DEVELOPMENTS IN MARITIME TECHNOLOGY AND ENGINEERING

Proceedings in Marine Technology and Ocean Engineering

BOOK SERIES EDITOR
Carlos Guedes Soares

EDITORIAL BOARD MEMBERS
R. Ajit Shenoi, Enrico Rizzuto, Fenando Lopez-Peña, Jani Romanov, Joško Parunov

ABOUT THE SERIES
The 'Proceedings in Marine Technology and Ocean Engineering' series is devoted to the publication of proceedings of peer-reviewed international conferences dealing with various aspects of 'Marine Technology and Ocean Engineering'. The Series includes the proceedings of the following conferences: the International Maritime Association of the Mediterranean (IMAM) Conferences, the Marine Structures (MARSTRUCT) Conferences, the Renewable Energies Offshore (RENEW) Conferences and the Maritime Technology and Engineering (MARTECH) Conferences. The 'Marine Technology and Ocean Engineering' series is also open to new conferences that cover topics on the sustainable exploration and exploitation of marine resources in various fields, such as maritime transport and ports, usage of the ocean including coastal areas, nautical activities, the exploration and exploitation of mineral resources, the protection of the marine environment and its resources, and risk analysis, safety and reliability. The aim of the series is to stimulate advanced education and training through the wide dissemination of the results of scientific research.

BOOKS IN THE SERIES
Volume 1: Advances in Renewable Energies Offshore, 2019, C. Guedes Soares (Ed.).
Volume 2: Trends in the Analysis and Design of Marine Structures, 2019, J. Parunov and C. Guedes Soares (Eds.).
Volume 3: Sustainable Development and Innovations in Marine Technologies, 2020, P. Georgiev and C. Guedes Soares (Eds.).
Volume 4: Developments in the Collision and Grounding of Ships and Offshore Structures, 2020, C. Guedes Soares (Ed.).
Volume 5: Developments in Renewable Energies Offshore, 2021, C. Guedes Soares (Ed.).
Volume 6: Developments in Maritime Technology and Engineering, 2021, C. Guedes Soares and T.A. Santos (Eds.)
Volume 7: Developments in the Analysis and Design of Marine Structures, 2021, J. Amdahl and C. Guedes Soares (Ed.).

Proceedings in Marine Technology and Ocean Engineering (Print): ISSN: 2638-647X
Proceedings in Marine Technology and Ocean Engineering (Online): eISSN: 2638-6461

PROCEEDINGS OF THE 5TH INTERNATIONAL CONFERENCE ON MARITIME TECHNOLOGY AND ENGINEERING (MARTECH 2020), LISBON, PORTUGAL, 16 – 19 NOVEMBER 2020

Developments in Maritime Technology and Engineering

Celebrating 40 years of teaching in Naval Architecture and Ocean Engineering in Portugal and the 25th anniversary of CENTEC

Volume 2

Editors

C. Guedes Soares

Centre for Marine Technology and Ocean Engineering (CENTEC), Instituto Superior Técnico, Universidade de Lisboa, Portugal

T.A. Santos

Ordem dos Engenheiros, Portugal

CRC Press is an imprint of the
Taylor & Francis Group, an **informa** business

A BALKEMA BOOK

CRC Press/Balkema is an imprint of the Taylor & Francis Group, an informa business

© 2021 the Author(s)

Typeset by Integra Software Services Pvt. Ltd., Pondicherry, India

The right of the Fifth International Conference on Maritime Technology and Engineering (MARTECH 2020) to be identified as author[/s] of this work has been asserted by him/her/them in accordance with sections 77 and 78 of the Copyright, Designs and Patents Act 1988.

All rights reserved. No part of this book may be reprinted or reproduced or utilised in any form or by any electronic, mechanical, or other means, now known or hereafter invented, including photocopying and recording, or in any information storage or retrieval system, without permission in writing from the publishers.

Although all care is taken to ensure integrity and the quality of this publication and the information herein, no responsibility is assumed by the publishers nor the author for any damage to the property or persons as a result of operation or use of this publication and/or the information contained herein.

Library of Congress Cataloging-in-Publication Data
A catalog record has been requested for this book

Published by: CRC Press/Balkema
　　　　　　　Schipholweg 107C, 2316 XC Leiden, The Netherlands
　　　　　　　e-mail: enquiries@taylorandfrancis.com
　　　　　　　www.routledge.com – www.taylorandfrancis.com

ISBN: 978-0-367-77374-8 (Set Hbk)
ISBN: 978-1-032-10699-1 (Set Pbk)
ISBN: 978-1-003-17107-2 (eBook)
DOI: 10.1201/9781003171072

Volume 1:
ISBN: 978-0-367-77376-2 (Hbk)
ISBN: 978-1-032-10693-9 (Pbk)
ISBN: 978-1-003-21658-2 (eBook)
DOI: 10.1201/9781003216582

Volume 2:
ISBN: 978-0-367-77377-9 (Hbk)
ISBN: 978-1-032-10696-0 (Pbk)
ISBN: 978-1-003-21659-9 (eBook)
DOI: 10.1201/9781003216599

Table of contents

Preface	xiii
Conference chairmen	xv
Organizing committee	xv
Scientific committee	xv
Technical programme & Conference secretariat	xvi
Sponsors	xvii

VOLUME 2

Ship performance

Augmenting ship propulsion in waves by flapping-foil thrusters — 3
K. Belibassakis

Effects of GPV datasets on WRF modelling of ocean surface wind in rough seas — 11
C. Chen, K. Sasa, T. Ohsawa & D. Terada

Experimental study of ship resistance in broken ice — 19
J.E. Gutiérrez-Romero, S. Ruiz-Capel, J. Esteve-Pérez, B. Zamora-Parra & J.P. Luna-Abad

Effect of optimal thruster location on DP operability of an offshore vessel — 27
F. Mauro, R. Nabergoj & J. Prpić-Oršić

The effect of spatial correlation of sea states on predicted extreme significant wave heights along ship sailing routes — 37
A. Mikulić, J. Parunov & M. Katalinić

Investigation of trim control devices on hydrodynamic characteristics of fast vessels — 45
M. Pedišić Buča & T. Prosinečki

Multiple evaluations of speed loss in rough sea voyages for 28,000-DWT bulk carrier — 53
K. Sasa, R. Uchiyama, C. Chen, D. Terada & J. Prpić-Oršić

Hydrofoil profile numerical analysis for low Reynolds number — 63
P.A.P. Souza, P.I.D. Lameira, H.P. Picanço, H.B. Moraes & L.C.P. Campos Filho

Ship hydrodynamics - CFD

Comparison between model test and numerical simulations for a container ship — 75
A.M. Chirosca & C. Gasparotti

Numerical investigation of monochromatic waves propagation over a submerged bar — 81
J.F.M. Gadelho & C. Guedes Soares

Comparative investigation on the hydrodynamic behavior of high-performance monohulls by CFD 91
J. Jiao, S. Huang & C. Chen

CFD investigation of submerged geometry effect on wave run-up around a fixed, vertical monopile in regular head waves 101
M. Mohseni & C. Guedes Soares

On the computation of the propulsive characteristics of a tanker 111
G. Tzabiras, H. Tserpes, S. Polyzos & D.E. Liarokapis

Numerical prediction of hydrodynamic coefficients of a submerged object with constant acceleration method 119
G. Xiang, S. Wang & C. Guedes Soares

Ship hydrodynamics - Manoeuvring

Modelling ship manoeuvrability using Recurrent Neural Networks 131
J.P. Araújo, L. Moreira & C. Guedes Soares

The variation in modal responses of a slamming-prone vessel during manoeuvres in open water 141
J.C. Bossau, C.M. van Zijl & A. Bekker

Optimal parameter estimation of empirical manoeuvring model using free-running ship tests 151
A.C. Costa, H.T. Xu & C. Guedes Soares

Preliminary review of shiphandling: Comparison between the literatures on naval architecture versus nautical sciences 159
H.O. Duarte, P.S.A. Michima, M.A.C. Carbajal & A.C.A. Oliveira

A new estimation concept for hydrodynamic derivatives of ship manoeuvrability using machine learning toolkits 169
L. Duan & T. Iseki

Reliability analysis of crabbing manoeuvre 177
V. Ferrari, S. Sutulo, A.P. Teixeira & C. Guedes Soares

Global and local path-planning algorithm for marine autonomous surface ships including forecasting information 187
M.A. Hinostroza & C. Guedes Soares

Study on the maneuverability of a ship in regular waves based on a unified seakeeping and maneuvering numerical model 197
S. Paramesh, P. Kumar & S. Rajendran

Z-drive escort tug manoeuvrability modelling: From model-scale to full-scale validation. 207
B. Piaggio, M. Viviani, M. Martelli & M. Figari

Local sensitivity analysis of a non-linear mathematical manoeuvring model 217
P. Pires da Silva, S. Sutulo & C. Guedes Soares

Instrumentation and data acquisition system for full-scale manoeuvrability tests on board of naval surface ships 227
P. Pires da Silva, M.A. Hinostroza, S. Sutulo & C. Guedes Soares

Investigation of performance of an identification program based on evolutionary optimization algorithms 235
S. Sutulo & C. Guedes Soares

Ship hydrodynamics – Seakeeping

Development of a three-dimensional frequency domain seakeeping code 247
A. Abbasnia, S. Sutulo, B. Callewaert & C. Guedes Soares

An operational investigation of wave slamming detection 255
J.C. Bossau & A. Bekker

The measurement and analysis of human comfort as a result of wave slamming on an ice-going vessel 265
M. Engelbrecht, A. Bekker & J. Muiyser

Experimental and numerical investigations of whipping responses of a 20,000TEU ultra large container carrier 275
Q.D. Feng, L.J. Wen, J.M. Wu, S. Wang & C. Guedes Soares

Improvement of ship hulls for comfort in passenger vessels 283
J. Gil Rosa, S. Wang & C. Guedes Soares

Experimental study on the wave loads including springing response of a very large crude carrier in regular head waves 297
Y. Lin, N. Ma, D. Wang & X. Gu

On the water entry problem of 2D wedges and bow flare section 305
P. Peddamallu, A.K. Menon & S. Rajendran

Assessment of ship motion responses to multi-peaked spectral models 319
L.Z.M. Silva, R. Vettor & C. Guedes Soares

Numerical analysis of water impact of spheres using mesh-free and mesh-based methods 329
S. Wang, C. Guedes Soares, J. González-Cao, J.M. Domínguez & M. Gómez-Gesteira

Ship hydrodynamics - Moorings

Experimental and numerical study of wave-induced ship motions and mooring loads of a tanker moored in Leixões port 341
H.S. Abdelwahab, C. Guedes Soares, L.V. Pinheiro, C.J.E.M. Fortes & J.A. Santos

Wind safety limits on ships docked with two different mooring systems 351
E. Díaz-Ruiz-Navamuel, A. Ortega-Piris, C.A. Pérez-Labajos & M.A. Andrés

Optimal mooring system deployment in line breakage condition 361
M. Liang, S. Xu, X. Wang & A. Ding

Investigation of long-term extreme mooring tensions by fully coupled dynamic analysis 371
S. Xu, C. Guedes Soares & C. Ji

Ship hydrodynamics - Resistance

Predicting head wave resistance for a KVLCC2 model using OpenFOAM 385
H. Islam & C. Guedes Soares

Investigation of the hydrodynamic properties of an inland container vessel 395
H. Islam, C. Guedes Soares, J. Kan, J. Liu & X. Wang

Fast ferry design – a case for the Gulf of Cádiz 403
M.J. Legaz, A. Querol, B. Flethes, M. Avalos & M.I. Ibrahim

An experimental investigation on the resistance and added resistance of two series 60 models with block coefficient 0.6 and 0.7 respectively 415
D.E. Liarokapis, G.P. Trachanas & G.D. Tzabiras

A review of FUNWAVE model applications in the propagation of waves generated by vessels 421
G.O. Mattosinho, G.F. Maciel, F.O. Ferreira, J.A. Santos & C.J.E.M. Fortes

Experimental and numerical study of added resistance in waves at low forward speeds 429
H. Orihara, H. Yoshida & K. Takagishi

Ship machinery

Auxiliary generator of a platform supply vessel based on fuel cell technology 441
M. Acanfora, T. Coppola, E. Fasano & L. Micoli

Analysis of ship performance data for the evaluation of marine engines emissions in ports 449
M. Altosole, F. Balsamo, L. Mocerino, F. Quaranta, U. Campora & E. Rizzuto

New methodologies for the study of transport phenomena in ship's ballast water 457
A. Amoresano, P. Iodice, G. Langella, L. Mocerino & F. Quaranta

Numerical modelling and analysis of the ambient conditions influence on the performance of a marine diesel engine 463
G. Benvenuto, U. Campora, M. Altosole & F. Balsamo

Condition analysis of air conditioning cooling water pumps 475
S. Lampreia, V. Vairinhos, V. Lobo & T. Morgado

A review of the use of Biodiesel as a green fuel for diesel engines 481
M. Tadros, M. Ventura & C. Guedes Soares

Sensitivity analysis of the steam Rankine cycle in marine applications 491
M. Tadros, M. Ventura & C. Guedes Soares

CO_2 treatment in an autonomous underwater vehicle powered by a direct methanol fuel cell 501
A. Villalba-Herreros, R. d'Amore-Domenech, R. Abad, T.J. Leo & E. Navarro

Renewable energy

Wave energy assessment in the São Roque do Pico Island for OWC installation 511
G. Anastas, J.A. Santos, L.V. Pinheiro & C.J.E.M. Fortes

A BEM for the performance of surge-type wave energy devices in variable bathymetry 519
K. Belibassakis & A. Magkouris

Evaluating trends and variability in Portuguese coastal wave energy potential using a 22 years high resolution hindcast 529
M. Bernardino, D. Silva & C. Guedes Soares

Pre-planning for Black Sea offshore wind farms: A wind speed dataset for three Romanian coastal locations 539
M. Burloiu & E. Rusu

Derivation of environmental contour by Direct Monte Carlo techniques 549
G. Clarindo & C. Guedes Soares

A review of mechanical analysis of submarine power cables 559
P. Fang, X. Jiang, H. Hopman & Y. Bai

Assessment of the wave conditions in the Azores coastal area 569
M. Gonçalves & C. Guedes Soares

Hydrodynamic Performance of Semi-Submersible FOWT Combined with Point-Absorber WECs 577
T.S. Hallak, D. Karmakar & C. Guedes Soares

Numerical and experimental analyses of a conical point-absorber moving around a hinge 587
T.S. Hallak, J.F. Gaspar, M. Kamarlouei & C. Guedes Soares

Experimental analysis of wind thrust effects on the performance of a wave energy converter array adapted to a floating offshore platform 597
M. Kamarlouei, J.F. Gaspar, T.S. Hallak, M. Calvário, C. Guedes Soares & F. Thiebaut

Experimental and numerical analysis of a spar platform subjected to regular waves 607
K. Raed, C. Guedes Soares & K. Murali

Experimental and numerical analysis of a spar platform subjected to irregular waves 617
K. Raed, C. Guedes Soares & K. Murali

Levelized cost of energy of offshore floating wind turbines in different case scenarios of the Madeira Islands 627
S. Ramos, H. Diaz, D. Silva & C. Guedes Soares

Dynamic analysis of submerged TLP wind turbine combined with heaving wave energy converter 639
J.S. Rony, D. Karmakar & C. Guedes Soares

An assessment of the wave energy in the European seas based on ERA5 reanalysis dataset 647
L. Rusu

Comparison of renewables (onshore wind, offshore wind, conventional PV) for Bozcaada Island in Turkey 653
A.E. Şentürk, E. Oğuz & D.D. Çiçek

Validation with satellite data of SWAN model for wave conditions at the Madeira archipelago 665
D. Silva & C. Guedes Soares

An integrated design approach for a self-float capable tension leg platform for wind energy 673
E. Uzunoglu & C. Guedes Soares

Fishing and Aquaculture

Validation of tools for the analysis of offshore aquaculture installations 685
T.A. Bernardo & C. Guedes Soares

Definition of landing profiles in the Portuguese coastal multi-gear fleet 693
A. Campos, V. Henriques, P. Fonseca, G. Araújo & J. Parente

A new approach to sustainable integrated cultures 699
J.P. Garcês, H. Quental-Ferreira, M. Theriaga, D. Neto & P. Pousão-Ferreira

Numerical modelling of full-scale aquaculture cages under uniform flow 705
Z.C. Liu, Y. Garbatov & C. Guedes Soares

The anchovy fishery by the Portuguese coastal seine fleet - landings and fleet characteristics 713
J. Parente, V. Henriques & A. Campos

Reducing uncertainties in Baltic herring and sprat abundance estimates: Alternative approach to acoustic analyses 721
E. Sepp, T. Raid, L. Saks, K. Hommik, T. Arula & O. Kaljuste

On UAV-assisted data acquisition for underwater IoT in aquaculture surveillance 729
Q. Wang, H.-N. Dai, Q. Wang & M.K. Shukla

Coastal structures

Modeling of navigability conditions of rivers in the Amazon and the occurrence of ENSO events 739
H.M. Borges, L.C.P. Campos Filho, N.M. de Figueiredo, R.S. Saavedra & P.I.D. Lameira

Optimizing the configuration of flow guide grid to reduce turbulence in a wave flume for coastal hydraulic research 747
D.M. Fellows, G. Nikolov & R. Kishev

Effect of vertical rigid wall on a moored submerged horizontal flexible porous membrane 757
Y.C. Guo, S.C. Mohapatra & C. Guedes Soares

The multi-objective optimisation of breakwaters using evolutionary approach 767
N.O. Nikitin, I.S. Polonskaia, A.V. Kalyuzhnaya & A.V. Boukhanovsky

Statistical analysis of the oil production profile of Campos' basin in Brazil 775
L.M.R. Silva & C. Guedes Soares

Waves and currents

Surface circulation in the Eastern Central North Atlantic 785
J.H. Bettencourt & C. Guedes Soares

Assessment of Hurricane Lorenzo metocean forecast 791
R.M. Campos, M. Gonçalves & C. Guedes Soares

Distribution and characteristics of extreme waves generated by extratropical cyclones in the North Atlantic Ocean 797
C.B. Gramcianinov, R.M. Campos, C. Guedes Soares & R. de Camargo

Autonomous observing systems in fishing vessels 805
A.M.P. Piecho-Santos, M.A. Hinostroza, T. Rosa & C. Guedes Soares

Modelling of the Surface Stokes drift in the Agulhas current system 809
S. Ponce de León, C. Guedes Soares & J.A. Johannessen

Simulation of hurricane Lorenzo at the port of Madalena do Pico, Azores, by using the
HIDRALERTA system 815
*M.I. Santos, L.V. Pinheiro, C.J.E.M. Fortes, M.T. Reis, V. Serrazina, E.B. Azevedo,
F.V. Reis & M. Salvador*

Author index 825
Book series page 827

Preface

Since 1987, the Naval Architecture and Marine Engineering branch of the Portuguese Association of Engineers (Ordem dos Engenheiros) and the Centre for Marine Technology and Ocean Engineering (CENTEC) of the Instituto Superior Técnico (IST), Technical University of Lisbon, (now University of Lisbon) have been organizing national conferences on Naval Architecture and Marine Engineering. Initially, they were organised annually and later became biannual events.

These meetings had the objective of bringing together Portuguese professionals allowing them to present and discuss the ongoing technical activities. The meetings have been typically attended by 150 to 200 participants and the number of papers presented at each meeting was in the order of 30 in the beginning and 50 at later events.

At the same time as the conferences have become more mature, the international contacts have also increased and the industry became more international so that the fact that the conference was in Portuguese started to hinder its further development with wider participation. Therefore, a decision was made to experiment with having also papers in English, mixed with the usual papers in Portuguese. This was first implemented in the First International Conference of Maritime Technology and Engineering (MARTECH 2011), which was organized in the year that Instituto Superior Técnico completed 100 years. Subsequently, three more MARTECH conferences have been organized, namely in 2014, 2016 and 2018, always with a broad scope.

In this Fifth International Conference of Maritime Technology and Engineering (MARTECH 2020), some special events have marked it as a special one. To start with, the Conference is associated with the commemorations of the 40th anniversary of the teaching of Naval Architecture at IST, which has gone through different study plans and phases of development. The Centre for Marine Technology and Ocean Engineering (CENTEC), which was created some years later, is commemorating its 25th anniversary, making this a joint commemoration.

The other special event that marked this Conference was the appearance of COVID-19, which started having a marked spread in Portugal in March 2020, leading to a postponement of the Conference from the planned date of May to November 2020. Against initial hopes, the situation was still very serious in October and thus the Conference was held mostly online with a small presence at IST in Lisbon.

Running the Conference online was a challenge, because of the little experience accumulated with this type of events and, of the difficulties in dealing with the time difference for the authors from Asia. Finally, a compromise solution was found, allowing the authors to present their papers and to follow most of the sessions in the morning and early afternoon in Europe.

The postponement of the Conference allowed a few more abstracts and papers to be accepted, so in the end, around 285 abstracts have been received and after the review process, about 180 papers were finally accepted and are included in this book. Without the presence of participants, the book finished up being produced and distributed after the Conference, which is not the usual procedure.

The Scientific Committee had a major role in the review process of the papers although several other anonymous reviewers have also contributed and deserve our thanks for the detailed comments provided to the authors allowing them to improve their papers. Participation is coming from research and industry from almost every continent, which is also a demonstration of the wide geographical reach of the conference.

The contents of the present books are organized in the main subject areas corresponding to the sessions in the Conference and within each group, the papers are listed by the alphabetic order of the authors.

We want to thank all contributors for their efforts and the sponsors for their support and we hope that this Conference will be continued and improved in the future.

C. Guedes Soares & T.A. Santos

Conference chairmen

Carlos Guedes Soares, *IST, Universidade de Lisboa, Portugal*
Pedro Ponte, *Ordem dos Engenheiros, Portugal*

Organizing committee

Tiago A. Santos, *Ordem dos Engenheiros, Portugal*
Ângelo Teixeira, *IST, Universidade de Lisboa, Portugal*
Dina Dimas, *Ordem dos Engenheiros, Portugal*
Manuel Ventura, *IST, Universidade de Lisboa, Portugal*
José Manuel Cruz, *Ordem dos Engenheiros, Portugal*
José Gordo, *IST, Universidade de Lisboa, Portugal*
Francisco C. Salvado, *Ordem dos Engenheiros, Portugal*
José Varela, *IST, Universidade de Lisboa, Portugal*
Paulo Viana, *Ordem dos Engenheiros, Portugal*

Scientific committee

Felice Arena, *Mediterranea Univ. of Reggio Calabria, Italy*
Ermina Begovic, *UNINA, Italy*
Kostas Belibassakis, *NTUA, Greece*
Marco Biot, *Università degli Studi di Trieste, Italy*
Elzbieta Bitner-Gregerseon, *DNVGL, Norway*
Evangelos Boulougouris, *University of Strathclyde, UK*
Rui Carlos Botter, *University of São Paulo, Brazil*
Sofia Caires, *Deltares, The Netherlands*
Nian Zhong Chen, *Tianjin University, China*
Ranadev Datta, *IIT Kharagpur, India*
Vicente Díaz Casas, *Universidad A Coruña, Spain*
Leonard Domnişoru, *Univ. Dunarea de Jos Galati, Romania*
Soren Ehlers, *Technische Universität Hamburg, Germany*
Saad Eldeen, *Port Said University, Egypt*
Bettar Ould el Moctar, *Univ. of Duisburg-Essen, Germany*
Segen F. Estefen, *UFRJ, Brazil*
Selma Ergin, *Istanbul Technical University, Turkey*
Massimo Figari, *University of Genova, Italy*
Thor I. Fossen, *NTNU, Norway*
Yordan Garbatov, *Instituto Superior Técnico, Portugal*

Sergio Garcia, *University of Cantabria, Spain*
Lorena García Alonso, *Univ. de Oviedo, Spain*
Peter Georgiev, *TU Varna, Bulgaria*
Hercules Haralambides, *Erasmus Univ. Rotterdam, The Netherlands*
Spyros Hirdaris, *Aalto University, Finland*
Zhiqiang Hu, *Newcastle University, UK*
Chunyan Ji, *Jiangsu Univ. Science & Technology, China*
Xiaoli Jiang, *TUDelft, The Netherlands*
Jean-Marc Laurens, *ENSTA Bretagne, France*
Debabrata Karmakar, *National Inst. Techn. Karnataka, India*
Faisal Khan, *Memorial University, Canada*
Pentti Kujala, *Aalto University, Finland*
Xavier Martínez, *Uni. Politécnica de Catalunya, Spain*
Alba Martínez-López, *Univ. Las Palmas Gran Canária, Spain*
Marcelo Ramos Martins, *University of São Paulo, Brazil*
Jakub Montewka, *Gdynia Maritime University, Poland*
Muk Chen Ong, *University of Stavanger, Norway*
Josko Parunov, *University of Zagreb, Croatia*
Apostolos Papanikolaou, *HSVA, Germany*
Preben T. Pedersen, *DTU, Denmark*
L. Prasad Perera, *Arctic University of Norway, Norway*
Jasna Prpić-Oršić, *University of Rijeka, Croatia*
Harilaos N. Psaraftis, *DTU, Denmark*
Suresh Rajendran, *IIT Madras, India*
Huilong Ren, *Harbin Engineering University, China*
Jonas W. Ringsberg, *Chalmers Univ. of Technology, Sweden*
Liliana Rusu, *University Dunarea de Jos Galati, Romania*
António Souto-Iglesias, *Univ. Politécnica de Madrid, Spain*
Maciej Taczala, *West Pomeranian University, Poland*
Wiesław Tarełko, *Gdansk University of Technology, Poland*
Michele Viviani, *University of Genova, Italy*
Deyu Wang, *Shanghai Jiao Tong University, China*
Jin Wang, *Liverpool John Moores University, UK*
Xinping Yan, *Wuhan University of Technology, China*
Shengming Zhang, *Lloyds Register, UK*
Peilin Zhou, *University of Strathclyde, UK*
Xueqian Zhou, *Harbin Engineering University, China*

Technical programme & Conference secretariat

Sandra Ponce, IST, *Universidade de Lisboa, Portugal*
Maria de Fátima Pina, IST, *Universidade de Lisboa, Portugal*
Sónia Vicente, IST, *Universidade de Lisboa, Portugal*
Bárbara Azevedo, IST, *Universidade de Lisboa, Portugal*
Mina Abbasi, IST, *Universidade de Lisboa, Portugal*

Sponsors

Ship Performance

Augmenting ship propulsion in waves by flapping-foil thrusters

K. Belibassakis
School of Naval Architecture & Marine Engineering, National Technical University of Athens, Greece

ABSTRACT: Flapping foils located beneath the ship's hull are investigated an unsteady thruster, augmenting ship propulsion in rough seas and offering dynamic stabilization. The foil undergoes a combined oscillatory motion in the presence of waves. For the system in the horizontal arrangement the vertical heaving motion of the hydrofoil is induced by the motion of the ship in waves, essentially ship's heave and pitch, while the rotational pitching motion of the foil about its pivot axis is set by an active control mechanism. A numerical BEM has been developed and applied to demonstrate that significant energy can be extracted from the waves. Furthermore, energy extraction under random wave conditions is studied and the effects of the wavy free surface are taken into account through the satisfaction of the corresponding boundary conditions. Numerical results concerning thrust coefficient are shown, indicating significant performance under variety of operating conditions. Preliminary results are presented concerning the applicability of the system for specific vessels for extracting energy from sea waves and augmenting ship propulsion in waves.

1 INTRODUCTION

Oscillating wings located beneath the ship's hull are investigated as unsteady thrusters, augmenting the propulsion of the ship in rough sea conditions. Initial attempts in this direction focused on the use of passively flapping wings to transform energy stored in ship motions to useful propulsive thrust, with simultaneous reduction of the motions of the ship; see Rozhdestvensky & Ryzhov (2003) and Wu et al (2019) for extensive reviews, and Naito & Isshiki (2005) for a review in flapping-bow wings on ship propulsion. This kind of biomimetic propulsion systems is subject of intensive investigation, since they are ideally suited for converting environmental (atmospheric or sea wave) energy to useful thrust, succeeding very high levels of propulsive efficiency; see, e.g., Triantafyllou et al (2000, 2004), Taylor et al (2010), Politis & Tsarsitalidis (2014). On the other hand, the complexity of kinematics of flapping wings necessitates the development of sophisticated power transmission mechanisms and control devices, as compared to the standard marine propeller systems, preventing at present its application as the main or sole propulsion system of ships.

A main difference between a biomimetic propulsor and a conventional propeller is that the former absorbs its energy by two independent motions, the heaving and the pitching motion, in contrast with marine propellers where power is transmitted through the rotating propeller axis. In real sea conditions, the ship undergoes a moderate or higher-amplitude oscillatory motion due to waves, and the vertical ship motion could be exploited for providing one of the modes of combined/complex oscillatory motion of a biomimetic propulsion system. At the same time, due to waves, wind and other factors, the ship propulsion energy demand in rough sea is increased well above the corresponding value in calm water for the same speed, especially in the case of bow/quartering seas. In the this work we present results from the investigation of the performance of actively controlled oscillating wings, located beneath the hull of the ship, operating as unsteady thrusters and augmenting the overall propulsion system of the ship. The main arrangement shown in Figure 1 consists of a horizontal wing undergoing combined vertical and angular oscillatory motion. The vertical motion is induced by ship heave and pitch, while the wing pitching motion about its pivot axis is actively set in terms of the ship motions.

A second arrangement has also been considered consisted of a vertical oscillating wing beneath the hull of the ship; see Belibassakis & Politis (2013). In this case, the transverse oscillatory motion is induced by ship rolling and swaying, and the pitching motion of the wing about its pivot axis is properly selected in order to produce thrust with significant generation of anti-rolling moment for ship stabilization.

In recent works by Belibassakis & Filippas (2015) and Filippas (2019), nonlinear BEM have been developed and applied to numerically simulate and study novel biomimetic systems based on oscillating hydrofoils operating in the presence of waves and currents, examined for extraction and exploitation of this kind of renewable marine energy resources for ships. It has been demonstrated by previous and ongoing research that flapping foil thrusters in waves, while travelling

DOI: 10.1201/9781003216599-1

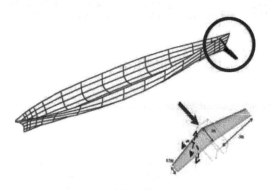

Figure 1. Ship hull equipped with a flapping wing located below the keel, at a forward station. Geometrical details of the flapping wings.

at constant forward speed, operate very efficiently, and could be exploited for augmenting the overall ship propulsion in waves by directly converting kinetic energy from ship motions to thrust; see, also Bockmann & Steen (2014). Predictions are found to be in agreement with CFD methods and experimental data; see e.g. De Silva & Yamaguchi (2012). First results indicate that high levels of efficiency are obtained in sea conditions of moderate and higher severity, under optimal control settings. In this work we present the peformance of the system under random wave conditions using active pitch control. More specifically, we consider operation of the foil in head waves characterized by a given frequency spectrum, corresponding to specific sea states. The effects of the wavy free surface are taken into account through the satisfaction of the corresponding boundary conditions. Numerical results concerning thrust coefficient are shown, indicating that significant efficiency can be obtained. The present analysis has been verified by recent experimental work; see, also Bockmann (2015), Bowker (2018). Thus, the present method can serve as a useful tool for the design, assessment and optimum control of such systems extracting energy from sea waves and augmenting marine propulsion.

2 FLAPPING THRUSTER IN WAVES

The main parameter controlling the unsteady thrust production of flapping systems, advancing at forward speed U, is the Strouhal number $St = 2f\,h_0/U$, where h_0 denotes the amplitude of the vertical wing motion, while Reynolds number is used to calculate viscous drag corrections. Also, the phase difference ψ between the two oscillatory motions is very important as far as the efficiency of the thrust development by the flapping system is concerned. In the single harmonic thrust producing case it usually takes the value $\psi=90°$ (see, e.g., Anderson et al 1998, Schouveiler et al 2005), in which case the required torque for wing pitching is found to be minimum when the pivot axis for the angular motion of the wing is located around $1/3 \div 1/4$ chord length from the leading edge. As a result of the simultaneous heaving and pitching motions of the biomimetic wing, in the case of horizontal arrangement (Figure 1), the instantaneous angle of attack is

$$\alpha(t) = \theta_H(t) - \theta(t) = \tan^{-1}\left(U^{-1}dh/dt\right) - \theta(t). \quad (1)$$

For relatively low amplitudes of harmonic motion and optimum phase difference $\psi=90°$, the angle of attack becomes $\alpha(t) = \left(U^{-1}h_0\omega - \theta_0\right)\cos(\omega t)$, which can be equivalently achieved by setting the pitch angle $\theta(t)$ proportional to $\theta_H(t)$ as follows

$$\theta(t) = w\tan^{-1}\left(U^{-1}dh/dt\right) \text{ and } \theta_0 = w\,h_0\omega/U. \quad (2)$$

In contrast to passively controlled flapping-wing thrusters (see, e.g., Murray & Howle 2003, Bøckmann & Steen 2013) in the present work an active system is studied based on the above parameter w, introduced in Politis & Politis (2014). The latter pitch control parameter usually takes values in $0<w<1$. Decreasing the value of $1-w$ the maximum angle of attack is reduced and the wing operates at lighter load. On the contrary, by increasing the above parameter the wing loading becomes strong and could lead to leading edge separation and dynamic stall effects. The above is exploited as an active pitch control rule of the flapping-wing thruster, not only for purely harmonic oscillations, but also in the general multichromatic case, applied to the time history of vertical oscillatory motion $h(t)$ of the wing. Thus, the instantaneous angle of attack, Eq(1), takes the form (Belibassakis & Politis 2013)

$$\alpha(t) = (1 - w)\tan^{-1}\left(U^{-1}dh/dt\right). \quad (3)$$

Moreover, the controlled angle of attack is limited in order to avoid excessive separation and dynamic stall effects.

In the case of the biomimetic system under the calm or wavy free surface, additional parameters enter into play, as Froude number(s) $F = U/(gL)^{1/2}$, with ℓ denoting the characteristic length(s) and g is gravitational acceleration, as well as frequency parameter(s) associated with the incoming wave, as $\mu = \omega^2 L/g$ and $\tau = \omega U/g$.

3 SHIP AND THRUSTER DYNAMICS

We consider a ship in head waves advancing at constant forward speed U. Linearized seakeeping analysis in the frequency domain (Lewis 1989) is used to obtain the motions and responses of the examined system (ship and flapping wing) in the vertical plane; see also Belibassakis and Politis (2013). The coupled equation of heave and pitch motion of the ship (with corresponding complex amplitudes ξ_{30} and ξ_{50}) is as follows (taking the origin at the centre of gravity):

$$D_{33}\xi_{30} + D_{35}\xi_{50} = F_{30} + X_{30}, \quad (4)$$

$$D_{53}\xi_{30} + D_{55}\xi_{50} = F_{50} + X_{50}, \quad (5)$$

where

$$\begin{aligned} D_{33} &= \left(-\omega_{en}^2(m + a_{33}) + i\omega_{en}b_{33} + c_{33}\right), \\ D_{35} &= \left(-\omega_{en}^2(a_{35} + I_{35}) + i\omega_{en}b_{35} + c_{35} + p\right), \end{aligned} \quad (6)$$

$$\begin{aligned} D_{53} &= \left(-\omega_{en}^2(a_{53} + I_{53}) + i\omega_{en}b_{53} + c_{53}\right), \\ D_{55} &= \left(-\omega_{en}^2(a_{55} + I_{55}) + i\omega_{en}^2 b_{55} + c_{55}\right), \end{aligned} \quad (7)$$

a_{jk} and b_{jk}, $j,k = 3,5$, are added mass and damping coefficients, m is the total mass of the ship and wing and $p = -i\omega_{en}Um$ is a Coriolis term. The involved hydrostatic coefficients are $c_{33} = \rho g A_{WL}$, $c_{35} = c_{53} = -\rho g(x_f A_{WL})$ and $c_{55} = m g GM_L$. The inertia coefficients involved in the above system are $I_{55} = mR_{yy}^2$ and $I_{35} = I_{53} = -m X_G$, where X_G is the long-center of gravity and R_{yy} the radius of gyration with respect to the transverse axis. For simplicity, only head waves ($\beta=180°$) are considered here as excitation of the hull oscillatory motion. In this case, the frequency of encounter (relative frequency) is

$$\omega_e = \omega + kU, \quad (8)$$

where k is the wavenumber of the incident waves ω is the absolute frequency, g is the acceleration of gravity and U the ship speed. The terms F_{j0}, $j = 3,5$ appearing in the right-hand side of Eqs.(6),(7) are the Froude-Krylov and diffraction vertical force and pitching moment (about the ship y-axis) amplitudes, respectively. Furthermore, the terms $X_{j0}, j = 3,5$ denote additional force and moment amplitudes due to the operation of the horizontal flapping wing as an unsteady thruster. The latter are dependent on heave (ξ_3) and pitch (ξ_5) responses of the ship, as well as to the incoming wave field. In general, due to the oscillatory thrust developed by the foil, ship responses are also coupled with surge motion. However, considering the large mass of ship, in conjunction with installation of energy storage and power feed smoothing systems, at first level of approximation that effect is neglected, as proposed by Belibassakis and Politis (2013).

Hydrodynamics of lifting surfaces attached to the hull, coupled with ship dynamics, have been studied extensively for hydrodynamics optimisation purposes. For example, passive and active foils used as anti-rolling stabilizers (e.g., Naito & Isshiki 2005). In the present work we exploit the approach developed in Belibassakis and Politis (2013) in the context of 3D BEM applications, to study the seakeeping performance of a vessel with attached foils; see also Sclavounos & Borgen (2004). Furthermore, Chatzakis & Sclavounos (2006) studied the problem of motion control of marine vehicles in rough seas coupled with the problem of dynamic positioning, using active foil systems. Developments and applications of control theory for marine vessels are extensively discussed in Fossen (2002). The complexity of the selected model depends on the properties of the controller and the desired performance of the controlled system, see, e.g., Sclavounos (2006), Thomas & Sclavounos (2007).

4 PERFORMANCE IN WAVES

4.1 Demonstrative example

As an example we consider a series 60-Cb060 ship hull form, with main dimensions' length L=50m, breadth B=6.70m, draft T=2.80m. The exact value of the block coefficient at the above draft is C_b=0.533. From hydrostatic analysis, the immersed volume in the mean position is 500m³, and the corresponding displacement in salt water, which equals the mass of the ship, is estimated to be Δ=512tn. Moreover, in the above draft, the wetted area of the hull is calculated S_{wet}=380m², the waterplane area A_{WL}=225m², the center of flotation x_f = -1.15m (LCF aft midship), the longitudinal moment of inertia of the waterplane is I_L=28800m⁴, and the corresponding metacentric radius BM_L=57.6m. The vertical center of buoyancy is KB=1.55m (from BL), and the longitudinal position is LCB=-0.266m. For simplicity, we consider the longitudinal center of gravity to coincide with the center of buoyancy, i.e. X_G=-0.266m (aft midship), Y_G=0, and KG=1.80m (from BL), and thus, the metacentric height in the above condition are estimated to be GM=0.9m. Also, the longitudinal metacentric height in the above condition is estimated to be $GM_L \approx BM_L$. Finally, the radii of gyration about the x-axis and y-axis, respectively, are taken R_{xx}=0.32B, R_{yy}=0.23L. The flapping wing propulsor is located at a distance x_{wing}=15m fore the midship section. The half-wing planform shape is trapezoidal and its span is s=6m. Moreover, the root and tip chords of the wing have lengths c_R=1m, c_T=0.5m, respectively, and the leading edge sweep angle is Λ=9.4deg. Also, the wing planform area is S_w=4.5m², and its aspect ratio AR=8. The wing sections are symmetrical NACA0012.

A low-order Rankine source based BEM, in the frequency domain, is used to obtain the seakeeping analysis of the hull in waves, and to treat the steady problem of the ship advancing with mean forward speed. Details can be found in Belibassakis & Politis (2013). In Figure 2 results are presented concerning the response of the

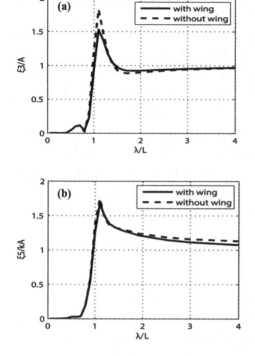

Figure 2. (a) Heave (ξ_{30}/A) and (b) pitch response (ξ_{50}/kA) of the examined ship hull against non-dimensional wavelength λ/L, for ship speed U=10.6kn (5.5m/s), with (bold line) and without (dashed line) the operation of the flapping thruster.

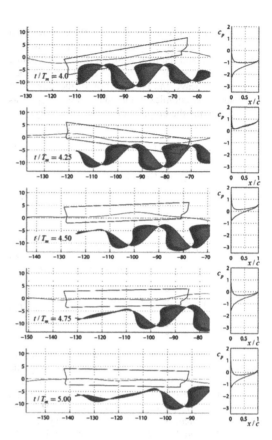

Figure 3. Simulation of the system operating at sea state 5.

system in head seas. To be more specific, in Figure 2(a) the normalized heave response with respect to the incident wave amplitude of the ship is plotted, without the operation of the flapping wing thruster, for various values of the non-dimensional wavelength and Froude numbers. The corresponding, ship-pitch response is shown in Figure 2(b). To illustrate the effect of flapping foil operation, in Figure 2(c) and 2(d), the same responses are presented in the case of Froude number 0.25 using dashed line. The modified responses taking into account the coupled ship-flapping wing dynamics are overplotted in the same figures using a thick solid line. We observe a significant reduction of the ship heaving motion, especially in the vicinity of the resonance condition. This result is indicative of the extraction of energy from ship motions by the flapping wing.

In the case of ship pitch motion, the operation of the flapping wing propulsor leads to reduction of the response, especially for wavelengths longer than the ship length. An extra effect, strongly connected with the reduction of ship responses, is the expected drop of the added wave resistance of the ship. Indicative results concerning the latter additional benefit are provided in Belibassakis & Politis (2013).

Concerning the thrust augmentation achieved by the operation of the flapping wing propulsor in head waves, is illustrated in Figure 3, as calculated by the present method. In particular, we consider the ship and flapping wing to travel at constant speed U=10.6kn, in head seas (β=180deg) corresponding to significant wave height Hs=5m, and peak period Tp=11s, corresponding to sea state 5. Numerical simulation of the system is presented in Figure 3 and 4. Results have been obtained using pitch control parameter w=0.5 and setting the pivot-axis concerning the self-pitching motion of the flapping foil at distance c/3 from the leading edge. In particular, in Figure 3 the profile of the ship travelling in random waves and positioned according to the response of the coupled ship-flapping wing system is shown at five instants within a time interval corresponding to one modal period.

In the same figure the trailing vortex curve modelling the foil's wake is plotted, including the calculated dipole intensity (potential jump) on the vortex sheet, which is illustrated by using arrows normal to the wake curve with length proportional to the local dipole strength. The latter result is associated with the memory effect of the generated lifting flow around the flapping foil operating in random incident waves. Moreover, in the right subplots of Figure 3 the instantaneous distribution of the pressure coefficient on the hydrofoil, at the same time instants, as calculated by the present method. From the calculated

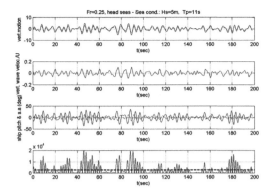
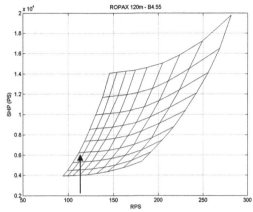

Figure 4. Responses of ship with horizontal flapping wing operating in head seas at ship speed U=10.6kn (F=0.25). (a) Vertical ship motion without (solid line) and with (dashed line) the effect of the flapping wing. (b) Vertical wave velocity at the flapping wing. (c) Calculated ship pitch (dashed line) and angle of attack (solid line) at the flapping wing, using w=50%. (d) Thrust production by the flapping wing (time history). The time average is indicated by using dashed line.

Figure 5. SHP-RPM(prop) diagram of each engine for twin screw passenger ferry with B4-55 propellers with propelelr pitch-ship speed grid: P/D=0.6:0.1:1.4 and ship speed range from Vs=14:1:22knots.

sectional pressure distributions, lift and thrust components are obtained at each time step by integration.

The results shown in the first subplot of Figure 4(a) concern the vertical motion at St.8, where the horizontal flapping wing is arranged. The second subplot (Figure 4b) shows the incident wave velocity at the same location, and in the next subplot (Figure 4c) the calculated time series of ship pitching angle together the angle of attack at wing sections are plotted. In the final subplot the thrust (in kp) produced by the horizontal flapping foil is shown, as calculated by setting the control pitch variable w=50%. We observe in the last subplot of Figure 4 that the thrust oscillations produced by the horizontal flapping wing in the considered sea condition are rather large, with a significant average value indicated by using dashed line. The latter compared to the bare hull resistance is of the same order of magnitude.

4.2 Realistic cases

We consider a ROPAX 120m with main dimensions Loa=120m, Lpp=107m, B=21m, stern Breadth=20m, T=5.3m (draft). The main propulsion system consists of two propellers of diameter D=4m. The propulsion performance is modeled by using B4-55 (as described in Politis & Tsarsitalidis 2014, table 3). For calculation purposes the following data are used for wake fraction, thrust deduction, rotative efficiency and shafting system efficiency: $1-t=0.95$, $1-w=0.95$, $\eta_R=1$, $\eta_S=0.98$. We obtain from this examples that propeller pitch set P/D=1.4 results in $U=17$knots with SHP=6230PS=4580kW (at 112 RPM propeller) per engine; see Figure 5.

In order to demonstrate the thrust augmentation in waves by the biomimetic system, we consider the ship motions at sea conditions 4-5 corresponding to significant wave height Hs=3m and peak period Tp=8sec for service ship speed U=17knots (Froude number Fn=0.265) in head waves. In this case we estimate vertical bow ship motion with rms amplitude h_σ=1.35m, and mean value of added wave resistance R_a=850kp which is of the order of 2.5% of the calm water resistance at the same ship speed.

The standard system with propeller pitch set at P/D=1.4 at U=17knots results SHP=6370PS= 4685kW (per engine). For the ship travelling in head waves with peak period T_p=8sec, the encounter peak frequency is 0.21Hz and the corresponding period drops to 4.7s. Using a wing with chord c=2.5m and span-to-chord ratio s/c=6 (which fits well in a forward station of the ferry), the Strouhal number of the flapping thruster is St=0.066. In this condition we obtain the following prediction concerning the behavior of flapping thruster $T_{flap}=6500$kp. The flapping propulsor is expected to reduce the ship responses and the vertical ship motion by 15% reducing also the thrust output approximately to the same level: $T_{flap}=5520$kp. Based on the above the propulsion system will operate at SHP=5380PS= 3955kW (per engine) leading to an improvement of fuel consumption and CO_2 emissions of the order of 16%.

4.3 Application to ship route in the North Sea

In order to provide more realistic results of the expected enhancement of the performance and the complementary of the proposed DF and flapping thruster system in waves, we consider a ship route in North Sea region. In particular, in Figure 6 the density of ship routing in the Central and Southern North Sea region is plotted using AIS data (https://www.marinetraffic.com/), and a selected point (55.05degN, 6.5degE) in the southern-central North Sea subregion is shown by using red dot.

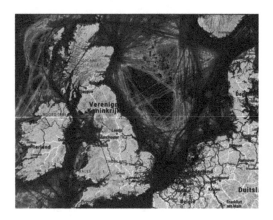

Figure 6. Ship route density of in the North Sea region from AIS data, and selected point (55.05degN, 6.5degE) shown by using red dot.

For this point wave data available from MetOcean View https://app.metoceanview.com/hindcast/sites/) are used to model the wave climatology, as presented in Figure 7 where a bivariate model of probability density for the specific point is shown. The mean and most probable values of wave parameters for this point (characteristic for the examined route) are:

Tm=6.78s, Hm=1.69m, $Tmpv$=6.37s, $Hmpv$=1.28m.

Next, in Figure 8 results are presented concerning the simulation of the ship engines performance, in complementarity with biomimetic flapping thruster. In this plot the upper solid lines indicate the increase of calculated SHP (in kW per engine) due to the waves (added resistance) and the lower solid line the expected imthruster in waves. The results are plotted against the significant wave height, while the overall mean values of SHP are indicated by using dashed lines in the graph. We obtain that overall the expected

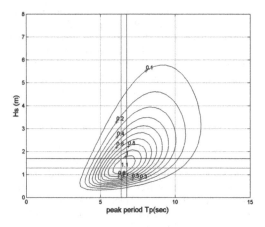

Figure 7. Bivariate density of significant wave height and peak period for the point (55.05degN,6.5degE) in the North Sea region.

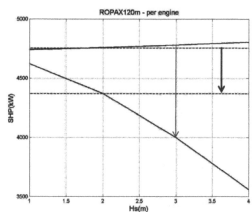

Figure 8. Simulation of the ROPAX ship engines performance, in complementarity with biomimetic flapping thruster.

performance enhancement of the ROPAX, is calculated to be 8%, while for Hs=4m it increases to 25%.

5 CONCLUSIONS

The performance of horizontal flapping thrusters located beneath the hull of the ship is investigated for augmenting ship propulsion in waves and offering dynamic stabliztion in rough seas. The wing undergoes a combined vertical (heaving) and self-pitching oscillatory motion, while travelling at constant speed in the presence of waves. The vertical wing motion is induced by ship heave and pitch. The pitching motion of the wing about its pivot axis is actively controlled in order to produce thrust, with significant reduction of responses and added wave resistance. Ship flow hydrodynamics are modeled in the framework of potential theory using Rankine source-sink formulation (Belibassakis & Politis 2013), and ship responses are calculated taking into account the additional forces and moments due to the above unsteady propulsion systems. Numerical results are presented indicating significant thrust produced by the examined biomimetic system and reduction of ship responses over a range of motion parameters.

The simulation model is used to simulate performance in various realistic senaria and various type of vessels indicating significant improvment in performance indices, including fuel consumption and emissions. Thus, the present method, after experimental verification, which is currently carried out in the towing tank of Ship and Marine Hydrodynamics Laboratory of National Technical University of Athens, can serve as a useful tool for the assessment, preliminary design and control of the examined thrust-augmenting devices, enhancing the overall performance of a ship in waves. In the same direction, application of more elaborate control methods would be beneficial for optimization of performance. Finally, the described model permits extension to various directions, as e.g., the inclusion of various non-linear effects (waves and ship hydrodynamics, dynamic stall) and consideration of hydroelasticity effects due to wing(s) flexibility.

REFERENCES

Anderson, J. M., Streitlien, K., Barrett, D.S., Triantafyllou, M.S., 1998. Oscillating foils of high propulsive efficiency. *J. Fluid Mechanics* 360: 41–72.

Belibassakis KA, Politis GK. 2013, Hydrodynamic performance of flapping wings for augmenting ship propulsion in waves. *Ocean Engineering* 72: 227–240.

Belibassakis K.A., Filippas, E., 2015, Ship propulsion in waves by actively controlled flapping foils, *Applied Ocean Research*, 52: 1–11.

Belibassakis K., 2012, A panel method based on vorticity distribution for the calculation of free surface flows around ship hull configurations with lifting bodies, *Sustainable Maritime Transportation and Exploitation of Sea Resources*, Rizzuto & Guedes Soares (Eds), Taylor & Francis Group, London, UK., Vol 1, pp 79–86.

Bøckmann E, Steen S. 2014, Experiments with actively pitch-controlled and spring-loaded oscillating foils. *Applied Ocean Research*, 48: 227–235.

Bøckmann E., *Wave propulsion of ships*, PhD thesis NTNU.

Bowker J. A. 2018, *Coupled dynamics of a flapping foil wave powered vessel*, PhD thesis Univ.Southampton.

Bowker J., Townsend N., Tan M., Shenoi R., Experimental analysis of submerged flapping foils; implications for autonomous surface vehicles, *OCEANS 2016* MTS/IEEE Monterey. IEEE, 2016, pp. 1–10.

Chatzakis I, Sclavounos P.D. 2006, Active motion control of high-speed vessels by state-space methods. *Journal Ship Research* 50(1).

Cusanelli D, Karafiath G.1997, Integrated wedge-flap for enhanced powering performance. In: Proceedings of Fourth International Conference on *Fast Sea Transportation Sydney FAST97*, Sydney.

De Silva, L.W.A., Yamaguchi, H., 2012, Numerical study on active wave devouring propulsion, *Journal Marine Science & Technology* 17: 261–275.

Filippas ES, Belibassakis KA. 2014, Hydrodynamic analysis of flapping-foil thrusters operating beneath the free surface and in waves. *Engin. Analysis Boundary Elem.* 41:47–59.

Filippas E.S., 2019, *Hydrodynamic analysis of ship and marine biomimetic systems in waves using GPGPU programming*, PhD thesis NTUA.

Fossen T I. 2002, *Marine Control Systems. Guidance, Navigation and Control of Ships Rigs and Underwater Vehicles*. Marine Cybernetics AS, Trondheim, Norway.

Lewis EV. 1989, *Principles of Naval Architecture*. Soc. Naval Architects & Marine Eng. (SNAME). New Jersey.

Murray M.M., Howle L.E., 2003, Spring stiffness influence on an oscillating propulsor, *Journal of Fluids and Structures* 17: 915–926.

Naito S, Isshiki H. 2005, Effect of bow wings on ship propulsion and motions. Applied Mechanics Reviews, 58 (4):253–268.

Nakos D., Sclavounos P., 1990. On steady and unsteady ship wave patterns. *Journ. Fluid Mech.* 215: 263–288.

Politis, G., Politis, K., 2014. Biomimetic propulsion under random heaving conditions, using active pitch control. J. Fluids Struct. 47, 139–149.

Rozhdestvensky KV, Ryzhov VA. 2003, Aerohydrodynamics of flapping wing propulsors. Progress in Aerospace Sciences vol.39:585–633.

Schouveiler L., Hover F.S., Triantafyllou M.S., 2005. Performance of flapping foil propulsion. *J.Fluids Struct.* 20: 949–59.

Politis G.K., Tsarsitalidis V.T., 2014, Flapping wing propulsor design: An approach based on systematic 3D-BEM simulations *Ocean Engineering* 84: 98–123.

Sclavounos PD, Huang YF. 1997, Rudder winglets on sailing yachts. *Marine Technology* 34(3):211–232.

Sclavounos P, Borgen H. 2004, Seakeeping analysis of a high-speed monohull with a motion control bow hydrofoil. *Journal of Ship Research* 48(2):77–117.

Sclavounos P. 2006, Intersections Between Marine Hydrodynamics and Optimal Control Theory. 21st Intern. Workshop on Water Waves and Floating Bodies. Loughborough, England.

Taylor GK Triantafyllou MS, Tropea C. 2010, *Animal Locomotion*. Springer Verlag.

Thomas BS, Sclavounos PD. 2007, Optimal control theory applied to ship maneuvering in restricted waters. *J. of Engineering Mathematics* 58:301–315.

Triantafyllou MS, Triantafyllou GS, Yue DKP. 2000, Hydrodynamics of fishlike swimming. *An. Review Fluid Mech* 32.

Triantafyllou MS, Techet AH, Hover FS. 2004, Review of experimental work in biomimetic foils. *IEEE J. Oceanic Eng.*, 29:585–594.

Wu Xia, Zhang X., Tian X., Li Xin, Lu W., 2020. A review on fluid dynamics of flapping foils, *Ocean Engineering*. 195: Article 106712.

Effects of GPV datasets on WRF modelling of ocean surface wind in rough seas

Chen Chen, Kenji Sasa & Teruo Ohsawa
Department of Maritime Sciences, Kobe University, Japan

Daisuke Terada
School of System Engineering, National Defense Academy, Japan

ABSTRACT: Understanding of the uncertainty of ocean surface wind forecast is of great importance for optimal ship routing, especially in rough sea condition. Data was collected from a bulk carrier during 2010–2016 covering both the Southern and Northern Hemispheres with high seasonal variability. Using the meteorological model, the Weather Research and Forecasting Model (WRF), numerical weather simulations were conducted for eight rough sea cases using the grid point value (GPV) datasets NCEP-FNL and ERA-Interim. Model results were validated by on-board observations. Results showed that optimum ship routing should use the high-resolution WRF model with NCEP-FNL initial and boundary conditions, when compared with the ERA-Interim, to generate ocean surface winds for a more accurate simulation performance in heavy weather.

1 INTRODUCTION

Ocean surface wind is of great importance in the generation of giant ocean waves, which could then lead to the high risk of ship safety and high cost of navigational fuel and time.

Nowadays, meteorological agencies around the world provide various kinds of weather services through their publication of datasets. As shown by the previous studies, different GPV datasets seem to provide reanalysis data with different uncertainties (Mooney et al., 2011, Carvalho et al., 2014, Huang et al., 2018).

Among those, the NCEP-FNL and ERA-Interim made from the NCEP and ECMWF are selected to provide initial and boundary conditions to the widely-used Weather Research and Forecasting model (WRF model).

Differences of these two different GPV datasets (NCEP-FNL and ERA-Interim) as well as the WRF downscaling simulation on the high wind generation of rough seas are studied, aiming at figuring out the uncertainties and then make the selection of the most accurate method generating ocean surface wind for ship routing.

Remote sensing using satellite have also been used for ocean state observations; however, temporal and spatial constraints limit their use for ship weather routing applications.

According to Vettor & Guedes Soares (2016), observations for wind and wave analyses in the southern hemisphere are currently insufficient for the development of a ship routing system.

Rather, high-resolution numerical weather simulations combined with on-board observations could become an efficient means of understanding ship performance in real seas with sufficient spatial and temporal resolution for rough-sea navigation.

2 ON-BOARD OBSERVATION

2.1 *Observation vessel*

On-board observations have been done on a 28,000 DWT class bulk carrier from 2010–2016.

With unfixed shipping routes, the ship has traversed oceans between Asian countries and areas of the Southern Hemisphere such as Oceania and South America, where the sea state is generally rougher when compared to the Northern Hemisphere due to the limited landmass. The ship dimension is shown in Table 1.

With a low operational speed (approximately 12 knots), it had less ability to avoid rough ocean states resulting in deleterious impacts on safety and efficiency.

2.2 *Observation cases*

Totally eight rough sea cases were selected covering both the Northern (cases 1–2) and Southern Hemispheres (cases 3–8) and large seasonal variability. The weather and ship locations for each case are detailed in Table 2.

Table 1. Dimension of the bulk carrier used for observations.

Length between Perpendiculars (LPP)	160.4 m
Breadth	27.2 m
Draft	9.82 m (fully loaded)

Table 2. Weather and ship conditions for each rough sea case.

Case #	Time	Location	Max. wind speed (m/s)
1	Sep 2010	East of Hokkaido	18.6
2	Jun 2011	South of Hokkaido	11.9
3	Sep 2013	Tasman Sea	15.9
4	Nov 2013	South of South Africa	14.6
5	Mar 2016	South of Australia	14.3
6	Mar 2013	Tasman Sea	11.5
7	Jun 2013	South of South Africa	22.3
8	Jun 2013	East of South America	15.0

Table 3. Physics options used in WRF simulation.

Microphysics	WRF Single-Moment (WSM) 3-class simple ice scheme
Long/Shortwave radiation	Rapid Radiative Transfer Model (RRTM)/Dudhia scheme
Surface layer	Monin-Obukhov Similarity scheme
Land surface	Noah Land-Surface Model
Boundary layer	Yonsei University (YSU) scheme
Cumulus	Kain-Fritsch (new Eta) scheme

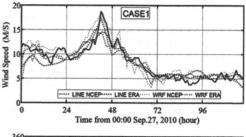

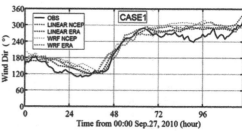

Case 1

3 NUMERICAL SIMULATION

In addition to the linear-interpolation of GPV datasets (the NCEP-FNL and ERA-Interim), the WRF model (Skamarock, 2008) was also used to generate the ocean surface wind fields.

As a next-generation mesoscale numerical weather prediction system designed for both atmospheric research and operational forecasting applications, the WRF model has been widely used for typhoon simulations and real-time forecasting (Jianfeng et al., 2005; Davis et al., 2008; Cha & Wang., 2013).

According to Carvalho et al. (2012), increasing domain resolution is not sufficient to improve model performance. Rather, they suggested that error minimization in the wind simulation could be achieved by testing and choosing a suitable numerical and physical configureuration for the region of interest together with the use of high resolution terrain data .

As the input and boundary condition data, both NCEP-FNL and ERA-Interim were used for the generation of near-surface winds. The WRF model was run with a spatial resolution of 0.1°. Detailed configureurations for the WRF model are shown in Table 3.

4 MODEL VALIDATION WITH ON-BOARD OBSERVATION

Ship observed and WRF simulated wind for all cases, averaged over a 10 minutes' time series recorded every second, are shown in Figure 1.

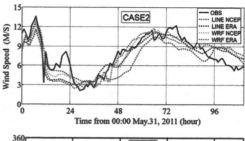

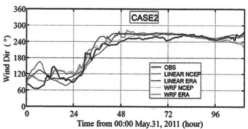

Case 2

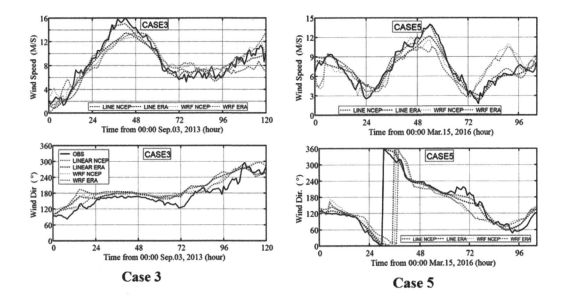

Case 3   Case 5

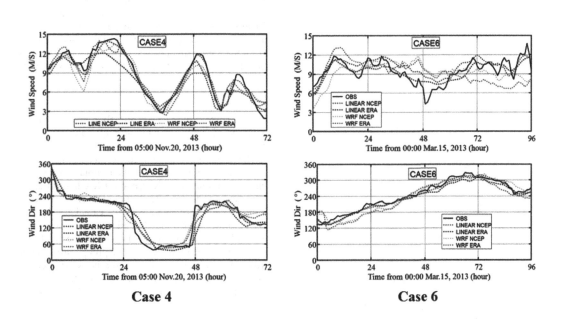

Case 4   Case 6

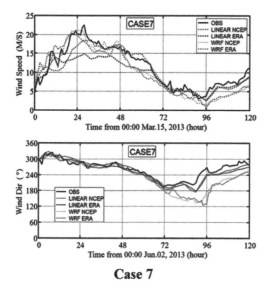

Case 7

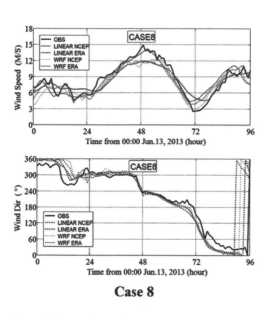

Case 8

Figure. 1. Comparisons of WRF model wind velocity for eight rough sea cases.

Generally speaking, as shown in Figure 1 where Black lines represent on-board observations, 'LINE NCEP' and 'LINE ERA' represent the wind velocity obtained by the linear interpolation of the NCEP and ERA-Interim datasets, and 'WRF NCEP' and 'WRF ERA' are wind velocity calculated by the WRF model, respectively; WRF results demonstrate a considerably reasonable replication of wind speed and direction for all cases.

The linear interpolation of NCEP-FNL tends to perform better for high wind for most cases, while the linear interpolation of ERA-Interim tends to underestimate high winds.

Moreover, owning to the downscaled simulations of the mesoscale model, WRF generates better results than linear interpolation for extremely high wind speed cases (Case 1, 7).

In terms of the wind direction, ERA-Interim tends to perform better than NCEP-FNL. A detailed analysis of the results as well as a discussion are presented in Section 5.

5 RESULTS AND DISCUSSION

5.1 Model evaluation statistics and classifications

Taking the factors of wind forcing on wave generation into account, Biases and RMSE data were classified as shown in Table 4.

Cases were grouped according to their maximum wind speed (wind strength): $V_{max} \leq 12$ m/s (cases 2 and 6), 12 m/s $\leq V_{max} \leq 15$ m/s (cases 4, 5, and 8), 15 m/s $\leq V_{max} \leq 20$ m/s (cases 1 and 3), and $V_{max} \leq$ 20 m/s (case 7) and the time period of risk (wind duration): the total period (including wind simulations for approximately one week) and peak period (the 12 hours prior to and after the highest wind).

5.2 Evaluation results

Figure 2 and Figure 3 are the Bias and RMSE of wind speed based on wind strength and wind duration, respectively.

Here, the 'linear-ncep' (red circle) and 'linear-era' (blue circle) represent the wind obtained by the linear interpolation of NCEP and ERA-Interim datasets, and 'wrf-ncep' (red triangle) and 'wrf-era' (blue triangle) are wind velocity calculated by the WRF model with input boundary conditions from the NCEP and ERA-Interim datasets, respectively.

As shown in Figure 2-A, four groups are formed from all simulated cases based on the wind strength as given in Section 5.1. It can be seen that for low wind speed cases (Case 2 and Case 6), ERA-Interim

Table 4. Classifications for Bias and RMSE calculations.

Group divisions	Details of group divisions			
Wind strength	$V_{max} \leq 12$	$12 \leq V_{max} \leq 15$	$15 \leq V_{max} \leq 20$	$V_{max} 20$
Wind duration	Total period (approximately one week)		Peak period (approximately one day)	

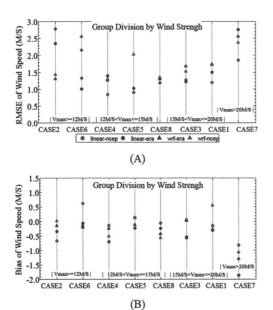

(A)

(B)

Figure. 2. Bias and RMSE of wind speeds based on wind strength.

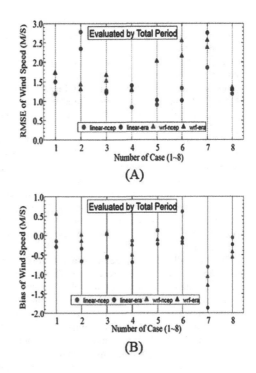

(A)

(B)

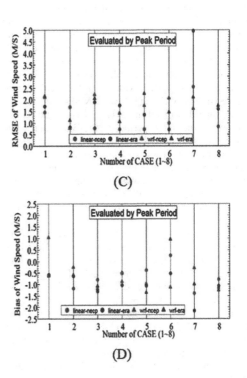

(C)

(D)

Figure. 3. Bias and RMSE of wind speed based on wind duration.

performs better with smaller RMSE values, while NCEP-FNL exhibits a better performance for extremely high wind speeds (Case 1 and Case 7) and most other high wind speed cases (Case 3, Case 4, Case 5, and Case 8).

Similar results are also shown in Figure 2-B, where ERA-Interim tends to have a steadier performance for low wind speed cases (Case 2 and Case 6) with smaller absolute Bias values, while NCEP-FNL can reproduce extremely high and high wind speed cases with a better accuracy.

Again, both Figure 3-A and Figure 3-C (RMSE values of "Total Period" and "Peak Period") show that NCEP-FNL generally simulates the extremely high and high wind speed cases more accurately when compared to ERA-Interim (Case 1, Case 3, Case 4, Case 5, Case 7, and Case 8).

While Figure 3-B and Figure 3-D (Bias values of "Total Period" and "Peak Period") show that owing to the downscaling effects, the WRF model can simulate the stronger (Case 7) and lower wind speed cases (Cases 2) more effectively when compared to the linear interpolation method, which tends to perform better for other relatively modest wind cases (Case 1, Case 3, Case 4, Case 5, and Case 8).

Furthermore, as shown in Figure 3-D, comparisons of Bias values show that although both NCEP-FNL and ERA-Interim tend to underestimate winds of the peak period for most cases, the absolute values of Bias in NCEP-FNL are generally smaller as compared to ERA-Interim, particularly for extremely high and high wind speed cases (Case 3, Case 4, Case 5, Case 7, and Case 8).

Moreover, NCEP-FNL shows a better performance for generating higher wind speed cases than ERA-Interim.

In Figure 4, Bias and RMSE of wind direction based on wind duration are given.

Generally, the RMSE values in Figure 4-A and Figure 4-C show that the ERA-Interim dataset performs better than the NCEP-FNL for the reproduction of wind direction.

Furthermore, the Bias values in Figure 4-B and Figure 4-D show that these modeling approaches tend to simulate the wind direction with a clockwise tendency when compared with observations for most cases, excluding the low wind periods of these cases, which can, in turn, show a better performance in generating wind direction for higher wind speed periods than for lower wind speed periods for these simulations.

Additionally, the averaged Bias and RMSE values of wind speed and wind direction obtained using different modeling approaches are also given for all rough sea cases, as shown in Table 5 and Table 6.

As shown in Table 5, all the absolute values in blue in the first and third columns ("Linear-FNL" and "WRF-FNL") are smaller than those in the second and fourth columns, showing that NCEP-FNL exhibits a better average performance when reproducing wind speeds of rough sea surfaces than that ERA-Interim, although ERA-Interim can better reproduce low wind cases (Case 2 and Case 6) and NCEP-FNL exhibits a better performance on extremely high and high wind speed cases (Case 1, Case 3, Case 4, Case 5, Case 7, and Case 8).

Moreover, both the absolute values of all averaged Bias and RMSE values of the peak period ("Ave-Bias-PEAK" and "Ave-RMSE-PEAK") are larger than that of all the averaged Bias and RMSE values of the total period ("Ave-Bias-Total" and "Ave-RMSE-Total"), showing a larger underestimation of the highest wind speed period (i.e., the peak period) than of the averaged lower wind period (i.e., the total period), as shown in Figure 2. This point shows a weakness of all methods in generating the peak wind strength in comparison to on-board observations.

Then, as seen in Table 5, the utilization of the WRF model can reduce the extent of underestimation considering the first two rows of "Ave-Bias-TOTAL" and "Ave-Bias-PEAK" (the absolute values of "WRF-FNL" and "WRF-ERA" are smaller than those of "Linear-FNL" and "Linear-ERA"). Furthermore, both of the RMSE values in "Ave-RMSE-TOTAL" and "Ave-RMSE-PEAK" show that NCEP-FNL performs better for the highest wind speed period (peak period) than ERA-Interim.

For the peak Period, the WRF downscaling method can perform better than the linear interpolation method for extremely high wind speed periods (Case 1 and Case 7), while linear interpolation of

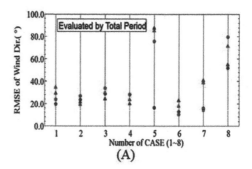

(A)

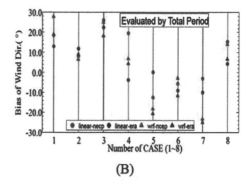

(B)

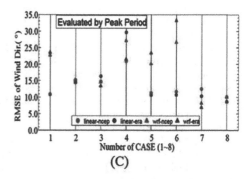

(C)

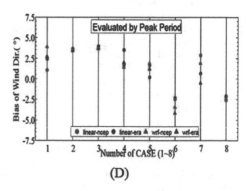

(D)

Figure. 4. Bias and RMSE of wind direction based on wind duration.

Table 5. Averaged Bias and RMSE of wind speed by using different modeling approaches: Linear-FNL, Linear-ERA, WRF-FNL as well as WRF-ERA.

	Linear-FNL	Linear-ERA	WRF-FNL	WRF-ERA	Ave.
Bias-Total	-0.20	-0.53	-0.19	-0.33	-0.31
Bias-Peak	-0.68	-1.05	-0.61	-0.68	-0.75
RMSE-Total	1.30	1.57	1.76	1.78	1.60
RMSE-Peak	1.22	1.85	1.69	1.73	1.62

Table 6. Averaged Bias and RMSE of wind direction by using different modeling approaches: Linear-FNL, Linear-ERA, WRF-FNL as well as WRF-ERA.

	Linear-FNL	Linear-ERA	WRF-FNL	WRF-ERA	Ave.
Bias-Total	8.35	3.62	4.46	-0.003	4.10
Bias-Peak	1.21	1.23	1.29	0.74	1.120
RMSE-Total	23.21	21.19	27.16	26.25	24.45
RMSE-Peak	14.31	15.35	19.00	18.79	16.86

NCEP-FNL exhibits better performance for high wind speed cases (Case 3, Case 4, Case 5, and Case 8). For low wind cases (Case 2 and Case 6), the results of the linear interpolation method agree better with the observations while the WRF downscaling method has a tendency to overestimate the results. In addition, averages of RMSE values of around 1.6 m/s for both the total and peak periods are shown for all the rough sea simulations.

It can be clearly seen from Table 6 that a combination of the WRF model and ERA-Interim (values in blue) can perform better than the combination the WRF model and NCEP-FNL (values in red) when generating the wind direction, as shown in the third and fourth columns ("WRF-FNL" and "WRF-ERA").

Moreover, both GPV datasets and modeling approaches tend to reproduce the wind direction better for high wind speed cases ("Ave-Bias-PEAK" and "Ave-RMSE-PEAK") than for low wind cases ("Ave-Bias-TOTAL" & "Ave-RMSE-TOTAL"). Furthermore, compared with the linear interpolation method, the utilization of the WRF model tends to lead to overestimation with a clockwise tendency in reproducing the wind direction at the peak wind strength period.

It should also be noted that the wind directions of both Case 5 and Case 8 are excluded for the calculation of RMSE in Table 6 because of the sudden variations resulting from the time delay of wind rotation, as shown in Figure 1. In addition, averages of RMSE values of around 25° and 17° for total and peak periods are obtained from all the rough sea simulations.

6 CONCLUSIONS

Eight rough sea navigation cases were investigated to determine the best GPV dataset and modeling approach for the estimation of ocean surface wind for optimum ship routing applications. Ocean surface winds were generated using linear interpolation of NCEP-FNL and ERA-Interim data, and WRF simulations.

Results were validated using on-board observations of wind velocity for eight rough sea cases. Owing to their geographic positions, these cases can be said to represent open ocean conditions.

Through all these weather and ocean simulations as well as the validation of results against on-board observations, we can draw the following conclusions for weather and simulations and ship navigation in open and rough seas:

For the wind speed simulations, results show that although all methods show a weakness in generating the peak period of wind speeds (the time of maximum wind speed), the NCEP-FNL tends to simulate better results for higher wind when compared with ERA-Interim, which also agrees with other studies, such as (Stopa, et al., 2014), who found that ERA-I generally underestimates the wind speed and wave height with lower standard deviations in comparison to observations while despite having a small positive bias, CFSR provides a better description of the variability of the observations and improved performance in the upper percentiles associated with extreme events.

Besides, by dividing analysis databases into overall conditions and extreme events, (Campos, et al., 2015) also argued that the lowest errors and best performance was obtained by CFSR, followed by HIPOCAS (REMO) at mid–high latitudes and ERA-Interim at low latitudes, and a significant underestimation of ERA-Interim for the peak of the storms was found, which can be associated with its coarse time and space resolution.

Therefore, compared with the ERA-Interim, the NCEP-FNL is recommended for ship routing because of its improved representation of strong winds during rough sea conditions, which is of great importance for ship safety and optimal routing.

Furthermore, the utilization of a high-resolution WRF model tends to increase the accuracy of wind simulations for extremely high wind when compared to the linear interpolation method, which tends to perform better for other relatively modest wind speed conditions.

ACKNOWLEDGEMENTS

We acknowledge the data providers of the National Centers for the Environmental Prediction Final Operation Model Global Tropospheric Analyses and the European Center for Medium-range Weather Forecasts Interim Reanalysis and the development groups of the Weather Research and Forecasting Model. We would like to thank Shoei Kisen Kaisha Ltd., Northstar Shipping Management Ltd., and the crew of the bulk carrier which collected the data used in this research.

REFERENCES

Carvalho, D., Rocha, A., Gómez-Gesteira, M., & Santos, C. (2012). A sensitivity study of the WRF model in wind simulation for an area of high wind energy. Environmental Modelling & Software, 33, 23–34.

Carvalho, D., Rocha, A., Gómez-Gesteira, M., & Santos, C. S. (2014). WRF wind simulation and wind energy production estimates forced by different reanalyses: Comparison with observed data for Portugal. Applied Energy, 117, 116–126.

Cha, Dong-Hyun and Yuqing Wang. "A dynamical initialization scheme for real-time forecasts of tropical cyclones using the WRF model." Monthly Weather Review 141.3 (2013): 964–986.

Campos, R.M. and Guedes Soares, C. "Assessment of three wind reanalyses in the North Atlantic Ocean." Journal of Operational Oceanography 10.1 (2017): 30–44.

Davis, C., Wang, W., Chen, S. S., Chen, Y., Corbosiero, K., DeMaria, M. & Reeves, H. (2008). Prediction of landfalling hurricanes with the advanced hurricane WRF model. Monthly weather review, 136(6), 1990–2005.

Huang, Danlian, and Shibo Gao. "Impact of different reanalysis data on WRF dynamical downscaling over China." Atmospheric Research 200 (2018): 25–35.

Mooney, P. A, F. J. Mulligan, and Rowan Fealy. "Comparison of ERA-40, ERA-Interim and NCEP/NCAR reanalysis data with observed surface air temperatures over Ireland." International Journal of Climatology 31.4 (2011): 545–557.

Sasa, K., Terada, D., Shiotani, S., Wakabayashi, N., Ikebuchi, T., Chen, C., & Uchida, M. (2015). Evaluation of ship performance in international maritime transportation using an onboard measurement system-in case of a bulk carrier in international voyages. Ocean Engineering, 104, 294–309.

Skamarock, W. C., J. B. Klemp, J. Dudhia, D. O. Gill, D. M. Barker, M. G Duda, X.-Y. Huang, W. Wang, and J. G. Powers, 2008: A Description of the Advanced Research WRF Version 3. NCAR Tech. Note NCAR/TN-475+STR, 113 pp. doi: 10.5065/D68S4MVH

Stopa, Justin E., and Kwok Fai Cheung. "Intercomparison of wind and wave data from the ECMWF Reanalysis Interim and the NCEP Climate Forecast System Reanalysis." Ocean Modelling 75 (2014): 65–83.

Vettor, R., and Guedes Soares, C. "Rough weather avoidance effect on the wave climate experienced by ocean-going vessels." Applied Ocean Research 59 (2016): 606–615.

Experimental study of ship resistance in broken ice

J.E. Gutiérrez-Romero, S. Ruiz-Capel, J. Esteve-Pérez, B. Zamora-Parra & J.P. Luna-Abad

Universidad Politécnica de Cartagena (UPCT), Cartagena, Murcia, Spain

ABSTRACT: The increase of the average temperature in artic regions is boosting the ice setback, which allows keeping the artic navigation routes open for longer periods, open new ones, and expand the commercial fishing. In fact, shipping lines are more and more enthusiastic about the potential that these new routes offer, given the save of time and energy cost that might provide compared to longer traditional routes. In this sense, this paper presents some issues regarding with experimentation carried out at CEHINAV Towing Tank (Spain) to study the ship resistance in broken ice. The tests were conducted using paraffin wax as simulated broken ice. First, some aspects regarding with ship ice navigation are exposed. Second, main particulars of a ship model based on B.I.O. Hesperides (Spanish Army) to carry out the towing tests are shown. Third, hypothesis used to configure tests are explained. Finally, some conclusions and results are exposed regarding with experimentation conducted.

1 INTRODUCTION

Since the industrial revolution, human activities have played a huge role in climate change. Pollutant greenhouse gases emissions have made global temperatures increase over the years driving to the melting of the ice on Earth's poles. This changing scenario may present challenges for all societies worldwide. On the other hand, adaptation might create new opportunities: Arctic shipping.

In recent decades, Arctic Sea ice extent experiments bigger differences between maximum (March) and minimum ice cover (September). As summer sea ice cover recedes year by year in the Arctic Sea, from North Eurasia to North America, following trends which vary depending on the region in Canadian Arctic waters, from 2.4% to 11.3% decade (Tivy et al., 2011), new sea routes remain open for ship traffic for a longer time.

Connections between North America and North-East Asia can be accomplished through the North West Passage instead of Panama Canal route; connections between North Europe and North-East Asia through the Northern Sea Route instead of Suez Canal, saving thousands of miles, days, emissions and size restrictions in both cases. Future greenhouse gases have a larger impact by midcentury. Distances will be shorter through the Trans-Polar Sea Route (Melia et al., 2016).

Due to these advantages, market opportunity in Arctic shipping is being considered by shipping companies and cargo vessels operators, mainly related to natural resources exploitation, new destination traffic and transit, according to scientific literature (Frédéric et al. 2016).

1.1 *State of art*

Whatever the reason may be to select a voyage through Arctic Sea, vessels will find several hazards and challenges in their way: from small floes to level ice, ridges and big icebergs (Bridges et al., 2018). As long as sea ice exists, ice-going vessels across the Arctic need to meet special requirements about ship's structure, power, subdivision and stability, hull strengthening and considerations about equipment and navigation among others. These requirements are defined by the Polar Code (IMO, 2014).

Interaction between hull and ice knowledge has made many researchers develop methods to predict ship's hydrodynamic resistance in ice infested waters. Lindqvist (1989) developed an empirical method to predict ship's resistance in level ice from research on full scale tests, by dividing ice resistance into crushing, bending and submergence components. Riska (1997) modified Lindqvist's equations based on empirical coefficients and validated a model with 13 sample vessels from full scale test. Including later developments in Computer Fluid Dynamics (CFD) have allowed researchers getting numerical models without the need of using full scale data, as the method developed by Jeong et al. (2017a) or the proposed by Su et al. (2010) to simulate ship maneuverability in level ice. Huang et al. (2019) gives a CFD combined with Discrete Element Method (DEM) approach to estimate ship-wave-ice interaction in circular ice floes, considering it will be the most representative ice condition in the future Arctic Sea.

Data for better understanding of ice-going ships' features, drove to the construction of ice tanks facilities for ice model testing. These facilities are used to

DOI: 10.1201/9781003216599-3

test ship's models, Arctic platforms, new technology developments as Azipod in Aker Arctic (Arctic, 2019), study the influence of resistance in brash ice channels and develop methodologies to properly test such conditions (Jeong et al., 2017a). These ice model testing facilities require high installation and maintenance costs, as well as high cost for tests development to produce refrigerated ice as EG/AD/S (diluted aqueous solution of ethylene glycol (EG), aliphatic detergent (AD), and Sugar (S)) (Timco, 1986).

Due to the high costs committed when producing ice in ice basins, some researchers have tried to carry out these tests in traditional towing tanks by using artificial ice, enabling lower costs at higher and more comfortable working temperatures. (Van Der Werff et al., 2015) used artificial ice in MARIN's Concept Basin made out of rigid polypropylene (PP) particles. They made a 'fishbone' presawn ice channel surrounded by large PP plates, similar to ice conditions in refrigerated model test facilities. Kim et al. (2013) made test at the Pausan National University towing tank with synthetic ice made of right triangle shaped fragments of semi-refined paraffin wax and compared the results with test of EG/AD/S and numerical methods.

This paper is aimed to give a methodology to simulate ice model tests with paraffin wax artificial ice. These tests were put into effect for small ice floes and ice cake according with sea ice navigation (WMO, 2014) with size distribution according to natural patterns distribution of sea ice (Toyota et al., 2011).

2 EXPERIMENTAL SET UP

In this section, the planning of the experimentation is explained. As pointed above the aim of this work is to present the results of experimentation to artificial paraffin wax ice floe and the influence of broken ice in ship resistance.

2.1 Ship model

The model selected to conduct the experimentation was based in a research ship of Spanish Army called B.I.O. Hespérides (CSIC, 2020). The main characteristics of full scale and ship model are shown in Table 1.

Figure 1 shows a photography of model built for tow test. This model was selected due to its long time periods in polar regions and the importance for Spanish polar research. The model also has a compromise bow (Grochowalski & Hermanski, 2011) valid for open drift water or navigation with certain size of ice floes.

2.2 Ice floe distribution and coverage

Key parameters for the experimentation are the selection of the coverage, the channel length, the ice floe distribution and the size.

Table 1. Main parameters of full scale and ship model selected to experimentation.

	Full scale	Model
Scale	1:1	1:21.43
Total Length (m)	82.588	3.824
Waterline length (m)	76.791	3.583
Breath (m)	14.591	0.681
Depth (m)	12.102	0.565
Draught	4.421	0.306
Full load displacement	2725.9 t	127.200 kg
Metacentric height (m)		0.186
Pitch radii of gyration (m)		0.850

Figure 1. Photography of B.I.O. Hespérides 1:21.43 model scaled built for experimentation.

2.2.1 Coverage and channel length

To conduct the experiment three coverages are selected according to typical sea navigation (CCG, 2012) in broken ice. Table 2 shows three types of coverages used to perform experimentations. The percentage of coverage is determined according with area used for resistance analysis.

Figure 2 shows three images obtained from experimentation with three paraffin wax ice floe coverages.

Channel length has been selected according to ITTC procedures and similar works (Van der Werff et al., 2015; Guo et al. 2018). It should be noted that ITTC procedures are stablished for level ice, not for test in broken ice. The channel dimensions were 25 × 3.8 meters enough to obtain resistance, trim and other significant value signals.

Table 2. Percentage of test channel area covered by synthetic ice floes.

	Percentage (%)	Type of water
Coverage 1	30	Very open drift
Coverage 2	45	Open drift
Coverage 3	60	Open drift

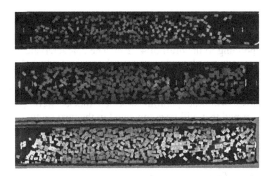

Figure 2. Total area covered by paraffin wax ice floes. Top: 30%. Centre: 45%. Bottom: 60%.

2.2.2 *Paraffin wax as artificial ice floes*

The experimentation of sea ice navigation requires the use of complex and expensive facilities. These have to be able to maintain suitable conditions to carry out sea ice experimentation. There exist few facilities around the world with real capacity for model testing of ice navigation.

However new techniques trying to reduce the costs of this type of infrastructure are appearing, boosted by the growing interest in studying the operation of ships and structures in polar areas. In the literature, two main trends can be noted related to ice modelling for experimental studies on the navigation of ships in the presence of surface ice.

The first is based on aqueous solution with different chemical compounds called EG/AD/S, as pointed in the introduction (Timco, 1989). This solution is very similar to sea ice and although it must be refrigerated, the required temperature is not as low as actual ice.

The second trend is the use of a paraffin wax whose mechanical characteristics is similar to sea ice, as well as the density. In order to reproduce the desired friction effect on the hull, it must be cut according to the specific ice scenario and the scale of the prototype. Main characteristics of paraffin wax are noted in Table 3.

The use of paraffin wax allows us to achieve one of the goals of this work, to obtain ship ice resistance in broken ice with a more affordable solution.

2.2.3 *Ice floe distribution and size*

The size and the distribution of ice floes along the channel length are important parameters to be considered. There is scarce information about the ice floe distribution for broken ice towing tank tests, in a literature review. Toyota et al. (2011) works have been used to select suitable size of paraffin wax blocks according to real patterns of polar areas. The statistics properties of ice floes are shown in Table 4. Assuming scale in variance in fracture patterns of ice floes and rectangular shape of broken ice the number of fragments N_{ma} can be determined as (Toyota et al., 2011)

$$N_{ma} = (1-f)(4f)^m N_o \quad (1)$$

being f a fragility coefficient, m the order of cell and N_o the number of ice blocks with biggest size used.

Typical sizes of ice floes in open drift waters have values less than 20 meters of diameter.

For this experimentation, two sizes are selected. First one is the base size with dimensions shown in Table 4, and second one is the one quarter of biggest block. Numbers of small pieces are determined taking m equal to 1 from Equation (1). Depending of area covered by piece of blocks and percentage of biggest blocks, different number of small pieces were obtained. Large number of blocks with different sizes in maximum percentage tested were required.

Distributions in free surface of piece of blocks were in random pattern, ensuring a homogeneous distribution of all space covered by paraffin wax blocks during tests.

2.3 Tow tank tests

The tests were conducted in a model basin with 100 m in length, 3.8 m. in width and 2.2 m. in depth at CEHINAV (Spain). Three Froude values corresponding with 2.0, 3.0 and 4.8 knots of the full-scale ship were selected. They are typical velocities in broken ice navigation. The overall tests consisted in:

- Open water resistance test.
- Open water self-propulsion test.
- Resistance test in broken ice.
- Self-propulsion test in broken ice.

Figure 3 shows a caption during the experimentation at model basin.

Table 3. Main parameters of synthetic paraffin wax used as synthetic ice.

	Value
Density	830 kg/m^3
Type	Macrocrystallines
Oil percentage (maximum)	0.5 %
Shape	Rectangular
Mean thickness	40 mm

Table 4. Statistics and fragility coefficient to determine the number of synthetic ice floes used in experimentation.

	Value
Fragility coefficient (f)	0.6
Mean thickness	40 mm
Percentage of biggest paraffin wax blocks	80 %
Mean length of biggest blocks	484 mm
Mean breath of biggest blocks	295 mm

Figure 3. Photography of experimentation conducted at model basin with 60 % of test area covered. Black points on paraffin wax ice blocks were used to track instant position during experimentation.

3 RESULTS

Prediction of total resistance in ship ice navigation is a key parameter for new Polar class ship design. Many works regarding ice resistance can be found, giving empirical or analytical formulation.

For instance, Lindqvist (1989) and Riska (1998) give formulation related with ice breaking models which considered the total resistance divided into several items: resistance due to breaking (R_{br}), resistance due to clearing (R_c), resistance due to buoyancy of piece of blocks (R_b) and resistance in open waters (R_o) so,

$$R_{ice} = R_{br} + R_c + R_b + R_{ci} \qquad (2)$$

For this work total resistance of ships in broken ice could be decomposed in (Kim et al., 2013; Grochowalski & Hermanski 2011):

$$R_{ice} = R_o + R_b + R_{ci} \qquad (3)$$

No breaking resistance is considered in this experimentation.

If total resistance is obtained from experimentation and simple formulation of Jeong et al. (2010) is used for buoyancy resistance, clearing resistance could be determined. Jeong formula for buoyancy resistance is,

$$R_b = C_B \Delta \rho g h_i B T \qquad (4)$$

being C_B the coefficient of ice buoyancy resistance, h_i the ice block thickness, B the beam of the ship, T the draught, $\Delta \rho$ the difference between water density and ice density and g the gravity acceleration.

3.1 Open water resistance

The hull has been tested in a load condition corresponding to the draft of 4.42 m. The characteristics of the rehearsed condition were shown in Table 1. Initially, towing and self-propelled tests without ice modeling were carried out. Subsequently, series of tests with the paraffin wax ice blocks were performed that will be commented in the next section.

Figure 4 shows the curve of ship resistance for different values of Froude number.

3.2 Total ice resistance

Several tow tests were performed to reduce uncertainty in resistance analysis. Figures 5, 6 and 7 show filtered resistance for nine runs with different Froude number for three coverages used in experimentation. As can be noted, the more percentage of area covered the more ship resistance in ice is observed.

Data was filtered using moving average to remove all noise of signal captured. Tables 5, 6, and 7 show mean, statistical deviation, covariance and other important parameters of runs conducted at CEHINAV. In these tables, it can be observed that significant increase on ship resistance is captured. More than 10 times higher if compared with open water resistance.

3.3 Buoyancy and clearing resistance

Using Jeong formulation (Jeong et al., 2010) buoyancy resistance can be determined. This term is determined as constant and independently of ship velocity. For these cases its value is approximately in the range of 0.69 to 0.98 Newtons. It can be considered as negligible if compared with total resistance. An example of buoyancy action of paraffin wax blocks can be noted in Figure 8.

Knowing the open water resistance (R_o) and total resistance in broken ice navigation (R_{ice}) it is possible to determine the resistance of clearing paraffin

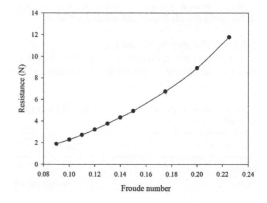

Figure 4. Open water resistance of ship model 1:21.43 for different Froude numbers tested.

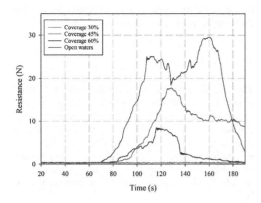

Figure 5. Filtered resistance for Froude number equal to 0.0375 for three coverages experimented compared with open water resistance.

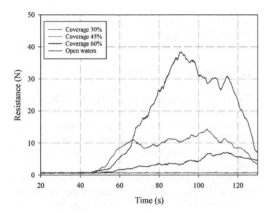

Figure 6. Filtered resistance for Froude number equal to 0.0563 for three coverages experimented compared with open water resistance.

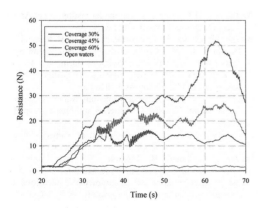

Figure 7. Filtered resistance for Froude number equal to 0.090 for three coverages experimented compared with open water resistance.

Table 5. Statistical parameters of resistance in Newtons for 2 knots.

Coverage	O.W.	30%	45%	60%
Mean	0.31	2.12	4.62	12.69
Variance	0.002	12.24	48.41	433.50
Standard dev.	0.04	3.09	6.77	20.28
RMS	0.10	3.80	8.22	23.94

(*) O.W. Open Waters.

Table 6. Statistical parameters of resistance in Newtons for 3 knots.

Coverage	O.W.	30%	45%	60%
Mean	0.71	2.63	6.47	12.75
Variance	0.003	155.53	96.16	394.52
Standard dev.	0.06	9.91	9.59	19.73
RMS	0.51	10.35	11.57	23.50

Table 7. Statistical parameters of resistance in Newtons for 4.8 knots.

Coverage	O.W.	30%	45%	60%
Mean	1.83	5.48	9.66	15.29
Variance	0.05	246.49	475.03	649.16
Standard dev.	0.23	13.66	20.54	25.32
RMS	3.39	14.89	22.83	29.61

Figure 8. Underwater eye fish capture with test at 45% coverage with paraffin wax blocks.

wax blocks. Figure 9 shows mean clearing resistance of each coverage tested.

3.4 Results comparison

As can be noted in Figure 10, an increase in coverage results in higher ship resistance. For low ship

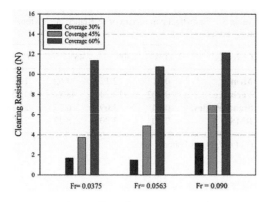

Figure 9. Clearing resistance of model for three Froude numbers and three coverages analyzed.

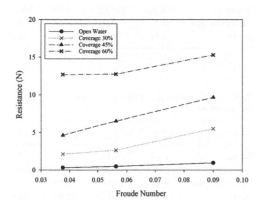

Figure 10. Total resistance of model for three Froude numbers and three coverages analyzed.

velocities, the change in resistance is not relevant if compared with the increasing due to different ice floes coverages.

It seems clear that the ice clearing resistance of ship is major component for this type of navigation if comparing with open water resistance and buoyancy resistance.

As can be noted from results obtained mean clearing resistance reaches values around 75 percent of total ship resistance in broken ice navigation. The buoyancy resistance is in the order of open water resistance for these cases in order of range of 12 percent of total resistance

Similar values can be obtained for clearing resistance if compared with formulation of Jeong model for 60 percent of concentration. Assuming ice floes were accumulated at bow of ship, instantaneous concentration of artificial ice floes are higher than value tested, reaching many times concentrations over 80 percent. In this case, clearing resistance obtained by formulation is equal to 11.82 N and the resulting from experimentation is equal to 12.11 N.

4 CONCLUSIONS

The use of artificial ice as paraffin wax could be a solution to obtain affordable solution avoiding high cost of ice tests. This solution might be used in traditional towing tank basins, open new possibilities and enable low cost facilities to investigate ship navigation in polar areas. However, more research should be added to delve in the use of paraffin wax ice blocks, the manage and the interaction with the hull.

As can be noticed, ship ice navigation increases the resistance considerably. Most of energy consumed by ship is wasted in clearing ice blocks. Open water results are only a little bit part of total resistance experienced by ship during its navigation.

From the experimentation can be observed that total ship resistance increases in order of ten times if compared with open water results.

ACKNOWLEDGEMENTS

The authors acknowledge CEHINAV whose facilities made this work possible.

Thanks to Luís Pérez Rojas, Ricardo Abad and CIMNE Naval research group for providing its knowledge and support to carry out this experimentation.

Thanks to Carlos López Pavón and Pablo Romero for providing their assistance during experimentation.

The research leading to these results has received funding from the Spanish Ministry for Economy and Competitiveness under Grants RTI2018-094744-A-C22 (NICESHIP).

REFERENCES

Arctic, A. 2019. 50 years of ice model testing. Aker Arctic Technology Inc. Finland. Online.

Bridges, R. Riska, K. Griewank, P. Lattes, P. Rampal, P. Bouillon, S. 2018. Constituents of Ice Navigation Systems from Ship Based Observations during Ice Transit of Kara Sea. 24th IAHR International Symposium on Ice, pp. 484–498. Vladivostok, Russia.

CCG. 2012. Ice Navigation in Canadian Waters. Canadian Coast Guard. Minister of Fisheries and Oceans Canada. Online.

CSIC. 2020. Unidad de Tecnología Marina. Consejo Superior de Investigación Científica. www.utm.csic.es

Frédéric, L. Leah, B. Mélanie, F. Pierre-Louis, T. Linyan, H. 2016. Polar seaways? Maritime transport in the Arctic: An analysis of shipowners' intentions II. Journal of Transport Geography. 5/7(C):105–114. http://dx.doi.org/10.1016/j.jtrangeo.2016.10.004.

Guo, C-y. Zhang, Z-t. Tian, T-p. Li, X-y. Zhao, D-g. 2018. Numerical Simulation on the Resistance Performance of Ice-Going Container Ship Under Brash Ice Conditions.

China Ocean Engineering. 32(5): 546–556. https://doi.org/10.1007/s13344-018-0057-2.
Grochowalski, S. Hermanski, G. Ship Resistance and Propulsion in Ice-Covered Waters: An Experimental Study. *Transactions SNAME*. 119: 67–92.
Huang, L. Tuhkuri, J. Igrec, B. Li, M. Stagonas, D. Toffoli, A. Cardiff, P. Thomas, G. 2019. Ship resistance when operating in floating ice floes: a combined CFD & DEM approach. Cornell University.
IMO. 2014. International Code for ship operating in Polar Waters. (POLAR CODE). MEPC 68/21/Add.1.
Jeong, S-Y. Lee, C-j. Cho, S-R. 2010. Ice Resistance Prediction for Standard Icebreaker Model Ship. Proceedings of the Twentieth (2010) International Offshore and Polar Engineering Conference. Beijing, China.
Jeong, S-Y. Jang, J. Kang, K-J. Kim, H-S. 2017a. Implementation of ship performance test in brash ice channel. *Ocean Engineering*. 140(1): 55–65. https://doi.org/10.1016/j.oceaneng.2017.05.008.
Jeong, S-Y. Choi, K. Kang, K-J. Ha, J-S. 2017b. Prediction of ship resistance in level ice based on empirical approach. *International Journal of Naval Architecture and Ocean Engineering*. 9(6): 613–623. https://doi.org/10.1016/j.ijnaoe.2017.03.007.
Kim, M-C. Lee, S-K. Lee, W-J. Wang, J-y. 2013. Numerical and experimental investigation of the resistance performance of an icebreaking cargo vessel in pack ice conditions. *International Journal of Naval Architecture and Ocean Engineering*. 5(1): 116–131 http://dx.doi.org/10.2478/IJNAOE-2013-0121.
Lindqvist, G. 1989. A straightforward method for calculation of ice resistance of ships. Proceedings of the 10th International Conference on Port and Ocean Engineering under Arctic Conditions, pp. 722–735. Lulea, Sweden.
Melia, N. Haines, K. Hawkins, E. 2016. Sea ice decline and 21st century trans-Arctic shipping routes. *Geophysical Research Letters*. 43(18):9720–9728. https://doi.org/10.1002/2016GL069315.
Riska, K. 1997. Performance of merchant vessels in ice in the Baltic. Espoo: Helsinki University of Technology, Ship Laboratory.
Timco, G.W. 1986. EG/AD/S: A new type of model ice for refrigerated towing tanks. *Cold Regions Science and Technology*. 12(2):175–195. https://doi.org/10.1016/0165-232X(86)90032-7.
Tivy, A. Howell, S.E.L. Alt, B. McCourt, S. Chagnon, R. Crocker, G. Carrieres, T. Yackel, J.J. 2011. Trends and variability in summer sea ice cover in the Canadian Arctic based on the Canadian Ice Service Digital Archive, 1960–2008 and 1968–2008. *Journal of Geophysic Research*. 116(C6), https://doi.org/10.1029/2009JC005855.
Toyota, T. Haas, C. Tamura, T. 2011. Size distribution and shape properties of relatively small sea-ice floes in the Antarctic marginal ice zone in late winter. *Deep Sea Research Part II: Topical Studies in Oceanography*. 58 (9-10): 1182–1193. https://doi.org/10.1016/j.dsr2.2010.10.034.
Su, B. Riska, K. Moan, T. 2010. A numerical method for the prediction of ship performance in level ice. *Cold Regions Science and Technology*. 60(3):177–188. https://doi.org/10.1016/j.coldregions.2009.11.006.
Van Der Werff, S. Joris, Brouwer, J. Hagesteijin G. 2015. Ship Resistance Validation Using Artificial Ice. 34th International Conference on Ocean, Offshore and Arctic Engineering. Newfoundland, Canada. https://doi.org/10.1115/OMAE2015-41804.
WMO. 2014. Sea Ice Nomenclature. World Meteorological Organization. Online.

Effect of optimal thruster location on DP operability of an offshore vessel

F. Mauro
Department of Engineering and Architecture, University of Trieste, Trieste, Italy

R. Nabergoj
NASDIS PDS d.o.o., Izola, Slovenija

J. Prpić-Oršić
Faculty of Engineering, University of Rijeka, Rijeka, Croatia

ABSTRACT: In the offshore industry, the thruster layout for dynamic positioning (DP) is not optimal to reach the maximum station-keeping capability. It is possible to optimise the position of the thrusters since early design stage applying a genetic algorithm-based optimisation procedure. The enhancements due to an optimal thruster configuration can be reported in the standard capability plot format as commonly done in the offshore industry. However, besides standard capability plots, additional calculations can be performed by explicitly considering the vessel's geographic operational areas. By adopting this novel approach, it is possible to associate to vessel's DP capability an operability index which is specific for the considered sea area and is in analogy of that adopted for ship motion criteria. In this way, the improvements of the optimised thruster configuration can be represented in terms of the increment of DP operability index in a selected sea area, instead of the capability plot area increase for standard conditions. The procedure is here applied to a reference Pipe-lay vessel, where the thruster layout has been optimised. The improvements are reported through both conventional capability plot and newly proposed DP operability index for the North Sea area.

1 INTRODUCTION

The increasing interest for offshore activities in deep water, requests the adoption of station-keeping systems capable to maintain a unit in a predetermined position with a preferential heading. Therefore, dynamic positioning systems are nowadays a primary attribute for an offshore unit (van 't Veer & Gachet 2011). However, the attention to this particular subsystem is not considered as a main project driver by designers in the early design stages of new vessels (Nabergoj 2011). This aspect is valid also for conversion of old units (van Wijngaarden 2012, Nabergoj et al. 2012), where the DP system is commonly subordinate to other issues, as e.g. the propulsion or the internal layout of the vessel (de Jongh et al. 2018). The general arrangement of an offshore unit is usually studied to optimise the layout of machinery and spaces needed to vessel's primary operations. Especially after conversions, the thruster location is forced in the available space remaining after the new equipments installation, often leading to non-symmetric configurations. Therefore, the main issue related to DP is principally referred to the thruster's size (Wichers et al. 1998). The selection of thrusters' devices is strongly influenced also by regulations given by Classification Societies, requiring the installation of more power to grant the station keeping of the vessel in case of multiple failures (ABS 2013, DNV-GL 2018). When the final size of thrusters' devices is chosen, it is possible to further improve the station keeping ability of an offshore vessel. In fact, applying an optimisation procedure based on genetic algorithm it is possible to obtain a thruster layout increasing the DP capability of the vessel (Mauro & Nabergoj 2019). The developed optimisation procedure is based on the maximisation of the area enclosed in the limiting environment curve plotted on the standard capability plots (IMCA 2000). That means, a standard calculation environment is used, referred to the specific wind-wave correlations used for the capability plot determination (Mauro & Nabergoj 2015). In any case, it is hard to quantify the effective capability increase given by a new thruster layout just evaluating the percentage of increase of the area enclosed in the limiting capability envelope. Moreover, a vessel is not always operating in a single sea area or in a condition similar to the standard one adopted in DP capability calculations. Therefore, it is convenient to evaluate vessel's DP performances with an alternative method, using a DP operability index (Mauro & Prpić-Oršić 2020). Being this approach oriented to initial design phase of a vessel, use is made of quasi-steady DP calculations (Virk et al. 2000).

DOI: 10.1201/9781003216599-4

Through this paper, the optimisation of the thruster layout is performed on a reference Pipe-lay vessel. The final optimal configuration is then compared to the original layout both with conventional capability plot and with DP operability index.

2 QUASI-STEADY DP CALCULATIONS

Even though time domain simulations can be used to evaluate the DP capability in early design stage (Smogeli et al. 2013, Lübke et al. 2015, Mauro and Gaudiano 2018), quasi-steady calculations allow to determine in a short time the capability curves. This can be obtained also in case not all the vessel's details are known, as it can be during the early-design stage.

A quasi-steady calculation requires the resolution of the equilibrium of forces and moments acting on the vessel, considering external loads and thruster actions. To this end, a thrust allocation algorithm has to be used to determine the thrust and the orientation of each thruster per each heading angle χ. This is done by solving the following system in the reference system described in Figure 1.

$$\begin{cases} \sum_{i=1}^{N} F_{X_{T_i}} = F_{X_{ext}} \\ \sum_{i=1}^{N} F_{Y_{T_i}} = F_{Y_{ext}} \\ \sum_{i=1}^{N} \left(F_{Y_{T_i}} x_{T_i} - F_{X_{T_i}} y_{T_i} \right) = M_{Z_{ext}} \end{cases} \quad (1)$$

where $F_{X_{T_i}}$s and $F_{Y_{T_i}}$s are the forces components delivered by the N actuators in direction x and y and x_{T_i} and y_{T_i} are the coordinates of the thruster locations from vessel midpoint O. The external forces that appear in the right term of system ((1)) are given by the simultaneous and collinear action of wind, waves and current plus additional forces as, for example, the pipe load for a Pipe-lay vessel.

The equilibrium system has more unknowns than equations, thus it can be solved with optimisation techniques (van Daalen et al. 2011, Johanson et al. 2014). However, also other mathematical methods can be use to solve the thrust allocation problem, adopting simpler and faster algorithms as the pseudo-inverse matrix (Valčić & Prpić-Oršić 2017, Ahani & Ketabdari 2019). In this study, having to deal with recursive optimisation procedures for the optimal thrusters' layout, this simple allocation algorithm has been used. The pseudo-inverse mathematical process needs to evaluate matrix $\mathbf{A}^+$ from system (1) written in the form $\mathbf{Ax} = \mathbf{b}$, where $\mathbf{x}$ is the unknown vector composed by $F_{X_{T_i}}$s and $F_{Y_{T_i}}$s, $\mathbf{b}$ contains the external forces and moments and $\mathbf{A}$ includes the thruster locations. Here, the singular value decomposition of $\mathbf{A}$ has been used to obtain $\mathbf{A}^+$. Then, the following solution can be found:

$$\tilde{\mathbf{x}} = \mathbf{A}^+ \mathbf{b} \quad (2)$$

This is the solution of system (1) having the minimal norm and, therefore, it can be considered as an optimum solution for the problem in the least square sense. Equation (2) does not ensure that all the available thrust is used per each active device. To allocate all the available thrust, a recursive method has been implemented (Mauro & Nabergoj 2019), allowing to satisfy the equilibrium constraint and respecting the maximum available thrust per each thruster. For compliance between the presented results, the same algorithm is used also for the operability determination.

Wind loads are determined at each encounter angle from non-dimensional coefficients according to the following formulations:

$$F_{X_W}(\chi) = \frac{1}{2} \rho_{air} V_W^2 A_T C_{X_W}(\chi) \quad (3)$$

$$F_{Y_W}(\chi) = \frac{1}{2} \rho_{air} V_W^2 A_L C_{Y_W}(\chi) \quad (4)$$

$$M_{Z_W}(\chi) = \frac{1}{2} \rho_{air} V_W^2 A_L L_{PP} C_{M_W}(\chi) \quad (5)$$

where A_T and A_L are the transversal and lateral projected area of the vessel superstructures respectively. L_{PP} is the length between perpendiculars, V_W is the wind speed and ρ_{air} the air density.

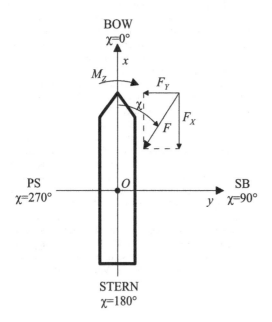

Figure 1. Reference system for DP calculations.

Current loads are evaluated with the same approach of wind, starting from heading-dependent non-dimensional coefficients C_{X_c}, C_{Y_c} and C_{M_c} but using the ship wetted surface S instead of lateral and transverse areas, water density ρ and current speed V_c.

For the wave loads, irregular sea conditions are considered, starting from drift coefficients and modelling the irregular sea with a spectrum:

$$F_{X_w}(\chi) = \rho g \nabla^{\frac{1}{3}} \int_0^\infty C_{X_w}(\omega,\chi) S_\zeta(\omega) d\omega \quad (6)$$

$$F_{Y_w}(\chi) = \rho g \nabla^{\frac{1}{3}} \int_0^\infty C_{Y_w}(\omega,\chi) S_\zeta(\omega) d\omega \quad (7)$$

$$M_{Z_w}(\chi) = \rho g \nabla^{\frac{2}{3}} \int_0^\infty C_{M_w}(\omega,\chi) S_\zeta(\omega) d\omega \quad (8)$$

where ∇ is the vessel volume, g is the acceleration of gravity and S_ζ is the wave amplitude energy spectrum function of the circular frequency ω. Using this approach it is possible to describe the stochastic process of an irregular sea by using the most appropriate wave spectrum for the environmental condition to be reproduced.

Non-dimensional coefficients for all the environmental loads can be derived from model tests, calculations or from simplified methods provided by Classification Societies. The developed DP software used for this study is capable to determine the environmental loads using non-dimensional coefficients coming from different sources, applying the above described procedures.

Even though the loads can be combined in different ways by changing incoming directions or relative contributions. Here, the loads are considered concurrent with a constant current speed, while the wind speed V_W and the wave parameters change according to a specific wind-wave correlation (IMCA 2000). This assumption cannot be representative of the worst possible environmental condition but is what is generally adopted as reference for preliminary DP calculations. To include dynamic effects inside the quasi-steady DP calculations, dynamic allowances can be used. According to regulations (DNV-GL 2018), a dynamic allowance coefficient of 1.25 has been used to increase the environmental loads at each heading angle.

The main output of a standard quasi-steady DP capability calculation is the capability plot (Figure 2), reporting the maximum sustainable wind speed at each heading.

3 ANALYSIS METHODS

A standard DP calculation is not capable to provide the results that are expected from the present study, means to evaluate the operability increase given by

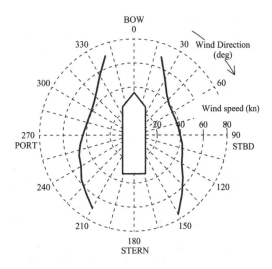

Figure 2. Example of a DP capability plot.

an optimal thruster layout. To this end, it is necessary to describe the methods used to evaluate the optimal thruster layout and to evaluate the operability of a DP system on the base of quasi-steady DP calculations.

3.1 Thruster layout optimisation

The optimisation of the thruster layout requires the adoption of a mathematical method aimed to increase the total DP capability of an offshore vessel. In the specific case of a DP analysis, the resolution of system (1) requires by itself the adoption of an optimisation algorithm. Therefore, the complete problem resolution requires the implementation of an optimisation procedure that should run multiple thrust optimisations at each step. The optimisation of the thruster layout may lead to the resolution of multiple issues, as for example the thruster locations and size. Here, only the optimal location has been considered.

To perform an optimisation, it is necessary define an objective function. The scope of this optimisation is to increase the vessel DP capability, which is traditionally reported on the capability plots as a function of the maximum wind speed $V_{W_{max}}$ that the system can hold at each encounter angle. Therefore, a reasonable choice for the objective function is the area included inside the limiting curve of a capability plot, being representative of the overall capability of a DP system (Mauro & Nabergoj 2019). This area can be identified with the following function:

$$A_{CP} = \int_0^{2\pi} [V_{W_{max}}(\chi)] d\chi \quad (9)$$

For the optimal thruster layout, the variables are the thruster locations x_{T_i} and y_{T_i}. Thus, to apply standard optimisation procedures like quadratic programming or non-linear optimisation processes, the objective function and the constraints should contain the unknowns. Function (9) does not directly include the thruster position, therefore a different optimisation technique has to be used. Here a procedure based on genetic algorithms has been adopted (Mauro & Nabergoj 2019). In the stated problem, the unknown thruster locations are not included in equation (9) but are included in matrix $\mathbf{A}^+$ that determines the resolution of the thrust allocation procedure. Then, to find the optimal solution, it is necessary to explore the possible changes of equation (0) inside the feasible location area for the thrusters on the analysed vessel. On this purpose, Genetic Algorithms (GA) can be used to find the solution inside a design space, searching an optimum value for the selected objective function. Even though the evolutionary process is based on a random procedure, the algorithm itself is not random at all, using the history of consecutive generation to direct the search into the optimal values of the design space. Especially in case of wide search spaces or multi-modal state space or n-dimensional surfaces, genetic algorithm can provide more benefits than conventional optimisation techniques (McCall 2005).

The optimisation procedure is also subjected to multiple constraints. In case of the adoption of genetic algorithm-based procedure they can be defined directly in the generation of the population. In fact, the procedure starts with the generation of a feasible initial population; in the specific, the process starts with the generation of the initial longitudinal coordinates of the thrusters:

$$X_{min_i} \leq x_{T_i} \leq X_{max_i} \qquad (10)$$

where X_{min_i} and X_{max_i} are the minimum and maximum possible longitudinal coordinates of each thruster.

Based on the values obtained for the longitudinal direction, the transverse coordinates of the thruster y_{T_i} can be generated. In this case a simple generation as per equation (10) is not advisable, being the final position of the thrusters subjected to the available space on the ship's flat of bottom. To this end, the shape of the flat of bottom should be included in the generation process according to the following formulation:

$$Y_{min_i}\big|_{x_{T_i}} \leq y_{T_i} \leq Y_{max_i}\big|_{x_{T_i}} \qquad (11)$$

where $Y_{min_i}\big|_{x_{T_i}}$ and $Y_{max_i}\big|_{x_{T_i}}$ are the maximum and minimum allowable transversal position for the thruster at a given x_{T_i}. In such a way the limitations can be given by the flat of bottom of the vessel or by another constraint due to internal layout.

In addition to constraints given by equations (10) and (11), other limitations can be provided. It is of utmost importance to determine the vessel DP capability to avoid interaction between the thrusters, which can decrease the effective total thrust delivered by a single actuator. Applying constraints (10) and (11) will not ensure that thrusters are located sufficiently distant one from each other to minimise interaction occurrence. This can be avoided adding a limiting distance between the rotation centres of the thrusters:

$$\sqrt{\left(x_{T_i} - x_{T_j}\right)^2 + \left(y_{T_i} - y_{T_j}\right)^2} \geq 4D_{M_{ij}} \qquad (12)$$

where $D_{M_{ij}}$ is the maximum between the ith and j^{th} thruster diameter. All the individuals respecting the constraints are evaluated using the objective function given in equation (9).

The adopted GA for the thruster layout optimisation problem is a real-valued algorithm, thus considering directly real numbers for the decision variables. At each iteration, the parents that have to be selected for the generation of new individuals are determined with a stochastic universal sampling method. The selection is based on the scaled values of the individuals, obtained according to their ranking. As additional option, it is possible to select a part of the population that will survive after the first generation step. Crossover and mutation operations can be controlled setting the probabilities p_c and p_m. The procedure stops after a specified number of iterations has been reached.

At the end of the process, the best individuals can be, therefore, considered as a near-optimal solutions to the analysed problem. Means the individual with the highest A_{CP} at the end of the process is representative of the optimal thruster location for the analysed vessel.

3.2 DP operability index

The conventional way to represent a preliminary DP analysis is using capability plots, representing the maximum sustainable wind that the DP system can face at each heading. As mentioned, the wind is linked to the wave conditions by means of a wind-wave correlation. The adoption of a wind-wave correlation did not ensure that the DP calculation will cover all the possible combination of wave height $H_{1/3}$ and wave period T_z that may occur in a specific sea area. In fact, wind-wave correlations establish V_W, $H_{1/3}$ and T_z triplets that are corresponding to just a few cells on a wave scatter diagram (Hogben et al. 1986), as reported in Figure 3. To overcome this issue, it is possible to change the traditional approach for DP capability determination and perform scatter diagram DP calculations (Mauro & Prpić-Oršić 2020). With this original approach it is possible to evaluate whether the DP system is capable or not to maintain the vessel in position per each couple $H_{1/3}$, T_z of the selected scatter diagram.

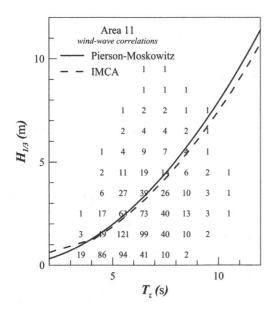

Figure 3. Wind-wave correlations on the wave scatter diagram of the North sea (Area11).

The calculations can be carried out per each vessel heading, determining the DP limiting curve on the scatter diagram.

To obtain the limiting curve on the scatter diagram it is necessary to define a correlation between wave, wind and current in a different way from standard DP capability analysis. The determination of V_W from a specific couple $H_{1/3}$, T_z can be done by means of simplified correlations, as e.g. using relationship derived by the Pierson-Moskowitz spectrum formulation:

$$T_z = \frac{2\pi}{g\sqrt[4]{\pi\beta}} V_W \qquad (13)$$

$$H_{1/3} = \frac{2}{g}\sqrt{\frac{\alpha}{\beta}} V_W^2 \qquad (14)$$

where α and β are two constant equal to 0.0081 and 0.74 respectively. The above equations identify the same V_W only for the $H_{1/3}$, T_z values of the Pierson-Moskowitz wind wave correlation (reported in Figure 3). For all the other combinations of the scatter diagram, equations (13) and (14) give two distinct values for V_W. A possible solution for this indetermination problem is to chose the maximum V_W value resulting from equations (13) and (14), which is representative of the maximum wind speed for each couple $H_{1/3}$, T_z.

For the current load, IMCA standards (IMCA 2000) have been applied, considering a constant current speed collinear with the other environmental loads. As in the previous calculations, also in this case a dynamic allowance coefficient of 1.25 is applied to the environmental loads.

With this environmental settings it is possible to perform DP calculations per each cell of the scatter diagram at each desired vessel heading. To this end, a single quasi-steady DP calculation is performed per each cell and heading, evaluating whether the DP system is holding the position or not. Thereafter, the operability is determined for the selected sea area with the following formulation:

$$OP_{DP} = \sum_{i=1}^{N_h} p_{h_i} \sum_{j=1}^{N_w} p_{w_j} I_{DP} \qquad (15)$$

where p_w is the probability associated with each specific N_w wave condition reported on the scatter diagram and p_h is the probability associated with each N_h heading of the vessel. Generally p_h can be considered as a constant between the different headings, however, in case it is specified by the operators, different values can be associated. OP_{DP} is determined also by the function I_{DP}, which is equal to 1 when the DP system holds the position or 0 when is not. The curve separating the area between I_{DP} equal to 0 and I_{DP} equal to 1 can be defined as DP critical curve for the selected heading. In Figure 4 the I_{DP} value is illustrated for a generic heading, reporting also the associated value of $\sum p_w I_{DP}$ in scale from 0 to 100.

As highlighted in (Mauro & Prpić-Oršić 2020), this method can be useful to compare different

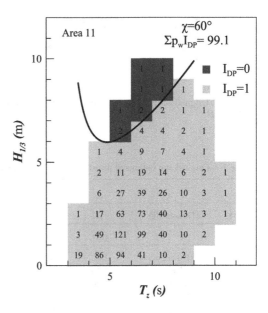

Figure 4. Determination of the OP_{DP} index on a wave scatter diagram.

vessels or thruster configurations with respect to the operability of the DP system.

4 TEST CASE

The methods described in the previous sections have been applied on a Pipe-lay vessel. Here, the general particulars of the original layout of the vessel are described, together with the comparison between original and optimised thruster layout by means of the DP operability index.

4.1 *The reference vessel*

The vessel selected for the application of the described procedure for the thruster layout optimisation is a Pipe-lay vessel (PLV) equipped with a stern stinger for S-lay operations. This PLV presents an asymmetrical layout both for the thruster layout and position of the stinger. This vessel has been selected because experimental data were available for the environmental loads, increasing the reliability of the obtained results.

The PLV is equipped with 6 steerable thrusters and 1 fixed bow tunnel thruster, however, only the 6 steerable devices are part of the DP system. The original thruster configuration is reported in Figure 5 and Table 1; here, it can be observed that the thruster have a fully asymmetrical layout. Moreover, the thrusters have also different sizes, leading to

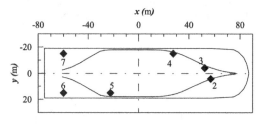

Figure 5. Original thruster configuration for the reference PLV vessel.

a complicate execution also for standard DP calculations. In the analysis, also the presence of the stinger has been considered, adding an external load of 490.5 kN in longitudinal direction to simulate the pipe tensioning. The load is applied at a distance of 4.0 meters from the vessel centreline. The experimental coefficients used for the calculation of environmental loads are including the presence of the stinger, because it was fitted on the model during the experiments.

4.2 *Optimal thruster layout*

The procedure described in section 3.1 has been applied to the reference PLV. The vessel has 6 thruster devices, however the aft-most thrusters (Thruster 6 and 7 according to Table 1) are used also for vessel's propulsion during transfer. For this reason, it has been decided to optimise the layout of the other 4 thrusters, keeping the position of the propulsive ones as a constant. In fact, thrusters 2-5 are installed on the flat of bottom, therefore, the strategies proposed for the position constraints of equation (11) can be applied. It can be observed that the original configuration is composed by a fore-group of two closely spaced thrusters located at two different longitudinal positions. Then, there is a middle group of two thrusters having a smaller size and located on the opposite sides of the vessel (thruster 4 at port side and thruster 5 on starboard side).

These 4 thrusters have been moved during the optimisation procedure, allowing the thruster to move along the vessel flat of bottom, with the additional constraint given by equation (12) applied to each thruster. Under these assumptions, the total amount of unknowns is 8, being the two coordinates of the thruster rotation centre along the flat of bottom. To ensure that the thrusters will not lay on the flat of bottom, the transverse bounds are automatically updated according to the available outreach.

With 8 unknowns, the populations generated at each step are composed of 64 members.

Table 1. Original and optimised thruster layout for the reference PLV.

					Original		Optimal	
NUM	Thruster ID	D	P_S	T	x_T	y_T	x_T	y_T
		(m)	(kW)	(kN)	(m)	(m)	(m)	(m)
2	RF Thruster	2.40	2050	338	57.0	4.2	68.4	0.2
3	LF Thruster	2.40	2050	338	52.3	-4.2	59.0	-1.0
4	LM THruster	2.00	1400	230	27.5	-15.0	20.3	2.9
5	RM Thruster	2.00	1400	230	-22.5	15.0	-12.7	-10.0
6	RA Thruster	2.40	2050	338	-60.0	15.0	-60.0	15.0
7	LA Thruster	2.40	2050	338	-60.0	-15.0	-60.0	-15.0

Being the process for the determination of the objective function complicate, it is not granted that the calculated A_{CP} value will increase at each iteration. For such a reason, the exit point for the genetic algorithm has been set to a predetermined number of iterations, that, for the selected case, has been set to 5000 (Mauro and Nabergoj 2019), using a p_c of 0.9 and a p_m of 0.05 for crossover and mutation probability. The convergence of the optimisation process is reported in Figure 6, showing a A_{CP} increase of about 9% with respect to original configuration. The resulting optimal thruster layout is shown in Figure 7 and in Table1. The optimal configuration has moved the two fore thrusters forward and, due to the flat of bottom constraint, close to the centreline. Thrusters 4 and 5 have been moved closer to midship and are switched of side with respect to the original configuration. Visualising the standard capability plots in Figure 8 it can be noticed that the capability increase is all in the beam and quartering

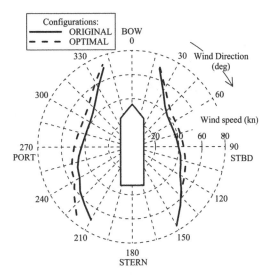

Figure 8. Capability plot comparison between original and optimised thruster layout.

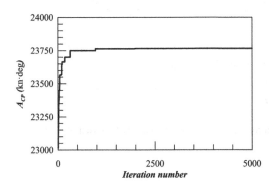

Figure 6. Genetic algorithm convergence diagram for optimal thruster location on the reference PLV.

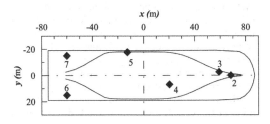

Figure 7. Optimal thruster location for the reference PLV.

headings, while the limiting curve is reduced for head sea condition.

Unfortunately, it is hard to quantify the benefits of the new thruster configuration by only considering the increase of A_{CP}. For such a reason, the operability of the DP system has been evaluated for the two configurations by means of the OP_{DP} index. Applying the calculation method described in section 3.2, it is possible to determine the operability of the original and optimised DP systems for the reference PLV. In Figure 9 the critical curves are shown for the two configurations, reporting the value of the $\sum p_w I_{DP}$ for the selected headings in step of 60 degrees. It can be noticed that the critical curves for the optimal thruster layout are higher than the original one, except for χ of 0 degrees, in accordance with the capability plots in Figure 8. Applying equation (15) with an equal probability p_h between the headings, than the original configuration has an OP_{DP} of 96.6 for the North Sea (Area 11). The optimal configuration, instead, has an OP_{DP} of 98.4, means the operability is increased by 1.8% with respect to the original configuration. An increase of 1.8% in annual operability means about 6.5 days of possible extra working days in one year.

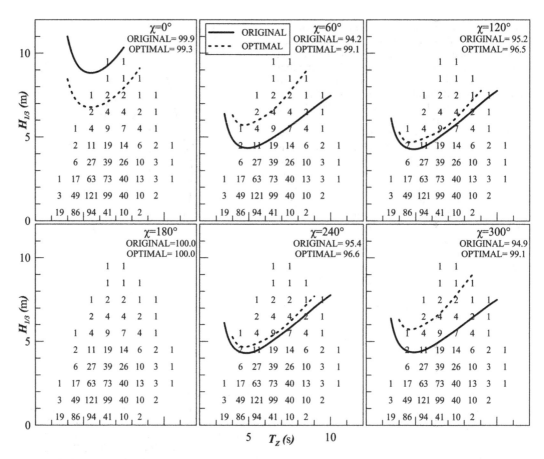

Figure 9. Critical curve comparison and $\sum p_w I_{DP}$ evaluation for the original and optimal thruster layout of the reference PLV in heeding steps of 60 degrees.

5 CONCLUSIONS

The current work presents the synthesis between two original procedures developed to improve and assess the DP capability of an offshore vessel. As first, the application of a thruster layout optimisation allows to increase the DP capability of a vessel, by finding the best location for the thrusters according to given constraints. Thereafter, the capability increase has been translated in operability increase, using the newly developed DP_{OP} operability index.

Applying the procedure to a reference PLV vessel, it was possible to observe how the capability increases by about 9% in terms of capability plot area A_{CP} influences the yearly operability of the offshore unit. In the specific, considering the North Sea as operational area, an operability increase of about one week of expected work has been evaluated. This results highlight that the optimisation of the thruster layout can be a benefit for the design of new offshore units. This is true also in case of conversion of old units, where maybe more constraints are present due to the existing vessel's layout. The optimisation procedure allows to find feasible solutions for the thruster locations, respecting the imposed constraints. Moreover, the possibility to evaluate the operability of the DP system in a given operational area by means of OP_{DP} index, allows to give more detailed informations to the designer and to the ship operator with respect to the expected performances of the DP system also during the early design stage.

In this specific work, only the North Sea environment has been investigated, however, the procedure can be applied to every area of interest for the operation of the vessel, giving an overall idea of the DP operability of the vessel in the most probable areas of operation.

At this stage, the location optimisation procedure is working by means of a simple allocation algorithm, thus the results and the reliability of the proposed method will further increase studying the application of more advanced algorithms for the thrust allocation process.

ACKNOWLEDGEMENTS

This work has been supported by the Croatian Science Foundation under the project IP-2018-01-3739 and by the University of Rijeka (projects uniri-tehnic-18-18 1146 and uniri-tehnic-18-266 6469).

REFERENCES

ABS (2013). Guide for dynamic positioning systems. Technical report, American Bureau of Shipping.

Ahani, A. & M. Ketabdari (2019). Alternative approach for dynamic-positioning thrust allocation using linear pseudo-inverse model. *Applied Ocean Research 90*, 101846.

de Jongh, M., K. Olsen, B. Berg, J. Jansen, & al. (2018). High-level demonstration of holistic design and optimisation process of offshore support vessel. In *Marine Design XIII*, Volume 1, pp. 203–214.

DNV-GL (2018). Assessment of station keeping capability of dynamic positioning vessels. Technical report, Det Norske Veritas - Germanischer Lloyd.

Hogben, N., N. Dacunha, & G. Olliver (1986). *Global Wave Statistics*. British Maritime Technology Limited.

IMCA (2000). Specification for dp capability plots. Technical report, IMCA.

Johanson, T., T. Fossen, & S. Berge (2014). Constrained nonlinear control allocation with singularity avoidance using sequential quadratic programming. *IEEE Transactions on Control System Technology 12*, 211–216.

Lübke, A., S. Krüger, & J. Christiansen (2015). Calculation of the dynamic positioning capability in time domain in early design stages. In *Proceedings of IMDC 2015*.

Mauro, F. & F. Gaudiano (2018). Station-keeping calculations in early design stage: Two possible approaches. In *NAV International Conference on Ship and Shipping Research*, pp. 372–379.

Mauro, F. & R. Nabergoj (2015). Integrated station-keeping and seakeeping predictions. In *Towards Green Marine Technology and Transport*, pp. 127–134.

Mauro, F. & R. Nabergoj (2019). Optimal thruster location on offshore dp vessels. *International Shipbuilding Progress 66 (2)*, 145–162.

Mauro, F. & J. Prpi´c -Orši´c (2020). Determination of a dp operability index for an offshore vessel in early-design stage. *Ocean Engineering 195*, 106764.

McCall, J. (2005). Genetic algorithms for modelling and optimisation. *Journal of Computational and Applied Mathematics 184*, 205–222.

Nabergoj, R. (2011). Station-keeping and seakeeping in offshore vessel design. In *Proceedings of 1st INT-NAM*.

Nabergoj, R., K. Ardavanis, L. Cok, & R. Faldini (2012). Upgrade after vessel refitting. In *Proceedings of the 10th International Conference on Hydrodynamics*.

Smogeli, O., N. Trong, B. Borhaug, & L. Pivano (2013). The next level dp capability analysis. In *Dynamic Positioning Conference*.

Valčić, M. & J. Prpić-Oršić (2017). Forbidden zone handling in optimal thrust allocation of dp vessels. In *Maritime Transportation and Harvesting of Sea Resources*, pp. 1043–1050.

van Daalen, E., H. Cozijn, C. Loussuran, & P. Hemker (2011). A generic optimization algorithm for the allocation of dp actuators. In *Proceedings of the International Conference on Offshore Mechanics and Arctic Engineering - OMAE*, Volume 1, pp. 87–94.

van 't Veer, R. & M. Gachet (2011). Dynamic positioning: Early design, capability and offsets—a novel approach. In *Proceedings of the International Conference on Offshore Mechanics and Arctic Engineering - OMAE*, Volume 3, pp. 755–764.

van Wijngaarden, A. M. (2012). Upgrades and conversions of floating offshore units. In *RINA, Royal Institution of Naval Architects - International Conference on ICSOT: Developments in Fixed and Floating Offshore Structures*, pp. 93–101.

Virk, G., H. Chiu, D. Deter, & C. van der Stoep (2000). Design of the dynamic positioning system for the drillship glomar c.r. luigs. In *Proceedings of the Annual Offshore Technology Conference*, Volume 2, pp. 437–450.

Wichers, J., S. Buitema, & R. Matten (1998). Hydrodynamic research and optimizing dynamic positioning system of deep water drilling vesels. In *Proceedings of the Annual Offshore Technology Conference*, Volume 4, pp. 553–564.

The effect of spatial correlation of sea states on predicted extreme significant wave heights along ship sailing routes

A. Mikulić & J. Parunov
Faculty of Mechanical Engineering and Naval Architecture, University of Zagreb, Zagreb, Croatia

M. Katalinić
Faculty of Maritime Studies, University of Split, Split, Croatia

ABSTRACT: Extreme significant wave heights that ship will encounter are usually predicted using available wave statistics for wave zones where the ship is intended to operate and by assuming that seas states are statistically independent. The aim of the present study is to investigate the effect that spatial correlation between sea states can have on predicted extreme values. The study is based on a database collected for the Adriatic Sea during 24 years of satellite measurements combined with numerical re-analysis. Spearman, Pierson, and Kendall correlation coefficients for seas states along the ship sailing route are determined. The probability of exceeding different significant wave heights along the route is calculated by assuming statistical independence and full correlation respectively. Thus, two bounding probability distributions of extreme significant wave heights for the one-year return period are established. These theoretical distributions are eventually compared with "measured" distributions of yearly extreme significant wave heights along the route, extracted from the database for each of 24 years.

1 INTRODUCTION

During the ship design phase, different design criteria are constituted upon marine structure. Design sea state or expected extreme wave condition is among the important design parameters. Bitner-Gregersen et al. (2016) presents comprehensive review on the state-of-the-art findings, procedures, as well as uncertainties associated with measuring, using, and forecasting wave data in general.

Design sea state for fixed offshore structures can be estimated using available wave statistics for relevant wave zone employing the initial distribution approach described in DNV (2010). The estimation procedure of design sea states for ships however, is more complicated due to a ship sailing in different regions. Namely, the ship is crossing different wave zones at different speeds and wave data for all relevant zones need to be combined. Procedure for the combination of different wave zones in a common scatter diagram is given in IACS Recommendation note. No.34 (IACS, 2000).

Procedure for estimating extreme sea states from the long-term probability distribution of sea states assumes the statistical independence of consecutive sea states. This assumption is not fully theoretically justified, as there is a temporal and spatial correlation of sea states that ship encounters. For fixed structures, the temporal correlation may be relevant, while for ship structures spatial correlation is more important. In addition, the correlation of seas states in different wave zones should be considered for ships (Mansour & Preston 1995).

1.1 *Aim and structure of the paper*

The aim of the present study is to investigate the effect that spatial correlation between sea states along the sailing route can have on predicted extreme values. The motivation for the study is the fact that the sea state encountered by a ship is somehow related to the preceding and following sea states. By considering that correlation, a more rational description of the wave environments for ship design may be formulated.

The main difficulty in establishing correlation coefficients is that uninterrupted records of wave data are required. For the present study, data for the Adriatic Sea are used, where all sea states are available for a period of 24 years. Such complete wave database enables us to determine correlation coefficients between successive sea states and different wave zones and to assess the consequences of the correlation on the predicted extreme values.

The description of the Adriatic region is given in section 2 along with characteristics of the used wave database. Correlations between geographical locations along the route are considered in section 3. Standard DNV methodology for long-term wave statistics is described in section 5. Section 5 reviews the effect of spatial correlation between sea states on predicted

DOI: 10.1201/9781003216599-5

extreme significant wave heights. The last section is allocated for final remarks and conclusions.

2 ADRIATIC SEA AND WAVE DATA

2.1 Adriatic Sea

The Adriatic Sea is in the central-north part of the Mediterranean Sea to whom is connected by the Strait of Otranto on the southeast side. It's stretching from the north-west to the south-east between the Dinaric mountain range in the east and Apennine in the west, having an average width 200 km. Surface wind waves in the Adriatic are limited by fetch. The longest fetch along the basin coincides with southeast winds yielding the highest recorded wave heights (10.87 m). The strongest winds, though, blow form northeast, across the basin, but having shorter fetch produce wave spectrums typical for partially developed sea states. More than 1000 islands along the east coast shelter the wave influence in that near-shore region. Relatively small sea depths that could influence the wave characteristics are found nearshore in the north-northeast part of the basin (Katalinić, et al, 2015).

2.2 WorldWave Atlas

WorldWave Atlas (WWA) is a high-resolution quality controlled and calibrated OCEANOR's wave (and wind) parameter database. WWA is primarily based on numerical wave model hindcast whose results are calibrated and improved by satellite altimetry measurements which are in turn verified with available buoys *in-situ* measurements. The database from operational runs of the WAM model at the European Centre for Medium-Range Weather Forecasts (ECMWF) was selected as the main component of the offshore database in WWA (Barstow et al. 2003) and all applicable satellite missions were considered for calibration.

The OCEANOR base for Adriatic is composed of 12 wind and wave parameters recorded at 39 different geographical locations over 6 hours' intervals, starting from the beginning of September 1992 till the end of January 2016. The parameters include wind speed and direction, main spectral wave parameters (e.g. significant wave height, peak spectral period, etc.), wave direction, with wind-waves and swell considered separately and combined. Geographical locations for which wave data are available are shown in Figure 1.

2.3 Maritime traffic in the Adriatic Sea

The shipping traffic in the Adriatic Sea is developed through the longitudinal and transversal sailing routes, as presented in Figure 2. Overlay of Figure 1 and Figure 2 suggest that the main fraction of the longitudinal traffic is going through locations: 3 - 5 - 7 - 15 - 17 - 19 - 24 - 25 - 29 – 32. The average distance between these adjacent locations (diagonal points) is approximately 38 nautical miles.

Figure 1. WWA database observations include 39 geographical locations uniformly distributed across the Adriatic Sea.

Assuming an average trade speed of 12.5 knots, it follows that the ship takes about 3 hours to cross the distance between two adjacent points.

3 SPATIAL CORRELATION ANALYSIS OF SEA STATES IN THE ADRIATIC

In statistical analysis, correlation is used to describe relationships between random variables or datasets that can be either quantitative or categorical. A correlation coefficient offers a way to numerically quantify the statistical relationship between examined data (Rao 1992). Therefore, here it is applied to describe dependence and the relationship between measurements of significant wave height (SWH) in the Adriatic. There are several different types of correlation coefficient available, but:

Figure 2. Main routes of maritime transportation routes across the Adriatic. Source: MarineTraffic.

- Pearson,
- Spearman Rank/Spearman's Rho and
- Kendall's Tau

are considered the most relevant ones for examined data end therefore applied.

Pearson's correlation coefficient (r) measures the strength and direction of the linear relationship between variables. Eventual nonlinearities between variables can't be taken into the account as it also cannot differentiate between dependent and independent variables. Pearson's correlation coefficient is calculated as follows:

$$r = \frac{\sum_{i=1}^{n}(X_i - \mu_X)(Y_i - \mu_Y)}{\sqrt{\sum_{i=1}^{n}(X_i - \mu_X)^2 \sum_{i=1}^{n}(Y_i - \mu_Y)^2}} \quad (1)$$

where n is the number of observations, X_i value of ith X observation, Y_i value of ith Y observation while μ_X and μ_Y are means of X and Y.

Spearman's rank correlation coefficient (ρ) or Spearman's Rho, represents the nonparametric version of the Pearson correlation coefficient, measuring statistical dependence between the ranks of two variables.

$$\rho = \frac{\frac{1}{n}\sum_{i=1}^{n}\left((R(X_i) - \mu_{Rx}) \cdot (R(Y_i) - \mu_{Ry})\right)}{\sqrt{\left(\frac{1}{n}\sum_{i=1}^{n}(R(X_i) - \mu_{Rx})^2\right)\left(\frac{1}{n}\sum_{i=1}^{n}(R(Y_i) - \mu_{Ry})^2\right)}} \quad (2)$$

Spearman's formula is presented in (2) where n is a number of variables $R(X_i)$ and $R(Y_i)$ denote ranks of ith X and Y variable while μ_{Rx} and μ_{Ry} are the mean ranks. It's easily noticeable that (2) is actually slightly modified (1) and it's chosen because with this form it can deal with tied ranks. As a measure of rank correlation, Spearman's correlation assesses monotonic relationships amongst datasets allowing also some nonlinearities to be described.

Kendall's Tau or Kendall rank correlation coefficient (τ) is a non-parametric measure that evaluates the strength of dependence between rankings of different variables. Some nonlinearities in datasets can also be taken into account by Kendall's Tau coefficient defined in the following expressions.

$$\tau = \frac{2K}{n(n-1)}$$

$$K = \sum_{i=1}^{n-1}\sum_{j=i+1}^{n} \xi(X_i, X_j, Y_i, Y_j) \quad (3)$$

$$\xi(X_i, X_j, Y_i, Y_j) = \begin{cases} 1 & if \quad (X_i - X_j)(Y_i - Y_j) > 0 \\ 0 & if \quad (X_i - X_j)(Y_i - Y_j) = 0 \\ -1 & if \quad (X_i - X_j)(Y_i - Y_j) < 0 \end{cases}$$

In terms of the strength of the relationship between variables, the value of all previously described correlation coefficients varies between +1 and –1. A value of ± 1 indicates a perfect degree of correlation between the two variables. As the value falls towards 0, the relationship becomes weaker. The relationship trend is indicated by the sign of the coefficient i.e. a positive relationship is indicated by the plus (+) sign whereas a minus (–) sign indicates a negative relationship.

Correlations between SWH values from every considered geographical location are calculated as 10 by 10 diagonal matrix also named correlation matrix. Correlations are calculated using the data for different geographical locations at the same time. The correlation matrices for the previously described correlation types are presented in Figures 3-5.

The distinct interpretation of calculated values of correlation coefficients is basically impossible. Therefore, by combining different recommendations from available literature, the paper outlines at least

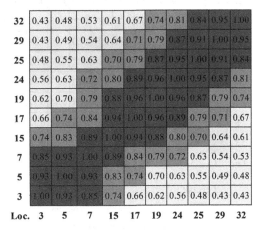

Figure 3. Pearson's correlation coefficient for SWH-s between different locations along the ship route in Adriatic.

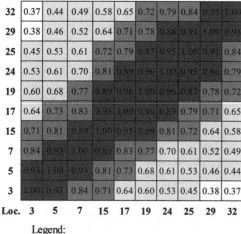

Loc.	3	5	7	15	17	19	24	25	29	32
32	0.37	0.44	0.49	0.58	0.65	0.72	0.79	0.84	0.95	1.00
29	0.38	0.46	0.52	0.64	0.71	0.78	0.86	0.91	1.00	0.95
25	0.45	0.53	0.61	0.72	0.79	0.87	0.95	1.00	0.91	0.84
24	0.53	0.61	0.70	0.81	0.89	0.96	1.00	0.95	0.86	0.79
19	0.60	0.68	0.77	0.89	0.96	1.00	0.96	0.87	0.78	0.72
17	0.64	0.73	0.83	0.95	1.00	0.96	0.89	0.79	0.71	0.65
15	0.71	0.81	0.89	1.00	0.95	0.89	0.81	0.72	0.64	0.58
7	0.84	0.93	1.00	0.89	0.83	0.77	0.70	0.61	0.52	0.49
5	0.93	1.00	0.93	0.81	0.73	0.68	0.61	0.53	0.46	0.44
3	1.00	0.93	0.84	0.71	0.64	0.60	0.53	0.45	0.38	0.37

Legend:

- Very strong positive relationship
- Strong positive relationship
- Moderate positive relationship
- Weak positive relationship

Figure 4. Spearman's Rho correlation coefficient for SWH-s between different locations along the ship route in Adriatic.

Loc.	3	5	7	15	17	19	24	25	29	32
32	0.26	0.30	0.34	0.41	0.47	0.53	0.60	0.65	0.81	1.00
29	0.26	0.32	0.37	0.46	0.52	0.59	0.68	0.75	1.00	0.81
25	0.31	0.37	0.44	0.53	0.60	0.70	0.82	1.00	0.75	0.65
24	0.37	0.44	0.51	0.62	0.71	0.83	1.00	0.82	0.68	0.60
19	0.43	0.50	0.59	0.72	0.84	1.00	0.83	0.70	0.59	0.53
17	0.46	0.54	0.64	0.83	1.00	0.84	0.71	0.60	0.52	0.47
15	0.53	0.62	0.72	1.00	0.83	0.72	0.62	0.53	0.46	0.41
7	0.66	0.79	1.00	0.72	0.64	0.59	0.51	0.44	0.37	0.34
5	0.78	1.00	0.79	0.62	0.54	0.50	0.44	0.37	0.32	0.30
3	1.00	0.78	0.66	0.53	0.46	0.43	0.37	0.31	0.26	0.26

Legend:

- Very strong positive relationship
- Strong positive relationship
- Moderate positive relationship
- Weak positive relationship

Figure 5. Kendall's Tau correlation coefficient for SWH-s between different locations along the ship route in Adriatic.

crude estimates for the strength of the correlation. Correlation coefficients between 0.20 and 0.39 represent a small association, coefficients between 0.40 and 0.69 represent a medium association, coefficients between 0.70 and 0.84 represent a large association and coefficients of 0.85 and above represent a considerably large association or relationship.

It's expected that each location has a perfect correlation with itself, while the further correlation between locations is decreased as the distance among them groves.

Pearson's correlation matrix given in Figure 3 suggests a very strong relationship not just for adjacent zones but also for the second following ones. Values of Spearman's correlation matrix (Figure 4) same as Kendall's correlation matrix (Figure 5) follow the same trend with somewhat quantitatively lower relationship magnitudes.

Even though values have no additional application they provide valuable insights and reason to further doubt the current calculation method which working on the assumption of statistically independent seas states that ship encounters on the sailing route.

The significant linear characteristics are also visible in Figure 6. The presented scatter diagram displays a relationship between successive significant wave heights along the ship route. High value (0.87) of the coefficient of determination (R^2) indicates the upcoming SWH (H_{s2}) changes relatively in line with the (H_{s1}) therefore enabling decent prediction of the successive sea state.

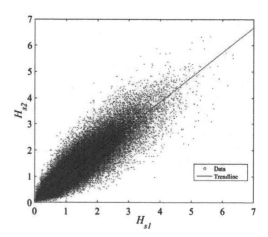

Figure 6. Relation of successive significant wave heights along the ship route. $R^2 = 0.87$.

4 STANDARD PROCEDURE FOR PREDICTING EXTREME SEA STATES

The Weibull-3p distribution (4) is used as an empirically based long term significant wave height distribution where α is the scale parameter, β is the shape parameter, and γ is the location parameter (DNV 2010).

$$F_{H_s}(h) = 1 - \exp\left[-\left(\frac{h-\gamma}{\alpha}\right)^\beta\right] \quad (4)$$

The distribution parameters are determined from the wave data for a specific zone by some fitting technique. The distribution of the annual maximum significant wave height $H_{s,max}$ can be obtained using short term wave height distribution as defined in (5).

$$F_{H_{s,max},1year}(h) = (F_{H_s}(h))^n \quad (5)$$

In the expression above $F_{Hs}(h)$ denotes the distribution of the significant wave height in an arbitrary t-hour sea state, where n is the number of t-hour sea states in one year. The annual extremes of the significant wave height can be assumed to follow a Gumbel distribution:

$$F_c(x_e) = \exp\left\{-\exp\left[-\left(\frac{x_e - U}{A}\right)\right]\right\} \quad (6)$$

Distribution parameters A and U are related to the mean (8) and standard deviation (7).

$$\sigma_e = \frac{\pi}{\sqrt{6}} A \quad (7)$$

$$\mu_e = U + 0.5772 \cdot A \quad (8)$$

It is recommended to base the annual statistics on at least 20-year of data points. It is further recommended to define the year as the period from summer to summer (DNV 2010).

5 IMPACTS OF SPATIAL CORRELATION UPON EXTREME SEA STATE

Defining the design sea state i.e. the probability of a ship encountering a severe storm depends on the ship route and the wave statistics in the zones along the route (Mansour & Preston 1995).

A procedure for long-term significant wave height probability calculation in one zone is described in section 4. The Nonlinear Least Squares (NLS) Data Fitting Method is initially used to fit Weibull-3p distribution onto significant wave height of different locations along the route (Katalinić, 2019).

After that, probability of no-exceeding different significant wave heights ($H_{s,j}$) along shipping route (i.e. for following geographical locations: 3 - 5 - 7 - 15 - 17 - 19 - 24 - 25 - 29 – 32) is calculated using previously fitted Weibull functions (4).

For the one journey probability of no-exceeding SWH is calculated by assuming statistical independence (9) and full correlation of wave zones (10) (Mansour and Preston, 1997).

$$F_{H_s}(H_{s,j}) = \prod_{i=1}^{n} F_{H_s,i}(H_{s,j}) \quad (9)$$

$$F_{H_s}(H_{s,j}) = \min_{i} F_{H_s,i}(H_{s,j}) \quad (10)$$

The probability of no-exceedance of extreme significant wave heights for the one-year return period is calculated by equation (11) for two bounding cases. The following equation is obtained combining (9) or (10) with (5) where variable n denotes the number of journeys through one year.

$$F_{H_{s,max},1year}(h) = \left(F_{H_s}(H_{s,j})\right)^n \quad (11)$$

Those two cases created assuming statistical independence and full correlation of sea states are then fitted with cumulative Gumbel distribution (6) using, NLS (Figure 7).

"Measured" annual extreme significant wave heights are extracted from the OCEANOR database for each of 24 years. The mean μ_e and standard deviation σ_e of measured extremes were calculated using expressions (12) and (13).

$$\mu_e = \frac{1}{n} \sum_{i=1}^{n} (x_{ei}) \quad (12)$$

$$\sigma_e = \sqrt{\frac{\sum_{i=1}^{n}(x_{ei} - \mu_e)^2}{n-1}} \quad (13)$$

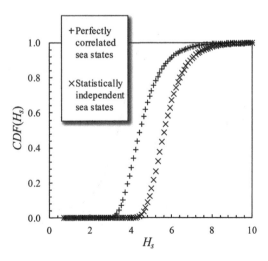

Figure 7. Probability of no-exceedance of extreme significant wave heights for the one-year return period.

Gumbel distribution parameters A and U are obtained by (7) and (8)

Probability density functions using the assumption of independence, full correlation, and actual measurements are calculated by equation (14) and presented in Figure 8.

$$f_c(x_e) = \frac{1}{A}\exp\left[-(\frac{x_e - U}{A})\right] \cdot \exp\left\{-\exp\left[-(\frac{x_e - U}{A})\right]\right\} \quad (14)$$

Two bounding probability distributions are compared in Figure 8 with "measured" distributions of yearly extreme significant wave heights along the route. The effect of correlation may be clearly seen in Figure 8. The most probable yearly extreme significant wave height reads 5.38 m and 4.16.m using statistical independence and full correlation respectively. "Measured" the most probable yearly significant wave height reads 4.68 m, which is between two bounding distributions.

The high values of the previously analyzed correlation coefficients are suggesting dependence between wave data in neighboring locations. Therefore, the assumption of statistical independence led to an exceedance of measured results. Also, because correlation coefficients haven't reached the ideal value of 1, results calculated assuming full correlation have underestimated measured ones.

It is evident that the commonly used assumption of statistical independence of the successive significant wave height leads to conservative results. Therefore, for a more precise and accurate approach, such conservativism should be limited when applying ship rational-based design and analysis.

The results presented in Figure 8 are in conjunction with the previously analyzed correlation coefficients. The placement of the measured results above the perfectly correlated and below statistically independent theoretical distributions indicates a partial correlation, which will be the focus of future research.

6 CONCLUSIONS

The paper explores the effect of spatial correlation between sea states along the shipping route on extreme value predictions. Conducted correlation analysis indicates a very strong relationship between successive sea states that ship encounters.

The probability of no-exceedance for different significant wave heights along the shipping route is calculated by assuming statistical independence and full correlation respectively. Two established bounding theoretical distributions are compared with "measured" distribution. Obtained results clearly indicate that the spatial correlation between successive sea states has a measurable effect on predicted extreme values. It can also be concluded that the sea states have the largest randomness at the beginning of the voyage, and then, due to the high correlation, encountered sea states are more or less interdependent and predictable from the already encountered sea states.

This result generates a motivation for further research to find an alternative, more rational approach for the definition of scatter diagrams for ship structural design and analysis. The effort will be put to quantitatively incorporate effects of correlation between successive sea states and between different wave zones into procedures for long-term sea state predictions.

ACKNOWLEDGEMENTS

This work has been fully supported by Croatian Science Foundation under the project IP-2019-04-2085. The WorldWaves data used in the study are provided by Fugro OCEANOR AS. The conference attendance has been partially supported by University of Zagreb.

REFERENCES

Barstow, S., Mørk, G., Lønseth, L., Schjølberg, P., Machado, U., Athanassoulis, G., Belibassakis, K.A., Gerostathis, T., Stefanakos, C. & Spaan, G. 2003. WORLDWAVES: Fusion of data from many sources in a user-friendly software package for timely calculation of wave statistics in global coastal waters.

Bitner-Gregersen, E.M., Dong, S., Fu, T., Ma, N., Maisondieu, C., Miyake, R. & Rychlik, I. 2016. Sea state conditions for marine structures' analysis and model tests. *Ocean Engineering* 119: 309–322.

DNV. 2010. Environmental conditions and environmental loads. *DET NORSKE VERITAS*, hlm.

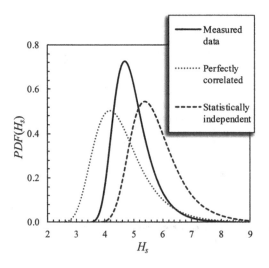

Figure 8. Probability density functions of the significant wave height yearly extremes.

IACS. 2000. Standard Wave Data (North Atlantic Scatter Diagramm) 34(34): 1–4.

Katalinić, M. 2019. Modelling of wind-generated waves in the Adriatic Sea for applications in naval architecture and maritime transportation., PhD Thesis, University of Zagreb (in Croatian)

Katalinić, M., Ćorak, M. & Parunov, J. 2015. Analysis of wave heights and wind speeds in the Adriatic Sea. *Maritime Technology and Engineering*, C. guedes Soares & T. A. Santos (EDs), Taylor and Francis Group, pp: 1389–1394.

Mansour, A.E. & Preston, D.B. 1995. Return periods and encounter probabilities. *Applied Ocean Research* 17(2): 127–136.

Rao, S.S. 1992. Reliability-based design. McGraw-Hill: New York.

Developments in Maritime Technology and Engineering – Guedes Soares & Santos (eds)
© 2021 Copyright the Author(s), ISBN 978-0-367-77377-9

Investigation of trim control devices on hydrodynamic characteristics of fast vessels

M. Pedišić Buča & T. Prosinečki
Brodarski Institute, Zagreb, Croatia

ABSTRACT: In order to optimize dynamic trim of representative fast vessel, various configurations of trim control devices such as trim tabs, wedges and interceptors are tested. Ship model of representative geometry was used and tested in the Large Towing Tank of Brodarski Institute. Geometry and position of trim control devices are systematically varied and tests are conducted for the wide range of Froude numbers including semi-planing and planing regimes. Main part of investigation refers to resistance tests, while configurations with most benefits were tested in self propulsion condition as well. Also, the analysis shows benefits of application of certain combination of trim control devices i.e. interceptors and trim tabs compared to application of interceptors or trim tabs only. Finally, it is demonstrated that putting effort into this specific phase of project development may lead to significant savings and improvements.

1 INTRODUCTION

Fast vessels undergo three different sailing regimes in order to achieve high speeds, as follows: displacement, semi-planing and planing regime. In the first regime (up to Fn = 0.4 – 0.6), overall vessel weight is completely supported by hydrostatic buoyancy force. In semi-planing regime (0.4 (0.6) < Fn < 1.0 (1.2)), hydrostatics forces become less important since hydrodynamic lift starts to overtake part of weight. Finally, at planing regime, the weight of the vessel is mainly supported by hydrodynamic pressure loads which lift the vessel (Fn> 1.0 (1.2)) (Faltinsen, 2005.).

In both, semi-planing and planing regimes dynamic trim angle and rise are pronounced, affecting the total resistance, changing seakeeping characteristics and making the operational environment less comfortable for people and cargo onboard. As it is known, the performance of planing hull is depending on the longitudinal position of centre of gravity (Savitsky, 2003). However, for the majority of the projects, centre of gravity cannot be easily varied in practice and therefore in order to optimize dynamic trim angle, trim control devices (in further text TCD) are used as follows: interceptors, trim tabs (flaps) and wedges. Among hydrodynamic benefits, criteria of application most commonly include simplicity, adaptability and installation and operational costs.

Within this study, for typical planing hull, application of interceptors, trim tabs and integrated trim tabs-wedges configurations and their combinations are tested.

Trim tabs or flaps are thin flat plates mounted at the transom. They are located symmetrically at the stern as an extension of the lower surface of the hull and their parametars are: span, chord and angle. With hinge connection to the hull, rotating around transversal axis and changing their angle in respect to waterline they allow high adaptability in different regimes. Flaps are used in pairs, located symmetrically. Likewise, stern wedges principle is similar, although they are integrated to the hull and not extending the aft portion of the hull. Their parameters are also chord, span and angle.

Practice of installing stern trim tabs started relatively early, and many studies concerning their performance have been published starting with Brown (1971) who performed a study on planing surfaces with trim tabs installed in order to generate data that would help planing hull designers, following Savitsky et al., (1976) who analysed previous experimental results and formed a tool suitable for design process, particularly estimation of planing performance in smooth and rough waters; which was basis for studies of U.S. Navy who carried out large amount of full scale experiments in military vessels. Decreasing the needed power between 10 – 15 % trim tabs have been widely used for projects of working, as well as military and pleasure craft nowadays.

Another TCD with similar principle is widely applied in modern hydrodynamics approach in decreasing trim angle and resistance, called interceptors. Interceptors are in a form of thin rectangular plates mounted at the transom of the hull and protruding vertically. Their main parameter is height and most usually they are located along the transom or at certain portion of the transom (tunnels i.e.) symmetrically. They can be of fixed or retractable type. Although drag coefficient usually increases as well as total resistance in displacement regime, the increase in lift coefficient is more significant than the hydrodynamic coefficient increment when planing, resulting in speed increase and gain of 10-15% of fuel efficiency (Day and Cooper, 2011).

2 SHIP MODEL AND TRIM CONTROL DEVICES DESCRIPTION AND SETTINGS

To investigate influence of the interceptors, wedges, integrated trim tabs-wedges and corresponding combinations for the same hull, influence on resistance values, dynamic trim angle and rise at LCB was determined through systematic experiments in the Towing Tank.

Model of typical planing hull form was used with the following characteristics: transom stern, single chine, two hydrodynamic tunnels, deadrise angle of $\beta = 20°$ and three pairs of spray rails. Model photo is given in Figure 1. Geometric non dimensional ship and model parameters are shown in Table 1.

Hull also featured standard set of appendages as follows: two propeller shafts and corresponding shaft brackets (one per shaft) and two rudders. For the resistance tests, false hubs were installed at the positions of the propellers. Photo of detail of setting of the appendages is presented in Figure 2.

Figure 1. Ship model, side view.

Table 1. Main model parameters.

Parameter	Unit	Value
L_{WL}/B_{WL}	[-]	3.590
B_{WL}/T	[-]	4.115
C_B	[-]	0.500
$C_{p,L}$	[-]	0.787
$LCB_{\%\,WL}$	[%] Lwl] *	-7.1
$L/\nabla^{1/3}$	[-]	4.70

Figure 2. Ship model, stern view – Apppendages.

Additionaly, different configurations of trim control devices have been installed at the stern. Interceptors have been varied in span and height; while wedges were varied in angle and trim tabs were varied in chord, span and angle.

In Table 2 and Figures 3-6 the set of variations and corresponding explanations are shown. Altogether, fourteen different variations are tested and elaborated within this study.

During the tests, resistance values were measured with load cell, rise (sinkage) values at LCB with potentiometer and dynamic trim values with inclinometer. Model in resistance test is shown in Figure 7.

Table 2. Tested configurations.

Trim Control Devices	Interceptor		Wedge or Integrated Wedge/Trim Tab		
	Position	Height	Chord Wedge+ Flaps	Span	Angle
		[% L_{wl}]	[% L_{wl}]	[% L_{wl}]	[deg]
Hull without Trim Control Devices	x	x	x	x	x
INT1	Full Transom	0.03	x	x	x
INT 2	Full Transom	0.06	x	x	x
INT 3	Tunnels	0.12	x	x	x
INT 4	Tunnels	0.17	x	x	x
INT 5	Tunnels	0.24	x	x	x
TT1	-	x	0.6 +1.7	3.6	14
TT2	-	x	0.6+1.7	4.9	5
TT3	-	x	0.6+1.7	4.9	10
C1	Tunnels	0.12	0.6+0.0	3.6	14
C2	Tunnels	0.12	0.6+1.7	3.6	14
C3	Tunnels	0.12	0.6+0.0	3.6	10
C4	Tunnels	0.12	0.6+2.5	3.6	5
C5	Tunnels	0.14	0.6+0.0	3.6	10

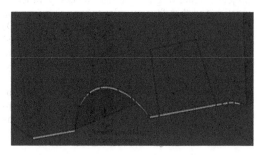

Figure 3. Set-up of Interceptors along Transom (INT1and INT2).

Figure 4. Set-up of Interceptors in Tunnels only (INT3, INT4 and INT5).

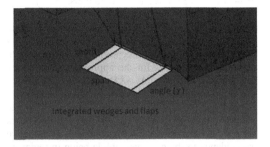

Figure 5. Set-up of Integrated Wedges-Trim Tabs (TT1-3).

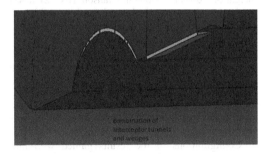

Figure 6. Set-up of Tunnel Interceptors and Integrated Wedges-Trim tabs (C1, C3, C5).

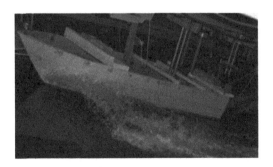

Figure 7. Model during resistance test.

Jeonghwa (2016) describes in more details the typical setting for measurement of resistance of high speed hulls.

In Table 3 corresponding values of Froude and Reynolds numbers for tests are presented.

Results are analysed on the basis of model measured values normalized for the reference temperature of t=20 deg. By using model measured values, influence of running wetted lengths and surfaces is neglected. Since the method of determination of these values is usually based on visual observations and includes significant degree of uncertainty, it was decided not to include them into analysis. Within this study main aim was to analyse trends and for the purpose of comparison and qualitative analysis such approach can be applied.

After the detailed evaluation in resistance condition was completed, short self-propulsion tests for two chosen set-ups were conducted as well. Tests were performed in accordance with ITTC Recommended Procedures and Guidelines 7.5-02-05-02, Propulsion Test (2017). Self-propulsion test was conducted at same displacement and draught as resistance test and two five bladed fixed pitch propellers were used. Tests were conducted via British Method and measurements were conducted with propeller dynamometers.

3 MEASUREMENTS AND RESULTS

Results are presented as values of ratios of model total resistance of hull with trim control devices and hull without trim control devices i.e. R_{WTC}/R_{WOTC} related to the volumetric Froude number as well as corresponding dynamic trim angles and rise values at LCB.

In the first part of analysis, results are grouped into three groups as follows:

- Configurations of interceptors (INT1 – INT5)
- Configurations of wedges and integrated wedges/flaps (TT1-TT3)
- Combinations of former two groups (C1-C5)

In the Figures 8, 9 and 10. the results for configurations of interceptors are presented.

As to the resistance values, application of interceptors was beneficial for all five tested configurations. The values of the dynamic trim for the hull configuration without trim control devices are excessive as it can be expected for this type of fast vessel and application of trim control devices is inevitable.

Table 3. Froude and Reynolds numbers for tested speeds.

Point No.	Re_M	Re_s	Fn	Fn_{vol}
1	1.2×10^7	1.2×10^8	0.62	1.34
2	1.9×10^7	1.7×10^8	1.08	2.23
3	2.4×10^7	2.7×10^8	1.42	2.90

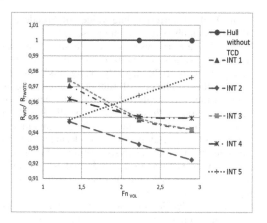

Figure 8. Effectiveness of interceptors.

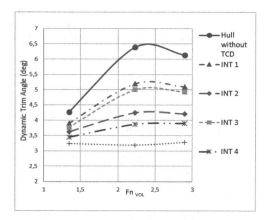

Figure 9. Influence of interceptors upon dynamic trim angle interceptors.

Four of the five tested configurations yielded same trend of improvement, i.e. contribution of interceptor was larger for higher speeds. Best results were obtained with interceptors aligned along the entire transom with height of 0.06% L_{wl} (INT 2) when the reduction of total resistance reached 8% at highest tested speed. Dynamic trim angle was reduced for about 2 degrees while rise values at LCB were reduced for about 1% of L_{wl}.

Results obtained with INT1, INT3 and INT 4 were similar regarding resistance reduction for all three tested speeds although some differences in dynamic trim and rise at LCB are present. For configuration of INT 5 where interceptors of height of 0.24% Lwl were located in the tunnels, the dynamic trim angle was reduced to approximately 3.2 deg which obviously presents the limiting value. Namely, in case of larger trim reductions, the benefits of application of interceptors will not be present anymore. Guidelines for the appropriate interceptor height were refered to Avci&Barlas (2019).

Application of interceptor of height of 0.03% L_{wl} along the transom (INT 1) and interceptors only in the tunnel regions of 0.12% L_{WL} (INT 3) i.e. four times more, yielded almost the same results. This can serve as guidance to the designers, while being in region of moderate values. But, application of interceptor of height of 0.06% L_{wl} along the transom (INT 2) proved to be best among tested configurations, while the tunnel interceptors with four times larger height of 0.24% L_{wl} (INT 5) did not yield similar benefits since the reduction of trim angle was larger. This might be attributed to the boundary layer thickness scale effects.

Interceptors of moderate height of 0.17% L_{wl} located in tunnels only, yielded uniform improvements for all three tested speeds, within 4-5%. Configurations INT 1 – INT 4 yielded improvement of 4.8% in average for all tested speeds.

Configurations of the results gained with integrated wedges and flaps are presented in Figures 11, 12 and 13.

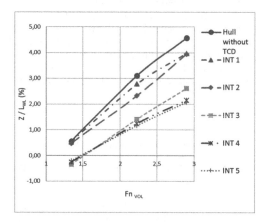

Figure 10. Influence of interceptors upon sinkage.

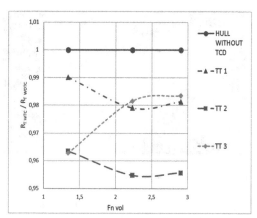

Figure 11. Effectiveness of integrated trim tabs/wedges.

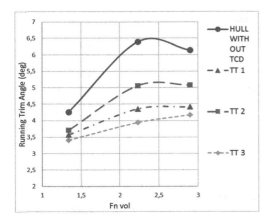

Figure 12. Influence of integrated trim tabs/wedges upon dynamic trim angle.

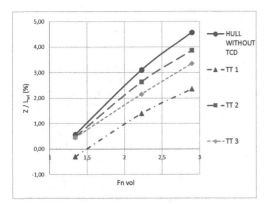

Figure 13. Influence of integrated trim tabs/wedges upon rise at LCB.

All three configurations yielded certain improvement of resistance, although less pronounced than for interceptors. The average resistance improvement for TT1 and TT2 was 3%. At the same time, reduction of dynamic trim angle was comparable with those obtained with interceptor configurations. Two configurations (TT1 and TT2) have similar trend i.e. for the higher speeds resistance decrease is larger, while configuration TT3 yields adverse trend.

Configuration TT3 causes largest decrements of the dynamic trim angles which are over 2 degrees, although still less than the lowest values obtained with interceptors. For the particular hull and proposed integrated trim tabs/wedges configuration application of interceptors only was more beneficial.

Configuration TT2 had larger span and smaller angle compared to TT1 which proved to be better for resistance values.

In the following Figure 14, Figure 15 and Figure 16 results related to the combinations of interceptors and wedges or integrated wedges/flaps are shown.

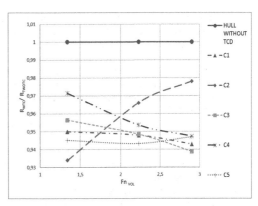

Figure 14. Effectiveness of combinations of TCD.

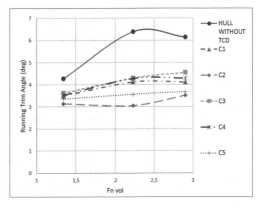

Figure 15. Influence of combinations of TCD upon dynamic trim angle.

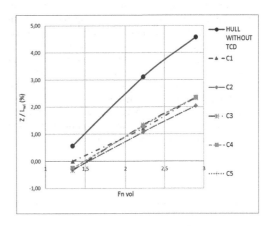

Figure 16. Influence of combinations of TCD upon rise at LCB.

For these cases, interceptors were located strictly in the tunnel region and wedges or integrated flaps/wedges were of the same span (3.6% of L_{WL}) differing in angle and chord.

As it can be seen from the results, again the improvement is present for all tested configurations and it is in average 4.9% for the tested speed range.

Four of five tested configurations have again the trend of larger resistance decrement for higher speeds, while one configuration (C2) yields adverse trend. Such behaviour is in compliance with research of Song et al. (2018). This configuration corresponds again to the lowest measured dynamic trim angles, somewhat above 3 degrees. In average, considering all tested speeds, best results were obtained for C1 and C5 (combinations of wedges and tunnel interceptors). Differences in savings for these two configurations were within 1%, while the differences in dynamic trim angle are significant and amount somewhat less than 1 degree.

For the further testing in self propulsion condition it is expected that lower values of dynamic trim angles will be beneficial for propulsion components and consequently self-propulsion results. Thrust affects dynamic trim value and rise at LCB.

In order to check these effects, self-propulsion tests were performed with the two configurations: C1 and C5. Since the model was fairly large it was possible to run the model in self propulsion condition. Usually, tested models are smaller and in the literature limited data are available concerning self-propulsion test results. Within this study, test results for the volumetric Froude numbers Fn=2.3 and Fn = 2.9 are given. For the tested values of Fn = 2.3 and Fn = 2.9 dynamic trim values are up to 0.9

1.5% of LWL larger compared to the resistance condition.

As the basis for the analysis, differences in delivered power (full scale values) and revolutions (full scale values) were analyzed.

In resistance condition, configuration C5 was only 0.5% better regarding resistance compared to C1. In self propulsion condition for both tested speeds Fn=2.3 and Fn = 2.9 the configuration C5 was 2% better regarding delivered power with 0.5% increment in revolutions and 1.5% reduction in thrust. This decrement of 2% for the particular project led to the speed improvement equivalent to 0.5 kn in full scale.

Finally, comparison between two most promising configurations in resistance condition is done and presented in Tables 4 and 6. It is INT 2

Table 4. Results of the most favourable configurations.

	Dynamic Trim Angle			Rise at LCB		
	(deg)			(%L$_{WL}$)		
Fnvol	INT 2	C1	delta	INT 2	C1	delta
1,34	3,63	3,49	0,14	0,48	0,00	0,48
2,23	4,24	4,12	0,12	2,32	1,22	1,10
2,90	4,21	4,11	0,10	3,94	2,36	1,58

Table 5. Results of the least favourable configurations.

	Dynamic Trim Angle			Rise at LCB		
	(deg)			(%L$_{WL}$)		
Fnvol	INT 5	C2	delta	INT 5	C2	delta
1,34	3,24	3,14	0,10	-0,20	0,26	0,06
2,23	3,19	3,00	0,19	1,16	1,31	0,15
2,90	3,28	3,51	0,23	2,07	2,36	0,29

Table 6. Savings for two most favourable and two least favourable configurations.

	R$_{WTCD}$/R$_{WOTCD}$			
Fnvol	INT 2	C1	INT5	C2
1,34	0,947	0,950	0,948	0,934
2,23	0,933	0,947	0,964	0,966
2,90	0,922	0,943	0,976	0,978
Avg	0,934	0,947	0,963	0,959

(0.06% Lwl interceptor along transom) and C1 (tunnel transoms 0.12% Lwl and wedge of 14 deg, chord of 0.06% Lwl and span of 3.6% Lwl.

Values of the dynamic trim angle are very similar, while certain difference in rise exists since for the interceptors only configuration where rise is more pronounced i.e. lift is larger. Differences in resistance reduction are in favour of INT2 configuration.

Likewise, only two configurations which resulted with the lower gain for higher speeds are compared in Table 5.

Again, values of the dynamic trim angle are very similar, but in this case values of rise are also more resembling resulting in similar resistance reductions for two higher speeds

Comparison of savings for these four configurations is given in the following Table 6.

It can be concluded that overall the gains are very similar for all tested configurations and for the particular project within range of savings of 5% and more there are various options available.

4 CONCLUDING REMARKS

Within this study, experimental research of influence of different configurations of trim control devices on resistance, dynamic trim angle and rise of representative fast vessel was conducted. Anaysis was conducted within range of Froude numbers Fn $_{VOL}$ = 1.34 – 2.9. Based on the analysis following conclusions can be drawn:

– All tested configurations yielded better results compared to the hull without trim control devices.

Maximum gain was 8% and it was achieved with interceptors located along the transom in height of 0.06% Lwl (INT2). Average gain for all tested options was somewhat less than 5%.
- Trim angle reduction via trim control devices is beneficial for resistance up to the certain point. In the particular case values of dynamic trim angle approaching 3 deg were diminishing positive effects.
- Application of wedges or integrated trim tabs/ wedges configurations without interceptor had lowest impact upon resistance improvement i.e. in average 3%.
- In self propulsion condition dynamic trim angles and rise values are significantly larger compared to the resistance condition. Therefore, it is intended to achieve as low dynamic trim angles as possible in resistance condition without deteriorating resistance values. It is expected for such configuration in self propulsion condition to yield improvement due to the improved wake field and propulsion components. Measured improvement in delivered power was within 2%.
- Although it is possible to predict in some extent influence of trim control devices, for „fine tuning" it is necessary to conduct experiments and/or CFD analyses

The analysis could be enhanced with the additional observation of stern wave system especially rooster tail in respect with the obtained results.

REFERENCES

Avci A.G., Barlas B. 2019, An experimental investigation of interceptors for a high speed hull, *International Journal of Naval Architecture and Ocean Engineering*, 11; 256–273

Brown, PW, 1971, An experimental and theoretical study of planing surfaces with trim flaps, *Stevens Inst of Tech Hoboken NJ*, Davidson Lab

Day A.H., Cooper C., 2011: An Experimental study of interceptors for drag reduction on high-performance sailing yachts, *Ocean.Eng.* 38 (8-9), 983–994

Faltinsen O., 2005.: Hydrodynamics of High-Speed Marine Vehicles, *Cambridge University Press*, New York

Jeonghwa S., Hak-Kyu C., Un-Cheul J., Dong K.L., Shin H.R., Chul-Min J., Jeahoon Y.: Model Tests on resistance and seakeeping performance of wave-piercing high-speed vessels with spray rails, International Journal of Naval Architecture and Ocean Engineering 8 (2016), 442–455

ITTC – Recommended Procedures and Guidelines, 7.5-02-05- 01: Testing and Extrapolation Methods, High Speed Marine Vehicles, Resistance Test (2011)

ITTC Recommended Procedures and Guidelines 7.5-02-05-02, Propulsion Tests (2017)

Savitsky D., 2003: On the subject of high speed monohulls, Presented to the Greek Section of the Society of Naval Architects and Marine Engineers, Athens, Greece, October 2nd

Savitsky D, Brown PW, 1976.: Procedures for hydrodynamic evaluation of planing hulls in smooth and rough water, *Marine Technology*, 13:381 – 400

Song K., Guo C., Gong J., Li P., Wang L., 2018.: Influence of interceptors, stern flaps and their combinations on the hydrodynamic performance of deep-vee ship, *Ocean Engineering 170*, 306–320

Multiple evaluations of speed loss in rough sea voyages for 28,000-DWT bulk carrier

K. Sasa, R. Uchiyama & C. Chen
Kobe University, Kobe, Japan

D. Terada
National Defense Academy, Yokosuka, Japan

J. Prpić-Oršić
University of Rijeka, Rijeka, Croatia

ABSTRACT: Loss of speed in a rough sea voyage is the most important factor for constructing an accurate optimal ship routing model. However, there is only a small database of ship performance measured in the real sea for some period. In this study, variations in weather conditions and ship performance are summarized for three cases of rough sea voyages. It is shown that there are two patterns of engine operation for the speed loss, and vertical acceleration is an effective parameter for estimating the switching point from natural speed loss to deliberate speed loss. Time series analysis is also effective in assessing the situation of deliberate speed loss.

1 INTRODUCTION

Over 10 billion tons of cargo is traded annually across the oceans, and the amount of cargo is forecasted to be 15 billion tons in 2050. This implies that our daily life cannot be sustained without a stable supply of maritime transportation. On the other hand, the demand of lower gas emission or fuel consumption makes the maritime transportation difficult as the amount of cargo increases. For decades, seafarers switched to temporarily employed foreign crews from permanently employed domestic ones. It could cause the lower maneuvering technique in rough seas. The optimal ship routing has been studied since the 1950s (Hanssen and James, 1960; Hagiwara et al., 1997; Maki et al., 2011), and is expected as one of the effective tools. Some studies point out that uncertainties exist in the estimation of weather conditions and speed loss in rough seas (Artessen, 1967; NordForsk, 1987; Tsujimoto et al, 2009; Prpić-Oršić and Faltinsen, 2012). However, there are very few validations because of the lack of an onboard measurement database. The authors measured the ship performance onboard in real seas for validation. Lu et al. (2017) showed a quantitative uncertainty of weather conditions that are measured onboard in the Southern Hemisphere. Sasa et al. (2017 and 2019) also analyzed measured ship performance, including speed loss and fuel consumption. More analyses of speed loss are necessary to find out common patterns or tendencies in rough sea voyages. It is also important to know the detailed operation of the main engines to discuss this problem. In this study, other cases of speed loss, including the Northern Hemisphere, are analyzed to find different tendencies in rough sea voyages. It is shown that there are two patterns of engine operation in rough sea voyages. Measured time series can be categorized into steady and unsteady ones, or linear and nonlinear ones. Thus, it seems possible to estimate the actual situation if the time series properties are sufficiently known. This has been shown in some related studies using statistical models (Park et al., 2000; Iseki and Terada, 2001; Terada, et al., 2002). A statistical time series analysis is conducted to clarify the operation of the main engine. A Time-Varying Auto Regressive (TVAR) model is applied to the measured revolution of the main engine to find features of a natural and deliberate loss of speed. Finally, the reduction in the uncertainty of speed loss is discussed using numerical analyses.

2 MEASUREMENT AND ANALYSIS OF SHIP PERFORMANCE FOR 28,000-DWT BULK CARRIER

2.1 *Onboard measurement*

The onboard measurement of ship performance has been conducted for 28,000-DWT class bulk carrier from June, 2010 to August, 2016. However, some mechanical problems arose on the disks, electric supply, etc. Thus, the actual period of measurement is 2–3 years or so. The inertial measurement equipment, NAV440, which can measure rotational motions and accelerations along the *xyz* axes, is installed inside the ship's bridge. In addition, the ship-land communication system is installed which outputs the measured parameters of position, speed over the ground, course, wind direction and speed, steering angle, engine revolution, engine power, shaft thrust, exhausted gas temperature, etc. The log speed is also measured. However, it shows abnormal value. The speed is evaluated by the speed over the ground. This information is recorded on a computer with communication software. A bulk carrier is a tramper without regular routes. This means that the ship visited various sea areas in the world. Main dimensions are 160.4 m in length, 27.2 m in width, 9.82 m of fully loaded draft, 14 knots of voyage speed. After the ship management was transferred to another company in 2012, the ship is mainly operated with 12 knots to save fuel. Measured data is recorded on laptops every 1 s from the ship-land communication system and 0.1 s from NAV440.

2.2 Situation of rough sea voyages

As mentioned in the previous section, the bulk carrier does not have regular routes during the measurement. The ship has mainly been in the North Pacific Ocean and the South Atlantic Ocean from 2010 to 2011. It has been in the Indian Ocean, the South Atlantic Ocean, the Tasman Sea, and the Pacific Ocean from 2013 to 2016. Figure 1 shows the ship's track during the measurement. Authors already showed 3 cases of rough sea voyages in the Southern Hemisphere (Lu et al., 2017; Sasa et al., 2017 and 2019). However, the number of analyzed cases was not sufficient to define the patterns of speed loss operation. Two cases were newly added to compare with the results of three cases already analyzed. Dates and sea areas in these three cases are shown in Table 1.

There are two cases of rough sea voyages in the Southern Hemisphere and one case in the Northern Hemisphere. Case C occurred offshore South Africa. Strong currents exist there, in addition to wind and waves. There are southern currents along the South American continent, too.

2.3 Weather conditions for three cases

Wind and wave conditions are summarized here. Figures 2–4 show the variation of averaged wind

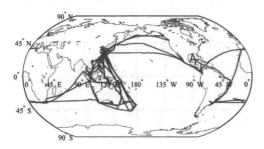

Figure 1. Ship track of 28,000-DWT class bulk carrier.

Table 1. Three cases of rough sea voyages.

Case	Period	Sea area	Voyage route
A	2010.9.27-2010.9.30	Pacific Ocean, Near Japan	From China to Mexico
B	2013.9.3-2013.9.7	Tasman Sea	From Australia to NZ
C	2013.6.1-2013.6.4	Indian Ocean and Atlantic Ocean	From China to Uruguay

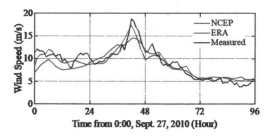

Figure 2. Variation of average wind speed (Case A).

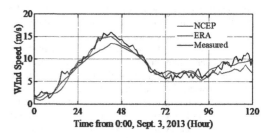

Figure 3. Variation of average wind speed (Case B).

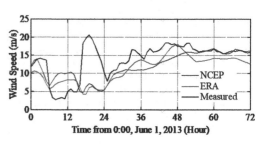

Figure 4. Variation of average wind speed (Case C).

speed at the ship's position for Cases A, B, and C. They include measured onboard value and reanalysis value (2-dimensional) distributed from the National

Center for Environment and Prediction, NCEP (NCEP-FNL), and the European Centre for Medium-range Weather Forecasting, ECMWF (ERA interim). There are no measured onboard wave data, and they are estimated by the third-generation wave model, Wave WATCH III. Figures 5–7 show a significant variation in wave height for Cases A, B, and C.

The maximum wind speed is 15–25 m/s, and the wave height is 4–7 m. It is obvious that there is a difference of 1–2 m in computed wave heights from the wind data of NCEP-FNL and ERA interim. Thus, the existence of uncertainty can be seen for wind waves.

2.4 *Analysis of the speed loss and engine parameters*

Various factors contribute to speed loss in rough sea voyages. Variations of ship speed, engine revolution,

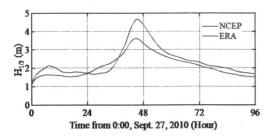

Figure 5. Variation of significant wave height (Case A).

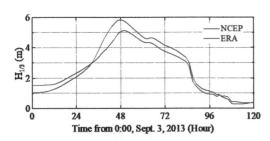

Figure 6. Variation of significant wave height (Case B).

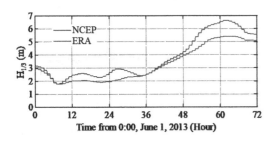

Figure 7. Variation of significant wave height (Case C).

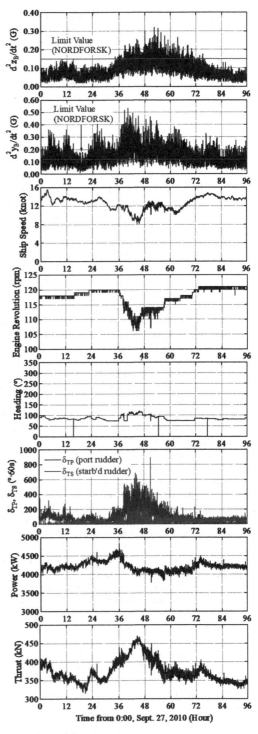

Figure 8. Variation of ship performance in rough sea voyages (Case A).

engine power, shaft thrust, pitch motion for Cases A, B, and C are shown in Figures 8–10. A significant loss of speed can be seen in these cases, and a large vertical acceleration is almost synchronized with a decrease in the ship speed, especially in Cases B and C. Typically, the speed of the ship gradually drops during the first 1–2 days and drops strongly starting from certain points. The engine revolution stays constant in the first stage, and drops down from a certain point, too. The marine engine is usually controlled to be at a constant revolution by adjusting the fuel injection in the governor. Because of the added resistance, the fuel injection is increased to achieve constant engine revolution in rough seas. Engine power increases with increasing fuel injection. The total resistance often exceeds the thrust in rough sea voyages, even if the latter is increased.

In Case A, the vertical acceleration exceeds the limit value of 0.15g by NordForsk (Nielsen, 1987) after approximately 36 h. Engine revolution stays at around 120 rpm until 36 h, and drops to 106 rpm in the next 12 hours. The speed of the ship gradually drops from 14 knots at 12 h to 12 knots at 36 h, and greatly drops to 8 knots at the same time with the engine revolution. The amount of rudder use per minute simultaneously increases for 24 hours, and the port steer is mainly used. The heading also varies from 75° to 120° at the same time. The engine power gradually tenses until 36 h, from 4,000 kW to 4,500 kW at the maximum value. It decreases to 4,000 kW after 36 h as the ship's speed decreases. On the other hand, the thrust increases from 24 to 45 h after the ship's speed and engine revolution decreased. In Case B, the vertical acceleration increases greatly from 44 h, at the same time there is a decrease in the ship's speed and engine revolution. The amplitude of the speed loss is around 8 knots, which continues for 2 days. The amount of steering is greater than that in Case A, and the starboard rudder is mainly used after the drop of ship speed. The power of the main engine does not increase until speed is lost. This situation with the engine operation differs from that in Case A. The thrust increases a bit just before 44 h, the start point of speed loss. It is known that thrust is more in Case B by 100 kN than that in Case A, although the engine power is larger in Case A by 500–1,000 kN than that in Case B. The ship was fully loaded in Case A and is ballasted in Case B. Thus, a greater engine power is necessary to make thrust in Case A. In Case C, the vertical acceleration exceeds the limit value at 40 h, and this is almost the same time as the engine revolution drops. The ship

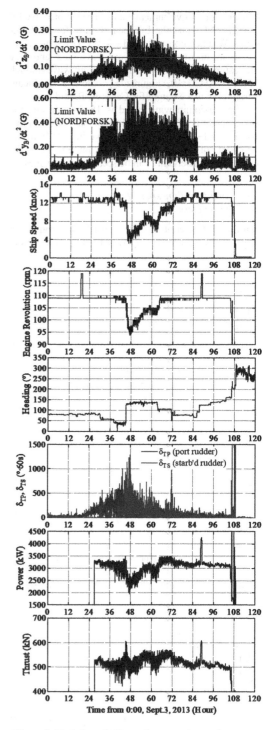

Figure 9. Variation of ship performance in rough sea voyages (Case B).

56

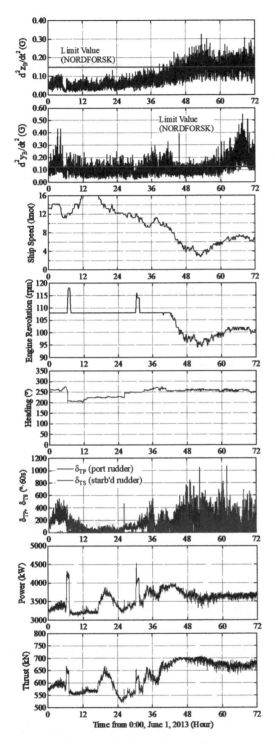

Figure 10. Variation of ship performance in rough sea voyages (Case C).

speed gradually decreases from 24 to 40 h, and greatly decreases after 40 h. It is also common that the amount of steering increases so much with a speed loss. Engine parameters are not recorded correctly in 0–24 h. The engine power and thrust continue to increase from 24 to 40 h, and they seem to be constant. The pattern of speed loss in Case C is very similar to Case A. The ship tried to maintain engine revolution when the added resistance in waves and winds reaches a certain point, and this can be regarded as a natural speed loss for 1–2 days. After the vertical acceleration exceeds the limit value, the deliberate speed loss occurs in the form of constant power control of the main engine. Situations with the main engine seem to be a typical torque-rich phenomenon in Cases A and C. However, the pattern is different in Case B.

In our future studies, it is necessary to make clear why there are two types of engine operations.

3 TIME-FREQUENCY ANALYSIS OF THE MAIN ENGINE REVOLUTION IN A ROUGH SEA VOYAGE

3.1 Time-Varying Autoregressive (TVAR) Method

Measured time series can be separated into steady and unsteady, linear and nonlinear. It seems possible to estimate the actual situations of ship operation. This analysis was already applied to the time series of ship motions when maneuvering a ship changed their properties. To analyze the loss of speed, which consists of the natural and deliberate loss, here the focus is on the operation of the main engine. Some characteristics for detecting natural and deliberate loss of speed are analyzed by using TVAR. The time series $y(n)$, measured at time t, is expressed as the summation of the previous time series with the coefficients and the observation noise as follows.

$$y(n) = \sum_{l=1}^{L} a_l(n) y(n-l) + v(n) \quad (1)$$

where $a_l(n)$ is the TVAR coefficient, L is the maximum number of time lags, $v(n)$ is the Gaussian white noise with zero average and variance σ^2. The estimation of $a_l(n)$ and σ^2 is important in the model. The estimation is conducted by using the state space model and the Akaike Information Criterion (AIC) (Kitagawa, 2010). The state vector, x_n, is formed using the TVAR coefficients. Time evolution of the space is modeled using a random walk model. The state space model is expressed as follows.

$$x_n = x_{n-1} + w_n$$
$$y_n = H_n x_n + v_n \quad (2)$$

where w_n is the Gaussian white noise, a vector with zero average, and σ^2 is the variance-covariance matrix, and H_n is the state space matrix. Eq. (2) is solved using the Kalman's algorithm, which consists of one-step prediction, smoothing, and filtering. The coefficients are determined from minimizing the value of AIC, which is

$$AIC = -2l\left(\hat{\theta}^*\right) + 2 \quad (3)$$

$$l\left(\hat{\theta}^*\right) = -\frac{1}{2}\left\{N\left(\log 2\pi\hat{\sigma}^2 + 1\right) + \sum_{n=1}^{N}\log\left(\tilde{d}_{n|n-1}\right)\right\} \quad (4)$$

$$\tilde{d}_{n|n-1} = H_n \tilde{V}_{n|n-1} H_n^T + \sigma^2 \quad (5)$$

$$\hat{\sigma}^2 = \frac{1}{N}\sum_{n=1}^{N}\frac{(y_n - y_{n|n-1})^2}{\tilde{d}_{n|n-1}} \quad (6)$$

$$V_{n|n-1} = \sigma^2 \tilde{V}_{n|n-1} \quad (7)$$

where $V_{n|n-1}$ is the provisional variance-covariance matrix of state x_n, and N is the number of data. Thus, the instantaneous spectrum, $S(f, n)$, can be obtained from TVAR coefficients and the estimated variance of measured noise is as follows.

$$S(f,n) = \frac{\Delta t \hat{\sigma}^2}{\left|1 - \sum_{l=1}^{L}\hat{a}_l(n)\exp(-2\pi i \Delta t fl)\right|^2} \quad (8)$$
$$\text{for } \left(-\frac{1}{2\Delta t} < f < \frac{1}{2\Delta t}\right)$$

where f is the frequency, Δt is the sampling period.

3.2 Data Analysis for Measured Time Series

Time series of measured data are analyzed for Case H. The ship has been in offshore South Africa from China to Uruguay in a half-loaded condition. As shown in Figure 11, great variations can be seen in the ship speed, ship heading, rudder angle, main engine revolution, etc. There are spike-shaped fluctuations in the main engine revolution, which correspond to the soot blow operation for an hour per day which increased the speed to 14 knots. As mentioned

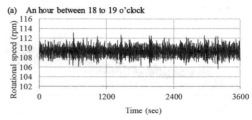
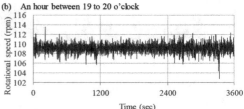
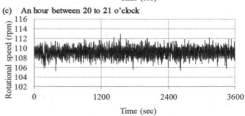
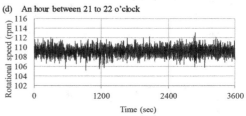
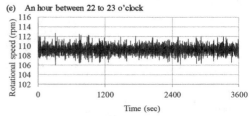

Figure 11. Time series of main engine revolution as the first statistical analysis (18:00-23:00, June 1, 2013).

before, the ship reduced speed to 12 knots to save fuel. These parts should be avoided in the analysis of time series, and the period from 18:00 to 23:00 on June 2 was chosen for analysis. A remarkable speed loss occurred immediately after this period. The first statistic result is shown in Figure 11 and Table 2. Shown are average values, median values, mode values, standard deviation, kurtosis, and skewness for the time series of the main engine revolution, and there are little differences between the average values and also the mode values over time. On the other hand, some differences can be seen in other parameters, especially in kurtosis and skewness.

Table 2. Statistical values in each term.

Term Items	18:00- 19:00	19:00- 20:00	20:00- 21:00	21:00- 22:00	22:00- 23:00
Mean	109.2	109.1	109.1	109.1	109.2
Median	109.2	109.1	109.1	109.1	109.2
Mode	109.9	109.3	109.9	108.7	109.9
Standard Deviation	1.026	0.968	0.996	1.010	0.944
Kurtosis	-0.102	0.980	0.016	0.058	0.062
Skewness	0.123	-0.209	-0.089	0.033	0.132

This shows that evaluating just the average value is not sufficient.

The instantaneous spectrum is estimated by TVAR method for main engine revolution. The order of model is defined as 40 here, and the search of noise variance is conducted every 6.8^{-k} (k =1, 2, ..., 10). Table 3 shows the model order and AIC value. It is obvious that the model order is less than 40 in all cases and that the data is correctly analyzed. If the system noise is greater, this means that the time-frequency property also varies strongly. The calculated results of instantaneous spectrum are shown in Figure 12.

The latest spectra are shown in the upward direction. Frequency and time are shown on the horizontal and vertical axes on a log-scale, and spectrum density is expressed using color contours. The interval of time and frequency is 1 minute and 0.05 Hz, respectively. There are many peaks in the spectrum from 18:00 to 19:00 o'clock, and the maximum values are in 0.065 Hz (15.4 s). Twin peaks around 0.065 Hz and 0.10 Hz (10 s) exist in the first half of the time period from 19:00, and they combine into one peak as the time goes until 20:00. The spectrum density becomes remarkable in long periods from 20:10 to 20:50, and the peak frequency gradually shifts from 0.095 Hz (10.5 s) to 0.07 Hz (14.3 s). The peak appears in long periods around 21:20, and the shape of the spectrum changes over time. Although the spectrum density is relatively low from 22:00 to 23:00, its shape has not changed over this period. These instantaneous spectra clearly show a trend in peak frequency. It is difficult to evaluate only from statistical values, such as average or standard deviation, etc. According to Sasa et al. (2019), it is

Table 3. Results of the TVAR modeling procedure.

Data	Model order	AIC
18:00-19:00	34	6532.866
19:00-20:00	19	6366.414
20:00-21:00	8	6954.746
21:00-22:00	12	6811.849
22:00-23:00	21	5871.915

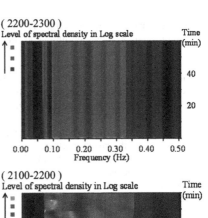

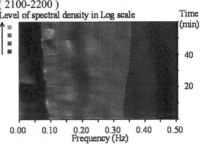

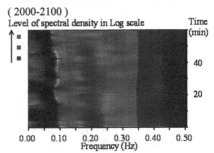

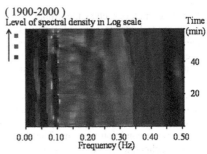

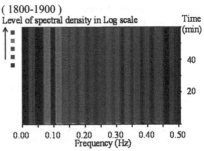

Figure 12. Estimated results of instantaneous spectrum (18:00-23:00, June 2, 2013).

shown that marine engineers typically operate the main engine when they monitor and decide on intentional actions for 20 minutes or so. These results may allow an accurate assessment of the operational status. The density of the spectrum increases in the low-frequency region from 20:20 to 20:50. This implies that intentional operation is included in this period due to a gradual variation in time series. These variations in instantaneous spectra can occur if marine engineers operate main engine slowly. As shown in Section 2, the speed loss is strongly correlated with the vertical acceleration, the deck wetness, the slamming, and the propeller racing, which are caused by pitch motion. If the variation in pitch or roll amplitudes is unsteady, it is necessary to consider the corrections to the variation of the main engine revolution.

4 CONCLUSIONS

Speed loss in rough sea voyages is analyzed from various aspects for a 28,000-DWT class bulk carrier in the global region. Main conclusions are as follows.

(1) Parameters are compared for three cases of rough sea voyages with speed loss. Vertical and lateral accelerations are compared with the Nord-Forsk limit values to evaluate deliberate speed loss. The vertical acceleration of 0.15g is coincides with the starting point of engine revolution dropping. On the other hand, the lateral acceleration is higher than the limit value of 0.12g in all cases.

(2) Other parameters such as the probability of slamming or deck wetness are also proposed. These parameters are being analyzed to validate the speed loss (Sasa et al., 2019). However, the estimation of range of speed loss is still unconstructed. This point will be studied in the future.

(3) The speed of the ship gradually decreases over 1–2 days, which can be prevented by increasing engine power. The added resistance continues to increase as the wave condition worsens. The ship switches to the deliberate speed loss at a certain point, which can be determined using vertical acceleration, the beginning of deck wetness or slamming, etc.

(4) Time series analysis is conducted for the measured engine revolution by TVAR method. The variation of instantaneous spectra shows that the engine revolution varied over 3 hours both in time and frequency domains. Especially, significant changes can be seen at 20:00-21:00, June 2, 2013, a couple of hours before the dropping in engine revolution. It is shown that the time-frequency spectrum is effective for estimating the loss of speed, including deliberate one.

(5) The amount of steering has greatly increased in all cases from the moment of switching to deliberate speed loss. The authors investigate the reason why the ship uses large steering angles when losing speed. It is necessary to show the relation with the speed loss or maneuvering in rough seas.

(6) Time domain analysis should be conducted for other parameters and periods after the switching point of deliberate speed loss, etc. There are multiple frequencies in the main engine revolution, and the deliberate speed loss has relation to low-frequency components of less than 0.05 Hz. According to the nationwide questionnaire, the period of engine operation is 20 minutes to 1 hour. Further analysis is necessary at these frequencies.

(7) The switching point from natural to deliberate loss of speed can be estimated from the measurement results. However, further analysis seems necessary to estimate the amplitude of the deliberate speed loss. Relation analysis with the wave condition, the ship motions, the steering condition, the main engine condition, etc., will be conducted.

ACKNOWLEDGEMENTS

The authors are deeply grateful to the Shoei Kisen Kaisha, Ltd. and the Imabari Shipbuilding Co., Ltd. for their cooperation in onboard data measurement for the 28,000-DWT class bulk carrier from 2010–2016. This study was financially supported by the Fostering Joint International Research (B) (Project No. 18KK0131, 2018-2022, submitted by Kenji Sasa) under Grants-in-Aid for Scientific Research, Japan Society for Promotion and Science. This study has been also supported by the Croatian Science Foundation under the project IP-2018-01-3739.

REFERENCES

Aertssen, G. 1967. Labouring of ships in rough seas with special emphasis on the fast ship, *Society of Naval Architects and Marine Engineers (SNAME) diamond Jubilee International Meeting*: 1–34.

Hagiwara, H., Shoji, R., and Sugisaki, A. 1997. A new method of ship weather routing using neural network, *Journal of the Tokyo University of Mercantile Marine, Natural Sciences*, 47: 21–29.

Hanssen, G.L., and James, R.W. 1960. Optimum ship routing, *J. Institute of Navigation*, 13(3): 253–272.

Iseki, T. and Terada, D. 2001. Study on real-time estimation of the ship motion cross spectra, *Journal of the Society of Naval Architects of Japan*, 190: 161–168. (in Japanese)

Kitagawa, G. 2010. Introduction to time series modeling, *CRC Press*.

Lu, L.F., Sasa, K., Sasaki, W., Terada, D., Kano, T., and Mizojiri, T. 2017. Rough wave simulation and validation using onboard ship motion data in the Southern Hemisphere to enhance ship weather routing, *J. Ocean Engineering*, 144: 61–77.

Maki, A., Akimoto, Y., Nagata, Y., Kobayashi, S., Kobayashi, E., Shiotani, S., Ohsawa, T., and Umeda, N. 2011. A new weather-routing system that accounts for ship stability based on a real-coded genetic algorithm, *Journal of Marine Science and Technology*, 16: 311–322.

Nielsen, I.R. 1987. Assessment of ship performance in a seaway, *NordForsk*, 91p.

Park, J.S., Otsu, K., Oda, H., Hirose, N., Ito, M. 2000. On the effect of rudder speed to batch adaptive roll reducible autopilot system, Journal of Japan Institute of Navigation, 102: 55–62. (in Japanese)

Prpić-Oršić, J. and Faltinsen, O.M. 2012. Estimation of speed loss and associated CO_2 emissions in a seaway, *J. Ocean Engineering*, 44: 1–10.

Sasa, K., Faltinsen, O.M., Lu, L.F., Sasaki, W., Prpić-Oršić, J., Kashiwagi, M., and Ikebuchi, T. 2017. Development and validation of speed loss for a blunt-shaped ship in two rough sea voyages in the Southern Hemisphere, *J. Ocean Engineering*, 142: 577–596.

Sasa, K., Takeuchi, K., Chen, C., Faltinsen, O.M., Prpić-Oršić, J., Valčić, M., Mrakovčić, T., Herai N. 2019. Evaluation of speed loss in bulk carriers with actual data from rough sea voyages, *J. Ocean Engineering*, 187: 1–19.

Terada, D., Yokokawa, S., and Iseki, T. 2002. Development of an onboard ship motion analyzer –I-, *Journal of Japan Institute of Navigation*, 106: 201–206. (in Japanese)

Tsujimoto, Kuroda, M., Shibata, K., Sogihara, N., and Takagi, K. 2009. On a Calculation of Decrease of Ship Speed in Actual Seas, *Journal of Japan Society of Naval Architect and Ocean Engineers*, 9: pp.79–85.

Hydrofoil profile numerical analysis for low Reynolds number

P.A.P. Souza, P.I.D. Lameira, H.P. Picanço, H.B. Moraes & L.C.P. Campos Filho
Universidade Federal do Pará, Belém, Brazil

ABSTRACT: In hydrofoil ship projects, it is important to choose the foil profile that provides the higher lift and the smaller drag minimizing the risk of cavitation. Moreover, hydrofoil ships have a higher drag on low speeds than conventional ships, highlighting the importance of low speeds analysis of the profile. This paper analyses 2212, 2309 and 4712 NACA profiles, used for hydrofoil applications, through bidimensional panel theory using the software XFOIL, and through bidimensional RANS equations and finite volume method using ANSYS FLUENT, with the objective to determinate the lift and drag coefficients for low Reynolds number. The analysis ranges from 0 to 15 degrees of attack angle, using a step of 2.5 degrees. The validation of the mesh for the finite volume method was made using experimental data from the E387 profile. According to the results obtained, the 4712 NACA profile has the highest lift-drag coefficient among the studied profiles.

1 INTRODUCTION

In hydrofoil ships, the hull is removed from the water due to hydrodynamic forces provided by the foils in which the force component perpendicular to the movement is called lift and the parallel component is called drag. This type of vessel has many applications in military and passenger transportation purposes since it can reach higher speeds due to the hull being removed from the water.

However, this type of vessel has a limitation in weight considering that it is limited by the lift generated by the foils. Another limitation of the hydrofoil project is cavitation which limits the maximum speed since this phenomenon can erode the surface of the foil and increase the drag of non-sharp leading-edge foils (Acosta, 1973). Therefore, it is important to determinate the profile used in hydrofoil projects so it can provide higher lift, lower drag without the risk of cavitation. Consequently, hydrodynamics analysis of the profile used for this application is of great importance.

Since the hydrofoil vessels need to reach a minimum speed to take off and considering that the hydrofoil vessels have higher drag compered to vessels without foils at low speeds highlight the importance of analysis for low Reynolds number. This analysis is more complex, due to the predominance of the viscous force instead of inertial and considering the limitation of the majority of turbulence models (Wilcox, 1994).

To determine the lift and drag coefficients to 2212, 2309 and 4712 NACA profile for the Reynolds number of 300000, it was used two methodologies: panel method and finite volume. The panel method analysis was made in the XFOIL software while the finite volume method was made in the ANSYS FLUENT software.

It was considered an attack angle from 0° to 15° with a step of 2,5°. The variation of attack angle is of great importance to the conception of the hydrofoil since the alteration of the attack angle alters the lift and drag generated by the profile.

2212, 2309 and 4712 NACA profiles were selected due to the analysis made by Putranto & Sullisetyono (2017), being those profiles used in hydrofoil projects. While the Reynolds number was selected due to the analysis made by Günel (2016) to the SG6043 profile. The profiles used are illustrated by Figures 1, 2 and 3.

2 METHODOLOGY

2.1 Panel method

The method used by the software XFOIL considers initially the potential flow (Drela, 1989b) and it can only determinate the lift coefficient initially. It is required a viscous analysis for the drag.

This methodology consists of discretizing only the foil and the wake, being N denotating the number of knots of the foil and N_w the number of knots of the wake.

The hypothesis considered are potential flow, the fluid does not go through the foil wall, that is, the speed normal to the panel of the foil is null and the Kutta condition on the trailing edge of the foil. The other condition considered is that the trailing edge is not sharp.

DOI: 10.1201/9781003216599-8

Figure 1. 2212 NACA Profile.

Figure 2. 2309 NACA Profile.

Figure 3. 4712 NACA profile.

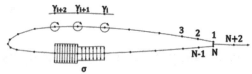

Figure 4. Discretization of the foil.

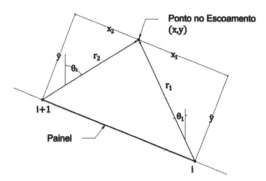

Figure 5. Local coordinates.

For the bidimensional flow, the flow around the foil is given by the superposition of the free flow, vorticity γ and source σ, according to the equation (1).

$$\Psi(x,y) = U_\infty y - V_\infty x + \frac{1}{2}\pi \int \gamma(s) \ln r(s;x,y) ds + \frac{1}{2\pi} \int \sigma(s) \cdot \theta(s;x,y) ds \quad (1)$$

In the equation 1, s is the coordinate of the edge of the foil and r is the distance vector between s and any point (x,y) of the domain, θ is the angle of the position vector r and U_∞ e V_∞ are components in $\hat{i}$ and $\hat{j}$ of the free flow velocity. Considering this equation, the foil discretization is given according to Figure 4.

It was also considered local coordinates for each panel. These coordinates are illustrated by Figure 5.

Considering the equation (1) and the local coordinate, utilizing Green's Function, we obtain the equation 2.

$$\psi(x,y) = U_\infty y - V_\infty x + \frac{1}{4\pi} \sum_{j=1}^{N+N_W} \psi_j^\sigma \cdot 2\sigma_j$$

$$+ \frac{1}{4\pi} \sum_{j=1}^{N-1} \psi_j^{\gamma+} \left(\gamma_{j+1} - \gamma_j\right) + \psi_j^{\gamma-} \left(\gamma_{j+1} - \gamma_j\right) \quad (2)$$

$$+ \frac{1}{4\pi} \left(\psi_j^\sigma |\hat{s} \times \hat{t}| + \psi_N^{\gamma+} |\hat{s} \times \hat{t}| \right)(\gamma_1 - \gamma_N)$$

Which ψ_{j^σ}, $\psi_{j^{\gamma+}}$ e ψ_{j^γ} are given by:

$$\psi_j^\sigma = \overline{x_2}\theta_2 - \overline{x_1}\theta_1 + \bar{y} \ln\frac{r_1}{r_2} \quad (2a)$$

$$\psi_j^{\gamma+} = \overline{x_1} \ln r_1 - \overline{x_2} \ln r_2 + \overline{x_2} - \overline{x_1} + \bar{y}(\theta_1 - \theta_2) \quad (2b)$$

$$\psi_j^{\gamma-} = \frac{\left[(\overline{x_1} + \overline{x_2})\psi_j^{\gamma+} + r_2^2 \ln r_2 - r_1^2 \ln r_1 + \frac{1}{2}(\overline{x_1}^2 - \overline{x_2}^2) \right]}{(\overline{x_1} - \overline{x_2})} \quad (2c)$$

Due to the necessity that the function is equal to a stream function ψ_0 for each knot of the foil analyzed, we have to a linear system of equations according to Equation 3. The coefficients a_{ij} e b_{ij} are determined by the equations (2a-c) for each knot of the discretized foil.

$$\sum_{j=1}^{N} a_{ij}\gamma_j - \psi_0 = U_\infty y_i - V_\infty x_i - \sum_{j=1}^{N} b_{ij}\sigma_j \quad (3)$$

Considering the Kutta's condition for the trailing edge, we have that $\gamma_1 + \gamma_N = 0$, resulting in a linear system of N+1 equations, allowing to determinate γ_i e ψ_o.

The system described by Equation (3) and the Kutta's condition can be solved using Gauss elimination, resulting in a solution dependent on the attack angle α described by the equation (4).

$$\gamma_i = \gamma_{0i} \cos \alpha + \gamma_{90i} \sin \alpha + \sum_{j=1}^{N} b_{ij}' \sigma_j; 1 \leq i \leq N \quad (4)$$

Which γ_{0i} and $\gamma 90i$ represent the distribution of the vorticity of the free flow for α equals to 0° and 90°, while $b_{ij}' = -a^{-1} b_{ij}$. Considering the potential free flow, the lift and its coefficient can be found, but the drag cannot be determinate. Considering $\sigma_j = 0$, the flow around the foil can be determinate, however, for viscous flow, the intensity of the sources cannot be determined, being additional conditions for the boundary layer for the resolution of the problem.

The equation for the boundary layer described by Drela (1989a) used for the methodology describes a boundary layer of compressive flow that uses energy and inertia coefficients. This equation is described by the formulation (5a-b).

$$\frac{d\theta}{d\xi} + (2 + H - M_e^2) \frac{\theta}{u_e} \frac{du_e}{d\xi} = \frac{C_f}{2} \quad (5a)$$

$$\theta \frac{dH^*}{d\xi} + (2H^{**} + H^*(1-H)) \frac{\theta}{u_e} \frac{du_e}{d\xi} = 2C_D - H^* \frac{C_f}{2} \quad (5b)$$

The term ξ refers to the coordinate in direction of flux lines, while η refers to the coordinate perpendicular to the flow. The fluid velocity at the boundary layer is denoted by u_e. θ is the momentum thickness, θ^* is the kinetic energy thickness, δ is the boundary layer, δ^* is the density thickness, H the shape parameter given by the displacement thickness over θ, H* is the kinetic energy shape parameter given by θ^* over θ, H** is the density shape parameter given by δ^* over θ while u_e is the boundary layer edge velocity and C_D is the dissipation coefficient.

2.2 RANS equations

The turbulent flow is the main phenomenon of fluid mechanics since most flows in nature are turbulent. The Navier-Stokes equations are applicable for turbulent as for laminar flow, however, there are many difficulties to model these flows, demanding high computational power for more complex problems. For engineering, one of the alternatives is to ignore the minor effects of turbulence and consider only the general and mean flow by doing a statistical approach.

The Reynolds Averaged Navier-Stokes equation considers that the properties of the flow can be decomposed in a mean and a floating part. Considering this approach and the Navier-Stokes equations, the continuity and conservation of momentum bidimensional equations can be written as (6) and (7) respectively.

$$\frac{\partial \bar{u}}{\partial x} + \frac{\partial \bar{v}}{\partial y} = 0 \quad (6)$$

$$\rho \bar{u} \frac{\partial \bar{u}}{\partial x} + \rho \bar{v} \frac{\partial \bar{u}}{\partial y} = -\frac{\partial \bar{p}}{\partial x} + \mu \nabla^2 \bar{u} - \rho \left[\frac{\partial \overline{u'^2}}{\partial x} + \frac{\partial \overline{u'v'}}{\partial x} \right] \quad (7a)$$

$$\rho \bar{u} \frac{\partial \bar{v}}{\partial x} + \rho \bar{v} \frac{\partial \bar{v}}{\partial y} = -\frac{\partial \bar{p}}{\partial y} + \mu \nabla^2 \bar{v} - \rho \left[\frac{\partial \overline{v'^2}}{\partial y} + \frac{\partial \overline{u'v'}}{\partial y} \right] \quad (7b)$$

The RANS equations are similar to the Navier-Stokes equation, differing only by the term related to the turbulence. This term can be written in the tensor form, called Reynolds's Tensor given by (8).

$$\begin{pmatrix} \tau_{xx} & \tau_{xy} \\ \tau_{yx} & \tau_{yy} \end{pmatrix} = -\rho \begin{pmatrix} \overline{u'^2} & \overline{u'v'} \\ \overline{u'v'} & \overline{v'^2} \end{pmatrix} \quad (8)$$

Only with the RANS equations, it is not possible to describe the flow, being needed additional equations. These additional equations are given by the turbulence model, that is, hypothesis for the turbulent flow. The model adopted was the SST k-ω model, developed by Menter (1994). This model combines the models k-ω and k-ε in which the k-ω is used for calculations for the interior of the boundary layer and the k-ε used for the free flow. The transition between the models is made using a blend function.

This model is said to be a two-equation model and considers that the fluctuation of the velocity is locally isotropic and the production and dissipation of turbulent kinetic energy are locally equal, being this hypothesis called local equilibrium. Another hypothesis adopted is the approximation of Boussinesq, that is, Reynolds's tensor is given by (9), which δ_{ij} is the Kronecker's delta and ν_T is the turbulent viscosity.

$$\tau_{ij} = \rho \nu_T \left(\frac{\partial u_i}{\partial x_j} + \frac{\partial u_j}{\partial x_i} \right) - \frac{2}{3} \rho k \delta_{ij} \quad (9)$$

The addition equations need to describe the flow refers to the kinetic energy of the turbulence, denoted by k, and the specific dissipation rate. Since this paper considers only stationary flow, its transient terms were neglected.

$$\frac{\partial(\rho k u_i)}{\partial x_i} = \tau_{ij}\frac{\partial u_i}{\partial x_j} - \beta^*\rho\omega k + \frac{\partial}{\partial x_j}\left((\mu+\sigma_k\mu_t)\frac{\partial k}{\partial x_j}\right) \quad (10)$$

$$\frac{\partial(\rho\omega u_i)}{\partial x_i} = \tau_{ij}\frac{\gamma}{\nu_T}\frac{\partial u_i}{\partial x_j} - \beta\rho\omega^2 + \frac{\partial}{\partial x_j}\left((\mu+\sigma_\omega\mu_t)\frac{\partial k}{\partial x_j}\right) + 2(1-F_1)\rho\sigma_{2\omega}\frac{1}{\omega}\frac{\partial k}{\partial x_j}\frac{\partial \omega}{\partial x_j} \quad (11)$$

$$\nu_T = \frac{k \cdot a_1}{\max\left[\frac{\omega \cdot a_1}{\alpha^*}; \Omega F_2\right]} \quad (12a)$$

$$\alpha^* = \frac{0,024 + \frac{Re_t}{6}}{1 + \frac{Re_t}{6}} \quad (12b)$$

$$Re_t = \frac{\rho k}{\mu \omega} \quad (12c)$$

Considering the turbulence model, the closure parameters and the boundary conditions, the finite volume method can be used to obtain the properties of the flow. The software ANSYS uses a correction for low Reynolds number. This correction modifies the turbulent viscosity equation, being the new equation given by (12a-c). The term a* is responsible to restrict the turbulent viscosity value.

2.3 Lift and drag

Knowing the properties of the flow around the foil, it is possible to determine the lift and the drag. The resulting hydrodynamic forces can be divided into two parts, one that refers to the pressure of the flow that acts normal to the foil's surface and a part that refers to shear stress that acts tangentially to the foil's surface. So, we can determine the drag and lift respectively using the equations (13) and (14). The term P represents the pressure on the surface of the foil, while τ represents the stress on the surface of the foil. The angle θ is determined by the vector normal to the surface in relation to the horizontal line, as illustrated by Figure 6. Since there is only

Figure 6. Pressure and shear on the foil.

considered bidimensional flow this paper, disregarding the foil's length and, so, the equations were adapted for curves integral, resulting in lift and drag given by force unit over length unit.

$$L = \oint_A (p\,sen\theta + \tau\,cos\theta)dA \quad (13)$$

$$D = \oint_A (-p\,cos\theta + \tau\,sen\theta)dA \quad (14)$$

For the calculation of the coefficients, we have that the lift and drag coefficient is given by the equations (15) and (16). The term U represents the velocity module while c represents the chord of the foil. It is worth mentioning that the coefficient is given by unit of length since it is a bidimensional analysis.

$$c_l = \frac{2L}{\rho U^2 c} \quad (15)$$

$$c_d = \frac{2D}{\rho U^2 c} \quad (16)$$

3 METHODOLOGY

For the profile analysis made by XFOIL developed by DRELA, the profiles were discretized in panels with 160 knots that, by default, have a unitary chord. The iteration limit was raised to 150. Afterward, the Reynolds number was considered 300000. After the calculations, the coefficients of lift and drag and inertia were shown.

For the analysis in CFD, it was used the software ANSYS 18 utilizing the FLUENT platform. A domain consisted of a semicircle of 25m o diameter and a rectangle with a total length of 27 m was adopted. The geometry of the foil was generated using coordinates of 60 points with a cosine spacing with 1m of chord. A sharp trailing edge foil was adopted.

A non-structured mesh with a thickness of the first layer of 4,4 10^{-2}mm was used. Being the y+ for the foil's wall verified after each simulation, since this value must stay below 1 to assure that the surface is well represented by the simulation. The total number of elements used was around $9 \cdot 10^5$ for each foil. As an example, Figures 7 and 8 illustrate the domain used. It is worth mentioning that in Figures 7 and 8, the number of elements was lowered to enhance visualization.

About the boundary conditions, the value of the inlet velocity was calculated according to the equation (17) using the Reynolds number of 300000, being the velocity decomposed. To not alter the mesh with the variation of the attack angle for each simulation, the inlet velocity components were altered. The components of the velocity adopted are described in Tables 1 and 2. The domain was characterized as liquid water at 20°C, having specific mass of 998,2 kg/m³ and dynamic viscosity μ of 0,001003 kg/m.s.

$$|\vec{v}| = \frac{Re \cdot \mu}{\rho \cdot c} \quad (17)$$

The SIMPLE velocity-pressure coupling was used, the spatial discretization of pressure, inertia and kinematic energy of turbulence and dissipations of second order. Beyond that, as explained before, the SST k-ω turbulence model was used. The convergence criterion used was 10-3 for the residual values. 3500 iterations were made, being additional iterations made in the case of non-convergence, especially continuity. The mean time of simulation was approximately 50 minutes.

Since the attack angle was obtained by altering the components of the inlet, a rotation matrix was

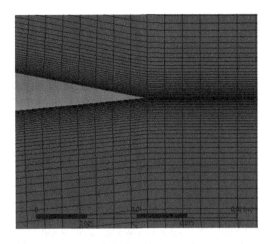

Figure 8. Trailing edge detail of the mesh.

Table 1. Velocity components for Reynolds number of 300000.

α	U	V
0°	0,301442	0,000000
2,5°	0,301155	0,013148
5°	0,300295	0,026272
7,5°	0,298863	0,039346
10°	0,296863	0,052344
12,5°	0,294297	0,065244
15°	0,291171	0,078019

Table 2. Lift coefficients- experimental x ANSYS.

			Difference	
α	Experimental	ANSYS	Absolute	%
0,0°	0,36561	0,367574	0,00197	0,5%
2,5°	0,61419	0,635761	0,02157	3,5%
5,0°	0,86881	0,895941	0,02713	3,1%
7,5°	1,12066	1,125852	0,00520	0,5%
10,0°	1,22240	1,228956	0,00656	0,5%
12,5°	1,22000	1,234562	0,01456	1,2%
15,0°	1,16191	1,197616	0,03571	3,1%

necessary for the rotation of the resulting force to determine the real lift and drag. The rotation matrix is described by equation (18), in which α is the attack angle and D' and L' are, respectively, the drag and lift obtained by the software.

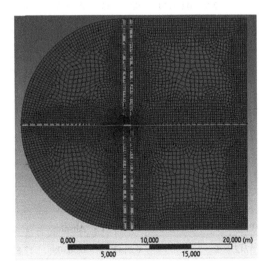

Figure 7. 2212 NACA profile mesh.

$$\begin{pmatrix} D \\ L \end{pmatrix} = \begin{bmatrix} \cos\alpha & -\mathrm{sen}\,\alpha \\ \mathrm{sen}\,\alpha & \cos\alpha \end{bmatrix} \cdot \begin{pmatrix} D' \\ L' \end{pmatrix} \quad (18)$$

4 VALIDATION

Considering the unavailability of experimental data of 2212, 2309 and 4712 NACA profiles, to ensure that the RANS equation methodology and the simulations befit the reality, it is necessary to validate the method. With this objective, experimental data of Morgado et al (2016) to the E387 profile for Reynolds Number of 200000 was used, considering the same mesh parameters. The results obtained are shown in Tables 2 and 3. Being the maximum observed difference of less than 5% for the coefficients.

5 RESULTS AND DISCUSSION

The data obtained are shown in Tables 4 and 5. The results obtained are also available in form graphics in Figures 9, 10, 11, 12, 13 and 14.

It was observed higher values for the lift coefficients obtained by ANSYS FLUENT. Similarly, the lift coefficients for drag obtained by ANSYS FLUENT were lower when compared to the results obtained by XFOIL. This is expected since the methodology used by XFOIL disregards the viscous effects initially.

The higher percentual difference for the lift occurs to the 2309 NACA profile, reaching 27,0% that represents 3,27 N/m for a foil the 1m of chord. While the higher difference for the drag was observed for the 2212 NACA profile, reaching 57,7%, however, this represents 0,0193N/m for a 1m foil.

The 4712 NACA profile presented the higher maximum lift and drag coefficient reaching values of 1,505 and 0,069439 respectively, this represents for a 1m chord foil a lift of 68,418N/m and drag of 3,146 N/m, being this result expected since it is the most asymmetric profile among the analyzed profiles.

The c_l/c_d ratio for each profile and attack angle are arranged in Table 6. According to the table, the higher ratio was obtained for the 4712 NACA profile for the attack angle of 5°.

Table 3. Drag coefficients - experimental x ANSYS.

α	Experimental	ANSYS	Absolute	%
0,0°	0,01097	0,011483	0,00052	4,7%
2,5°	0,01204	0,012596	0,00056	4,6%
5,0°	0,01366	0,014298	0,00064	4,7%
7,5°	0,01956	0,020495	0,00093	4,8%
10,0°	0,03265	0,03391	0,00126	3,9%
12,5°	0,05300	0,055273	0,00227	4,3%
15,0°	0,11000	0,105782	0,00422	3,8%

(Difference columns: Absolute, %)

Table 4. Lift coefficients - XFOIL x ANSYS (Re 300000).

Profile	α	C_l XFOIL	C_l ANSYS	Absolute	%
2212	0	0,2027	0,196728	0,0060	2,9%
	2,5	0,5410	0,522843	0,0182	3,4%
	5	0,7696	0,742569	0,0270	3,5%
	7,5	1,0119	0,957388	0,0545	5,4%
	10	1,2430	1,141413	0,1016	8,2%
	12,5	1,3427	1,287095	0,0556	4,1%
	15	1,3290	1,232319	0,0967	7,3%
2309	0	0,2674	0,195335	0,0721	27,0%
	2,5	0,5133	0,459230	0,0541	10,5%
	5	0,767	0,715754	0,0512	6,7%
	7,5	0,9918	0,938513	0,0533	5,4%
	10	1,1754	1,098330	0,0771	6,6%
	12,5	1,2025	1,203373	0,0009	0,1%
	15	0,7972	0,876851	0,0797	10,0%
4712	0	0,4774	0,512017	0,0346	7,3%
	2,5	0,8258	0,741091	0,0847	10,3%
	5	1,0827	0,976166	0,1065	9,8%
	7,5	1,2405	1,169608	0,0709	5,7%
	10	1,3791	1,315041	0,0641	4,6%
	12,5	1,4840	1,420046	0,0640	4,3%
	15	1,5304	1,505004	0,0254	1,7%

Table 5. Drag coefficients - XFOIL x ANSYS (Re 300000).

Profile	α	C_l XFOIL	C_l ANSYS	Absolute	%
2212	0	0,00800	0,012617	0,00462	57,7%
	2,5	0,00979	0,013133	0,00334	34,1%
	5	0,01229	0,014394	0,00210	17,1%
	7,5	0,01496	0,017633	0,00267	17,9%
	10	0,01763	0,021688	0,00406	23,0%
	12,5	0,02868	0,034353	0,00567	19,8%
	15	0,05602	0,064403	0,00838	15,0%
2309	0	0,00687	0,010609	0,00374	54,4%
	2,5	0,0081	0,011367	0,00327	40,3%
	5	0,01045	0,013569	0,00312	29,9%
	7,5	0,01701	0,019876	0,00287	16,8%
	10	0,02889	0,022248	0,00664	23,0%
	12,5	0,05436	0,045723	0,00864	15,9%
	15	0,01047	0,017126	0,00666	63,6%

Profile	α	C_d XFOIL	C_d ANSYS	Absolute	%
4712	0	0,0173	0,014222	0,00308	17,8%

(Continued)

Table 5. (Cont.)

Profile	α	C$_l$ XFOIL	C$_l$ ANSYS	Difference Absolute	%
	2,5	0,01276	0,015695	0,00293	23,0%
	5	0,01173	0,016762	0,00503	42,9%
	7,5	0,01883	0,023333	0,00450	23,9%
	10	0,02842	0,032354	0,00393	13,8%
	12,5	0,04151	0,047094	0,00558	13,5%
	15	0,06196	0,069439	0,00748	12,1%

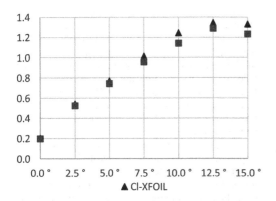

Figure 9. Lift coefficients of 2212 NACA profile (Re 300000).

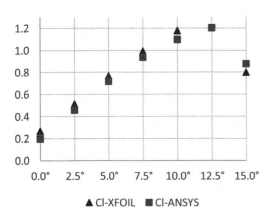

Figure 10. Lift coefficients of 2309 NACA profile (Re 300000).

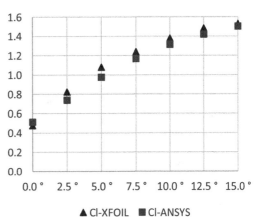

Figure 11. Lift coefficients of 4712 NACA profile (Re 300000).

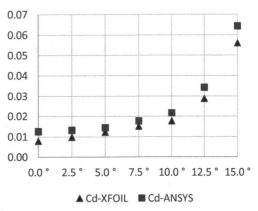

Figure 12. Drag coefficients of 2212 NACA profile (Re 300000).

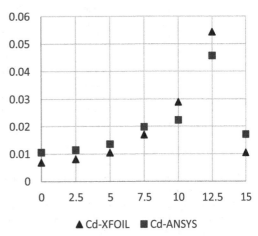

Figure 13. Drag coefficients of 2309 NACA profile (Re 300000).

6 CONCLUSIONS

The methods used for the foil analysis are valid and can be applied as a tool for the hydrofoil ship project, since the analysis in XFOIL, previously validated, as well as in ANSYS FLUENT was valid,

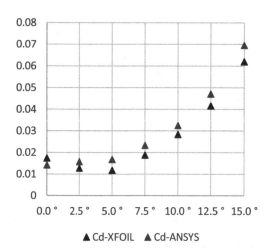

Figure 14. Drag coefficients of 4712 NACA profile (Re 300000).

Table 6. Lift-Drag Coefficient - XFOIL x ANSYS.

Profile	α	XFOIL Cl/Cd	CFD Cl/Cd
2212	0	25,34	15,59
	2,5	55,26	39,81
	5	62,62	51,59
	7,5	67,64	54,29
	10	70,50	52,63
	12,5	46,82	37,47
	15	23,72	19,13
2309	0	38,92	18,41
	2,5	63,37	40,40
	5	73,40	52,75
	7,5	58,31	47,22
	10	40,69	49,37
	12,5	22,12	26,32
	15	76,14	51,20
4712	0	27,60	36,00
	2,5	64,72	47,22
	5	92,30	58,24
	7,5	65,88	50,13
	10	48,53	40,65
	12,5	35,75	30,15
	15	24,70	21,67

which show an error less than 5% in the validation with experimental data.

Considering the attack angles with the maximum and minimum of the coefficients of lift, drag, and stol, it is highlighted the correspondence between the methods. However, there is a difference between the values of the coefficients obtained by XFOIL and ANSYS FLUENT, being the maximum difference of 10,3% for the lift and 57,7% for the drag. But it is worth mentioning that the percentage the variation is high but, numerically this variation is in the order of 10^{-2}. According to Rumanujam et al. (2015), the its methodology underestimates the drag since XFOIL uses boundary layer formulation that considers streamwise coordinates and consequently considers the boundary layer edge velocity instead of the free flow velocity resulting in a significant change in foil performance since the drag is usually two orders of magnitude lower than the lift.

Although the methodology used by XFOIL results in quick analysis and less complex of the flow around the foil, the results are not precise as the methodology used by ANSYS FLUENT. Besides that, the XFOIL software is deficient in the analysis of the foil, especially in pressure distribution and velocity around the foil and, consequently, in analysis of cavitation. So, the XFOIL software is indicated to foil analysis in the conceptual steps of the project while the ANSYS analysis is indicated to a more refined analysis.

The analysis described in this paper is of great importance for the study of hydrofoil before taking off, however, high Reynolds number analysis is still necessary for a hydrofoil project. The methodology described in this paper may also be applied to high Reynolds number, with minor changes, which is the main difference in the low Reynolds number correction.

The 4712 NACA profile showed a higher lift-drag ratio even when they have higher values of drag, results similar to the one obtained to Putranto & Sulisetyono (2017) for high Reynolds number.

REFERENCES

Acosta, A.J. Hydrofoils and Hydrofoil Craft. Annual Reviews of Fluid Mechanichs. California Institute of Tecnology. 1973. p161–184.

Abraham, R. & Marsden, J. E. & Ratiu, T. Manifolds, tensor analysis, and applications. 2 ed. New York: Springer-Verlag, 1988.

Drela, M. Integral boundary layer formulation for blunt trailling Edges. Massachusetts Institute of Technology: Department of Aeronautics and Astronautics. 1989. p 59–68.

Drela, M. XFOIL: an analysis and design system for low reynolds number airfoil. Massachusetts Institute of Technology: Department of Aeronautics and Astronautics. Lecture Notes in Engineering, Vol 54. 1989. p 1–12.

Eppler, R. Airfoil design and data. Berlin: Sringer-Verlag Berlin Heidelberg. 1990.

Günel, O. & Koç, E. & Yavuz, T. Comparison of CFD and XFOIL airfoil for low reynolds number. International Journal of Energy Applications and Technologies Vol. 3, 2016. p 83–86.

Harlow, F. H. & Welch, J. E. Numerical calculation of time-dependent viscous incompressible flow of fluid with free surface. Physics of Fluids, vol.8. 1965.

Menter, F.R. Two-equation eddy viscosity turbulence models for engineering applications. AIAA Journal. 1994. P 1597–1604.

Morgado, J. et al. Xfoil vs CFD performance predictions for high lift low reynolds number airfoil. Elsevier: Aerospace Sciencie and Technology. 2016.

Putranto, T. & Sulisetyono, A. Lift-drag coefficient and form factor analyses of hydrofoil due to the shape and angle of attack. International Journal of applied Engineering Research. Vol. 12. 2017. P 11152–11156.

Rumanujam, G. et al. Improving Airfoil Drag Prediction. 34th Wind Energy Symposium. American Institute of Aeronautics and Astronautics. San Diego, 2015.

Verteeg, H.K. & Malalasekera, W. An introduction to computational fluid dynamics: The finite volume method. Nova York: Longman Scientific & Technical. 1995.

Wilcox, D. C. Turbulence modeling for CFD. 1ed. La Cañada: DCW Industries. 1994.

Ship hydrodynamics - CFD

Comparison between model test and numerical simulations for a container ship

A.M. Chirosca & C. Gasparotti
"Dunarea de Jos" University of Galati, Galati, Romania

ABSTRACT: Computational fluid dynamics (CFD) techniques are improving and now are frequently used to augment, and occasionally replace, physical experiments. In this paper, the free surface viscous flow around a bare hull model is simulated with two CFD software (FINE Marine, a CFD product of NUMECA and ANSYS CFD) and compared to the results obtained during the experimental tests. The bare hull model studied in this paper is DTC (Duisburg Test Case), a typical 14000 TEU container ship, developed at the Institute of Ship Technology, Ocean Engineering and Transport Systems (ISMT) for benchmarking and validation of the numerical methods. Regarding the solution obtained, it can be noticed a satisfactory agreement between towing test results and the computation results. Comparative to NUMECA analysis, where the mean difference over the speed domain between model test and numerical simulation is about 2.16%, for ANSYS case, the medium percentage difference is 2.98%.

1 INTRODUCTION

Nowadays, container ships are constantly becoming larger and are required to carry more loads and travel at faster speeds and it's vital to find accurate methods to obtain the design data that are establish. An essential step in ship design is hydrodynamic performance evaluation.

Examining the dynamics of a container ship is extremely important for designers from the point of view of ship itself and of the waterways in which they travel. For a large container ship several factors affect the operation, these include the overall length, beam, draught, shape of the hull, displacement, velocity and distribution of the weight and buoyancy. A restricted channel has influencing factors such as width, depth, geometry and under-keel clearance.

All these factors can affect the three main issues for a ship in shallow water: sinkage, trim and resistance.

The resistance of a ship is not a new concept, but the changing environment of container ships specifications requires there to be continual effort into improving resistance prediction methods. Even though model testing of ships in towing tanks has been an excellent approach to determining resistance values (and sinkage and trim) up to now, with an increasing need for accuracy and our understanding of numerical simulations improving, a more sophisticated analysis is needed.

A number of container ship research hull forms have been developed over the years, which are representative of designs of the time. Examples of these include:

- "Duisburg Test Case" ("DTC"), designed by the University of Duisburg-Essen, Germany in 2012, representative of a 14,000 TEU Post-Panamax container ship;
- "KRISO Container Ship" ("KCS"), designed by Korean Research Institute Ships and Ocean Engineering (KRISO), representative of a Panamax container ship;
- "JUMBO" designed by SVA Potsdam, Germany in 1995, representative of a 5,500 TEU Post-Panamax container ship;
- "MEGA-JUMBO" designed by VWS Berlin, Germany in 2001, the design ship for the Jade Weser port in Germany, representative of a 12,000 TEU Post-Panamax container ship;
- "Hamburg Test Case" ("HTC"), a model of the container ship "Teresa del Mar", built by Bremer Vulkan in 1986 and still in service;
- "S-175", a somewhat simplified hull shape used for model testing benchmarking.

In this paper, a comparative analysis of the numerical approach and experimental results was performed, related to the free viscous flow around the bare hull of a container ship. Also, a comparative analysis between NUMECA and ANSYS is performed.

Hull geometry and experimental model tests data were available from performs in the experimental facility from SVA Postdam, Nietzschmann in 2010.

2 CASE STUDY

For our case, the hull tested was DTC. "Duisburg Test Case" (DTC), designed by the University of Duisburg-Essen, Germany in 2012, is representative for a 14,000

DOI: 10.1201/9781003216599-9

TEU Post-Panamax container ship, which has been tested in the Hamburg and the Postdam model basin.

The main characteristics of the hull are presented in Table 1:

DTC (Figure 1) is a single-screw vessel with a bulbous bow, large bow flare, large stern overhang and a transom.

The resolution of CFD problems involves three main steps: spatial discretization of the flow domain, computation and visualization of the results.

Meshing is an important step in any computational method, since the accuracy of the solution can be directly related to the sizes and shapes of the mesh elements. Choosing the appropriate meshing strategy is therefore an important aspect of any computational work.

The simulation part includes the actual computations of the discretized problem. The computational requirements vary depending on the problem size and the level of complexity of both the geometry and physics.

The processing of the results for providing useful data and plots is called post-processing. In the post-processing part, the results of the simulation are analyzed. Here the data from computations are visualized in a more illustrative format. However, this stage is not limited only to visualization. Most importantly, the results must be confirmed to be reliable. In addition, post-processing often includes calculation of new derived quantities, based on the original results.

Table 1. Main particulars of DTC in design loading condition.

Main characteristics	Model Scale	Full Scale
Length between perpendiculars L_{BP} [m]	5.976	355
Waterline breadth B_{WL} [m]	0.859	51
Draught midship T_m [m]	0.244	14.5
Trim angle θ [°]	0	0
Volume displacement ∇ [m^3]	0.827	173467
Block coefficient c_B [-]	0.661	0.661
Wetted surface S_W [m^2]	6.243	22032
Design speed v [knots]	3.244	25

Figure 1. DTC hull.

3 NUMERICAL APPROACH

For the numerical approach, in this paper, two software have been used: FINE Marine NUMECA CFD and ANSYS Fluent CFD.

FINE Marine is a CFD product of NUMECA International. This software suite is dedicated to marine applications and integrates a full-hexahedral unstructured mesh generator (HEXPRESS), a free-surface RANSE solver (ISIS-CFD) and a dedicated flow visualizer (CFView).

NUMECA offers a complete spectrum of software focused on turbo machinery fluid-dynamic simulation. The main advantages of this software are: the semi-automatic generation of control volumes starting from the blade profile CAD drawings, the capability of inserting geometrical details (fillet, leakage and cavities), the semi-automatic treatment of film-cooling holes and the possibility of manually building specific geometries.

ANSYS Fluent is a CFD software used in the ship design to model flow, turbulence, heat transfer, and reactions for industrial applications. In this simulation some modules included in the ANSYS CFD Package (Workbench 19.2) were used:

- SpaceClaim – defining geometry module;
- Meshing – module used for discretization of the body and the fluid domain;
- Fluent – module used as solver for the water flow around the body;
- Solution – the mathematical model used;
- Results – present the graphical and numerical solution.

The software is based on a cutting-edge physical mode and is able to perform thermo-fluid-dynamic simulations for engineering applications. It includes an accurate and robust solver and its usage capabilities are enlarged by the possibility of using moving and deforming meshes and of implementing user-defined-functions for inserting new models and modifying the old ones.

As NUMECA, ANSYS includes a post-processing environment entirely integrated in the graphic interface allowing an immediate and simple visualization of result.

The same settings were used in both ANSYS FLUENT and NUMECA.

Domain size is defined according to the length overall (Loa) of the ship. The computational domain extends 1.5Loa in front of the ship hull, 3Loa behind the hull, 1.5Loa in the side, 1Loa above ship hull and 1.5Loa under the keel of the model.

The computation was made for a range of six speeds from 1.335 to 1.668 meters/second, each different speed being computed separately. Water and air properties were defined for fresh water at 16 degrees.

Time configuration was properly used according to a steady flow and the turbulence model selected was k-omega (SST-Menter).

The surge motion defined as a ½ sinusoidal ramp law is imposed, beginning from an initial time of 0 seconds to 3.6 seconds and an initial velocity from 0 m/s to a final velocity of 1.335 m/s or one of the other values of the six velocities studied. Sway, roll and yaw are considerate fixed.

The no-slip boundary condition was imposed on the hull surface of the DTC model, that is, the fluid particles on the body move with body velocity.

4 NUMERICAL SIMULATION RESULTS

Resistance was computed for a range six speeds from 1.335 to 1.668 meters/second and compared with the available data from model tests conducted in the model test basins SVA Potsdam, Nietzschmann in 2010. The results are shown in Figures 2-11.

Tz0 (Figure 4) represents the evolution of the translation of the center of gravity of the body along Z-axis in the initial frame of reference.

In Table 2 and Figure 12 are presented the percentages differences between the numerical simulation and experimental results. A relative satisfactory agreement can be noticed. The medium percentage difference over the speed domain is about 2.16 %.

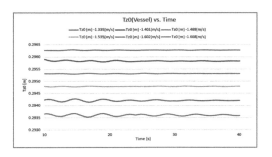

Figure 4. Sinkage for all six speeds computed.

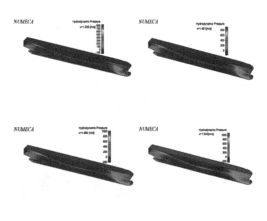

Figure 5. Hydrodynamic pressure for all six speed – Perspective view (NUMECA).

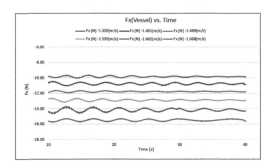

Figure 2. Fx for all six speeds computed.

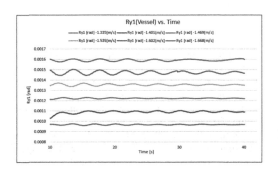

Figure 3. Trim angle for all six speeds computed.

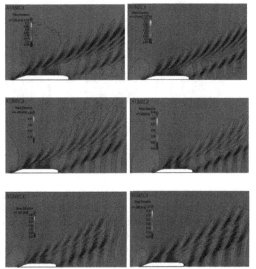

Figure 6. Wave Elevation for all six speeds (NUMECA).

77

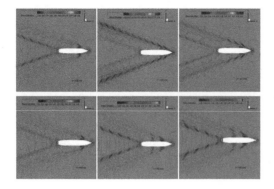

Figure 7. Wave Elevation for all six speeds (Tecplot).

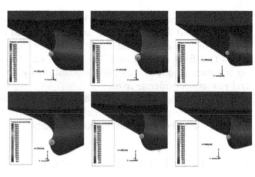

Figure 10. Pressure (normal stress) for all six speeds – Aft View (Tecplot).

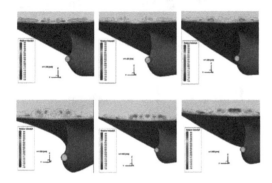

Figure 8. Relative Velocity on X-axis for all six speeds - Aft View (Tecplot).

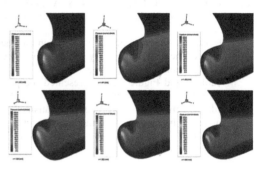

Figure 11. Pressure (normal stress) for all six speeds – Fore View (Tecplot).

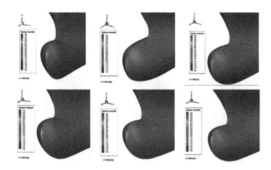

Figure 9. Relative Velocity on X-axis for all six speeds - Fore View (Tecplot).

From the analysis using ANSYS Fluent software, the total resistance for each speed was obtained. Regarding the solution obtained, it can be noticed a satisfactory agreement (as we can see in Figure 13 and Table 3) between towing test results and the computation results.

Table 2. Comparison of total resistance between experimental test and numerical simulation.

v [m/s]	R_T- model test [N]	R_T- NUMECA simulation [N]	Error ε [%]
1.335	20.34	19.674	3.2%
1.401	22.06	21.646	1.8%
1.469	24.14	23.572	2.3%
1.535	26.46	25.796	2.5%
1.602	28.99	28.542	1.5%
1.668	31.83	31.284	1.7%

But the numerical simulation can be improved, in order to increase the level of accuracy related to the total resistance. If finer meshes would have been used and if the number of time steps would be increased, we would have received more accurate values for this case.

Comparative to NUMECA analysis, where the medium percentage difference over the speed domain between model test and numerical

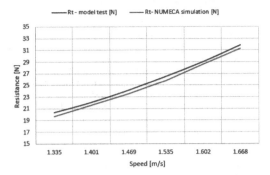

Figure 12. Comparative diagram between model tests and NUMECA simulation.

Table 3. Comparison of total resistance between experimental test and numerical simulation.

v [m/s]	R_T- model test [N]	R_T- ANSYS simulation [N]	Error ε [%]
1.335	20.34	20.764	2.08%
1.401	22.06	21.690	1.68%
1.469	24.14	24.478	1.40%
1.535	26.46	27.230	2.9%
1.602	28.99	30.274	4.42%
1.668	31.83	33.562	5.44%

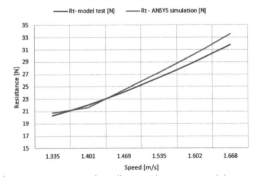

Figure 13. Comparative diagram between model tests, NUMECA and ANSYS.

simulation is about 2.16 %, for ANSYS case, the medium percentage difference is 2.98%.

As we can see in Figure 14 and Table 4, NUMECA generated better solutions than ANSYS Fluent, comparative to the model test regarding the simulation of the free surface around DTC model.

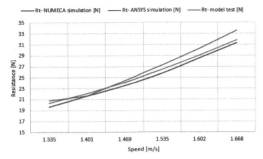

Figure 14. Comparative diagram between model tests, NUMECA and ANSYS.

Table 4. Comparison of total resistance between NUMECA simulation and ANSYS simulation.

v [m/s]	R_T- model test [N]	R_T- NUMECA simulation [N]	R_T- ANSYS simulation [N]
1.335	20.34	19.674	20.764
1.401	22.06	21.646	21.690
1.469	24.14	23.572	24.478
1.535	26.46	25.796	27.230
1.602	28.99	28.542	30.274
1.668	31.83	31.284	33.562

5 CONCLUSIONS

In this study, hydrodynamics of a benchmark ship, Duisburg Test Case, are computationally investigated. Although the hull form exists only as a virtual CAD model and as two models in different scales, the lines of the hull represent a typical hull form for modern post-panamax container vessels.

The benefits of CFD compared to traditional fluid flow experiments are many:

– Relatively low cost, no need to set-up and run physical experiments
– Speed, set-up for a CFD problem is faster than for a physical one. In addition, changes to the original design can be made quickly.
– Comprehensive data can be extracted from CFD, whereas a physical test case can only provide data from a limited number of locations. In addition, there is no testing apparatus interacting with the flow.
– Greater control of the set-up of the experiment. Conditions which would be di☐cult or impossible to achieve in a physical test can be easily created in CFD.

The CFD analysis of the flow was performed with Fine Marine NUMECA software. A comparative analysis between NUMECA and ANSYS was performed.

For our case, more accurate solutions were obtained using NUMECA, instead of using ANSYS simulation. The medium percentage difference between model tests and numerical simulation was 2.16% for NUMECA and 2.98% for ANSYS.

In conclusion, the main advantage of CFD comes from its ability to fulfill both Froude and Reynolds similarities meaning that model-scale results and full-scale results can be directly calculated while providing a great deal of detail about the flow. However, the absolute accuracy of CFD is still under concern and final decisions about the predictions of resistance and propulsive factors are still made by model tests.

REFERENCES

A. M. Chirosca (2019), Master Thesis: *Numerical Simulation of the Free Surface Viscous Flow around a Bare Hull Model*. Faculty of Naval Architecture, "Dunarea de Jos" University of Galati

El. Moctar, O., Shigunov, V. and Zorn, T. (2012). *Duisburg Test Case: Post-panamax container ship for benchmarking, Ship Technology Research Schiffstechnik* Vol. 59, No. 3, pp. 50–64

ISMT (2012). http://www.uni-due.de/ISMT/. Institute of Ship Technology, Ocean Engineering Project Best Roll Transport Systems, University Duisburg-Essen

Nietzschmann, T. (2010*)*, SVA Potsdam Model Basin: *Widerstands- und Propulsionsversuch für das Modell eines Containerschiffes*

NUMECA Fine/Marine (2017), *Theoretical Manual ISIS-CFD v6.2.*

NTNU –Norwegian University of Science and Technology (2014), *Numerical Investigation of Free Surface Flow*

ANSYS (2016), *Tutorial ship hull - Free Surface Flow around a Ship Hull Using ANSYS Fluent*

Numerical investigation of monochromatic waves propagation over a submerged bar

J.F.M. Gadelho & C. Guedes Soares
Centre for Marine Technology and Ocean Engineering (CENTEC), Instituto Superior Técnico, Universidade de Lisboa, Lisbon, Portugal

ABSTRACT: The main objective of this work is to study numerically the propagation of monochromatic waves over a submerged bar. The CFD model used in this study is OpenFOAM and solves Navier-Stokes equations. The free surface elevations time series of the Beji & Battjes (1993) experimental cases are used to calibrate and validate the numerical model. Results demonstrate that the numerical model describes with high accuracy the complex and highly non-linear phenomenon of wave energy exchange from low to high frequency harmonics over the submerged bar. The model can also predict implicitly the wave breaking but, in these cases, cannot reproduce satisfactorily the wave transformation in the back of the bar.

1 INTRODUCTION

The study of ocean waves near the coastline is a very interesting subject and it is necessary for practical applications in coastal engineering and wave energy conversion systems. The correct design of submerged bars is important, for example, to create surf zones that dissipate wave energy. It can also be used as a focusing energy method for wave energy converters.

In shallow water regime, the wave's interaction with the bottom topography frequently provokes refraction, diffraction, shoaling, damping and breaking of the wave.

The damping process due to bottom friction, for most wind waves with wave periods less than 10 s, is described by Lin (2008) as a significantly dependent process of the viscous effects within the boundary layer. This suggests that for numerical modelling of the wave propagation over a submerged bar the viscous effects cannot be neglected.

Nonlinear wave interaction is also a phenomenon that must be taken into account in the numerical modelling of submerged bars. Tick (1963) proposed the secondary interaction theory that in part explains the phenomenon. Later, Hasselmann (1968) established the theory for calculating the net energy transfer among different wave modes. The theory is the basis for all wave energy spectral models to compute nonlinear wave energy transfer.

The most common nonlinear process for wave energy transfer from low frequency to high frequency is the process of second harmonic generation or also called frequency doubling Lin (2008).

In particular cases of monochromatic waves travelling over submerged bars, typically, the energy is transferred from the generated wave to a transmitted wave that has twice the frequency of the generated wave. This phenomenon has been witnessed by several authors who made scaled experimental investigations on the damping action of submerged bars or obstacles (Beji & Battjes, 1993 and 1994; Drouin & Ouellet, 1988; Johnson et al. 1951; Rey, et al. 1992). Also field observations, in full scale, reported by Byrne (1969), and Dingemans (1989) show similar results compared to the laboratory experiments.

In the past three decades, with the exponential increase of computational power combined with more efficient numerical methods, numerical modelling of wave flumes with submerged bars became a very useful tool.

Several authors developed numerical models of submerged bars based on Boussinesq equations or Navier-Stokes equations. While the first are typically lighter in terms of CPU costs the accuracy of the results is limited to wave shoaling, weak nonlinearity and the wave breaking needs a trigger (Klonaris, et al., 2013; Schäffer et al., 1993; Tissier et al., 2012). On the other hand, models based on the Navier-Stokes equations are generally fully non-linear, take into account viscous effects and can model implicitly wave breaking, but the computational effort is much higher (Gadelho et al., 2014; Higuera et al., 2013a,b; Jacobsen, 2011; Ji et al., 2017; Kamath et al., 2015 and 2017; Li & Lin, 2010 and 2012).

In the present work, a CFD model based on OpenFOAM coupled with a wave generation and absorption toolbox is used to replicate the experimental

DOI: 10.1201/9781003216599-10

submerged bar case of Beji & Battjes (1993). The calibration of the model is done essentially for the non-breaking case, where results of different meshes and high order numerical schemes are compared. The validation presented also accounts for the wave breaking cases. Most of the above presented studies don't account for this phenomenon, and the only one that shows good results for monochromatic waves (Kamath et al., 2017), needs a high demand computational power, approximately 5 000 CPU core hours for a simulation length of 60 s.

The final goal of this work is to present a fine-tuned numerical model that can deal with the non-linear phenomenon of wave energy exchange from low to high frequency harmonics. At the same time, the model deals with wave breaking without the need of high computational demand. The present results show that the longest simulation for the plunging waves took about 250 CPU core hours. Which is 20 times faster than the CFD model presented by Kamath et al. (2017).

2 METHODS

The methodology used to develop, calibrate and validate the numerical wave flume, that describes the wave propagation over a submerged bar, is based on the comparison of the free surface elevation time series with experimental results and analytical formulations. The process is done in two parts.

In the first part, a methodology is presented to calibrate the wave flume without any structure. The results are compared with analytical Stokes second order waves.

In the second part, four monochromatic wave conditions were used to calibrate and validate the numerical model. The calibration was based on the non-breaking waves of Dingemans (1994) experimental case. The validation was made to the long non-breaking, long spilling and long plunging waves of Beji & Battjes (1993) experiments.

3 PHYSICAL MODEL DESCRIPTION

The experimental case of Beji & Battjes (1993) represents the wave transformation over a submerged bar both with regular and irregular waves. They made these experiments to elucidate the phenomenon of high frequency energy generation observed in the power spectra of waves traveling over submerged bars.

The experiments were carried out in the wave flume of the Department of Civil Engineering, Delft University of Technology. The flume has a length of 37.7 m, width 0.8 m, and height 0.75 m. During the entire set of experiments the still water level over the horizontal bottom was 0.4 m. The bottom profile selected for the experiments is shown in Figure 1.

A submerged trapezoidal bar was constructed, consisting of an upslope of 1:20 and a 2 m horizontal crest followed by a 1:10 downslope. The height of

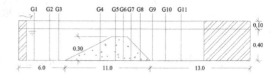

Figure 1. Physical and Numerical model shape setup. Water depth is 0.40 m. With the representation of the relaxation zones in the inlet and outlet (horizontal scale 10 times smaller).

the horizontal plane section was 0.3 m above the bottom of the flume.

The water depth in the deep region was 0.4 m and reduced to 0.1 m in the shallowest region above the horizontal part. At the end of the flume opposite to the wave generator, a plane beach with a 1:25 slope was used as a wave absorber. Some coarse material was placed on the beach to reduce the reflection even further.

The free surface elevations were recorded with parallel-wire resistance gauges at 8 different locations with a sampling frequency of 10 Hz.

Later, Dingemans (1994) replicated the experimental setup with a linear scale of 2 compared to the measurements of Beji & Battjes (1993). He employed more two free surface elevation gauges in the back of the bar.

4 NUMERICAL MODEL DESCRIPTION

The main CFD (computational fluids dynamics) software used in this work is the release version 2.4.0 of the open source software OpenFOAM (Open Source Field Operation and Manipulation) running on Ubuntu 16.04 operating system (OpenFOAM, 2019).

OpenFOAM offers users freedom to customize and extend its existing functionality by programing new solvers. The library waves2Foam (Jacobsen, Fuhrman & Fredsøe, 2012) is a toolbox used to generate and absorb free surface water waves. Currently the method applies the relaxation zone technique (active sponge layers) and a large range of wave theories are supported. Moreover, the relaxation zones can take arbitrary shapes. The free surface elevation is tracked by a Volume of Fluid (VOF) method.

This tool has a built-in waveFoam solver (based on the native's interFoam solver) that solves incompressible free surface Newtonian flows using the Navier–Stokes equations coupled with a volume of fluid method. This method determines the fraction of the fluid that exists in each cell.

5 NUMERICAL WAVE FLUME CALIBRATION

Originally, the numerical model works as a 3D model. To simulate a 2D wave flume, it is used only one cell in the transverse direction and imposed a slip condition at the back and front boundaries. Relaxation zones were employed to absorb waves in the inlet (wave generation) and outlet (artificial beach).

The domain used is a box with 30.0 m of length, 0.5 m of height and 0.01 m of width, with the initial free surface elevation at 0.4 m from the bottom of the domain.

The chosen Cartesian coordinates are x direction is parallel to the flume length, y direction parallel to the flume height and z direction parallel to the flume width. The x origin is located in the left boundary of the domain, where the waves are generated, and y origin is located in the initial free surface elevation.

The calibration of the present wave flume without structure focused on two sensitivity analysis. One regarding the mesh refinement and another related to the dimensions of the relaxation zones.

The mesh refinement sensitivity analysis was made by ranging the size of the cells (from 0.005 m to 0.01 m) and local refinement near the initial free surface elevation. No relaxation zone was employed and to prevent reflection, the domain was extended in x direction to 60.0 m.

To maintain a maximum efficiency and avoid extreme propagation errors, all meshes were made considering two criteria:

- Aspect ratio of the cells not bigger than 4:1;
- Volume ratio of neighbor cells not bigger than 4:1.

The incident wave is the same to all simulations. It is regular with a wave height, $H = 0.02$ m, wave period, $T = 2.02$ s and wave length, $\lambda = 3.74$ m.

The free surface elevations were recorded along the wave flume at $n\lambda$ (n = 1,2,...,10) and compared with the analytical Stokes second order waves (Dean & Dalrymple, 1991) described by equation (1):

$$\eta = \frac{H}{2} cos(kx - \sigma t) + \frac{H^2 k}{16} \frac{cosh\ kh}{sinh^3\ kh} (2 + cosh\ 2kh)\ cos2(kx - \sigma t) \quad (1)$$

where t represents time, x the horizontal position. The regular wave parameters are: wave height, $H = 0.02$ m, period, $T = 2.02$ s and water depth, $h = 0.4$ m. k is the wave number and $\sigma = 2\pi/T$.

A spectral evaluation of the wave energy along the wave flume was made. The validation criterion of the mesh was to preserve at least 95% of the energy at 8 λ (29.92 m) compared to the generated wave. The ideal base mesh, which maintain accurate results with no significant CPU cost, is structured with 600 000 cells ($\Delta x = \Delta y = 0.005$ m).

The relaxation zone geometry employed is the rectangular relaxation shape. Several horizontal dimensions were tested in the inlet and outlet ranging between 1/4 λ to 3 λ.

It was concluded that for this type of wave flume the minimum horizontal dimensions are 1/4 λ in the inlet and 1.5 λ in the outlet. The values of 1.0 m and 6.0 m were used for the inlet and outlet horizontal dimensions, respectively.

6 RESULTS

Four wave conditions were used to calibrate and validate the numerical model of the submerged bar. The calibration was based on the non-breaking waves of Dingmans (1994) experimental case. The validation was made comparing the results with the long non-breaking, long spilling waves and long plunging waves of Beji & Battjes (1993) experiments. The characteristics of the monochromatic waves used are presented in Table 1.

In any CFD numerical model there must be a balance between accuracy, stability and speed to solve the partial differential equations that governs the physics modelled. These factors are all dependent and are related normally to the mesh size, numerical schemes employed, and the hardware used in the simulations. If higher accuracy is needed, a more refined mesh or higher order numerical scheme must be employed on the model. In practice, to maintain a certain criterion of convergence the time step must be less than a certain time. Otherwise, round-off or truncation errors can be magnified, instead of damped, causing errors to grow exponentially leading to an unstable solution. In CFD usually a courant number (Courant, et al., 1967) is used to maintain the numerical stability and must be defined. In the present work a variable time step is computed with a maximum courant number of 0.25 for all simulations.

Taking into account the literature review, and in particular Jacobsen (2011) where he describes that the discrepancies on the back of the bar are related to the order of accuracy of the numerical schemes, it is obvious that this order of accuracy must be changed.

In OpenFOAM the discretization schemes can be defined in the dictionary fvschemes, for the terms: timeScheme: first and second time derivatives; gradSchemes: gradient; divSchemes: divergence; laplacianSchemes: Laplacian; interpolationSchemes: cell to face interpolations of values; snGradSchemes: component of gradient normal to a cell face; wallDist: distance to wall calculation.

In the present work, a Gauss Cubic scheme (Cubic) is employed in the gradSchemes and divSchemes. The results are compared with two meshes of the Gauss Linear schemes (Linear) and also with the experimental results. The characteristics of the simulations for 50 s of simulation are described in Table 2 and the main parameters of the Linear and Cubic numerical schemes are described in Table 3.

Table 1. Characteristics of the waves used in the calibration and validation of the numerical model.

Waves	H (m)	T (s)	Breaking Type
Wav1	0.020	2.02	Non-breaking
Wav2	0.022	2.50	Long non-breaking
Wav3	0.040	2.50	Long spilling
Wav4	0.050	2.50	Long plunging

Table 2. Characteristics of the simulations for 50s.

Sim	Mesh (cells)	fvSchemes	CPU Time (h)
Sim1	522k	Linear	21
Sim2	130k	Cubic	18
Sim3	522k	Cubic	80

Table 3. Main parameters for Linear and Cubic numerical schemes employed.

fvSchemes	Linear	Cubic
ddtSchemes		
default	Euler	Euler
gradSchemes		
default	Gauss linear	Gauss cubic
grad(U)	Gauss linear	Gauss cubic
grad(alpha1)	Gauss linear	Gauss cubic
divSchemes		
div(rho*phi,U)	Gauss limitedLinearV 1	Gauss cubic
div((muEff*dev(T(grad(U)))))	Gauss linear	Gauss cubic
div(phi,alpha)	Gauss MUSCL	Gauss cubic
div(phirb,alpha)	Gauss interface Compression	Gauss interface Compression

The hardware setup is a regular desktop with an Intel® Core™ i3-2120 CPU @ 3.30GHz × 4 with 8Gb RAM. The simulations to calibrate the wave flume with a submerged bar run for 50 s and have the same incident wave (Wav1, see Table 1).

The representation of the domain of the numerical wave flume and the position of the numerical wave gauges for the Dingemans (1994) setup is represented in Figure 1. The position of the wave gauges is described in Table 4 for the Dingemans (1994) setup and also for the Beji & Battjes (1993). A snapshot of the computational mesh for x = 11.0 m to 13.0 m for simulation wav4 at 50.0 s is presented in Figure 2.

Figure 2. Snapshot of the computational mesh for x = 11.0 m to 13.0 m with representation of the free surface elevation for simulation wav4 at 50.0 s.

Based on the mesh sensitivity analysis the refined mesh is about 522 000 cells which results of a base mesh with 600 000 cells generated with the block-Mesh tool and was adjusted to the bar geometry with the snappyHexMesh tool. The coarser mesh is generated the same way, but with a cell size two times bigger in the x and y directions, which results in a mesh with about 130 000 cells. The coarser mesh is used in sim2 to test the stability of the cubic numerical scheme and the accuracy of the results with a much faster numerical setup compared to the slower sim3.

The water wave statistics are presented in Table 5. In this work, Hs is defined as the mean wave height (trough to crest, using the zero-crossing definition) of the highest third of the waves. This way only the biggest waves (most energetic) contributes to the statistical analysis. The peak wave period (Tp) which is the period associated with the most energetic waves Hs, was also evaluated.

In Figure 3 is represented the proportion of significant wave height of the experimental results to the simulations in all gauges along the wave flume.

The results of the free surface elevations recorded in the last 7 gauges of the three simulations for Wav1 are compared with the experimental results in Figures 4-10.

The energy spectral density of the waves in the gauges for Wav1 is presented in Figure 11.

The validation cases are presented for Wav2, Wav3 and Wav4. Considering the results obtained in the calibration analysis performed for the numerical wave flume with the submerged bar, all the

Table 4. Gauge horizontal position along the wave flume in meters.

Gauge	Dingemans (1994)	Beji and Battjes (1993)
G1	2.0	6.0
G2	4.0	11.0
G3	5.2	12.0
G4	10.5	13.0
G5	12.5	14.0
G6	13.5	15.0
G7	14.5	16.0
G8	15.7	17.0
G9	17.3	-
G10	19.0	-
G11	21.0	-

Table 5. Water wave statistics: Hs calculated in all gauges for the experimental and numerical results.

Gauges	Experimental	Sim1	Sim2	Sim3
G1	0.022	0.021	0.021	0.021
G2	0.022	0.021	0.021	0.021
G3	0.020	0.020	0.021	0.020
G4	0.026	0.025	0.025	0.025
G5	0.034	0.033	0.035	0.034
G6	0.036	0.037	0.036	0.037
G7	0.032	0.034	0.032	0.033
G8	0.027	0.030	0.027	0.028
G9	0.026	0.031	0.025	0.025
G10	0.022	0.028	0.026	0.026
G11	0.031	0.036	0.033	0.034

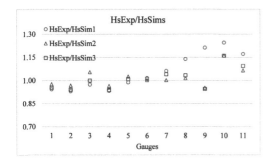

Figure 3. Significant wave height comparison between the experimental results and the numerical simulations in the 11 gauges.

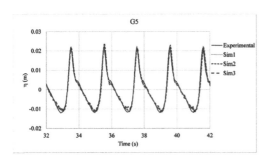

Figure 4. Free surface elevations time series in G5 for Wav1.

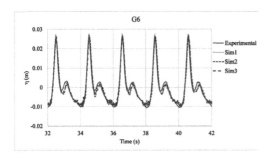

Figure 5. Free surface elevations time series in G6 for Wav1.

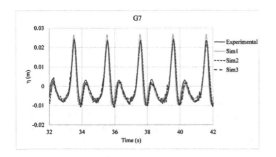

Figure 6. Free surface elevations time series in G7 for Wav1.

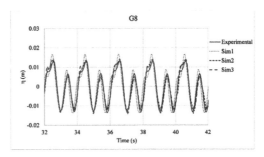

Figure 7. Free surface elevations time series in G8 for Wav1.

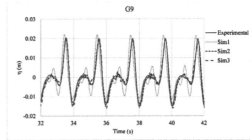

Figure 8. Free surface elevations time series in G9 for Wav1.

numerical parameters for the validation cases are the same as those used in sim3.

The comparison of the free surface elevation time series in G1 to G8 for Wav2 with the physical experiments of Beji and Battjes (1993) is presented in Figure 12. The results of the free surface elevations time series for the Wav3 case are presented in Figure 13.

Also, the evolution of the wave over the bar for Wav4 for times $5.5T + 1/8T$, $5.5T + 2/8T$, ..., $5.5T + 8/8T$ is presented in Figure 14. The longest simulation for the plunging waves took about 250 hours CPU core time, which is about 20 times faster than the study presented by Kamath et al. (2017).

7 DISCUSSION

Regarding the calibration of the model, and for Wav1, the free surface elevation time series are presented from Figures 4-10 for the last 7 wave gauges. It is observed that in the first four gauges the three simulations perform almost the same, showing the evolution of the wave profile along the upward slope identical to the physical results.

All of the simulations assume, what is described as, a saw-toothed configuration at gauge 5 (Figure 4).

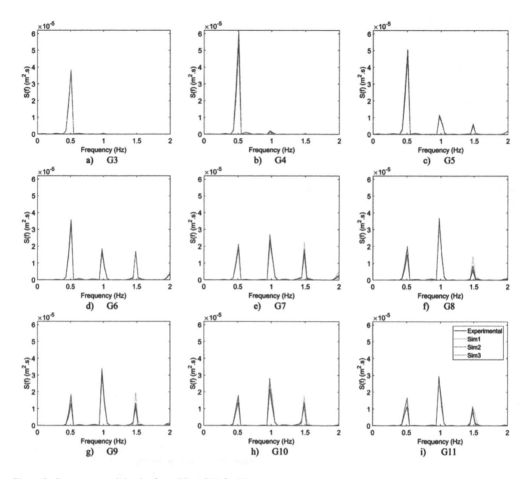

Figure 9. Energy spectral density from G3 to G11 for Wav1.

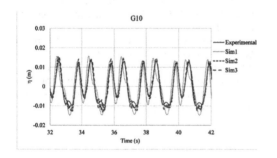

Figure 10. Free surface elevations time series in G10 for Wav1.

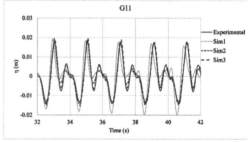

Figure 11. Free surface elevations time series in G11 for Wav1.

Also, the energy spectral density of the water waves of gauge 5 (Figure 11c) shows that is evident the energy spread to harmonics of higher frequency for both numerical and physical results.

In these gauges, the cubic simulations (sim2 and sim3) show some irregularities in the wave trough that are not present in the experimental results. These differences are probably related to numerical viscosity that is much less in the cubic numerical scheme.

The physical profile transformation of the wave in the top of the bar at gauge 6, becomes evident by presenting a second crest (Figure 5). Differences between numerical results also becomes noticeable. Sim1 (linear) seems to perform better representing

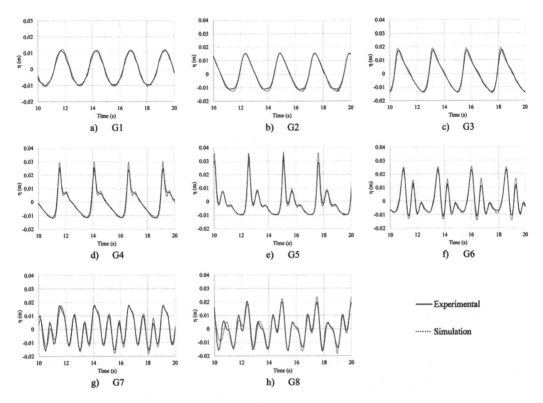

Figure 12. Free surface elevation time series in G1 to G8 for Wav2.

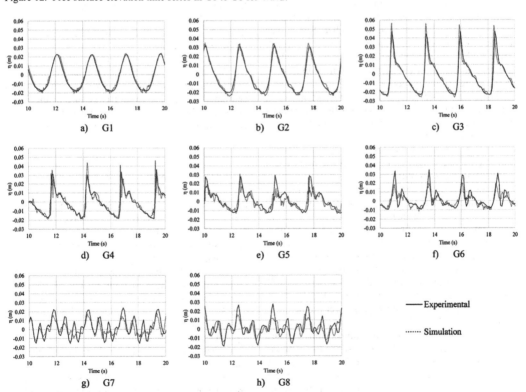

Figure 13. Free surface elevation time series in G1 to G8 for Wav3.

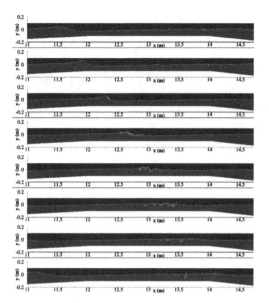

Figure 14. Evolution of the wave over the bar for Wav4 for times $5.5T + 1/8T, 5.5T + 2/8T, ..., 5.5T + 8/8T$.

the trough and the second higher crest, but over predicts the higher crest of the wave. Sim2 and sim3 (cubic) continues to present some noise in the trough of the wave. In the downward slope of the bar, at gauge 7 (Figure 6) and compared to gauge 6, physical results show that the first crest becomes smaller, while the second crest becomes higher. Sim1 over predicts the first crest and under predicts the second. Sim2 and sim3, present better results by predicting the crest heights, but once again presents some noise in the trough of the wave.

The energy spectral density of the water waves at gauge 7 (Figure 11e) shows that, for the experimental results, the second harmonic is the one that starts to have more energy.

Sim2 and sim3 follows the same spectral behavior, but strangely sim1 indicates that the most energetic harmonic is the third one.

In the back of the bar, from gauge 8 to 11 (Figures 7-10), experimental results show an evident decomposition of the wave in three harmonics. Also, the spectrum analysis confirms this observation (Figures 11f-11i). This is where sim1 presents unsatisfactory results, by over predicting in most of the gauges the wave crests. Also, the wave phase is not well described. Generally, sim2 and sim3 describes well the wave shape (with a little advantage for sim3), but the crest amplitudes are slightly over predicted.

Overall, sim3 (cubic) can describe very well the wave propagation in all the wave flume. Sim1 (linear) that share the same mesh, fails to describe the harmonics behavior in the back of the bar. This suggests that for the present case, the performance of the numerical scheme plays an important role in the physical description of the exchange of energy between harmonics.

Using a coarser mesh in sim2, with evident CPU time saving, lead to similar results compared to sim3, only losing crest amplitudes at the far back of the bar, at gauge 11.

The peak period Tp is well predict by all simulations in all gauges. Based on Table 5, it is also observed that all simulations can predict with good accuracy Hs until G7. After this gauge, Sim1 over predicts Hs up to 25%. Sim2 and Sim3 have almost the same values for Hs and predict with accuracy Hs, with differences up to 15% (Figure 3).

The validation results of the free surface elevations for Wav2 (long non-breaking waves) are presented in Figure 12. Overall the results of the numerical model describe very well the wave transformation along the The validation results of the free surface elevations wave flume. The shape of the wave is well described in all gauges, but the wave crests are slightly over predicted by the numerical model.

The validation results of the free surface elevations for Wav3 (long spilling waves) are presented in Figure 13. The results show that the numerical model can predict the wave shape in the first four gauges, but over predicts the wave crests (Figures 13a-13d). At gauge 5 and onwards (corresponds to 14.0 m, which is the start of the downward slope), the model fails to reproduce the wave shape in all gauges. This can be explained by the fact that the VOF method that OpenFOAM uses does not give the exact position of the free surface elevation. Instead, it gives the fraction of each fluid in each cell, resulting in an erroneous fluid interface position. Also, the spatial discretization over the bar might be insufficient.

Although results of the wave evolution over the bar for Wav4 (Figure 14) show that the model can predict the plunging wave breaker x position, that is estimated to be 12.2 m and is in line to the results presented by Kamath et al. (2017). It is also observed that emulsion air water is evident after the wave breaking.

8 CONCLUSIONS

Results demonstrate that the numerical model can generate and accurately model wave propagation over a submerged bar as well as it can describe the processes of wave transformation and wave energy exchange from low to high harmonics.

The use of cubic parameters in the numerical scheme demonstrated to improve the results of the free surface elevations time series in the back of the bar. This is where the complex and high non-linear phenomenon of wave energy exchange from low to high harmonics is dominant. On the other hand, some disturbances are observed on the trough of the wave.

Results for the wave breaking cases show that the present numerical model cannot reproduce satisfactorily the wave transformation in the back of the bar, probably related to the VOF method that OpenFOAM uses to track the free surface elevation. Although, the horizontal plunging breaker positions is well represented.

ACKNOWLEDGEMENTS

The first author has been funded by the University of Lisbon, and CENTEC within a PhD grant. This work was performed within the scope of the Strategic Research Plan of the Centre for Marine Technology and Ocean Engineering (CENTEC), which is financed by the Portuguese Foundation for Science and Technology (Fundação para a Ciência e Tecnologia - FCT) under contract UIDB/UIDP/00134/2020.

REFERENCES

Beji, S. and Battjes, J. A., 1993. Experimental investigation of wave propagation over a bar. *Coastal Engineering*, 19(1-2): 151–162.

Beji, S. and Battjes, J. A., 1994. Numerical simulation of nonlinear wave propagation over a bar. *Coastal Engineering*, 23(1-2): 1–16.

Byrne, R. J., 1969. Field occurrences of induced multiple gravity waves. *J. Geophys. Res.*, 74 (10): 2590–2596.

Courant, R., Friedrichs, K., and Lewy, H., 1967. [1928], On the partial difference equations of mathematical physics, *IBM Journal of Research and Development*, 11 (2): 215–234.

Dean, R. G. and Dalrymple, R. A., 1991. *Water Wave Mechanics for Engineers and Scientists*. Singapore: World Scientific Publishing Co. Pte. Ltd, 353p.

Dingemans, M.W., 1989. Shift in characteristic wave frequency; some spectra in wave basin and in Haringvliet region, Delft Hydraulics, *Tech. Rep. H 0616*, Part II, 56 p.

Dingemans, M. W., 1994. Comparison of computations with Boussinesq-like models and laboratory measurements. Technical University of Delft: *Report N H1684.12*.

Drouin, A. and Y. Ouellet, 1988. Experimental study of immersed plates used as breakwaters. *Proceedings of the 21th Coastal Engineering Conference* (Malaga, Spain), Part 3, pp. 2272–2283.

Gadelho, J.F.M.; Lavrov, A., and Guedes Soares, C., 2014. Modelling the effect of obstacles on the 2D wave propagation with OpenFOAM, In: Guedes Soares, C. and López Peña, F., (eds.), *Developments in Maritime Transportation and Exploitation of Sea Resources*, London: Taylor and Francis Group, pp. 1057–1065.

Hasselmann, K., 1968. Weak-interaction theory of ocean waves. In: M. Holt (ed.), *Basic Developments in Fluid Dynamics: Vol. 2*, London: Academic Press, pp. 117–182.

Higuera, P., Lara, J. L., and Losada I. J., 2013a. Realistic wave generation and active wave absorption for Navier-Stokes models Application to OpenFOAM®. *Coastal Engineering*, 71: 102–118.

Higuera, P., Lara, J. L., and Losada I. J., 2013b. Simulating coastal engineering processes with OpenFOAM®. *Coastal Engineering*, 71: 119–134.

Jacobsen, N. G., 2011. *A Full Hydro- and Morphodynamic Description of Breaker Bar Development*. Denmark: Technical University of Denmark, Department of Mechanical Engineering, Ph.D. dissertation. DCAMM Special Report no. S136.

Jacobsen, N. G.; Fuhrman, D. R., and Fredsøe, J., 2012. A Wave Generation Toolbox for the Open-Source CFD Library: OpenFoam. *Int. J. Numerl. Meth. Fluids*, 70(9): 1073–1088.

Ji, Q., Dong, S., Luo, X., and Guedes Soares, C., 2017. Wave transformation over submerged breakwaters by the constrained interpolation profile method, *Ocean Engineering*, 136: 294–303.

Johnson, J. W.; Fuchs, R. A., and Morison J. R., 1951. The damping action of submerged breakwaters, *Eos Trans. AGU*, 32(5): 704–718.

Kamath, A., Bihs, H., Chella, M. A. and Arntsen Ø. A., 2015. CFD Simulations of Wave Propagation and Shoaling over a Submerged Bar. *Aquatic Procedia*, 4: 308–316.

Kamath, A., Chella, M. A., Bihs, H., and Arntsen Ø. A., 2017. Energy transfer due to shoaling and decomposition of breaking and non-breaking waves over a submerged bar. *Engineering Applications of Computational Fluid Mechanics*, 11(1): 450–466.

Klonaris, G. Th., Memos, C. D. and Karambas, Th. V., 2013. A Boussinesq-type model including wave-breaking terms in both continuity and momentum equations. *Ocean Engineering*, 57: 128–140.

Li, Y. and Lin, M., 2010. Wave-body interactions for a surface-piercing body in water for finite depth. *Journal of Hydrodynamics* 22(6): 745–752.

Li, Y. and Lin, M., 2012. Regular and irregular wave impacts on floating body. *Ocean Engineering* 42: 93–101.

Lin, P., 2008. *Numerical Modeling of Water Waves*. London: CRC Press, 504p.

OpenFOAM, 2019. OpenFOAM - The open source CFD toolbox, http://www.openfoam.com/.

Rey, V.; Belzons, M. and Guazzelli, E., 1992. Propagation of surface gravity waves over a rectangular submerged bar. *J. Fluid. Mech.* 235: 453–479.

Schäffer, H. A.; Madsen, P. A., and Deigaard, R., 1993. A Boussinesq model for waves breaking in shallow water. *Coastal Engineering* 20: 185–202.

Tick, L. J., 1963. Nonlinear probability models of ocean waves. *Proceedings of Ocean Wave spectra Conference* (Easton, Maryland, USA), pp. 163–169.

Tissier, M., Bonneton, P., Marche, F., Chazel, F., and Lannes, D., 2012. A new approach to handle wave breaking in fully non-linear Boussinesq models. *Coastal Engineering* 67: 54–66.

Comparative investigation on the hydrodynamic behavior of high-performance monohulls by CFD

J. Jiao, S. Huang & C. Chen
School of Civil Engineering and Transportation, South China University of Technology, Guangzhou, China

ABSTRACT: In order to develop monohull with lower resistance and higher seakeeping ability, wave-piercing deep-V hull and two kinds of bow appendage are developed and compared with a round bilge hull. The roll stability, calm water resistance and seakeeping performance of ships are comparatively investigated by CFD solver. The influence of mesh number on the simulation of ship resistance and motions in regular waves is also analyzed. The results indicate that deep-V hull has better roll and pitch stability than round bilge hull. The water drop-shaped bulbous bow is helpful in the reduction of resistance of deep-V hull at high speed. The semi-submerged bow has more effect in the improvement of pitch stability of deep-V hull compared with the drop-shaped bulbous bow.

1 INTRODUCTION

Ship seakeeping directly affect the habitability, usability and safety of both merchant and naval ships (Lloyd, 1989). To data, although high performance ship such as wave-piercing catamaran, trimaran and pentamaran are becoming mature and widely adopted due to their good seakeeping ability, monohull is still the first choice at ship design phase due to its obvious advantage such as simplified configuration and high structural strength. Compared with the traditional round bilge type monohull, deep-V type monohull with wave-piercing bow has obvious advantage in roll stability, seakeeping and stealth performance. The damage on local structure of bow caused by green water and slamming can be largely reduced by adopting the scheme of wave-piercing bow.

It is known that large water drop-shaped bulbous bow could reduce the wave-making resistance of ship. Till now, water drop-shaped bulbous bow has been widely applied on bow flare ships. However, the application of water drop-shaped bulbous bow on deep-V hull is rarely seen, this study will investigate this aspect. On the other hand, although ship roll motion can be effectively reduced by ship anti-roll tank and fin stabilizer techniques (Jin et al., 2004), ship pitch reduction is difficult to realize due to the longitudinal moment of inertia of ship is much larger compared with the transverse moment of inertia. Kihara et al. (1985) developed semi-submerged bow (SSB) and used it to improve the pitch stability of a 40-meter long vessel. Sun et al. (2013) investigated the effect of SSB on the seakeeping of a 1000 tonnage class deep-V hull by tank model test.

The effects of vertical motion reduction of SSB can be attributed to the viscous damping force and lift force generated due to relative vertical movement of SSB against fluid. The lift force is generated when the appendage advancing with an attack angle (caused by pitch). The motion stabilization is achieved since the damping force and lift force are always opposite to the vertical movement direction of bow. The conventional potential flow theory assumes the fluid to be inviscid and, therefore, cannot accurately predict the motions of deep-V hull with SSB. Recently, with the development of computer calculation power, CFD technique is widely used in the field of naval architecture and ocean engineering (Kim, 2011). Jiao et al. (2018) calculated the 2D hydrodynamic coefficients of cross-section of deep-V hull by CFD method and then substituted the hydrodynamic coefficients into a strip theory based ship motion equation to take the fluid viscosity effect into account. Sun et al. (2016) predicted wave-induced motions of a catamaran equipped with semi-submerged bow by CFD and compared with tank model experimental data.

In this paper, a traditional round bilge monohull is adopted as a basic model, deep-V monohull with two different kinds of bow appendage are designed and optimized to achieve better comprehensive hydrodynamic performance. CFD method is used to investigate the calm water resistance and seakeeping behavior of these ships. The influence of bow appendage on ship hydrodynamics is also analyzed.

2 GOVERNING EQUATIONS

This paper studies the hydrodynamic behavior of ship in waves based on CFD technique. In a Cartesian coordinate system, incompressible Newtonian fluid motion conforms to both the continuity and the momentum conservation equations that shown in Eq.(1) and Eq.(2):

$$\nabla \cdot \mathbf{v} = 0 \quad (1)$$

$$\frac{\partial U_i}{\partial t} + \frac{\partial (U_i U_j)}{\partial x_j} = -\frac{1}{\rho}\frac{\partial P}{\partial x_i} + \frac{\partial}{\partial x_j}\left[\mu\left(\frac{\partial U_i}{\partial x_j}+\frac{\partial U_j}{\partial x_i}\right)\right] - \frac{\partial \overline{u'_i u'_j}}{\partial x_j} \quad (2)$$

where $\mathbf{v}$ is velocity of fluid, ρ is the fluid density, μ is the dynamic viscosity coefficient, U_i and U_j are mean velocity of fluid in i and j direction (i, j=1,2,3), u'_i and u'_j are the fluctuation velocity in i and j direction, P represents the time mean value of pressure, the Reynolds mean stress is computed based on Boussinesq's assumption:

$$\overline{u'_i u'_j} = -v_t\left(\frac{\partial U_i}{\partial x_j}+\frac{\partial U_j}{\partial x_i}\right) + \frac{2}{3}\delta_{ij}k \quad (3)$$

The Realizable k-ε turbulence model is applied to solve the equations. The turbulent kinetic energy (k) and dissipation of turbulent energy (ε) equations are shown as follows:

$$\frac{\partial(\rho k)}{\partial t} + \frac{\partial(\rho k u_i)}{\partial x_i} = \frac{\partial}{\partial x_j}\left[\left(\mu+\frac{\mu_t}{\sigma_k}\right)\frac{\partial k}{\partial x_j}\right] + G_k - \rho\varepsilon \quad (4)$$

$$\frac{\partial(\rho\varepsilon)}{\partial t} + \frac{\partial(\rho\varepsilon u_i)}{\partial x_i} = \frac{\partial}{\partial x_j}\left[\left(\mu+\frac{\mu_t}{\sigma_\varepsilon}\right)\frac{\partial \varepsilon}{\partial x_j}\right] + \rho C_1 E\varepsilon - \rho C_2 \frac{\varepsilon^2}{k+\sqrt{v\varepsilon}} \quad (5)$$

where the critical coefficient C_1 and C_2 are functions of mean and turbulence flows, respectively. The Planck constant for k and ε are respectively set at σ_k=1.0 and σ_ε=1.2. The pressure and velocity coupling problem is solved by using the semi-implicit method for pressure-linked equations (SIMPLE) algorithm.

The free surface is captured using the Volume of Fluid (VOF) model. The volume of fraction is governed by the following equation:

$$\frac{\partial a_q}{\partial t} + \frac{\partial(u_i a_q)}{\partial x_i} = 0 \quad (6)$$

where a_1 and a_2 respectively represent the volume fraction of water and air, a_q represents the volume fraction of water.

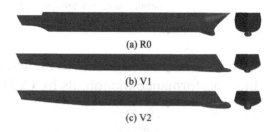

(a) R0

(b) V1

(c) V2

Figure 1. General view of ship hulls.

Table 1. Main dimensions of the ship models.

Item	Symbol	R0	V1	V2
Scale	C	1:50	1:50	1:50
Waterline length (m)	L	3.227	3.600	3.600
Breadth (m)	B	0.403	0.480	0.480
Depth (m)	D	0.31	0.28	0.28
Drought (m)	T	0.14	0.14	0.14
Displacement (kg)	Δ	94.21	113.15	114.54

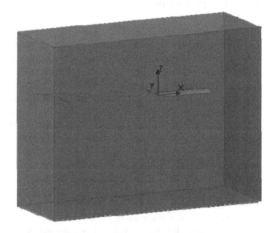

Figure 2. Fluid domain with ship model.

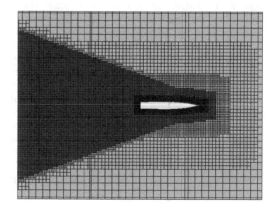

Figure 3. Meshes on free surface.

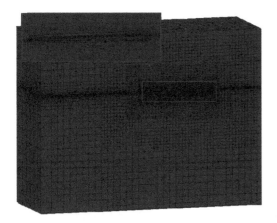

Figure 4. Surface mesh near the hull for seakeeping simulation.

3 NUMERICAL MODEL SETUP

3.1 *Ship hull model*

Three ship hulls are involved for investigation in this study. A traditional round bilge type monohull (R0) is used as a basic reference. Two deep-V type wave-piercing monohulls with the same main hull body while equipped with two different kinds of bow appendage are used for comparative study. V1 is equipped with a SSB, and V2 is equipped with a water drop-shaped bulbous bow. Overview of the three monohulls is shown in Figure 1. Main dimensions of the ships are listed in Table 1.

3.2 *Numerical method*

The CFD numerical simulations in this study were conducted by using the STAR-CCM+ commercial software. A numerical wave tank was established with a dimension of $-2.0L<x<2.0L$, $0<y<1.5L$, $-2.0L<z<1.0L$. In order to reduce computational complexity and time, only half of the hull (the port side) and fluid domain is represented. A symmetry plane forms the centerline domain face in order to accurately simulate the other half of the model. The fluid domain with a model is shown in Figure 2. Velocity inlet boundary condition was applied on the inlet, top, bottom and two side boundaries of the numerical tank, and pressure outlet boundary condition was applied on the outlet. No-slip wall was applied at the body surface. Damping technique was adopted near the outlet boundary to prevent wave reflection. Unstructured meshes were used for volume grid generation. Local view of meshes on the free surface around V1 for calm water resistance calculation is shown in Figure 3.

The definition of boundary condition in ship seakeeping simulation is different from that in calm water resistance simulation. Velocity inlet was applied at the boundaries of inlet, outlet, two sidewalls and bottom of the fluid domain; pressure outlet was applied at the top boundary. Local mesh refinement was applied around

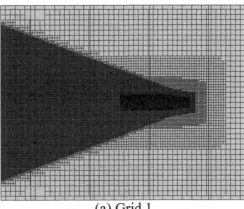

(a) Grid 1

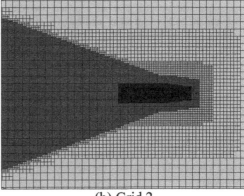

(b) Grid 2

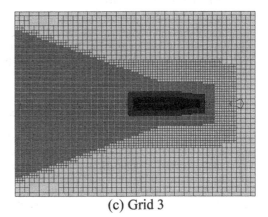

(c) Grid 3

Figure 5. Mesh on the free surface for calm water resistance.

the free surface and hull body. The vertical range of the wave height was divided into at least 20 layers of mesh, and at least 80 layers of mesh were refined within a wave length. A boundary layer mesh of 6 near the hull is selected ($y+$ value lies in 30–90). The grid around V1 that used for seakeeping calculation is shown in Figure 4. Wave forcing technique was used near the outlet for wave absorbing (CD-adapco, 2019). Overset mesh

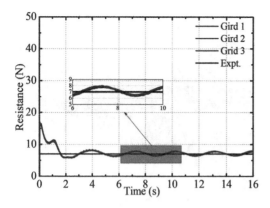

Figure 6. Time series of resistance by different grid scheme.

technique was adopted and an interface was created between the background region and the overset region to transfer fluid information. Ship motion was simulated using Dynamic Fluid Body Interaction (DFBI) and the model was free to heave and pitch motions.

4 MESH CONVERGENCE ANALYSES

In this section, the influence of mesh density on the results of ship calm water resistance and seakeeping behavior is analyzed and discussed. The optimized mesh scheme will be used for the subsequent numerical simulations.

4.1 *Ship calm water resistance*

To accurately capture the detailed flow information, the mesh around ship and free surface was refined. Meshes with dimension of 0.072m, 0.102m, 0.144m (respectively corresponding to 2.00%, 2.83%, 4.00% ship length) were used to generate the fluid domain near ship. Views of the mesh on the free surface around V1 for different schemes are shown in Figure 5.

In the calm water resistance simulation, time step of 0.01 s was selected, turbulence model of Realizable k-ε was used. The calculated resistances of V1 at a speed of 1.309 m/s (full-scale 18 knots) by different mesh schemes in comparison with experimental value are shown in Figure 6 and Table 2. Figure 7 presents the wave pattern generated by the advancing ship for different mesh schemes. It is found that the scheme of Grid 2 is a compromise between calculation accuracy and cost.

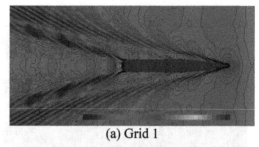

(a) Grid 1

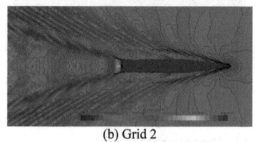

(b) Grid 2

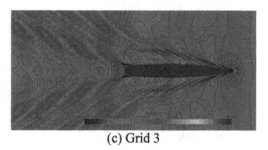

(c) Grid 3

Figure 7. Wave generated by advancing ship in calm water.

4.2 *Ship seakeeping in regular wave*

Different mesh schemes were also generated for the convergence analyses of ship seakeeping simulation. Meshes with dimension of 0.072m, 0.102m, 0.144m (respectively corresponding to 2.00%, 2.83%, 4.00% ship length) were used to generate the fluid domain near the ship. Comparative view of the mesh on the free surface around V1 for different schemes is shown in Figure 8.

In the seakeeping simulation, time step of $T_e/200$ was selected, where T_e denotes wave encounter period. Typical condition of wave length to ship length ratio 1.1, wave height of 50 mm (full-scale 2.5 m) and model speed 1.309 m/s (full-scale 18

Table 2. Calm water resistance by different grid schemes.

Scheme	Mesh No./M	Numerical value/N	Experimental value/N	Deviation	CPU time/h
Grid 1	1.28	7.010	7.084	1.04%	15.7
Grid 2	0.72	6.878	7.084	2.91%	9.5
Grid 3	0.43	6.762	7.084	4.55%	6.9

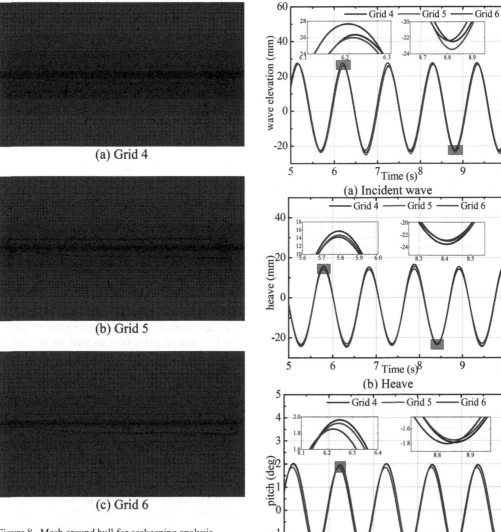

Figure 8. Mesh around hull for seakeeping analysis.

knots) sailing in head wave is selected. Figure 9 and Table 3 shows a comparison of the simulated incident wave (at L/6 ahead of bow) and ship heave and pitch motions by different mesh schemes with model V1. Figure 10 shows the free surface pattern around the advancing ship when at hogging phase. It is seen that the scheme of Grid 5 is a compromise between calculation accuracy and cost.

5 COMPARISON OF SHIP HYDRODYNAMIC BEHAVIOR

5.1 Free rolling decay

A comparison of the free rolling decay curves of the three ships by releasing them with an initial roll angle of 15 degrees is shown in Figure 11.

Figure 9. Time series of wave and ship motions in regular waves.

The obtained dimensionless roll damping coefficient of R0 is $2\mu=0.035$ which shows good agreement with the experimental value of 0.034. The calculated roll natural period for R0, V1 and V2 are 1.667s, 1.421s and 1.161s, respectively. The calculated dimensionless roll damping coefficient for R0, V1 and V2 are 0.035, 0.063 and 0.085, respectively. The results indicate that the roll stability of deep-V hull is largely improved

Table 3. Ship motions by different grid schemes.

Scheme		ζ_a/mm	Z_a/mm	θ_a/deg	CPU time/h	Mesh No./M
Experimental value		25	18.9	1.83		
Grid 4	Numerical value	25.2	18.8	1.87	145.3	6.97
	Deviation	0.80%	0.53%	2.19%		
Grid 5	Numerical value	25.1	18.7	1.85	96.1	4.83
	Deviation	0.40%	1.06%	1.09%		
Grid 6	Numerical value	24.6	18.5	1.80	58.5	2.06
	Deviation	1.60%	2.12%	1.64%		

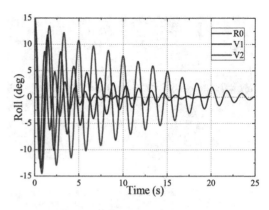

Figure 11. Roll decaying curves of the hulls.

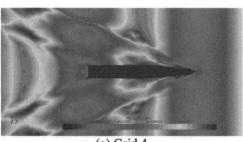

(a) Grid 4

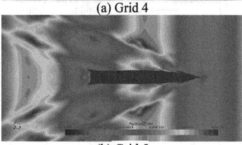

(b) Grid 5

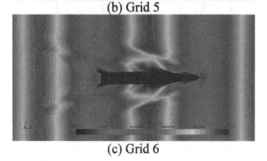

(c) Grid 6

Figure 10. Free surface pattern around the advancing ship.

compared with the R0, which can be attributed to the sharp bilge behavior of deep-V type main hull. The V2 that equipped with water drop-shaped bow performs better than the SSB type V1 hull due to the contribution of water drop-shaped bulbous bow to the side projection area of the hull.

5.2 *Ship calm water resistance*

A comparison of ship calm water resistance correspond to unit displacement as well as the sinkage and trim value at full-scale speed ranging from 12 to 42 knots is shown in Figure 12. As is seen from the curves, resistances of the three ships are almost identical at low and middle speed range. The resistance of V2 hull becomes lower than R0 and V1 with the increasing speed due to the relatively small wave-making resistance of wave-piercing bow and water drop-shaped bulbous bow. The sinkage increased with the increasing speed and the value of V2 is always larger than R0 and V1. Trim of the ships remains unchanged at speed Fn<0.35, while obviously trim by stern occurs with increasing speed due to the fluid dynamic lift. The simulated body surface pressure and streamline around bow of the three ships at speed Fn=1.309 (full-scale 18 knots) are compared in Figure 13.

It is also important to understand the added resistance behavior of ship in waves, which is useful for the evaluation of Energy Efficiency Design Index (EEDI) of ship. Generally, the wave added resistance of ship with wave-piercing bow is smaller compared with round bilge hull due to its better seaworthiness. On the other hand, the complex and expensive bulbous bows are incorporated in hull forms to reduce the drag. Therefore, a good balance between the bluntness and the sharpness of hull form should be considered so that the design scheme is a compromise between utility and cost.

5.3 *Ship seakeeping in regular waves*

Comparison of the calculated incident wave (at L/6 ahead of bow) and heave and pitch motions of the

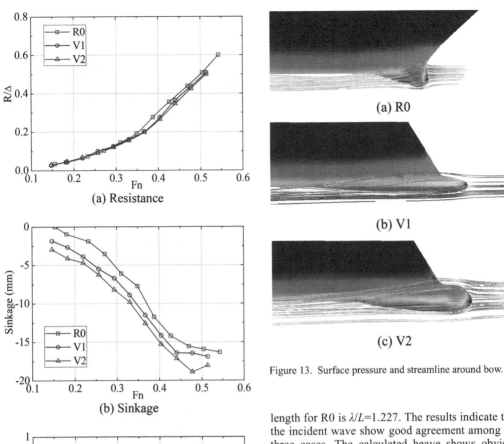

Figure 12. Comparison of calm water navigational performance of ships.

Figure 13. Surface pressure and streamline around bow.

ships are shown in Figure 14. The results correspond to the condition of wave length to ship length ratio 1.1, wave height of 50 mm (full-scale 2.5 m) and model speed 1.309 m/s (full-scale 18 knots) in head wave. It should be noted that since ship length of R0 is shorter than V1 and V2, the actual wave length for R0 is $\lambda/L=1.227$. The results indicate that the incident wave show good agreement among the three cases. The calculated heave shows obvious asymmetry in crest and trough, which can be explained by the fact that the heave oscillates around its mean value. The amplitude of heave and pitch of V1 is obviously lower than V2 due to the effect of SSB. The heave amplitude of R0 is the smallest due to the fact that the encounter frequency exceeds the resonant frequency of heave at $\lambda/L=1.227$. The crest value of pitch is generally larger than trough value for all the three ships, this show similar phenomenon with the fact of trim by bow of ship in calm water at this speed. Figure 15 shows the surface pressure on bow area of the ships at hogging phase. As is seen, there exist high stress zone on the large bulbous bow of V2, and this therefore should be concerned at ship structural design stage.

More comprehensive results for ship motion responses in different wave lengths and wave heights need to be provided for the comparison of ship seakeeping performance. But due to the space and content limitation of conference paper, these results can be referred in our reference Jiao et al. (2015), Sun et al. (2014). This conference paper only provides one typical condition for a comparative study of the three ships' seakeeping behavior.

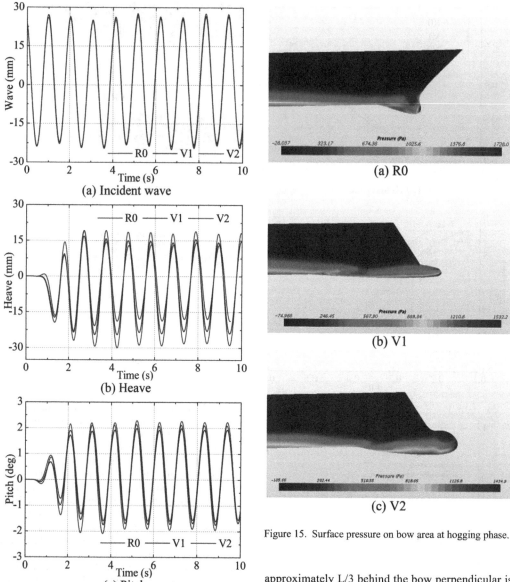

Figure 14. Time series of wave and ship motions in regular waves.

Figure 15. Surface pressure on bow area at hogging phase.

To further validate the CFD method used in this study, comparison of the heave and pitch motions of V2 between CFD calculation and tank model measurement is shown in Figure 16. Generally, the results show good agreement with each other. However, CFD method overestimates the crest of heave value. A visual comparison of the free surface pattern of V2 when the wave crest was approximately L/3 behind the bow perpendicular is shown in Figure 17. The CFD simulation well captured the flow physics of wave ship interaction phenomena.

The severity of green water on deck is important for the evaluation of ship seakeeping. The wave-piercing bow has more advantage in the reduction of impact loads caused by green water or slamming compared with the flare bow of round bilge hull. Sun et al. (2015) has concluded that the green water frequency of deep-V monohull has been largely reduced compared with round bilge monohull by both small-scale model tank test and large-scale model sea trial measurement.

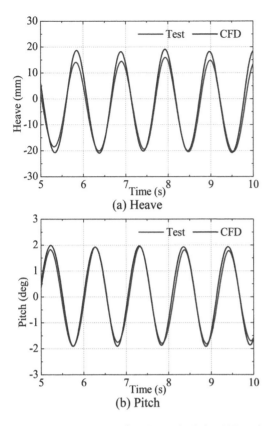

Figure 16. Comparison of motions of V2 by CFD and experiment.

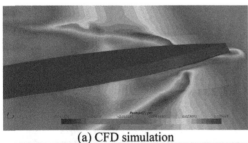

(a) CFD simulation

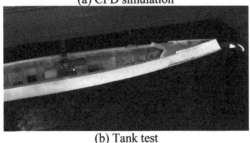

(b) Tank test

Figure 17. Visual comparison of free surface pattern around V2.

6 CONCLUSIONS

This paper comparatively investigates the hydrodynamic behavior of three different ships by CFD method. Deep-V monohull was developed and two different bow appendages were designed for it to further improve ship hydrodynamic behavior. The objective of research and development of ship with good seakeeping performance was well achieved. The deep-V hull shows good performance in roll stability and seakeeping compared with traditional round bilge hull. The water drop-shaped bulbous bow could obviously reduce ship resistance at high speed. The SSB type hull contributes more to the pitch stability of hull compared with the water drop-shaped bulbous bow.

REFERENCES

CD-adapco. 2019. *User Guide STAR-CCM+ Version 14.02*.

Jiao, J. Sun, S. Ren, HJ. 2015. Integrative performance optimization of hybrid monohull based on numerical simulation and model experiment. *Proceedings of the Twenty-fifth (2015) International Ocean and Polar Engineering Conference*, 21-26 June 2015, Kona, Big Island, Hawaii, USA

Jiao, J. Sun, S. Li, J. et al. 2018. A comprehensive study on the seakeeping performance of high speed hybrid ships by 2.5D theoretical calculation and different scaled model experiments. *Ocean Engineering* 160: 197–223.

Jin, H. Zhao, W. Qi, Z. et al. 2004. Study on integrated balance method for large ships. *Journal of Ship Mechanics* 8(4): 42–47. (in Chinese)

Kihara, K. & Tazawa, M. 1985. Development of a new hull form with semi-submerged bow for high speed craft. *The Society of Naval Architects of Japan* 157: 459–466.

Kim, S. 2011. CFD as a seakeeping tool for ship design. *International Journal of Naval Architecture and Ocean Engineering* 3(1): 65–71.

Lloyd, A.R.J.M. 1989. *Seakeeping: ship behaviour in rough weather*, E. Horwood.

Sun, S. Miao, Q. Zhao, X. et al. 2013. Research on ship-form of 1000 tons hybrid monohull. *Ship Science and Technology* 35(6): 6–10. (in Chinese)

Sun, S. Tian, B. Zhao, X. et al. 2014. Model test analysis of hydrodynamics of appendages of hybrid monohull. *Journal of Shanghai Jiao Tong University* 48(4): 482–487. (in Chinese)

Sun, S. Ren, H. Zhao X. et al. 2015. Experimental study of two large-scale models' seakeeping performance in coastal waves. *Brodogradnja* 66(2): 47–60.

Sun, H. Jing, F. Jiang, Y. et al. 2016. Motion prediction of catamaran with a semi-submersible bow in wave. *Polish Maritime Research* 23(1): 37–44.

CFD investigation of submerged geometry effect on wave run-up around a fixed, vertical monopile in regular head waves

M. Mohseni & C. Guedes Soares
Centre for Marine Technology and Engineering (CENTEC), Instituto Superior Técnico, Universidade de Lisboa, Lisbon, Portugal

ABSTRACT: Wave-structure interaction and accurate prediction of wave run-up height induced by ocean waves is essential for safe and cost effective design of fixed and floating offshore structures exposed to a harsh environment. Taking into consideration, wave scattering types identified by Swan et al. (2015) and lateral progressive edge waves, in this paper, the influence of change in underwater volume on the nonlinear wave field surrounding the single fixed monopile and corresponding wave run-up harmonics is investigated. In order to study wave-monopile interaction, the analysis is performed numerically using Unsteady Reynolds-Averaged Navier-Stokes/VOF model based on OpenFOAM® framework. For the simulations, the monopile is assumed vertical and surface piercing with a circular cross-section and the incident wave is considered plane progressive fifth-order Stokes, regular and non-breaking in deep water. The harmonic analysis of local free surface elevation indicates that the scattered wave field around the monopile involves high harmonics wave run-up.

1 INTRODUCTION

In recent years, the offshore industry has moved towards deeper water and harsher environments. Offshore structures are expected to have an acceptably low probability of failure so as to survive most severe sea states. Wave-structure interaction and accurate prediction of air gap, wave run-up height and forces induced by ocean waves is essential for safe and cost effective design of fixed and floating offshore structures exposed to a harsh environment.

Potential flow theory is the common numerical approach to study the wave run-up height and forces on a surface piercing bodies in the presence of progressive water. The diffraction of surface water waves around surface piercing cylinders is a classical problem, which has been investigated in a large number of studies over many decades. These include the linear diffraction theory approach of McCamy and Fuchs (1954), the second-order frequency domain calculation procedure presented by Kriebel (1990, 1992), Isaacson & Cheung (1994) and Buchmann et al. (1998) and second order time domain calculation approach of both Buchmann et al. (1997) and Isaacson & Cheung (1993). Based on the benchmark study by Nielsen (2003), Stansberg et al. (2005) remarked that non-linear tools based on potential theory have some limitations due to model wave-breaking and viscous effects in simulating non-linear wave-body interaction flows. Higher-order potential flow effects have been analyzed by several authors but tools are still in the developing phase.

Physical experimentation is one of the most common approaches for studying wave-structure interaction. The benchmark experiments of Kriebel (1990, 1992) for regular wave run-up on a circular cylinder in water of finite depth have subsequently been compared with a number of wave run-up calculation procedures. Niedzwecki et al. (1992) performed a small-scale experimental study to investigate wave run-up on rigid full-length and truncated circular cylinders under regular and random sea conditions. Morris-Thomas et al. (2003, 2004), conducted a series of experiment to study cross-section effects on harmonics of wave run up on the fixed vertical surface piercing cylinder using monochromatic progressive waves. They compared the experimental results with a solution of diffraction theory by WAMIT and concluded that with long wave theory, the wave run-up is well predicted. Ramirez et al. (2013) studied wave run-up of irregular waves on vertical monopiles by conducting large-scale experiments with a focus on the near breaking and breaking waves. Swan et al. (2005, 2015) highlighted the importance of nonlinear wave scattering from a slender vertical surface piercing column and also investigated the nonlinear, higher-harmonic, wave loading experimentally and characterized high-frequency wave scattering around the cylinder. They also explained, why low-order diffraction solutions are inappropriate.

Wave-structure interaction is highly nonlinear and cannot be predicted well by potential theory and it shows the need for computational efforts for accurate predictions, Danmeier (2008) and Bøckmann (2014). In the recent years, several types of research have been carried out on the study of the wave run-up on monopiles and columns of large semisubmersibles using Computational Fluid Dynamics (CFD) based Navier-Stokes equations. In order to evaluate the capabilities of state-of-the-art CFD codes for wave run-up simulation for single/multiple surface-piercing cylinders in regular non-breaking waves, the ITTC Ocean Engineering Committee (OEC), (ITTC, 2013), provided a benchmark tests based on experimental data measured from MOERI and MARINTEK for single (1C) and four circular cylinders (4C), respectively. Cao et al. (2017) and also Sun et al. (2016) utilizing OpenFOAM without the inclusion of any turbulence model, they conducted simulations of the wave run-up around a truncated vertical cylinder for various wave conditions. Comparing the numerical results with the aforementioned published experimental data the accuracy of the solver was validated, and then they investigated the effects of wavelength and steepness on wave amplification around the cylinder and maximum wave run-up height, as well. Yoon et al. (2016) employing CFDShip-Iowa with no-turbulence and then the inclusion of turbulence model of blended k–ε/k–ω based isotropic and anisotropic RANS, and DES approaches with near-wall or wall functions, similarly did this investigation. Paulsen et al. (2013) performed numerical computations of wave loads on surface piercing circular cylinders at intermediate water depths for non-linear regular and irregular waves, phase-focused irregular waves and multidirectional irregular waves using a fully nonlinear-coupled solver. Chen et al. (2014) numerically investigated the nonlinear interaction of non-breaking regular and focused waves with a vertical surface piercing cylinder for different wave conditions. They used OpenFOAM and compared the numerical results with physical experiments performed at the Danish Hydraulic Institute (DHI). Lin et al. (2017), discussed the effects of wave nonlinearity and scattering on run-up heights and wave loads by comparing the wave steepness parameter and scattering parameter for three different types of wind turbine foundations. They conducted the numerical simulation, based on the commercial software FLUENT with k-ε turbulence model.

The high-frequency and nonlinear wave field involves in some important phenomena of wave scattering Type 1&2 identified by Swan et al. (2005, 2015) and lateral progressive edge waves, Chaplin et al. (1997).Taking into account these important contributions, Mohseni et al (2018) investigated the physics of high-frequency and nonlinear wave scattering and wave run-up around a single fixed cylinder under different wave conditions in deepwater. Following their work, in this paper the influence of change in underwater volume on the nonlinear wave field surrounding the single fixed monopile and corresponding wave run-up harmonics is investigated.

2 NUMERICAL MODEL

In order to study wave-monopile interaction, the analysis is performed numerically using interFoam version 2.2.2. It is a three-dimensional Unsteady Reynolds-Averaged Navier-Stokes/VOF model solver for two incompressible, isothermal, immiscible fluids based on OpenFOAM® framework. The governing URANS equations are discretised in the fluid domain using the finite volume method(FVM) on a static mesh. The interface between phases is captured via the Volume of Fluid (VOF) technique Hirt & Nichols, (1981), in which the system is treated as a mixture of both fluids using an indicator function (α) marking the content of each cell. $\alpha = 1$ denotes a pure water cell, $\alpha = 0$ marks a pure air cell, and $(0 < \alpha < 1)$ represents the interfacial cells. The continuity, Navier-Stokes and VOF equations solved by the model are as follows:

$$\nabla .(\rho U) = 0 \quad (1)$$

$$\frac{\partial \rho U}{\partial t} + \nabla .(\rho U U) = (-\nabla P^*) - ((\boldsymbol{g}.\boldsymbol{X})\nabla \rho) + \begin{pmatrix} \nabla U . \nabla \mu_{eff} \\ + \nabla . \left(\mu_{eff} \nabla U \right) \end{pmatrix} + (\sigma k \nabla \alpha) \quad (2)$$

$$\frac{\partial \alpha}{\partial t} + \nabla .(U\alpha) + \nabla .[U_c \alpha (1-\alpha)] = 0 \quad (3)$$

where all the bold letters indicate a vector field. U is the velocity vector, ∇ denotes the gradient operator, t is the time. ρ is fluid density, calculated as a weighted average of the densities of water and air (ρ_w and ρ_a):$\rho = \alpha \rho_w + \rho_a(1-\alpha)$). P* is the pressure in excess of the hydrostatic, namely $\mathbf{P}^* = \mathbf{p} - \rho \boldsymbol{g}.\boldsymbol{X}$ in which p is the total pressure, X is the Cartesian position vector, and g is the gravity acceleration vector. μ_{eff} represents the effective dynamic viscosity of the fluid, comprised by the molecular dynamic viscosity μ and the turbulent viscosity μ_t. Following the work by Mohseni et al. (2018) as the diffusion term in Navier-stokes equation with only fluid viscosity can reasonably account the turbulence effects due to local wave breaking around cylinder at low and medium incident wave steepness, in this work the turbulent viscosity is set to zero and No-Turbulence model is considered.

The last term on the right of Equation 2 is the surface tension force, in which σ is the surface tension coefficient; k is the mean curvature of the interface. In Equation 3, U_c is artificial interface-compression velocity aimed at maintaining a sharp interface which acts only at the interface between the fluids $(0 < \alpha < 1)$, in the normal direction to the free surface. In addition, to ensure the sharpness and boundedness of time advanced VOF field, an interface compression scheme called MULES is implemented in InterFoam.

There are several built-in numerical schemes in OpenFOAM for the numerical approximation of the PDE terms in the governing equations Equations 1, 2 and 3. An overview of the discretization schemes used in this work has been presented by Mohseni et al (2018). In this work the PISO algorithm is used to deal with the pressure and velocity coupling.

The discretization procedure converts the given partial differential equation into a corresponding system of linear algebraic equations, with one equation for each control volume (computational cell). This system is solved using the iterative procedure where the iteration loop is stopped when some prescribed condition is fulfilled. In order to improve the convergence rate, the equations' system can be preconditioned, i.e. multiplied by a suitable preconditioning matrix. In this study, for symmetric matrices, the Preconditioned Conjugate Gradient (PCG) solver with Diagonal-based Incomplete Cholesky (DIC) preconditioner is used. In the case of asymmetric matrices, the Preconditioned Bi-Conjugate Gradient (PBiCG) with Diagonal-based Incomplete Lower-Upper (DILU) preconditioner is adopted, OpenCFD (2012).

In this paper, the numerical wave tank for wave generation/absorption is replicated with IHFOAM toolbox Higuera et al. (2013). Therefore the 5th-order Stokes wave theory, presented in Skjelbreia and Hendrickson (1960), is used in all the simulations at the fixed inlet wave boundary. At the at outlet boundary a passive absorbing method of cell stretching in combination with IHFOAM active wave absorption is used to ensure efficient wave damping. The Numerical Wave Tank which is used to study wave-body interaction can be assumed as a closed rectangular domain consisting of a box with a body inside. It includes 7 boundaries that named after their physical representation as Inlet (1), Outlet (3), Bottom (1), Top (1) and Body (1). Each of the geometrical boundaries requires a set of numerical type boundary conditions to specify the boundary data for each of the flow variables including the phase fraction, Velocity and Pressure which has been presented by Mohseni et al (2018). For all simulations, calm water state with no surface waves, and initial hydrostatic pressure distribution are used as an initial condition.

According to Muzaferija & Peric, (1997), accurate wave generation requires at least a second-order time integration method and for stability, it is required that the wave propagates less than half a cell per time step. In this paper, with regard to the wave simulations by Mohseni et al. (2018) to provide reasonably accurate wave specification and kinematics a fixed time step is utilized and the Courant number for the solver, (Co_{max}), and for the free surface, $(alphaCo)$, are kept smaller than 0.2. Throughout the simulation, data from individual wave probes are sampled at 50 Hz to ensure capturing all the wave features through propagation. In a post-processing step, the vertical coordinates where the iso-contour of phase fraction of $(\alpha = 0.5)$ is taken to be the position of the free surface interface at each time step.

3 GRID CONVERGENCE AND VALIDATION OF NUMERICAL MODEL

Having an appropriate NWT that can provide accurate wave generation and propagation with small numerical dissipation and dispersion is necessary. Therefore, in this section, the grid and time step refinement study and Comparisons with experimental data are performed to obtain appropriate and optimum wave and body mesh resolution.

In this paper, the influence of a change in underwater volume on the wave field surrounding the monopile and corresponding wave run-up harmonics is investigated. The physics of Wave scattering and wave run-up on monopile involves the interaction of single surface piercing cylinder with surface gravity incident waves which are propagating over a flatbed in an unbounded domain. The fixed structure is considered as rigid, vertical and surface monopile with a circular cross-section. The surface gravity incident wave is also assumed to be non-breaking, regular, long-crested and unidirectional fifth-order Stokes wave propagating over a flatbed in deep water.

In this work the benchmark experiments provided by ITTC (OEC) (ITTC, 2013) was employed for validation purpose. Hence, following the wave conditions and body specifications by the mentioned experiments, all of the simulations are performed in the model scale of $(\gamma = 1/50.314)$ based on the Froude similitude with the assumption of constant gravity acceleration and also air and water fluid properties. For the purpose of this study, wave condition with wave period of T=7s and moderate wave steepness of H/L=1/16 is considered, Table 2.

Following the dimensional analysis by Mohseni et al. (2018), Table 1, the $(Reynolds(Re))$ number is in the order of (10^7) for both full and scale models which indicates the flow regime for steady flow interacting a circular cylinder is already turbulent and the friction effects are negligible.

The $(Froude(Fr))$ number is very small for steady flow, which indicates that gravity effects are dominants. It also suggests that there is small free surface amplification that can be neglected. The KC number is also small where the separation behind the cylinder doesn't occur and the inertia or diffraction effects will dominate, Sumer & Fredsøe (2006). The $(Weber(We))$ is sufficiently greater than unity for both full and model scale, therefore, surface tension effect cannot affect the wave run-up around the cylinder. Regarding the range of aforementioned non-dimensional parameters for both full and scale models, it can be concluded the scale effect can be neglected and Froude similitude is appropriate with respect to the physics of the problem.

Table 1. Selected incident wave condition and given physically non-dimensional parameters.

Case name			T7S116
T [s]	7	KC	0.9381
H [m]	4.777	Fr	0.031
L [m]	76.44	2a/L	0.210
H/L	1/16		
Re	Full: 0.6186E+007 Model: 0.1733E+005	We	Full: 184.8623 Model: 3.6742

Table 2. Spatial and temporal discretization data.

Parameter	Mesh A	Mesh B	Mesh C
$H/\Delta z$	42	30	22
$L/\Delta x$	141	100	71
$D/r_{Refinement1}$	72	51	36
$D/r_{Refinement2}$	90	64	46
$N_{Tangential}$	226	160	113
$T/\Delta t$	17500	8750	7000
Total grid points (M)	13.512	9.56	6.75

The computational domain dimensions and computational mesh with free-surface plane and symmetry plane are illustrated in Figure 1. The whole computational domain is discretised by blocks of hexahedral cells using blockMesh. The steep and high-frequency waves around the body are highly deformed, and propagate in radial directions. Therefore an extra mesh refinement around the body is also necessary besides the free-surface region. The computational domain is divided into two parts, main tank to study the physics of problem and damping zone surrounding the main tank in a horizontal plane to damp these scattered waves and avoid reflections back into the computational domain. The origin of the coordinate system is defined at the bottom left of the corner at the inlet boundary, positive x-axis pointing downstream and z-axis pointing upward. In the case of the body region, the up and down-stream length in the x-direction and the main domain half-width in the y-direction is **2D** for all cases. The assumption of the deep-water condition, the water depth is **1L** and air-part has the height of **3D**. The damping zone length in the y-direction is **2D** and in the x-direction is **3L**. In order to avoid the contamination of the inlet boundary with scattered/reflected waves propagating in the negative x-axis, the size of the wave region in the x-direction is set to **3L**. In order to record time histories of free surface elevation, an arrangement of wave probes is used. The top view of wave probes at 10 locations in a radial pattern in the vicinity of the cylinder is illustrated in Figure 2. The wave probes at distances of $(r/D = 0.513)$ are considered as on-body probes.

A grid-space and time step refinement study were carried out by Mohseni et al. (2018) to find optimum mesh arrangement that can correctly represent the

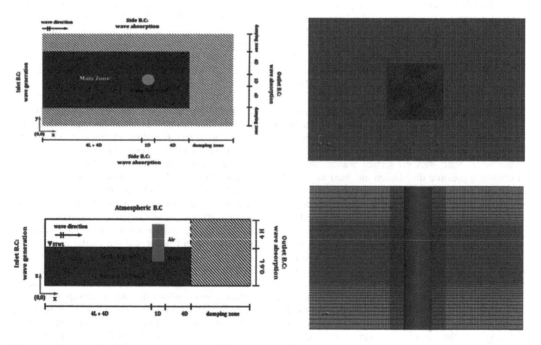

Figure 1. Computational domain, geometry, and boundary conditions,(Left), Computational mesh including horizontal cross section at SWL,(Up), symmetry plane,(down).

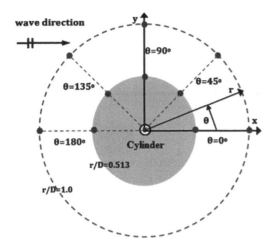

Figure 2. Locations of wave probes around the single circular cylinder.

wave filed around the monopile. The study was performed for the triple solutions of Mesh A, Mesh B and Mesh C, Table 2, with The refinement factor of $\sqrt{2}$ for both spatial and temporal discretization based on the Grid Convergence Index (GCI) method by Stern et al. (2001). Following the result of this study it was found the mesh-setup B is a fair choice that can provide sufficiently satisfactory results for the solution of wave elevation around the monopile.

where, $L/\Delta x$ is number of cells per wavelength, $H/\Delta z$ is number of cells per wave height, $N_{Tangential}$ is number of cells around the cylinder, $D/r_{Refinment1}$ the number of cells in the normal direction, $D/r_{Refinment2}$ is the number of cells in the outer refinement zone and $T/\Delta t$ is the time non-dimensional time step.

Mohseni et al. (2018) also compared the numerical results obtained from the Navier-Stokes solver with the experimental data, which was provided by ITTC (OEC) (2013) for the mean value, 1st and 2nd harmonics are free surface elevation around the monopile. Figure 3, shows the comparison of normalized 1st and 2nd harmonics and mean value of wave elevation along the center plane in terms of wave probes location x/D which is normalized by incident wave amplitude A_1. It was shown that there is a good agreement for moderate steep incident waves of H/L=1/16.

4 RESULTS

In this paper, the influence of a change in underwater volume on the wave field surrounding the cylinder and corresponding wave run-up harmonics is investigated. Here, the change in underwater volume is associated to change in vertical surface-piercing cylinder draft, with or without attached substructure. In this regard, the simulations are conducted for four geometries, which are illustrated in Figure 4. The geometries related to change in the draft without attached substructure include two cylinders of Truncated1 (draft 1.5D), Truncated2 (draft 0.5D). Truncated cylinders, are used for buoyancy in a range of floating structures including semi-submersibles, spar buoys and Tension-Leg Platforms (TLPs) as well as floating offshore wind applications. The other two geometries of SubStr1 and SubStr2 are composed of a substructure and the two cylinders of Truncated1 and Truncated2, respectively. This attached substructure is a disk with circular cross-section and diameter of (3D) which can be taken as heave plate or part of the pontoon of offshore floating oil/gas platforms (Semi-submersibles, TLPs) and base column of floating platform based offshore wind turbines.

As it is seen in Figure 4, the width of each cylinder at the intersection of STWL and the circular cross-section is the same for all of the geometries and equal to (1D) which results in identical wave diffraction number. In the present analysis, the cylinder geometry of Truncated1 is taken as reference2 case. The spatial contour of wave field around the given geometries for the arrival of three wave phases of the crest, trough and zero up crossing at the front stagnation point of the cylinder is illustrated at Figures 6-8 by the top and side view. Figure 5 shows the comparison of normalized mean value and harmonics of the wave elevation

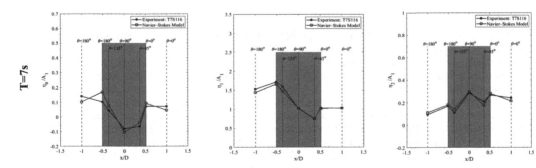

Figure 3. Normalized harmonics of wave elevation around the cylinder, for wave condition of T=7s, H/L=1/16, (vertical solid line (r/D=0.513) and vertical dash line (r/D=1.0)).

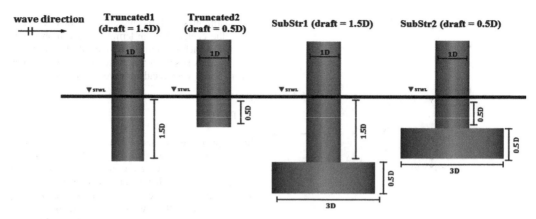

Figure 4. The geometries related to change in vertical cylinder draft, with or without attached substructure. under the wave condition of (T=7s, H/L=1/16) in deep water.

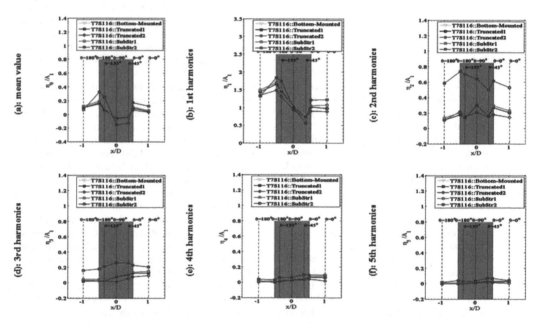

Figure 5. Comparison of normalized mean value and harmonics of wave run-up around the vertical cylinder under wave condition of (T=7s, H/L=1/16), (vertical solid line (r/D=0.513) and vertical dash line (r/D=1.0)).

around the given geometries in terms of wave probes location(x/D). Change in underwater volume as it can, primarily affect the reflection, is important in the context of wave scattering and resultant wave amplification around the cylinder. Comparing the simulation results by cylinder of Truncated1 and Truncated2 the wave scattering and also harmonic pattern are maintained. However, the reduction in the draft and consequently reflection by underwear volume for cylinder of Truncated2 lead in the reduction of both wave elevation and corresponding harmonics at the given wave probes, see Figures 6-8 (a&b). On the contrary, in the case of cylinder of Truncated1 and also increasing the draft more than (1.5D), the excess reflection by underwater volume and also the developed vorticity from the cylinder bottom, cannot reach the free surface and affect the wave scattering and related wave run-up around the cylinder.

For SubStr1 in comparison to the reference2 case where they both have an identical draft, the effect of attached substructure is apparent. As it is seen in Figures 6-8 (c) and also in Figure 5, the attached substructure enhances the surrounding wave field and related harmonics. Taking to account the

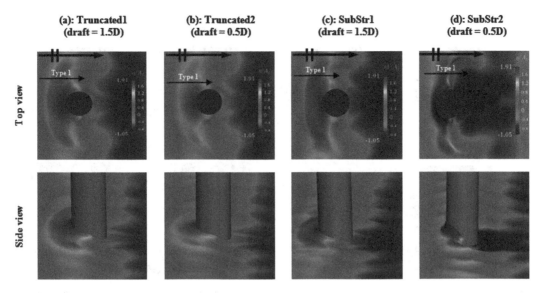

Figure 6. Spatial contours of the free surface elevation around the vertical cylinder under wave condition of (T=7s, H/L=1/16), with the arrival of wave crest at the front point.

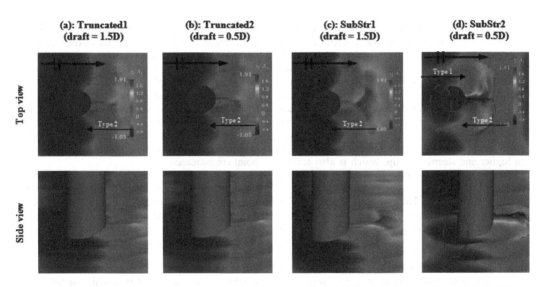

Figure 7. Spatial contours of the free surface elevation around the vertical cylinder under wave condition of (T=7s, H/L=1/16), with the arrival of wave trough at front point.

identical results by Bottom-Mounted and Truncated1 cylinders, there is a weak wave-substructure interaction for the case of SubStr1 at a draft of (1.5D) which leads in small change while maintaining the trend for the mean value and first five harmonics in comparison to the reference2 case, see Figure 5. The wave field around SubStr1 experiences locally shallow water due to the presence of attached substructure. In shallow water, as we know, the waves are non-dispersive and the propagation speed depends on the local depth. Therefore as it is seen in Figures 6-8 (c), there is a reduction in wave scattering propagation velocity, which is more evident by steeper crest and flatter trough at the circular extension that is affected by attached substructure.

The effect of attached substructure on wave run-up which is similar to the effect of the cone-shaped foundation is also involved wave upwelling. De Vos et al. (2007), showed that the shape of the foundation substantially affects the maximum run-up level where for the cone-shaped foundation it leads to increasing the expected run-up value. During the

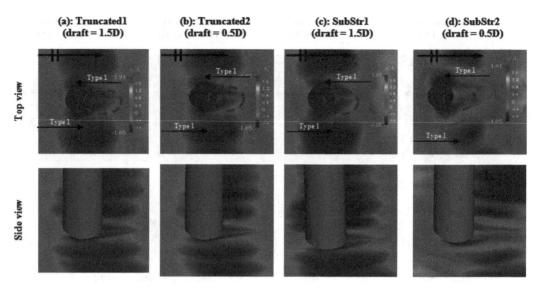

Figure 8. Spatial contours of the free surface elevation around the vertical cylinder under wave condition of (T=7s, H/L=1/16), with the arrival of the wave zero up crossing at the front point.

interaction of wave passing the cylinder with the substructure, a reflection of water particles in an upward direction results in a local free surface amplification, which is known as wave upwelling effect, Taylor-(1989). With regard to assumption of identical diffraction number and incident wave condition, wave upwelling locally steepens the wave scattering and contribute to wave amplification around the vertical cylinder. Increasing the wave steepness enhances the wave kinematics and results in higher and steeper run-up, which is also accompanied by a notable local wave breaking around the cylinder.

For the cylinder of Truncated2, it was shown that there is a small reflection by underwater volume due to smaller draft comparing to the reference2 case. In the case of SubStr2 which is a combination of cylinder Truncated2 and the attached substructure, this small reflection is augmented by the wave upwelling. Thus, there is significant enhancement by wave scattering and run-up, see Figures 6-8 (d) and also corresponding harmonics, see Figure 5. Comparing the reference2 case and SubStr2, the significant increment for 1st harmonics is observed at Figure 5. This increment is about 10% and 20% at front and back stagnation point, respectively. In addition, there is a considerable reduction from front corner to back corner in comparison to the other cases for 1st harmonics. This is caused by energy reduction of lateral edge waves, which in this case it is more related to the notable local wave breaking/dissipation. For SubStr2, the collision of lateral edge waves at back stagnation point in combination with wave upwelling results in considerably strong local flow and higher and steeper run-up which is more evident at the spatial contour of Figure 7 (d). It was explained before that, the interaction of wave trough at back stagnation point leads in the reduced run-up in the form of wave scattering Type1. As it is seen in Figure 6, this run-up is less evident for cylinder Truncated 1 and Truncated 2 while it is more evident in the case of SubStr1 and SubStr2. Accordingly, as the presence of substructure becomes apparent, the harmonics higher than 1 and also mean value at back stagnation point are increased.

During the movement of the lateral edge waves in the upstream direction, there is strong and nonlinear interaction with opposing incident wave at or about the trough, which results in large 2nd and 3rd harmonics and also mean value at the back corner, shoulder and front corner points, see Figure 5. Considering the harmonics higher than first for all given geometries except SubStr2, the nonlinearity is more notable at half backward part while in the case of SubStr2, the nonlinearity at front stagnation point is also significant which is evident in the 2nd harmonics and mean value. This is related to the occurrence of the second run-up at this point, see Figure 7 (d). The edge waves traveling in an upstream direction can pass the shoulder point but eventually can reach the forward corner point before the arrival of the zero-up crossing. This is associated to the considerable reduction of edge waves energy cause by strong interaction with the vertical cylinder and also insufficient propagation time as a result of small propagation speed and also incident short wave condition. Therefore occurrence of this second run-up at the front point is related to the wave scattering Type1 which is caused by the interaction of some point about the incident wave trough and the attached substructure.

5 CONCLUSIONS

In this work, the influence of a change in underwater volume on the wave field surrounding the cylinder and corresponding wave run-up harmonics was investigated. Change in underwater volume as it can, primarily, affect the reflection. Comparing the simulation results by a cylinder of Truncated1 and Truncated2 the wave scattering and also harmonic pattern are maintained. However, the reduction in the draft and consequently reflection by underwear volume for a cylinder of Truncated2 lead in the reduction of both wave elevation and corresponding harmonics at the given wave probes. On the contrary, in the case of the cylinder of Truncated1 and also increasing the draft more than (1.5D), the excess reflection by underwater volume and also the developed vorticity from the cylinder bottom, cannot reach the free surface and affect the wave scattering and related wave run-up around the cylinder.

For SubStr1 in comparison to the reference2 case where they both have an identical draft, the effect of attached substructure is apparent. It was shown that the attached substructure enhances the surrounding wave field and related harmonics. Taking to account the draft of (1.5D) for SubStr1, it caused small change while maintaining the trend for the mean value and first five harmonics in comparison to the reference case. The wave field around SubStr1 experiences locally shallow water due to the presence of attached substructure. Therefore as it was observed, there is a reduction in wave scattering propagation velocity which is more evident by steeper crest and flatter trough at the circular extension that is affected by attached substructure. The effect of attached substructure was also involved in wave upwelling.

Following the assumption of identical diffraction number and incident wave condition, wave upwelling locally steepens the wave scattering and contribute to wave amplification around the vertical cylinder, which is also accompanied by notable local wave breaking around the cylinder. In the case of SubStr2, the small reflection due to a small draft of the vertical cylinder was augmented by the wave upwelling. Thus, it caused significant enhancement by wave scattering and run-up and also corresponding harmonics. For SubStr2, the collision of lateral edge waves at back stagnation point in combination with wave upwelling resulted in considerably strong local flow and higher and steeper run-up. It was mentioned that for reference case, nonlinearity is more notable at half backward part while in the case of SubStr2, the nonlinearity at front stagnation point was also significant. This was related to the occurrence of the second run-up at this point in the form of the wave scattering Type1. This run-up was caused by the interaction of some point about the incident wave trough and the attached substructure.

ACKWNOWLEDGEMENTS

The first author has been funded by the project HYDROELASTWEB, which is funded by the Portuguese Foundation for Science and Technology (Fundação para a Ciência e a Tecnologia - FCT) under contract 031488_770 (PTDC/ECI-EGC/31488/2017). This work was performed within the scope of the Strategic Research Plan of the Centre for Marine Technology and Ocean Engineering (CENTEC), which is financed by the Portuguese Foundation for Science and Technology (Fundação para a Ciência e Tecnologia - FCT) under contract UIDB/UIDP/00134/2020.

REFERENCES

Buchmann, B., Skourup, J., Cheung, K., 1997. Run-up on a Structure Due to Waves and Current. *Proceeding of the Seventh International Offshore and Polar Engineering Conference*.

Buchmann, B., Ferrant, P., Skourup, J., 1998. Run up on a body in waves and current, fully nonlinear and finite order calculations. *13th International Workshop on Water Waves and Floating Bodies* 1, pp. 9–1

Bøckmann A, Pâkozdi C, Kristiansen T, Jang H, Kim J. An experimental and computational development of a benchmark solution for the validation of numerical wave tanks. In: *Proc ASME 33rd Int Conf Ocean*. 2014.

Cao, H. J., Wan, D. C. (2017). Benchmark computations of wave run-up on a single cylinder and four cylinders by naoe-FOAM-SJTU solver. *Applied Ocean Research*. 65, 327–337.

Chen, L. F., Zang, J., Hillis, A. J., Morgan, G. C. J., and Plummer, A. R., 2014. Numerical investigation of wave–structure interaction using OpenFOAM. *Ocean Engineering*, 88, 91–109.

Chaplin, J. R., Rainey, R. C. T. & Yemm, R. W. 1997. Rining of a vertical cylinder in waves. *Journal of Fluid Mechanics*, 250: 119{147}.

Danmeier DG, Seah RKM, Finnigan T, Roddier D, Aubault A, Vache M, et al. Validation of wave run-up calculation methods for a gravity-based structure. In: *Proc ASME 27th Int Conf Offshore Mech and Arctic Eng*. 2008.

De Vos, L., Frigaard, P., De Rouck, J., 2007. Wave run-up on cylindrical and cone-shaped foundations for offshore wind turbines. *Coast. Eng*. 54,17–29.

Hirt, C.W., Nichols, B.D., 1981. Volume of fluid (VOF) method for the dynamics of free boundaries. *J. Comput. Phys*. 39 (1), 201–225.

Higuera, P., Lara, J.L., Losada, I.J., 2013a. Realistic wave generation and active wave absorption for Navier–Stokes models application to OpenFOAM. *Coastal Eng*. 71, 102–118.

Isaacson, M.d.S.Q., Cheung, K., 1993. The time domain solution for wave-current interaction with a two-dimensional body. *Applied Ocean Research* 15 (1), 39–52.

Isaacson, M.d.S.Q., Cheung, K., 1994. Correction factors for non-linear run-up and wave force on a large cylinder. *Canadian Journal of Civil Engineering* 21, 762–769.

ITTC 2013. OEC Workshop on VIV and Wave Run-up held in Nantes, France October 17–18, 2013.

Kriebel, D., 1990. Nonlinear wave diffraction by the vertical circular cylinder. Part 1: Diffraction theory. *Ocean Engineering* 17, 345–377.

Kriebel, D., 1992. Non-linear wave interaction with a vertical circular cylinder. Part II: wave run-up. *Ocean Engineering* 19 (1), 75–99.

Lin, Y., Chen, J., Lu, P., 2017. A CFD model for simulating wave run-ups and wave loads in case of different wind turbine foundations influenced by nonlinear waves. *Ocean Engineering* 129 (2017) 428–440.

MacCamy RC, Fuchs RA. Wave forces on piles: A diffraction theory. *Beach Erosion Board Office of the Chief Engineers, Department of the Army, Technical Memorandum no.* 69; 1954 1–17.

Muzaferija, s., Peric, m., 1997. computation of free surface flows using the finite-volume method and moving grids. *numerical heat transfer, part b: fundamentals*. volume 32, 1997 - 4.

Morris-Thomas MT. An investigation into wave run-up on a vertical surface piercing cylinders in monochromatic waves, *Ph.D. Thesis, The University of Western Australia*; 2003.

Morris-Thomas MT, Thiagarajan KP. The run-up on a cylinder in progressive surface gravity waves: harmonic components. *Applied Ocean Research* 2004;26:98–113.

Mohseni M, Esperanca P T, and Sphaier S H 2018. Numerical study of wave run-up on a fixed and vertical surface-piercing cylinder subjected to regular, non-breaking waves using OpenFOAM. *Applied Ocean Research* 79228–52.

Nielsen FG. Comparative study on airgap under floating platforms and run-up along platform columns. *J Mar Struct* 2003;16:97–134.

Niedzwecki JM, Duggal AS. Wave runup and forces on cylinders in regular and random waves. *J Waterway, Port, Coastal, Ocean Eng* 1992;118(6):615–34.

OpenCFD Ltd (2012). OpenFOAM: The open source computational fluid dynamics (CFD) toolbox. https://openfoam.org/release/2-2-0/.

Paulsen, B.T., Bredmose, H., Bingham, H.B., Jacobsen, N. G., 2014. Forcing of a bottom mounted circular cylinder by steep regular water waves at finite depth, *J. Fluid Mech.* (2014) vol. 755, pp. 1–34.

Ramirez, J., Frigaard, P., Lykke Andersen, T., and Christensen, E., 2011. Numerical modeling of wave run-up: regular waves. In Twenty-first. *International Offshore and Polar Engineering Conference: ISOPE*.

Ramirez, J., Frigaard, P., Lykke Andersen, T., De Vos, L., 2013. Large-scale model test investigation on wave run-up in irregular waves at slender piles. *Coast. Eng.* 72, 69–79.

Skjelbreia, L., Hendrickson, J.A. Fifth order gravity wave theory. *Proc. 7th Coastal Eng Conf., The Hague (1960)*, pp. 184–196.

Stern F, Wilson RV, Coleman HW, Paterson EG. A comprehensive approach to verification and validation of CFD simulations-Part 1: methodology and procedures. *ASME J Fluids Eng* 2001;123:793–802.

Stansberg, C.T., Kristiansen, T., 2005. Non-linear scattering of steep surface waves around vertical columns. *Appl. Ocean Res.* 27 (2), 65–80.

Swan C, Masterton S, Sheikh R, Cavalletti A. Wave forcing and wave scattering from a vertical surface-piercing cylinder. Paper no. 67158. *Proceedings of the 24th OMAE conference*, Halkidiki, Greece.

Sumer, b. m. & Fredsø, j. 2006 hydrodynamics around cylindrical structures. *world scientific*.

Swan C, Sheikh R. The interaction between steep waves and a surface piercing column. *Phil Trans R Soc A* 2015;373(2033).

Sun, L., Zang, J., Chen, L., Taylor, R. E., Taylor, P. H. (2016) Regular waves onto a truncated circular column: A comparison of experiments and simulations, Applied Ocean Research 59, 650–662.

Yoon, S.-H., Kim, D.-H., Sadat-Hosseini, H., Yang, J., and Stern, F., 2016. High-fidelity CFD simulation of wave run-up for single/multiple surface-piercing cylinders in regular head waves. *Applied Ocean Research* 60, 620–642.

On the computation of the propulsive characteristics of a tanker

G. Tzabiras, H. Tserpes, S. Polyzos & D.E. Liarokapis
National Technical University of Athens, LSMH, Athens, Greece

ABSTRACT: The present work deals with the prediction of the horsepower and *RPM* of a tanker during sea trials by applying an in house CFD code. The code solves the steady RANS equations in calm water using the finite volume approach. A hybrid surface-tracking method is employed to calculate the free-surface and the propeller is modeled according to the actuator disk approximation. The main goal of the paper is to investigate the influence of the turbulent model on the acquired results. In this respect, two turbulence models are examined i.e. the standard k-ε and the k-ω-SST. The computed results at the speed of the sea trials are compared to the measured data at full displacement. Besides, a ballast condition is studied in order to explore the behavior of the two models in two quite different situations.

1 INTRODUCTION

The prediction of the required horsepower (*SHP*) and propeller revolutions (*RPM*) of a ship moving in steady forward speed in calm water is one of the most significant issues in marine hydrodynamics. Therefore, it is the main goal of any CFD method which can be applied to solve the self-propulsion problem during sea trials.

The majority of the relevant CFD approaches is concerned with the solution of the RANS equations. Therefore, their success depends strongly on the turbulence model which is employed. Although the Reynolds stress models seem to predict successfully many complicated features in stern flows, two equation models are applied in the majority of practical problems since they demand significantly lower computing power. Two widely used, among them, are the k-ε model of Launder & Spalding (1972) and the k-ω-SST model of Menter (1993). The main advantage of the first one relies on the fact that it is a universal model which is applicable anywhere in a flow-field. On the contrary, the k-ω-SST is essentially a two-zonal model, depending on local geometrical characteristics and has been designed to calculate more accurately the field variables in thick or separated boundary layers.

The aim of the present work is to study the influence of these turbulence models on the predicted *SHP* and *RPM* of an existing tanker during sea trials. An in-house CFD code has been employed, which solves the steady RANS equations under a pre-determined free-surface. The propeller operation is approximated by an actuator disk and self-propulsion is achieved by an iterative procedure. In order to compare the results in two cases having substantially different shapes, i.e. with and without transom, a full load and a ballast condition are examined.

2 THE NUMERICAL METHOD

The employed method has been developed at the Laboratory for Ship and marine Hydrodynamics of NTUA. It solves the RANS equations in a body fitted structured mesh as shown in Figure 1. The three regions (I), (II) and (III) refer to three different grid topologies. Region (I) consists of a C-O grid following a sequence of transverse planes which intersect on the axis Zc. Region (II) represents an H-O grid which is formed by transverse planes to the longitudinal symmetry axis x, while region (III) forms a typical H-H grid which is generated when a dry or wet transom stern exists, Tzabiras & Polyzos (2015). In any case, the 2D grids on the transverse planes are generated following the conformal mapping technique as described by Tzabiras & Kontogiannis (2010). In order to apply as far as possible high grid resolutions, the three blocks are created in a restricted domain underneath the pre-determined free surface boundary FS. The free-surface is calculated according to the hybrid potential-viscous flow method of Tzabiras & Polyzos (2015).

The RANS code employs a sequence of orthogonal curvilinear systems bounded on each transverse plane. In such a system the three velocity components are denoted as (u_i, u_J, u_l) and the u_I- momentum equation reads:

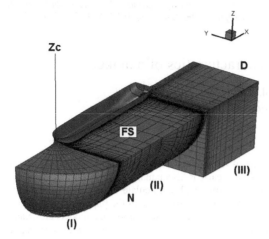

Figure 1. The mesh around the hull.

$$C(u_i) = -\frac{1}{h_i}\frac{\partial p}{\partial x_i} + \rho u_j^2 K_{ji} + \rho u_l^2 K_{li}$$
$$- \rho u_i u_j K_{ij} - \rho u_i u_l K_{il} + (\sigma_{ii} - \sigma_{jj})K_{ji}$$
$$+ (\sigma_{ii} - \sigma_{ll})K_{li} + \sigma_{ij}(2K_{ij} + K_{lj}) \qquad (1)$$
$$+ \sigma_{il}(2K_{il} + K_{jl}) + \frac{1}{h_i}\frac{\partial \sigma_{ii}}{\partial x_i} + \frac{1}{h_j}\frac{\partial \sigma_{ij}}{\partial x_j} + \frac{1}{h_l}\frac{\partial \sigma_{il}}{\partial x_l}$$

where (h_i, h_j, h_l) are the metrics, K_{ij} the curvatures of the orthogonal system, ρ the fluid density, p the static plus the hydrostatic pressure, σ_{ij} the stress tensor and the lhs of equation (1) represents the convective terms:

$$C(\Phi) = \frac{\rho}{h_i h_j h_l}\left[\frac{\partial(h_j h_l u_i \Phi)}{\partial x_i} + \frac{\partial(h_i h_l u_j \Phi)}{\partial x_j} + \frac{\partial(h_i h_j u_l \Phi)}{\partial x_l}\right] \qquad (2)$$

The stress tensor components are associated to the deformation tensor through:

$$\sigma_{ii} = 2\mu_e e_{ii} = 2\mu_e\left[\frac{1}{h_i}\frac{\partial u_i}{\partial x_i} + u_j K_{ij} + u_l K_{il}\right]$$
$$\sigma_{ij} = \mu_e e_{ij} = \mu_e\left[\frac{h_j}{h_i}\frac{\partial}{\partial x_i}\left(\frac{u_j}{h_j}\right) + \frac{h_i}{h_j}\frac{\partial}{\partial x_j}\left(\frac{u_i}{h_i}\right)\right] \qquad (3)$$

The effective viscosity in Equation 3 is defined as:

$$\mu_e = \mu + \rho\nu_t \qquad (4)$$

where ν_t stands for the turbulent (or eddy) viscosity which is calculated according to the adopted turbulence, two-equation model. When the k-ω-SST model is employed, the equation for the kinetic energy of turbulence k reads:

$$C(k) = \frac{1}{h_i h_j h_l}\left[\frac{\partial}{\partial x_i}\left(\sigma_k \mu_t \frac{h_j h_l}{h_i}\frac{\partial k}{\partial x_i}\right) + \frac{\partial}{\partial x_j}\left(\sigma_k \mu_t \frac{h_i h_l}{h_j}\frac{\partial k}{\partial x_j}\right) + \frac{\partial}{\partial x_l}\left(\sigma_k \mu_t \frac{h_i h_j}{h_l}\frac{\partial k}{\partial x_l}\right)\right]$$
$$+ G - \beta^* \rho \omega k \qquad (5)$$

The second Equation (6) refers to the specific dissipation ω:

$$C(\omega) = \frac{1}{h_i h_j h_l}\left[\frac{\partial}{\partial x_i}\left(\sigma_\omega \mu_t \frac{h_j h_l}{h_i}\frac{\partial \omega}{\partial x_i}\right) + \frac{\partial}{\partial x_j}\left(\sigma_\omega \mu_t \frac{h_i h_l}{h_j}\frac{\partial \omega}{\partial x_j}\right) + \frac{\partial}{\partial x_l}\left(\sigma_\omega \mu_t \frac{h_i h_j}{h_l}\frac{\partial \omega}{\partial x_l}\right)\right]$$
$$+ \frac{\gamma}{\nu_t}G - \beta^* \rho \omega^2 + 2\rho(1 - F_1)\frac{\sigma_\omega}{\omega}\frac{1}{h_j^2}\frac{\partial k}{\partial x_j}\frac{\partial \omega}{\partial x_j} \qquad (6)$$

According to the k-ω-SST model the turbulent kinematic viscosity is calculated according to the formula:

$$\nu_t = \frac{a_1 k}{\max[a_1 \omega, |rot(\vec{c})|F_2]} \qquad (7)$$

In the above Equations 5-7 the constants σ_k, σ_ω, β^* and the functions F_1, F_2 are defined as in the original paper of Menter (1993), while G represents the generation term of the turbulence kinetic energy. Essentially, this model separates the flow-field above the body surface in two regions, which are determined according to the local flow parameters and the normal distance from the surface. It has been developed in order to calculate effectively complex flow-fields, like those appearing in stern flows past full ship forms.

On the other hand, the k-ε model is more universal and is applied by solving two transport equations which hold for all regions in the flow-field. The k-equation is quite similar to Equation 5, but using different constants. The second equation, regarding the energy dissipation rate ε, is written as:

$$C(\varepsilon) =$$
$$\frac{1}{h_i h_j h_l}\left[\frac{\partial}{\partial x_i}\left(\sigma_\varepsilon \mu_t \frac{h_j h_l}{h_i}\frac{\partial \varepsilon}{\partial x_i}\right) + \frac{\partial}{\partial x_j}\left(\sigma_\varepsilon \mu_t \frac{h_i h_l}{h_j}\frac{\partial \varepsilon}{\partial x_j}\right) + \frac{\partial}{\partial x_l}\left(\sigma_\varepsilon \mu_t \frac{h_i h_j}{h_l}\frac{\partial \varepsilon}{\partial x_l}\right)\right]$$
$$+ C_1 \frac{\varepsilon}{k}G - C_2 \rho \frac{\varepsilon^2}{k} \qquad (8)$$

while, the eddy viscosity is calculated as:

$$\nu_t = C_\mu \frac{k^2}{\varepsilon} \qquad (9)$$

The constants σ, C_1, C_2 and C_μ are defined according to the original work of Launder & Spalding (1972).

The momentum and the turbulence model (RANS) equations are solved numerically by applying the finite volume method in a staggered grid arrangement. In the resulting non-linear algebraic equations, the convective terms are approximated according to the second order MUSCL scheme associated with the minmod limiter, while the diffusive and the source terms are approximated using central differences. The solution follows the SIMPLE algorithm, where the RANS equations are solved following a marching scheme, while the pressure (continuity) equation is treated as fully elliptic. Dirichlet boundary conditions are applied on the external boundary N of Figure 1 for the flow variables. The velocity components and the pressure on this boundary are calculated by the potential flow solution performed around the hull and the free-surface, Tzabiras (2014). On the free-surface, FS in Figure 1, the kinematic condition is fulfilled (zero normal velocity) wile for the pressure and the turbulence quantities Neumann conditions are applied. In order to calculate the flow variables above the solid boundary in a uniform way for both turbulence models, the standard wall function method is employed. Finally, on the exit plane D, open-type conditions hold, Tzabiras (2004).

The self-propulsion problem is solved by adopting the actuator disk model. Only the axial body forces are taken into account and their distribution along the blade are calculated by the lifting line approach, Politis (1985). To introduce this model, the effective wake is approximated according to the open water numerical experiment as described by Tzabiras (1996), (1997). The propeller thrust is calculated following an iterative procedure so that its final value equals the total resistance of the ship. This procedure is also followed when the free-surface problem is solved, since the stern wave is influenced by the propeller operation.

3 THE TEST CASE

3.1 Characteristics of the tanker

The main characteristics of the tanker under investigation are shown in Table 1. In this Table, L_{BP} represents the length between perpendiculars, L_{OA} the length overall, B the ship's beam, T the draft at full load condition (FL) during sea-trials, Δ the corresponding displacement and C_B the block coefficient. The speed of the ship in the trials was equal to 16.04 knots, the Froude number based on L_{OA} equal to 0.175 and the Reynolds number equal to 1.3×10^9. The shape of the

Table 1. Characteristics of the ship (sea trials).

L_{BP}(m)	220
L_{OA}	226.2
B(m)	32.24
T (m)	12.2
Δ(tons)	76509
C_B	0.86
Speed (kn)	16.04
Fr No	0.175
Re No	1.3×10^9

hull with the bulbous bow and the transom stern is shown in Figure 2.

3.2 Computations at full load condition

Computations at full load have been conducted in order to compare the computed *SHP* and *RPM* with those measured at sea-trials. At first, the free-surface has been calculated by applying the hybrid method of Tzabiras & Polyzos (2015), which employs the potential solution up to (about) the middle of the ship. At the stern and wake regions, where the viscous phenomena are dominant, a full RANS solver is applied to find iteratively the free-surface boundary. As aforementioned, the propeller effect is taken into account in these calculations.

The calculated bow wave at full load is shown in Figure 3. Although the Froude number is relatively

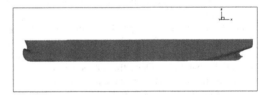

Figure 2. The hull shape.

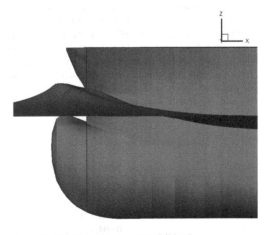

Figure 3. Calculated bow wave at full load.

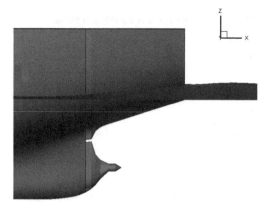

Figure 4. Calculated stern wave at full load (wetted transom).

low, the bulb generates a relatively high wave above, which is attenuated after the fore perpendicular. Figure 4 shows the stern wave formation around the wetted transom and the near wake. This wave is strongly influenced by viscous effects since the flow presents a recirculation area after the transom, while the potential solution calculates a significantly higher wave in the same area.

Next, the RANS equations have been solved under the calculated surface, as described in the previous section. The external boundary N of the calculation domain in Figure 2 was placed at a distance of $0.44L_{BP}$ from the center plane and the exit plane D at a distance of $0.5L_{BP}$ after the transom. In order to achieve, as far as possible, accurate results two sub-domains have been applied. The first one (bow) includes the C-grid around the bow and the parallel body up to $0.7L_{BP}$ from the fore-perpendicular. In this part of the field the flow is characterized by a thin boundary layer and is essentially parabolic, Once the solution is performed, assuming that at the last plane the pressure is calculated by the potential flow solution, the input boundary conditions of the second sub-domain are calculated using linear interpolation. This sub-domain covers the stern part, the transom and the near wake and it is characterized as stern-transom, including two grid topologies.

In order to study the effect of grid resolution, three grid densities were tested using the k-ω-SST model. The three grids are characterized as coarse, medium and fine and their characteristics are depicted in Tables 2, 3 and 4. In these Tables, N_1, N_2 and N_3 denote the number of grid nodes along

Table 2. Characteristics of the coarse grid.

Region	No of grid points ($N_1N_2N_3$)
bow	161x27x60
stern	161x27x60
transom	59x28x50
total	0.604240M

Table 3. Characteristics of the medium grid.

Region	No of grid points ($N_1N_2N_3$)
bow	321x54x120
stern	321x54x120
transom	119x56x100
total	4.826560M

Table 4. Characteristics of the fine grid.

Region	No of grid points ($N_1N_2N_3$)
bow	481x81x190
stern	481x81x190
transom	189x85x150
total	17.21493 M

Table 5. Grid dependence tests.

Grid	$C_T \times 10^3$	%Diff.
Coarse(0.6M)	2.429	
Medium(4.8M)	2.493	2.567
Fine(17.2M)	2.510	0.677

the longitudinal, the circumferential and the transverse directions, respectively. The coarse grid comprises about 0.6M, the medium 4.8M and the fine 17.2M grid points. The calculated total resistance coefficients C_T with the three grids are compared in Table 5. C_T is defined as:

$$C_T = \frac{R_T}{1/2\rho S v_S^2} \quad (10)$$

where R_T is the total resistance of the ship, S its wetted surface and v_s the ship's speed. The total resistance is the sum of the friction component R_F and the pressure component R_P, i.e. $R_T = R_F + R_P$. The column characterized as % Diff. in Table 5 shows the percentage difference between the examined and the previous grid. The difference in C_T between the medium and the coarse grid is about 2.5%, while is drastically reduced to 0.67% between the fine and the coarse. Therefore, it was considered that the fine grid could be reliable for the comparison purposes of the present work and has been used in all other cases.

Computations were performed by applying a sequential grid refinement technique, Tzabiras (1996), and almost 1000 steady-state, iterative steps (sweeps) were needed to obtain convergence with the fine grid. Convergence was achieved when the non-dimensional residuals of the momentum and continuity

Table 6. Calculated resistance characteristics.

Turb. model	k-ω-SST	k-ε	Diff%
$C_F \times 10^3$	1.581	1.647	+4.17
$C_P \times 10^3$	0.929	0.908	-2.26
$C_T \times 10^3$	2.509	2.555	+1.85
$R_T(N)$	9.877×10⁵	1.006×10⁶	+1.85
EHP(KW)	8,144	8,294	+1.85
$1-w_n$	0.731	0.720	-1.50

Table 7. Calculated propulsion characteristics.

Turb. model	k-ω-SST	k-ε	Diff%
$C_F \times 10^3$	1.584	1.651	+4.22
$C_P \times 10^3$	1.296	1.291	-0.38
$C_T \times 10^3$	2.881	2.941	+2.00
$T(N)$	1.134×10⁶	1.157×10⁶	+2.03
DHP(KW)	11,392	11,615	+1.95
RPM	103.38	103.52	+0.13
$1-t$	0.871	0.869	-0.23
$1-w_e$	0.709	0.697	-1.69
J	0.499	0.490	-1.80
K_T	0.171	0.175	+2.34
$10K_Q$	0.238	0.241	+1.26
η_P	0.574	0.567	-1.22

equations, Tzabiras and Kontogiannis (2010), were below 5×10⁻⁴. The non-dimensional y^+ values of the adjacent to the wall nodes ranged between 100 and 400, which is a suitable range for the applicability of wall functions at high Reynolds number ship flows.

Integrated results concerning the simple resistance problem, i.e. without propeller in operation, are presented in Table 6. The last column in this Table shows the percentage differences between the k-ω-SST and k-ε models, regarding the first one as basic. The friction coefficient C_F and the pressure coefficient C_P are defined by Equation (10), where R_T is replaced by R_F and R_P accordingly. Evidently, the highest difference (4.17%) is observed for C_F, indicating that the flow exhibits higher velocities close to the body surface in the stern region, when the k-ε model is applied. This is, somehow, a reasonable result since the k-ω-SST model has been theoretically designed to predict more accurately stern flows. The pressure coefficient C_P presents the opposite trend, i.e. it appears by 2.26% higher with the k-ω-SST. Consequently, the total coefficient C_T shows a lower difference of 1.85% between the two models. Obviously, this difference remains the same in the results for the total resistance R_T and the effective horsepower EHP. Finally, the calculated nominal wake fraction $1-w_n$ is by 1.5% higher with the k-ω-SST model.

To perform self-propulsion calculations, the general features of the real propeller during the sea-trials were adopted: propeller diameter D = 6.8m, four blades, pitch ratio *P/D = 0.8*, and expanded area ratio A_E/A_0 = 0.525. According to the drawings, the propeller mid-plane was placed 8.36 m in front of the transom. Since no data were available concerning the open water tests, the Wageningen B-Series were employed in order to calculate the delivered horse power DHP and propeller revolutions RPM. In order to achieve the equality of the thrust to the total resistance, 45 external iterations were necessary, using 30 internal sweeps per external iteration.

The calculated propulsive characteristics are presented in Table 7, where T in (N) stands for the thrust, DHP in (KW) for the delivered horsepower, $1-t$ for the thrust deduction factor, $1-w_e$ for the effective wake and J, K_T, K_Q, η_p are the non-dimensional advance, thrust, torque and propeller efficiency coefficients, respectively. The integrated results show a slight increase of C_F with both models with respect to the resistance data of Table 6, while the percentage difference between them remains the same. On the contrary, the pressure coefficient C_P is significantly increased by almost 45% in both cases showing that the propeller operation affects mainly the pressure field and contributes essentially to the thrust deduction factor $1-t$. A negligible difference is observed for $1-t$ between the two models, while the effective wake fraction $1-w_e$ varies slightly (1.69%) and follows the same trends as the nominal wake fraction. The most significant results are those concerning DHP and RPM. The k-ω-SST model predicts a lower by almost 2% DHP than the k-ε, while both models give practically the same RPM.

The measured SHP and RPM during the sea-trials are compared to the calculated ones in Table 8. In calculations, it is assumed that DHP = 0.99 SHP in order to derive SHP. It is remarkable that both models give surprisingly good results for SHP. The k-ω-SST predicts a lower by 0.16% value than the measured, while the k-ε gives higher SHP by 1.97%. With both models RPM are under-predicted by 1.5%. Nevertheless, it should be mentioned that simplifications which have been adopted, influence more or less computations. Important among them are: the Wageningen adoption, the operation of the actuator disk without taking into account the torque effects and the interaction with the rudder.

3.3 *Computations at ballast condition*

The draft of the ballast condition which has been examined was equal to T = 8,5 m and the corresponding displacement Δ = 49,800 t. In this draft, the still waterline intersects the bulb and forms a cruiser-type stern, i.e. the transom appears above the water level. The same situation is observed after the calculation of the free-surface, as shown in Figures 5 and 6 corresponding to the bow and stern wave formation.

The basic geometrical characteristics of the calculation domain have been the same as in the full load condition, but the grid topology differs because of

Table 8. Comparison of measured to calculated results for SHP and RPM.

	SHP (KW)	Diff%	RPM	Diff%
measured	11,526		105	
calc. k-ω-SST	11,507	-0.16	103.38	-1.54
calc. k-ε	11,733	+1.97	103.52	-1.41

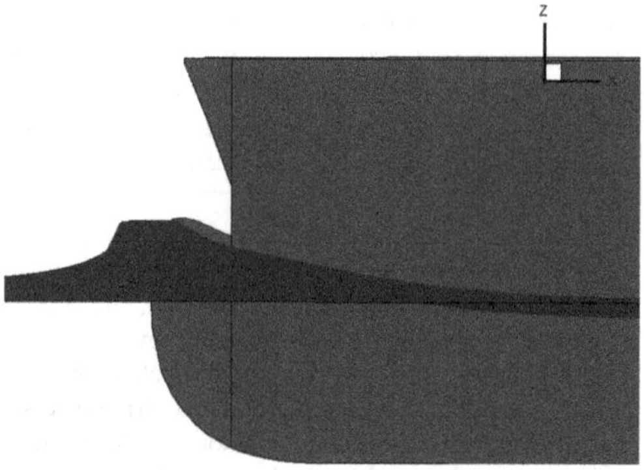

Table 9. Characteristics of the grid at ballast condition.

Region	No of grid points ($N_1N_2N_3$)
bow	481x81x190
stern	631x60x190
total	14.59599 M

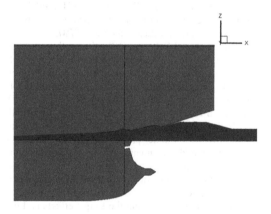

Figure 5. Calculated bow wave at ballast condition.

Table 10. Calculated resistance characteristics at ballast condition.

Turb. model	k-ω-SST	k-ε	Diff%
$C_F \times 10^3$	1.548	1.615	+4.13
$C_P \times 10^3$	1.140	1.157	+1.49
$C_T \times 10^3$	2.688	2.772	+3.12
R_T(N)	8.873x10^5	9.150x10^5	+3.12
EHP(KW)	7,315	7,543	+3.12
$1-w_n$	0.608	0.624	+2.63

C_T is higher by 3.12% in the second case, and this difference holds also for R_T and EHP. On the contrary, the nominal wake fraction with k-ε is, in this case, higher by 2.63%

In Table 11, the calculated propulsion characteristics concerning the ballast condition are presented. The main conclusion is that the integrated resistance coefficients are both higher with the k-ε model, resulting in a higher DHP by almost 7%. This result is mainly due to the different percentage increase of C_P when self-propulsion is performed. The computed RPM differ also by 2%. These results show that the differences in the predictions by the two models are more pronounced than in the case of the full load, implying that the relevant computations are sensitive with regard to draft changes.

Figure 6. Calculated stern wave at ballast condition.

the absence of the transom stern. Therefore, the stern sub-domain comprises only one block covering the stern area and the near wake. Only one grid has been tested, similar to the fine grid applied in full load computations. The characteristics of the grid in the two sub-domains of bow and stern are depicted in Table 9.

The integrated resistance coefficients in the ballast condition are presented in Table 10. As in the previous case, the friction coefficient C_F predicted with the k-ω-SST model is lower by 4.13% than the one predicted with k-ε, while C_P follows now the same trend, being slightly lower. Therefore, the total coefficient

Table 11. Calculated propulsion characteristics at ballast condition.

Turb. model	k-ω-SST	k-ε	Diff%
$C_F \times 10^3$	1.550	1.618	+4.22
$C_P \times 10^3$	1.507	1.599	+6.01
$C_T \times 10^3$	3.057	3.217	+5.20
T(N)	1.009x10^6	1.062x10^6	+5.20
DHP(KW)	9,183	9,839	+7.15
RPM	94,83	96.78	+2.00
$1-t$	0.879	0.873	-0.68
$1-w_e$	0.617	0.623	+0/97
J	0.473	0.469	-1.25
K_T	0.182	0.184	+1.09
$10K_Q$	0.248	0.250	+0.81
η_P	0.553	0.550	-0.55

4 CONCLUSIONS

The present work has been concerned with the prediction of the propulsive characteristics of a full scale tanker, using two different two-equation turbulence models, i.e. the k-ω-SST and the k-ε. Numerical calculations have been performed in the full load as well as in a ballast condition corresponding to different flow situations. The comparison between the calculated and measured data during sea-trials, have shown that the predictions are rather reliable. In both cases, it has been found that the k-ε has the trend to over-predict the friction coefficient, while the pressure coefficient varies smoothly. As a consequence, the total resistance coefficient follows the trends of C_F and results in a higher total resistance, thrust and delivered horsepower. However, if we are concerned with the required engine characteristics at full load, the differences can be considered as insignificant.

REFERENCESS

Launder, B.E. & Spalding, D.B., 1974. The numerical computation of turbulent flows. *Computation Methods in Applied Mechanics and Engineering*, 269–289.

Menter, F. 1993. Zonal two equation turbulence models for ae- rodynamic flows. *24th Fluid Dynamics Conference, AIAA, paper no 93–2906, Orlando, Florida*.

Politis, G.K., 1985. A lifting line equivalent profile method for propeller calculation. *Journal of Ship Research*, 29, 241–251.

Tzabiras, G.D., 1996. A numerical study of actuator disk pa-rameters affecting the self-propulsion of a tanker. *Int Shipbuilding Progress*, 1, 55–47.

Tzabiras, G.D. 1997. A numerical study of additive bulb ef-fects on the resistance and propulsion characteristics of a full ship form. *Ship Technology Res.*, 44, 98–108.

Tzabiras, G.D. 2004. Resistance and self-propulsion simulations for a Series-60, c_B=0.6 hull at model and full scale. *Ship Technology Res.*, 51, 21–34.

Tzabiras, G.D. & Kontogiannis, K., 2010.An integrated method for predicting the hydrodynamic performance of low c_B ships. *Computer Aided Design Journal*, 42, 985–1000.

Tzabiras, G. 2014. The effect of free-surface simulations on the resistance and propulsion characteristics of a ship. *2nd International Conference on Maritime Technology and Engineering, MARTECH 2014*, An Proc. Lisbon, 903–912.

Tzabiras, G.D. & Polyzos, S.P., 2015. A hybrid numerical me-thod for calculating self-propulsion characteristics of ships. *IMAM 2015 Int. Conference*, Pula, Croatia, 51–58.

Numerical prediction of hydrodynamic coefficients of a submerged object with constant acceleration method

G. Xiang, S. Wang & C. Guedes Soares
Centre for Marine Technology and Ocean Engineering (CENTEC), Instituto Superior Técnico, Universidade de Lisboa, Lisbon, Portugal

ABSTRACT: The hydrodynamic coefficients of a submerged object are predicted through constant acceleration method, which is implemented by the CFD tool OpenFOAM. The object is assumed to be fixed and passed by the downward water flow with constant acceleration. In the constant acceleration method, the added mass force can be obtained at the moment that acceleration flow just begins or disappears by subtracting the drag force from the total hydrodynamic force. The CFD predictions for a two-dimensional cylinder and a three dimensional prism are compared with corresponding theoretical values and available experimental values. The good agreement indicates the capability of the CFD method into predicting the hydrodynamic coefficients of a submerged object.

1 INTRODUCTION

The force exerted by a fluid on a bluff body has been of interest to researchers and designers for many years. The complexity of the research has ranged from the simple static case to complicated accelerating cases. When considering an unsteady velocity flow situation, the fluid particles around the object generate an additional inertial force, added mass force.

Added mass should be widely taken in to account in naval architecture and ocean engineering. At the stage of design analysis, added mass must be known to predict the required minimum power to accelerate the ocean vessels such as surface ships, unmanned underwater vehicles (UUV) and submarines, because the added mass can easily become very high compared to the mass of the vessel itself. During operations of installation of heavy equipment in the seabed, the coupling motion between the suspended system, the support vessel and the equipment to be installed is likely to excite the whole system to be in unstable state. Added mass of each component should be obtained for dynamic analysis of the whole installation system. When it comes to the installations of underwater equipment such as manifolds using crane lifts, the challenges of installing these structures in deep water depths not only regard to the capabilities of the installation equipment, but also an efficient and safe installation procedure and analysis. At this time, accurate prediction of hydrodynamic coefficients such as added mass coefficient and drag coefficient are required.

There are mainly three methods to estimate the added mass of an object including the potential flow method, constant acceleration method and forced oscillation method. Fernandes & Mineiro (2007) introduced all these three methods in the added mass of a model manifold for the purpose of deep-water deployment. The first method is implemented using WAMIT (2005) while the latter two methods are realized experimentally. However, for saving cost, many researchers applied these three methods either numerically or analytically.

Potential flow method usually indicates solving the Laplace equation for the velocity potential of irrotational water flows using some panel methods such as boundary element methods (BEM). The surface of the moving object is discretized to many panels to approximate the object surface, and dipole or the combination of sources and dipoles are attached on each panel so as to determine velocity potential, then obtain added mass.

Geisbert (2007) utilized BEM based software to simulate a body accelerating in a flow or resting in a moving fluid and then determine the forces and moments acting on the body. The unsteady flow characteristics is solved using potential flow theory, the doublets and sources over the time history for the body under the assumption that the effects of viscosity are largely confined to a thin boundary layer on the body surface. Lin & Liao (2011) applied the fast-multiple boundary element method (FMBEM) into calculating the added mass coefficients of complicated three dimensional (3D) underwater bodies such as sphere and spheroids and SUBOFF submarine. It is found that the FMBEM is computationally much more efficient than the traditional BEM to predict added mass coefficients of complicated underwater bodies. Koo & Kim (2015) developed a two-dimensional frequency-domain Numerical Wave Tank (NWT) technique to calculate the values of the added masses for the vertical movement of various two-dimensional body sections at various water depth, and wave frequency. Nokob & Yeung (2018) applied Galerkin approach into hyper singular boundary-integral equation to study the added mass and moment of inertia of infinitely thin plates of arbitrary shapes particularly those plates with openings or holes in an infinite potential field. Lagrange et al. (2018) presented a new analytical method based on potential theory for the added mass of two cylinders next to each other, with different radius and distances between.

Forced Oscillation Method is divided into two branches based on oscillating the body or the flow around the body. Uchiyama (2003) applied the finite element method to study the added mass and damping of a circular cylinder oscillating in an air–water bubbly mixture enclosed by a concentric shell. The floor effect has been studied by changing the diameter ratio of the cylinder to the shell. With diameter ratio increasing, the added mass coefficient increases as well. Zhang & Ishihara (2018) presented large eddy simulations to predict the added mass coefficient of a forced oscillated model with multiple heave plates. The simulated drag and added mass coefficients agreed well with the water tank test. Geometric parameters, such as spacing ratio, diameter ratio and aspect ratio are systematically studied on how they affect the added mass coefficient.

Although the oscillating body method can solve the problem well, it requires too much time cost and very high calculating resources because the mesh around the body needs to be dynamically changed and adapted to the movement of the body at each time step. Thus, oscillating flow method may be a good alternative. Zoontjes et al. (2009) compared both methods: oscillating body and oscillating flow method into calculating the add mass and damping coefficients of suction piles using CFD. The authors found that both methods can give very good results for both closed and open hatch conditions. But the computational costs for oscillating flow method is much lower than the oscillating body method.

However, the main drawback of the forced oscillation method is that the predicted added mass coefficient may be influenced by the wake induced by the oscillating body because the oscillating body may run into its wake. At this time, constant acceleration method stands out because the wake induced by the translational body is left far behind. Like forced oscillation method, constant acceleration method can be also divided into two branches: accelerating flow and accelerating body. Hu & Liu (2010) applied two methods: constant acceleration method and potential theory based surface panel method into assessing the added mass coefficient of components of deep sea mining system. In the constant acceleration method, the accelerated body moving in the water is simulated by commercial computational fluid dynamics (CFD) software, Fluent. Raza et al. (2012) also presented CFD code, Fluent to compute the added mass of ellipsoids. The constant acceleration method is based on unsteady, inviscid model and dynamic mesh technique for transient simulation of body motions.

Yang et al. (2017) utilized the dynamic mesh technique in CFX fluid simulation software to simulate the accelerating submarine-launched missile during the water-exit process. By comparing the results of the numerical simulation and the calculation of theoretical model, the e□ectiveness of this added mass calculation method is verified. Without taking the floor or seabed effect into account, accelerating flow method is much more efficient than accelerating body method because accelerating flow method only needs to solve the static mesh instead of dynamic mesh in accelerating body method. Thus accelerating flow method deserves more attentions.

Mishra et al. (2011) applied the accelerating flow method based on CFD software, Fluent into the calculation of translational added mass coefficient of axisymmetric underwater bodies in both longitudinal and transverse directions. The simulated added mass coefficient of sphere and infinitely long circular cylinder through accelerating the flow shows good agreement with their analytical solutions of the added mass.

In this paper, the constant acceleration method is proposed to predict the hydrodynamic coefficients for different submerged objects such as cylinder, prism. The accelerating flow is applied and realized by OpenFOAM. The steps to calculate the added mass coefficient are provided in detail. The validation of the methodology is obtained by the good agreement between simulated drag, added mass coefficients and corresponding analytical solutions and experimental data.

2 METHODOLOGY

2.1 *Constant Acceleration Method*

Constant acceleration method is an efficient approach to calculate the added mass of a submerged object. Usually we applied two ways of implementing accelerations. One is accelerating the object in the still water while the other is accelerating the water flow past the fixed object. The former has been experimentally studied by Fernandes & Mineiro (2007). But when studying the added mass numerically, the former requires remeshing or dynamic mesh techniques for each time step while the latter just used a predefined static mesh for each time step. In CFD simulations, to reduce the calculation time, the latter way of accelerating flow is used in present paper.

2.2 *Accelerating flow past a fixed body*

According to the Morison equation for a fixed body in an oscillatory flow, the total force acting on the fixed body can be expressed as a summation of drag force F_d and inertial force F_I

$$F_t = F_d + F_I \quad (1)$$

where

$$F_I = \rho \, C_m V a \quad (2)$$

$$C_m = C_a + 1 \quad (3)$$

As a result, by substituting Eq. (2) into Eq. (3), the equation to calculate the added mass coefficient C_a can be obtained:

$$C_a = \frac{F_I}{\rho V a} - 1 \quad (4)$$

Derived from Eq.(1), the inertial force F_I can be obtained by subtracting the drag force from the total force.

$$F_I = F_t - F_d \quad (5)$$

where,
ρ: the density of the water
V: the volume of the cylinder
a: the acceleration of the flow
C_a: the added mass coefficient
C_m: inertial coefficient

During the simulations, one force jump can be observed that happens at the moment accelerating flow just starts. At this moment, in addition to the drag force, F_d, there will be an instantaneous inertial force F_I caused by the accelerations. Furthermore, one force drop that happens at the moment accelerating flow just ends can be observed. With the disappearing of the accelerations, the inertial force F_I will also become zero, thus the force drop comes up.

Therefore, the critical feature to determine the added mass are the instantaneous changes of acceleration that are introduced

2.2.1 *Governing equation*
The governing equations for the unsteady incompressible flow past a fixed cylinder are the conservation equations for mass and momentum, namely the continuity and Navier–Stokes (N–S) equations expressed by Eq. (6) and Eq. (7) respectively

$$\frac{\partial U_i}{\partial x_i} = 0 \quad (6)$$

$$\frac{\partial U_i}{\partial t} + \frac{\partial (U_i U_j)}{\partial x_j} = -\frac{1}{\rho}\frac{\partial P}{\partial x_i} + \frac{1}{\rho}\frac{\partial \tau_{ij}}{\partial x_j}$$
$$+ \frac{\partial}{\partial x_j}\left[\mu\left(\frac{\partial U_i}{\partial x_j} + \frac{\partial U_j}{\partial x_i}\right)\right] \quad (7)$$

According to the literature, the most appropriate model is the k-ω SST turbulence model. This is due to its superior treatment of the viscous near wall region in addition to accounting for the effects of stream-wise pressure gradients. The SST version also accounts for the transport of turbulent shear stresses. These features are important in accurately modeling the boundary layer separation process, which is of paramount importance in obtaining good results for flow over bluff bodies. The k-ω SST model can be used as flow application without extra damping functions and is able to capture flow separation. Thus k-ω SST two equation model is adopted for considering turbulence.

$$\frac{\partial(\rho k)}{\partial t} + \frac{\partial(\rho k U_i)}{\partial x_i} = \frac{\partial}{\partial x_j}\left[(\mu + \mu_t \sigma_k)\frac{\partial k}{\partial x_j}\right] \quad (8)$$
$$+ P_k - \rho \beta^* k \omega$$

$$\frac{\partial(\rho \omega)}{\partial t} + \frac{\partial(\rho \omega U_i)}{\partial x_i} = \frac{\partial}{\partial x_j}\left[(\mu + \mu_t \sigma_\omega)\frac{\partial \omega}{\partial x_j}\right] +$$
$$\gamma \frac{\omega}{\kappa} P_k - \rho \beta \omega^2 + 2(1 - F_1)\rho \frac{1}{\omega \sigma_{\omega,2}}\frac{\partial k}{\partial x_j}\frac{\partial \omega}{\partial x_j} \quad (9)$$

The constants of this model are provided in Menter et al. (2003).

3 ADDED MASS OF A 2D CIRCULAR CYLINDER

To validate the CFD based constant acceleration method into predicting the added mass of an object, a relatively simple model, a 2D cylinder is selected for the first trial. Many existing results about drag coefficient of 2D cylinder have been published (Horner 1970, Gao et al., 2018), and the theoretical value of added mass coefficient of a 2D cylinder is known from potential theory.

3.1 *Flow domain and boundary conditions*

The 2D cylinder with the diameter of $d = 0.02$m, is fixed in the domain in Figure 1. The boundary conditions of both sides are wall. The inlet of the downward water flow is defined at the top boundary while

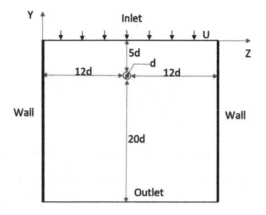

Figure 1. The computational domain.

the outlet is defined at the bottom boundary. The velocity at the inlet is varying according to a predefined time profile. The distance between the cylinder to the both sides is $s=12d$ to avoid side wall effects on the water flow. The distance of the cylinder to the inlet is $5d$ to make sure the flow is developed before reaching the cylinder. The cylinder is located $20d$ away from the outlet to avoid reflecting flow at the outlet and to fully express the wake stream behind the cylinder.

At the first stage, a low constant velocity (0.1 m/s) is applied until the simulation results converge. Then a constant acceleration is suddenly imposed. At the end of the acceleration ramp, a high constant velocity (0.5 m/s) is reached thereafter. In the simulations, four velocity profiles with different accelerations $a = 0.01g$, $0.02g$, $0.03g$, and $0.04g$ are shown in the following time profile A, B, C and D respectively.

Profile A:
$$U = \begin{cases} 0.1 & t < 20s \\ 0.1 + 0.04g \times t & 20 \leq t \leq 20.25s \\ 0.2 & 20.25s < t \end{cases}$$

Profile B:
$$U = \begin{cases} 0.1 & t < 20s \\ 0.1 + 0.06g \times t & 20 \leq t \leq 20.166s \\ 0.2 & 20.166s < t \end{cases}$$

Profile C:
$$U = \begin{cases} 0.1 & t < 20s \\ 0.1 + 0.08g \times t & 20 \leq t \leq 20.125s \\ 0.2 & 20.166s < t \end{cases}$$

Profile D:
$$U = \begin{cases} 0.1 & t < 20s \\ 0.1 + 0.1g \times t & 20 \leq t \leq 20.1s \\ 0.2 & 20.1s < t \end{cases}$$

3.2 Mesh set up and solver settings

Figure 2 Shows the mesh arrangement for the whole computational domain. The local refinement block around the cylinder has been used for capturing the flow characteristics at the surface of the cylinder. The time step is set to match the minimum element size so that the stability criteria the Courant Number (Co < 0.5) can be met. All the following simulations are based on OpenFOAM 2.4.0 and calculated with 36 cores' parallel processing. An unsteady Reynolds Averaged Numerical Simulation (URANS) solver is applied together with its PIMPLE algorithm (Xiang et al. 2020). The tool box, GroovyBC, part of swak4Foam in OpenFOAM is adopted to realize the varying velocity with time at the inlet boundary.

3.3 Steps to calculate added mass coefficient

Corresponding to Profile B, there will be a predicted added mass coefficient, C_a. The estimation of C_a will follow the steps below:

1. Get the inertial force, F_{I1} by subtracting the drag force F_d from the total force F_t at the moment the acceleration ramp begins as shown in Figure 3.
2. Get the inertial force, F_{I2} by subtracting the drag force F_d from the total force F_t at the moment the acceleration ramp ends as shown in Figure 3.
3. Get the inertial force, F_I by average of F_{I1} and F_{I2}.
4. Substitute F_I into Eq. (4) to get C_a.

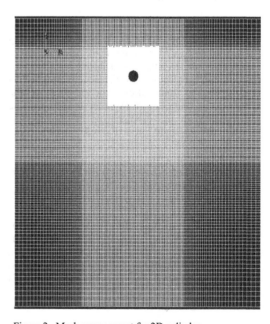

Figure 2. Mesh arrangement for 2D cylinder.

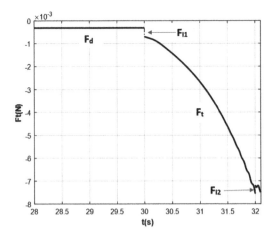

Figure 3. Time history of total force acting on the cylinder under Profile B.

3.4 Sensitivity study

In sensitivity study, the added mass coefficient of the 2D cylinder under the specified velocity Profile B has been calculated.

Table 1 gives information about the sensitivity study on the effect of mesh size and time step on the drag coefficient of the 2D cylinder at incoming velocity 0.5m/s, Re=1×104. Figure 4 shows the effect of mesh size and time step on the variation of the hydrodynamic force and corresponding added mass coefficient under velocity profile B.

By increasing the number of elements and decreasing the time step, the predicted drag coefficient and the added mass coefficient are very close. So, the settings with the refined mesh and the minimum time step in Case 3 are adopted for the rest of simulations.

3.5 Validation study

3.5.1 Drag coefficient
Table 2 compares the simulated drag coefficients for a 2D cylinder with corresponding experimental data in Horner (1970) and Gao et al. (2018).

3.5.2 Added mass coefficient
To accurately get the added mass coefficient of a circular cylinder, multiple simulations are run under different velocity profiles. Figures 5-6 present the

Table 1. Drag coefficient of the 2D cylinder with different grid and time resolution at incoming velocity 0.5m/s, $Re=1\times10^4$.

Case	Quality	Element	Time step(s)	C_d
1	Coarse	1×150×150	0.0001	1.17
2	Medium	1×180×180	0.00004	1.18
3	Fine	1×200×200	0.00002	1.19

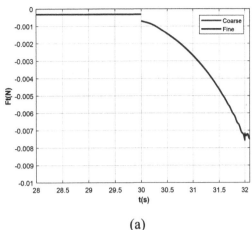

(a)

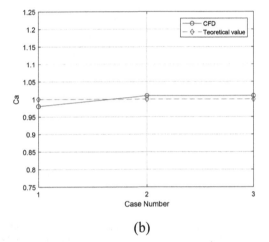

(b)

Figure 4. Comparison of simulated results due to different space and time resolutions, (a) variation of total force with time, (b) added mass coefficient.

Table 2. Drag coefficients of 2D cylinder.

	Re	Cd
Horner (1970)	2000	1.0
Gao et al.(2018)	2000	1.05
Present	2000	1.05
Horner (1970)	10000	1.1
Gao et al.(2018)	10000	1.4
Present	10000	1.2

time varying total force acting on the cylinder following inlet velocity Profile A, B, C, and D, respectively. It is observed that the total force at acceleration ramp stage is oscillating significantly under velocity profile with low acceleration, Profile A when a =0.01g. This may be because the inertial force induced by the low acceleration is very small and unstable compared

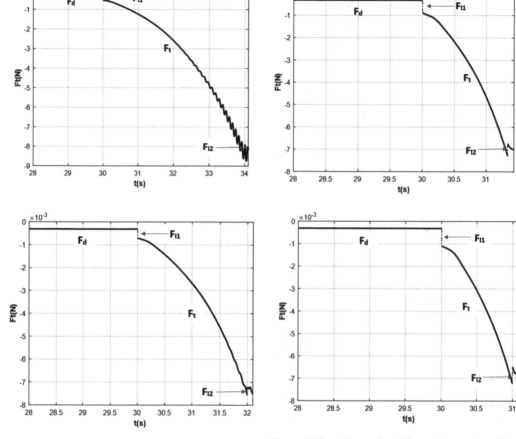

Figure 5. Time history of total force acting on the cylinder under different velocity profiles: Profile A at the top, Profile B at the bottom.

Figure 6. Time history of total force acting on the cylinder under different velocity profiles: Profile C at the top, Profile D at the bottom.

with the drag force. The simulation results may be also easily influenced by numerical noises.

As shown by Table 3, Ca for the 2D cylinder is found almost independent of imposed acceleration though Ca under profile A, a=0.01g, is 1.07 slightly larger than 1.01 under velocity profiles with relatively high accelerations: profile B, C, and D.

At last, C_A calculated by the average of C_a for each velocity profile in the Table 3 is the final value we will use for comparisons with theoretical values as shown in Table 4.

$$C_A = \frac{\sum_1^N C_a}{N} \quad (10)$$

It is found that the simulated drag coefficients match the experimental values very well. The simulated added mass coefficient of the 2D cylinder is 1.02, which is very close to the theoretical value of 1.0.

Table 3. Added mass coefficient of a 2D cylinder under each profile.

Profile	a	$F_{I1}(N)$	$F_{I2}(N)$	$F_I=0.5(F_{I1}+F_{I2})$	C_a
A	0.01g	0.00019	0.000201	0.000195	1.07
B	0.02g	0.000379	0.000377	0.000378	1.01
C	0.03g	0.000569	0.000566	0.0005675	1.01
D	0.04g	0.000759	0.000756	0.0007575	1.01

Table 4. Comparison of C_A with theoretical value.

	C_A
CFD	1.02
Theoretical value	1.00

4 ADDED MASS OF A MANIFOLD

4.1 Flow domain and boundary conditions

The prism with dimensions of H×L×B (H=0.147m, L=0.475m, B=0.243m) is fixed in the domain in Figure 7. The distance of the nearest face of the prism to the left or right side is S_1 =2.5H, to the top is S_2 =4B, to the bottom is S_4 =10B, to the front or back side is S_3 =2.5L.

The top boundary is defined to be inlet for velocity to simulate the downward water flow past the fixed prism. The velocity at the inlet is varying according to a predefined time profile. Generally multiple simulations with different predefined velocity profiles are used to calculate the added mass coefficient of the prism in specified direction.

For example, for longitudinal added mass coefficient (x directional) of the prism, the inlet velocity range is 0.1m/s-0.5m/s with following four predefined time profiles:

Profile A:
$$U = \begin{cases} 0.1 & t < 50s \\ 0.1 + 0.01g \times (t-50) & 50 \leq t \leq 54s \\ 0.5 & 54 < t < 60s \end{cases}$$

Profile B:
$$U = \begin{cases} 0.1 & t < 50s \\ 0.1 + 0.02g \times (t-50) & 50 \leq t \leq 52s \\ 0.5 & 52 < t < 60s \end{cases}$$

Profile C:
$$U = \begin{cases} 0.1 & t < 50s \\ 0.1 + 0.03g \times (t-50) & 50 \leq t \leq 51.33s \\ 0.5 & 51.33 < t < 60s \end{cases}$$

Profile D:
$$U = \begin{cases} 0.1 & t < 50s \\ 0.1 + 0.04g \times (t-50) & 50 \leq t \leq 51s \\ 0.5 & 51 < t < 60s \end{cases}$$

For vertical (z directional) and transverse (y directional) added mass coefficients, the inlet velocity range is 0.1m/s-1m/s.

The bottom boundary is set to be outlet for pressure. Four vertical sides are defined as solid wall boundaries. The prism can be rotated to align the side of interest of the prism with the water flow direction to study the different directional added mass coefficients of the prism. For example, in Figure 7 is showing the settings for studying transverse (y directional) coefficient with side B aligned with the flow direction.

4.2 Mesh set up and solver

Figure 8 Shows the mesh arrangement for the whole computational domain with a local refinement block around the prism. Wall function has been used to reduce dependency on mesh for capturing boundary layer properties.

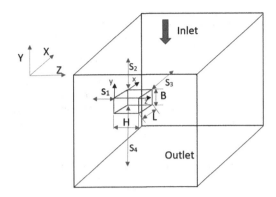

Figure 7. Description for the model and the computational domain.

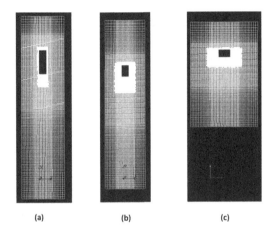

Figure 8. Mesh arrangement for prism, (a) longitudinal (b) transverse (c) vertical.

4.3 Sensitivity and validation study

For the purpose of the grid sensitivity study, the drag coefficient and added mass coefficient are both calculated and compared with corresponding experimental data. Table 5 gives information about the effect of grid resolution on the drag coefficient of the prism in z direction at incoming velocity 1m/s. Figure 9 shows the effect of grid resolution on the variation of the hydrodynamic force and the added mass coefficient under velocity profile F. It is found that the drag coefficient and the added mass coefficient are very close in cases 1-3 although finally become much closer to corresponding experimental values in Fernandes and Mineiro (2007) by increasing the number of elements.

Table 6 gives information about the sensitivity study on the effect of time step on drag coefficient in z direction. Figure 10 shows the effect of time step on the variation of the hydrodynamic force with time and the added mass coefficient. By reducing time step, it can be seen that the drag coefficient and the added mass coefficient both start to

Table 5. Drag coefficient of the prism with different grid resolution at incoming velocity 1m/s, $Re=1.47\times10^5$.

Case	Quality	Element	Cd
1	Coarse	100×75×40	1.38
2	Medium	125×100×50	1.39
3	Fine	150×125×80	1.41
Experiment		-	1.42

Table 6. Drag coefficient of the prism with different time step at incoming velocity 1m/s, $Re=1.47\times10^5$.

Case	Time step(s)	Cdz
4	0.005	1.40
5	0.002	1.41
6	0.001	1.41

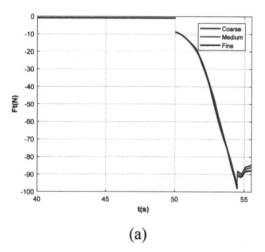

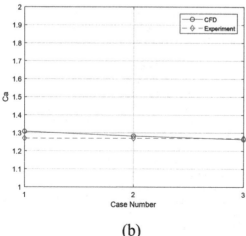

Figure 9. Comparison of simulated results due to different space resolutions, (a) variation of total force with time, (b) added mass coefficient.

get converged and become much closer to corresponding experimental values by Fernandes & Mineiro (2007).

All the above numerical results show a weak dependence on either grid or time step. But it should be noted that the large time step may cause instability of the numerical simulations by increasing the courant number. Therefore, a relatively small time step is preferred to ensure the convergence. Consequently, the fine grids used in Case 3 and a time step of 0.001s used in Case 6 are adopted in the following numerical simulations.

Table 7 compares the simulated drag coefficients of a prism in direction x, y and z with corresponding experimental data in Fernandes and Mineiro (2007). In experiment, there are many holes inside of the physical manifold model as shown in Figure 11 while in CFD are using an enclosed envelope of the manifold with smooth surface. The porosity effects may make the measured drag coefficient in experiment larger than the predicted. By taking into account both porosity effects in the experiment and side wall effect in the simulations, the CFD predicted drag coefficients is very close to the measured drag coefficient at last as expressed by Table 7.

As mentioned by Fernandes & Mineiro (2007), the prism with larger frontal area experiences larger drag coefficient. For example, with the prism having the largest frontal area, C_d in z direction is much larger than in x direction and y direction.

The final simulated directional added mass coefficients C_A as expressed by Eq. (10) are compared with corresponding experimental data by Fernandes & Mineiro (2007) and Wamit predicted value by Fernandes & Mineiro (2008) in Table 8. Figure 12 compares the simulated added mass coefficients C_a in direction x, y and z under different velocity profiles.

The CFD simulated added mass coefficient of the prism agrees well with the WAMIT predicted value by Fernandes & Mineiro (2008) but differs slightly from the experimental values by Fernandes & Mineiro (2007). In longitudinal and vertical direction, CFD simulated and WAMIT predicted added mass coefficients are both slightly larger than the experiment while in transverse direction, CFD and WAMIT predicted values are smaller than experiment. The

Table 7. Drag coefficients of a prism in x, y and z direction.

	Fernandes and Mineiro(2007)		Present
Rex		2.38×10^5	
Cdx	1.16		1.05
Rey		2.43×10^5	
Cdy	1.23		1.22
Rez		1.47×10^5	
Cdz	1.42		1.41

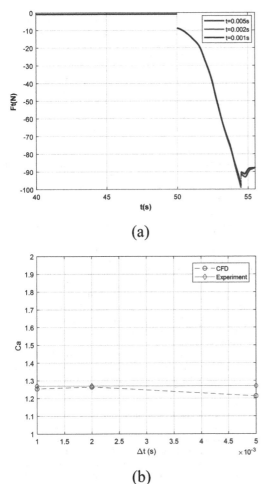

Figure 10. Comparison of simulated results due to different time resolutions, (a) variation of total force with time, (b) added mass coefficient.

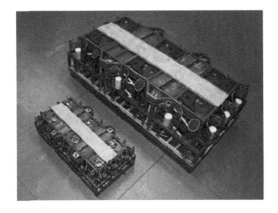

Figure 11. Model scale prism tested in Fernandes & Mineiro (2007).

Table 8. Comparison with theoretical value.

C_A	CFD	WAMIT	Experiment
Longitudinal	0.28	0.26	0.24
Transverse	0.62	0.60	0.71
Vertical	1.32	1.31	1.27

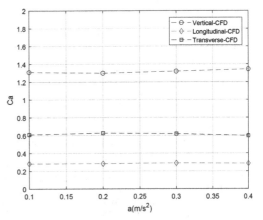

Figure 12. CFD simulated directional added mass coefficients compared with experimental data under different accelerating flows.

porosity effects will influence the added mass coefficient according to the arrangement of the components of the manifold model in the experiment.

5 CONCLUSIONS

In this paper, a CFD based constant acceleration method is proposed and applied into studying the hydrodynamic coefficients of different submerged objects such as cylinder and prism using Open-FOAM. The steps to calculate the added mass coefficient of the submerged object are introduced. The effect of using different constant accelerations is found to be very small by applying different velocity profiles at the inlet boundary. Finally, the accuracy of this methodology into predicting the drag and added mass coefficient is validated by the good agreement with corresponding analytical solutions and experimental data. It is pointed out that porosity effect is an important factor which need to be further studied in the future.

ACKNOWLEDGEMENTS

This work contributes to the Strategic Research Plan of the Centre for Marine Technology and Ocean Engineering (CENTEC), which is financed by the Portuguese Foundation for Science and Technology

(Fundação para a Ciência e Tecnologia - FCT) under contract UIDB/UIDP/00134/2020.

REFERENCES

Fernandes, A.C., & Mineiro, F.P.S. 2007. Assessment of hydrodynamic properties of bodies with complex shapes. Appl Ocean Res, 29, pp. 155–166.

Fernandes, A.C., & Mineiro, F.P.S. 2008. Corrigendum to "Assessment of hydrodynamic properties of bodies with complex shapes" [Appl. Ocean Res. 29 (2007) 155–166]. Appl Ocean Res, 30, pp. 341–344.

Gao W., Nelias D., & Liu Z., 2018. Numerical investigation of flow around one finite circular cylinder with two free ends. Ocean Engineering, Vol. 156:373–380.

Geisbert, J.S. 2007. Hydrodynamic Modeling for Autonomous Underwater Vehicles Using Computational and Semi-Empirical Methods. Master Thesis submitted to the Faculty of the Virginia Polytechnic Institute and State University.

Hoerner, S., 1965 (2nd ed.). Fluid Dynamic Drag; Practical Information on Aerodynamic Drag and Hydrodynamic Resistance. Hoerner Fluid Dynamics, Bakersfield, Calif.

Hu X.Z., & Liu S.J., 2010. Simulation and calculation of hydrodynamic forces of components of deep sea mining system. 2010 International Conference on Digital Manufacturing & Automation. December 18-20, 2010. Changsha, China.

Issa R.I., 1995. Rise of total pressure in frictional flow. AIAA Journal, Vol.33 (4):772–774.

Koo, W., & Kim, J. 2015. Simplified formulas of heave added mass coefficients at high frequency for various two-dimensional bodies in a finite water depth Int. J. Nav. Archit. Ocean Eng., 7, pp. 115–127.

Lagrange R. Delaune X., Piteau P., & Borsoi L., 2018. A new analytical approach for modeling the added mass and hydrodynamic interaction of two cylinders subjected to large motions in a potential stagnant fluid. Journal of Fluids and Structures. 77:102–114.

Lin, Z.L., & Liao, S.J. 2011. Calculation of added mass coefficients of 3D complicated underwater bodies by FMBEM. Commun Nonlinear Sci Numer Simulat,16, pp. 187–194.

Menter, F.R., Kuntz, M., & Langtry, R. 2003. Ten years of industrial experience with the SST turbulence model. In Proceedings of the fourth international symposium on turbulence, heat and mass transfer, pages 625–632, Antalya, Turkey, Begell House.

Mishra V., & Bhattacharya S., 2011. Translational Added Mass of Axisymmetric Underwater Vehicles with Forward Speed Using Computational Fluid Dynamics. Journal of Ship Research, Vol. 55, No. 3, September 2011, pp. 185–195.

Nokob, M.H., & Yeung, R.W. 2018. Added mass of thin flat plates of arbitrary shapes with possible openings. Appl Ocean Res, 79, pp. 149–159.

Raza N., Mehmood I., Rafiuddin H., & Rafique M., 2012. Numerical simulation of added mass determination of standard ellipsoids. Proceedings of 2012 9th International Bhurban Conference on Applied Sciences & Technology (IBCAST), 9-12 Jan. 2012, Islamabad, Pakistan.

Uchiyama, T., 2003. Numerical prediction of added mass and damping for a cylinder oscillating in confined incompressible gas–liquid two-phase mixture. Nuclear Engineering and Design, 222, pp. 68–78.

WAMIT, 2005. WAMIT user manual — Versions 6.2, 6.2PC, 6.2S, 6.2SPC, WAMIT. Incorporated and Massachusetts Institute of Technology. 2005

Xiang G., Wang S., & Guedes Soares C., 2020. Study on the motion of a freely falling horizontal cylinder into water using OpenFOAM. Ocean Engineering, 196, 106811

Yang J., Feng J.F., Li Y.L., Liu A., Hu J.H., & Ma Z.C., 2017. Water-exit process modeling and added-mass calculation of the submarine-launched missile. polish maritime research, Special Issue 2017 S3 (95) 2017 Vol. 24; pp. 152–164.

Yamamoto, T., Nath, J. & Slotta, L., 1974. 'Wave forces on cylinders near plane boundary.' Journal Waterway, Port, Coastal Ocean Engineering Divisions, ASCE 100.

Zhang S.N., & Ishihara T., 2018. Numerical study of hydrodynamic coefficients of multiple heave plates by large eddy simulations with volume of fluid method. Ocean Engineering.163:583–598.

Zoontjes R., Siegersma H., & Ottens H., 2009. Using CFD to Determine Heave Added Mass and Damping of a Suction Pile. Proceedings of the ASME 2009 28th International Conference on Ocean, Offshore and Arctic Engineering OMAE2009 May 31 - June 5, 2009, Honolulu, Hawaii, USA.

Ship hydrodynamics - Manoeuvring

Modelling ship manoeuvrability using Recurrent Neural Networks

J.P. Araújo, L. Moreira & C. Guedes Soares
Centre for Marine Technology and Engineering (CENTEC), Instituto Superior Técnico, Universidade de Lisboa, Lisbon, Portugal

ABSTRACT: Recurrent Neural Networks are used to learn a ship's manoeuvrability behaviour from experimental data obtained from tests with a scale model. The goal of the study is to assess the performance of ship manoeuvrability models developed using Recurrent Neural Networks trained with low amounts of noisy experimental data from zig zag and circle tests, performed according to the IMO standards. Due to the small size of the ship model, wind interference was noticeable in all recorded tests. Two models were trained, one to predict zig zag manoeuvres, and another one to predict circle manoeuvres.

1 INTRODUCTION

Neural networks have previously been used to learn ship manoeuvrability models from numerical simulation data (Moreira & Guedes Soares 2003), simulation data with added noise (Moreira & Guedes Soares 2005) and experimental data collected from full scale trials (Moreira & Guedes Soares 2012). The goal of this paper is to assess the performance of ship manoeuvrability models developed using RNNs trained with low amounts of noisy experimental data from zig zag and circle tests, performed according to the IMO standards (IMO 1993).

Over the last 20 years, Artificial Neural Networks (ANNs) have been applied successfully to a wide array of problems in naval architecture and ocean engineering. Among these problems is the modelling of ship manoeuvrability.

Mathematical models for ship manoeuvrability exist, such as the Abkowitz model (Abkowitz 1980), the MMG model (Ogawa & Kasai 1978), the Nomoto model (Nomoto et al. 1956, Nomoto and Taguchi 1957), a model for hard manoeuvres (Sutulo & Guedes Soares 2015), and others discussed in Sutulo & Guedes Soares (2011).

The parameters of these models can be estimated using system identification techniques, which typically involve performing a set of experiments (for example, the previously mentioned IMO Circle and Zig Zag tests). Several methods are available, such as the ones described in Sutulo & Guedes Soares (2014), Perera et al. (2016), Xu et al. (2018) and Wang et al. (2019).

The ship can also be treated as a black box, and modelled using an appropriate tool. ANNs have been used for parameter estimation in Luo & Zhang (2016), where the weights of the network corresponded to parameters in the Nomoto model. The network learns these parameters from samples obtained experimentally. Another approach, developed in Rajesh & Bhattacharyya (2008), uses a feedforward ANN to learn the behaviour of the non linear terms of the mathematical model, using data obtained through numerical simulation. This ANN is then used in simulations to replace the calculation of the non linear terms, as the model would demand.

Another ANN architecture which has been used to model ships are the Recurrent Neural Networks (RNNs). In a RNN, the current output depends on the past outputs, that is, the output of the network at a certain time instant is fed recurrently to the network in the following time instants. They have been used for black box identification. Different architectures (inputs, outputs, number of layers, number of neurons) have been tested.

In Hess & Faller (2000), a RNN with 56 inputs, 4 layers and 6 outputs was used to learn the ship manoeuvrability model from experimental tactical circle data obtained from full scale trials in the open sea. The inputs to the network were forces, moments, and linear and angular velocities. The outputs were the linear and angular velocities of the next time step.

In Moreira & Guedes Soares (2003), a RNN with 4 inputs, 3 layers and 2 outputs was used to learn the manoeuvrability model of a ship from numerical data obtained through simulation. The inputs were the ship speed and rudder orders, along with the sway velocity and yaw rate of the previous time step, and the outputs were the sway and yaw rate at the current time instant. A few years later, Moreira & Guedes Soares (2005) showed that the same RNNs were robust to the addition of white noise to simulation data, and in Moreira & Guedes Soares (2012), RNNs were applied to the modelling of a Catamaran using data from full-scale experimental trials.

DOI: 10.1201/9781003216599-15

More recently, deep learning techniques such as Long Short Term Memory Networks (LSTM, an improvement over the RNNs mentioned previously) have been applied to the same problem (Woo et al. 2018). Other machine learning techniques, such as Support Vector Machines, have also been applied to this problem (Luo et al. 2014, Xu et al. 2018, Xu and Guedes Soares 2020).

This paper continues the work done by Moreira & Guedes Soares (2012), considering much less data. The RNNs studied have the advantage of having very few parameters (only 72 weights to be learned, compared to the 42,101 of the LSTM network), making them very fast to train. The low amount of parameters also prevents overfitting, helping to ensure a good generalisation performance. A model structure that achieves good generalisation performance with low amounts of data is very attractive for simulation and control applications.

Section 2 contains a description of the manoeuvring tests, along with a summary of the experimental data that was collected, and the preprocessing steps performed before using it for training and testing. Section 3 describes the architecture and training procedure of the proposed RNN based model. Section 4 presents the results obtained using the model. These results are then discussed in Section 5, where they are also compared with results achieved by models being used for similar tasks under similar conditions. Finally, section 6 summarises the results.

2 DESCRIPTION OF MANOEUVRING TESTS

2.1 Experimental setup

The experiments carried out to collect the data used in this article are described in (Xu et al. 2018) and in (Hinostroza et al. 2018). The tests were carried at "Piscina Oceânica" in Oeiras, Portugal. This pool has length 50m, and breadth 20m.

The main dimensions of the model (Figure 1) are described in Table 1. The sensors onboard

Figure 1. Ship model used to carry the tests. Reproduced with permission.

Table 1. Dimensions of the ship model.

Chemical Tanker Model Length	
Length (mm)	2587.5
Breadth (mm)	426.2
Draught (mm)	102
Propeller diameter (mm)	82.2
Design speed (m/s)	0.984
Scaling coefficient	65.7

included a real time kinematic GPS, IXSEA inertial sensors (to measure surge, sway, and roll, pitch and heading angles), ultrasonic anemometer (to measure wind speed and direction) and incremental encoders (to measure rudder angles and propeller rotations per minute). The sampling time was $T_s = 0.2s$.

2.2 Available data

Four zig zag tests and two circle tests are provided (Table 3). Table 2 describes the data collected on each test.

In total, 5229 data points are provided (2348 from circle tests, and 2881 from zig zag tests). Since the forward speed reference was not available, it was replaced in the model with the recorded RPM values. These values were very noisy, and therefore they were replaced with a step signal of height equal to the average of the RPM value.

Due to the small amount of data points with both 0 RPM and 0 rudder angle, these data points (257 + 478 = 735 data points) were discarded (neither used for training or testing; it was verified that these data points occurred either at the beginning or at the end of the tests, which ensured that no causality links were broken with their removal). Along with these, other data points (such as initial transient trajectories) were discarded to ignore a behaviour which was not part of the manoeuvre.

Table 2. Data collected for each test.

Column	Description
1	Time
2	Surge (m)
3	Sway (m)
4	Heave (m)
5-7	Roll, pitch and yaw (Degrees).
8-9	u, v (Velocity, m/s)
10	Velocity of heave(m/s)
11-13	Longitude, latitude and height (DGPS)
14	Rudder angle input
15	Measured rudder angle
16	RPM of the shaft
17-18	Wind velocity and direction

Table 3. Data available for the Circle and Zig Zag tests.

Dataset name	Data points available	Rudder angle range (degrees)	RPM value	Average wind speed (m/s)	Average wind direction (degrees)
ZigZag30	748	[−30, 30]	856	1.3671	96.34
ZigZag30_1	614	[−30, 30]	873	1.1166	88.83
ZigZag20_new	565	[−20, 20]	844	1.0986	87.99
ZigZag20_for validation	954	[−20, 20]	669	1.5483	94.32
turning_20_2	992	[0, 20.356]	486	0.6480	138.02
turning_26_4	1356	[0, 26.418]	491	0.5368	149.76

Although wind conditions were not very adverse, due to the small size of the scale model it could be noticed that all tests had been affected by wind. For circle tests, the wind vector was estimated according to the method described in Moreira & Guedes Soares (2012). This estimate was calculated over a wide range of points, to assess the consistency of wind speed and direction over the course of the test. There was a notable change in wind direction for the turning_26_4 dataset, and therefore the first 250 data points (50 seconds of data), where wind direction was different from the one measured in what remained of the test, were discarded. There was also some fast variation in wind direction in the first 30 time instants (6 seconds) of the turning_20_2 dataset. These points were also neglected. The root mean square of the wind speed residual

$$V_{wind}^{RMS} = \sqrt{\frac{1}{n-1}\sum_{i=1}^{n}||v_i - V_{wind}||^2}$$

was 22.63% and 35.42% of the estimated wind velocity for data sets turning_20_2 and turning_26_4, respectively. This was above the 20% threshold mentioned in Moreira & Guedes Soares (2012) for considering wind homogeneous. Even so, the two trajectories were corrected taking into consideration the estimated wind vector, and were used for training.

For zig zags it was not possible to perform this correction, and the model was expected to learn the manoeuvre with the effect of wind. Wind conditions (both velocity and direction) were similar during the four zig zag tests, and therefore the zig zag model could be trained in the data of all four zig zag tests, and similarly tested in all four of them.

After the preprocessing steps outlined in this section, 1693 points remained for circle tests, and 1649 remained for zig zag tests.

3 NEURAL NETWORK TRAINING

The model used had four inputs

- Rudder angle $\theta(k)$
- RPM (k), replacing the forward speed reference in Moreira & Guedes Soares (2012)
- Sway speed at previous time step $v(k-1)$
- Yaw rate at previous time step $r(k-1)$

and two outputs

- Sway speed at current time step $v(k)$
- Yaw rate at current time step $r(k)$

The yaw rate was estimated from the yaw data using forward finite differences

$$r(k) \approx \frac{\psi(k+1) - \psi(k)}{T_s}$$

where T_s is the sampling time (0.2 seconds, in this case). Both the sway and yaw rate signals were smoothed using a moving average filter

$$v_{smooth}(k) = \frac{1}{5}\sum_{i=-2}^{2} v(k-i)$$

The first and last elements of v and r were kept, and the second and penultimate were smoothed according to

$$v_{smooth}(2) = \frac{1}{3}\sum_{i=-1}^{1} v(2-i)$$

$$v_{smooth}(n-1) = \frac{1}{3}\sum_{i=-1}^{1} v(n-1-i)$$

For the yaw rate signal only one pass of the filter was necessary. The sway velocity signal required four passes of the filter to smooth out the quantisation noise. Failing to smooth out this noise resulted in the network learning a model with a terrible closed-loop performance.

Connecting inputs and outputs was a single hidden layer with 10 neurons. Following the advice in LeCun et al. (1998), the activation function used was tanh.

$$\tanh(x) = \frac{e^{2x} - 1}{e^{2x} + 1}$$

Due to the dependence of the network output on its previous outputs, RNNs need to be trained in a different way than feedforward neural networks. A possible approach at training is to unfold the network and, at each training iteration, feed it with the experimental value of sway and yaw rate, instead of the network prediction. This is called open loop training, and allows for a quick initialisation of the network weights, which can then be fine-tuned with closed loop training (that is, we only give the network the initial conditions, and calculate our current output using the previous outputs of the model).

When training in open loop, the network is fed with the actual past values of sway and yaw rate, it is not mandatory to follow a specific order when feeding the samples for training, and so samples from various tests can be mixed. This helps to avoid overfitting to a specific test. When training in closed loop, several consecutive points of experimental data (both control action and expected output) have to be fed to the network, and it is not possible to concatenate several different tests (this would lead to discontinuities between them, which the network would try to model). This requires the network to be trained in closed loop for each test at a time, which may lead to overfitting a specific test. In order to avoid this, the networks in this article were trained in open loop, but kept or discarded based on their closed loop performance in the test data. Closed loop performance was defined as the sum of network performance on the individual data sets. The training procedure was as follows

1. Prepare the input and output data for each model.
2. Train 10 networks in open loop. Evaluate them based on their closed loop performance.
3. Train 20 additional networks. If any of the new networks performs better than the initial 10, discard the worst initial network, and keep the new one.

This procedure was used to ensure robustness to the randomness of the training (random initial weights). The 10 best networks were kept. The purpose behind storing 10 networks was to assess the effect of using an average of several good models instead of using only the best model.

It can be seen in Table 3 that the wind conditions during the zig zag tests were very similar, but different from the wind conditions of circles. Due to this difference in wind conditions, it did not make sense to train a model on zig zag data and validate it on circle data, or vice versa. Two separate models were trained, one for each type of test. The training data points were all concatenated into two arrays, one for zig zag tests and another one for circle tests. Each of these two arrays was then split according to the following proportions

- 80% of the data points used for training,
- 10% of the data points used for validation,
- 10% of the data points used for testing

Input and output values were scaled to fit the interval [-0.8, 0.8], to avoid the activation function saturation.

The training algorithm chosen was Bayesian Regularization (Foresee & Hagan 1997). It was chosen due to its ability to handle small and noisy data sets. In this algorithm, we wish to minimize a loss function of the form

$$L(x) = \alpha \sum_i (y_i - \hat{y}(x_i))^2 + \beta \sum_j w_j^2$$

which is a weighted sum of the sum of squared errors $(y_i - \hat{y}(x_i))^2$ and the sum of the square of the value of the network weights w_j. The values α and β control how much importance we give to each quantity. If $\beta \neq 0$, there will be a trend to choose simpler models, which helps to prevent overfitting. The algorithm takes turns at minimising $L(x)$ (using the Levenberg-Marquardt algorithm) and updating α and β, until convergence is reached.

Training was done in MATLAB. By default, this algorithm does not use a validation data set. However, after training several models, it was noticed that the error in the test set achieved a minimum and then degraded significantly, while residual training performance gains were being obtained. Therefore, a validation data set was configured in order to stop the training after 6 consecutive iterations of validation set performance degrading.

Only 1045 seconds of experimental data were available, and out of these 377 seconds had to be discarded (they corresponded to time intervals which were not part of the manoeuvre, had harsh wind conditions, were clearly outliers, etc.). In the end, 668 seconds of data remained for training and testing. Out of these, 338 seconds were of circle tests, and the remaining 330 seconds were of zig zag tests. For comparison, Moreira & Guedes Soares (2012) used 5704 seconds of circle data and 1713 seconds of zig zag data to train similar models.

4 RESULTS

4.1 Zig Zag

Figures 2 and 3 show the predicted and experimental sway velocity values and yaw rates for data set ZigZag30. It is worth noticing the discontinuities in the sway velocity values. These occur at the time instants when the rudder angle changes, and are not surprising if we consider that neural networks approximate continuous functions. A variation of 60° can be considered as a discontinuity, and therefore it is reasonable to expect jumps in the predicted variables. It is worth noticing, however, that the network has managed to cope very well with these discontinuities.

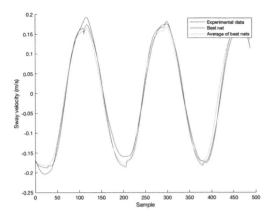

Figure 2. Experimental and predicted sway velocity for data set ZigZag30.

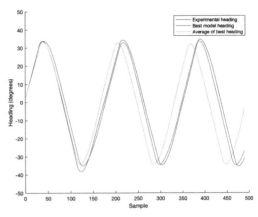

Figure 4. Experimental and predicted heading for data set ZigZag30.

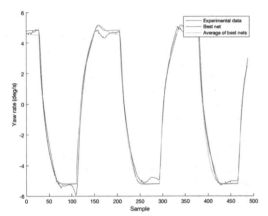

Figure 3. Experimental and predicted yaw rate for data set ZigZag30.

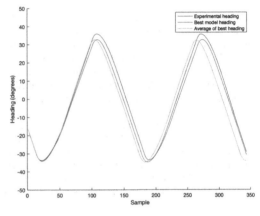

Figure 5. Experimental and predicted heading for data set ZigZag30_1.

The parameter used to assess the model error in zig zag tests is the average heading error, that is, the average of the heading errors at each time sample. The relative errors were obtained by normalizing the absolute error with the maximum value of rudder deflection (30° or 20°, depending on the test). Figures 4 to 7 show the evolution of experimental and predicted heading along all of the four the tests. Table 4 summarises the absolute and relative errors for each test.

4.2 Circle

For assessing the performance of the model in circle tests, the tactical diameter and the final position of the ship are of interest. The tactical diameter is defined as the distance between two points whose heading differs by 180°. Several of these diameters were sampled from the experimental data and their average computed

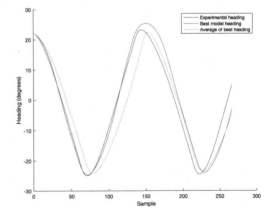

Figure 6. Experimental and predicted heading for data set ZigZag20_new.

135

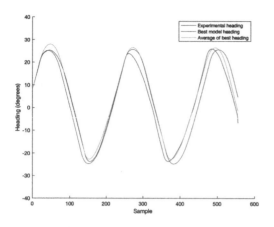
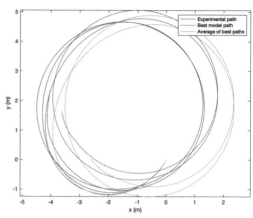

Figure 7. Experimental and predicted heading for data set ZigZag20_for validation.

Figure 8. Experimental and predicted trajectory for data set turning_20_2.

to obtain the estimate of the real tactical diameter. The same was done to the trajectories obtained from the models, in order to obtain the predicted tactical diameter. The relative error in x and y position is the difference between the real and modelled values, divided by the real tactical diameter. These values are presented in Table 5, and the trajectories (real and predicted) are shown in Figures 8 and 9.

Only two data sets were available, with the only difference between them being the rudder angle. Since neural networks are expected to be good interpolators, it is possible to assess if the network generalizes well by giving as input rudder angles in between 20° and 26°. Since no data is available, it is not possible to quantify the error of these simulations. However, a qualitative assessment can be done based on the simulated tactical diameters. Figure 10 shows the simulated trajectories for rudder angles of 20°, 22°, 24° and 26°. The trajectories for angles 22 and 24 fall in between the trajectories for angles 20 and 26, as would be expected. The tactical diameters are 5.35 and 5.21 meters, respectively for rudder angles 22° and 24°, which is within the [5.01, 5.82] range established by the manoeuvres with rudder angle 20° and 26°. The trajectory for 24° seems to have a constant diameter. Regarding the trajectory for 22°, the diameter varies along the manoeuvre.

Table 4. Maximum absolute and relative error of the heading predictions.

Dataset name	Average heading error (°) Best model	Average heading error (°) Average of models	Associated relative heading error (%) Best model	Associated relative heading error (%) Average of models
ZigZag30	3.03	10.59	10.1	35.29
ZigZag30_1	2.49	5.09	8.3	16.98
ZigZag20_new	2.84	4.63	14.21	23.17
ZigZag20_for validation	3.88	1.86	19.42	9.32

Table 5. Tactical diameter and final circle position errors.

	Dataset name	Experimental value (m)	Best simulated value (m)	Error (%)	Average simulated value (m)	Error (%)
Diameter	turning_20_2	5.70	5.66	0.69	5.82	2.05
	turning_26_4	5.04	5.03	0.25	5.01	0.60
Final x	turning_20_2	-4.03	-3.63	7.17	-2.62	24.73
	turning_26_4	-1.08	-2.40	26.22	-1.57	9.70
Final y	turning_20_2	2.34	1.63	12.40	0.03	40.43
	turning_26_4	4.41	4.86	9.00	4.98	11.32

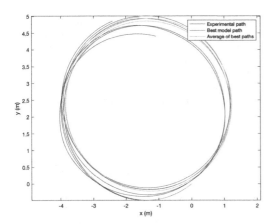

Figure 9. Experimental and predicted trajectory for data set turning_26_4.

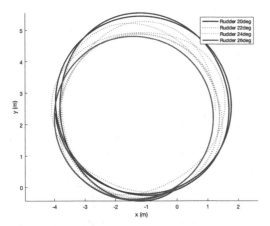

Figure 10. Simulated trajectories for different rudder angles. The full lines show the trajectories with rudder angles for which experimental data was available. The dotted lines show the manoeuvres simulated using the network for rudder angles for which no experimental data was available.

5 DISCUSSION OF THE RESULTS

Regarding the Zig Zag model, the network has managed to learn the low frequency component of the sway and yaw rate signals. For sway predictions, the greatest problem are the discontinuities in the rudder angle, which carry on to the sway velocity. Using the average of several networks helps to smooth out these discontinuities, although they are never completely smoothed out. This does not pose a problem for the yaw rate prediction. Heading is obtained by integrating the yaw rate. The heading curves shown in Figures 4 to 7 were obtained by simulating directly the manoeuvre, that is, the counter-rudder order was given when the simulated heading reached the target value. Using the best model generally gives lower average heading errors than when using the average of several models. The average value of the heading error when using the best model is around 3°. In relative terms, this error is always above the 7% obtained in Moreira & Guedes Soares (2012). Even so, it is clear that the network learned the behaviour associated with the Zig Zag manoeuvre. What it did not learn accurately were the specific parameters of the ship, such as overshoot value. Therefore, the conclusion is that to obtain a Zig Zag manoeuvre simulator this amount of data suffices. In order to obtain a simulator of the model, more data is required.

For the Circle model, the maximum relative error of the tactical diameter is 2%, when considering the average of 10 networks as our prediction. Considering only the best network, the maximum relative error is 0.7%, a value comparable to the 0.5% obtained in Luo et al. (2014). This indicates that, even with low amounts of data, neural networks are able to learn the tactical diameter with excellent accuracy. The relative errors in position are larger, sometimes being as high as 26%. However, the absolute errors are of 1 meter at most. The question that remains is whether this error continues to be 1 meter in full scale trials (with tactical diameters of 200 meters, for example), or if it scales proportionally. The model was also assessed in terms of its ability to simulate Circle trajectories with rudder angles that were not seen in the training set. For both trajectories, the average tactical diameter was within the interval it would be expected to be. However, the tactical diameter of one of the trajectories (rudder angle at 22°) oscillates along the manoeuvre, as if the rudder angle was changing. This reduces the trust in the simulator, but could be fixed by training the network with more data, and more rudder angles.

The errors when considering the average of several networks tend to be larger than when considering only the best network. However, it should be noted that all networks were trained in the same training data. Using the average of different networks trained on different partitions of the full data set might yield better results when averaging several network outputs. The only conclusion that can be drawn from this paper is that using the average of several models trained on the same data is not guaranteed to bring any improvement.

This last paragraph hints at the interest of applying k-fold cross validation, which consists in splitting the full data set into k parts, and then training k different models using as training data the k different combinations of $k - 1$ parts. The output of these k models can then be combined into a final output, for example.

Another venue which has not been studied so far is the sensitivity analysis to the number of hidden neurons of this RNN architecture. 10 hidden neurons have been shown to suffice so far, but a study such as the one performed in (Rajesh & Bhattacharyya

2008) would allow an assessment of the robustness of this architecture, and would also reveal whether it is possible to keep the same results with simpler architectures. The Bayesian Regularization algorithm can also be exploited for this, as one of its outputs is the effective number of parameters. If two models have similar performance and the same number of effective parameters after training with Bayesian Regularization, we can discard the model architecture with more trainable parameters and keep the simpler one.

Finally, over the last years, the consensus in the machine learning community has been that the best activation function to use is the Rectified Linear Unit (ReLU)

$$h(x) = \max(0, x)$$

It would also be interesting to study how using it (instead of tanh) affects the performance of the models.

6 CONCLUSIONS

The RNN architecture studied has been shown to perform satisfactorily when trained with low amounts of data, even if partially corrupted by noise.

For zig zag manoeuvres, the learned model was good enough to simulate the manoeuvre, although with a relative error which in some cases was almost the double of the relative error obtained in previous works. This indicates that 330 seconds of zig zag test data are not enough to train a good model, and therefore more zig zag test data should be collected before training a model.

For circle manoeuvres, the simulator achieves low error values on the training and test data. The errors in the tactical diameter are comparable with error values obtained in previous works. Only 338 seconds of circle test data were available. This amount of circle test data sufficed to train a circle model, while also being much less than the 5704 seconds of data used in Moreira & Guedes Soares (2012). Therefore, it can be concluded that a short amount of circle test data is enough to train a good circle model. The model generalised well for some rudder angles which interpolated the rudder angles seen in the training data. Although the performance of the model was reasonable, it would clearly benefit from additional training data in some of these rudder angles (namely 22°).

ACKNOWLEDGMENTS

This work was performed within the Strategic Research Plan of the Centre for Marine Technology and Ocean Engineering (CENTEC), which is financed by Portuguese Foundation for Science and Technology (Fundação para a Ciência e Tecnologia - FCT) under contract UIDB/UIDP/00134/2020. The first author would like to thank Haitong Xu for the many conversations and insights provided about ship manoeuvring modelling and for providing the experimental data used in this paper.

REFERENCES

Abkowitz, M. A. (1980). Measurement of hydrodynamic characteristics from ship maneuvring trials by system identification. *SNAME Transactions 88*, 283–318.

Foresee, F. D. & M. T. Hagan (1997). Gauss-newton approximation to Bayesian learning. In *Proceedings of the International Joint Conference on Neural Networks*.

Hess, D. & W. Faller (2000). Simulation of ship maneuvers using recursive neural networks. In *Proceedings of 23rd symposium on naval hydrodynamics*, pp. 17–22.

Hinostroza, M., H. Xu, & C. Guedes Soares (2018). Path-planning and path-following control system for autonomous surface vessel. In C. Guedes Soares and A. P. Teixeira (Eds.), *Maritime Transportation and Harvesting of Sea Resources*. Taylor & Francis Group; pp. 991–998.

IMO (1993). Interim standards for ship manoeuvrability. *IMO Resolution A.751 (18)*.

LeCun, Y., L. Bottou, G. Orr, & K. Müller (1998). *Neural Networks: Tricks of the Trade* (First ed.)., Chapter Efficient BackProp. Springer.

Luo, W., L. Moreira, & C. Guedes Soares (2014). Manoeuvring simulation of catamaran by using implicit models based on support vector machines. *Ocean Engineering 82*, 150–159.

Luo, W. & Z. Zhang (2016). Modeling of ship maneuvering motion using neural networks. *Journal of Marine Science and Application 15*(4), 426–432.

Moreira, L. & C. Guedes Soares (2003). Dynamic model of manoeuvrability using recursive neural networks. *Ocean Engineering 30*(13), 1669–1697.

Moreira, L. & C. Guedes Soares (2005). Analysis of recursive neural networks performance trained with noisy manoeuvring data. In C. G. Soares, Y. Garbatov, and N. Fonseca (Eds.), *Maritime Transportation and Exploitation of Ocean and Coastal Resources*. Taylor & Francis Group; pp. 733–744.

Moreira, L. & C. Guedes Soares (2012). Recursive neural network model of catamaran manoeuvring. *The International Journal of Maritime Engineering RINA, 154*, A–121 – A–130.

Nomoto, K. & K. Taguchi (1957). On steering qualities of ships (2). *Journal of Zosen Kiokai 1957*(101), 57–66.

Nomoto, K., K. Taguchi, K. Honda, & S. Hirano (1956). On the steering qualities of ships. *Journal of Zosen Kiokai 1956*(99), 75–82.

Ogawa, A. & H. Kasai (1978). On the mathematical model of manoeuvring motion of ships. *International Shipbuilding Progress 25*(292), 306–319.

Perera, L. P., P. Oliveira, & C. Guedes Soares (2016). System identification of vessel steering with unstructured uncertainties by persistent excitation maneuvers. *IEEE Journal of Oceanic Engineering 41*(3), 515–528.

Rajesh, G. & S. Bhattacharyya (2008). System identification for nonlinear maneuvering of large tankers using artificial neural network. *Applied Ocean Research 30*(4), 256–263.

Sutulo, S. & C. Guedes Soares (2011). Mathematical models for simulation of manoeuvring performance of ships. In C. Guedes Soares, Y. Garbatov, N. Fonseca, and A. P. Teixeira (Eds.), *Marine Technology and Engineering*. Taylor & Francis Group; pp. 661–698.

Sutulo, S. & C. Guedes Soares (2014). An algorithm for offline identification of ship manoeuvring mathematical models after free-running tests. *Ocean Engineering 79*, 10–25.

Sutulo, S. & C. Guedes Soares (2015). Development of a core mathematical model for arbitrary manoeuvres of a shuttle tanker. *Applied Ocean Research. 51*, 293–308.

Wang, Z., Z. Zou, & C. Guedes Soares (2019). Identification of ship manoeuvring motion based on nu-support vector machine. *Ocean Engineering 183*, 270–281.

Woo, J., J. Park, C. Yu, & N. Kim (2018). Dynamic model identification of unmanned surface vehicles using deep learning network. *Applied Ocean Research 78*, 123–133.

Xu, H. & C. Guedes Soares (2020). Manoeuvring modelling of a containership in shallow water based on optimal truncated nonlinear kernel-based least square support vector machine and quantum-inspired evolutionary algorithm. *Ocean Engineering 195*, 106676.

Xu, H., V. Hassani, M. A. Hinostroza, & C. Guedes Soares (2018). Real-time parameter estimation of nonlinear vessel steering model using support vector machine. In *Proceedings of the 37th International Conference on Ocean, Offshore and Arctic Engineering (OMAE 2018)*, Madrid, Spain. Paper OMAE2018-78234.

Xu, H., M. A. Hinostroza, & C. Guedes Soares (2018). Estimation of hydrodynamic coefficients of a nonlinear manoeuvring mathematical model with free-running ship model tests. *International Journal of Maritime Engineering (RINA Transactions Part A) 160*(A3), A–213–A–215.

The variation in modal responses of a slamming-prone vessel during manoeuvres in open water

J.C. Bossau, C.M. van Zijl & A. Bekker
Sound and Vibration Research Group, Department of Mechanical and Mechatronic Engineering, Stellenbosch University, South Africa

ABSTRACT: Slamming and whipping responses are investigated through full-scale measurements on a slamming-prone vessel. Purposely-executed manoeuvres were performed to enable a systematic investigation of slamming and whipping, whereby the relative heading and vessel speed was altered with respect to consistent wave states. An accelerometer array throughout the ship hull was used to determine the wave slamming impact site, rigid body motion and resulting hull flexure from wave-induced vibration. The operational modal analysis technique confirmed that the first bending mode dominates the high-frequency response of the hull when the ship encounters following waves during stationary or low-speed operations. Head-on wave encounters result in significant rigid body motion, but do not elicit global bending of the ship structure.

1 INTRODUCTION

Wave-induced vibration - springing and whipping - affect ship safety (Mao et al. 2010). Springing is defined as continual hull girder vibration resulting from resonant excitation by waves. In this case the wave encounter frequency (or its harmonics) match the fundamental bending mode of the ship hull girders. Whipping is the oscillatory response that follows impulsive impacts from wave slamming, green water or under-water blasts (Dessi 2014). Whipping is associated with the ringing of the natural frequencies of the global hull structure, which will die out depending on the structural damping inherent to the hull. The operational fatigue contribution of whipping can be significant (30 to 40%) (Mao et al. 2010). Whipping responses of flexible ship structures may be modelled by expressing the total vibration response as the superposition of structural modes. Each mode is characterised by four parameters, namely a natural frequency, damping ratio, mode shape and generalised mass. Natural frequencies describe the dominant rates of oscillation, while damping ratios are related to the magnitude and duration of the whipping response. Mode shapes provide the relative motion between different locations on the structure. In order to predict the severity of ship vibrations, accurate estimates of modal parameters, especially damping, are required (Jensen 2001). The present investigation focusses on whipping responses of the South African polar supply and research vessel, SA Agulhas II (SAAII). Her ice-going hull design features large bow flare angles, with the anticipated implication of bow slamming in rough seas. However, the ship is designed with a flat, extended, transom which causes stern slamming. Stern slamming is problematic on the SAAII as it causes extensive whipping during stationary operations in low sea states in waves $\leq$ 1m, and inhibits oceanographic work (Omer & Bekker 2016). Paramount, cracks have occurred during the first 5 years of her operational life at the midship transition between the fore-deck and superstructure. Soal (Soal 2014) investigated acceleration measurements on the vessel and showed that vibration in the stern and bow reach levels where damage is possible and probable (BS ISO 20283-2 2008), although the standard is not expressly purposed to assess the transient responses associated with slamming and whipping. Omer & Bekker (2016) showed that whipping responses last for as long as 40 seconds on the SAAII and that bow- and stern slamming events produce responses which are associated with the first and second bending modes of the hull structure. The effect of whipping on the 30 year service life of the SAAII is yet unquantified.

The present investigation aims to compare the respective magnitudes of whipping responses that arise from clearly segregated bow and stern slamming on the SAAII. This would serve to inform if stern slamming is likely to accelerate fatigue damage of the hull structure significantly, thereby limiting the expected service life of her original design intent. Sequences of vessel manoeuvres were performed with the instrumented ship on full scale, whereby the incident wave angle and encounter frequency were respectively adjusted by systematically re-orientating the ship and changing the vessel speed with respect to the present wave state. This allows clear identification of wave

DOI: 10.1201/9781003216599-16

slamming sites on the ship hull, from which ship responses to bow slamming and stern slamming could be sensibly segregated using measurements from an accelerometer array. Operational modal analysis techniques are used to identify the fundamental vertical bending modes (VBM) of the hull, along with their associated natural frequencies, mode shapes and damping ratios and excitation magnitude.

2 METHOD

2.1 *Vessel and instrumentation*

The SAAII spearheads the logistical support and oceanographic research of the South African National Antarctic Programme. The vessel is purposed for ice-going voyages to Antarctica, but spends $\geq 85\%$ of her operations in open water in oceanographic voyages along the South African coast and the stormy Southern Ocean (Babanin et al. 2019). The ship is instrumented with seven pairs of accelerometers throughout her hull structure (see Figure 1). These sensors measure vertical acceleration, thereby serving multiple purposes including vertical the determination of vertical rigid body motion, pitch, wave impact site and hull flexure. A limitation includes that she is not instrumented with strain gauges to enable the direct measurement of strain cycles (Mao et al. 2010).

2.2 *Manoeuvres*

The research mandate of the South African Southern oCean seAsonal Experiment (SCALE) enabled the execution of two sequences of open water manoeuvres, for the systematic investigation of slamming and whipping responses. The first sequence of *stationary manoeuvres* studied the effect of a consistent wave state on the ship when she operates on station. The relative heading of the stationary vessel was systematically adjusted as demonstrated in Figure 2, where the red arrows labelled A to E indicate the waves approaching the vessel at 0°, 315°, 90°, 135° and 180° respectively. As the ship hull is symmetric

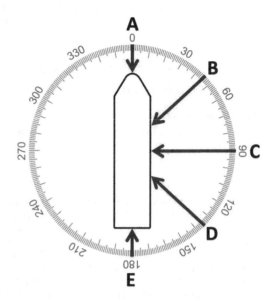

Figure 2. Relative heading with waves approaching the vessel from (A)0°, (B)45°, (C)90°, (D)135° and (E)180°.

relative headings between 180° and 360° are classified with responses between 0° and 180° to simplify reporting where this is sensible. The ship was maintained on station for 15 minutes at each heading. The second sequence entailed *manoeuvres at speed*. The vessel was orientated to voyage in head seas with waves approaching at 0°. After the ship reached the desired test speed of 3 kn, 6 kn or 9 kn respectively constant operations were sustained for 15 minutes. Constant speed manoeuvres were repeated for the relative headings of 45°, 225° and 180°.

2.3 *Slamming detection*

Figure 3(a) presents a measurement from a typical slamming impulse, followed by transient oscillations of whipping. Signal processing techniques are employed to extract the peak acceleration amplitude associated with the time of a wave impact.

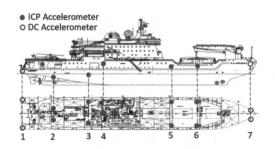

Figure 1. Layout of acceleration sensors for measurements in the vertical direction. 1 - Steering gear, 2 - Stern thruster, 3 - Engine store, 4 - Ceiling, 5 - Cargo hold aft, 6 - Cargo hold front, 7 - Bow.

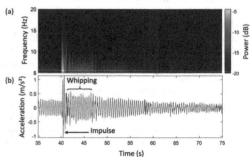

Figure 3. (a) A sample of an acceleration time signal of slamming and whipping with the (b) associated spectrogram.

A spectrogram, Figure 3(b), presents combined time and frequency information of the signal. Wave slamming results in broadband excitation and excites a range of frequencies, which appear as a vertical line at the time of impact (Omer and Bekker 2016). The thickness of line features depend on the frequency resolution of the spectrogram. The whipping response is indicated by the frequency which follows the slamming impulse.

$$F(\omega,\tau) = \int_{-\infty}^{\infty} f(t)\psi^*(t-\tau)e^{-j\omega t} dt \quad (1)$$

The frequency domain transformation is performed using the short-time Fourier transform (STFT, Eq. 1). It applies a window function $\psi(t)$ at time τ, and computes the Fourier transform of the windowed signal. The parameters ω and τ control the modulation and translation of the window function respectively (Kiymik et al. 2005). To achieve a good time resolution, frequency resolution is sacrificed due to the fixed time window length (Loughlin et al. 1992). Bekker & Van Zijl (2019) explored the ability of the Morlet wavelet to detect striated slamming features and present the procedure and background as a stepwise discussion. Similarly, slamming produces lines in Morlet scalograms, which allow for slamming detection with the drawback of computational expense. Line detection is served by the conversion of spectrograms to black and white images and subsequent use of the Hough transform to detect the coordinates of vertical lines (Duda and Hart 1972) which are mapped back to the time domain.

2.4 Operational modal analysis

Operational modal analysis (OMA) provides the means to extract modal parameters of a linear, time-invariant lumped-parameter system using output measurements only (Brincker and Ventura 2015). Assuming that the inputs are stochastic white noise quantities, modal parameters may be identified from the output correlation matrix in the time domain and output power spectral density (PSD) matrix in the frequency domain. The output correlation matrix, $R_{yy}(\tau)$ is defined as (Bendat and Piersol 1980):

$$R_{yy}(\tau) = \mathbf{E}[y(t-\tau)y(t)^T] \quad (2)$$

Where **E** is the expected value operator and $y(t)$ is the output vector. The output spectral density matrix, $G_{yy}(f)$ is defined as the Fourier transform of the output correlation matrix. In this paper, two OMA identification techniques are used. Frequency domain decomposition (FDD) is a simple OMA algorithm which estimates natural frequencies and mode shapes directly from singular values of the output PSD matrix. Since output PSDs are related to vibration energy, response spectra may further be used to quantify the magnitude of modal responses. The Multiple-input Ibrahim Time Domain (MITD) technique identifies modal parameters from output correlation functions. This includes accurate damping estimates which are important for fatigue and extreme loading analysis (ISSC Committee II.2).

2.4.1 Frequency domain decomposition (FDD)
If the modal coordinates are uncorrelated, then the PSD matrix is diagonal.

$$G_{yy}(f) = \phi G_{qq}(f)\phi^T = USU^T \quad (3)$$

Therefore, if the mode shapes are orthogonal, Eq. (3) results in a singular value decomposition (SVD) of the vibration response PSD matrix. The matrix U consists of singular vectors and the diagonal matrix S consists of singular values. The singular values of the spectral density matrix can be used to generate a plot of the auto spectral densities of the modal coordinates. Peaks in the first singular value are used to identify modal frequencies. The corresponding mode shape is acquired from the first singular vector in U (Brincker et al. 2007).

2.4.2 Multiple-input Ibrahim Time Domain (MITD)
Assuming white noise excitation and wide-sense stationary conditions, the output correlation matrix is related to modal properties according to Eq. (4) (Brincker and Ventura 2015):

$$R_{yy}(\tau) = \Phi e^{\Lambda t}\Gamma \quad (4)$$

Where $\Phi \in \mathbf{C}^{l \times n_m}$ is the mode shape matrix. $\Lambda \in \mathbf{C}^{n_m \times n_m}$ is the diagonal pole matrix and $\Gamma \in \mathbf{C}^{n_m \times l}$ is modal participation matrix. The elements of the pole matrix are related to the natural frequencies and damping ratios of individual modes (Maia and Silva 1997). The MITD technique extracts modal parameters from the output correlation matrix according to the steps outlined in Figure 4. Further details on the MITD technique are well documented in classical texts (Allemang and Brown 1987, Maia and Silva 1997). The results of the MITD algorithm is multiple identifications of poles and mode shapes at increasing model orders. This includes both physical and spurious poles. In theory, physical poles will be identified consistently with increasing model order and will satisfy stabilisation criteria. In this context, stable means that modal parameter estimates at some model order, k, will be similar to an estimate from the previous model order, $k-1$, within some tolerance:

$$\frac{|f_k - f_{k-1}|}{|f_k|} \leq \delta f, \frac{|\zeta_k - \zeta_{k-1}|}{|\zeta_k|} \leq \delta \zeta \text{ and}$$

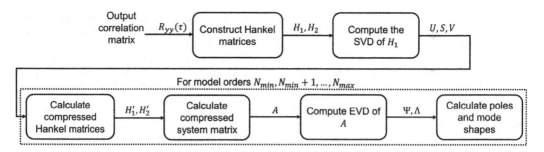

Figure 4. Steps of the MITD OMA algorithm. Step 1: Hankel matrices, $H_0(\tau)$ and $H_1(\tau)$, are formed from the output correlation matrix, where $H_1(\tau) = H_0(\tau + \Delta\tau)$. Step 2: Calculate the SVD of H_0. This involves the solution of a regression problem that fits modal parameter matrices to the output correlation matrix according to Eq. 4. As with all regression problems, *a priori* knowledge of the model order, N of data is required. In most practical applications, the model order is unknown and common practise is to repeat the identification (Step 3) for multiple model orders ranging between some minimum and maximum model order, $N = N_{min}, ..., N_{max}$). In Step 4, compressed Hankel matrices are formed by post-multiplying H_0 and H_1 with the first N columns of the left singular vector of the SVD. Step 5: The system matrix, A is calculated from the compressed Hankel matrices. Step 6: Eigen value decomposition (EVD) of the system matrix is used to determine poles and mode shapes (Step 7).

$$MAC(\Phi_k, \Phi_{k-1}) \geq M \quad (5)$$

The MAC (Φ_i, Φ_j) function is a measure of similarity between two or more mode shapes and is defined as follows (Maia and Silva 1997):

$$MAC(\Phi_i, \Phi_j) = \frac{\left(|\Phi_i|^T|\Phi_j|\right)^2}{\left(|\Phi_i|^T|\Phi_i|\right)\left(|\Phi_j|^T|\Phi_j|\right)} \quad (6)$$

A high MAC value indicates high similarity whereas a low MAC value indicates low similarity. A useful tool to discriminate between physical and spurious poles is a stabilisation diagram where modal parameters, such as natural frequency, are plotted versus increasing model order.

3 RESULTS

3.1 Case studies and basic analysis

Figure 5 presents root-mean-square (r.m.s) of acceleration measured at different locations on the hull during stationary manoeuvres (0 knots) and for the manoeuvres at speed (3,6 and 9 knots). Wave state parameters (i.e. wave period, significant wave height and wavelength) recorded during the manoeuvres are included in this figure. Further, the relative headings are indicated for the stationary manoeuvres (0°, 315°, 90°, 135° and 180°) and manoeuvres at speed (0°, 315°, 135° and 180°). The grey bar represents the total acceleration r.m.s. This includes both low-frequency rigid body motion and flexural vibration between 0 and 8Hz. The red bar represents the contribution of flexural motion (≥1 Hz) to the total r.m.s acceleration, while the blue bar represents the r.m.s value associated with VBM1 at 2.25Hz. Overall consideration of the ship manoeuvres show that the highest total r.m.s level occurs when the vessel voyages into head seas (0 degrees relative heading) at 9 knots (930mm/s^2). For this case, flexure contributes only about 22 % of total vibration r.m.s. acceleration. For the stationary manoeuvres, vibration r.m.s generally increases as relative heading changes from 0° (head seas) to stern-quartering and following seas (135° and 180°). The contribution of flexure concurrently increases with a contribution of 10 % at a relative heading of 0° to 88% at a relative heading of 180°.

3.2 FDD

The measurement results are investigated in the frequency domain by calculating the PSDs of the accelerometer channels, for each of the relative headings considered. Figure 4 presents the PSDs for DC sensors at the bow and stern for stationary manoeuvres in the frequency range of 0 to 32Hz. The first significant peak at 0.13Hz (close to the encounter frequency of the wave conditions, 0.11 to 0.13Hz), indicates that a significant amount of rigid body motion is present in the vessel motion. The peaks around 2.25Hz and 4.09Hz are associated with the first and second VBM as confirmed in OMA by (Soal 2014) and (Van Zijl 2020). Earlier investigation (Omer and Bekker 2016)determined that wave slamming on the SAAII excites the first two bending modes, as such the signals are band-pass filtered and further analysis considers the frequency range from 1 to 9Hz. An FDD modal analysis was conducted for two open water manoeuvre sequences, performed on the same date, where both the speed at which the vessel was travelling and the orientation with respect to the direction of waves approaching the vessel was adjusted. For the FDD analysis, a PSD matrix is calculated for a sample frequency of 64Hz. The singular value decomposition (SVD) is computed for each

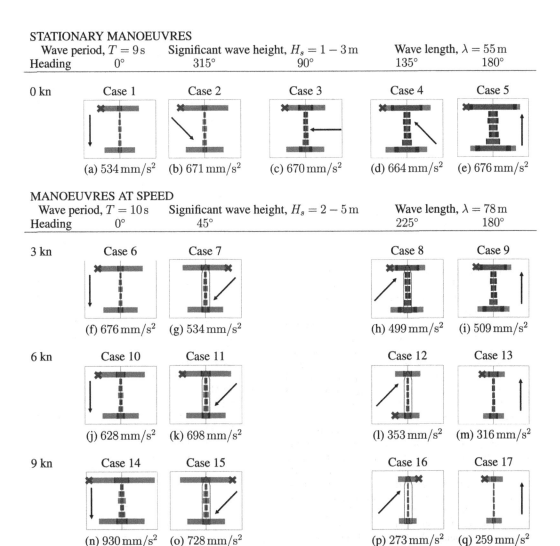

Figure 5. A summary of the operational case studies. Grey bars - overall vertical r.m.s. acceleration level, Red bar - flexural vibration (≥ 1Hz), Blue bar - Contribution of VBM1 at 2.25Hz. X indicates the maximum r.m.s. location across the ship structure, reported alongside the sub-figure headings.

frequency line. The mode shapes of the first two modes are extracted from the peaks in the first singular value and represented in Figure 5. The shaft frequency may cause harmonic contamination of the results. The shaft speed varies up to 140 rpm (and often operates at this speed, 2.33Hz), which may influence the VBM1. The two modes are excited well for the first set of singular values, s_1 for all of the relative headings considered. Therefore, only the first set of singular values are considered.

3.3 MITD

Output correlation matrices with 512 positive time lags were calculated for the different case studies

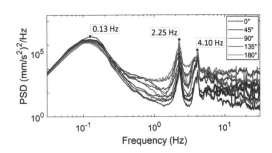

Figure 6. PSDs of stationary manoeuvre with 2048-point Hanning window, 50% overlap, frequency resolution of 0.313Hz.

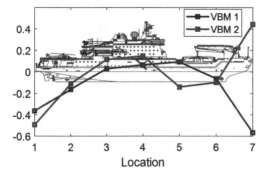

Figure 7. Mode shapes of VBM1 at 2.25Hz (blue) and VBM2 at 4.09Hz (green).

Table 1. Modal frequency f_n and damping ζ_n for the first two VBM of the SAAII during manoeuvre tests.

STATIONARY MANOEUVRES

	Mode	0°	45°	90°	135°	180°
0 kn	VBM1					
	f_n [Hz]	2.26	2.27	2.26	2.25	2.24
	ζ_n[%]	0.860	0.519	0.657	0.845	0.784
	VBM2					
	f_n [Hz]	4.09	4.10	4.09	4.01	4.09
	ζ_n[%]	0.660	0.482	1.39	1.01	1.38

MANOEUVRES AT SPEED

	Mode	0°	45°	90°	135°	180°
3 kn	VBM1					
	f_n [Hz]	2.26	2.26		2.26	2.26
	ζ[%]	0.379	0.827		0.497	0.492
	VBM2					
	f_n [Hz]	4.08	4.09		4.08	4.08
	ζ_n[%]	0.841	0.544		0.394	0876
6 kn	VBM1					
	f_n [Hz]	2.25	2.25		2.25	2.25
	ζ_n[%]	0.829	0.537		0.341	0.300
	VBM2					
	f_n[%]	4.07	4.07		4.08	4.09
	ζ_n[%]	0.710	0.402		0.690	1.12
9 kn	VBM1					
	f_n [Hz]	2.22	2.22		2.23	2.23
	ζ_n[%]	0.812	0.657		0.771	0.512
	VBM2					
	f_n [Hz]	4.00	4.01		4.02	4.04
	ζ_n[%]	1.34	0.769		0.481	1.67

using the Welch method (Brandt 2011). To reduce bias errors, the first four samples and noise "tail" of the correlation functions were discarded before modal parameters were estimated using the MITD technique. Model orders ranging from 2 to 250 were used and "stable" pole estimates corresponding to the first and second VBM were manually selected for each case. An example of a stabilisation diagram with mode indicator function (MIF) overlaid is presented in Figure 8. Only stable poles are shown (with $\delta f = 0.01$, $\delta \zeta = 0.1$ and $M = 0.98$, refer Eq.5 and estimates corresponding to the first and second VBM are highlighted. Table 2 presents the natural frequencies and damping ratios as determined from the MITD analysis. The variation in natural frequency and damping are presented in Figure 9 and Figure 10. Generally, natural frequency decreases with increasing speed. Variation in natural frequency is approximately 2.3% and 2.5% for VBM1 and VBM2, respectively. There is more variation in the damping than natural frequency. Damping of VBM1 varies between 0.3 and 0.85 % (183 % difference) while damping of VBM2 varies between 0.39 and 1.74 % (346 % difference).

3.4 *Manoeuvre results*

The first set of singular values, s_1 from the CPSD matrix are plotted for all manoeuvres in Figures 11 and 12. The same VBM govern the structural response

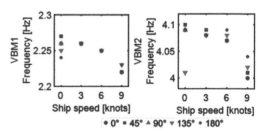

Figure 9. Changes in the stiffness of the first two VBM of the SAAII for varying speed and heading.

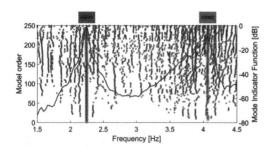

Figure 8. MITD stabilization diagram.

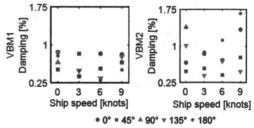

Figure 10. Changes in damping of the first two VBM of the SAAII for varying speed and heading.

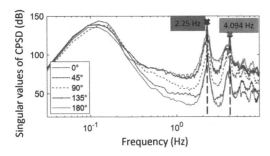

Figure 11. First singular values of CPSD matrix for waves approaching at 0°, 45°, 90°, 135° and 180° for the stationary manoeuvres.

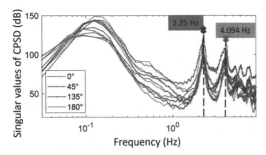

Figure 12. First singular values of CPSD matrix for waves approaching at 0°, 45°, 90°, 135° and 180° for ship manoeuvres at speed.

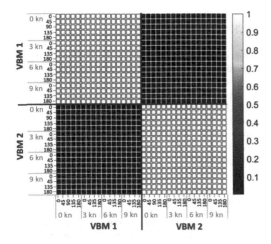

Figure 13. MAC matrix corresponding to the first two VBM for all case studies.

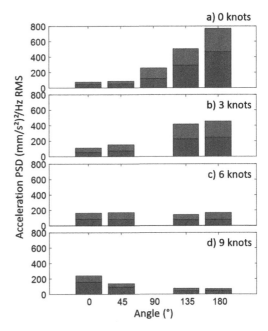

Figure 14. Stacked bar graphs that summarize the RMS values of VBM1 and VBM2 for different ship velocities and relative headings.

throughout both manoeuvre sequences, at 2.25Hz and 4.09Hz. Figure 11 cross-modal assurance criteria (MAC) matrix is calculated for the manoeuvres considered. This serves to evaluate the similarity in the identified mode shapes for respective maneuvers. The analysis shows that the mode shapes for each mode remains consistent despite changing operating conditions ($MAC \approx 1$). Yet, when the first and second VBM are compared, $MAC \approx 0$ which confirms that VBM1 and VBM2 comprise distinct mode shapes. Figure 11 summarizes the energy contained in the VBM by determining the RMS acceleration value from the area under the PSD curve. The frequency range for the area integration was determined by specifying a $MAC \geq 0.9$ of the singular value mode shapes. Figure 11(a) shows that the RMS values grow tenfold as the stationary vessel is re-orientated from head seas to following seas. Combined consideration of this result with that of Figure 9 highlights that the rigid body motion of the ship in the vertical direction remains largely similar regardless of heading, but that the bending response of the structure increases, reaching a maximum in following seas. Notably the bending response in following seas decreases systematically as the vessel increases speed away from the approaching waves. VBM1 (at 2.25Hz) is dominant and corresponds to the hogging-sagging mode shape. Note that the bar graph is a stacked representation; therefore, the total energy accumulates both of the VBM. In order to associate the bending responses of the vessel with slamming incidence, Figure 15(a) presents the number of slams detected for both the port and starboard accelerometer signals. The slams indicated relate to the earliest peak detected in the acceleration signal across all of the accelerometer signals for every slamming incident in the time signal. It is expected that sensors

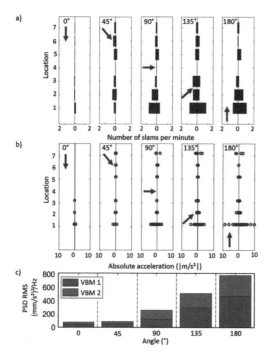

Figure 15. Stationary manoeuvre a) number of slams, b) absolute-peak magnitude of slams and c) RMS value associated with the VBM.

closest to the site of impact will peak earlier than sensors situated further away (Bekker and Van Zijl 2019). Figure 15(b) plots the absolute acceleration magnitude obtained for each peak detected. The number of waves that first impact the hull at the stern increases when the stationary vessel operates in following and stern quartering seas. Further, the peak magnitude of the acceleration measurements is greatest at the stern under these conditions. Figure 15(c) illustrates the RMS values associated with the first two VBM at each relative angle. In turn, larger magnitude slams induce a larger whipping response due to the high energy associated with the VBM when slamming is prevalent.

4 DISCUSSION & CONCLUSIONS

The results indicate that the vessel motion response is high in head seas, but mostly attributed to rigid body motion. When the ship is operated on station, wave action elicits a large flexural response, especially in following seas. This is significant for the SAAII, as many oceanographic research activities are conducted near the stern when she is stationary. Past experiences show that safety is affected in these regions due to violent wave action at the stern. The RMS values of the bending response increased tenfold for stern waves compared to bow waves for the stationary manoeuvres in the same wave state. This coincides with a pronounced increase in the number of slams identified from accelerometer measurements at the stern. Excessive bending of the hull structure in following seas is mitigated when the relative velocity between the incoming waves and the stern structure is increased. When modal parameters of the SAAII are considered, the natural frequency decreases while damping ratio increases, with increasing ship speed. This agrees with another OMA study by (Orlowitz and Brandt 2014) on a Ro-Lo ship and may be attributed to hydro-dynamic and hydro-elastic effects during fluid-structure interaction. Structural damping affects the magnitude and duration of whipping responses and are important for extreme loading and the mitigation of whipping to reduce fatigue damage (ISSC Committee II.2). In a study by (Storhaug & Kahl 2015), container vessels with 5% structural damping were found to be significantly more susceptible to torsional vibration damage than similar vessels with structural damping of 10%. In the context of existing literature the SAAII exhibits lower damping values during stern slamming (between 0.3 and 0.78% for VBM1), along with very large vibration magnitudes, which imply that the contribution of whipping to fatigue damage may have implications for the remaining useful life of the hull. Current conclusions seem to warrant the future pursuit of a full-scale investigation of hull fatigue life expenditure on the SAAII, with techniques that utilize direct measurements of strain, typically at the midship, for example (Mao et al. 2010, Thompson 2016).

ACKNOWLEDGEMENTS

This work is funded through the National Research Foundation (NRF) South African National Antarctic Programme (SANAP Grant No.110737). Research voyages for the Southern oCean seAsonal Experiment (SCALE) were enabled by the Department of Science and Innovation. The support of the Department of Environment, Forestry and Fisheries and the Captain and Crew of the S.A. Agulhas II is thankfully acknowledged.

REFERENCES

Allemang, R. & D. L. Brown (1987). Experimental Modal Analysis and Dynamic Component Sythesis - Volume 3 - Modal Parameter Estimation. pp. 131.

Babanin et al. (2019). Waves and Swells in High Wind and Extreme Fetches, Measurements in the Southern Ocean. *Frontiers in Marine Science 6*, 361.

Bekker, A. & C. M. Van Zijl (2019). The use of line detection to identify random impulses in long time histories. In *International Operational Modal Analysis Conference*, Copenhagen, Denmark.

Bendat, J. & A. Piersol (1980). *Engineering applications of correlation and spectral analysis*.

Brandt, A. (2011). *Noise and Vibration Analysis: Signal Analysis and Experimental Procedures*.

Brincker, R., P. Andersen, & N. J. Jacobsen (2007). Automated frequency domain decomposition for operational modal analysis. *Conference Proceedings of the Society for Experimental Mechanics Series*.

Brincker, R. & C. Ventura (2015). *Introduction to Operational Modal Analysis*.

BS ISO 20283–2 (2008). Mechanical vibration Measurement of vibration on ships Part 2: Measurement of structural vibration, Geneva, Switzerland.

Dessi, D. (2014, jan). Whipping-based criterion for the identification of slamming events. *International Journal of Naval Architecture and Ocean Engineering 6*(4), 1082–1095.

Duda, R. O. & P. E. Hart (1972). Use of the Hough Transformation to Detect Lines and Curves in Pictures. *Communications of the ACM 15*(1), 11–15.

ISSC Committee II.2. Dynamic response report. In *Proceedings of the 20th International Ship and offshore Structures Congress*, pp. 151–154.

Jensen, J. J. (2001). *Load and global response of ships*.

Kiymik, M. K., I. Güler, A. Dizibüyük, & M. Akin (2005). Comparison of STFT and wavelet transform methods in determining epileptic seizure activity in EEG signals for real-time application. *Computers in Biology and Medicine 35*(7), 603–616.

Loughlin, P. J., J. W. Pitton, & L. E. Atlas (1992). Proper time-frequency energy distributions and the Heisenberg uncertainty principle. In *Proceedings of the IEEE-SP International Symposium on Time-Frequency and Time-Scale Analysis*, pp. 151–154.

Maia, N. & J. Silva (1997). *Theoretical and Experimental Modal Analysis*.

Mao, W., J. W. Ringsberg, & I. Rychlik (2010). The effect of whipping/springing on fatigue damage and extreme response of ship structures. *Proceedings of the International Conference on Offshore Mechanics and Arctic Engineering - OMAE 2*(September 2014), 123–131.

Omer, H. & A. Bekker (2016). Detection of wave slamming sites from ship deflections. *Research and Development Journal of South Africa 32*, 50–57.

Orlowitz, E. & A. Brandt (2014). Operational modal analysis for dynamic characterization of a Ro-Lo ship. *Journal of Ship Research 58*(4), 216–224.

Soal, K. (2014). *Vibration response of the polar supply and research vessel the S.A. Agulhas II in Antarctica and the Southern Ocean*. Ph. D. thesis, Stellenbosch University.

Storhaug, G. & A. Kahl (2015). Full scale measurements of torsional vibrations on Post-Panamax container ships. *Proceedings of the 7th International Conference on Hydroelasticity in Marine Technology*, 151–154.

Thompson, I. (2016). Validation of naval vessel spectral fatigue analysis using full-scale measurements. *Marine Structures 49*, 256–268.

Van Zijl, C. M. (2020). Operational Modal Analysis on the SA Agulhas II.

Optimal parameter estimation of empirical manoeuvring model using free-running ship tests

A.C. Costa, H.T. Xu & C. Guedes Soares
Centre for Marine Technology and Ocean Engineering (CENTEC), Instituto Superior Técnico, Universidade de Lisboa, Lisbon, Portugal

ABSTRACT: This work concerns the identification of hydrodynamic coefficients of a specific mathematical manoeuvring model using an optimization method with free-running tests. A nonlinear manoeuvring model is proposed, and the hydrodynamic coefficients are computed using empirical equations. In order to search the optimal values, the least-square method combined with the singular value decomposition was used to optimize the values of the hydrodynamic coefficients, where zig-zag manoeuvre tests were used as training data. The validation is carried by comparing the result of the experiments and the model completed with the coefficients identified by the least square method.

1 INTRODUCTION

Ever since the beginning of the 20th century several studies on ship manoeuvring models have been carried, focusing on finding the most complete model, understanding of the manouevers and simulating them (Sutulo and Guedes Soares, 2011). In 2008 the Manoeuvring Committee of the ITTC (Hochbaum et al., 2008) put together a overview of several methods used to predict the manoeuvering properties, mainly, hydrodinamic coefficients and derivatives, to obtain the equations of motion (Figure 1 and Figure 2).

Regarding the hydrodynamic coefficients, their accuracy can be different depending on the method chosen for their assessment, as seen in Figure 2. According with the previous figures, it seems that the methods must be used individually. However, it is when combined that better results are achieved. Data from empirical formulas, system identification, databases can be combined with free running or full-scale tests to provide more accurate hydrodynamic coefficients (Luo, 2016; Wang et al., 2014).

Additionally, captive model tests have higher reliability concerning the hydrodynamic coefficients but are more expensive than free running tests (Viviani et al., 2007; Sutulo & Guedes Soares, 2004, 2006). Moreover, accuracy of these coefficients is very important, in order to reduce the costs and time spent computing them (Viviani et al., 2007) and to have a more exact model (Haddara and Wang, 1999). Like so, is important to understand the identifiability of some parameters of these mathematical models.

Identifiability means that the parameters can or not be uniquely identified from the relations between the inputs and output. It can be seen different if the analysed systems are linear or non-linear. For linear systems, if all the parameters of a model can be entirely identified from the relation between the input and outputs, is possible to say that the parameters are identifiable. Contrary wise, for non-linear systems there is not possible to understand if this definition is applicable. There are also parameters that are not identifiable (Hwang, 1980). Is possible that some parameters that are identified are mathematically correct but not physically (parameters drift), but it doesn't mean that it does not predict the motions well. For less complicated models, such as the Nomoto models, the parameter drift can be neglected when compared with more complicated ones as the Abkwotiz model (Luo, 2016).

Other problem comes with the parameter cancelation, which diminishes the coefficients accuracy and as consequence the simulation accuracy (Viviani et al., 2007; Hwang, 1980; Xu et. al., 2019). To prevent this, the best option is to try to do not compute a large number of hydrodynamic coefficients at the same time (Viviani et al., 2007).

As said previously, the tests can be combined with other methods to obtain the hydrodynamic coefficients. The one studied in this paper is system identification using the Least Square Methods. Other system identification methods, as the Extended Kalman Filter, Maximum Likehood Estimation (Perera et al. 2016), SVM (Luo et al. 2014; Xu et. al., 2020a,b) Genetic Algorithm (Xu et. al., 2018; Sutulo and Guedes Soares, 2014) and Particle Swarm Optimization (Luo et al. 2016) can also be adopted to compute these values. System identification is a very practical and reliable manner to obtain hydrodynamic coefficients, which improves if combined

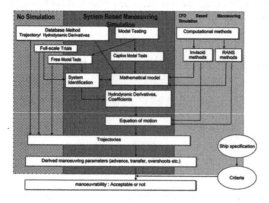

Figure 1. Overview of manoeuvring work (Hochbaum et al., 2008).

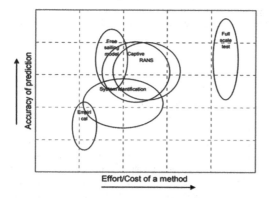

Figure 2. Methods to predict manoeuvring models - cost vs. accuracy (Hochbaum et al., 2008).

with free running tests (Luo 2016, Zhang and Zou, 2011). Depending on some initial parameter values of the studied object, the use of the Least Square Method can lead to some problematic results. However, as early as in 2000, it was seen that the association of free running tests with this method, gives satisfactory results for hydrodynamic coefficients, them being well identified (Le & Kose, 2000). However, the Least Square Method is not able to fight multicolinearity, which has a big influence on the identification of this parameters and is a cause for parameter cancelation (Farrar & Glauber, 1967). Nevertheless, combined with Singular Value Decomposition (SVD) is possible to achieve a better result (Golub & Reinsch, 1971).

Hydrodynamic coefficients often are identified from models as the Abkowitz model, Nomoto model, MMG model (Zhang & Zou, 2011). Using a set of motion equations, normally sway, surge, yaw and if relevant roll motion the mathematical models are often complex in a manner that the hydrodynamic forces and moments are expanded to their Taylor Expansion, where the hydrodynamic coefficients are found. These are taken as being constant in time.

The main goal of this work is to show that Least Square Method combined with the Truncated Singular Value Decomposition (TSVD) (Chan & Hansen, 1990), a particular form of the Singular Value Decomposition, can actually improve the results of the hydrodynamic coefficients. A comparison between the application of the Classical Least Square Method and the one combined with the Truncated Singular Value Decomposition is made, and conclusions about the final results and uncertainties of values are taken.

2 NONLINEAR EMPIRICAL MANOEUVRING MODEL

To have a satisfactory mathematical model, it is mandatory that it predicts well the motions of the object (full scale or model) without any need of physical tests. Is good that they can also be used for hard manoeuvres that are better tests in low speed (Sutulo and Guedes Soares, 2015). It normally contains differential equations of motion and to define the behaviour of auxiliary components as propeller shafts and steering gears, and climate interferences (eg. wind and waves).

There are six degrees of freedom to represent all the motions in the ships. Most of mathematical models consider only 4 degrees of freedom, defining a surface ship. These are surge, sway, yaw and roll. In this study, the roll motion was also neglected, only keeping the surge, sway and yaw equation, as the ship is only considered to move in the horizontal plane and in still water. The motions are also in still water, with no waves or wind considered (Sutulo and Guedes Soares, 2015), as given by:

$$\begin{cases} (m+\mu_{11})\dot{u} - mvr - mx_G r^2 = \frac{\rho V^2}{2} LT \cdot X_q' + X_p \\ (m+\mu_{22})\dot{v} + (mx_G+\mu_{26})\dot{r} + mur = \frac{\rho V^2}{2} LT \cdot Y_q' \\ (mx_G+\mu_{26})\dot{v} + (I_{zz}+\mu_{66})\dot{r} + mx_G ur = \frac{\rho V^2}{2} L^2 T \cdot N_q' \end{cases}$$
(1)

where the added mass coefficients are μ_{11}, μ_{22}, μ_{26} and μ_{66}, the moment of inertia I_z, the centre of gravity x_G, the forces on the hull and rudder X_q and Y_q and moment on the hull and rudder N_q and also the force X_p caused by the propeller, V is the ground speed, and $V^2 = u^2 + v^2$. The motions defined on equations 1 represent the standard Euler equations for a ship that moves in the horizontal plane and can be reformulated as:

$$\begin{aligned} X_q' &= X_{uu}' u^2 + X_{vr}' v' r' + X_{\delta\delta}' \delta_r^2 \\ Y_q' &= Y_0' + Y_v' v' + Y_r' r' + Y_{vvv}' v'^3 + Y_{vvr}' v'^2 r' + Y_\delta' \delta_r \\ &\quad + Y_{vv\delta}' v'^2 \delta_r + Y_{\delta\delta v}' \delta_r^2 v' + Y_{\delta\delta\delta}' \delta_r^3 \\ N_q' &= N_0' + N_v' v' + N_r' r' + N_{vvv}' v'^3 + N_{vvr}' v'^2 r' + N_\delta' \delta_r \\ &\quad + N_{vv\delta}' v'^2 \delta_r + N_{\delta\delta v}' \delta_r^2 v' + N_{\delta\delta\delta}' \delta_r^3 \end{aligned}$$
(2)

In the case of this study, the values wanted are the ones from the adjustment coefficients $k_{xuu}, \ldots, k_{n\delta\delta\delta}$, which are the ones missing to compute the final hydrodynamic coefficients $X'_{\delta\delta}, \ldots, N'_{\delta\delta\delta}$.

$$X'_{uu} = -k_{xuu}\frac{2mC_{TL}}{\rho L^2 T}; X'_{vr} = -k_{xvr}\frac{1.3\mu_{22}}{\rho L^2 T}$$
$$X'_{vr} = -k_{xvr}\frac{1.3\mu_{22}}{\rho L^2 T}$$
$$X'_{\delta\delta} = k_R k_{x\delta\delta} X'_{\delta\delta 0}; Y'_0 = k_{y0} Y'_{00}; N'_0 = k_{n0} N'_{00}$$
$$Y'_v = k_{yv}(1+b_1\tau')Y'_{v0}; N'_v = k_{nv}(1+b_3\tau')N'_{v0}$$
$$Y'_r = k_{yr}(1+b_2\tau')Y'_{r0}$$
$$N'_r = k_{nr}(1+b_4\tau')(N'_{r0}+m'x'_G u') \quad (3)$$
$$Y'_\delta = k_R k_{y\delta} Y'_{\delta 0}; N'_\delta = k_R k_{n\delta} N'_{\delta 0}$$
$$Y'_{vvv} = k_{yvvv} Y'_{vvv0}; N'_{vvv} = k_{nvvv} N'_{vvv0}$$
$$Y'_{vvr} = k_{yvvr} Y'_{vvr0}; N'_{vvr} = k_{nvvr} N'_{vvr0}$$
$$Y'_{\delta vv} = k_R k_{y\delta vv} Y'_{\delta vv0}; N'_{\delta vv} = k_R k_{n\delta vv} N'_{\delta vv0}$$
$$Y'_{\delta\delta v} = k_R k_{y\delta\delta v} Y'_{\delta\delta v0}; N'_{\delta\delta v} = k_R k_{n\delta\delta v} N'_{\delta\delta v0}$$
$$Y'_{\delta\delta\delta} = k_R k_{y\delta\delta\delta} Y'_{\delta\delta\delta 0}; N'_{\delta\delta\delta} = k_R k_{n\delta\delta\delta} N'_{\delta\delta\delta 0}$$

$$b_1 = 0.6667; b_2 = 0.8; b_3 = -\frac{0.27 N'_{v0}}{Y'_{v0}}; b_4 = 0.3$$
$$k_H = \frac{2T}{L}; k_{11} = 0.25 k_H; k_{22} = 2\frac{T}{B}\left(1-\frac{1}{2}\frac{B}{L}\right);$$
$$k_{66} = 2\frac{T}{B}\left(1-1.6\frac{B}{L}\right)$$
$$I_{zz} = 0.0625 mL^2; C_{TL} = 0.07$$
$$\mu_{11} = k_{11}m; \mu_{22} = k_{22}m; \mu_{66} = k_{66} I_{zz}; \mu_{26} = \mu_{22} x_G$$
$$X'_{\delta\delta 0} = -0.02; Y'_{00} = -0.0008; N'_{00} = 0.00059$$
$$Y'_{v0} = -0.244; N'_{v0} = -0.0555$$
$$Y'_{r0} = 0.067; N'_{r0} = -0.0349$$
$$Y'_{\delta 0} = -0.0586; N'_{\delta 0} = 0.0293$$
$$Y'_{vvv0} = -1.702; N'_{vvv0} = 0.345$$
$$Y'_{vvr0} = 3.23; N'_{vvr0} = -0.1032$$
$$Y'_{\delta vv0} = -0.25; N'_{\delta vv0} = -0.1032$$
$$Y'_{\delta\delta v0} = -0.0008; N'_{\delta\delta v0} = 0.00264$$
$$Y'_{\delta\delta\delta 0} = 0.00975; N'_{\delta\delta\delta 0} = -0.00482$$
$$(4)$$

Values such as the dimensions, mass, center of gravity (x_G), moment of inertia and added masses, from the model used in the free running tests are known a priori (Table 1). From the tests the values of velocity of surge, sway and yaw are also taken from the tests. Thus, the main importance is to compute the hydrodynamic coefficients, in order to have a complete model. In equation 2 the forces and moments are nondimensional, as well as the values of velocities.

3 MANOEUVRING TEST USING FREE-RUNNING CONTAINER SHIP MODEL

In this section, a free-running ship model is used to carry out the manoeuvring tests in a swimming pool. This type model has been used for experimental validation of various methods of guidance and control (Moreira & Guedes Soares, 2011).

The vessel model considered in this paper is a scaled container, presented in Figure 3. The main dimensions of the ship model are given in Table 1. The ship model is from a conventional ship, it has one propeller and one rudder in the aft.

Hardware system of the free-running ship model consists of all the sensor and actuators, as illustrated in Figure 3. The hardware system is further divided into two groups: Onboard and offshore control centre. The on-board system is composed by propeller, rudder and set of sensors, internal measurement unit, yaw rate sensor, electrical motors and industrial Wi-Fi unit, where all the signals are synchronized using a Compact-RIO and stored in a laptop. It is used to control the self-running model remotely (Ferrari et al. 2015).

The software architecture is mainly programmed by LABVIEW software. The software architecture consists of several program loops: FPGA loop, real-time loop and TCP/IP loop. The FPGA loop is associated with collecting data from the sensors (i.e. GPS, internal

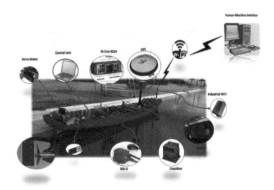

Figure 3. The free-running ship model during the manoeuvring tests.

Table 1. Main dimensions of the container model.

Length (m)	3.24
Breadth (m)	0.43
Draught (estimated at the tests) (m)	0.14
Ship weight (kg)	108.58
Water Depth (m)	0.185
Propeller diameter (m)	0.10

measurement unit, yaw rate sensor etc.) and controlling the actuation of propeller and rudder sub-systems that have been programmed under a reconfigurable FPGA platform in LABVIEW. The sensor data has been incorporated into a network shared variables that are forecasted along the entire network.

The TCP/IP loop is associated with a real-time processor and the Human Machine Interface (HMI) is used for analysis, post-processing, data logging, communications and control of the ship model. The TCP/IP loop is implemented under wireless communication through the industrial Wi-Fi unit. The Zig Zag 30°-30° manoeuvring test was carried out successfully and the result is given in Figure 5, where the yaw angle, yaw rate and yaw accelerations are presented. Figure 6 give the surge and sway speed during the tests.

4 OPTIMAL PARAMETER ESTIMATION METHOD

To compute the hydrodynamic coefficients, the Least Square Method was first used, which is one of the most common in identification of these values (Xu et al., 2019). Its main goal is to diminish the error of the squared residual value, r, which means, minimize the sum, S, of the squared difference between the data value, y_i, and the estimation, $\widehat{y_i}$:

$$S = \sum_{i=1}^{n} r_i^2 = \sum_{i=1}^{n} (y_i - \widehat{y}) \quad (5)$$

Figure 4. Sensors and actuators installed on the ship model.

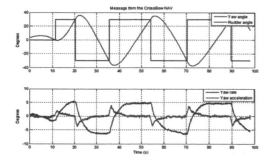

Figure 5. The Zig Zag 30°-30° manoeuvring test.

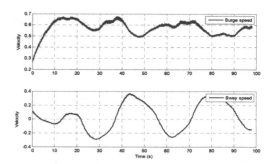

Figure 6. The surge and sway speed in the Zig Zag 30°-30° manoeuvring test.

In the case of the hydrodynamic coefficients, the equations 3, 4 and 5, can be written as follow:

$$Y = X\theta \quad (6)$$

The vector Y represents the sway, surge and yaw positions (outputs), the matrix X represents the inputs, and the vector θ the values of adjustment coefficients, which are the values wanted.

As said before, the main goal of the Least Square Method is to diminish the error squared residual value, which is known as the *'chi-squared'*. In this study, this depends on the input matrix X, output vector Y and the parameter matrix θ:

$$\chi^2(\theta) = (X\theta - y)^T V_y^{-1} (X\theta - y)^T \quad (7)$$

To find the minimum error, the derivative of χ^2 needs to be zero, when the parameter θ is equal to the estimated one:

$$\frac{\partial \chi^2}{\partial \theta}\bigg|_{\theta=\widehat{\theta}} = 0 \Leftrightarrow X^T V_y^{-1} X \widehat{\theta} - X^T V_y^{-1} y = 0 \quad (8)$$

Finally, we get the equation 9, which relates the estimated parameters with the inputs and outputs from the data:

$$\widehat{\theta} = \left[X^T V_y^{-1} X\right]^{-1} X^T V_y^{-1} y \quad (9)$$

Even though the Least Square is widely used, there are some disadvantages. One of them being the noise of the data that affects the results of the parameters' estimation (Xu et al., 2019).

As stated before, the problem of parameter drift is very real and it is impossible to eradicate, due to physical reasons, being the main reason the multicolinearity (Hwang, 1980).

Multicolinearity results from the fact that the input variables are interdependent, when they are supposed to be independent. As expected, this will have impact on the final estimations of the parameters, something that the Least Square Method is not able to solve (Farrar & Glauber, 1967). This means, that the input variables have a mathematical relation between themselves and when one changes, other can be affected by it. If they are interdependent, there is no manner to understand which ones are more important, considering the impact on the calculations of the parameters.

All of this complies with the parameter cancelation and drift, and the fact that a big number of coefficients should not be evaluated at the same time, in order to avoid these problems.

As said before, since the calculation of a big number of parameters is not recommendable, and the fact that the Least Square Method can't deal with these problems, the use of an algorithm combined with the LSM is appropriate. Singular Value Decomposition has been applied with the LSM in order to obtain better results for the parameters (Xu et al., 2019; Golub & Reinsch, 1971).

SVD uses the singular values of the input matrix to diagonalize it with the singular values and create orthonormal bases from the eigenvalues and eigenvector of the input matrix:

$$X = U\Sigma V^T \quad (10)$$

In equation 12, the general formulation of the Singular Value Decomposition of the matrix $X_{m \times n}$ is expressed, as dependent on the orthonormal bases for the column space, the orthonormal base for the rows and the diagonal matrix of the singular values (U, V and Σ respectively).

In order to build smaller matrixes to diminish the parameter cancelation and multicollinearity, is possible to apply the Truncated Single Value Decomposition (TSVD), which eliminates the smallest singular values of the input matrix (Chan & Hansen, 1990). It reduces the initial rank of the input matrix X and constructs a new input matrix X_n with n rows, corresponding to the n singular values that were kept:

$$X_n = U_n \Sigma_n V_n^T \quad (11)$$

Like so, the new matrix does not suffer from the problem of multicollinearity and parameter cancelation, avoiding parameter drift and providing better results.

Is important to notice that this method is only used, in this paper, for the sway force and yaw moment, as there are only 3 coefficients on the surge force, and the Least Square Method alone can compute them without the concern of being to many variables. This means that one expects similar predictions for the classical LSM and the LSM combined with TSVD for the surge force.

5 PARAMETER ESTIMATION OF THE MANOEUVRING MODEL

To understand if there is an improvement from the classical Least Square Method, to the one combined with the Truncated Singular Value Decomposition is important to simulate the manoeuvring model, analysing the results of the surge and sway forces, the yaw moment.

In this section, the fit of the force and moments curves and the coefficients, for both applications are going to be compared and discussed.

The coefficient of determination R^2 is a good evaluator for the fit of the forces and moments. Is know that the value of R^2 vary between 0 and 1, meaning that the prediction is better when closer to 1, and gets worse when closer to 0.

In the Figure 7, for the Least Square Method combined with the Truncated Singular Value

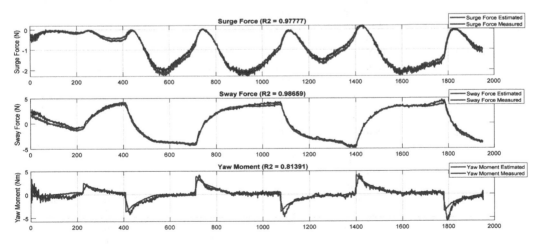

Figure 7. Comparison between predicted and measured surge and sway forces, and yaw moment – Zig Zag 30°-30° – Classical LSM.

Decomposition, is possible to understand that the estimated curves are well fitted to the ones from the measured data. Moreover, the high values of the R^2, confirm the good fit of the predictions for the measured data.

The same can be said about the results for the fit from the classical Least Square Method. The R^2 is still very high, being even better for the sway force (Figure 8).

However, as stated before, the classical LSM does not perform well when computing a large number of variables. Hence, is expected that when comparing the coefficients, even with a good fit of the manoeuvring models concerning the forces and moment, these present a considerable difference, bettering with the combination of LSM with the TSVD (Table 2).

The uncertainty of a coefficient, can be due to the noise of the data and is given by the error

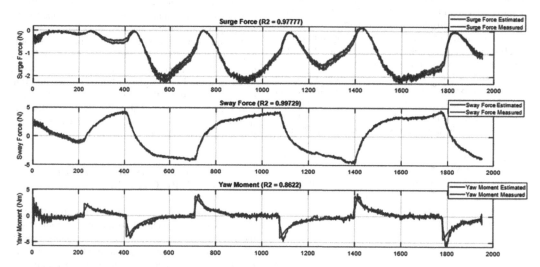

Figure 8. Comparison between predicted and measured surge and sway forces, and yaw moment – Zig Zag 30°-30° – LSM combined with SVD.

Table 2. Computed Coefficients for Zig Zag 20°-20° and Zig Zag 30°-30°.

		Classical LSM			LSM combined with TSVD	
	Coef.	Value	Uncertainty	Coef.	Value	Uncertainty
Surge	k_{uu}	5.09E+00	13.98%	k_{uu}	5.09E+00	13.98%
	k_{xvr}	1.50E+02	0.38%	k_{xvr}	1.50E+02	0.38%
	$k_{x\delta\delta}$	-1.17E+00	134.54%	$k_{x\delta\delta}$	-1.17E+00	134.54%
Sway	k_{y0}	-4.40E+02	1.16%	k_{y0}	-2.84E+00	8.02%
	k_{yv}	-1.06E+01	3.02%	k_{yv}	-3.52E+00	12.22%
	k_{yr}	1.09E+02	0.34%	k_{yr}	1.05E+02	0.76%
	k_{yvvv}	8.20E-01	31.87%	k_{yvvv}	-9.64E+00	5.22%
	k_{yvvr}	-1.09E+00	10.95%	k_{yvvr}	-3.66E+00	6.96%
	$k_{y\delta}$	4.03E+14	149.16%	$k_{y\delta}$	-8.40E+00	6.65%
	$k_{yvv\delta}$	-1.22E+00	158.41%	$k_{yvv\delta}$	5.02E+01	7.53%
	$k_{yv\delta\delta}$	1.44E+4	3.17%	$k_{yv\delta\delta}$	7.03E-02	9.46%
	$k_{y\delta\delta\delta}$	8.83E+15	149.16%	$k_{y\delta\delta\delta}$	3.83E-01	6.65%
Yaw	k_{n0}	-4.24E+02	5.30%	k_{n0}	3.49E+00	73.98%
	k_{nv}	-9.05E+01	6.57%	k_{nv}	-1.62E+01	26.15%
	k_{nr}	9.90E+01	2.57%	k_{nr}	1.04E+02	2.76%
	k_{nvvv}	3.98E+00	105.98%	k_{nvvv}	-1.37E+01	30.80%
	k_{nvvr}	8.83E-01	139.15%	k_{nvvr}	-2.08E+00	58.52%
	$k_{n\delta}$	7.02E+15	48.57%	$k_{n\delta}$	1.31E+02	1.45%
	$k_{nvv\delta}$	-9.80E+00	155.89%	$k_{nvv\delta}$	1.72E+01	89.27%
	$k_{nv\delta\delta}$	-6.68E+03	6.83%	$k_{nv\delta\delta}$	1.74E-01	123.92%
	$k_{n\delta\delta\delta}$	1.56E+17	48.57%	$k_{n\delta\delta\delta}$	-5.89E+00	1.45%

propagation matrix, V_θ, depending on the optimal values of the coefficients θ and the diagonal matrix of Y, V_Y:

$$V_{\hat{\theta}} = \left[\frac{\partial \hat{\theta}}{\partial y}\right] V_y \left[\frac{\partial \hat{\theta}}{\partial y}\right]^T \quad (12)$$

High uncertainties can mean that the coefficients are not as reliable as others.

In Table 2, for the classical LSM, there are five values above 100% of uncertainty, comparing with only one for the LSM combined with the TSVD. Hence, the addition of the Truncated Singular Value Decomposition improved the reliability of the values, by decreasing the problem of the parameter cancelation and multicollinearity. Analysing the Table 2 along with Figures 3-4, confirms that sometimes, even if the methods can predict the manoeuvring motions, their values deviate from being actually good values, and close to the real ones (Luo, 2016). The remain uncertainties are due to the fact that the free running tests were carried outside, affected by wind and waves, and the fact that some sensors were not good enough to capture the movement of the model satisfactorily.

6 CONCLUSIONS

In this paper, optimal parameter estimation was carried out and discussed, comparing the classical Least Square Method and the Least Square Method combined with the Truncated Singular Value Decomposition. The TSVD was used to improve the results of the LSM and deal with the multicollinearity and parameter cancellation, that the Least Square can't solve if the number of variables is too large. A manoeuvring model was introduced, and the methods were applied to it. The data was taken from a free running test carried in the outside of the Oeiras Pool. In this study, is proved that even with good fit for the forces and moments curves with or without the use of TSVD, the uncertainty of the majority of the coefficients decreases with the TSVD. Thus, the parameter cancellation and multicollinearity are diminished as proposed and expected. However, some uncertainty remains. This can be because the noise of the initial data, which can be eliminated if there were better weather conditions, or if the tests were carried inside closed doors. Additionally, with the use of better sensors that only capture the movements of the model instead of also other movements in the space of the test.

ACKNOWLEDGEMENTS

This work was performed within the Strategic Research Plan of the Centre for Marine Technology and Ocean Engineering (CENTEC), which is financed by Portuguese Foundation for Science and Technology (Fundação para a Ciência e Tecnologia-FCT) under contract UIDB/UIDP/00134/2020. The experiments with the vessel model were not possible without the collaboration of Eng. José Costa, Coordinator of the "Piscina Oceanica", Oeiras, Portugal, who allowed the realization of the maneuvering tests in their installations.

REFERENCES

Chan, T. F. & Hansen, P. C. (1990). Computing truncated singular value decomposition least squares solutions by rank revealing qr-factorizations. *SIAM Journal on Scientific and Statistical Computing*, 11(3):519–530.

Farrar, D. E. & Glauber, R. R. (1967). Multicollinearity in regression analysis: the problem revisited. *The Review of Economic and Statistics*, pages 92–107.

Ferrari, V.; Perera, L. P.; Santos, F. P.; Hinostroza, M. A.; Sutulo, S., & Guedes Soares, C. 2015. Initial experimental tests of a research-oriented self-running ship model. Guedes Soares, C. & Santos T.A. (Eds.). *Maritime Technology and Engineering. London*, UK: Taylor & Francis Group; pp. 913–918.

Golub, G. H. & Reinsch, C. (1971). Singular value decomposition and least squares solutions. *In: Linear Algebra*, pages 134–151. Springer.

Haddara, M. R. & Wang, Y. (1999). Parametric identification of manoeuvring models for ships. *International Shipbuilding Progress, 46(445):*5–27.

Hochbaum, A., Stern, F., Agdrup, K., Broglia, R., Kim, S., Perdon, P., Quadvlieg, F., Yasukawa, H., & Zou, Z. (2008). *The manoeuvring committee: final report and recommendations to the 25th ittc.*

Hochbaum, A., Stern, F., Agdrup, K., Broglia, R., Kim, S., Perdon, P., Quadvlieg, F., Yasukawa, H., & Zou, Z. (2008). The manoeuvring committee-final report and recommendations to the 25th ittc. *In 25th International Towing Tank Conference. Fukuoka, Japan, volume 1*, pages 143–208

Hwang, W.-Y. (1980). Application of system identification to ship maneuvering. PhD thesis, Massachusetts Institute of Technology.

Le, M.-D. & Kose, K. (2000). Estimation of ship hydrodynamic coefficients at low speed range and application to control ships. *The Journal of Japan Institute of Navigation, 103*:33–39.

Luo, W. (2016). Parameter identifiability of ship manoeuvring modeling using system identification. *Mathematical Problems in Engineering*, 2016.

Luo, W. L.; Guedes Soares, C., & Zou, Z. 2016. Parameter Identification of Ship Manoeuvring Model Based on Support Vector Machines and Particle Swarm Optimization. *Journal of Offshore Mechanics and Arctic Engineering*. 138 (3): 031101.

Luo, W. L.; Moreira, L., & Guedes Soares, C. 2014. Manoeuvring Simulation of Catamaran by Using Implicit Models Based on Support Vector Machines. *Ocean Engineering*. 82:150–159.

Perera, L. P.; Oliveira, P., & Guedes Soares, C. 2016. System Identification of Vessel Steering with Unstructured Uncertainties by Persistent Excitation Maneuvers. *IEEE Journal of Oceanic Engineering*. 41(3):515–528.

Sutulo, S. & Guedes Soares, C. 2004. Synthesis of Experimental Designs of Manouevring Captive-Model Tests with Large Number of Factors. *Journal of Marine Science and Technology;* 9(1):32–42

Sutulo, S. & Guedes Soares, C. 2006. Development of a Multifactor Regression Model of Ship Maneuvering Forces Based on Optimized Captive-Model Tests. *Journal of Ship Research.* 50(4):311–333.

Sutulo, S. & Guedes Soares, C. (2011). Mathematical models for simulation of manoeuvring performance of ships. Guedes Soares, C. Garbatov Y. Fonseca N. & Teixeira A. P., (Eds.). *Marine Technology and Engineering.* London, UK: Taylor & Francis Group; 661–698.

Sutulo, S., & Guedes Soares, C., (2014). An algorithm for offline identification of ship manoeuvring mathematical models from free-running tests. *Ocean Eng. 79,* 10–25.

Sutulo, S., & Guedes Soares, C., (2015). Development of a core mathematical model for arbitrary manoeuvres of a shuttle tanker. *Appl. Ocean Res.* 51, 293–308.

Viviani, M., Bonvino, C. P., Depascale, R., Conti, F., & Soave, M. (2007). Identification of hydrodynamic coefficient from standard manoeuvres for a serie of twin-screw ships. *2nd International Conferenceon Marine Research and Transportation, Naples, Italy,* pages 99–108.

Wang, X.-G., Zou, Z.-J., Xu, F., & Ren, R.-Y. (2014). Sensitivity analysis and parametric identification for ship manoeuvring in 4 degrees of freedom. *Journal of Marine Science and Technology, 19(4):*394–405.

Xu, H.T., Hinostroza, M.A., & Guedes Soares, C., (2018). Estimation of Hydrodynamic Coefficients of a Nonlinear Manoeuvring Mathematical Model with Free-Running Ship Model Tests, *Int. J. Marit. Eng., 160 (A3):*A213–225.

Xu, H., Hassani, V., & Guedes Soares, C. (2019). Uncertainty analysis of the hydrodynamic coefficients estimation of a nonlinear manoeuvring model based on planar motion mechanism tests. *Ocean Engineering, 173:*450–459.

Xu, H. T. & Guedes Soares, C., (2019). Hydrodynamic coefficient estimation for ship manoeuvring in a shallow water using an optimal truncated LS-SVM. *Ocean Engineering, 191, pp.* 106488.

Xu, H. T. & Guedes Soares, C., (2020). Manoeuvring modelling of DTC in Shallow Water based on Optimal Truncated Nonlinear Kernel-based Least Square Support Vector Machine and Quantum-inspired Evolution Algorithm. *Ocean Engineering, 195, pp.* 106676.

Xu, H. T., Hassani V. & Guedes Soares C., (2020a). Truncated least square support vector machine for model simplification and parameter estimation of a nonlinear manoeuvring model based on PMM tests. *Applied Ocean Research*, 97, 102076.

Xu, H. T., Hassani V. & Guedes Soares C., (2020b). Comparing Generic and Vectorial Nonlinear Manoeuvring Models and parameter estimation using Optimal Truncated Least Square Support Vector Machine, *Applied Ocean Research, 10.1016/j.apor.2020.*102061.

Zhang, X.-G. & Zou, Z.-J. (2011). Identification of Abkowitz model for ship manoeuvring motion using ε-support vector regression. *Journal of Hydrodynamics, 23(3):*353–360.

Developments in Maritime Technology and Engineering – Guedes Soares & Santos (eds)
© 2021 Copyright the Author(s), ISBN 978-0-367-77377-9

Preliminary review of shiphandling: Comparison between the literatures on naval architecture versus nautical sciences

H.O. Duarte, P.S.A. Michima, M.A.C. Carbajal & A.C.A. Oliveira
Department of Mechanical Engineering, Federal University of Pernambuco, Recife, Pernambuco, Brazil

ABSTRACT: Today, port constraints (e.g., channel depth) are the main limiting factor to increasingly large ships, so it is in the interest of Naval Architects (NAs) to understand the practical aspects of shiphandling in ports. However, most of the ship hydrodynamics learned by NAs either focus on deep water or, when covering shallow waters, sometimes differ too much from the opinion of experienced mariners. It is important that NAs understand shiphandling not only based upon hydrodynamic calculations, but also upon field experience of pilots and professional mariners. In this review, we summarize and compare basic principles (pivot point, separation and cavitation, directional stability, sinkage, squat and trim) and other characteristics (propeller, rudder, effect of wind and current) that influence shiphandling, comprising the literature on naval architecture and nautical sciences. Our aim is to highlight main gaps of understanding between the designer and the practitioner, for mutual awareness and possibly special consideration by the designer when thinking of ship maneuverability.

1 INTRODUCTION

Ships are designed and constructed to be handled with maximum safety and minimum tug assistance costs in ports and waterways, so it is desirable that to make the best possible use of knowledge on the practical aspects of tug use in ports, ship maneuverability and control, squat and interaction with shallow water, banks and other vessels. The maneuverability and control trade-offs in ship design, given a chosen hull, are usually based on ship hydrodynamic theory (e.g., bow-thruster efficiency as a function of ship speed, stopping distance). However, most of the ship hydrodynamics learned by NAs either focus on deep water or, when covering the behavior of ships in shallow and narrow waters, sometimes differ too much from the opinion of experienced mariners. Although naval architecture and nautical sciences are areas that should be integrated, there seems to be a gap between them. This work aims to reduce this gap by making a review on the literature about shiphandling not only based upon the hydrodynamicist point of view (i.e., naval architecture references), but also upon actual experience of practicing pilots and professional mariners (i.e., nautical science references).

We focus on the behavior of ships in restricted waters such as ports and waterways. The content of this paper is not based on the authors' personal opinion. All comments and statements are based on the literature and the references are provided along the paper. Our references were published by hydrodynamicists and experienced mariners who sometimes agree or disagree, as is commented case by case. Most references have been used in recent syllabus for pilotage certification or licensing (e.g., in qualification exams for applicants to pilot licensing in Brazilian waters (DPC, 2011)).

In section 2, we provide a summary of the NA's versus the mariner's point of view regarding basic principles such as pivot point, separation and cavitation, directional stability, trim, sinkage and squat. In sections 3, 4, 5 we summarize, respectively, the importance of the propeller, rudder and wind/current in shiphandling, as seen by the NA versus the mariner. In section 6, we discuss the main convergences and disparities in the bibliography. Finally, we conclude with the most important aspects of these subjects to NAs and suggestion for future works (section 7). Unless specified otherwise, "ship" refers to "conventional displacement ship with a righthand turning single screw".

2 BASIC PRINCIPLES

Regarding shiphandling in restricted waters, there are six general sources of forces considered to be bearing on a ship independent of any other vessel, i.e.: propeller, rudder, mooring lines, anchors, wind and current. The first four are controllable from the ship itself. Although the wind and current are not controllable, advantage can be taken on them to favor the desired maneuver if properly planned (Crenshaw, 1975). Additionally, there may also be forces on the ship due to

DOI: 10.1201/9781003216599-18

the use of bow/stern thrusters or tugs (Fragoso & Cajaty, 2002; Hensen, 2018; MacElrevey & MacElrevey, 2018).

All these six forces can cause acceleration, but this acceleration will only result in linear or rotational movement towards the acting force after overcoming inertia, which is great for a ship of thousands of tons. Thus, the response time between a maneuvering order and the resulting movement of a ship is long.

Before proceeding to the explanation of the general forces and their implications in ship design, we must define some basic principles: pivot point, separation and cavitation, Directional Stability (DS), trim and its relation with directional stability.

2.1 Pivot point

Naval architecture references explain the Pivot Point (PP) as the instantaneous center of rotation of the ship in combined yaw and sway motion. It can be found at the intersection of the perpendicular line that passes at the center of curvature of the trajectory over the centerline of the ship. In the turning maneuver, PP varies with the ship speed and the rudder angle. The drift angle at this point is zero and increases as the distance from that point increases (Lewis, 1988). Although usually located on the center line, depending on the maneuver and the local draft (whether in deep water or restricted water), PP may be tilted by shifting the pivot point off the center plane of the vessel (Asgari, 2018).

In nautical science references, the pivot point is an imaginary floating point around which a vessel turns when forced into a directional change. The form of the submerged body, rudder size and type, trim, under keel clearance (UKC) and direction of movement all affect the PP. The exact location of the pivot point is therefore not stationary but variable (Hensen, 2018).

There are different opinions about the approximate location of the PP when a ship is in a steady turn with forward thrust and port or starboard rudder, although all authors agree that it is between LOA/3 and LOA/5 aft of the bow. According to Hensen (2018) and Miguens (1996), the PP settles in a position approximately LOA/3 aft of the bow. For Mandel (1953) apud Lewis (1988), for most ships the PP is somewhere between the bow and about LOA/5 aft of the bow. Whereas for Fonseca (2019), it is between LOA/3 and LOA/4 aft of the bow.

This explains why a bow thruster is not effective to assist in a turning (the turning lever from the bow thruster to the PP is very short). Bow thrusters are more useful for maneuvers at very low speeds (< 2 knots), e.g.: to move the bow laterally in a docking/undocking, steer the ship when going astern, hold the ship alongside a wharf or pier, hold the ship into the wind at slow speeds and when anchoring (MacElrevey & MacElrevey, 2018).

For tug use in ports, the pivot point is very important for effective tug position. Regarding the need to add turning to the ship by tug action or not, the length of the turning lever will be chosen by deciding the position of tug action, respectively far from PP or near it. Attention should paid to the fact that PP also changes position when tug forces are applied. For more details see Hensen (2018).

2.2 Separation and cavitation

Separation and cavitation are of great importance for the ship performance, fuel consumption, propeller lifetime and maintenance costs, and for shiphandling. Such phenomena will disturb the resulting forces, and cause vibration and difficulty in maneuvering.

To the NA separation plays an important role in ship resistance. For certain speeds, a flow past a blunt body will face a flow with a thin boundary layer upstream, and the pressure decreases along the surface towards to the rear, where it encounters increasing pressure and breaks off, or separates into a broad wake, deflecting the mainstream (White, 2010). The wake of eddies increases the local kinetic energy and drop in pressure, unbalancing the resultant forces in advance direction. As a result, the net force from pressure at fore region towards to aft of the body will be greater. The discrepancy will increase the power needed to overcome inertia and develop advance speed. This mechanism can be observed on the hull, rudder and other appendages. Through this mechanism, separation increases fuel consumption.

By similar mechanism, high loadings on a screw propeller will increase the local velocity of particles, which will drop the local pressure. When the pressure assumes values that are lower than the so-called vapor pressure, water changes to gas phase, creating vapor cavities. This phenomenon is known as cavitation. There will be, beyond certain critical revolutions, a progressive break-down in the flow and a consequent loss of thrust, which may prevent the ship from reaching a desired speed (Harvald, 1983). Besides other drawbacks like noise and vibration, two biggest problems brought by this phenomenon are loss of efficiency, thus more consumption of fuel, and damage of blades by erosion of their surface when the bubbles implode cyclically, leading to higher maintenance costs. More detailed explanation can be found in Lars, Hoyte & Raven (2010) and Harvald (1983).

To the mariner, separation and cavitation are as follows:

- Water is a continuous media, which means it does not have "gaps" or "holes". But if a volume of water is moved rapidly (e.g., by the propeller blade, by the ship's hull), so that the pressure difference is not enough to fill the gap quickly, a "gap" will occur. This phenomenon is known as separation (Crenshaw, 1975). It occurs in the propeller turning rapidly, in the rudder with large angles (rudder may stall) and especially around the stern of bunt ships e, causing the so-called separation resistance.

- The higher the velocity, the lower the pressure, so in a high velocity flow (e.g., turning blades) the velocity gets so high and the pressure so low that it reaches the water vaporization point. Water particles around the propeller blades vaporize like boiling water (small explosions). This phenomenon is known as cavitation.

2.3 Directional stability

NAs look at DS as a tool to predict whether the ship will be easily deviated from the straight-line trajectory by disturbances when in transit. The NA estimates the degree of stability of the ship through the DS Index (DSI). Negative values indicate unstable hulls and positive but close to zero values indicate low stability, which suggests the need to add a flat structure such as a skeg aft of the ship.

In the analysis to determine the DSI, the properties of the loads from the added mass and damping, which are associated to the so-called hydrodynamic derivatives, create forces and moments. However, the DSI is more influenced by the steering moment due to a variation of the lateral speed of the hull, (Kobylinski, 2003).

The NA will use only the most important maneuver equations of sway and yaw. Considering the coupled equation in matrix form is, see Routh (1877):

$$A\ddot{q} + B\dot{q} + Cq = 0 \qquad (1)$$

With:

$$A = \begin{bmatrix} m - Y_{\dot{v}} & -Y_{\dot{r}} \\ -N_{\dot{v}} & I_z - N_{\dot{r}} \end{bmatrix}, B = \begin{bmatrix} -Y_v & mU - Y_r \\ -N_v & -N_r \end{bmatrix},$$

$$\dot{q} = \begin{bmatrix} v(t) \\ r(t) \end{bmatrix}, C = 0$$

Where q is the vector of positions of the ship in sway, $v(t)$, and yaw, $r(t)$; m, Iz are ship mass and inertia, respectively, U is the ship forward speed, and Y_v, $Y_{\dot{v}}$, Y_r, $Y_{\dot{r}}$, N_v, $N_{\dot{v}}$, N_r, $N_{\dot{r}}$ are the hydrodynamic derivatives, in notation according to Lewis (1988).

The solutions for $v(t)$ and $r(t)$ can be obtained by assuming their shape is as follows:

$$v(t) = v_0 e^{\lambda t}; \quad r(t) = r_0 e^{\lambda t}$$

From what the characteristic equation 2 is obtained:

$$\begin{bmatrix} m - Y_{\dot{v}} & -Y_{\dot{r}} \\ -N_{\dot{v}} & I_z - N_{\dot{r}} \end{bmatrix} \begin{bmatrix} v_0 \\ r_0 \end{bmatrix} \lambda e^{\lambda t}$$
$$+ \begin{bmatrix} -Y_v & mU - Y_r \\ -N_v & -N_r \end{bmatrix} \begin{bmatrix} v_0 \\ r_0 \end{bmatrix} e^{\lambda t} = \begin{bmatrix} 0 \\ 0 \end{bmatrix} \qquad (2)$$

The particular solution is obtained when the matrix has no inverse. So, determinant is zero.

$$\Delta(\lambda) = \begin{vmatrix} (m - Y_{\dot{v}})\lambda - Y_v & -Y_{\dot{r}}\lambda + mU - Y_r \\ -N_{\dot{v}}\lambda - N_v & (I_z - N_{\dot{r}})\lambda - N_r \end{vmatrix} = 0$$

$$\Delta(\lambda) = \bar{A}\lambda^2 + \bar{B}\lambda + \bar{C} = 0$$

The two roots of the polynomial are:

$$\lambda_{1,2} = \frac{-\frac{\bar{B}}{\bar{A}} \pm \sqrt{\left(\frac{\bar{B}}{\bar{A}}\right)^2 - 4\frac{\bar{C}}{\bar{A}}}}{2}$$

Hence, the solutions will be formed by the linear combination:

$$v(t) = v_1 e^{\lambda_1 t} + v_2 e^{\lambda_2 t}; \quad r(t) = r_1 e^{\lambda_1 t} + r_2 e^{\lambda_2 t}$$

Where: v_1, v_2, r_1, r_2 are integration constants. As can be seen from the solutions above, if λ_1 and λ_2 are negative, $v(t)$ and $r(t)$ will tend to zero over time, which means that the ship will straighten its trajectory at the end of the disturbances. Thus, the ship is directionally stable if $\lambda_1 < 0$ and $\lambda_2 < 0$. Also, looking at C, if N_v is positive, then stability is assured. However, usually for ships, N_v is negative (bow predominates in this hydrodynamic derivative). Therefore, the final criterion for DS is:

$$\sigma_H = Y_v N_r + N_v(m\bar{U} - Y_r) > 0 \qquad (3)$$

σ_H *is the DSI in horizontal plane.*

If the ship is sailing in restricted waters, or even with ships operating in proximity to one another, then the hydrodynamic derivatives are severely altered see Eloot & Vantorre (2011). For shiphandling in a channel, the farther from the symmetry line of the channel, the greater will be the interaction with the nearest side of the channel and the more unbalanced will be the side forces and yawing moments, which makes course-keeping more difficult. This is also known as "bank effects" MacElrevey & MacElrevey, (2018). For a review of bank effects see Duarte et al. (2016).

To the mariner, a ship can have positive, negative, or neutral DS, i.e. assuming there are no external forces (MacElrevey & MacElrevey 2018):

- Positive DS: ship tends to stabilize at one course ($ROT \to 0$) when rudder is put amidships.
- Negative DS: ship turns at an increasing rate ($ROT \to \infty$) when the rudder is put amidships. These ships require more attention when turning.
- Neutral DS: ship continues to steer at the present rate ($ROT = k$) or continues its present course until external forces act.

As a great number of beamy full-bodied ships are launched (e.g., VLCCs, ULCCs), especially those with open sterns and full sections forward, the directionally unstable condition has become common. After a directionally unstable ship has started a swing, amidships rudder will not be enough to check that swing and stabilize on a course. To steady up, she will need large amounts of rudder to the opposite direction of the turn. She becomes difficult to steer and needs more attention. These ships are commonly called by mariners as "cranky" ships (MacElrevey & MacElrevey, 2018).

The following design characteristics will increase/decrease the DS of a ship (Hensen 2018, MacElrevey & MacElrevey 2018):

- Increases as length increases.
- Increases as the resistance the submerged body increases.
- Decreases as block coefficient (C_b) increases.
- Decreases as the length/beam ratio decreases.
- Decreases as the area of the forward sections increases relative to the area of the after sections (as the pivot point shifts ahead).

2.3.1 *Trim, sinkage, squat and directional stability*

The directional stability of a vessel depends on geometric characteristics of the hull, among which are slenderness, operating draft and trim. Slender forms perform better, an increased trim by the stern increases directional stability for fine sterns, whereas for round and full sterns usually skegs are indicated. The increase of deadwood or fixed skeg area aft lead to an increase in directional stability (Molland, 2008).

The trimmed condition of a ship is associated to change in relative position between the centers of gravity and buoyancy, usually due to changes in load and draft conditions. The NA can calculate the position of the center of buoyancy for each condition the projected submerged area relative to the vertical center plane of the hull. Alternatively, the hydrodynamic derivatives of equation 1 can be directly corrected by approximation, using the regression equations by Clarke (1983) coupled with Inoue & Kijima (1981, 1982) to correct trim, and Ankudinov (1985) for large angles of yaw. The trim condition will be of greater influence on the directional stability through some aspects, one is the position of the propeller relative to interface air-water (IAW) – whether it will be too close and cause aeration or it will be more immerse and comparatively less susceptible to cavitation. Other aspect of influence is the change in the center of application of the net drift force applied by the environment to the hull. The trim by stern condition will displace the position of the center of buoyancy to aft, so that in low advance speeds the yawing moment caused by a side current force will turn the bow to opposite transversal direction, which tends to help resuming ship position at route after disturbances. Conversely, the trim by head brings poor performance in directional stability. Hence, in a yawing maneuvering, the tugboat would take advantage if it pushes the hull at the head.

From the shiphandler's point of view, DS depends on the shape of the submerged body. The body itself cannot be altered for a ship underway. So, DS will only alter due to changes in trim, sinkage and by the squat effect. Squat is the decrease in UKC caused by forward motion. As a ship moves forward she develops a mean bodily sinkage together with a trimming effect. The sum of sinkage and trim, at the point where UKC is reduced the most, is called squat. It can happen by the head (when the UKC reduction is greater at the bow) or by the stern (when the UKC reduction is greater at the stern). For more details on the squat effect see MacElrevey & MacElrevey (2018) and Barrass (1995).

If a ship moves from deep into shallow water, the presence of the seabed will have an effect on the hull pressures and the squat effect will alter. When a ship squats by the head in shallow waters, it increases the forward sections of the submerged body, so the center of buoyancy moves forward, causing the ship to be more directionally unstable. Shiphandlers associate ships that squat by the head in shallow waters with directionally unstable ships. For a review of shallow water effects see Duarte et al (2016).

A commonly accepted rule of thumb to anticipate if a ship will squat by the head or by the stern in shallow water is (MacElrevey & MacElrevey (2018)): full-bodied ships ($C_b > 0.75$) will tend to squat by the head, e.g., large tankers and bull carriers; ships with finer lines ($C_b < 0.7$) will tend to trim by the stern, e.g., containerships.

Assuming there is not a strong wind on the higher bow, a ship usually steers better when the trim by the stern increases (i.e., drag increases).

3 PROPELLER

From the NA's point of view, the propeller is a device that provides thrust for the hull to overcome the net resistance force needed to develop a chosen speed in a route. According to Mandel (1960), one or more screw propellers rotating behind the hull will directly and indirectly influence the maneuverability. The direct action will be produced by the propeller itself, without its action on the hull or rudder, whereas the indirect influence results from the flow conditions around the stern of the ship, disturbed by the action of the propeller. Those disturbances will also induce effects on hull and rudder compared to the case with no propeller(s), influencing the stability and control derivatives. The author states that on ships with an odd number of propellers or with any number of unirotating propellers, they will introduce substantial forces and moments with $v = \delta = \dot{r} = 0$ approximately (δ: angle of rudder), i.e., even though with controls-fixed, straight-line stability, those ships cannot sail a straight course with rudder angle held at zero, hence a small drift angle and small rudder angle are needed, and the increase of projected area of the rudder to incident flow, bigger resistance will happen.

The origin of forces and moments by a right-handed single-screw ship, for example, is that the wake field behind it has an upward component throughout the propeller disk, resulting in a larger thrust in starboard than in port. Consequently, the center of application of the net thrust will not be at the vertical center plane of the hull, but slightly displaced to starboard, inducing a light yaw moment to port. Opposite-rotating propellers will individually generate opposite net forces and thus will not be much affected by this effect.

During a turn, the propeller will be subject to an extra flow increasing its angle of attack. The straightening influence of the hull on the angle of attack can be significative, and eventually cause undesirable vibrations and abrupt drop of thrust due to stall. For more details, see Mandel (1960) and Sileo & Steen (2011). Due to the rotation of the propeller itself, and intensified by the turning motion of the ship, the pressure distribution at starboard and port side is non-symmetric, especially at the aft. Depending on the composition of superposed flow of propeller rotation and turning direction, a net drift force is applied at the stern, so that the hull acts as a big rudder at non-zero angle of incidence, applying a yaw moment on the overall system. Regardless of the direction of rotation and number of propellers, there will be a lateral force to starboard in starboard turns and to port in port turns, hence for propellers located at stern, the direct effects exerted by them to the hull is favorable to directional stability and unfavorable to turning. According to Davidson (1945) apud Lewis (1988), the indirect detrimental influence of propeller by such effect can be alleviated if the propeller disk can be contained within the wake by the hull.

The aeration, caused by proximity of the propeller to the water surface (also called "ventilation", "suction" or "shallow water submergence effect" by mariners), as well as the emergence of the propeller also cause lateral forces and yaw moments, which are very important in starting, stopping and backing. The last two are even more important for operations in crowded waters or in proximity to fixed structures.

At low speeds the wake by the hull is negligible, so there is a loss of torque on the upper blade, bringing unbalance in comparison to the lower blade. This increments the tendency of the stern to move in the direction of motion of the upper blade. The unbalanced pressure between upper and lower blades is also observed when starting from zero speed in a back motion. The discharge flow from the backing propeller moves forward against the hull and, due to hull geometry, the portion of hull above propeller shaft axis has more surface area perpendicular to water incidence from propeller, and consequently is more affected by it than the lower portion (Figure 1).

In an eminent collision situation with forward speed, considering open waters (side space not limited), advantage of this phenomenon can be taken by reversing and highly loading the right-handed propeller rotation to favor a turning to starboard and at the same time reduce speed, and so avoid the collision. The effect of the ship turning to starboard when the propeller turns astern is known by NAs as the "Hovgaard Effect" and by mariners as the "twist effect". This effect can also be used to advantage in many other situations of ship handling, e.g.: make a turn in a canal or river that would not be possible to make with only engine ahead and rudder; to swing the stern towards the berth in a portside docking; to sweep a lee for the pilot (i.e., position the ship's side against swell and sea so the other side has calm waters and it is safer for the pilot launch to come alongside and for the pilot to embark/disembark).

From the mariner's point of view, the objective in designing a propeller is to produce the maximum

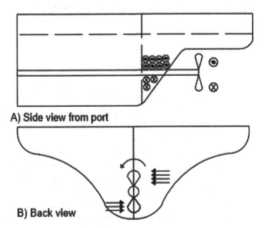

Figure 1. Unbalanced pressure between upper and lower blades as an effect of propeller action on the hull. A: side view, with inflow direction from upper and lower blades of the propeller to the hull indicated by circles. X-marked: pressure into the plane of the image, dot-marked: pressure out of the plane of the image. The number of arrows and circles indicate the intensity of pressure applied at each portion of the hull surface. B: back view, with inflow direction from upper and lower blades of the propeller to the hull indicated by horizontal arrows.

thrust along the line of the shaft from a given rotational force or torque applied to the shaft itself. Thus, propellers are designed to generate longitudinal force (ahead or astern), but in an actual ship the propeller will also always generate a side force to port or starboard. This side force is always very significant at slow maneuvering speeds and for some intricate maneuvers (e.g., portside docking at a pier) it will be even more important than the longitudinal force itself (Crenshaw, 1975).

The direction of the side force depends only on the rotation of the propeller (Crenshaw, 1975). When it turns to starboard, it generates a side force to starboard. When the propeller turns to port, it generates a side force to port.

The side force to port when turning astern is more pronounced, because the discharge of a backing propeller is directed against the stern of the ship and tends to bank up against the starboard side of the counter. Therefore, conventional ships turn significantly to starboard when the propeller turns astern ("twist effect"). Consider the following standard maneuver used by Masters to familiarize with their ship. "*While proceeding at 6 knots ahead put the engine half astern and the rudder amidships. Do nothing further except collect required data as the ship comes to a stop. [...] You will find that the ship changes heading significantly [to starboard], in some cases as much as 80 to 90 degrees in shallow water and somewhat less in deep water*" (Macelrevey & Macelrevey, 2018).

The side force of a propeller turning ahead is less significant. Small ships may present a smaller turning diameter to port than to starboard. However, these differences are insignificant for large ships such as VLCCs and ULCCs (Macelrevey & Macelrevey, 2018).

3.1 *Twin screw ships*

We find most twin-screw ships turning outboard when going ahead (i.e., right-handed starboard screw and left-handed port screw). The propellers turn in opposite directions when driving ahead or astern, so the side forces then cancel.

The outboard turning increases turning ability, e.g., for a turn to port, independently of rudder position, the pilot can put the right screw ahead and left screw astern. This generates a couple along centerline of the ship that tends to turn it to port. Also, a side force to starboard will happen at both screws, adding up and generating a double side force (on stern) to starboard, favoring the ship turn to port (Figure 2). The advantage of outboard turning is the smaller turning diameter.

Conversely, a vessel with inboard turning screws, when trying to make a turn using the propeller as a couple generates a side force opposite to this binary. Inboard turning propeller is often used on twin screw tugs. The main advantage is higher propeller efficiency. A disadvantage is the large turning

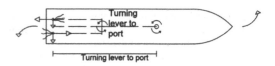

Figure 2. Twin screw ship using the couple "one engine ahead and the other astern" to generate a turning moment to port that reinforces the turning moment from the rudder. Outboard turning screws increases turning ability.

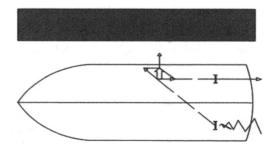

Figure 3. Flanking maneuver. Twin screw tug (inboard turning) moving sideways to starboard. Port engine ahead and starboard engine astern while applying port rudder. The side forces of the propellers reinforce the side thrust to starboard. Adapted from Hensen (2018).

diameter (Hensen, 2018). Another advantage is that inboard turning allows tugs to move sideways (so-called "flanking") even without a bow thruster (Figure 3). By setting the port engine ahead and starboard engine astern while applying port helm, the tug can move sideways to starboard. In the flanking maneuver, the propeller couple (ahead-astern) is used to move the bow to starboard while the rudder is used to move the stern also to starboard.

From the NA's point of view (Mandel, 1960), in comparison to single-screw ships, the resulting turning moment from such operation – one propeller astern, one ahead – will be relatively small, especially if the shafts are not parallel but converge forward. The effectiveness or even feasibility of the operation also depends on stern geometry, which defines the effects of the propellers on the hull. Most twin or quadruple-screw ships with single rudders have poor maneuvering qualities at low speeds compared to ships with rudders located in the race of the propeller.

4 RUDDER

At slow and moderate speeds (e.g., shiphandling in a channel, approaching berth, docking, undocking), most ships do not respond well to the rudder if the propeller is turning slow, so that there is not a good flow of water past the rudder. This may be a problem in restricted waters, since the ship must proceed at slow speeds to avoid accidents while requiring flow from the propeller through the rudder to steer the ship. If a ship is not responding well to the rudder, increasing engine revolutions for long periods of time increases speed, which is undesirable in restricted waters. The tendency of new ships with smaller rudders (to reduce resistance) makes the shiphandler's task even more difficult, so they use the commonly known "kick ahead" i.e., proceed at a moderate speed and use greater engine revolutions only for a short period of time with the rudder in the desired position, once the ship responds, decrease engine revolutions. *"By using the engine in this manner for only as long as need to obtain the desired results, the shiphandler can usually overcome any inherent deficiencies in the ship's design"* (Macelrevey & Macelrevey, 2018).

The "kick ahead" is a very common practice, particularly used with diesel ships, since immediate large changes in revolutions can be obtained. A turbine ship increases revolutions more slowly, so more care is necessary to keep the ship speed down while controlling it. The "kick astern" is also common practice and for some maneuvers, e.g., back and fill, the ship handler alternately uses it alternated with kick ahead several times in a short period time, at the risk of exhausting the supply of starting air. Hence, larger rudders, despite the bigger resistance and fuel consumption at cruising speed, allow safer maneuvers. Likewise, greater volumes of starting air, although occupying more space, reduce the likelihood of accidents in ports and associated costs during lifetime of a ship.

5 WIND AND CURRENT

In ordinary conditions, the resultant external force acting on a ship can only be originated in the aerodynamic and hydrodynamic forces acting on the hull, superstructure and appendages. Despite the importance of the aerodynamic forces, for example, for turning moments in ships with large windage areas, the NA usually ignores aerodynamic forces for standard maneuvers when studying the turning and maneuvering of ships, where they will be considered only as disturbing forces.

To the shiphandler, it is very important to understand the effect of wind and current on the ship maneuverability, as will be further explained. He must think ahead of the ship and use wind and current to its best advantage, instead of reacting to these forces as they occur.

Mariners use a simple rule of thumb to judge the predominance of wind or current from different directions, i.e.: 30 knots of wind is equivalent of 1 knot of current (Crenshaw, 1975; MacElrevey & MacElrevey, 2018).

When designing the ship's freeboard and superstructure, ship designers usually make calculations to evaluate the air and wind resistance at cruising speed, since it increases the ship's resistance to ahead motion, increasing fuel consumption and so increases operational costs. However, they usually ignore other costs related to the shape and dimensions of the freeboard at slow maneuvering speeds. As speed decreases (e.g., ship arriving at the port of destination), the effect of wind becomes more significant to the ship control. The lower the ship's speed, the greater the effect of wind and the more difficult to steer in a steady course. The main factor determining how much effect the wind will have on steering is the freeboard or "sail area" that the ship presents (MacElrevey & MacElrevey, 2018).

At very slow maneuvering speeds, a relation between the type of ship, velocity of wind, V_w, and velocity of ship, V_{ship}, can be used as an indicator to anticipate a safe minimum speed that will not significantly affect steering, i.e.:

- For high-sided ships (passenger, container, liquefied natural gas, or other high freeboard vessels) the wind becomes significant when $V_w \geq 3 \times V_{ship}$.
- For a loaded tanker, when $V_w \geq 5 \times V_{ship}$.
- Other types of ships, e.g. general cargo, will fall between these two ratios, depending on their superstructure configuration (MacElrevey & MacElrevey, 2018).

For example, a passenger with many decks of closed balconies trying to steer on a channel at speeds lower than 5 knots, will certainly have difficulties when $V_w \geq 15$ knots and may require tugs or bow/stern thrusters. Hence, more "sail area" may increase not only operational costs with fuel, but also with thrusters (construction and maintenance costs) and/or tug service (operational costs).

The layout of the superstructures will also influence on how the ship will react to the wind as speed is reduced. The center of pressure of the wind (CPW) or, center of lateral resistance, on the hull determines the behavior of the ship in the wind. Most ship configurations have their superstructures and deck cargo more concentrated astern than ahead, so the CPW will fall somewhere between amidships and the stern. These ships will behave as follows with rudder amidships (MacElrevey & MacElrevey, 2018):

- When going ahead, the ship will tend to turn against the wind (upwind) (Figure 4 (a)).
- When dead in the water, the ship will tend to lie beam to the wind (Figure 4 (b)).
- With sternway, the ship will want to back against the wind (Figure 4 (c)).

This is a rule of thumb for the majority of ships.

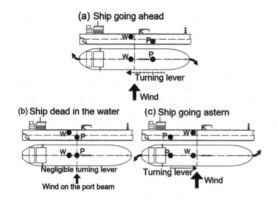

Figure 4. (a) Oil tanker dead in the water tends to lie beam to the wind; (b) Oil tanker going ahead tends to turn against the wind; (c) Oil tanker going astern tends to back against the wind.

6 DISCUSSION

The hydrodynamicist is concerned with building and solving sophisticated mathematical models that represent the maneuvering characteristics of a ship design to evaluate different design alternatives and see how they change the maneuvering performance. On the other hand, the shiphandler must deal with the ship as built. A pilot must understand the maneuvering characteristics of a wide variety of ships to anticipate the ship response to a set of actions. For example, when turning the ship around a bend with a strong wind, when approaching the berth, when coming alongside. Sophisticated calculations are unnecessary and even inconvenient, since the pilot will not have enough time for that.

Based on experience, pilots have been using rules of thumb to predict the ship's behavior in a practical way, which may be useful for ship design. Some examples:

- The ship squats by the head in shallow waters when her $C_b > 0.8$ and so DS will decrease. Steering becomes more difficult.
- The bow thruster is not reliable to assist in turns at moderate speed. It is not effective when ship speed is greater than 2 knots.
- The lower the ship's speed the greater the importance of the wind.
- For high-sided ships, the wind will become significant when $V_w \geq 3 \times V_{ship}$. For heavy ships, when $V_w \geq 5 \times V_{ship}$.

Following are the main connections between what NAs get from theory and calculations and the shiphandlers' point of view concerning maneuvering.

- Separation and cavitation are seen by NAs as power efficiency losses and possible local damage in the case of cavitation, incurring in costs. To the shiphandler both are disturbances to the rudder, hull and propeller forces that bring vibration, difficulty and unpredictability in maneuvering. Vibration in shallow waters indicates too high ship speed.
- For NAs, increased DS is sometimes associated with worse maneuvering performance due to the larger turning diameter. However, most pilots prefer more directional stable ships as they steer better in shallow waters.
- On many routes vessel length and draft has increased to the maximum allowed limit of the port. Disregarding technological advances, increasing the ship's beam may be the only way to increase carrying capacity and the operator's profit, so it has become a tendency in merchant ship design to increase the beam for a same length, resulting in low length-to-beam ratio, which decreases DS. A possible solution has been to fit these ships with twin skegs, twin rudders and twin screws, as is the case of V-Max tankers (Wärtsilä, 2019).
- Regarding twin screws with twin rudders, NA books underestimate the importance of the couple (one engine on ahead and the other on astern) to make turns. Shiphandlers books state that, for outboard turning, the turning ability of ships increases significantly, while inboard turning are more useful for tugs because they can move sideways without a bow-thruster.

7 CONCLUSIONS

In this study, we have conducted a preliminary review on shiphandling, comprising the literature on naval architecture and nautical sciences. Basic principles are reviewed in Section 2. The influence of the propeller, rudder and wind/current in shiphandling are presented in Sections 3, 4 and 5, respectively. The rules of thumb used by pilots, and the main connections of concepts between ship designers and mariners are summarized in Section 6. Based on this review, conceptual gaps between ship designers and mariners are identified and discussed in Section 6.

There is not a common agreement in the literature. Therefore, we recommend that neither NAs nor mariners should rely their theoretical knowledge on a single publication, but better study an extensive bibliography to understand the main possibilities. The recommended references are in the bibliography section, from which the present concepts were extracted. All comments and conclusions do not include the authors' personal opinions, but solely what is found in the literature. Some comments/conclusions may be trivial, not accurate or even not correct, but such judgement does not belong to the purpose of this work.

For future works, we propose: more research on the topics raised in the discussion section in order to investigate what is correct and not correct, especially when there are contradictory conclusions in the literature; and reviewing other important forces in shiphandling such as anchors, mooring lines and tugs.

REFERENCES

Ankudinov, V. 1985. Ship Manoeuvring Simulation Model Including Regimes Of Slow Speeds And Large Drift Angles. Report For The First International Maritime Simulation Symposium, Munich, Germany

Asgari, P. 2018. Roll Damping Estimation Via Sway-Roll Coupled Equation And The Moirc (Most Often Instantaneous Rotation Center) Consideration. Universidade Federal do Rio de Janeiro.

Barrass, C.B. 1995. Ship Squat. In Squat Interaction Manoeuvring, Humberside Branch Seminar: The Nautical Institute, 21–33.

Clarke D., Gedling P. & Hine G. 1983. The Application Of Manoeuvring Criteria In Hull Design Using Linear Theory, Transactions Rina, Vol. 125, Pp. 45–68.

Crenshaw, S. R. 1975. Naval Shiphandling (4th Edition: 1975). Annapolis (Maryland): Naval Institute Press.

Davidson, K.S.M. 1945. Concerning The Differences In Minimum Turning Diameters Of Cruisers And Destroyers, ETT Technical Memo 73.

Dewhurst, P., Knight, W. & Boothroyd, G. 2001. Product Design For Manufacturing And Assembly. New York: Marcel Dekker,

Dongkon, L. & Kyung-Ho, L. 1999. An Approach To Case-Based System For Conceptual Ship Design Assistant. Expert Systems With Applications. 16:2 97–104.

DPC. 2011. Normam-12 - Normas Da Autoridade Marítima Para O Serviço De Praticagem. Marinha Do Brasil, Diretoria De Portos E Costas (Dpc).

Duarte, H.O. et al. 2016. Review of Practical Aspects of Shallow Water and Bank Effects. Transactions of the Royal Institution of Naval Architects Part A: International Journal of Maritime Engineering 158: 177–86.

Eloot, K. & Vantorre, M. 2011. Ship Behaviour In Shallow And Confined Water: An Overview Of Hydrodynamic Effects Through Efd.: 20.

Fayol, H. 1949. General And Industrial Management. London: Translation By Constance Stotts, Sir Isaac Pitman & Sons, 1949

Fonseca, M.M. 2019. *Arte Naval*. 1th Ed. Rio De Janeiro: Serviço De Documentação Da Marinha.

Fragoso, A.O & Cajaty, M. 2002. Rebocadores Portuários. Rio De Janeiro: Conapra.

Harvald S.A. 1983. Resistance and propulsion of ships, Volume 12 de Ocean engineering,Edição ilustrada Editora Wiley, Num. págs. 353 páginas.

Hensen, H. 2018. Tug Use In Port, A Pratical Guide (3rd Edition). London: The Nautical Institute.

Inoue, S., Hirano, M. & Kijima, K. 1981. Hydrodynamic Derivatives on Ship Manoeuvring, International Shipbuilding Progress, No. 321, Vol. 28.

Inoue, S., Hirano, M. & Kijima, K. 1982. Takashina, J., A Practical Calculation Method of Ship Maneuvering Motion, International Shipbuilding Progress, No. 336, Vol. 29

Kobylinski, L.K. 2003. Directional Stability Of Ships And Safe Handling. In Marine Technology V, ed. Wessex institute of technology., 213–22.

Lamb, T. 2003. Ship Design And Construction. 2. Ed. Jersey City: The Society Of Naval Architects & Marine Engineers.

Lamb, T. 2003. Design/Production Integration. Em Lamb, Thomas (Ed.) - Chapter 14: Ship Design And Construction. Jersey City: Society Of Naval Architects And Marine Engineers. Isbn 0939773104. P. 14.1 —-14.70.

Lars, L., Hoyte, C. & Raven, J. 2010. Randolph Paulling. Ship Resistance And Flow. Ed. J. Randolph Paulling. Society Of Naval Architects And Marine Engineers.

Lewis, E.V. 1988. Principles Of Naval Architecture. Society Of Naval Architects.

Macelrevey, D.H. & Macelrevey, D.E. 2018 - Shiphandling For The Mariner. Atglen, Pa: Schiffer Publishing Ltd.

Mandel, P. 1953. Some hydrodynamic aspect of appendage design. Transactions of the society of Naval Architects and Marine Engineers, Vol. 61, pp. 464–515.

Mandel, P. 1960. The Potentialof Semi-submerged in Rough Water Operation, New England Section Paper, Soc. Nav. ARchitectus Marine Engrs., MAr.

Miguens, Altineu Pires. 1996. *Navegação: A Ciência e a Arte*. Rio de Janeiro: DHN.

Molland, A.F. 2008. Marine Rudders and Control Surfaces: Principles, Data, Design and Applications Hardcover September 12 by Stephen R. Turnock Anthony F. Molland

Moyst, H. 2001. Optimizing The Integration Of Ship Design With Construction: A Linear Programming Approach. Halifax: Master's Dissertation, Department Of Industrial Engineering, Dalhousie University

Pianc. 1992. Capability of ship manoeuvring simulation models for approach channels and fairways in harbours: Report of Working Group no. 20 of Permanent Technical Committee II, Supplement to PIANC Bulletin, No. 77, 49 pp.

Routh, E.J. 1877. A Treatise On The Stability Of A Given State Of Motion: Particularly Steady Motion.

Ross, J. M. 1993. Integrated Ship Design And Its Role In Enhancing Ship Production. Ship Production Symposium. Williamsburg Virginia: The National Shipbuilding Research Program.

Sileo, L. & Steen, S. 2011. "Lateral Force And Turning Moment On A Reversing Ship." Http://Www.Marinepropulsors.Com/Smp/Files/Downloads/Smp11/Paper/Ta3-4_Sileo.Pdf.

Taylor, F. W. 1911. Principles Of Scientific Management. New York: Harper & Row.

Ulrich, K.T. & Ellison, D.J. 2005. Beyond Make-Buy: Internalization And Integration Of Design And Production. Production And Operations Management. 14:3 (2005) 315–330.

Wärtsilä. 2019. V-Max Tankers STENA VISION and STENA VICTORY. Consult. dec. 17 2019 https://www.wartsila.com/encyclopedia/term/v-max-tankers-stena-vision-and-stena-victory.

White, F. M. (2010), "Fluid Mechanics", (7th edition), New York, NY: McGraw-Hill Science/Engineering/Math pp 428–430

A new estimation concept for hydrodynamic derivatives of ship manoeuvrability using machine learning toolkits

L. Duan & T. Iseki
Tokyo University of Marine Science and Technology, Tokyo, Japan

ABSTRACT: Results of PMM (pure swaying) tests are analysed by a new estimation concept. The analysis program is written in *Python* with importing *"Scikit-learn"* library. Several measured time series of pure swaying tests are decomposed as data points and considered as a kind of Big-data including measurement noises. In the stochastic analysis, the data points are scattered in a 3D space and the hydrodynamic derivatives are evaluated as slopes of the optimum fitted surface. The contour map of the surface provides many information for making up mathematical models of ship manoeuvrability. This concludes that the machine learning toolkits can be applied to evaluation of ship manoeuvring performances.

1 INTRODUCTION

In the design stage of ships, it is very important to predict their manoeuvring performances. Captive model tests, such as oblique towing tests and circular motion tests with rotating arm mechanism, are commonly carried out, and are effective to evaluate the hydrodynamic derivatives precisely. On the other hand, PMM (Planar Motion Mechanism) tests are also carried out to estimate the hydrodynamic derivatives. Especially, PMM tests in a circulating water channel are not very accurate but are convenient and practical. In the analysis of measured forces, harmonic analyses are usually applied to decompose the measured signals into the velocity related force and the acceleration related force. The harmonic analysis is also effective to remove the noises that are the effect of turbulent flows in the water channel. In some cases of PMM tests, however, the estimated hydrodynamic derivatives show the dependency on the frequency and the amplitude of forced motions. Physical understanding of the frequency dependency is not so easy. One of the authors tried to develop a real-time estimation method of hydrodynamic derivatives in order to investigate the frequency dependencies in detail (Iseki 2019, Sekine et al. 2017, Uchibori et al. 2016, Yamanaka et al. 2016).

On the other hand, machine learning techniques have been applied in many research fields and achieved many successes recently. *Python* is one of the most useful computer languages for machine learning because many kinds of libraries are provided as the toolkits. *"Scikit-learn"* is an open-source project library for machine learning and widely used in many fields.

In this paper, the results of PMM (pure swaying) tests are analysed by a new estimation concept. The analysis program is written in *Python* with importing the *"Scikit-learn"* library. Several measured time series of PMM tests are decomposed as data points and considered as a kind of Big-data including measurement noises. In the analysis, the data points are scattered in a 3D space and the hydrodynamic derivatives are evaluated as slopes of the optimum fitted surface. The contour map of the surface provides many information to understand the dependency on the frequency and the amplitude of forced motions. It is shown that the machine learning toolkits can be used to evaluate ship manoeuvring performances.

2 PMM TESTS AND THE ANALYSIS

2.1 Model experiment

The model experiments were conducted using the vertically circulating water channel of Tokyo University of Marine Science and Technology (TUMSAT). The photo and specifications are shown in Figure 1 and Table 1, respectively. A model ship of the series 60 was used and the principal particulars are listed in Table 2. The simple PMM system equipped on the channel can provide sway motion (±0.4m max), yaw motion (±30°max) with the period from 8s to 20s. The hydrodynamic forces acting on the model were measured by a 3-component load cells which was set between the connecting strut and the model ship. The data was measured every 0.2s and recorded by a laptop computer. A scene of the experiments are shown in Figure 2.

DOI: 10.1201/9781003216599-19

Figure 1. Vertically circulating water channel of TUMSAT.

Table 1. Specifications of vertically circulating water channel.

Main particulars	Contents
Type	2 inpeller type
Dimension	L 12.4m × W 2.3m × H 5.2m
Observation part	L 3.3m × W 1.5m × d 0.8m
Flow speeds	0 – 2.5m/s
Control type	Inverter control

Table 2. Model ship (series 60).

Main particulars	Contents
Length (P.P.)	1200 mm
Draught	68.6 mm
Cb	0.7
Scale ratio	1/101.6

Figure 2. The model ship under PMM tests.

2.2 Pure swaying tests

Pure swaying tests in the circulating water channel were conducted with various flow velocities and the swaying amplitude.

Figure 3 shows the results of a pure swaying test. The flow velocity was fixed to 0.88m/s, and the swaying amplitude and the period were set to 0.3m and 9.84s, respectively. The graphs indicate the time histories of the longitudinal force (X_{LC}), lateral force (Y_{LC}), yaw moment (N_{LC}) that were measured by the 3-component load cells. The swaying motion (*Sway* in the figure) was measured by a potentiometer. The graphs are also indicating the results of harmonic analyses. The suffix "-*H*" means the results of harmonic analyses with the swaying frequency. The suffixes "-*H2*" and "-*H3*" mean the non-linear components analysed by the doubled and tripled swaying frequencies of the swaying motion, respectively. The measured data involves some noises due to surface ripples and turbulent flows in the channel, however, it can be seen that the noises were successfully removed, compared to analysed results.

2.3 Equations of motions

Motion equations of the pure swaying test considered in this paper are expressed as follows:

$$X_{LC} = X_{\dot{v}}\dot{v} + X_v v + X_{vv} v^2 \quad (1)$$

$$Y_{LC} = -(m + m_y)\dot{v} + Y_v v + Y_{vvv} v^3 \quad (2)$$

$$N_{LC} = N_{\dot{v}}\dot{v} + N_v v + N_{vvv} v^3 \quad (3)$$

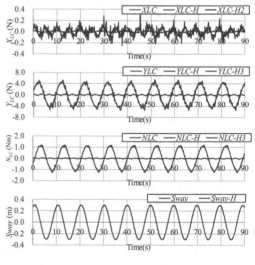

Figure 3. Time histories of the longitudinal force (X_{LC}), lateral force (Y_{LC}), yaw moment (N_{LC}) measured by the load cells, and the swaying motion (*Sway*) measured by the potentiometer.

where X_{LC}, Y_{LC}, N_{LC} are the measured forces and the moment, $X_{\dot{v}}$, X_v, X_{vv}, m_y, Y_v, Y_{vvv}, $N_{\dot{v}}$, N_v, N_{vvv} are the hydrodynamic derivatives to be estimated.

Theoretically, the hydrodynamic derivatives $X_{\dot{v}}$ and X_v should become zero. In the actual measurement, however, the non-uniform flow in the water channel yields a certain value for the hydrodynamic derivatives. On the other hand, the X_{vv} appears clearly with a doubled swaying frequency. The drag force acting on the ship's hull becomes maximum when the ship crosses the centre line of the swaying motion and takes minimum value at the both sides. The drag force appears periodically regardless of the swaying direction, and the frequency becomes double of the swaying frequency.

2.4 Results of harmonic analyses

In harmonic analyses, the measured forces and the moment are decomposed into the proportional components of the swaying velocity and the swaying acceleration. In order to evaluate the non-linear hydrodynamic derivatives, the measured signals should be decomposed by the doubled and tripled swaying frequencies. The harmonic analysis is also effective to remove the noises caused by the surface ripples and turbulent flows in the water channel. Therefore, it should be noted that the harmonic analysis acts as a signal filter and removes much information.

Table 3 shows the estimated non-dimensional hydrodynamic derivatives. Non-dimensionalizations of the hydrodynamic derivatives are carried out by dividing the both sides of Equations 1 and 2 by $\rho L d U^2/2$ and Equation 3 by $\rho L^2 d U^2/2$, respectively. The concrete form of the non-dimensionalized hydrodynamic derivatives are as follows:

$$X'_{\dot{v}} \text{ or } m'_y = \frac{X_{\dot{v}} \text{ or } m_y}{\frac{1}{2}\rho L^2 d}, \quad X'_v \text{ or } Y'_v = \frac{X_v \text{ or } Y_v}{\frac{1}{2}\rho L d U},$$

$$X'_{vv} = \frac{X_{vv}}{\frac{1}{2}\rho L d}, \quad Y'_{vvv} = \frac{Y_{vvv}}{\frac{1}{2}\rho L d}, \quad N'_{\dot{v}} = \frac{N_{\dot{v}}}{\frac{1}{2}\rho L^3 d}, \quad (4)$$

$$N'_v = \frac{N_v}{\frac{1}{2}\rho L^2 d U}, \quad N'_{vvv} = \frac{N_{vvv}}{\frac{1}{2}\rho L^2 d}.$$

where ρ, L, d and U are the water density, ship length, draught and flow velocity, respectively. As mentioned in the previous section, the hydrodynamic derivatives X'_v, $X'_{\dot{v}}$ and X'_v should become zero theoretically, therefore, the derivatives take small values in Table 3. On the other hand, the X'_{vv} takes rather large value based on the drag force acting on the ship's hull.

Figure 4 shows the change of the nine non-dimensional hydrodynamic derivatives with the swaying period. The pure swaying tests were carried out in the same flow velocity U=0.88m/s. The swaying period was changed eight times from 9.84s to 16.41s. In the graph, it can be seen that the linear

Table 3. Estimated non-dimensional hydrodynamic derivatives by harmonic analyses.

Coef.	value	Coef.	value	Coef.	value
X'_v	0.0025	Y'_v	-0.3401	N'_v	-0.1337
$X'_{\dot{v}}$	-0.0004	m'_y	0.3609	$N'_{\dot{v}}$	-0.0102
X'_{vv}	-0.0721	Y'_{vvv}	-2.9285	N'_{vvv}	-0.1066

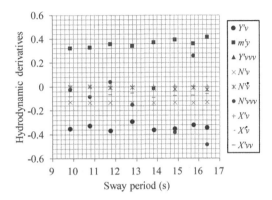

Figure 4. Non-dimensional hydrodynamic derivatives of eight pure swaying tests carried out in the same flow velocity.

hydrodynamic derivative m'_y shows a dependency on the swaying period slightly, compared to other linear hydrodynamic derivatives. On the other hand, N'_{vvv} seems to be unstable because of the small signal of the swaying acceleration. In order to obtain more accurate results from the data with noises, more reasonable stochastic analysis is required.

3 ANALYSIS BY USING PYTHON PROGRAM AND THE LIBRARIES.

Python is one of the most popular programing languages for the machine learning. The various libraries are the reason why *Python* is frequently used in many research fields. *Pandas*, *NumPy*, *Matplotlib*, *SciPy* and *"Scikit-learn"* are the libraries that are provided as parts of a package called *Anaconda*. Especially, *"Scikit-learn"* is very famous as a machine learning library for *Python*. In this paper, the program was written by *Python* 3.7.6 and the libraries are used for 3D visualization and stochastic analysis.

3.1 Python and the library SciPy

Figure 5 shows a 3D plot result of the harmonic analysis of lateral force (Y'_{LC}). The bottom coordinate axes are the non-dimensional sway velocity and the acceleration. The vertical axis denotes the non-dimensional lateral force (Y'_{LC}). The eight rings

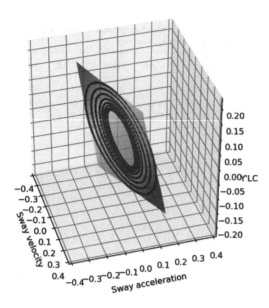

Figure 5. 3D plot of the results of harmonic analyses for lateral force (Y'_{LC}).

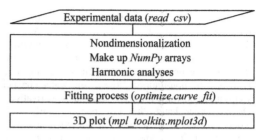

Figure 6. Flowchart of the algorithm implemented for Figure 5.

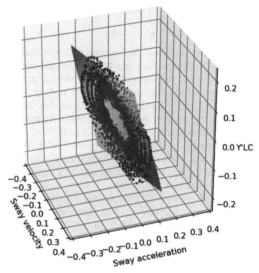

Figure 7. 3D plot of the raw data of the lateral force (Y'_{LC}) and the fitted surface.

plotted in the 3D graph are the trajectories of the pure swaying tests. The plane indicated in the graph was fitted by the module "*optimize.curve_fit*" of "*SciPy*" library. The fitted surface seems to be a plane because the scattered data is the results of harmonic analyses. Each ring belongs to a plane and the planes almost the same. Looking at the plane, the slopes are negative with respect to both axes on the bottom. It means that Y'_{LC} acts as the drag force that is proportional to the sway velocity and acceleration.

The algorithm implemented for Figure 5 consists of four parts (Figure 6). The first part is the file-reading routine in which the module "*read_csv*" of "*Pandas*" library is used. In the second part, after nondimensionalization, the data were transformed to arrays using "*NumPy*" library. Using the "*NumPy array*", harmonic analyses could be carried out without *for-loops* or *while-loops*. In the third part, Equation 2 was fitted using "*optimize.curve_fit*" of "*SciPy*" library. Finally, the 3D graph was drawn using "*mpl_toolkits.mplot3d*" of "*Matplotlib*" library. Therefore, it can be said that most of the program can be completed by calling various modules.

Figure 7 shows a 3D plot of the raw data of lateral force (Y'_{LC}). The only difference from Figure 5 is the Y'_{LC} was not filtered by the harmonic analysis. If the raw data of lateral force (Y'_{LC}) can be directly fitted by an optimum curved surface, there is no need to carry out harmonic analyses. The curved surface can be defined by Equation 2. It means that the equation of motion can be recognized as an equation of a curved surface and the coefficients coincide with the hydrodynamic derivatives. Compared to Figure 5, it is observed that the curvature of the surface becomes slightly large. This means that the measured data includes non-linearity.

Figure 8 shows a contour map of the optimum surface of Figure 7. It can be seen that the contour lines descend in the upper right direction, and it means that the lateral force (Y'_{LC}) is acting as a drag force that is proportional to the sway velocity and the sway acceleration. Moreover, the slightly curved contour lines are indicating the existence of a non-linear relationship.

Table 4 shows comparisons of non-dimensional hydrodynamic derivatives estimated by harmonic analyses and the curve fitting module of "*SchiPy*". The results of "Harmonic" is the same results listed in Table 3. On the other hand, the "*Curve_fit*" and "*Curve_fit* (raw)" are showing the results estimated from the fitted surface shown in Figure 5 and 6, respectively. Looking at the Y'_{vvv} results, the "*Curve_fit*" shows smaller value compared to the "*Curve_fit* (raw)". It can be considered that the non-linear components were filtered by the harmonic analysis. Therefore, it can be said that the curve fitting procedure to

Table 4. Non-dimensional hydrodynamic derivatives estimated by harmonic analysis, curve fitting to the harmonic analysed Y'_{LC} and curve fitting to the raw Y'_{LC} data points.

Coef.	Harmonic	Curve_fit	Curve_fit (raw)
Y'_v	-0.3401	-0.3766	-0.3364
m'_y	0.3609	0.3438	0.3423
Y'_{vvv}	-2.9285	-1.6095	-3.4678

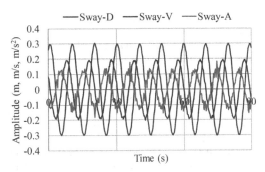

Figure 9. Time histories of the measured swaying displacement (Sway-D) and the numerically evaluated velocity (Sway-V) and acceleration (Sway-D).

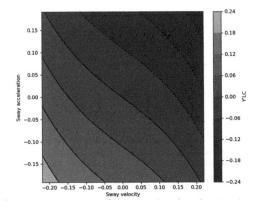

Figure 8. Contour map of the curved surface fitted to the raw data of the lateral force (Y_{LC}).

the raw data is effective to estimate the non-linear component of the hydrodynamic derivatives.

3.2 Analysis using machine learning library "Scikit-learn"

It has been shown that harmonic analyses can be considered as a kind of filtering procedure. Therefore, the curve fitting to the raw data can be considered as better estimating procedure for non-linear hydrodynamic derivatives. However, the results discussed in the previous section are based on the theoretically estimated velocities and accelerations. The actual procedure in the previous section is as follows. Firstly, the harmonic analysis is applied to the measured swaying displacement and the actual frequency and the amplitude are estimated. Secondary, the signal of velocities and accelerations are theoretically generated using the estimated frequency and amplitude. Therefore, numerical differentiation of the raw swaying motion data can be considered as the second choice and considered to be advantageous in nonlinear analysis. The numerical differentiation was carried out by "*np.gradient*" of "*NumPy*" library to estimate the velocity and the acceleration in this section.

Figure 9 shows time histories of the measured swaying displacement (Sway-D), the velocity (Sway-V) and the acceleration (Sway-A) that were evaluated by numerical differentiation. There seems to be no noises in the measured sway displacement.

Looking at the Sway-A, however, rather large fluctuation can be seen in the time histories. Of course, some amount of the fluctuation came from the numerical differentiation, but the actual rattling of the PMM system must be included in the fluctuation. Therefore, it can be considered that easy application of harmonic analysis to the sway displacement can be a risk of deleting important signals. In order to increase the accuracy of the curve fitting, number of data points should be increased from the stochastic viewpoint. In this section, 44,649 data points are introduced from 99 pure swaying tests.

Figure 10 shows a 3D plot of the 44,649 raw data points from 99 pure swaying tests. Looking at the fitted surface, it can be seen that the curvature with respect to the sway velocity axis becomes slightly large compared to Figure 7. In this analysis, Equation 2 is still the equation of the curved surface to be fitted. Therefore, it can be said that the choice of the

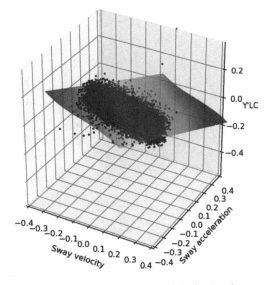

Figure 10. 3D plot of the raw data and the fitted surface.

function is important and can have a significant effect on the fitted results.

Figure 11 is the same 3D plot with Figure 10, but the function to be fitted is a cubic polynomial of the sway velocity and acceleration. Therefore, 10 coefficients, including constant term, were provided by the fitting process. In the Python program, the module "*optimize.curve_fit*" of "*SciPy*" library, indicated in Figure 6, was simply replaced by the module "*linear_model.BayesianRidge*" of "*Scikit-learn*" library. Modification of the program codes is very simple due to the extensive modules of libraries. Looking at the fitted curved surface, over fitting situation can be seen. The cause seems to be due to outliers in the upper right and the outliers are mainly caused by numerical differentiation for the swaying acceleration shown in Figure 9.

Figure 12 is a 3D plot of the raw data of 99 pure swaying tests, but 447 data points, that are indicated by red markers in the graph, were neglected as outliers by using the module "*LocalOutlierFactor*" of "*Scikit-learn*" library. The parameter called "*contamination*" was set to 0.01. The curved surface was also fitted by "*linear_model.BayesianRidge*".

Table 5 shows comparisons of non-dimensional hydrodynamic derivatives estimated by the module "*Curve_fit*" of "*SchiPy*" library and the module "*BayesianRidge*" of "*Scikit-learn*" library with/without considering outliers. The "*BayesianRidge*" is applied to a cubic polynomial function, while the "*Curve_fit*" is applied to Equation 2. Therefore, many hydrodynamic derivatives, that are not used in ordinary cases, are also evaluated. Comparing the two "*BayesianRidge*", considerable difference cannot be observed. This concludes that the outliers don't affect the estimates so much.

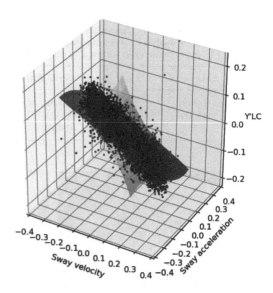

Figure 12. 3D plot of the raw data and the fitted surface by "*linear_model.BayesianRidge*" of "*Scikit-learn*" with "*LocalOutlierFactor*". The red colored markers were ignored as outliers in the fitting process.

Table 5. Comparison of non-dimensional hydrodynamic derivatives estimated by curve fitting and the module "*BayesianRidge*" of "Scikit-learn" with/without outliers.

Coef.	Curve_fit	BayesianRidge with outliers	BayesianRidge without outliers
Y'_v	-0.3476	-0.3488	-0.3420
m'_y	0.2482	0.2940	0.3133
Y'_{vv}	N/A	-0.0862	-0.0781
$Y'_{v\dot{v}}$	N/A	0.0365	0.0261
$Y'_{\dot{v}\dot{v}}$	N/A	-0.0185	0.0179
Y'_{vvv}	-3.1364	-3.1185	-3.2524
$Y'_{vv\dot{v}}$	N/A	3.1060	3.4091
$Y'_{v\dot{v}\dot{v}}$	N/A	0.1895	-0.7280
$Y'_{\dot{v}\dot{v}\dot{v}}$	N/A	0.9476	1.5728

Figure 13 shows contour map of the curved surface that is shown in Figure 12. Compared to Figure 8, the patterns of contours are quite different, and curvature of the lines is suggesting a non-linear relationship between the lateral force (Y'_{LC}) and the sway velocity and the sway acceleration. This can be concluded that mathematical models for ship manoeuvrability should be examined by referring to the contour map obtained by many experimental results.

Figure 14 is a 3D plot of the raw longitudinal force (X'_{LC}) data of 99 pure swaying tests. The red markers are indicating the neglected outliers by using the module "*LocalOutlierFactor*" of "*Scikit-learn*" library. The parameter called contamination was set to 0.01. In this case, Equation 1 was not adopted as the function to be fitted. However,

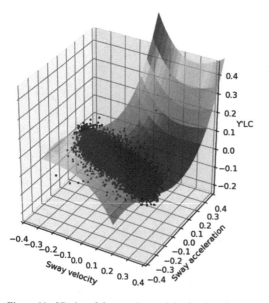

Figure 11. 3D plot of the raw data and the fitted surface by "*linear_model.BayesianRidge*" of "*Scikit-learn*".

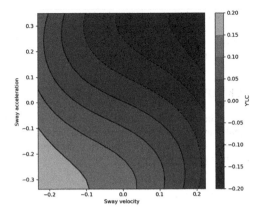

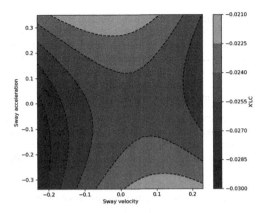

Figure 13. Contour map of the curved surface fitted to the raw data of the lateral force (Y'_{LC}).

Figure 15. Contour map of the curved surface fitted to the raw data of the lateral force (X'_{LC}).

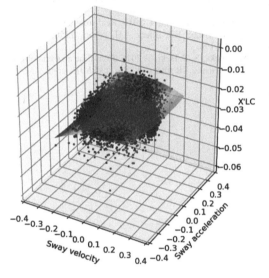

Figure 14. 3D plot of the raw longitudinal force (X_{LC}) data of 99 pure swaying tests and the fitted surface by "*linear_ model.BayesianRidge*" of "*Scikit-learn*" with "*LocalOutlierFactor*". The red colored markers were ignored as outliers in the fitting process.

considering symmetry, the function to be fitted was assumed to be a quadratic polynomial of the sway velocity and acceleration. The curved surface was fitted by the module "*linear_model.BayesianRidge*" of "*Scikit-learn*" library. There can be seen the large curvature with respect to the sway velocity axis and it coincides with the non-linearity of the X'_{vv} based on the drag force acting on the ship's hull.

Figure 15 shows contour map of the fitted surface that is shown in Figure 14. Compared to Figure 13, the pattern of contours is quite different and indicates saddle-shaped surface of the longitudinal force (X'_{LC}). The saddle-shape appears when many experimental points are analyzed simultaneously. This can

Table 6. Estimated non-dimensional hydrodynamic derivatives by harmonic analyses and the module "*BayesianRidge*" of "Scikit-learn" with use of "*LocalOutlierFactor*".

Coef.	Harmonic	BayesianRidge
X'_v	0.0025	0.0055
$X'_{\dot{v}}$	-0.0004	0.0017
X'_{vv}	-0.0721	-0.0590
$X'_{v\dot{v}}$	N/A	-0.0305
$X'_{\dot{v}\dot{v}}$	N/A	0.0218

be said as an advantage of using a machine learning library.

Table 6 shows comparison of non-dimensional hydrodynamic derivatives estimated by harmonic analysis and the module "*BayesianRidge*" of "*Scikit-learn*" library with use of "*LocalOutlierFactor*". In this application, the "*BayesianRidge*" is applied to a quadratic polynomial function. As mentioned in the section 2.3, the hydrodynamic derivatives $X'_{\dot{v}}$ and X'_v should become zero theoretically. On the other hand, the time history of the longitudinal force (X_{LC}) in Figure 3 is suggesting existence of X'_{vv}. As shown by Table 6, the second order hydrodynamic derivatives take larger value compared to the linear hydrodynamic derivatives. This concludes that the machine learning toolkits are very useful for understanding the overall trends of mathematical models of ship manoeuvrability.

4 CONCLUSIONS

In this paper, the results of PMM (pure swaying) tests were analysed by a new estimation concept. The analysis program was written by *Python* with importing the "*Scikit-learn*" library that is often used in the machine learning. Several measured time series of pure swaying tests were analyzed as a kind of Big-data involving measurement noises. In the analysis, the data points were scattered in a 3D space and the hydrodynamic derivatives were evaluated as slopes of the optimum fitted surface. The results obtained in this paper are summarized below:

- The fitted surface to the scattered data points has negative slopes with respect to velocity and acceleration axes. This means that the hydrodynamic force acts as the drag force proportional to the sway velocity and acceleration.
- The curve fitting procedure to the raw data is effective to estimate the non-linear component of hydrodynamic derivatives.
- Definition of the function to be fitted has a risk of deleting important signals that indicating non-linear component of hydrodynamic derivatives.
- Removal of the outliers doesn't affect the estimates so much in use of the module *"Bayesian-Ridge"* of *"Scikit-learn"*.
- Mathematical models for ship manoeuvrability should be examined by comparing to the contour map obtained by many experimental results.

This concludes that the machine learning toolkits are very useful for understanding the overall trends of mathematical models of ship manoeuvrability.

ACKNOWLEDGEMENTS

The authors express sincere gratitude to Mr. Yuta Tanaka and Haruto Tasaki, undergraduate students of Tokyo University of Marine Science and Technology.

REFERENCES

Iseki, T. 2019. Real-time estimation of the ship manoeuvrable range in wind. *Ocean Engineering* 190. https://doi.org/10.1016/j.oceaneng.2019.106396.

Sekine, S., Ohta, Y. & Iseki, T. 2017. Real-time Analysis of Non-linear Hydrodynamic Derivatives, *Proc. Asia Navigation Conference*.Zhanjiang.

Uchibori, U. & Iseki, T. 2016. Real-time analysis of PMM tests using IIR filters - II., Proc. 135th JIN conf., 195–196.

Yamanaka, S. & Iseki, T. 2016. Real-time analysis of PMM tests using IIR filters - I., Pro. 134th JIN conf., 152–153.

Reliability analysis of crabbing manoeuvre

V. Ferrari
Maritime Research Institute Netherlands (MARIN), Wageningen, The Netherlands

S. Sutulo, A.P. Teixeira & C. Guedes Soares
Centre for Marine Technology and Ocean Engineering (CENTEC), Instituto Superior Técnico, Universidade de Lisboa, Lisbon, Portugal

ABSTRACT: In this study reliability analysis methods are applied to the crabbing manoeuvre of a ship. The objective is to express the crabbing capability of a ship in terms of probability of failure, rather than a simple yes/no verification which does not take into account any uncertainties in the mathematical model. To this purpose three reliability methods are presented and applied to the case of a ship sustaining a transverse wind force. These methods are the First Order-Second Moment, the First Order Reliability Method with Rosenblatt transformation and a Monte Carlo simulation. A more complex case, with longitudinal, transverse and rotational equilibrium requirements, is also assessed with Monte Carlo simulations. With these reliability methods it is possible to overcome some limitations of static crabbing calculations, such as assuming a constant wind and using conservative empirical coefficients for safety. Moreover, deriving the crabbing capability in this way provides more information than a standard crabbing analysis thanks to the estimation of the probability of failure.

1 INTRODUCTION

Crabbing is the sideways movement of a ship used for leaving a berth unassisted, in presence of external forces. It is a complex low-speed manoeuvre that requires the use of all propulsive devices (main propellers, rudders or pods, tunnel thrusters) in order to balance the environmental disturbances. It applies in particular to passenger ships, which have tight schedules, must leave the berth unassisted and have large superstructures resulting in high wind loads acting on the vessel. The crabbing capability is defined as the maximum wind speed, for a given direction, at which the ship is able to maintain position. Above that wind speed the ship will start drifting. For each wind direction this limit wind speed is calculated and the resulting limit curve is typically shown in a wind angle – wind speed polar plot.

This polar plot is derived considering a simple equilibrium of forces. If the forces generated by the ship are higher than the environmental ones, then the ship is able to maintain position. The outcome of the analysis is a yes/no answer: either the ship is able to sustain the wind or not. However, with this approach many assumptions have to be made, regarding the wind and the ship propulsion. First, the wind is assumed to be constant in time since no gusts are taken into account. Secondly, some assumption have to be made regarding the propulsion model. It is difficult to estimate the thruster-hull and rudder-hull interactions, and these values may even change in time due to small adjustments performed by the captain, changes in the flow around the tunnels and rudders, and in long-term loss of efficiency due to wear. The typical way of taking into account all these uncertainties is to use a conservative approach. The estimated crabbing capability of the ship will be somewhat lower than the actual one in order to have some margin for wind speed and thruster efficiency fluctuations. However, this approach can quickly become too restrictive and may lead to unrealistic results when choosing for instance the tunnel thrusters characteristics.

A more advanced possibility is to include these uncertainties in the mathematical mode. By expressing them as random variables, the crabbing capability can be defined in terms of *probability of failure* (POF), instead of a static wind speed limit. The polar plot provides more detailed and reliable information, and it is easier to choose the correct tunnel thruster design for the limit conditions. The present paper illustrates how random variables can be included in a crabbing model and how the probability of failure can be derived. At first only the pure transverse wind force (1 degree of freedom) is considered as a test-case. A First Order-Second Moment (FOSM) method is applied and the probability of failure is calculated using Cornell's reliability index. Successively, more accurate First Order Reliability Method (FORM) and Monte Carlo simulation are conducted for calculating the probability of failure and the results are compared with the simplified

DOI: 10.1201/9781003216599-20

FOSM approach. Finally the probabilistic crabbing capability is calculated for the more general case of 3 degrees of freedom, including surge, sway and yaw displacements.

2 MODELLING OF WIND FORCES

2.1 Wind speed

It is important to correctly model the wind variation in time. In the present approach the total wind speed $v(t)$ is assumed to be the sum of a mean component $\bar{v}$ and a zero-mean random fluctuation $v'(t)$:

$$v(t) = \bar{v} + v'(t). \quad (1)$$

The wind fluctuation is to be derived from a wind speed spectrum. In this case the Davenport spectrum is used (first presented in Davenport, 1961), a wind speed spectrum derived for coastal winds. This is considered appropriate for the crabbing manoeuvre which usually happens in harbour. The spectrum is defined as follows:

$$S(\omega) = 4\kappa L \bar{v} \frac{\chi}{2\pi(1+\chi^2)^{4/3}},$$
$$\chi = \frac{\omega L}{2\pi \bar{v}}, \quad (2)$$

where ω is the angular frequency [rad/s], κ is the surface drag coefficient, usually assumed 0.025 for wind over seas, L is a scale length, usually 1200 m for the Davenport spectrum and $\bar{v}$ is the 1-hour average wind speed measured at 10 m height. An example of the spectrum for $\bar{v} = 10$ m/s is shown in Figure 1.

From this spectrum it is possible to generate random time series of wind fluctuation. Assuming a stationary and ergodic process, these series will have a mean $\bar{v}$ and standard deviation σ_w, which can be calculated directly from the spectrum using Parseval's theorem:

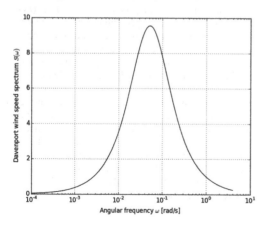

Figure 1. Davenport wind speed spectrum.

$$\sigma_w^2 = \int_0^\infty S(\omega) d\omega. \quad (3)$$

In order to avoid unrealistically extreme tail values, the wind speed v is eventually defined by a truncated Gaussian distribution, cutting at 3 standard deviations from the mean:

$$v \sim N_T(\bar{v}, \sigma_w, \bar{v} \pm 3\sigma_w). \quad (4)$$

2.2 Wind forces

The wind forces are typically calculated by means of wind coefficients c_X, c_Y and c_N for the longitudinal force F_X, transverse force F_Y and yaw moment F_N respectively, as function of the wind direction ε, using the following equations:

$$F_X = \tfrac{1}{2} C_X(\varepsilon) \rho_{air} A_F v^2,$$
$$F_Y = \tfrac{1}{2} C_Y(\varepsilon) \rho_{air} A_L v^2, \quad (5)$$
$$F_N = \tfrac{1}{2} C_N(\varepsilon) \rho_{air} A_L L v^2,$$

where ρ_{air} is the density of the air, A_F is the frontal area of the ship's above-water part exposed to the wind, A_L the lateral windage area and L the characteristic ship length. The main issue is defining the wind coefficient for the ship in exam in an accurate way. There are several methods available, ranging from simple statistical coefficients to advanced RANSE-based CFD calculations or experimental wind tunnel tests. All these methods provide some slightly different results, making it difficult to discern the actual values of the coefficients and adding thus more uncertainty to the overall problem. An example of the scatter derived by using different methods for predicting the coefficients can be found for instance in Haddara & Guedes Soares (1999). In order to take this uncertainty into account in the present model, also the wind coefficients are assumed to be random variables. They are modelled with a uniform distribution, with mean equal to the value obtained by the method chosen and one standard deviation from the mean as bound, estimated on the scatter of experimental data. Some numerical values are proposed later when discussing an actual example.

$$C_X \sim \mathcal{U}(\mu_{CX} - \sigma_{CX}, \mu_{CX} + \sigma_{CX}),$$
$$C_Y \sim \mathcal{U}(\mu_{CY} - \sigma_{CY}, \mu_{CY} + \sigma_{CY}), \quad (6)$$
$$C_N \sim \mathcal{U}(\mu_{CN} - \sigma_{CN}, \mu_{CN} + \sigma_{CN}).$$

In reality there might also be variations of the areas exposed to the wind (e.g. due to a slightly different loading condition) and the characteristics of the air (e.g. due to a different temperature), but it is assumed that the uncertainty deriving from these small variations is already taken into account by the wind coefficients.

3 MODELLING OF SHIP FORCES

Quadvlieg & Toxopeus (1998) present a mathematical model for the ship forces during a crabbing manoeuvre, which will be used here for modelling the ship forces. Here only the theoretical model is presented, some numerical values are proposed later when discussing an actual example.

3.1 Tunnel thrusters

The tunnel thrusters' thrust can be estimated using the simple empirical formula $T_T \, [N] = 100P_T \, [kW]$. However due to the tunnel efficiency and thruster-hull interactions, the resulting net side force Y_T is different from the nominal thrust T_T:

$$\frac{Y_T}{T_T} = \eta_T, \quad (7)$$

where η_T is the thruster-hull efficiency. This value might change depending on the geometry of the tunnel, the presence of shallow water and quay effects, currents in the harbour affecting the thrusters' flows, etc. For these reasons this thruster efficiency is assumed to be a random variable that accounts for all uncertainties related to tunnel thrusters. Two variables are considered: η_{BT} and η_{ST} for the bow and stern thrusters, respectively, which have different characteristics in terms of efficiency. On the other hand it is assumed that all bow thrusters work in the same conditions and similarly for the stern ones. The random variables are assumed to be described by a truncated normal probability density function with means μ_{BT}, μ_{ST} and standard deviations σ_{BT}, σ_{ST}:

$$\eta_{BT} \sim N_T(\mu_{BT}, \sigma_{BT}, \mu_{BT} \pm 3\sigma_{BT}),$$
$$\eta_{ST} \sim N_T(\mu_{ST}, \sigma_{ST}, \mu_{ST} \pm 3\sigma_{ST}). \quad (8)$$

The resulting transverse forces Y generated by the propellers, assuming that the longitudinal forces X are negligible, are for the bow thrusters

$$\begin{aligned} X_{BT} &\approx 0 \\ Y_{BT} &= q_{BT} \eta_{BT} T_{BT} \\ N_{BT} &= \eta_{BT} T_{BT} \sum_{i=1}^{q_{BT}} x_{BT}^{(i)} \end{aligned} \quad (9)$$

and similarly for the stern thrusters

$$\begin{aligned} X_{ST} &\approx 0 \\ Y_{ST} &= q_{ST} \eta_{ST} T_{ST} \\ N_{ST} &= \eta_{ST} T_{ST} \sum_{i=1}^{q_{ST}} x_{ST}^{(i)} \end{aligned} \quad (10)$$

where q_{BT} and q_{ST} are the number of bow and stern thruster, respectively, $x_{BT}^{(i)}$ and $x_{BT}^{(i)}$ are the longitudinal position of the i-th bow and stern thruster, respectively.

3.2 Main propellers

The propellers are in push-pull mode, that is, one is in ahead mode (positive RPM or pitch in case of controllable pitch propeller) and the other astern (negative RPM or pitch). In this way the ship can be in longitudinal equilibrium while providing thrust to the rudder. The thrust of each propeller is found using directly an allocation algorithm, as detailed in Section 3.4, without considering the propeller revolutions. However, a relationship between thrust and power must be found, so that the maximum available thrust based on the maximum power can be taken into account in the algorithm. This can be done by using a propeller 4-quadrant open-water curves approximations such as those given by Dang et al. (2013), then finding the propeller rotation frequency corresponding to the maximum power of the ahead and astern propellers, P_{Ah} and P_{As} respectively:

$$\begin{aligned} P_{Ah} &= C_Q(0) \tfrac{1}{2} \rho \tfrac{\pi}{4} D_P^3 (0.7\pi n D_P)^2 2\pi n \\ P_{As} &= C_Q(\pi) \tfrac{1}{2} \rho \tfrac{\pi}{4} D_P^3 (0.7\pi n D_P)^2 2\pi n \end{aligned} \quad (11)$$

where C_Q is the generalised torque coefficient given by the approximations, ρ is the water density, D_P is the propeller diameter and n is the propeller rotation frequency. The latter can be found from the equations above and inserted in the formulae for the thrust:

$$\begin{aligned} T_{Ah} &= C_T(0) \tfrac{1}{2} \rho \tfrac{\pi}{4} D_P^2 (0.7\pi n D_P)^2 \\ T_{As} &= C_T(\pi) \tfrac{1}{2} \rho \tfrac{\pi}{4} D_P^2 (0.7\pi n D_P)^2 \end{aligned} \quad (12)$$

where C_T is the generalised torque coefficient. In this way the maximum thrust can be calculated and used as constraint in the allocation algorithm. Similarly to the tunnel thrusters, all uncertainties are assumed to be included in the main propellers-hull interaction coefficient ξ_P, which is modelled with a truncated Gaussian distribution with mean μ_P and standard deviation σ_P.

$$\xi_P \sim N_T(\mu_P, \sigma_P, \mu_P \pm 3\sigma_P). \quad (13)$$

The resulting hull forces generated by the propellers, assuming that the transverse force (the so-called wheel effect) is negligible, are:

$$X_P = \xi_P(T_{Ah} - T_{As})$$
$$Y_P \approx 0$$
$$N_P = \xi_P T_{Ah} y_P + \xi_B T_{As} y_P \quad (14)$$

where y_P is the transverse position of the propellers.

3.3 Rudders

The formulation for the rudder forces is based on Sutulo & Guedes Soares (2015). It is assumed that the rudder behind the ahead propeller is deflected, while the other one is set to 0 degrees and does not provide any force. Moreover, since in this study the ship is stationary, all the flow at the rudder is generated only by the ahead propeller, so the formulation can be simplified. These simplifications are already included in the following formulae.

The axial induced velocity at infinity behind the propeller in bollard pull regime is:

$$w_{a0\infty} = \sqrt{\frac{2|T_{Ah}|}{\rho \frac{\pi}{4} D_P^2}}. \quad (15)$$

At zero ship speed this velocity is the same as the total jet velocity at infinity $w_{a\infty}$. With this value it is possible to calculate the longitudinal velocity of the part of the rudder inside the slipstream:

$$w_a(\bar{x}) = \frac{1}{2} \kappa k_w(\bar{x}) w_{a\infty}. \quad (16)$$

The coefficient κ is recommended to be 0.68. The relative signed distance from the propeller to the rudder $\bar{x}$ is defined as:

$$\bar{x} = \frac{2(x_P - x_R)}{D_P} \operatorname{sign} T \quad (17)$$

where T is the draught. This distance is used for calculating the distance factor k_W:

$$k_w(\bar{x}) = \left[\left(1 + \frac{\bar{x}}{\sqrt{1+\bar{x}^2}}\right) \kappa_T(T)\right] \operatorname{sign} T, \quad (18)$$

with $\kappa_T(T)$ defined as:

$$\kappa_T(T) = \begin{cases} 1.0 & \text{at } \bar{x}T \geq 0, \\ 0.7 & \text{at } \bar{x}T < 0. \end{cases} \quad (19)$$

In case of bollard pull the only contribution to the total velocity at the rudder V_R comes from the total jet velocity at infinity $w_{a\infty}$ already defined.

Other important parameters are the lift and drag coefficients C_L and C_D. They are functions of the rudder attack angle α, which in the case of bollard pull is identical to the rudder deflection angle δ. In the case of zero sweep angle the rudder lift coefficient can be estimated as:

$$asC_L = \left(\frac{2\pi a_\infty \lambda_R}{\sqrt{\lambda_R^2 + 4} + 2a_\infty} + \frac{C_d}{\lambda_R}|\alpha|\right)\alpha, \quad (20)$$

where a_∞ is the viscosity correction factor, taken equal to 0.9, λ_R the rudder aspect ratio, and C_d is 0.8 assuming a rudder with faired tip. The drag coefficient is

$$C_D = C_{D0} + \frac{C_L^2}{\pi a_\infty \lambda_R}. \quad (21)$$

Assuming a NACA-0015 profile, the profile drag coefficient C_{D0} is equal to 0.0065. The lift and drag coefficients are combined together to calculate the normal coefficient, assuming to be in pre-stall regime:

$$C_N = C_D \sin \alpha + C_L \cos \alpha. \quad (22)$$

Another parameter to be defined in order to calculate the rudder forces is the area exposed to the slipstream A_{RP}. It can be calculated as:

$$A_{RP} = \frac{h_{RP}}{h_R} A_R, \quad (23)$$

where h_R, A_R are the rudder height and area, respectively, and h_{RP} the height invested by the propeller, taken as $\approx D_P$. All elements are now available for calculating the normal force generated by the rudder, recalling that at zero ship speed outside the propeller slipstream there are no other contributions to the force:

$$F_N = \frac{1}{2} \rho C_N(\alpha) k_d A_{RP} V_R^2, \quad (24)$$

where the jet deflection reduction factor k_d simplifies to 1 in case of zero ship speed. The rudder forces in ship-fixed coordinates are:

$$\begin{aligned} X_R &= -c_R F_N \sin\delta, \\ Y_R &= c_R(1+a_H) F_N \cos\delta, \\ N_R &= x_R Y_R - y_R X_R, \end{aligned} \quad (25)$$

where c_R represents the uncertainty for the rudder forces and a_H is the rudder-hull interaction coefficient. The latter is calculated as (Inoue et al., 1981): $a_H = 0.633 C_B - 0.153$. The uncertainty c_R is modelled with a truncated Gaussian distribution with mean μ_R and standard deviation σ_R.

$$c_R \sim N_T(\mu_R, \sigma_R, \mu_R \pm 3\sigma_R). \quad (26)$$

3.4 Thrust allocation

The thrust allocation algorithm sets the thrust of each component so that the ship remain in longitudinal, transverse and rotational balance against wind loads. It still uses a deterministic approach considering only mean values of the random variables. The uncertainty analysis is performed afterwards, as described in Chapter 4.

Based on the assumptions described in previous sections, the resulting equations of equilibrium are:

$$\begin{cases} X_P(T_{Ah}, T_{As}) + X_R(T_{Ah}) + \\ \qquad F_X(\bar{v}, \varepsilon) = 0, \\ Y_{BT}(T_{BT}) + Y_{ST}(T_{ST}) + Y_R(T_{Ah}) + \\ \qquad F_Y(\bar{v}, \varepsilon) = 0, \\ N_P(T_{Ah}, T_{As}) + N_{BT}(T_{BT}) + N_{ST}(T_{ST}) + \\ \qquad N_R(T_{Ah}) + F_N(\bar{v}, \varepsilon) = 0. \end{cases} \quad (27)$$

Given an average wind speed $\bar{v}$ and direction ε we obtain a system of 3 equations in 4 unknowns: T_{Ah}, T_{As}, T_{BT} and T_{ST}. It is then possible to use some minimisation techniques such as least-square fitting for finding the thrusts.

4 RELIABILITY ANALYSIS

4.1 Test-case

In the next sections the reliability analysis is applied to a test-case, a generic expedition cruise ship presented by Grin et al. (2018) and Ferrari et al. (2018). The ship has the characteristics shown in Table 1.

The wind coefficients are estimated using data from Brix, 1993. The random variables are defined in Table 2, based on Ferrari et al. (2018).

4.2 Case study: Pure transverse wind force

As initial simplified scenario we consider a pure transverse wind force, which does not generate any

Table 1. Characteristics of the test-case.

Length between perpendiculars	120.0m
Breadth	17.0m
Draught	4.0m
Frontal windage area	334.0 m²
Lateral windage area	1987.0m²
Each propeller's diameter	3.0m
Each rudder's area	8.75m²
Each bow thruster's diameter	1.2m
Stern thruster's diameter	1.2m

Table 2. Characteristics of the random variables.

VARIABLE	MEAN μ	ST.DEV. σ	DISTRIB. TYPE
Push-pull coefficient ξ_P	0.9	0.1	Truncated Gaussian
Bow thruster efficiency η_{BT}	1.2	0.1	Truncated Gaussian
Stern thruster efficiency η_{ST}	1.0	0.1	Truncated Gaussian
Rudder coefficient c_R	1.0	0.1	Truncated Gaussian
Longitudinal wind coefficient c_X	0.4	0.1	Uniform
Transverse wind coefficient c_Y	0.9	0.15	Uniform
Rotational wind coefficient c_N	0.08	0.01	Uniform

longitudinal force nor yaw moment. This happens only for beam winds acting an a perfectly fore/aft symmetric area exposed to the wind. This is obviously not the case in reality, but nonetheless this assumption allows to study a simple case not too far from reality in case for instance of cruise ships.

To study this scenario three approaches are used: first the First Oder-Second Moment technique is applied, calculating the probability of failure by means of Cornell's reliability index, then a First Order Reliability Method is applied, and finally a more accurate Monte Carlo simulation is performed. See Melchers and Beck (2018) for more details on the methods for structural reliability analysis.

4.2.1 Cornell's reliability index

In case of pure transverse wind the equilibrium condition becomes:

$$Y_{BT} + Y_{ST} + Y_R + F_Y = 0 \quad (28)$$

assuming that the main propellers are able to keep the ship longitudinally and rotationally in equilibrium. The limit state function g can be defined as:

$$g(\eta_{BT}, \eta_{ST}, c_{UR}, c_Y, v) = Y_{BT} + Y_{ST} + Y_R + F_Y \quad (29)$$

that is positive when the ship is able to balance the wind force and negative when the wind speed is too high. It is then possible to use the First Oder-Second Moment technique to estimates the limit state function's mean and standard deviation. The vector of random variables u is:

$$u := [\eta_{BT}, \eta_{ST}, c_{UR}, c_Y, v]^T \quad (30)$$

and consequently

$$\begin{aligned} E[g] &= g(\mu_{BT}, \mu_{ST}, \mu_R, \mu_{CY}, \bar{v}), \\ Var[g] &= \sum_{i=1}^{5} \left(\frac{\partial g}{\partial u_i}\right)^2 Var[u_i] \end{aligned} \quad (31)$$

assuming that all random variables follow normal distribution and are independent. Cornell's reliability index β is then calculated as:

$$\beta = \frac{E[g]}{\sqrt{Var[g]}} \quad (32)$$

and according to Cornell's method, the probability of limit state violation $P(g \leq 0)$, denoted as probability of failure, is:

$$P_{fC} = \Phi(-\beta), \quad (33)$$

where $\Phi(\cdot)$ indicates the cumulative normal Gaussian distribution function.

4.2.2 First Order Reliability Method

First Order Reliability Methods offer a more sophisticated approach for calculating the probability of failure of non-linear limit state functions. They are based on transforming the non-random variables to independent and normally distributed ones, then using the Jacobian matrix for deriving the limit state equation in this new domain, thus allowing the calculations of the probability of failure. Among the possible transformation here the Rosenblatt one is used, based on the procedure described by Melchers & Beck (2018). Each of the normal variables y_i are calculated as:

$$y_i = \Phi^{-1}[F_i(u_i)], \quad (34)$$

where $F_i(\cdot)$ is the cumulative distribution function corresponding to the i-th random variable. Then, each ij element of the Jacobian matrix J is calculated as:

$$J_{ij} = \frac{\partial y_i}{\partial x_j} = \frac{1}{\phi(y_i)} \frac{\partial F_i(x_i)}{\partial x_j}, \quad (35)$$

where $\phi(\cdot)$ is the normal Gaussian probability density function. Since the hypothesis is made that all random variables are independent, the gradient of the cumulative distributions $\partial F_i / \partial x_j$ is 0 if $i \neq j$ and can be evaluated numerically otherwise. With the inverse Jacobian matrix J^{-1} and the gradient of the limit state function $\partial g / \partial x$ it is possible to obtain the components of the gradient of the limit state function in normalised space g_y:

$$\frac{\partial g_y}{\partial y} = J^{-1} \cdot \frac{\partial g}{\partial x}. \quad (36)$$

With the above, the following components can be calculated:

$$c_i = \lambda \frac{\partial g_y}{\partial y_i}, \quad (37)$$

where λ is an arbitrary constant. These components allow to derive the direction cosines:

$$\alpha_i = \frac{c_i}{\sqrt{\left(\sum_i c_i^2\right)}}. \quad (38)$$

Finally, the β index can be calculated:

$$\beta = -y^T \cdot \alpha \quad (39)$$

from which the probability of failure is evaluated using Eq. (33).

4.2.3 Monte Carlo simulation

Cornell's method is an approximated approach that approximates the limit state function with second-order terms of the Taylor series and assumes that the probability density function of the system $f_u(u)$ is Gaussian. However this may not be the case. The exact probability of failure involves calculating the integral of the density function over the failure region $g(u) \leq 0$:

$$P_f = \int_{g(u) \leq 0} f_u(u) du. \quad (40)$$

Since $f_u(u)$ involves a product of multiple Gaussian distributions (the term $c_Y v^2$) it is difficult to evaluate analytically. Nonetheless it is possible to use the Monte Carlo simulation technique to estimate the integral. To this purpose Eq. (40) can be rewritten as:

$$P_f = \int_{\mathrm{IR}^5} I(u) f_u(u) du, \quad (41)$$

with

$$I(u) = \begin{cases} 0 & \text{if } g(u) > 0, \\ 1 & \text{if } g(u) \leq 0. \end{cases} \quad (42)$$

By randomly generating a certain number q_{MC} of samples of the vector u, it is possible to calculate numerically the corresponding values of the function $I(u)$. The probability of failure estimated with the Monte Carlo method is thus the expected value of this sample:

$$P_{fMC} = \mathrm{E}[I] = \frac{1}{q_{MC}} \sum_{k=1}^{q_{MC}} I(u^{(k)}). \quad (43)$$

It is convenient to use the inverse transformation technique to generate the random samples of u. For the random variables that follow a Gaussian probability density function, let $U \sim unif(0,1)$. For the i-th component of the vector u the random value is calculated as $u_i = \mathcal{N}^{-1}(\mu_i, \sigma_i)(U_i)$. All these random values generate one realisation $u^{(k)}$ of the random vector u used as input to the function I. A similar procedure is used for the variables that are described by a uniform distribution.

4.2.4 Numerical example with comparison of the three approaches

The three approaches previously described are applied to the test-case presented in Section 4.1 for the case pure transverse wind, without longitudinal force nor yawing moment. The probability of failure is calculated using for different average wind speeds, keeping the optimal thrust settings constant. The Monte Carlo results are based on 1000 simulations. In this way the graph shown in Figure 2 is obtained.

It can be seen that for the expected static wind limit all methods predict a probability of failure of about 50% at 14 m/s, but if the wind speed changes the probability of failure increases or decreases accordingly. The Monte Carlo curve has a 99% confidence interval of ± 1.4 and $\pm 1.2\%$ at 20 and 30 m/s, respectively. It can be seen that the Cornell index does not predict the same trend as the Monte Carlo simulation, possibly because the wind speed appears in a non-linear term in Eq. (5) whereas the Cornell

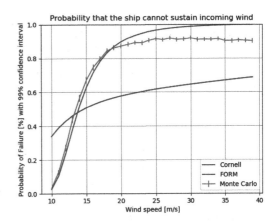

Figure 2. Probability of failure estimated with Monte Carlo and Cornell index methods for pure transverse force case.

method is a linearised one. The curve of the First Order Reliability Method matches well with the Monte Carlo simulation up to 20 m/s, above which it tends to slightly overpredict the probability of failure. This shows that in general FORM approaches could be a good compromise between accuracy and computation time.

4.3 General case

As mentioned previously, the case of pure transverse wind force is a useful reference but not entirely realistic. The ship will have to balance in reality the longitudinal, transverse and rotational wind loads at the same time. The resulting equation of equilibrium in 3 degrees of freedom are:

$$\begin{cases} X_P + X_R + F_X = 0, \\ Y_{BT} + Y_{ST} + Y_R + F_Y = 0, \\ N_P + N_{BT} + N_{ST} + N_R + F_N = 0. \end{cases} \quad (44)$$

The corresponding limit state equations are thus:

$$\begin{aligned} g(u_X) &= X_P + X_R + F_X, \\ g(u_Y) &= Y_{BT} + Y_{ST} + Y_R + F_Y, \\ g(u_N) &= N_P + N_{BT} + N_{ST} + N_R + F_N, \end{aligned} \quad (45)$$

where u_X, u_Y and u_N are the vector of random variables for each equation, defined as:

$$\begin{aligned} u_X &:= [\xi_P, c_{UR}, c_X, v]^T, \\ u_Y &:= [\eta_{BT}, \eta_{ST}, c_{UR}, c_Y, v]^T, \\ u_N &:= [\xi_P, \eta_{BT}, \eta_{ST}, c_{UR}, c_N, v]^T. \end{aligned} \quad (46)$$

The Monte Carlo technique can be used for finding the overall probability of failure also in this more general case, considering that the system is safe only if all limit state equations are satisfied at the same time. The operator to be used is thus:

$$I_{XYN}(u_X, u_Y, u_N) = \begin{cases} 0 & \text{if } g_X(u_X) > 0 \ \wedge \\ & g_Y(u_Y) > 0 \ \wedge \\ & g_N(u_N) > 0, \\ 1 & \text{otherwise.} \end{cases} \quad (47)$$

Random values for u_X, u_Y, and u_N are generated using the procedure detailed in Section 4.2.3, obtaining many realizations $u_X^{(i)}$, $u_Y^{(j)}$ and $u_N^{(k)}$. The POF is then computed as the sum of the I_{XYN} operator calculated with all possible values of these random variables:

$$P_{fMC} = \frac{1}{q_{MC}} \sum_i \sum_j \sum_k I_{XYN}(u_X^{(i)}, u_Y^{(j)}, u_N^{(k)}). \quad (48)$$

The results are shown in Figure 3. Also in this case the Monte Carlo results are based on 1000 simulations. The 99% confidence interval is ±1.6 and ±1.4% at 20 and 30 m/s, respectively In comparison with the simple 1-dimensional case, the probability of failure is now higher, being very close to 1 for wind speeds above 26 m/s. This is due to the fact that the ship must now satisfy the equilibrium in longitudinal, transverse and rotational directions, which increases the difficulty of sustaining the wind.

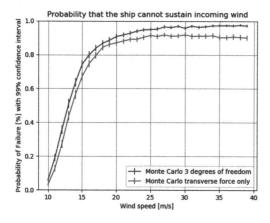

Figure 3. Probability of failure estimated with Monte Carlo method for for general case.

5 CONCLUSIONS

This paper demonstrates how reliability methods can be applied to analysing the crabbing manoeuvre of a ship obtaining probability of failure over any wind speed range for a given wind direction, thus providing more information than a simpler pass/fail analysis. This approach lifts some limitations of static calculations, such as assumption of a constant wind, and makes not necessary application of conservative empirical safety coefficients.

Three methods were tested for a scenario with only transverse wind force: the First-Order-Second-Moment (FOSM) method, the First-Order Reliability Method (FORM) with Rosenblatt transformation, and the Monte Carlo simulation. Due to the non-linearity of the mathematical model, the FOSM method failed to provide a proper prediction of the probability of failure. On the contrary, the FORM was found to be in good agreement with the Monte Carlo simulations. Therefore for the purpose of determining the probability of failure in crabbing, the FORM approach could be a good compromise between accuracy and computation time. A more realistic case with three degrees of freedom was further investigated by means of the Monte Carlo simulation. The results showed an increase in the probability of failure, thus illustrating the importance of taking into account all three degrees of freedom in crabbing modelling.

This study opens some possibilities for further research. Finding an extension of the FORM to three degrees of freedom could provide a simpler alternative to the Monte Carlo simulations. Moreover, the wheel effect, that is, the transverse force generated by the main propellers turning in the same direction, is disregarded in the present formulation, due to the increase in the complexity of the problem. This effect is limited but still relevant during a crabbing manoeuvre, therefore deriving a more detailed formulation with its influence included would give more reliable results.

ACKNOWLEDGMENTS

The study was partly supported by the project NAVAD, IC&DT–AAC n.º02/SAICT/2017 ``Simulation of manoeuvrability of ships in adverse weather conditions'' funded by the Portuguese Foundation for Science and Technology (FCT).

REFERENCES

Brix, J., 1993. "Manoeuvring Technical Manual". *Seehafen Verlag GmbH*, Hamburg, Germany.

Dang, J., van den Boom, H. J. J., Ligtelijn, J. Th., 2013. "The Wageningen C- and D-series propellers". *FAST Conference 2013*, Amsterdam, The Netherlands.

Davenport, A. G., 1961. "The spectrum of horizontal gustiness near the ground of high winds". *Quarterly Journal Royal Meteorological Society*, Vol. 87, pp. 194–211.

Ferrari, V., Kisjes, A., Quadvlieg, F. H. H. A., 2018, "Quantifying the uncertainty of the crabbing capability", *OMAE 2018*, Madrid, Spain.

Grin, R., Bandas, J., Ferrari, V., Rapuc, S., Abeil, B., 2018. "On the importance of service conditions and safety in ship design”. *IMDC 2018*, Helsinki, Finland.

Haddara, M. R. & Guedes Soares, C., 1999. "Wind loads on marine structures". *Marine Structures*, 12, pp. 199–209.

Inoue, S., Hirano, M., Kijima, K., Takashina, J., 1981. "A practical calculation method of ship manoeuvring motions". *International Shipbuilding Progress*, Vol. 28, No. 235, pp. 207–222.

Melchers, R. E. & Beck, A. T., 2018. "Structural reliability analysis and prediction". 3rd Edition. *John Wiley & Sons Ltd.*.

Quadvlieg, F. H. H. A. & Toxopeus, S., 1998. "Prediction of crabbing at early design stage". *PRADS 1998*, The Hague, The Netherlands.

Sutulo, S. & Guedes Soares, C., 2015. "Development of a core matematical model for arbitrary maneouvres of a shuttle tanker". *Applied Ocean Research*, Vol. 51, pp. 293–308.

Global and local path-planning algorithm for marine autonomous surface ships including forecasting information

M.A. Hinostroza & C. Guedes Soares
Centre of Marine Technology and Ocean Engineering (CENTEC), Instituto Superior Técnico, Universidade de Lisboa, Lisbon, Portugal

ABSTRACT: This paper presents a novel technique for global and local path-planning of autonomous surface ships, which is based in the fast-marching square method and includes forecasting data, to compute an optimal path in a global route, such as transatlantic voyages. The global path-planning employs the fast marching square method and the ship responses in waves to compute a global path, while the local planner is utilized to manage the near-field changes. The local path-planning is based in angle-guidance fast marching square method and computes an optimal path in a small complex region including dynamic and static obstacles. In order to validate the developed system a set of numerical simulations were carried out. From these simulations the influence of the forecasting information in the computation of the optimal path was observed.

1 INTRODUCTION

Recently, advances in navigation technologies and increases in robot intelligent have attracted the attention of the shipping and maritime sector, with the objective of developing the first unmanned surface ship for autonomous shipping in a near future (Liu et al., 2019). The unmanned ships have several benefits, such as the reduction of the number of causalities, risks and lower costs, as they can operate with minimal personal involvement. Thus, The Roll-Royce company has successfully tested in 2018 the world's first fully autonomous ferry in the archipelago south of the city of Turku, Finland (Roll-Royce, 2018). Roll-Royce has announced that remotely controlled local ships are expected in 2020 and fully autonomous ships in 2030, Figure 1 presents the Roll-Royce prototypes of unmanned ship. Furthermore, the Kongsberg Maritime company has announced the World's first autonomous cargo vessel, YARA Birkeland, which is expected to navigate in the Norwegian fjords and is projected for fully autonomous operation by 2020 (Kongsberg Maritime, 2017).

Due to these advances in the autonomous ships, the International Maritime Organization (IMO) takes steps to address autonomous ships, abording topics such as how safe, secure and environmentally sound are the maritime autonomous surface ships operations (IMO, 2019). Furthermore, DNV-GL Releases Autonomous and Remotely Operated Ship Guidelines, to help build a safety culture around these new technologies for autonomous shipping, DNV-GL has released a new class guideline covering autonomous and remotely operated ships (DNV-GL, 2019).

According to the current phase of autonomy, unmanned ships are designed to perform missions and navigate by themselves, and to achieve this, a considerable amount of research has been done, specifically in the field of path planning, which seeks an optimal path in a marine complex environment including static (islands, buoys) and dynamic (other vessels).

In Kim et al. (2014) an angular rate-constrained path planning algorithm for unmanned surface vehicles, including simulations and experiments has presented. In Liu et al. (2019) a path-planning for autonomous ships was presented. The path planning algorithm was developed based upon the angle guidance fast marching square method, which is able to calculate the optimal path according to vehicle's motion constraints. The system was been validated in both real field trials and computer-based simulations proving a small USV is able to autonomously navigate in different maritime environments.

Later in Hinostroza et al. (2018, 2019) path-planning for a small ASV and a team of ASVs were presented, respectively. The motion planning is based in an extension of the AFMS method, including a fuzzy logic collision avoidance unit based in COLREGs rules and regulations for navigation. It is important to notice that the route planning and collision avoidance are events of very different temporal and spatial scales, therefore, normally, these subsystems work independently as can be seen in the diagram block presented in Hinostroza et al. (2019).

DOI: 10.1201/9781003216599-21

Figure 1. (a) Falco ferry - autonomous surface vessel, (b) prototype of unmanned ships (Rolls-Royce).

In this paper a novel approach is presented for the global and local path-planning for unmanned ships. The global path-planning is sub-module in charge to compute the route for the ship in large areas, such as Mediterranean (Vettor et al, 2016) or Atlantic routes (Vettor & Guedes Soares, 2016). This module can compute the fast and/or safe route, based in weather forecast information and the ship responses in waves in addition to the fast marching square method (Liu & Bucknall, 2016). The local path-planning is able to compute the safe path in a small area, taking into consideration the unnamed ship dimension, the dynamic obstacles (other ships) and static obstacles (buoys), which cannot be detected a-priori and the angle-guidance fast-marching square method.

Figure 2 presents the diagram lock of the developed system, where the local and global path-planning are presented. The input for the global algorithm, are the world map, the forecasting information and the ship RAOs and characteristics, then the safe and/or fast route is computed. This route is the input for the local planning unit, this unit calculates the more specific path in a given region, this local path-planning uses the angle-guidance FMS method, and the static and moving obstacles.

The remaining part of this paper is organized as follows: Section 2 presents the mathematical formulation of the global and local path-planning. The numerical simulation for the global path-planning are addressed in section 3. Section 4 presents the numerical simulation of the local path-planning for ASVs. Section 5 briefly introduces the computational costs and section 6 is the conclusion.

2 MATHEMATICAL FORMULATION OF PATH-PLANNING UNIT

In this section the mathematical formulation of the global and local path planning unit system is presented. The path-planning system is responsible to compute a suitable path for ASVs. From the literature, a broad spectrum of efficient and intelligent path planning techniques were presented, such as: (a) optimization methods, which can directly produce optimal trajectories or paths that might include sophisticated characteristics, such as, fuel saving, weather routing, formation control, and scheduled missions. (b) Heuristic search algorithms such as the A* search algorithm which is a widely used grid-based strategy, which can quickly find an optimal path with the least number of nodes. (c) Potential fields, where is defined a potential field (PF), where the objectives are assigned with attractive fields, while obstacles are distributed with repulsive fields. (d) Hybrid path planning which consists in global and local path planning approaches, where the global path-planning employs the Dijkstra method to compute a global path, while a local planner is utilized to manage the near-field changes that arise to the previously defined path.

In this paper the hybrid-planning approach is used. Mainly, because in a global path planning system, the computed path is poor in reacting to unknown obstacles (small buoys, other ships). In contrast, a local/reactive navigation method works well in dynamic and initially unknown environment. Thus, this paper presents a global a local path-planning method, working together, Figure 3 presents a diagram flux of the algorithm proposed in this paper. The first part of the algorithm, is to compute the global path, based in a global map (world map), and the forecasting information (ERA interim data) and the ship responses in waves, later, a local path-planning unit computes the optimal path, in a restricted area, based in the ship length and local fixed and moving obstacles (islands, ships). It is important to notice that the algorithm is designed iteratively and has capabilities to recompute the optimal path, in case of a global path, encounter and unknow obstacle.

2.1 Global path-planning formulation

The formulation of the global path planning unit is a combination between the traditional fast marching square method and the forecasting information. Thus, this global path-planning system is based in the work presented in Vettor & Guedes Soares (2016). The main objective is this module is to compute the optimal path in a large area, such as transatlantic routes. The inputs for this module are the forecasting information (ERA), the global map grid and ship characteristics.

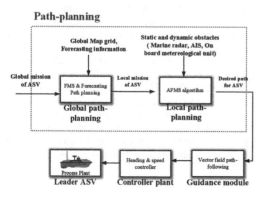

Figure 2. Diagram block of the global and local path-planning modules.

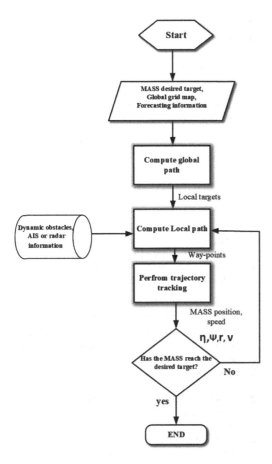

Figure 3. Diagram flux of the path-planning algorithm.

2.1.1 Fast marching square method

One of the problems associated with path planning by directly using the FMM method is that the generated path is too close to obstacles, such a drawback is especially impractical for ASVs, because near distance areas around obstacles are usually shallow water, which is not suitable for marine vehicles to navigate. Hence, it is important to keep the planned path a certain distance away from obstacles. To tackle this problem, Garrido et al. (2011) has proposed a new algorithm named the fast-marching square (FMS) method. The basic concept behind the FMS is to apply the conventional FMM algorithm twice but with different purposes.

2.1.2 ERA interim forecasting information

The knowledge of the actual environment in which ships operate is one of the most important aspects to be considered in a path-planning. The historical weather data are available from several sources depending on the wideness of the area covered and the model used. Local measurements from buoys or weather stations are extremely valuable meteorological resources, but of scarce operational use for marine vehicles if not integrated in a wider model, Guedes Soares et al. (2011). Figure 4 shows the annual mean Hs from the ERA interim data. The Earth surface have been divided according to a grid of 1°x1° and all the observations made within each panel of the grid in a pre-defined period have been considered in the computation of the mean Hs for that area.

2.1.3 Ship responses in waves

An efficient motion planning unit needs the ship behaviour information to provide trustworthy results. Associating the RAOs with a given wave spectrum S_ζ, the ship response spectra S_R can be easily determined as shown in Guedes Soares (1990) like,

$$S_R(\omega,\theta) = RAO(\omega,\theta)^2 . S_\zeta(\omega,\theta) \quad (1)$$

where ω and θ are the wave frequency and direction, respectively. Figure 5 presents an example of calculation of the vertical acceleration at the bridge in a quartering short-crested sea-state defined by the directional wave spectrum.

For the algorithm instead of only considering ship responses it is often convenient to refer to their negative effect on ship operations. In the following the most important effects to be considered are briefly described. Table 1 summarizes the rms criteria for vertical and lateral accelerations, and roll angle and the corresponding working and living conditions onboard. the most dangerous motions are roll. Excessive roll amplitudes result in great inclination of the deck and fast degradation of human performance (Cox & Lloyd, 1977) with possible falls of people and objects. Excessive lateral accelerations may cause movement of the cargo, which may be particularly dangerous for instance for containerships or RO-RO and compromise the effectiveness of the personnel. Vertical acceleration is the main cause of seasickness thus it has to be contained.

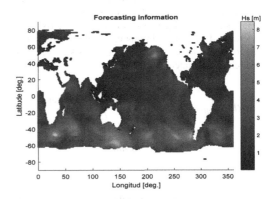

Figure 4. Mean Hs from ERA interim data (Vettor & Guedes Soares, 2016).

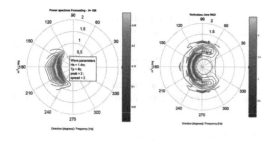

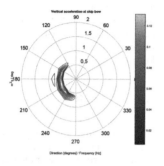

Figure 5. (a) Generated wave (b) Transfer function of the vertical acceleration and (c) Response spectrum.

Table 1. Examples of rms criteria for different working conditions (Vettor & Guedes Soares, 2016).

Root Mean Square criterion		
Vertical acceleration	Lateral acceleration	Roll
0.20g	0.10g	6.0°
0.15g	0.07g	4.0°
0.10g	0.05g	3.0°
0.05g	0.04g	2.5°
0.02g	0.03g	2.0°

2.1.4 Risk coefficient definition

Besides acting as constraints to ensure the safety limits not to be overstepped, safety can also be included in the objectives to minimize the risk or to increase the comfort. In this case, all responses must be reduced to a single factor, a risk coefficient, which is calculated as follows,

$$RISK_{coeff} = \frac{1}{2}[\max(\frac{\max\_seakeeping\_criteria_i}{Limit_i}) + \max(\frac{mean\_seakeeping\_criteria_i}{Limit_i})] \quad (2)$$

The ratio aims to normalize all the seakeeping effects in a value in the range [0,1] depending on the distance from the respective limit, such as 1 corresponds to the most extreme conditions that the ship can stand.

In the global path-planning method including the forecasting information, the total value of each node in the optimization procedure are calculated using a weight for each parameter, i.e. map of obstacles, map of Dijkstra propagation and the coefficient risk, here identified e.g. as x, y and z respectively. It means that the hyperplane is a plane that can be defined by

$$M_{AFMS} = \frac{s_x}{s_z}M_{FMM} - \frac{s_y}{s_z}M_{Forecasting} \quad (3)$$

where s_x, s_y and s_z are the importance values given by the algorithm to safe distance to obstacles, fast route and avoid the dangerous situation respectively.

2.2 Local path-planning formulation

The local path-planning formulation is based in the AFMS method and a collision avoidance unit. In this section the algorithm is based in the work presented in Hinostroza et al. (2019).

2.2.1 Angle-guidance fast marching square algorithm

Based on the kinematic motion of the USV, the AFMS is developed with its pseudocode shown in Hinostroza et al. (2019). It uses the fast-marching square as the base algorithm, and in order to make the generated path compliant with USV's motion constraints.

2.2.2 Path-following module

To track the predefined trajectory, the autonomous ships must be capable of following the desired heading angles. The vector field guidance law (Xu and Guedes Soares, 2016) is used to generate a vector field around the predefined path. The vectors indicated the desired heading angle, as presented in Figure 6. If the ships follow the vectors' direction, it will end up following the path successfully.

As shown in the Figure 6, the solid line between the waypoints is the predefined path. The area between the red dashed lines, which lie at a distance τ on each side of the path, indicates the transition region. A vector field around the path is constructed, as presented in Figure 6. If the distance, d, is greater than the predefined constant, τ, it means that the ships are outside the transition region. Then the guidance laws will force the ship to travel towards the path at a constant desired heading angle, χ^e, which is called entry angle. When the vehicle is inside the transition region ($d < \tau$), the desired heading is calculated using Eq. (4). χ^f The rate of transition is controlled by a gain, $k > 1$.

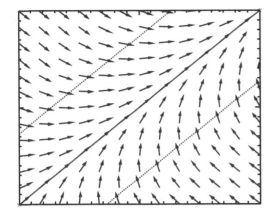

Figure 6. Vectors generated using vector field guidance law.

The vector field guidance is given (Xu & Guedes Soares, 2016),

$$\chi^d = \begin{cases} \chi^f - \text{sgn}(y_e)\chi^e & \text{if } x \geq \tau \\ \chi^f - \text{sgn}(y_e)\left(\frac{|y_e|}{\Delta}\right)^k \chi^e & \text{if } x < \tau \end{cases} \quad (4)$$

where χ^d is the desired course angle and is defined as $\chi^d = \psi^d + \beta.\psi^d$ is the desired heading angle, β is the sideslip angle, which can be measured directly. χ^f is the angle of the path. χ^e is the entry course angle, when the ship located outside the transition area. y_e is the cross-track error. k and Δ are the predefined parameters.

2.2.3 Collision avoidance unit

The collision avoidance unit is composed by two blocks i.e. collision detection and the fuzzy-logic algorithm, (Hinostroza et al. 2019). The collision detection block uses the distance and time to the closest point of approach between vessels to detect potential conflicts, using COLREGs rules and regulation. The fuzzy-logic block uses linguistic variables to characterize encounter situation between the ASVs team and a dynamic obstacle, target ship. Then, using fuzzy-rules compute changes in heading and speed in order to avoid collision.

3 NUMERICAL SIMULATIONS FOR GLOBAL PATH-PLANNING

This section presents numerical simulations of the global path-planning algorithm. In order to test the algorithm in a real case a real Mediterranean route is chosen for simulation. The starting point is the Genoa containership terminal and the target destination are the port in Rotterdam. For simulation a real ship has chosen and the RAOs are computed using an inhouse seakeeping code, based in a strip theory. The forecasting information for simulations are from the ERA interim data.

3.1 Ship for simulations

The ship selected for simulations is a container ship from the "Mediterranean shipping company", Table 2 presents the main particulars of the ship. Figure 7 presents the Msc Oscar container ship during his operation.

In order to compute the ship responses in waves, and to compute the coefficient risk for the global path-planning, is important to calculate the ship response amplitude operators for the ship, in this study the RAOs were calculated using an in house code, presented in Fonseca & Guedes Soares (1998).

3.2 Chosen route

The chosen route for simulation is from Genoa port, to Rotterdam port, this route is also operated by the Mediterranean shipping company, Figure 8 presents the starting and target location of the vessel.

3.3 Simulation results-case A

In order to compute the optimal path, is necessary a pre-processing of the grip map. For it is

Table 2. Ship for simulations.

MSC Oscar Container ship	
Overall Length(m)	395.47
Breadth(m)	59.08
Draught (estimated at voyage) (m)	6.7
Displacement (estimated at trials) (ton)	199273
Speed cruise (kn)	15
Flag	Panama
IMO number	9703291
Built year	2014

Figure 7. MSC Oscar, container ship of 19224 TEU.

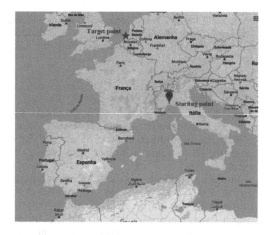

Figure 8. Selected route Genoa to Rotterdam, carried by Mediterranean shipping company.

Figure 11 shows the risk associated when the ship is navigating in a Mediterranean route. This figure presents the risk associate with the roll, acceleration in the bridge, slamming, risk of freeboard and the total risk for the computation of an optimal route, according to algorithm presented in Figure 3.

From the previous plots and performing calculation to compute the global path planning algorithm leads to Figure 12, which shows three different route solutions. In black is the route without consideration of the ERA interim forecasting data, in green is a method with forecasting information and in red in a method including only the 80% of forecasting information, given an intermediate solution. From this plot it is possible to see the influence of the

important to consider that 1° in longitude is more than 1° in latitude. Figure 9 shows the transformation of the global map into a grid map.

Figure 10 presents the forecasting information from ERA interim data for simulations, in these figures is important to notice that the information collected in the web site is provided for 1°x1° resolution, the data was interpolated for more accuracy resolution. In this figure is important to notice that, some regions are plotted in blue, which means no information. In this case they are considered as zero values for the wave parameters.

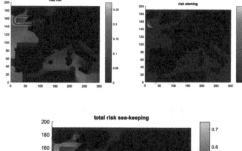

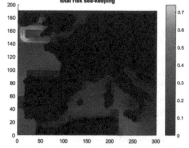

Figure 11. Example of calculation of the risk coefficient.

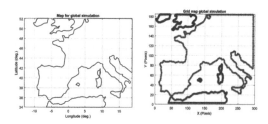

Figure 9. (a) Global map in GPS coordinates and (b) in a grid map.

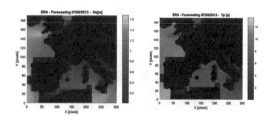

Figure 10. ERA-interim forecasting information 07/06/2013.

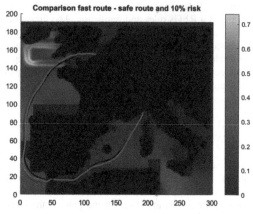

Figure 12. Optimal routes with and without forecasting information.

forecasting information into the computation of the optimal path. The algorithm avoids the dangerous situations based in the risk map presented in Figure 11.

3.4 Simulation results -case B

In order to show the influence of the forecasting data, a new simulation for a different case B is presented in this subsection. In case A, the influence of the forecasting information in the final route is almost not perceptible, therefore, in this case B a high wave is simulated. As is possible to see in Figure 13, where waves of Hs=3m of significant wave height are simulated.

Figure 14 presents three optimal paths computed with the global path planning. In this figure it is possible see that the route in black line, does not consider the forecasting information. The path in red considers the forecasting information and avoids the bad weather, the green route is an intermediate solution case between the previous two. In this simulation the influence of the bad weather can be observable.

4 NUMERICAL SIMULATIONS FOR LOCAL PATH-PLANNING

In order to validate the local path-planning algorithm, numerical simulations were carried out, in a small area considering static and moving obstacles. The place for this simulation is chosen a 4x4 km² area in the estuary of the Tagus river, Portugal, for this simulation a static obstacle and a moving obstacle was considered. The guidance and control module for the simulations were taken from Hinostroza et al. (2019). The trajectory tracking uses the vector-field path following algorithm.

4.1 Place for numerical simulations

In this case the area chosen for the simulation is a square area of 4Km side length, as is presented in Figure 15. This area includes a part of the Tagus estuary in Lisbon, Portugal. Figure 15 also shows the map grid map generated.

4.2 Simulation results

Table 3 presents the model configuration of the numerical simulations for the local path planning algorithm. In this simulation, the starting point is located in a point at the entrance of the Tagus river estuary and the target in the Navy dock in "Alfeite". This simulation includes one static obstacle and one dynamic obstacle (a moving ship).

Figure 16 presents the initial configuration for the simulation. The simulated static obstacles are plotted

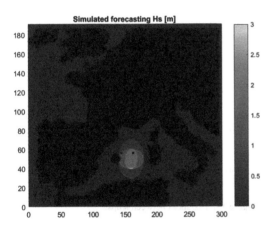

Figure 13. Forecasting data for simulation case B.

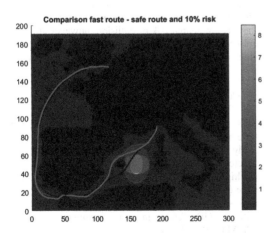

Figure 14. Case B – Global path planning.

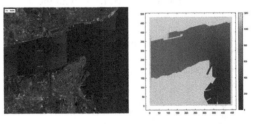

Figure 15. (a) Generation of the grid map from aerial picture, (b) Potential map (Ms).

Table 3. Model configurations for simulations.

ASV	Leader
Start point (pix.)	(15,250)
Initial heading (º)	30
Des. target (pix.)	(360,70)

193

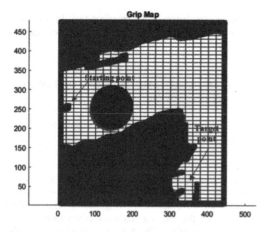

Figure 16. Initial configuration for simulation.

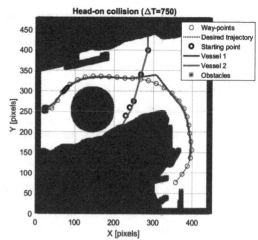

Figure 18. Path planning computed with local algorithm.

in blue or red and distributed in the map randomly in a 450x450 [pixels^2] and a start point in the initial position.

Figure 17 presents the computed local path; this path was calculated at the begining of the ASV mission. This figure also addresses a gradient colour plot from the angle-guidance fast marching square method. In colour plot, the points with a highest value, yellow points, represents how complicate is pass through that points.

Figure 18 shows the final trajectories of the autonomous surface vehicle during the execution of the desired mission. In this figure, the trajectory is on magenta line, the dynamic obstacle trajectory is plotted in green. The desired trajectories path, calculated from AFMS algorithm, are represented by way-points in asterisk. From this plot it is possible to see the modification of the formation shape when the ASV passes through a bottleneck at the begin of the task, and also, how the ASV changes his path in order to avoid a potential collision with the moving obstacle.

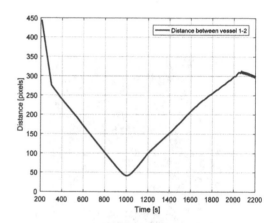

Figure 19. Distances between ships.

Figure 19 displays the distance between the autonomous surface vehicle and the dynamic obstacle during the execution of the mission task. From this plot it is possible to see that in a given moment, there is a potential risk of collision, however after the collision avoidance maneuvers, the distance between ships increases above to the minimal safe distance.

5 COMPUTATIONAL COST

This section presents a study of the computation time for the fast-marching square algorithm. This study is important because the main constrain of a deterministic approach in path-planning system is the high computational resources required to run the code (Song et al., 2019). The numerical simulations, in this study, were performed in a Core i7, 2.6 GHz with 8 GB RAM memory computer, running a MATLAB ® 2017b.

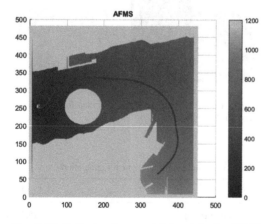

Figure 17. Optimal path computed based in the AFMS method.

Table 4. Analysis of the computation cost for 4 cases.

Grid dimensions [Pixels²]	Number Obstacles	Computational time (sec.)
[50,50]	1	3.62
[100,100]	1	5.7
	2	5.4
[200,200]	1	23
	2	20
[500,500]	1	310

During the numerical simulations it was identified that the most computational time is used to calculate the *Ms* (colour grid map), in the FMM method. Thus, Table 4 shows the mean time to compute the colour grid map, in maps from a small 50x50 pixels² to a big 500x500 pixels² grid map.

From this table it can be observed that the computational time increases exponentially with the area of the grip map, and decreases with the number of obstacles, because it reduces the number of nodes to be calculated from the free space to expand the solution.

Furthermore, from this table it is important to notice that the best option for a real time application is a map grid of 100x100 pixels and it has a bad performance for a map above of 500x500 pixels. It is principally, because the module needs to calculate the potential map applying the angle-guidance fast marching square for each different distribution of static and dynamic obstacles

6 CONCLUSIONS

A novel approach for the global and local path planning system of autonomous surface vehicles was presented. The global path-planning algorithm was validated in a realistic scenario, a Mediterranean route between Genoa and Rotterdam container terminal. Furthermore, the local path-planning algorithm was tested in a small region in the estuary of the Tagus River, Portugal. From these simulations the good behaviour of the system was verified. The major contribution of this paper is the inclusion of the forecasting data into the fast-marching square method to compute a more realistic path. From the simulations, the good performance of the system was found. Also, a computational analysis was carried out, and was detected that the best option for a real-time path-planning is a map grid of 100x100 pixels.

ACKNOWLEDGEMENTS

This work was performed within the Strategic Research Plan of the Centre for Marine Technology and Ocean Engineering (CENTEC), which is financed by Portuguese Foundation for Science and Technology (Fundação para a Ciência e Tecnologia-FCT) under contract UIDB/UIDP/00134/2020. The first author has been funded by a PhD scholarship from the University of Lisbon, and the Centre for Marine Technology and Ocean Engineering (CENTEC) under the contract *BD/579/2016*. The authors are grateful with R. Vettor who provided the forecasting information for simulations.

REFERENCES

Cox, G. G., & Lloyd, A. R. (1977). Hydrodynamic design basis for navy ship roll motion stabilization.

DNV-GL, (2019), Autonomous and remotely-operated ships, https://www.dnvgl.com/maritime/autonomous-remotely-operated-ships/index.html

Fonseca, N., & Guedes Soares, C. (1998). Time-domain analysis of large-amplitude vertical ship motions and wave loads. *Journal of Ship Research*, 42(2), 139–152.

Garrido S., Moreno L., Lima P.U., (2011). Robot formation motion planning using fast marching, *Robot. Auton. Syst.* 59,675–683.

Guedes Soares, C. (1990). Effect of spectral shape uncertainty in the short term wave-induced ship responses. *Applied Ocean Research*, 12(2), 54–69.

Guedes Soares C., L. Rusu, M. Bernardino, P. Pilar, (2011). An operational wave forecasting system for the portuguese continental coastal area, *Journal Operational Oceanography*, 4, pp. 17–27.

Hinostroza, M.A., Xu, H.T. and Guedes Soares, C., (2017), "Path-planning and path following control system for autonomous surface vessel", *Maritime Transportation and Harvesting of Sea Resources*, Guedes Soares, C. & Teixeira A. P., (Eds.), Taylor & Francis Group, London, pp. 991–998.

Hinostroza, M.A., Xu, H.T. and Guedes Soares, C., (2018) "Motion Planning, Guidance and Control System for Autonomous Surface Vessel" In *Proceedings of the 37th International Conference on Ocean, Offshore and Arctic Engineering (OMAE 2018)*, V11BT12A016, https://doi.org/10.1115/OMAE2018-78537

Hinostroza, M. A., Xu, H., & Guedes Soares, C. (2019). Cooperative operation of autonomous surface vehicles for maintaining formation in complex marine environment. *Ocean Engineering*, 183, 132–154.

IMO (2019), Guidelines for Maritime Autonomous Surface Ships (MASS), http://www.imo.org/en/MediaCentre/HotTopics/Pages/Autonomous-shipping.aspx

Kim, H., Kim, D., Shin, J. U., Kim, H., & Myung, H. (2014). Angular rate-constrained path planning algorithm for unmanned surface vehicles. *Ocean Engineering*, 84, 37–44.

KongsbergMaritime, 2017. Autonomous ship project, key facts about YARA Birkeland. URL, https://www.km.kongs berg.com/ks/web/nokbg0240.nsf/AllWeb/4B8113B707A50A4FC125811D00407045?OpenDocument

Liu, Y., & Bucknall, R. (2016). The angle guidance path planning algorithms for unmanned surface vehicle formations by using the fast marching method. *Applied Ocean Research*, 59, 327–344.

Liu, Y., Song, R., & Bucknall, R. (2019). Intelligent Tracking of Moving Ships in Constrained Maritime

Environments Using AIS. *Cybernetics and Systems*, *50* (6), 539–555.

Rolls-Royce, (2018), "Autonomous ships: The next step," Available:http://www.rolls-royce.com/

Song, R., Liu, Y., & Bucknall, R. (2019). Smoothed A* algorithm for practical unmanned surface vehicle path planning. *Applied Ocean Research*, *83*, 9–20.

Vettor, R., & Guedes Soares, C. (2016). Development of a ship weather routing system. *Ocean Engineering*, *123*, 1–14.

Vettor, R.; Tadros, M.; Ventura, M., and Guedes Soares, C. (2016). Route planning of a fishing vessel in coastal waters with fuel consumption restraint. Guedes Soares, C. & Santos T. A., (Eds.), *Maritime Technology and Engineering 3* London, UK: Taylor & Francis Group; pp. 167–173.

Xu, H., & Guedes Soares, C. (2016). Vector field path following for surface marine vessel and parameter identification based on LS-SVM. *Ocean Engineering*, *113*, 151–161.

Study on the maneuverability of a ship in regular waves based on a unified seakeeping and maneuvering numerical model

S. Paramesh, Praveen Kumar Ch & Suresh Rajendran
Department of Ocean engineering, IIT Madras, India

ABSTRACT: Maneuverability of a ship in regular waves is numerically investigated in this paper. A unified seakeeping and maneuvering numerical model is used for assessing the ship behavior in waves. A crude oil carrier (KVLCC2) model is used for studying the ship's maneuvering behavior. The wave exciting forces are calculated based on strip theory. The Froude-Krylov and the restoring forces are calculated for the exact wetted surface area and the diffraction forces are calculated for mean wetted surface area. The hydrodynamic derivatives and the control surface, i.e., the propeller and the rudder, are modelled based on empirical data available in the existing literature. The equation of motion is solved in the body frame. An autopilot is designed based on PID controller and tested for the model operating in waves. Effectiveness of the PID controller in regular waves is numerically investigated by navigating the ship in the desired trajectory through way point guidance, using a line of sight (LOS) guidance algorithm.

1 INTRODUCTION

Maneuvering is an important topic in the field of naval architecture to study the behavior of ships in calm water. Maneuvering motions are curvilinear in nature and the maneuvering performance of a ship is traditionally assessed from the experiments conducted in calm water. These tests play an important role in the assessment of the maneuvering characteristics of ships. However, information obtained from this study may differ significantly in real sea conditions. The introduction of the Energy Efficiency Design Index (EEDI) by IMO has put limitations on installed engine power. Hence it is imperative to study the maneuvering performance of ships in actual sea conditions.

Researchers have adopted different techniques to develop a unified numerical model in order to study the behavior of ships in real sea conditions. Typically seakeeping equations of motion is solved in the frequency domain and Response Amplitude Operators (RAOs) are calculated to estimate the ship motions (i.e., roll, pitch and heave). However, the maneuvering equation of motion is directly solved in the time domain. One way of combining these two models is to consider the motions due to seakeeping as the disturbance at the output of the maneuvering model. The shortcomings of this approach are well cited in Perez et al. (2004). Cummins (1962) developed a frequency-independent formulation to represent radiation forces in which an impulse function was used to represent the wave memory effect. Based on this approach, Bailey et al. (1997) developed a unified model and the simulation results were compared with the traditional seakeeping and maneuvering performance of the ship. Skeijic & Faltinsen (2008) adopted a two-time scale approach to solving maneuvering problems combined with seakeeping. In the present study, a unified numerical model is developed and wave exciting forces are calculated for time-varying wetted surface area and these forces are combined with the maneuvering model and solved in a single time scale.

The second part of this paper deals with the development of a controller based on PID control law for heading control of ships using the mathematical model mentioned above. Ships are generally underactuated vehicles and the trajectory tracking is actually achieved through heading control. Fossen et al. (2003) developed a control system for trajectory tracking of marine vehicles applying a Line of sight (LOS) algorithm. Guerreiro et al. (2014) applied a model-based control technique, nonlinear model predictive control (NMPC), for trajectory tracking of the autonomous surface craft. The author considered the state constraints in the form of penalties in the cost function and the input constraints are made inherent in the nonlinear model in order to reduce the computational burden. The proposed algorithm is also tested for real-time implementation on a Catamaran model. Zheng et al (2014)) compared the performance of Nonlinear Model Predictive (NMPC) and Linearized Model Predictive Control (LMPC) technique for trajectory tracking of surface vessels in calm water in terms of computational facility required for the optimization of the quadratic objective function, accuracy and the efficiency of the

DOI: 10.1201/9781003216599-22

two methods. Fossen et al. (2015) developed an adaptive controller in order to compensate for the drift due to the environmental disturbance in the trajectory tracking problem. Several other authors have developed different control techniques in order to improve the performance as well as to compensate for the environmental disturbances. Though there are several advanced control techniques available in the literature, the PID control technique is still widely implemented in industrial applications because of its feasibility and easy to implement in real-time. In the present study, forces and moments due to waves are calculated numerically and these forces are considered in the equation of motion of ships in calm water. A PID controller is designed for heading control and the performance of the design is numerically tested for trajectory tracking application. The input constraints such as rudder limits and rudder rate limits are included implicitly in the model. A LOS guidance system is used for reference heading generation for the ship to navigate through way-points.

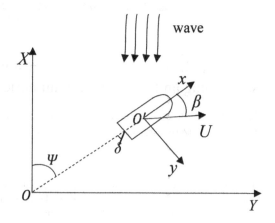

Figure 1. Ship's frame of reference.
X-O-Y – Inertial Frame or global frame
x-O'-y – Body frame.

2 UNIFIED NUMERICAL MODEL

Rajendran et al. (2015, 2016) presented a body non-linear time-domain method based on strip theory for seakeeping calculation. The numerical tool is further modified in order to study the maneuvering of ships. The 4DoF equation of motion of a ship having surge, sway, roll and yaw degrees of freedom in waves is given by the following expression

$$[(M+A(0))]\dot{v} + C_{RB}v + N(0)v = F_P + F_R \\ + F_H + F_{FK} + F_D + F_{Rest} \quad (1)$$

Where M- mass matrix, $A(0)$ – Low frequency added mass matrix, C_{RB} – Coriolis component matrix due to rigid mass and $N(0)$ – Coriolis component matrix due to added mass. F_P, F_R, F_H, F_{FK}, F_D, F_{Rest} are respectively propeller, rudder, hydrodynamic, Froude-Krylov, diffraction and restoring forces. Velocity vector $v = [u, v, p, r]$ is defined in body frame and the position vector $\eta = [x, y, \Phi, \psi]$ is measured w.r.t global frame as shown in Figure 1.

$$\dot{\eta} = R(\eta)v \quad (2)$$

$R(\eta)$ is the transformation matrix from the body frame to the global frame

3 CALCULATION OF FORCES/MOMENTS

3.1 Propeller thrust

The hydrodynamic force due to propeller motion in the surge direction is given by

$$F_{Propeller} = (1-t_p)T \quad (3)$$

Where t_p thrust deduction factor and the propeller thrust (T) is calculated based on the expression

$$T = \rho n_p^2 D_p^4 K_t(J_p) \quad (4)$$

The propeller details are given in Table 1 and $K_t(J_p)$ is calculated based on the empirical relation available in Yasukawa & Yashimura (2014).

3.2 Hydrodynamic force/moment

Hydrodynamic force/moment acting on the hull (F_H) in each degree of freedom is calculated based on Yasukawa & Yashimura (2014) and is given by,

$$X_H = -R_0 + X_{vv}v^2 + X_{vr}vr + X_{rr}r^2 + X_{vvvv}v^4 \quad (5)$$

Table 1. KVLCC2 ship and model particulars.

Particulars	Full scale	model Scale (1:45.7)
Length between Perpendiculars L_{bp} (m)	320	7
Breadth B (m)	58	1.27
Draft D (m)	20.8	0.46
Displacement Δ (m^3)	312600	3.27
Longitudinal center of Gravity x_G (m)	11.2	0.25
Block coefficient C_b	0.810	0.810
Propeller dia. D_p (m)	9.86	0.216
Rudder height H_R (m)	15.80	0.345
Rudder Area A_R (m^2)	112.5	0.0539

$$Y_H = Y_v v + Y_r r + Y_{vvv} v^3 + Y_{vvr} v^2 r + Y_{vrr} v r^2 + Y_{rrr} r^3 \quad (6)$$

$$N_H = N_v v + N_r r + N_{vvv} v^3 + N_{vvr} v^2 r + N_{vrr} v r^2 + N_{rrr} r^3 \quad (7)$$

$$K_H = Y_H \left(\frac{\Delta}{2} + 0.4061 \right) \quad (8)$$

where X_H, Y_H, N_H, K_H are hydrodynamic forces acting on the hull in the surge, sway, yaw and roll directions, respectively. The hydrodynamic derivatives corresponding to the hull considered in this paper are obtained from Yasukawa & Yashimura (2014).

3.3 Rudder force/moment

The force/moment due to steering in the surge, sway, roll and yaw directions are given by the following expressions

$$X_R = -(1 - t_r) F_N \sin\delta$$
$$Y_R = -(1 + a_H) F_N \cos\delta \quad (9)$$
$$N_R = -(x_R + a_H x_H) F_N \cos\delta$$

where X_R, Y_R and N_R respectively are rudder force in surge, sway and yaw directions.

3.4 Wave exciting force/moment

The exciting force on the body due to the action of waves can be resolved into two components, namely, the force due to the incident wave velocity potential and the force due to the diffracted wave velocity potential. The surge excitation forces are calculated based on a semi-empirical formula as given in Rajendran et al. (2015a, 2015b).

The Froude-Krylov exciting force/moment, due to the incident wave velocity potential, is calculated by assuming the ship as a slender body. The ship is discretized along the length into a finite number of strips, each having a uniform cross-section. The Section curves defining the cross-section of each strip are further discretized into a finite number of line segments. The instantaneous position and orientation of each line segment are calculated with reference to the global reference frame. The dynamic pressure at the centroid of each line segment is calculated using the following expression based on linear wave theory,

$$p_d = -\rho \frac{\partial \Phi_I}{\partial t} \quad (10)$$

where Φ_I – Incident velocity potential and is defined in the global frame as given in the expression below,

$$\Phi_I = \frac{Ag}{\omega} e^{Kz} \cos(KY \sin\gamma - KX \cos\gamma + \omega t + \varepsilon) \quad (11)$$

where K is the wave number and X, Y is the position of the vessel measured in the global reference frame, ω_0 is the frequency of the incident wave and γ is the incident wave heading angle measured in the global frame. The position and orientation of the vessel as well as the wave heading are being updated in the global/universal reference frame (X-O-Y) at every time step. Hence the effect of encounter frequency is taken into account in the time-domain simulation.

Forces/moments in each degree of freedom are calculated by integrating the dynamic pressure given by the following expression.

$$F_{FK_j}^U = \int_{x_{as}^U}^{x_{fs}^U} \left[\sum_{port}^{stbd} \left[p_d . dl \, n_j^U \right] \right] dx \quad j = 1, 2 \ldots 6 \quad (12)$$

Diffraction forces are calculated using Incident velocity potential (Φ_I) and radiation velocity potential (Φ_R) based on Haskind relationship. Haskind relationship for total wave exciting forces is given by,

$$F_i(\omega) = \rho \iint_S \left[\Phi_I \frac{\delta \Phi_R}{\delta n} - \Phi_R \frac{\delta \Phi_I}{\delta n} \right] ds \quad (13)$$

The force due to diffracted waves is given by the following expression,

$$F_d(\omega) = \rho \iint_S -\Phi_R \frac{\delta \Phi_I}{\delta n} ds \quad (14)$$

The longitudinal, lateral and yaw drift forces/moments plays an important role in maneuvering of ships. The developed numerical tool partially takes account of the second order drift forces through estimation of the body nonlinear Froude-Krylov forces and restoring forces for the exact wetted surface. However, a complete formulation should involve all three components i.e. incident, radiation and diffraction potentials. The wave direction w.r.t the global frame is shown in Figure 2.

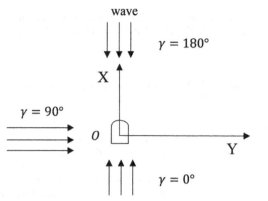

Figure 2. Wave direction with reference to global frame.

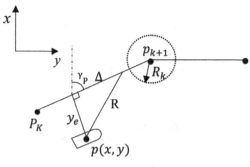

Figure 4. LOS guidance system geometry.

4 CONTROLLER DESIGN

A PID controller is integrated with the above model in cascade to achieve the heading control of the ship, as shown in Figure 3. A LOS guidance system, as represented in Figure 4, is integrated with the unified model and PID controller to generate the reference heading (ψ_{ref}) based on the way-points. This reference heading is compared with the actual heading and the error signal is fed to the controller. The control law adopted in the controller design is given by,

$$\delta(t) = K_p(\psi_d - \psi_a) + K_d r + K_i \int_0^t (\psi_d - \psi_a) dt \quad (15)$$

Where K_p, K_d and K_i are proportional, derivative and integral gains of PID controller, respectively. The response was simulated in Simulink and the gains were adjusted to have minimum rise time and the overshoot.

4.1 LOS guidance system

The line of sight (LOS) approach has been widely adopted in the literature for trajectory tracking applications because of its simplicity and guaranteed stability properties such as uniform semi-global exponential stability (USGES), as proved in Fossen et al. (2015). The ships are generally underactuated vehicles i.e., conventional ships have propeller(s) for speed control and rudder for direction control and no independent control over the sway direction. Hence through the LOS guidance approach, the desired output is reduced from 3 DOF i.e. (X_d, Y_d, ψ_d) to 2 DOF i.e. (ψ_d and u_d).

LOS guidance has two main functions. The first function is to calculate the desired heading angle and the second function adopts a mechanism to select the next way-point. The desired heading $\psi_d(t)$ is computed based on vessel's current position $p(x, y)$ and the deviation (cross-track error (y_e)) from the desired path at any given point in time. It resembles a helmsman where he intuitively selects the desired heading angle based on the vessel's position and a look-ahead distance. In this paper, a constant look-ahead distance (Δ) and the cross-track error (y_e) is used to compute the desired heading angle. The desired trajectory is assumed to be straight lines joining the way-points p_k and p_{k+1} where the subscript $k=1,2...n-1$ indicates the way-point and n is the number of way-points.

The desired heading angle is given by (M.Lekkas & Fossen 2013),

$$\psi_d = \gamma_p + \operatorname{atan}\left(\frac{-y_e}{\Delta}\right) - \operatorname{atan}\left(\frac{v}{u}\right) \quad (16)$$

where $\Delta = sqrt(R^2 - y_e^2)$

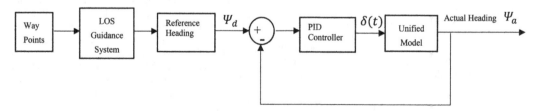

Figure 3. Block diagram of an autopilot system integrated with PID controller and LOS guidance system.

$$\gamma_P = atan2(y_{k+1} - y_k, x_{k+1} - x_k)$$

The way-points are selected from the way-points table based on the criteria that the ship position $p(x,y)$ lies within the circle of radius R.

$$(x - x_k)^2 + (y - y_k)^2 < R_{k+1}^2 \qquad (17)$$

where R is a constant and its value as suggested in the literature should be less than or equal to two times the ship length $(R_{k+1} \leq nL_{pp})$.

5 MODEL DETAILS

The geometric details of KVLCC2 ship is given in Table 1 for the full ship and the model of 1:45.7 scale. The numerical study is done on model of 7 m length.

Ship response was simulated for different wave conditions and the results are presented in section 6. Detailed wave conditions are given in the Table 2.

6 SIMULATION RESULTS

The simulation was carried out for a KVLCC2 ship model of 1:45.7 scale. The Froude number considered in the simulation is $F_n = 0.142$. The desired trajectory is assumed to be straight lines joining the way-points (X_d, Y_d) which are given in Table 3. A numerical method based on 4th order Runge-Kutta method with constant time step (h=0.1) is adopted for solving the equations of motion. The ship is initially at the origin (0, 0). The ship moves with a constant forward speed of U=1.1 m/s, which corresponds to a propeller speed of 690 rpm.

Rudder saturation limits: $-35deg \leq \delta \leq 35deg$
Rudder rate limit $\dot{\delta} = 11.92 \ deg/sec$
PID Controller gains: K_p= 5, K_d= 25 and K_i= 0.05

Table 2. Wave details.

Wave Heading (°)	Amplitude (m)	Angular frequency (rad/sec)
0	0.0350	2.21
60	0.0350	2.21
180	0.0350	2.21

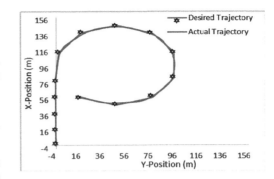

Figure 5. Trajectory of the ship in head wave using PID controller.

6.1 Case 1: Simulation results for head waves

The vessel is numerically tested in a regular wave with an amplitude of 0.035m (wave steepness $ka=0.175$) and a frequency of 2.21 rad/s, which corresponds to a wave to ship length ratio of 1.8 and wave heading of 180°. The plot in Figure 5 and in Figure 6 (a), (b), (c), (d) shows respectively the trajectory of the ship in head waves, corresponding rudder angle input, ship positions and deviation from the desired path, motions in roll and yaw. We can notice from Figure 5 that the ship is able to follow the trajectory and the controller is effective in providing the required control force without violating the saturation limits of the rudder input. From Figure 6(a) we can also notice that between 0–120 seconds, where the vessel travels in straight line, the corresponding rudder angle input and roll motion is negligible. The deviation of the ship trajectory from the desired trajectory is at most 8m near way-points which is satisfactory as the vessel is underactuated and through LOS guidance, it is expected to have such deviations. The mean value of the roll is about 1° towards port while turning to the right.

6.1.1 Wave exciting Force/Moment

The exciting force/moment due to incident waves is shown in Figure 7 (a), (b), (c), (d) for 4 DOF. The wave exciting force in sway, roll and yaw is quite insignificant when the ship is in between the way-points (0, 0) and (115, 2) owing to the port-starboard symmetry of the hull and the ship travels in a straight line. This occurs between 0–120 seconds (approx.) and hence not shown in the plots except for surge motion. As the ship

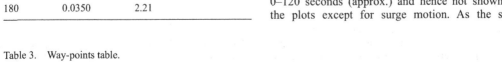

Table 3. Way-points table.

X_d(m)	0	20	40	60	80	115	140	150	140	115	85	60	50	60
Y_d (m)	0	0	0	0	0	2	20	50	80	100	100	80	50	20

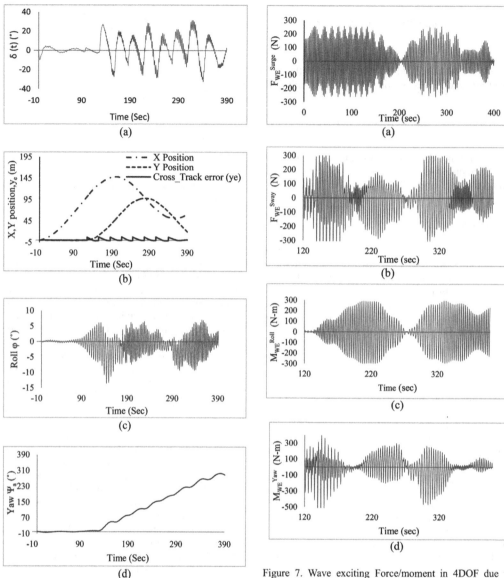

Figure 6. Simulation results: (a) Rudder input δ (t). (b) Ship position, cross track error y_e, (c) Motion in roll and (d) Motion in yaw during the trajectory tracking in head waves.

Figure 7. Wave exciting Force/moment in 4DOF due to incident regular waves during trajectory tracking in head waves. (a), (b) force in surge, sway directions and (c), (d) moment in roll, yaw directions.

enters the oblique sea condition after 130 seconds the surge force becomes negligible and the force/moment in sway, roll and yaw become dominant. We can also notice that the ship encounters waves with different frequencies in its course. For example, the heading angle of the ship is between 0–180° up to 280 seconds and the ship travels in head waves. During this period, the encountered frequency varies from 2.21–2.85 rad/sec. Wave exciting frequency between 280–350 seconds varies from 2.21–1.7 rad/sec. During this period, the ship experiences the following waves as the heading angle is 180< ψ_a <270°. Hence the effect of encounter frequency is captured.

6.2 *Case 2: Simulation results for Oblique waves*

The vessel is also tested in oblique waves with an amplitude of 0.035m and a frequency of 2.21 rad/s, which corresponds to a wave to ship length ratio of 1.8 and wave heading of 60°. The ship trajectory, corresponding rudder angle input and ship positions

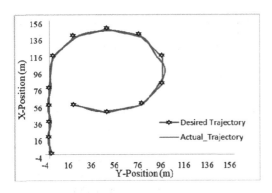

Figure 8. Trajectory of the ship in oblique waves using PID controller.

and deviation from the desired path, motions in roll and yaw are given respectively, in Figure 8, 9 (a), (b), (c), (d) below. As the ship is experiencing the beam waves, the ship is being drifted away from the desired path in the beginning, as against in the case of head waves.

The rudder angle input is within the saturation limits. The mean roll angle during turning is 0.7 degrees towards port and it is maximum between the way-points (140, 80) and (115,100). The deviation from the desired path is also maximum between the way-points (140, 80) and (85,100). This is the case when the model almost experiences the beam sea condition.

6.2.1 *Total Force/Moments*

The force/moment in 4DOF experienced by the ship due to incident waves when it is following the trajectory given in Figure 8 under oblique waves is shown in Figure 10 (a), (b), (c), (d). The contribution of the wave exciting force up to 130 seconds in sway is more when compared to surge and more in yaw when compared to roll. This is due to the fact that the ship travels in straight line during this period and the waves acting on bow of the model imparts a yaw moment. The surge force is dominant when the ship position is in between way points (85,100) and (50,50), when the model experiences the following wave condition. The roll moment is maximum between the way points (140, 80) and (115,100).

7 CONCLUSION

A unified numerical model integrated with PID controller and LOS guidance system was developed and the effectiveness of the controller in heading control is studied numerically for trajectory tracking application. The numerical study was done for regular waves of different wave headings i.e. head, following and oblique waves. It is observed that, based on the numerical study, the performance of PID

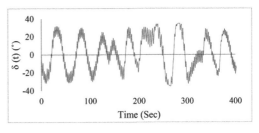

(a)

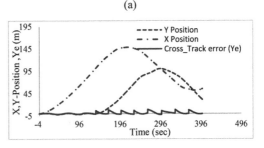

(b)

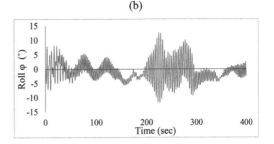

(c)

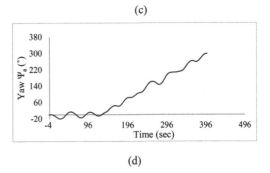

(d)

Figure 9. Simulation results: (a) Rudder input δ (t). (b) Ship position, cross track error y_e, (c) Motion in roll and (d) Motion in yaw during the trajectory tracking in oblique waves.

controller in following and head wave conditions is satisfactory and in oblique waves the performance though satisfactory not as good as in head waves.

Going forward, the accuracy of the unified numerical model and real time implementation of the PID controller will be studied through free running autonomous ship models.

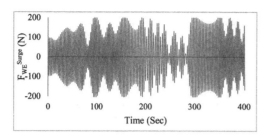

(a)

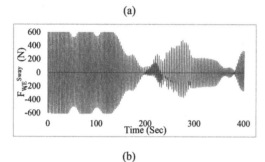

(b)

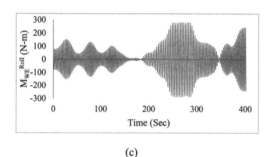

(c)

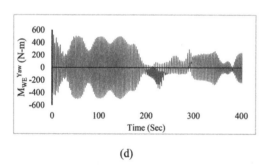

(d)

Figure 10. Wave exciting force/moment in 4DOF acting on the ship during trajectory tracking in oblique waves. (a), (b) Force in surge, sway directions and (c), (d) Moment in roll, yaw directions.

ACKNOWLEDGEMENTS

This project is partially funded by the Science and Engineering Research Board (SERB) under the project no: CRG/2018/004807. The authors are indebted to Prof. Antonio Pascoal, Associate professor at Instituto Superior Technico (IST), Portugal for providing insights of control system design and to Prof. Ranjith Mohan, Associate professor at IIT Madras, India for his technical advice during the course of this work.

SYMBOLS

$R(\eta)$	Transformation matrix from Body reference frame to Universal reference frame
n_p	Speed of the propeller (rpm)
D_p	Diameter of the propeller (m)
T	Propeller Thrust (N)
t_p	Thrust deduction factor
t_r	Steering deduction factor
a_H	Rudder force increase factor
x_R	Longitudinal coordinate of rudder position (m)
x_H	Longitudinal coordinate of acting point of the additional lateral force (m)
ρ	Density (kg/m^3)
A	Wave amplitude (m)
ω	Incident wave frequency (rad/sec)
K	Wave number
ε	Phase difference (radians)
F_{FK}^U	Froude-Krylov force measured in universal reference frame (N)
γ	Wave heading angle (radians)
P_d	Dynamic pressure (N/m^2)
n_j	Generalized unit normal to the hull surface
x_d, y_d	Desired positions of the ship (m)
Y_e	Cross-track error (m)
$\delta(t), \delta$	Rudder angle input (degree)
u_d	Desired forward speed (m/s)
Ψ_d	Desired heading (degree)
F_N	Rudder normal force (N)
F_{WE}, M_{WE}	Wave exciting force (N), moment (N-m)

REFERENCES

Bailey, P.A., 1997. A unified mathematical model describing the maneuvering of a ship travelling in a seaway. *Trans RINA*, 140, pp.131–149.

Cummins, W.E., 1962. The impulse response function and ship motions. Schiffstechnik 9:101–109.

Fossen, T.I., Breivik, M. and Skjetne, R., 2003. Line-of-sight path following of underactuated marine craft. *IFAC proceedings volumes*, 36(21), pp.211–216.

Fossen, T.I., Pettersen, K.Y. and Galeazzi, R., 2014. Line-of-sight path following for dubins paths with adaptive sideslip compensation of drift forces. *IEEE Transactions on Control Systems Technology*, *23*(2), pp.820–827.

Guerreiro, B.J., Silvestre, C., Cunha, R. and Pascoal, A., 2014. Trajectory tracking nonlinear model predictive control for autonomous surface craft. *IEEE Transactions on Control Systems Technology*, *22*(6), pp.2160–2175.

Lekkas, A.M. and Fossen, T.I., 2013. Line-of-sight guidance for path following of marine vehicles. *Advanced in marine robotics*, pp.63–92.

Perez, T., Fossen, T.I. and Sorensen, A., 2004. A discussion about seakeeping and manoeuvring models for surface vessels. *Centre for Ships and Ocean Structures (CESOS), Technical Report No. MSS-TR-001*.

Rajendran, S., Fonseca, N. and Guedes Soares, C., 2015a. Simplified body nonlinear time domain calculation of vertical ship motions and wave loads in large amplitude waves. *Ocean Engineering*, *107*, pp.157–177.

Rajendran, S., Fonseca, N. and Guedes Soares, C., 2015b. Effect of surge motion on the vertical responses of ships in waves. *Ocean Engineering*, *96*, pp.125–138.

Rajendran, S., Fonseca, N. and Guedes Soares, C., 2016. Body nonlinear time domain calculation of vertical ship responses in extreme seas accounting for 2nd order Froude-Krylov pressure. *Applied Ocean Research*, *54*, pp.39–52.

Skejic, R. and Faltinsen, O.M., 2008. A unified seakeeping and maneuvering analysis of ships in regular waves. *Journal of marine science and technology*, *13*(4), pp.371–394.

Sutulo, S. and Guedes Soares, C., 2006. Development of a multifactor regression model of ship maneuvering forces based on optimized captive-model tests. *Journal of ship research*, *50*(4), pp.311–333.

Yasukawa, H. and Yoshimura, Y., 2015. Introduction of MMG standard method for ship maneuvering predictions. *Journal of Marine Science and Technology*, *20*(1), pp.37–52.

Zheng, H., Negenborn, R.R. and Lodewijks, G., 2014. Trajectory tracking of autonomous vessels using model predictive control. *IFAC Proceedings Volumes*, *47*(3), pp.8812–8818.

Z-drive escort tug manoeuvrability modelling: From model-scale to full-scale validation

B. Piaggio, M. Viviani, M. Martelli & M. Figari
Department of Naval Architecture and Marine, Electrical, Electronic, Telecommunications Engineering (DITEN)
Polytechnic School of Genoa University, Genova, Italy

ABSTRACT: A deep insight into the manoeuvring characterisation of a broader class of Azimuthal Stern Drive Escort tugs (ASD) is undertaken with the scope of defining a parametric manoeuvring simulation code for the free-sailing and towing operations. To this end, given a simple set of tug design parameters (main dimensions, skeg size, azimuthal size, propeller pitch, main engines, etc.), a physics-based 4-DOF mathematical prediction tool for the dynamic behaviour of the ASD tug has been developed in calm seas. Two independent validation processes have been provided to prove the suitability of the modelling: the first model-scale, while the second full-scale. The present paper presents the free-sailing full-scale validation of a different but compatible hull, having dimensions, propulsion, skeg characteristics significantly different with respect to the "parent-design" (RM2812) used to develop the code principally. The verification involved the measurements purposely performed during sea trials onto two sister-ship ASD new-buildings (RM3213).

1 INTRODUCTION

Tugs represent a challenging market for work-boat designers and operators. The general increase in the size of merchant vessels requires the use of tugs with increasingly better performances in terms of bollard pull, and not only. This design goal can be achieved by increasing tugs size and power; however, some disadvantages can occur. Ships of medium size are not prepared to sustain high push forces onto the side shell safely, or extremely high wire pulls onto the vessels' bollards. On the other hand, large size tugs are not optimal for assistance in restricted/busy harbour waters and, last but not least, tugs of significant size/power implies, for the operators, high overall capital investments and high daily costs. Furthermore, indirect towing features are becoming increasingly demanded and complex to be estimated: the development of large hydrodynamic forces for steering or braking an assisted ship is a matter of hull and propulsion system integrated design, with considerable implications on vessel's dynamics and stability; Figure 1 shows a schematic of an escort operation.

Although the primary explicit purpose of a tug design is to achieve good manoeuvring and pull performances when assisting a ship, either in berthing direct assistance (*low-speed*) or in escort indirect mode (*high-speed*), the tools available for designers to predict these type of performances are customarily based onto personal expertise. Correlations with known results of previous similar projects are generally comforted by the consideration that a tug offering good results in terms of stability and bollard pull performances will surely be a good platform to achieve adequate manoeuvring/assistance capabilities.

The manoeuvring capabilities, together with stability margins, are the main characteristics required to any tug, and especially Escort tugs. To adequately exploit the available direct and indirect pull performances, the present state of the art tug design in only a few cases involves manoeuvrability simulation tools (Quadvileg and Kaul 2006, Allan et al. 2019, Piaggio et al. 2019, Li and Calisal 2005). Instead, simulation tools are widely adopted with very good feedback in naval applications (Martelli 2015a, Martelli 2015b, Michetti et al. 2010), as well as in small vessels (Capasso et al. 2016).Indeed, good results in terms of indirect towing performances predictions can be achieved both through EFD (Artyszuk 2014, Waclawek and Molyneux 2000, Molyneux and Bose 2007, Molyneux and Earle 2001) and CFD (Çağrı Aydın et al. 2018, Smoker et al. 2016) investigations of flow patterns around tug's hull in steady drifting modes, but requiring at the same time great expertise of the CFD tools.

Moreover, higher forecasting effort and abstraction are demanded when dealing with the predictability of unsteady and transitional manoeuvrability-propulsive dynamics, if not adequately supplied of a thorough physical-based mathematical tool. With this purpose, the need for a breakthrough in escort tug design is also hinted in Allan et al. 2019 where the authors presented a simulation tool to analyse dynamic scenarios during

DOI: 10.1201/9781003216599-23

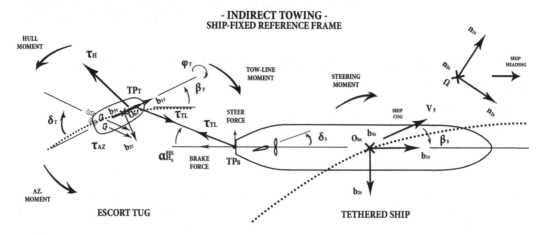

Figure 1. Escort scheme - System of systems.

escort operations, including failures. From a scientific point of view, the main challenge is to fill the existing gap in between the low-speed and high-speed manoeuvrability approaches, and then – a fortiori – in-between the model-scale and full-scale scenarios dynamics. A research project had been established to face the above-mentioned challenges.

1.1 The research project

The Rosetti Marino shipyard and the Naval Architecture and Marine Technology research group of the Genoa University have therefore addressed a project research program devoted to developing a specific computational tool capable of describing the dynamics and the manoeuvrability of an ASD tug when assisting a ship in berthing operations or escort mode. The shipyard-university partnership has the aim to achieve sound engineering results by merging the existing robust shipyard background with a new, simulation oriented, scientific approach.

In this sense, the settling of a new tug's hull was supported by a new simulation tool, with the scope of realising a manoeuvring and propulsion forecasting tool for ASD tugs at an early design phase. The goal of the project is the definition of a parametric simulator code for the dynamic manoeuvring behaviour of ASD tugs, that allows, after introduction of a simple set of design information (main dimensions, skeg size, choice of main engines, etc.) a reasonable prediction of the dynamic behaviour of the ASD tug in calm sea.

The authors presented the first batch of the tug manoeuvring performance simulation in (Piaggio et al.2019, Piaggio et al. 2019). In this instance, a novel MMG-inspired 4-DOF mathematical modelling for azimuthal stern drive escort tugs was settled down and validated by means of suitable free-sailing escort tests carried out at the model tank basin in model scale.

The present paper, on the other hand, presents a first insight into the full-scale cross-validation of the same modelling by means of purposely devised sea trials, which were carried out onto similar vessels to the project's prototype.

2 CASE STUDY

2.1 The RM2812 prototype

A new 28 × 12m sized tug design has been carried out to produce the reference set of data for the development of the manoeuvring simulator. The idea behind is the development of a medium-size tug's hull, capable of good performance in ahead/astern directions (maximum achievable speed, low wave pattern), fulfilling with large margins the requirements for tugs stability (RESOLUTION MSC.415(97) entering into force on 1st January 2020). The presence of a medium-size skeg has the aim to achieve good escort performance without impairing low-speed manoeuvring readiness. A double hull configuration (side protection) allows hull damages survivability in accordance with the requirements of RESOLUTION MSC.235-(82) for OSV ships. In particular, the specific new tug design has the following characteristics:

- bollard pull: 65-70 tonnes
- maximum speed: 12.5 knots
- fixed pitch propellers
- high stability margins

A summary of the main characteristics of the prototype tug is described in Table 1; the General arrangement of the RM2812 is shown in Figure 2. The project was fully developed into the basis of a specific propulsion selection that covered both the main engines (2000 kW/shaft) and the main propulsors. MTU 16V4000 M63, to be coupled to RR US205 P20 FP, 2.4 m diameter, were chosen as the basic propulsion set for this purpose.

Table 1. RM2812 - Main particulars.

Length	L_{OA}	28.4	m
Breadth	B	12	m
Height	D_H	4.95	m
Full Draught	T_d	4.05	m
Operative Draught	T	3.7	m
Azimuthals	D	2.4	m
Design Speed	V_d	12.5	kts
Power	P_B	2x2000	kW
Bollard Pull	BP	>65	t

3 MATHEMATICAL MODEL

The *Escort Tug*, is a scalable, parametric and customizable Azimuthal Stern Drive tug: hull, skeg and azimuthal hydrodynamics have been meticulously investigated and included into an MMG-like physical modelling, including interactions. Shaft and engine dynamics are detailed. The tug is studied in full 4-DOF with an emphasis on inclining moments and heel hydrodynamic effects, which notably jeopardise the towage operational safety. The parametric modelling concept enables the design of each component.

3.1 Tug dynamics

Vessel Hydrodynamics Canonical 4-DOF Rigid-body dynamics equations are applied to the vessel and referred onto the Body-Fixed basis **b** — *frame* — i.e. the planar manoeuvrability is fully coupled with the roll effect.

Tug's hydrodynamics modelling embraces hull and skeg forces τ_{H+s}, and azimuthal forces τ_{AZ} — comprehensive of their reciprocal interactions. A brief summary of the main functional dependencies is below presented. Complete details can be found in Piaggio et al. 2019, Piaggio et al. 2020, Piaggio et al. 2020.

1. ***Hull+Skeg*** The hull+skeg regressor $\hat{\Phi}'$ of the generic hydrodynamic force and moment is formally defined as a 5th order multivariate polynomial of the vessel's kinematics:

$$\hat{\Phi}' = \sum_{i=0}^{n-1} \mu_i \left(v'^{\alpha_i} r'^{\beta_i} \phi^{\gamma_i} \right) + \mu_{\dot{v}} \dot{v}' + \mu_{\dot{r}} \dot{r}' \quad (1)$$

where $\alpha_i, \beta_i = 0, 1, 2, 3, 4, 5$, $\gamma_i = 0, 1, 2, 3$ and $\alpha_i + \beta_i + \gamma_i \leq 5$. A Time Domain Multi-Run LSQ approach must be adopted to identify the hydrodynamic derivative parameters for the

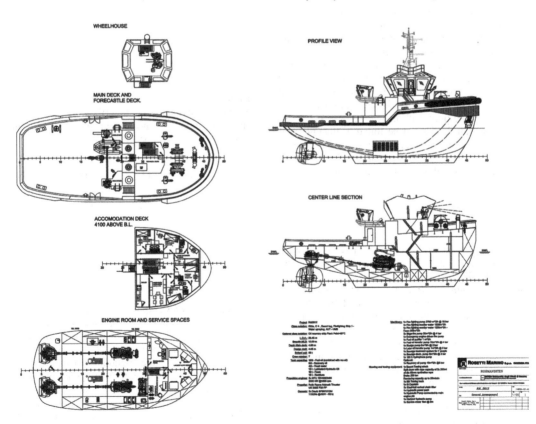

Figure 2. RM2812 - General arrangements.

longitudinal X and lateral Y forces, and the yaw N and roll K moments.

2. **Azimuthals** The complete hydrodynamic characterisation of the two Azimuthals in oblique flow requires a model representation spanning the entire working domain of the advance angle ε (i.e. hydrodynamic pitch angle) and azimuthal angle δ. The entire response surfaces of the total axial longitudinal force $\tilde{X}_{AZ}$, the total transversal force $\tilde{Y}_{AZ}$ and the propeller torque Q are investigated in uncoupled and coupled dependence from the variables. The non-dimensional coefficients (Eq. 2) are defined in the azimuthal-fixed reference system rotated by the azimuthal angle (i.e. longitudinally aligned with the propeller shaft), with $V_t = (V_a^2 + (0.7\pi n D)^2)^{0.5}$ and $A_O = \pi D^2/4$.

$$C_X(\delta, \varepsilon) = \frac{\tilde{X}_{AZ}(\delta, \varepsilon)}{0.5\rho V_t^2 A_O} \quad (2a)$$

$$C_Y(\delta, \varepsilon) = \frac{\tilde{Y}_{AZ}(\delta, \varepsilon)}{0.5\rho V_t^2 A_O} \quad (2b)$$

$$C_Q(\delta, \varepsilon) = \frac{Q(\delta, \varepsilon)}{0.5\rho V_t^2 A_O D} \quad (2c)$$

3. **Skeg Series** Starting from the reference set-up model tested in tank, model differentials are evaluated in terms of total longitudinal X, transverse Y, yaw moment N and roll moment K employing a dedicated CFD campaign. Explicit dependency from the chord length $l' = l - l_0/L$ and the span $h' = h - h_0/T$ is analysed with respect to the tug's original main particulars, both in the pure drift and in the pure yaw scenarios. Full details can be found in Piaggio et al. 2020 The forces variation $\hat{d\Phi}'$ with respect to the one obtained by the original configuration Φ_0, are made non-dimensional through the tug data:

$$\hat{d\Phi}' = \frac{\Phi}{1/2\rho A_T V^2} - \frac{\Phi_o}{1/2\rho A_{T_o} V^2} \quad (3)$$

where the lateral area A_T is corrected considering the variation of skeg lateral area from the original.

4. **Hull-Azimuthal Interactions** The alteration of the propeller inflow can be modelled through a variation of the propeller working point in terms of effective attack angle δ_e and effective advance angle ε_e. Such variations expressed as $\Delta\delta_e$ and $\Delta\varepsilon_e$ and given as a function of the local drift angle and the azimuthal angle, are summed to the ideal geometric open water inflow (Eq. 4). The drift angle and the yaw rates represent the main functional dependencies of such variations.

$$\bar{C}_X = C_X(\delta_e + \Delta\delta_e, \varepsilon_e + \Delta\varepsilon_e) \quad (4a)$$

$$\bar{C}_Y = C_Y(\delta_e + \Delta\delta_e, \varepsilon_e + \Delta\varepsilon_e) \quad (4b)$$

$$\bar{C}_Q = C_Q(\delta_e + \Delta\delta_e, \varepsilon_e + \Delta\varepsilon_e) \quad (4c)$$

5. **Azimuthal-Hull Interactions** The influence of the azimuthals on the hull is back kept into account by employing an extended MMG-like model (Eq. 5) by which the forces are corrected in function of the drift angle β, the azimuthal angle δ, and the heel angle ϕ. Each force exerted on the azimuthal is firstly rotated in the tug's reference system by the helm angle δ. The yaw and roll moments are consequently defined according to their geometric positioning. Subsequently, forces and moments perceived by the *hull+skeg* system are corrected through the interaction factors a_H and its application point x_{aH}. The amplification of the hull forces and moments is hence assumed proportional to the corresponding azimuthal contributions of forces rotated in the hull reference.

$$X_{AZ} = (1 - t(\beta, \delta))\, a_H(\phi)\, \bar{X}_{AZ} \quad (5a)$$

$$Y_{AZ} = [1 + a_H(\beta, \phi)]\, \bar{Y}_{AZ} \quad (5b)$$

$$N_{AZ} = [x_P + x_{aH} a_H(\beta)] a_H(\delta)\, Y_{AZ} \quad (5c)$$

$$K_{AZ} = z_P\, Y_{AZ} \quad (5d)$$

Propulsion Plant The port and starboard-line propulsion plant dynamics are described through-out the dynamical coupling in-between the engines, the shaft-lines, and the propellers as in Eq. (6a-6c).

$$2\pi I^* \dot{n} = Q_{Eng} + Q_f + Q_P \quad (6a)$$

$$P_{Eng} = 2\pi Q_{Eng}(n_{Eng}, \dot{m}_f) \quad (6b)$$

$$\dot{m}_f = k_p(n_{set} - n) + k_i \int_0^t (n_{set} - n) \\ - k_{aw}(\dot{m}_f - \bar{\dot{m}}_f(n))\, d\tau \quad (6c)$$

1. **Shaft Dynamics** (Eq. (6a)) — the torque disequilibrium is evaluated comparing the propeller request Q_P and the engine provided torque at brake Q_{Eng}, accordingly to the reduction gear ratio i, and up to the frictional efficiency of the shaft-line η_s. The overall total polar inertia I^* reduced to the slow shaft is thus considered through the kinetic energy conservation of the $i-$th rotating part - i.e. subject to $1/2\, I^* \omega_{Eng}^2 = \sum 1/2\, I_i \omega_i^2$. Consistently, the

propulsive efficiencies from the generated thrust to the brake power are within included in the modelling of the frictional term.

2. **Engine Dynamics** (Eq. (6b)) — accordingly to a simplified thermodynamic modelling approach for real-time simulators Altosole_ENGINES, Altosole_ENGINES2, a mixed static and dynamic technique is adopted, where: the stroke is reduced to a static model governed by the fed fuel flow-rate $\dot{m}_f$ and the turbocharger is driven by its slower and primary dynamics. The modelling encompasses medium and high-speed diesel engines in the range of tug applications.

3. **Governor Dynamics** (Eq. (6c)) — engine's fuel-rack governor controls the flow-rate amount $\dot{m}_f$ to be fed to each engine accordingly to the design working range – i.e. idle and max speed – and torque limitations. According to the revolution's error between the set-point and the feedback $e_n = n_{set} - n$, a proportional and integral controller (PI) is complementary designed with an anti-windup functionality (AW) to simulate the inner protections of the engine. In particular, the latter part decreases the integral action of over-saturated requests which are trespassing the non-linear torque threshold. This is realised in terms of the corresponding fuel-rate saturation thresholds $\bar{\dot{m}}_f(n)$, which depends itself on the actual engine's rate of revolutions. k_p, k_i, and k_{aw} suitably represent and tune the individual actions, guaranteeing stability to the system.

3.2 Model identification

The manoeuvrability characteristics of marine vessels are traditionally of great interest in the field of naval architecture. When dealing with classic merchant ship configurations, the literature provides mathematical regression models. On the other hand, the literature addressing tug manoeuvring is indeed quite poor, and no published parametric model was found available; the authors addressed then the topic by three complementary approaches: experimental investigation with towing tank tests, CFD calculations, full-scale trials.

EFD Captive Model Testing The RM2812 escort tug prototype was built in 1:11 model scale (Figure 1). The model was fitted with two ducted azimuthal thrusters, a centre skeg, bow fenders, deck, bulwarks and superstructure for escort tests. In addition to the standard resistance, propulsion and bollard pull tests (ahead and astern), a manoeuvrability experimental campaign was performed with a three-step approach. The first part of the manoeuvring tests concerned the hull+skeg testing, the second one investigated the azimuthals only functioning, and the latter the combined system hull+skeg+azimuthals reciprocal interactions. Due to the nature of escort manoeuvering, the investigation concerned large-amplitude drift angles, yaw velocities and combined effects, with particular attention also to the heel effect on planar motions. Pure drift tests with working azimuthals were investigated in PMM tests to reproduce the hydrodynamics of the complex hull+skeg+azimuthals interactions. A summary of the experimental manoeuvring campaign is proposed in (Piaggio et al. 2019).

CFD Model Extended Series In parallel to the tank tests, CFD simulations were performed in order to test and validate numerical procedures to evaluate hydrodynamic forces. An extended series of tests have been carried out starting from the RM2812 original prototype through CFD, in order to extend the acquired hydrodynamical knowledge to some variation of variables and geometries – mainly, the skeg size, the draught and the scale. The scope of the two EFD and CFD campaigns was to merge the respective experiences into a unique mathematical modelling formulation of the manoeuvrability of a wider series of tugs. The proposed methodology is proposed in (Figari et al. 2019, Piaggio et al. 2020, Piaggio et al.2020). Among the scope of the CFD analysis, the investigation of skeg variation effects since the early design stages is the main focus. Skeg dimensions were varied, and different skeg geometries were considered, all generated by keeping the skeg leading-edge fixed in the original position and modifying its length/aspect ratio.

4 VALIDATION PROCESS

The degree of accuracy and agreement of the code with experimental data has been verified through two independent comparisons.

As the code has been developed starting from the prototype RM2812, whose model was thoroughly tested in towing tank, the first natural validation tries to reproduce the available manoeuvring Escort tests that have been performed with the tug's model

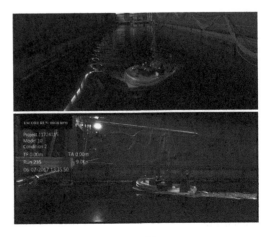

Figure 3. RM2812 - Escort model tests.

(Figure 3). In a previous work (Piaggio et al. 2019) the results of *Escort model-tests* reproduction have been widely discussed.

The second validation test case here presented concerns the simulation of the *Free Sailing full-scale* measurements performed during sea trials on two 32 × 13m sistership ASD new-buildings – namely yard hulls 118 and 119 (Figure 4). Hull and skeg geometries of two vessels are depicted in Figure 5. Characteristics of the new buildings tested are summarised in Table 2. This comparison allowed to check the simulator capability to describe the performances of a different hull, having dimensions, propulsion, skeg characteristics significantly different but non-dimensionally compatible with respect to the "parent design" used to develop the code principally. The programme was purposely-devised as a first full-scale benchmark.

Table 2. RM2812 vs RS3213 - Main characteristics.

	RM2812	RS3213	
Length	28.4	32.0	m
Breadth	12.0	13.2	m
Full Draught	4.05	4.5	m
Ops Draught	3.70	4.2	m
Ops Displacement	660	900	t
Skeg Depth	1.1	1.68	m
Skeg Length	16.2	16.0	m
Skeg Area	18.4	28.9	m^2
Centre of Mass	[14.8 0 3.9]	[15.9 0 4.2]	m
GMT	2.4	2.1	m
Az Diameter	2.4	2.8	m
Az Position	[3.70 ± 2.7 0.82]	[4.64 ± 2.8 0.2]	m
Speed	12.5	13.5	kn
Bollard Pull	6.5	90	t
Power	2x 2'000	2x 2'555	kW

4.1 Full-scale experimental set-up

The experimental measurement campaign involved a three-sided synchronised acquisition system (Table 3 - Figure 6). Both Global Navigation Satellite System + Compass and Inertial Navigation System were installed onboard and logged. Azimuthals were instrumented for measuring shafts' torque and revolutions. Azimuth control set-point and feedback signals were collected by the recording system from the proprietary control system. The engine's powering, fuel index and turbocharger dynamics were separately acquired from the proprietary automation system. Velocities and attitudes are filtered, processed and transferred to the standard reference, positioned at vessel's mid-length, on the waterline.

Figure 4. RS3213 - Full-scale tests.

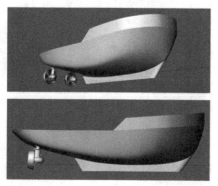

(a) RM2812

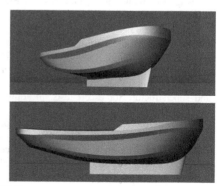

(b) RS3213

Figure 5. Z-drive escort tugs.

Table 3. Sea Trials - experimental set-up.

Station	Instrument	Signal
Bridge PC	GNSS (GPS) Compass Towing Load-Cell	Latitude & Longitude, Speed & COG Mag. Heading Tension
ECR PC	INS (Gyro.+Mag. +Acc.) Shaft Tachometer & Torquemeter Azimuthal's Automation	Attitude (Euler Angles) & Accelerations Revolutions & Torque Pitch, Revolutions & Angles
ER PC	Engine Automation Turbocharger Automation	Revolutions & Power Load & Fuel Index Pressure & Temperatures

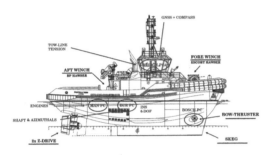

Figure 6. RS3213 - Experimental set-up.

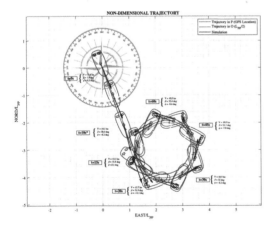

Figure 7. RS3213 - Turning test @ 27 deg – trajectory.

4.2 Sea-trials

The sea-trials programme included progressive runs, bollard pull tests, turning circle, zig-zag, free and crash stop, slam start, pure rotation on the spot, pure drift/crabbing, Dieudonnè spiral ahead and astern for benchmarking purposes. Tests were performed offshore Ravenna (ITA), in the northern Adriatic Sea.

At the actual preliminary stage of the validation, the only turning manoeuvres are presented. Zig-zag and Dieudonne' spiral will be the object of future work.

In the following paragraphs, the turning ability measured at sea is compared with simulation results. Turning Circle manoeuvres are depicted (Figures 7, 8). The main macroscopic characteristics are summarised in the following figure 9. Non-dimensional advance, transfer, tactical diameter over the length are summarised together with absolute velocity loss, max heel, asymptotic yaw rate, drift angle, and heel angle, where: the markers depict sea-trials results; the dashed lines represent simulation outcomes. All the graphs are presented with the azimuth angle in the abscissa. A satisfactory agreement with sea-trials is found, matching in average the portside and starboard repetitions at sea, whose asymmetry can be ascribed to current and wind effects.

Then, a complete set of time-series and trajectory is presented for C119's 27 deg to portside sample manoeuvre in Figures 7 and 8, respectively. These include all the main kinematic and dynamic quantities such as: absolute velocity, surge and sway velocity components, drift angle, vessel heel and trim attitude, yaw rate, heading and course over ground, together with azimuthal's angles and the engine powering. Markers represent the measured quantities during the sea-trials, while the solid line illustrates simulation results. Both transient phases, overshooting dynamics and steady regime behaviour are very well retraced by the models in all 4-DOF, demonstrating the suitability of the simulation model (Figure 9). Moreover, engines' dynamics and asymmetric loading is parallelly caught on both the port side and the starboard side shaft-lines.

5 CONCLUSIONS

The presented parametric mathematical structure for Azimuthal Stern Drive tugs proposes to encompass a broader class of Escort vessels, with tunable main particulars, stability/weight properties, draught, skeg size, and azimuthal characteristics. Starting from the RM2812 prototype project model and its RANSE-supplement series in skeg geometry, the design variables are suitably tuned in order to match the two RS3213 ASD tugs tested full-scale at sea in free-sailing. In particular, even if the hulls are different in main particulars and local forms, the two RS3213 vessels well match the RM2812 in all the dimensional ratios and conveniently suit for benchmarking purposes the parametric structure of the mathematical modelling.

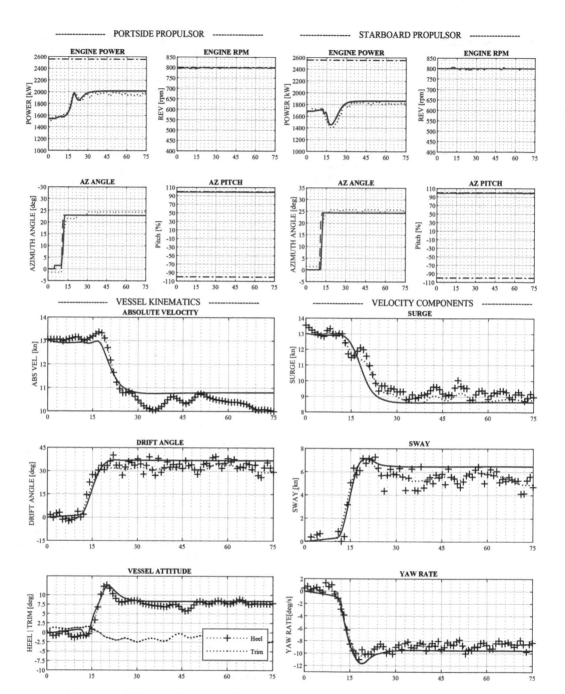

Figure 8. RS3213 - Turning test @ 27 deg - Simulation time-series.

In conclusion, the physics-based and MMG-inspired mathematical parametric architecture of the model satisfactorily encompass all the main dynamics, and thus it is suitably found able to represent the manoeuvrability of a specific but broader class of Azimuthal Stern Drive Escort tugs. It is evident that in the case of units with notably different dimensional ratios, supplementary experiments or numerical calculations would be necessary to include possible effects into the modelling. In this sense, a further benchmarking case study at sea would be broadly beneficial to prove simulator's robustness and wideness of applicability.

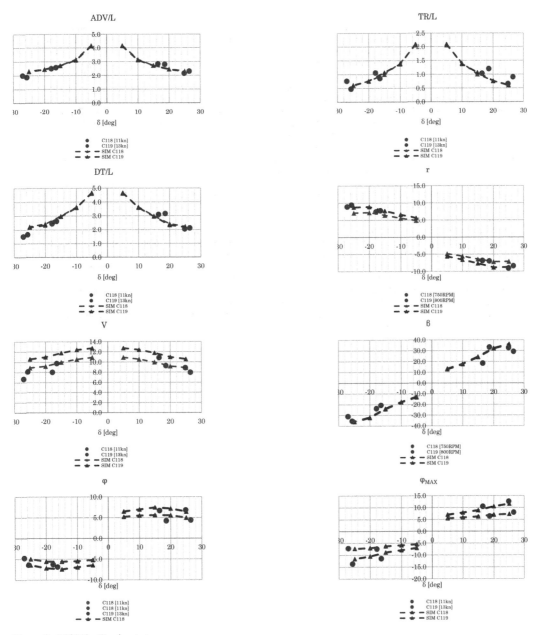

Figure 9. RS3213 - Turning tests.

REFERENCES

Allan, R., B. Smoker, M. Shives, V. Hertog, & S. Newbury (2019). Escort tug safety: Accounting for dynamic scenarios in design and operations. In *Tugnology - Liverpool UK*, pp. Day 1,Paper 5.

Altosole, M., G. Benvenuto, U. Campora, M. Laviola, & R. Zaccone (2017). Simulation and performance comparison between diesel and natural gas engines for marine applications. *Proceedings of the Institution of Mechanical Engineers Part M: Journal of Engineering for the Maritime Environment* 231(2), 690–704.

Altosole, M., U. Campora, M. Figari, M. Laviola, & M. Martelli (2019). A diesel engine modelling approach for ship propulsion real-time simulators. *Journal of Marine Science and Engineering* 7(5).

Çağrı Aydın, U. O. Ünal, U. C. Karabulut, & K. Sarıöz (2018). Practical computational procedures for predicting steering and braking forces of escort tugs. *Ocean Engineering* 166, 159–171.

Artyszuk, J. (2014). Steady-state manoeuvring of a generic asd tug in escort pull and bow-rope aided push operation. *TransNav: International Journal on Marine Navigation and Safety of Sea Transportation* 8.

Capasso, C., O. Veneri, E. Notti, A. Sala, M. Figari, & M. Martelli (2016, Nov). Preliminary design of the hybrid propulsion architecture for the research vessel "g. dallaporta". In *2016 International Conference on Electrical Systems for Aircraft, Railway, Ship Propulsion and Road Vehicles International Transportation Electrification Conference (ESARS-ITEC)*, pp. 1–6.

Figari, M., L. Martinelli, B. Piaggio, L. Enoizi, M. Viviani, & D. Villa (2019). An All-round Design-to-Simulation Approach of a new Z-Drive Escort Tug Class. *Journal of Offshore Mechanics and Arctic Engineering*, 1–29.

Li, Y. & S. M. Calisal (2005). Numerical simulation of ships manoeuvrability in wind and current, with escort tugs. *Marine Technology 42 No. 3*, 159–176.

Martelli, M. (2015a, 01). *Marine Propulsion Simulation: Methods and Results*.

Martelli, M. (2015b). *Marine Propulsion Simulation: Methods and Results*. De Gruyter.

Michetti, S., M. Ratto, A. Spadoni, M. Figari, M. Altosole, & G. Marcilli (2010, Oct). Ship control system wide integration and the use of dynamic simulation techniques in the fremm project. In *Electrical Systems for Aircraft, Railway and Ship Propulsion*, pp. 1–6.

Molyneux, D. & N. Bose (2007). Escort tug at large yaw angle: Comparison of cfd predicitions with experimental data. *Transactions of the Royal Institution of Naval Architects Part B1*.

Molyneux, W. & G. Earle (2001). A comparison of forces generated by a hull and three different skegs for an escort tug design. *Research Report, Fort St. John. National Research Council Canada Institute of Marine Dynamics*.

Piaggio, B., L. Enoizi, L. Martinelli, M. Figari, & N. Faggioni (2019). Rosmanditen: A theoretical and experimental insight into asd tug manoeuvrability. In *Tugnology - Liverpool UK*, pp. Day 1,Paper 4.

Piaggio, B., D. Villa, & M. Viviani (2020). Numerical analysis of escort tug manoeuvrability characteristics. *Applied Ocean Research 97*, 102075.

Piaggio, B., D. Villa, M. Viviani, & M. Figari (Expected 2020). Numerical analysis of the skeg effect on escort tug manoeuvrability. *Applied Ocean Research*.

Piaggio, B., M. Viviani, M. Martelli, & M. Figari (2019). Z-drive escort tug manoeuvrability model and simulation. *Ocean Engineering*.

Quadvileg, F. & S. Kaul (2006). Development of a calculation program for escort forces of stern drive tug boats. *19th International International Tug and Salvage Convention*.

Smoker, B., B. Stockdill, & P. Oshkai (2016). Escort tug performance prediction using computational fluid dynamics. *Journal of Ship Research 60(2)*, 61–77.

Waclawek, P. & D. Molyneux (2000). Prediction the performance of a tug and tanker during escort operatioins using computer simulations and model tests. *SNAME Transactions 108*, 21–43.

Local sensitivity analysis of a non-linear mathematical manoeuvring model

P. Pires da Silva
Portuguese Navy Research Center (CINAV), Portuguese Naval Academy, Almada, Portugal
Centre for Marine Technology and Ocean Engineering (CENTEC), Instituto Superior Técnico, Universidade de Lisboa, Lisbon, Portugal

Serge Sutulo & C. Guedes Soares
Centre for Marine Technology and Ocean Engineering (CENTEC), Instituto Superior Técnico, Universidade de Lisboa, Lisbon, Portugal

ABSTRACT: This work performs a local sensitivity analysis on a naval vessel manoeuvring mathematical model in order to identify the relevant input parameters, the force or moment coefficients, for the relevant outputs, such as yaw rate, drift, and peak overshoot. The mathematical model is solved, and the reference results are obtained. These results are compared with those obtained in sea trials for a real naval vessel in order to calibrate the mathematical model. The perturbation is induced in the external forces in surge, sway and yaw. Using a simple metric, it is possible to find and present the relevant parameters of the mathematical model for this naval ship.

1 INTRODUCTION

Ship manoeuvring mathematical models constitute an important part of all existing bridge and desktop manoeuvring simulators. As these simulators must provide high simulation speed in real or accelerated time and at the same time they must guarantee good realism of simulations, the used models must represent a kind of compromise between complexity and effectiveness. This requirement immediately rejects potentially the most accurate models presuming in-the-loop CFD computations. Instead, much faster holistic or modular models representing sets of ordinary differential equations depending on a limited number of parameters are applied. The values of these parameters must be specified to assure acceptable adequacy of simulation. For these purpose, offline CFD computations or physical captive-model tests can be used but typically the thus obtained values of the parameters of the model must be adjusted or tuned which can be performed either manually or using system identification methods often on the basis of available full-scale trials.

In the both cases, information about sensitivity of the model to variations of the parameters can be very helpful. This fact triggered several sensitivity studies performed by a number of researchers as Kose & Misiag (1993) that studied the sensitivity of the MMG mathematical model on the uncertainties in its parameters' estimation. These authors investigated the parameter variation - hull added masses $(\mu_{11}, \mu_{22}.I_{zz})$, hull linear derivatives $(Y_v, Y_r.N_v, N_r)$ and the interaction parameters of rudder and propeller $(\varepsilon, \kappa.\gamma_r)$ - effect on the performance of the zigzag manoeuvre and 35 degree starboard turning manoeuvre. The performance parameters considered were first and second overshoot angles, initial turning ability, tactical diameter, advance and transfer. In each simulation only one parameter was disturbed while keeping the other parameters at their undisturbed values. This sensitivity analysis of the MMG mathematical model showed that the model parameters' variations had distinct effects on the estimated manoeuvring performance, being the most influencing parameters $Y_v.N_v, N_r$ and the least influencing $\mu_{11}, \mu_{22}.I_{zz}$. This sets the requirements regarding the accuracy of the manoeuvring model parameter estimation. That is, in which parameters one must put more accuracy effort.

Other authors such as Wang et al. (2014) performed a sensitivity analysis based on simulated spiral test using the 4-DOF manoeuvring mathematical model from Blank et al. (2002). A direct method proposed by Yeo & Rhee (2006) for sensitivity analysis of hydrodynamic coefficients was implemented, and the mathematical model simplified by omitting the coefficients of smaller sensitivity according to the sensitivity analysis results. Then 10/10, 20/20 zigzag tests and 35 turning circle manoeuvre were simulated with the original and the simplified mathematical models. By comparing the simulation results obtained by the original and the simplified models, the effectiveness of the sensitivity analysis and the validity of the simplified model were demonstrated. The authors showed that coefficients, X_u, X_{uu}, and X_{uuu} have a major influence on surge motion; $X_u, Y_v, Y_{v|v|}, Y_\delta, Y_{\delta u}, N_v, N_r,$

DOI: 10.1201/9781003216599-24

$N_{r|v|}$, $N_{\theta u}$, N_δ and $N_{\delta u}$ have a remarkable influence on sway and yaw motion; X_u, Y_v, $Y_{v|v|}$, Y_v, $Y_{v|r|}$, Y_r, Y_δ, $Y_{\delta u}$, N_v, N_r, N_δ, $N_{\delta u}$, K_v, $K_{v|v|}$, $K_{r|r|}$, $K_{r|v|}$, $K_{\theta u}$, K_δ and $K_{\delta u}$ have an important influence on roll motion.

Ishiguro et al. (1996) argue that at the early design stage, ship designers will cover a variety of hull forms. Thus, it may be interesting for them to know the level of prediction accuracy for different hull forms. It may be also important to know the parameters that most strongly affect the results of the prediction. Therefore they performed, a sensitivity study on the simulation parameters of Kijima's prediction tool (1993) in order to extract those which most affect the results of prediction, that is the parameters that should be paid attention at the design stage. The simulation parameters were categorized in four parts, linear hydrodynamic derivatives, non-linear hydrodynamic derivatives, interaction coefficients and inertial coefficients. They named "relative sensitivity" the ratio of change in estimated results when each parameter is individually increased 10%. It becomes 1.0 when the estimated relevant index increases 10% by the 10% increase of a given parameter. They concluded that almost every linear hydrodynamic derivative affects significantly the predicted results. These sensitivities become higher with lowering course stability of the hull. This tendency is particularly remarkable in the prediction of overshoots of Z-manoeuvres. So, it is concluded that linear hydrodynamic derivatives should be determined carefully and precisely as possible.

All in all, having made significant effort to estimate the parameters of a mathematical model: what is the sensitivity of the model to each of its parameters?

What are the parameters that affect the estimation of the manoeuvring performance mostly and, consequently, how precisely they should be estimated?

Having a generic mathematical model adapted to a naval frigate, this work aims to find the relevant parameters of the mathematical model to the output of the: turning, zigzag and spiral manoeuvres. This evaluation makes use of a global sensitivity analysis.

2 MANOEUVRING MATHEMATICAL MODEL

For the present work a 3DOF's, (u – surge velocity (m/s), v – sway velocity (m/s) and r – yaw velocity (rad/s)) non-linear model is used, which is the standard Euler system of equations for a ship considered as a rigid body moving in the horizontal plane in the form:

$$\begin{aligned}(m+\mu_{11})\underline{\dot u}-mvr-mx_gr^2 &= X_q+X_p\\(m+\mu_{22})\underline{\dot v}+(mx_g+\mu_{26})\underline{\dot r}+mur &= Y_q\\(mx_g+\mu_{62})\underline{\dot v}+(I_{zz}+\mu_{66})\underline{\dot r}+mx_gur &= N_q\end{aligned} \quad (1)$$

where the forces on the hull (h) and rudder (δ) are grouped as quasi-steady forces/moment (underscore q) on the hull and rudder in surge, sway, and yaw respectively.

The forces on the right-hand side of equation (1) may be represented as:

$$\begin{aligned}X_q &= X'_q \tfrac{\rho V^2}{2} LT;\\Y_q &= Y'_q \tfrac{\rho V^2}{2} LT;\\N_q &= N'_q \tfrac{\rho V^2}{2} L^2 T\end{aligned} \quad (2)$$

where X'_q, Y'_q, N'_q are the dimensionless force/moment coefficients, ρ is the water density, $V^2 = u^2 + v^2$ is the squared instantaneous ship speed, L is the length of the ship and T is the draught amidships. For the solution of the nonlinear system of equations a non-dimensionalized form of forces defined as multivariate third-order regression polynomials depending, besides of the rudder angle, on the non-dimensional velocities,

$$u' = \frac{u}{V};\; v' = \frac{v}{V};\; r' = \frac{rL}{V} \quad (3)$$

is used, since the forces on the right hand side of equation may be represented as cubic regression polynomial models for hydrodynamic hull forces on a symmetric hull in 3DOF taken in various forms, with some terms dropped as insignificant, are usually associated with the name of Abkowitz (1964) and Crane (1989) being often referred to as "*truncated Taylor expansions*":

$$\begin{aligned}X'_q &= X'_{uu}u'^2 + X'_{vr}v'r' + X'_{\delta\delta}\delta_R^2\\Y'_q &= Y'_0 + Y'_v v' + Y'_r r' + Y'_{vvv} v'^3 + Y'_{vvr} v'^2 r'\\&\quad + Y'_\delta \delta_R + Y'_{\delta vv} v'^2 \delta_R + Y'_{\delta\delta v} v' \delta_R^2 + Y'_{\delta\delta\delta} \delta_R^3\\N'_q &= N'_0 + N'_v v' + N'_r r' + N'_{vvv} v'^3 + N'_{vvr} v'^2 r'\\&\quad + N'_\delta \delta_R + N'_{\delta vv} v'^2 \delta_R + N'_{\delta\delta v} v' \delta_R^2 + N'_{\delta\delta\delta} \delta_R^3\end{aligned}$$

$$(4)$$

where for twin screw ship, initial steady nonsymmetric forces or moments may be considered null, thus $Y'_0 = 0$ and $N'_0 = 0$.

The coefficients in equation (4) and the constant base parameters are defined by Sutulo & Guedes Soares (2014). The propeller force model is adapted from Sutulo & Guedes Soares (2014). The propulsion model for the propeller surge force is based on that described by the 4-quadrant model proposed by Oltmann & Sharma (1985), but adjusted by means of the adjustment procedure described by Sutulo & Guedes Soares (2011). A first order non-linear model by Sutulo & Guedes Soares (2015) for the steering gear was also included in the overall model.

3 MANOEUVRING SIMULATION MODEL SET UP AND PROGRAMMING

The model expressed in equation *(1)* was extended with the kinematic equations needed for transformation of the quasi-velocities, v, r from ship coordinate frame to earth coordinate frame, given as:

$$\dot{\eta} = u\,sin\psi + v\,cos\psi \\ \dot{\xi} = u\,cos\psi - v\,sin\psi \quad (5)$$

with the positive senses as presented in Figure 1.

The solver uses the explicit initial conditions: $u(0) = V_0$; $v(0) = 0$; $r(0) = 0$; $\delta(0) = \delta_0$ and implicit initial conditions: $\psi(0) = 0$ (which in MATLAB corresponds to bow upwards); $\zeta(0) = 0$; $\xi(0) = 0$, and runs dimensional calculations in each timestep equilibrium. It calculates the instantaneous ship speed:

$$V = \sqrt{u^2 + v^2} \quad (6)$$

Then using nondimensional relations in Eq. *(7)*, it calculates the non-dimensional quasi-velocities u', v', r'.

Forces are calculated using equations *(4)* and *(7)* @ each timestep.

$$X_p = T_E = \frac{1}{2}(1 - t_p)A_d C_T V_B^2 \quad (7)$$

where X_p is the effective thrust (T_E), t_p is the thrust deduction coefficient, A_d is the propeller disk area, C_T is the generalized thrust coefficient and V_B is the propeller effiective total blade velocity.

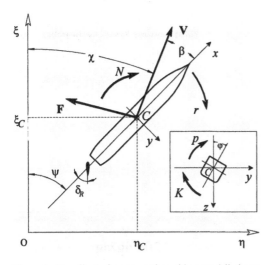

Figure 1. Coordinate frames: surface ship case (all shown angles and angular velocities are positive).

4 SENSITIVITY ANALYSIS

Sensitivity analysis (SA) of a model output aims to quantify the relative importance of each input model parameter in determining the value of an assigned output variable. Many different methods have been developed for SA. The various techniques can be classified in two main branches: global SA and local SA (Homma & Saltelli, 1996).

Global SA focuses on the output uncertainty over entire range of values of the input parameters. In this approach SA can help to identify key parameters whose uncertainty affects most the output. In local SA emphasis is on elucidating the key parameters in a complex system, not with respect to the output uncertainty, but with respect to the output itself.

In local SA one is interested in some kind of derivative (or Jacobian) of the model output say Y_i with respect to the model input, say X_i, that is, one is interested in $\partial Y_i / \partial X_i$, possibly normalized by means of standard deviations of the input or output variables themselves. In this context, aiming at the evaluation of the derivatives, model input parameters may be changed by generally small fraction of their nominal value, the fraction being the same for all the parameters. The input parameter interval thus explored does not represent our uncertainty about that parameter (Homma & Saltelli, 1996). In local SA only one point of the parameters space is explored, and parameters are changed one at the time (Saltelli et al. 2004).

In this work it is intended to analyse the mathematical behaviour of the 3DOF nonlinear model to a small perturbation on external forces. This perturbation is believed to be in the fractional range expected for the input parameters, in order to determine which of the them are more important in influencing the model output. This sensitivity analysis may classified as local sensitivity analysis since it was not studied the level of uncertainty of the input parameters and its propagation to the output parameters in a global sense, which may be related to the uncertainty of the ship trim, draft and displacement through its operational life as discussed by Silva & Guedes Soares (2016). The known parameters are part of a model that is good enough to represent the naval vessel manoeuvring behaviour without wind and waves. This behaviour is studied by performing global perturbation of the external forces.

5 VALIDATION OF THE MATHEMATICAL MODEL AND ALGORITHM

Considering manoeuvring trials of Portuguese Navy frigates, it is possible to make a partial parameter identification from the turning circle manoeuvre. That was done and with these parameters identified it was possible to approximate the behaviour of the 3 DOF generic model to the naval vessel behaviour.

5.1 Tuning the 3DOF nonlinear mathematical model

In order to tune the mathematical model to this particular ship, an exhaustive search was made on the input parameters, KRudd and kR (the Correction Factors for tuning vessel to match known turning values from Sea Trials) and on the output parameters: non-dimensional yaw rate r', the Transfer time TRt, the Transfer distance, TRd, the Advance time, ADt, the Advance distance, ADd, the Tactical Diameter time, $D_T t$, the Tactical Diameter distance, $D_T d$, in order to minimize the error in % to the sea trials results.

5.2 Manoeuvring simulation results

Figure 2 presents the graphical results from the tuned mathematical model for the 20° turning manoeuvre.

Table 1 presents the differences between the simulation results and the sea trial data for the turning circle manoeuvre.

Figure 3 shows the graphical results from the tuned mathematical model for the zigzag manoeuvre.

Table 2 depicts the relevant parameter output from the zigzag manoeuvre.

Table 1. Mathematical model results for turning manoeuvre.

Parameter	Rudder angle - 10°	Rudder angle - 20°	Rudder angle - 30°
	Difference to trial data [%]		
r'	+12.5	+3.25	-8.7
D_T	-14.0	-3.0	+10.3

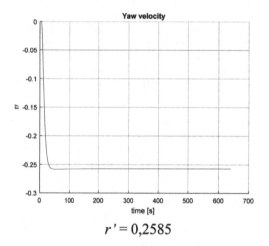

$r' = 0,2585$

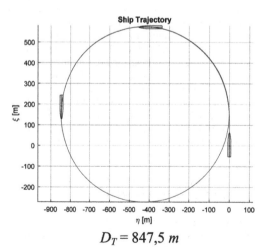

$D_T = 847,5\ m$

Figure 2. Results of the simulations with the tuned mathematical model – 20° turning manoeuvre.

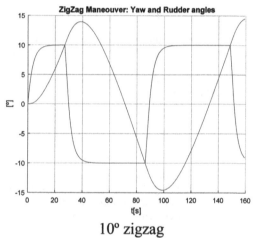

10° zigzag

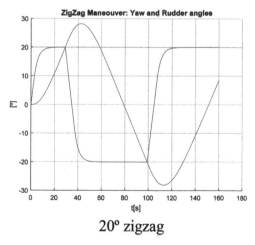

20° zigzag

Figure 3. Results of the simulations with the tuned mathematical model – zigzag manoeuvre.

Table 2. Mathematical model results for zigzag manoeuvre.

Parameter	ZigZag 10°	ZigZag 20°
1st peak overshoot (°)	3.94	8.3
2nd peak overshoot (°)	4.53	8.1

5.3 Manoeuvring simulation results – spiral manoeuvre

Figure 4 presents the graphical results from the tuned mathematical model for the spiral manoeuvre.

The minimum surge velocity ratio is 0.72.

The results obtained from the tuned mathematical model are the reference output parameters considered for the sensitivity analysis.

6 SENSITIVITY ANALYSIS OF THE 3DOF NONLINEAR MATHEMATICAL MODEL

In this work it is intended to analyse the behaviour of the 3 DOF nonlinear model to a small perturbation on external forces, that is, a sensitivity analysis is performed that may be classified as local sensitivity analysis. Total perturbation of the external forces is performed.

6.1 Total Perturbation of force/moment components

It is intended to study the effect of perturbing globally the forces, in DOF's X, Y and N, in the relevant output parameters for the manoeuvring tests simulated so far – turning circle, zigzag and spiral.

The perturbation is performed using perturbation factors $\Delta X'$, $\Delta Y'$ or $\Delta N'$ affecting the second member of equations (4). Therefore, the non-dimensionalized equations of perturbed forces may be written as:

$$X'_q = \left(X'_{uu}u^2 + X'_{vr}v_r r_r + X'_{\delta\delta}\delta_R^2\right) + \Delta X',$$

$$Y'_q = \left(Y'_0 + Y'_v v' + Y'_r r' + Y'_{vvv}v'^3 + Y'_{vvr}v'^2 r' + Y'_\delta \delta_R + Y'_{\delta vv}v'^2 \delta_R + Y'_{\delta\delta v}v'\delta_R^2 + Y'_{\delta\delta\delta}\delta_R^3\right) + \Delta Y',$$

$$N'_q = \left(N'_0 + N'_v v' + N'_r r' + N'_{vvv}v'^3 + N'_{vvr}v'^2 r' + N'_\delta \delta_R + N'_{\delta vv}v'^2 \delta_R + N'_{\delta\delta v}v'\delta_R^2 + N'_{\delta\delta\delta}\delta_R^3\right) + \Delta N' \quad (8)$$

The perturbations must be specified in order to investigate their influence on the simulation output. Let us assume a constant fractional perturbation expressed as:

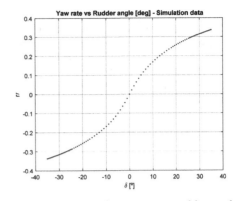

a) Nondimensional yaw rate vs rudder angle

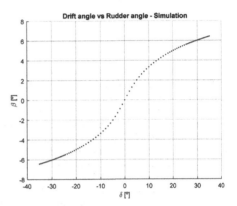

b) Drift angle rate vs rudder angle

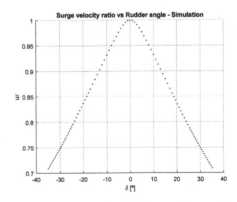

c) Surge velocity ratio (u/V) vs rudder angle

Figure 4. Results of the simulations with the tuned mathematical model – spiral manoeuvre.

$$\Delta X' = C_X X'_q$$
$$\Delta Y' = C_Y Y'_q \quad (9)$$
$$\Delta N' = C_N N'_q$$

Where the perturbation coefficients C_X, C_Y and C_N are constants, that will assume all the combinations of discrete values presented in Table 3. When all the coefficients take the value 0, results of the undisturbed model are obtained. Those are taken as the reference results of the simulated manoeuvring performance of the naval frigate.

Then the equation of non-dimensional forces can be written as:

$$X'_q = \left(X'_{uu}u'^2 + X'_{vr}v'r' + X'_{\delta\delta}\delta_R^2\right)(1+C_X')$$
$$Y'_q = \left(Y'_v v' + Y'_r r' + Y'_{vvv} v'^3 + Y'_{vvr} v'^2 r' + Y'_\delta \delta_R + Y'_{\delta vv} v'^2 \delta_R + Y'_{\delta\delta v} v' \delta_R^2 + Y'_{\delta\delta\delta} \delta_R^3\right)(1+C_Y')$$
$$N'_q = \left(N'_v v' + N'_r r' + N'_{vvv} v'^3 + N'_{vvr} v'^2 r' + N'_\delta \delta_R + N'_{\delta vv} v'^2 \delta_R + N'_{\delta\delta v} v' \delta_R^2 + N'_{\delta\delta\delta} \delta_R^3\right)(1+C_N')$$ (10)

The sensitivity analysis started by one-at-the-time or OAT perturbation method, which gave a total of 6 simulations (variants) per manoeuvre and respective rudder angles, that is a total of 36 simulations.

Those simulations and the reference motion (variant #0) are identified as the variants in Table 4. Figure 5 presents the "variant #0" and the bounds of the ship behaviour in some of simulated manoeuvres.

Then the total combination of the perturbation coefficients was used, giving a total of 27 perturbation combinations and 162 simulations/runs. Those simulations and the reference motion were using the logic of (Table 4).

For the sensitivity analysis, the chosen performance parameters (relevant output results - Y_i) are:

- in turning manoeuvre: r', D_T,
- in zigzag manoeuvre: α_{01}, α_{02},
- in spiral manoeuvre: $\left(\frac{dr'}{d\delta}\right)_{\delta \to 0}$, $max|r'|$, $max|\beta|$, $min|V_{inst}/V|$

whose quadratic distance to the undisturbed value of the parameter, thus the reference value (Y_{ref}), is normalized to the reference values, equation *(11)*. Another metric could be used as well, equation *(12)*, but it doesn't enhance the different effects of different parameters.

$$\frac{(Y_i - Y_{ref})^2}{Y_{ref}}$$ (11)

Table 3. Perturbation coefficients.

Perturbation coefficients	Values
C_X	{−0.2, 0, 0.2}
C_Y	{−0.2; 0; 0.2}
C_N	{−0.2; 0; 0.2}

$$\frac{\sqrt{Y_i^2 - Y_{ref}^2}}{Y_{ref}}$$ (12)

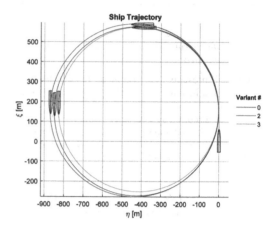

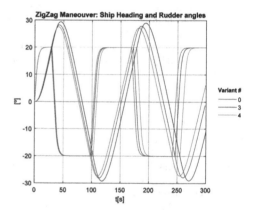

6.1.1 Turning manoeuvre

Figure 6 and Table 5 show the most relevant perturbation factors in turning manoeuvre for global force perturbation performed in OAT mode without combinations.

From Figure 6 and Table 5 it can be seen that the common most influential variants for yaw rate and tactical diameter, are the 20% perturbation in sway and the 20% perturbation in yaw: $-0.2Y_q$; $-0.2N_q$ (minus means less force in that degree of freedom), and the surge forces have almost no influence in turning manoeuvre output parameters.

From the sensitivity analysis resulting when the input parameters (total forces) are perturbed in all possible combinations of the three degrees of freedom, results that the common most influential perturbations for yaw rate and tactical diameter, are the

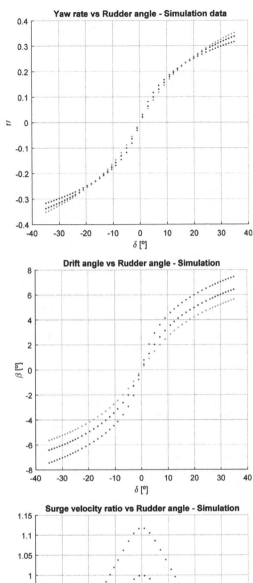

Figure 5. Results of the simulations for total perturbation of force/moment components, OAT.

combinations of 20% perturbation in sway and the 20% perturbation in yaw: $0.2Y_q$; $0.2N_q$ (minus means

Table 4. Total perturbation of force/moment components, OAT.

Variant #	$\Delta X'/X'_q$	$\Delta Y'/Y'_q$	$\Delta N'/N'_q$
0	0	0'	0
1	−0.2	0	0
2	0	−0.2	0
3	0	0	−0.2
4	0	0	0.2
5	0	0.2	0
6	0.2	0	0

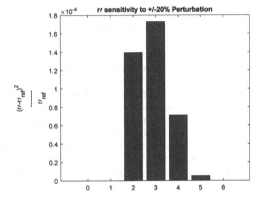

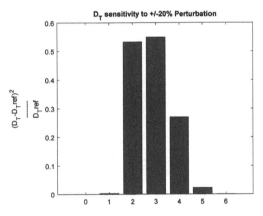

Figure 6. Example of sensitivity analysis of turning manoeuvre for, 20° rudder angle. Perturbed forces: OAT X'_q; Y'_q; N'_q.

Table 5. Most influential perturbation variants in turning manoeuvre: total perturbation OAT.

Rudder angle	most influential variants for r'	most influential variants for D_t
10° Port	2 and 5	2 and 5
20° Port	2 and 3	2 and 3
30° Port	2	2

less force in that degree of freedom), and the surge forces have almost no influence in turning manoeuvre output parameters.

In both sensitivity analysis, the 20% perturbation in sway force *per se* is relevant with 30° rudder angle.

It may be summarized that the relevant forces in the turning manoeuvre are the sway force - Y_q – and yaw moment - N_q, as expected. With increasing angle, the sway force becomes more relevant which agrees with increasing centripetal force with increasing rudder angle.

6.1.2 *Zigzag manoeuvre*

Figure 7 and Table 6 present the most relevant perturbation factors the 20° zigzag manoeuvre for global force perturbation performed in OAT mode without combinations.

From the OAT sensitivity analysis it can be verified that the common most influential perturbations the 10° and 20° peak overshoot, is the 20% perturbation in Yaw: $-0.2N_q$ (minus means less force in that degree of freedom), and the surge forces have almost no influence in zigzag manoeuvre output parameters.

From the sensitivity analysis resulting from when the input parameters are perturbed in all possible combinations of the three degrees of freedom, the common most influential perturbations for 10° and 20° peak overshoot, are the combinations of 20% perturbation in Sway and the 20% perturbation in Yaw: $0.2Y_q$; $0.2N_q$ (minus means less force in that degree of freedom), and the surge forces have almost no influence in zigzag manoeuvre output parameters.

It may be summarized that the relevant forces in the zigzag manoeuvre are the sway force - Y_q – and yaw moment - N_q, as expected.

6.1.3 *Spiral manoeuvre*

Figure 8 and Table 7 present the most relevant perturbation factors in spiral manoeuvre for total force perturbation performed in OAT mode without combinations.

From Figure 8 and Table 7 it can be seen that the common most influential perturbations for rate of turn vs. rudder angle gradient at the origin - $\left(\frac{dr'}{d\delta}\right)_{\delta\to 0}$, maximum yaw rate – r', and drift is the 20% perturbation in Sway. Surge Forces perturbations have the most influence in surge speed ratio, where the other perturbations do not have any significant contributes.

It may be summarized that the relevant forces in the outputs of the spiral manoeuvre are the sway force - Y_q – and less clearly the yaw moment - N_q. For the surge speed ratio, the most important input perturbation is that on surge forces.

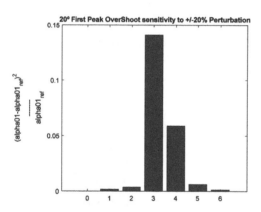

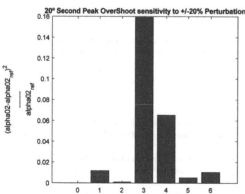

Figure 7. Example of sensitivity analysis of zigzag manoeuvre for 20°. Perturbed forces: OAT X'_q; Y'_q; N'_q.

Table 6. Most influential perturbation cases in zigzag manoeuvre: total perturbation OAT.

Rudder angle	most influential variants for 1st peak overshoot	most influential variants for 2nd peak overshoot
10°	3	3
20°	3	3

Table 7. Most influential perturbation cases in spiral manoeuvre: global perturbation OAT.

most influential perturbations on $\left(\frac{dr'}{d\delta}\right)_{\delta\to 0}$	most influential perturbations $(max|r'|)$	most influential perturbations $(max|\beta|)$	most influential perturbations V_{inst}/V
2 and 5	2 and 5	2 and 5	1 and 6

7 CONCLUSIONS

The mathematical model of the naval vessel under study was tuned within 8% mean error relatively to the available trials data, which is considered fair enough, since the trials were made with wind Beaufort 6 and wave Douglas 2, while the mathematical model does not account for wind and wave.

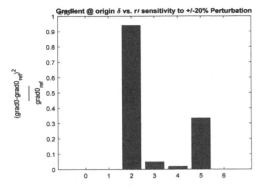
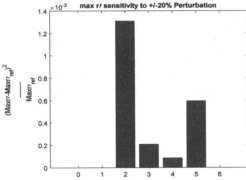
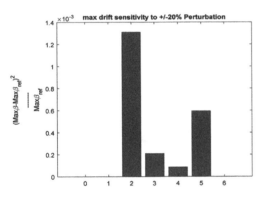
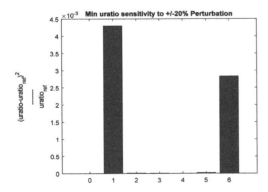

Figure 8. Sensitivity analysis of spiral manoeuvre. Perturbed forces: OAT X'_q; Y'_q; N'_q.

In this work it was intended to analyse the behaviour of the 3 DOF nonlinear model to a small perturbation on external forces. This perturbation is believed to be in the fractional range expected for the input parameters, in order to determine which of the them are more important in influencing the model output. Total perturbation of the external forces was performed. From the total perturbation sensitivity analysis, it may be summarized that the relevant forces in the turning manoeuvre and zigzag manoeuvre are the sway force Y_q and Yaw Moment N_q. With increasing angle, the sway force becomes more relevant. With 20° angle it seems that yaw moment becomes more relevant in zigzag manoeuvre. It came out also that the relevant forces in the outputs of the Spiral Manoeuvre are the sway force - Y_q - and less clearly the yaw moment - N_q. surge forces perturbations have the most influence in surge speed ratio, but the other two perturbations have also some significance.

Finally, it seems that with 20° rudder angle the model have different behaviour with reduction of force being more influential than an increase. The ultimate reason of that behaviour needs more in-depth analysis. At the moment it can only be said that this happens for this ship type.

ACKNOWLEDGEMENTS

The work was performed within the NAVAD project "Simulation of manoeuvrability of ships in adverse weather conditions" which is co-funded by the European Regional Development Fund (Fundo Europeu de Desenvolvimento Regional - FEDER) and by the Portuguese Foundation for Science and Technology (Fundação para a Ciência e a Tecnologia - FCT) under contract 02/SAICT/032037/2017. This work contributes to the Strategic Research Plan of the Centre for Marine Technology and Ocean Engineering (CENTEC), which is financed by the Portuguese Foundation for Science and Technology (Fundação para a Ciência e a Tecnologia - FCT) under contract UIDB/UIDP/00134/2020.

REFERENCES

Abkowitz, M. A. (1964). *Lectures on Ship Hydrodynamics -Steering and Manoeuvrability*. Report Hy-5, Hydro- and Aerodynamics Laboratory, Lingby, Denmark.

Crane, C., Eda, H., & Landsburg, A. (1989). Controllability. Em E. Lewis (Ed.), *Principles of Naval Architecture* (pp. 191–365). Jersey City, N.J.: SNAME.

Homma, T., & Saltelli, A. (1996). Importance Measures in global sensitivity analysis of nonlinear models. *Realbility Engineering and System Safety*, 52, 1–17.

Ishiguro, T., Tanaka, S., & Yoshimura, Y. (1996). A study on the accuracy of the recent prediction technique of ship's maoeuverability at early stage design. Em M. Chislett (Ed.), *Marine Simulation and Ship Manoeuvrability 1996*, (pp. 547–561). Copenhagen.

Kijima, K., & Tanaka, S. (1993). On a Prediction method of ship manoeuvring characteristics. *MARSIM'93* (pp. 285–294). St. John's, Newfoundland: Curran Associates, Inc.

Kose, K., & Misiag, W. (1993). A Systematic procedure for predicting manoeuvering performance. *International Conference on Marine Simulation and Ship Manoeuveravbility 1993*. *1*, pp. 331–340. St. John's, Canada: Curran Associates, Inc.

Oltmann, P., & Sharma, S. (1985). Simulation of combined engine and rudder maneuvers using an improved model of hull-propeller-rudder interactions. *Proceedings of 15th ONR Symposium on Naval Hydrodynamics*, (pp. 83–108). Hamburg, Washington, D.C.

Perez, T., & Blanke, M. (2002). *Mathematical Ship Modeling for Control Applications*. Technical Report, The University of Newcastle; Technical University of Denmark, Dept. of Electrical and Computer Engineering; Section of Automation at Ørsted.DTU.

Saltelli, A., Tarantola, S., & Ratto, M. (2004). *Sensitivity analysis in practice - A Guide to assess Scientific Models*. Chichester: John Wiley & Sons.

Silva, P. P., & Guedes Soares, C. (2016). Uncertainty Modelling in Ship Manoeuvring Models. Guedes Soares, C. & Santos T. A., (Eds.) *Maritime Technology and Engineering 3*, London, UK: Taylor & Francis Group; pp. 361–369.

Sutulo, S., & Guedes Soares, C. (2011). Mathematical models for simulation of manoeuvring performance of ships. Guedes Soares, C., Garbatov Y., Fonseca N. & Teixeira A. P., (Eds.). *Marine Technology and Engineering*. London, UK: Taylor & Francis Group; pp. 661–698.

Sutulo, S., & Guedes Soares, C. (2014). An algorithm for offline identification of ship manoeuvring mathematical models from free-running tests. *Ocean Engineering, 79*, 10–25.

Sutulo, S., & Guedes Soares, C. (2015). Development of a core mathematical model for arbitrary maneuvers of a shuttle tanker. *Applied Ocean Research, 51*, 293–308.

Wang, X.-G., Zou, Z.-J., & Xu, F. (2014). Sensitivity analysis and parametric identification for ship manoeuvring in 4 degrees of freedom. *Journal of Maritime Science and Technology, 19*, 394–405.

Yeo, D., & Rhee, K. (2006). Sensitivity analysis of submersibles manoeuvrability and its application to the design of actuator inputs. *Ocean Engineering, 33*, 2270–2286.

Instrumentation and data acquisition system for full-scale manoeuvrability tests on board of naval surface ships

P. Pires da Silva
CINAV - Portuguese Navy Research Center, Almada, Portugal
Centre for Marine Technology and Ocean Engineering (CENTEC), Instituto Superior Técnico, Universidade de Lisboa, Lisbon, Portugal

M.A. Hinostroza, S. Sutulo & C. Guedes Soares
Centre of Marine Technology and Ocean Engineering (CENTEC), Instituto Superior Técnico, Universidade de Lisboa, Lisbon, Portugal

ABSTRACT: A monitoring and data acquisition system is being developed, including an inertial measurement unit, a fibre-optics gyrocompass, a high-precision GPS unit, and a wireless weather station. Ships' own sensors data, will be used also. All the sensors will be synchronized by a controller that runs a real-time application developed in LabView®. The system is to be used in full-scale manoeuvring trials with three ships operated by the Portuguese Navy. The parameters to be recorded are: the instantaneous vessel's geographical coordinates; the speed over the ground; the course over the ground; the heading; the heave, roll and pitch angles and the corresponding velocities and accelerations; accelerations in surge and sway; the relative wind, the engines rpm, the ship log speed, and the instantaneous propeller pitch. For tests in rough weather, a wave radar sensor will also be installed.

1 INTRODUCTION

The availability of suitable and reliable mathematical models of ships is very important for improving the operation of ships. When these models are implemented in interactive simulators with virtual reality, they contribute to improving the practice of operators, who will be able to control ships more effectively and efficiently and with a higher level of security.

This work aims to address the preparation of full-scale sea trials to be performed in both calm water and rough seas to validate mathematical models for simulating manoeuvring motion of naval surface displacement ships in adverse weather conditions i.e. under action of wind and seas.

1.1 Origin and relevance of full-scale trials

Within naval architecture, the theory of ship manoeuvrability was the last mastery of hydrodynamics and dynamics of ships to emerge and mature. The state of the art in this area until the late 1930s is well exposed by (Schoenherr, 1939) in the first edition of the well-known *Principles of Naval Architecture* (PNA). The situation, however, changed considerably in the early 1960s, when the second revised edition of the PNA was published, and the chapter on manoeuvrability, written by (Mandel, 1965). The content has been reproduced with minor changes in the third edition of the same reference book (Crane, Eda, & Landsburg, 1989). In the early 1960s, substantial progress occurred in understanding the hydrodynamics of curvilinear movement and the most essential theoretical analysis of the directional stability of straight motion was completed. During the next three decades, the evolution and advancement of manoeuvrability theory resulted in certain qualitative changes.

However, it became clear that further development was conditioned by the progress of computing technology. Most computational difficulties were related to the modelling of complex nonlinearities, which required restrictions on the complexity of treatable mathematical models. In the late 1970s, it seemed that a mathematical model of manoeuvrability of any desired complexity could be relatively easily encoded and executed on a common digital computer. As such, computer simulation made available products based on the theory of manoeuvrability of ships much requested by ship operators. The simulation of manoeuvrability and associated research became very important, as it served as the basis for ship simulators of varying complexity for instruction or entertainment purposes. The software

DOI: 10.1201/9781003216599-25

implemented in these simulators comprises two relatively independent and equally important components:

- the mathematical model, which describes the dynamics of the ship, along with the necessary environmental factors
- the graphical interface required for realistic interaction between operator, instructor or student with simulated ship.

While the graphical interface is the clearly visible component, the dynamic model (what gives credible motion to virtual ships, according to the laws of physics), is hidden and is only felt through simulator reactions to control actions and simulated exogenous factors (wind, current, waves, etc.). Generally, it is necessary that the central model corresponds to a certain real ship and its responses are, in the ideal case, identical to those of the real ship, although the complete similarity cannot yet be achieved (Sutulo & Guedes Soares, 2011). The study and validation of manoeuvrability models as the core of the system, is a demanding, complex and nontrivial task.

In the 1990s, exponential growth in computing power and low-cost availability in relation to the total cost of a simulator program eliminated simulator hardware as an important limiting factor in the application of simulation to the design of ships. Instead, the cost of obtaining data for mathematical models, processing these data, and visual scenario development emerged as the dominant costs in simulation of marine environments. (Webster, 1992).

In the second decade of the 21st century, according to (Zhu, Hahn, Wen, & Bolles, 2017), the main methods for estimating the manoeuvrability model include: experiments in a towing tank, experiments with captive models (Sutulo & Guedes Soares, 2006), (Sutulo & Kim, 1998), system identification combined with large-scale model tests or free-running model tests and computational fluids dynamics (CFD). Among the above mentioned methods, the system identification combined with the full-scale or free running model has become an attractive and sufficient technique to estimate the ship maneuverability model due to its relatively high cost-benefit ratio (Zhu, Hahn, Wen, & Bolles, 2017).

It is underlying and inherent in all methods for estimating the maneuverability model the uncertainty derived from different sources, as discussed by Pires da Silva et al. (2016), both in the design phase of the ship and during its operational life, since the variables that influence the performance of manoeuvrability (e.g. displacement, trim and draft) estimated during the design phase will only be confirmed during the sea trials and will vary throughout its operational life. In full-scale trials, to these uncertainties it must be added those derived from the weather and waves and those from each of the data acquisition setup sensor and equipment.

1.2 Full-scale trials: challenges and data acquisition setups evolution

Although preferable, full-scale trials are time consuming and cost demanding. Their preparation implies selection of real ships, study and analysis of the ship's own sensing and data network capabilities, analysis of the need and technological level for external data acquisition setup, detailed planning and budgeting of the data acquisition setup and ship sea trials. In addition, the execution of the full-scale sea trials under the planned weather and wave conditions is and will always be a major challenge, for obvious reasons. Therefore, is not surprising that good data available from full-scale sea trials are scarce.

Nevertheless, some research using full-scale trials on military platforms in open sea have been made, as those by Guedes Soares et al (2002, 2004). where results of full-scale manoeuvrability tests are presented, carried out with two speedboats and a corvette, operated by the Portuguese Navy, in order to identify their manoeuvring characteristics. There were performed 68 tests (approximately 23 tests per ship) but only the results of 53 (approx. 18 per ship) were eligible. Those tests were the turning circle (at various speeds and rudder angles), spiral, zigzag, stop and acceleration manoeuvers. The data acquisition setup comprised a differential GPS, odometer, magnetic compass and anemometer. The data were acquired in real time, on a portable computer running a LabView® application, developed specifically for those trials. The manoeuvring trials plan was established taking into account both the recommendations of the code for manoeuvrability tests proposed by IMO (1993) (1994) and a research carried out previously by Francisco & Guedes Soares (2000), which indicated the manoeuvres that are potentially more likely to efficiently identify the hydrodynamics characteristics of the vessel.

Other full-scale trials are described by Guedes Soares et al. (1999) regarding manoeuvring characteristics of a fast catamaran carried out within a period of 6 months in the estuary of the Tagus river. This paper refers as a common problem of full-scale manoeuvring trials the wind-generated disturbances due to windy weather during practically all test runs due to the impossibility of adapting the test schedule to weather conditions. It is also mentioned that the wind factor was complemented by the river current. As result, only a fraction of collected data was considered as suitable for analysis of manoeuvring performance of the catamaran. As the wind perturbations are in fact hardly avoidable in most cases, an attempt was undertaken to register the instantaneous relative wind velocity so that the aerodynamic forces could be incorporated into the mathematical model and identified together with the hydrodynamic forces. In these trials two sets of equipment with the Differential Global Positioning System (DGPS) were used: that of type

SERCEL NDS-54, which was part of the ship navigational equipment, and an additional set of type Magellan PROMARKX-CM, which was part of the measurement equipment brought onboard. The global time received from the GPS and the computer clock time were both recorded. The recording sampling time was equal to one second for the GPS data and 0.2–0.25 seconds, for most of the remaining parameters.

Addressing also a catamaran ferryboat in confined waters full-scale trials, Sutulo et al. (2000) describe some methods for the quantification of the action of the wind and the current, using the data collected in the full-scale tests of manoeuvrability done by Guedes Soares et al. (1999) described above. The results obtained demonstrated the possibility of mitigating the disturbing influence of environmental effects and the paper presents a method for treating the effect of wind and current in order to reduce errors that can be caused by the presence of these effects.

Sutulo et al. (2008) using previous lessons learnt from full-scale trials and the technological advance in data acquisition equipment describe a set of equipment and software for measuring and recording the kinematic parameters of surface vessels. The set includes a fiber-optics gyro compass, a high precision GPS unit, a yaw rate sensor and an anemometer. A special application, developed in the G language of LabView®, performs the synchronized recording of data. This data acquisition system was applied in passive full-scale trials i.e. instrumented observations of normal operation of catamarans in the Tagus river estuary in March 2008. During the tests, the system was complemented with simultaneous high definition videoing of the control parameters. The use of a video camera prevented direct connection to the ship's circuits. The authors conclude that the data acquisition system did not seem to solve all the problems of the full-scale trials. The most sensitive difficulties in assembling the set of sensors on the ship come from the need to pass the very heavy and long coaxial cables of the GPS antenna and of the anemometer. Some selected results of the mentioned passive tests were presented by Sutulo et al. (2009). The setup measurement and data acquisition system is similar to the one described by Sutulo et al. (2008). In total, 54 berthing and unberthing events were recorded. The main result of the study is a set of relatively high quality full-scale data obtained as result of instrumented observations of berthing and unberthing processes.

In the reviewed literature, most of the research focuses on commercial ship hulls as object of study and less on naval hull types (Figure 1). Therefore, it is important to collect

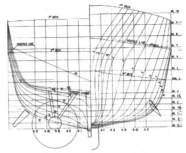

a) Frigate Hull - 1990s

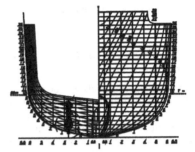

b) Early 21st century - Offshore Patrol Vessel (OPV)

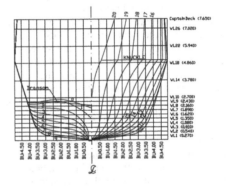

c) Early 21st century - Coastal Patrol Vessel (CPV)

Figure 1. Three types of body plane of naval hulls. From 1990's to the 1st decade of the 20th century. Courtesy of the Portuguese Navy.

more data on naval surface ships hull types which are usually slenderer and faster than most commercial monohulls.

2 PREPARATION OF DATA ACQUISITION SYSTEM FOR SEA TRIALS

The success of full-scale trials, and the quality of the data collected, depend on many factors, among which the quality of instrumentation is of primary importance. However, full-scale trials, especially those for scientific purposes, are generally quite expensive and as result are rarely executed. There is no standard, off-shelf equipment sets on the market, and each hydrodynamic centre develops its own system, using, where possible, available sensors developed for other applications, connected to a controller with port modules and to a laptop PC where all measured parameters are recorded during testing.

This project and the coordination of the sea trials involves researchers from CENTEC and CINAV, as well as interactions with Navy Operational Command, Navy Directorate of Ships, and the designated ships.

2.1 Relevant parameters and monitoring and acquisition system

Full-scale manoeuvring trials will be performed with three ships: a Replenishment Ship (RS), an Offshore Patrol Vessel (OPV), and a Coastal Patrol Vessel (CPV), operated by the Portuguese Navy, and representing different operational profiles and different levels of the sensing technology and integration, varying from fully standalone analogic sensors to fully integrated digital networks.

During the trials, the following parameters will be registered: the instantaneous WGS-84 geographical coordinates of the vessel; the speed over the ground; the course over the ground; the heading; heave, the roll and pitch angles and the corresponding velocities and accelerations; accelerations in surge and sway; the relative wind vector, the engines rpm, the ship log speed, and the instantaneous propeller pitch.

For tests in waves, the wave radar sensor WM-2 providing relative displacements of the system with respect to water surface will be installed. The collected data together with those related to the ship motions will be sufficient for estimating the two-dimensional wave spectrum.

Due to the different levels of sensors integration, in some ships is possible to have the same signal from two systems, allowing redundancy as shown on the "source" column of Table 1. Preventing possible difficulties in collecting some signals, these are categorized as "critical", "important", "if possible" and "important for rough weather", according to their criticality for proper system identification as presented in Table 1.

Depending on the type of ship, part of the variables can be obtained by on-board sensors (e.g. GPS position and time, rudder angle, anemometer, SOG, COG) as redundancy to portable external sensors provided by CENTEC. Transversal to all designated ships is the critical need to obtain the rudder angle in real time by digital signal (non-redundant signal).

Replenishment Ship (RS)

Offshore Patrol Vessel (OPV)

Coastal Patrol Vessel (CPV)

Figure 2. Designated ships. Courtesy of Portuguese Navy under NAVAD project.

2.2 Data collection setup

The setup for these full-scale sea trials to be performed in both calm water and rough seas will use ship's own sensors raw data as redundant (except for rudder deflection) to the parallel set that includes at least the items in Table 2 and Figure 3:

– wave radar sensor TSK WM-2.
– Embedded Controller from National Instruments cRIO 9037 with C# modules.
– Laptop PC running a LabVIEW real-time application for monitoring and acquisition of ship parameters.

Besides these sensors and equipment, some connections to the ship's own sensors and control circuits will be performed. Figure 4 presents a diagram with the layout of the data connection setup in ships without digital network, but with ECDIS with NMEA protocol for navigation sensors.

Table 1. List of parameters to be collected during full-scale sea trials and respective ship sensor (if available).

#	Parameter ID	Signal Source
Critical Parameters		
1	u: speed relative to water	Ship Odometer - ECDIS
2	V: Speed Over Ground (SOG)	Ship GPS – ECDIS* and Portable 10Hz GPS unit
3	ψ: heading angle	Ship ECDIS* and Portable IMU**
4	r: rate of yaw	Ship PMS*** and Portable IMU**
5	ξ, η, χ : Cartesian coordinates relative to the ground and Course Over Ground – (COG)	Ship GPS – ECDIS* and Portable 10Hz GPS unit
6	δ; rudder angle	Ship PMS*** or rudder angle indicator on the bridge
7	WGS-84 instant geographic coordinates	Ship GPS – ECDIS* and Portable 10Hz GPS unit.
Important		
8	Relative wind intensity and direction	Ship ECDIS* or Ship PMS*** and Portable Wi-Fi Meteo Station
If Possible		
9	ϕ: roll angle	Ship Gyro and Portable IMU**
10	n: shafts rotation frequencies (rpm)	Ship PMS***
11	Propeller Pitch (if applicable)	Ship PMS***
12	Rudder order	to investigate
13	rpm order	to investigate
Important for rough weather		
14	Wave motion	wave radar sensor TSK WM-2
15	θ: pitch angle	Ship Gyro and Portable IMU**
16	w: velocity of heave	Ship Gyro and Portable IMU**
17	$\dot{u}, \dot{v}, \dot{w}, \dot{\phi}, \dot{\theta}, \dot{\psi}$:inertial 6 dof accelerations	Ship Gyro and Portable IMU**

* Electronic Chart Display and Information System;
** Inertial Measurement Unit;
*** Platform Management System

In Figure 5 is presented a diagram with the layout of the data connection setup in ships with platform management system (PMS) and ECDIS.

In all designated ships it is possible to have part of the signals of Table 2 in ASCII files, concerning sensors that provide data to the ECDIS (GPS, anemometer, odometer, gyrocompass) from navigation network (NN) in NMEA protocol. This is possible, since there is a *"device master"* equipment on the bridge, where signals can be recorded to the laptop PC using an Ethernet port (RJ45). The

Table 2. List of equipment external to the ship platform for full-scale sea trials.

– one inertial measurement unit Crossbow NAV440,
– one IXSea Octans Mk III Fibre Optic Gyrocompass (FOG),
– one 10Hz high-precision GPS unit,
– a wireless weather station "Davis Vantage"
– wave radar sensor TSK WM-2.
– Embedded Controller from National Instruments cRIO 9037 with C# modules.
– Laptop PC running a LabVIEW real-time application for monitoring and acquisition of ship parameters.

"device master" has a tool *(PortVision* software) where using the *"Wcom2 - Test terminal"*, the data in NMEA protocol can be viewed and recorded by com emulated ports. This method requires separate and sequential start of data recording, by each COM port, that is, by each sensor. In data analysis, the date/hour/minute/second recording start of each sensor will be different, although no greater difficulties are predicted given the clock of the signals being unique, that of ship GPS.

In ships with Platform Management System (PMS) it is possible to collect digital propulsion data in *"csv"* files, including the rudder angle. However, NN and PMS signals are not synchronized in time, which always makes it necessary to use the independent set of sensors and CENTEC data collection system, with connection to some on-board sensors (e.g. rudder angle, shaft rotation, CPP) as shown in Figure 4 and Figure 5. In ships without PMS, the signals from the rudder angle, shaft rotation and CPP must be digitalized from analog indicators.

3 PLANNED FULL-SCALE SEA TRIALS

As part of preparation of the sea trials and while alongside before departure is necessary to have:

– actual draught measurement,
– actual vertical and longitudinal position of the centre of mass of the ship.
– list of tanks with filling liquid characteristics and level (before and after the trials).

Ideally, two series of sea trials should be carried out for each ship:

Series 1 - ideally performed without wind and waves, or as much as possible up to sea/wind Douglas 3/Beaufort 3.

Series 2 - sea/wind conditions above Douglas 3/ Beaufort 3.

In series 1 it will be performed the standard manoeuvring sea trials at different velocities. Series 2 begins with the identification of the wave spectrum. For this it is necessary to keep the ship steady and heading the predominant waves for about 20

IMU Crossbow NAV400

IXSea Octans fibre Optic Gyrocompass

GPS antenna and receiver

Wireless weather station "Davis Vantage pro"

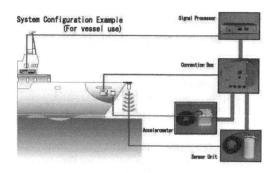

Wave radar TSK WM-2 (courtesy of Tsurumi-Seiki Co.,Ltd)

Compact-RIO 9004 from National Instruments and C# acquisition modules

Laptop PC running a real-time LabView® application

Figure 3. Portable external sensors and equipment for synchronized data collection.

minutes. Then a series of manoeuvres in waves at different velocities will be performed. It is estimated that in total 6 hours will be required for series 1 and —7 hours for series 2 to conclude the full-scale sea trials on each ship. That means at least 3 days of preparation and execution per ship.

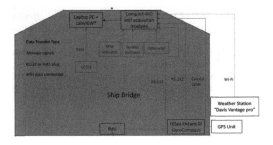

Figure 4. Scheme of on-board setup for data Acquisition. Ship without digital networks.

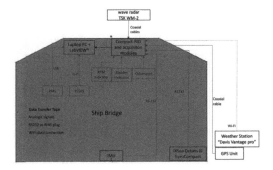

Figure 5. Scheme of on-board setup for data Acquisition. Ships with digital networks.

4 CONCLUSIONS

The history, relevance and reasoning for the use of full-scale manoeuvring trials on the improvement of ship simulators was presented. Then a system for monitoring and data acquisition in full-scale manoeuvrability tests on board of naval surface ships was described. Detailed information of the onboard instrumentation was addressed. During the instrumentation stage of the trials preparation, several arrangements of equipment were tested, and the best solution was chosen. This solution was to locate the acquisition system in the bridge of the ship, and the IMUs at the center of the ship. The rudder deflection angle in one ship is to be measured by an indirect method, using a laser sensor in the steering gear compartment.

ACKNOWLEDGEMENTS

This work was performed within the NAVAD project "Simulation of manoeuvrability of ships in adverse weather conditions", which is co-funded by the European Regional Development Fund (Fundo Europeu de Desenvolvimento Regional - FEDER) and by the Portuguese Foundation for Science and Technology (Fundação para a Ciência e a Tecnologia - FCT). This work contributes to the Strategic Research Plan of the Centre for Marine Technology and Ocean Engineering (CENTEC), which is financed by the Portuguese Foundation for Science and Technology under contract UIDB/UIDP/00134/2020.

REFERENCES

IMO (International Maritime Organization). (1993). *IMO Resolution A.751(18): Interim Standards for Ship Manoeuverability*. International Maritime Organization. London: IMO.

Crane, C., Eda, H., & Landsburg, A. (1989). Controllability. In E. Lewis (Ed.), *Principles of Naval Architecture* (pp. 191–365). Jersey City, N.J.: SNAME.

Francisco, R., & Guedes Soares, C. (2000). Identificação e Simulação das Características de Manobra de Navios. *O Mar e os Desafios do Futuro* (pp. 185–209). Lisboa: Edições Salamandra.

Guedes Soares, C., Sutulo, S., Francisco, A., Santos, F.M., & Moreira, L. (1999). Full-scale measurements of the manoeuvering capabilities of a catamaran. *RINA International Conference on Hydrodynamics of High Speed Craft* (pp. 1–12). London: RINA.

Guedes Soares, C., Sutulo, S., Francisco, R., Moreira, L., & Laranjinha, M. (2002). Ensaios de manobrabilidade em lanchas e corvetas. *O Mar Fonte de Desenvolvimento Sustentado* (pp. 251–270). Lisboa: Salamandra.

Guedes Soares, C.; Francisco, R. A.; Moreira, L., and Laranjinha, M. Full-Scale Measurements of the Manoeuvering Capabilities of Fast Patrol Vessels, Argos Class. Marine Technology. 2004; 41(1):7–16.

IMO (International Maritime Organization). (1994). Explanatory notes to the interim standards for ship maoeuverability. *Circular MSC/Circ. 644*. London: IMO.

Mandel, P. (1965). Ship maneuvering and control. In J. Comstock (Ed.), *Principles of Naval Architecture* (pp. 463–606). New York: SNAME.

Pires da Silva, P., & Guedes Soares, C. (2016). Uncertainty modeling in ship maneuvering models. *Marine Technology and Engineering 3* (pp. 361–369). London: Taylor & Francis Group.

Schoenherr, K. (1939). Steering. In E. Henry, L. Chapman, & Rossell (Ed.), *Principles of Naval Architecture* (pp. 197–233). New York: SNAME.

Sutulo, S., & Guedes Soares, C. (2006). Development of a multi-factor regression model of ship maneuvering forces based on optimized captive-model tests. *Journal of Ship Research*, 50, 311–333.

Sutulo, S., & Guedes Soares, C. (2011). Mathematical models for simulation of manoeuvring performance of ships. In C. e. Guedes Soares (Ed.), *1st International Conference of Maritime Technology and Engineering, MARTECH 2011. 1*, pp. 661–698. Lisbon: Taylor & Francis.

Sutulo, S., & Kim, S. Y. (1998). Systematic Approach to PMM/Rotating Arm Experiment Planning, Parameter Estimation, and Uncertainty Analysis. *International Symposium and workshop on Force Acting on a Manoeuvering Vessel*. Val de Reuil, France.

Sutulo, S., Moreira, L., & Guedes Soares, C. (2000). Análise do efeito do vento e corrente nas provas de manobrabilidade de navios. *O Mar e os Desafios do Futuro* (pp. 211–230). Lisboa: Edições Salamandra.

Sutulo, S., Paço, A., & Guedes Soares, C. (2009). Full-scale observations of berthing and unberthing processes of fast displacement catamarans. *FAST 2009-10th International Conference on Fast Sea Transportation*, (pp. 491–503). Athens.

Sutulo, S., Pascoal, R., & Guedes Soares, C. (2008). Sistema de Instrumentação e Aquisição de Dados para Ensaios e Observações de Manobrabilidade nos Navios. In Guedes Soares, C. & Costa Monteiro C., (pp. 525–538). Lisboa: Salamandra.

Webster, W. (1992). *Shiphandling Simulation, Application to Waterway Design*. Washington D.C.: National Press.

Zhu, M., Hahn, A., Wen, Y., & Bolles, A. (2017, September 7). Identification-based simplified model of large container ships using support vector machines and artificial bee colony algorithm. *Applied Ocean Research, 68,* 249–261.

Investigation of performance of an identification program based on evolutionary optimization algorithms

S. Sutulo & C. Guedes Soares

Centre for Marine Technology and Ocean Engineering, Instituto Superior Técnico, Universidade de Lisboa, Lisbon, Portugal

ABSTRACT: The paper describes continuation of studies carried out in the application of system identification for estimation of parameters of ship manoeuvring mathematical models. A new version of a versatile identification algorithm based on various metrics and global optimizations schemes is described. The algorithm was tested on artificial training data characterized by a very high level of the Gaussian white noise. The presented results confirm sufficient effectiveness and robustness of the algorithm which is now considered as sufficiently matured for application to real-world experimental data.

1 INTRODUCTION

Significance of adequate and accurate mathematical models for ship manoeuvring is evident and undisputable. Unfortunately, construction of such models for surface displacement ships is not an easy task in spite of a broad variety of approaches and methods continuously applied and refined in course of several decades (Sutulo & Guedes Soares 2011). Of all such methods, those based on the system identification (SI) look especially attractive due to some their special features (Jang & Phan 2004).

In a broader sense, it is possible to interpret every method avoiding direct measurements or computations of required components of hydrodynamic forces as a SI-method. In particular, this interpretation applies even to the well-known procedure of determination of the parameters of the mathematical model from oscillatory captive-model tests performed with planar-motion mechanisms (PMM): in this case some forces are measured directly but results of these measurements (mean values, out-of-phase and in-phase amplitudes) cannot be directly imported into the model and some processing is required, see e.g. (Sutulo & Guedes Soares 2006, 2007). However, typically the SI-approach in manoeuvring is interpreted as restauration of the parameters of a ship mathematical model from kinematical measurements performed with full-scale ships or self-running scaled models. As many of these parameters define the hydrodynamic forces acting upon a ship in manoeuvring motion one can also talk about indirect estimation of those forces. In practice this estimation turns out rather complex primarily due to large number of the parameters to be estimated and to the fact that real-world kinematical measurements are noisy. These two circumstances can lead to biased estimates and inadequate resulting models.

As a rather extended review of literature on SI can be found in earlier publications by Sutulo & Guedes Soares (2011, 2014, 2015, 2018) only few latest articles on this topic are commented below.

It can be noticed that most of latest contribution in ship dynamics applications of SI exploit the so-called Support Vector Regression (SVR) technique. And often this technique is complemented with some optimization method for selecting optimal values of the insensitivity and regularization parameters. In particular, Luo & Cong (2016) combined SVR with the particle swarm optimization procedure. In this study SI was aimed at synthesizing an optimized automatic steering controller. However, the study was based on simplistic Norrbin model for ship manoeuvring. SVR combined with the ABC optimization was used by Zhu et al. (2019) for identifying a relatively simple quasi-polynomial model. A much more complex polynomial regression model with 34 parameters was used by Wang et al. (2019) who applied an improved version of SVR. However, the number of regression coefficients seems to be excessive and it is not clear whether in this case the SVR method was able to mitigate possible multicollinearity effect. The same doubt applies to the study described in (Liu et al. 2019) where even 40 parameters were involved. Specifics of that contribution consists in using a sum of two training manoeuvres as the input record. An identification algorithm was used by Dai et al. (2019) for estimating parameters of a linear heave-and-pitch model. Salient feature of this study is implementation of a multi-objective genetic algorithm constructing a Pareto front of suitable solutions. Finally, Wang et al. (2020) made an attempt to synthesize an optimized multi-level pseudo-random excitation sequence which, according to their data, lead to better parameter estimation than after a zigzag test.

The common feature of the above commented contributions dealing with manoeuvring was a seemingly insufficient validation of the estimated models. For instance, in no one case a comparison of the spiral curves was performed while the authors came to conclusion that this can be critical for comparative assessment of different models for the same object (Sutulo & Guedes Soares 2019).

After having analysed multiple studies dedicated to the SI and its application to ship manoeuvrability the authors had performed a kind of synthesis of a number of approaches which resulted in a new algorithm firstly described in (Sutulo & Guedes Soares 2014). Of course, similarities with some earlier contributions can be traced but some new ideas were also exploited. In particular, selection of responses subject to comparisons and used in the identification process is different from that adopted in most studies and for the first time the Hausdorff metric was used for quantifying distances between the original and simulated responses. The restauration was carried out not only from original training responses but also from the responses polluted with the white noise. While identification from clean records was successful with all tested metrics, only the Hausdorff metric performed well with polluted records.

In the next contribution by the authors (Sutulo & Guedes Soares 2015) the number of estimated parameters was increased from 11 to 22 and a more general variant of the Hausdorff metric was applied. However, it was further realised that some of the parameters (the added mass coefficients) should not be subject to identification to avoid multicollinearity problems and in (Sutulo & Guedes Soares 2018) the number of parameters was reduced to 19.

Results presented in the last two cited publications were quite satisfactory and even good when the algorithm was run on clean records but the same algorithm failed completely on polluted ones. As long as this failure coincided with substantial augmentation of the dimension of the factor space, the latter was suspected to be responsible for poor performance of the method caused by premature convergence of the genetic and ABC algorithm to a wrong local extremum which may be expected in high-dimensional problems. At the same time, it was discovered that the ABC algorithm (Kang et al. 2011) showed somewhat inferior performance as compared to that of the simple genetic algorithm (GA). And the authors' further efforts were direct toward improvement of the used implementation of the GA. Unfortunately, the authors had to ignore the recommendation to implement the so-called "messy" GA which was claimed to have superior performance and resistance to premature convergence (Haupt & Haupt 2004). The problem lay in absence of a sufficiently detailed description of such algorithm in the literature: rather some hints could only be found.

Hence, the authors decided to concentrate on improvements of the earlier developed simple GA code and its parameters using recommendations given in the literature, see (Cooley 1999), (Mitsuo & Runwei 2000), and (Reeves & Rowe 2002). Besides augmentation of the population size, of the allowed convergence base and of the chromosome length, two variants of the tournament selection method and two additional scaling methods were implemented. Also, a much better method was used for transformation of the objective function (distance between the responses) to the fitness function dealt with by the GA.

All new variants of optimization were preliminarily tested on more than 100 test functions described by Haupt & Haupt (2004) and by Kang et al. (2011) and coded by the authors for that purpose. While quite satisfactory results were obtained on the multimodal test functions with the dimension of the factor space up to 24, no improvements were reached with the identification problem itself. As the premature convergence was still suspected as being responsible for this setback, an additional optimization method was implemented: the direct quasi-random search based on the Sobol sequences (Press et al. 1992). This method had been used earlier by the authors in another applications (Sutulo & Guedes Soares 2004, 2007b) and proved to be inferior to GA but by its nature it is completely free of any kind of premature convergence.

Although the direct quasi-random search per se did not resolve the problem, its implementation and test runs helped to trace an error in the format of polluted records used after 2014. After this flaw was eliminated the performance of the identification program started to meet the expectations.

The study described in the present paper is similar to those carried out earlier i.e. a completely defined ship mathematical model of medium complexity was used to obtain training responses serving as surrogate kinematical measurements used for restauring the parameters through minimization of the distance between the training and reproduced responses. Besides elimination of the mentioned flaw in the polluted training data, an improved version of the GA and the quasi-random search were tested for the first time.

2 SHIP MATHEMATICAL MODEL

2.1 *Equations of motion*

The same 3DOF holistic ship manoeuvring mathematical model of medium complexity as used earlier by the authors (Sutulo & Guedes Soares 2014, 2015, 2018) was operated in this study. The description, which follows, is rather brief and the reader is encouraged to consult the previous publications cited above.

The underlying set of ordinary differential equations of ship dynamics can be written as:

$$\mathbf{M}\dot{\mathbf{x}} = \mathbf{F}(\mathbf{x}, \boldsymbol{\theta}, \delta^*), \qquad (1)$$

where **M** is the inertial matrix, **x** is the state vector, **F** is the right-hand side vector, **θ** is the vector of parameters subject to estimation with the SI algorithm, and δ^* is the rudder order.

The inertial matrix is:

$$\mathbf{M} = \begin{pmatrix} m+\mu_{11} & 0 & 0 & 0 \\ 0 & m+\mu_{22} & mx_G+\mu_{26} & 0 \\ 0 & mx_G+\mu_{26} & I_{zz}+\mu_{66} & 0 \\ 0 & 0 & 0 & 1 \end{pmatrix}, \quad (2)$$

where m is the ship's mass, x_G is the abscissa of the centre of mass, I_{zz} is the moment of inertia, and $\mu_{11}, \mu_{22}, \mu_{26}, \mu_{66}$ are the added mass coefficients.

The vector of state variables can be represented as the column matrix:

$$\mathbf{x} = (u, v, r, \delta_R)^T, \quad (3)$$

where u, v, r are the velocities of surge, sway and yaw respectively, and δ_R is the rudder angle. All state variables depending on the time t, and the upper dot in (1) means derivative with respect to this time.

The right-hand side function in (1) can be represented as

$$\mathbf{F} = \begin{pmatrix} mvr + mx_G r^2 + X_P + X_H(V, v', r', \delta_R; \boldsymbol{\theta}) \\ -mur + Y_H(V, v', r', \delta_R; \boldsymbol{\theta}) \\ -mx_G ur + N_H(V, v', r', \delta_R; \boldsymbol{\theta}) \\ F_\delta(\delta_R, \delta^*) \end{pmatrix}, \quad (4)$$

where X, Y are the surge and sway forces, N is the yaw moment; the subscript P corresponds to the propeller, H—to the hull with the rudder; $V = \sqrt{u^2 + v^2}$ is the ship speed, $v' = v/V$, $r' = rL/V$ are the dimensionless velocities, and L is the ship length.

In this model the components X_P and F_δ are independent of adjustable parameters and their detailed description is given in (Sutulo & Guedes Soares 2011, 2015b).

To predict trajectories of a manoeuvring vessel, the equations (1) must be complemented with the following kinematical equations:

$$\begin{aligned} \dot{\xi}_C &= u\cos\psi - v\sin\psi, \\ \dot{\eta}_C &= u\sin\psi + v\cos\psi, \\ \dot{\psi} &= r, \end{aligned} \quad (5)$$

where ξ_C, η_C are the instantaneous advance and transfer of the ship and ψ is the heading angle. However, these equations are not involved into the identification process as they contain no identifiable parameters.

2.2 Hydrodynamic forces depending on adjustable parameters

The forces with the subscript H are represented as

$$X_H = X'_H \frac{\rho V^2}{2} LT, \quad Y_H = Y'_H \frac{\rho V^2}{2} LT,$$
$$N_H = N'_H \frac{\rho V^2}{2} L^2 T, \quad (6)$$

where ρ is the water density, T is the draught, and the dimensionless force/moment coefficients are approximated with the following regression polynomials:

$$\begin{aligned} X'_H &= \kappa_1 X'_{uu} u'^2 + \kappa_2 X'_{vr} v'r' + \kappa_3 X'_{\delta\delta} \delta_R^2, \\ Y'_H &= Y'_0 + \kappa_4 Y'_v v' + \kappa_5 Y'_r r' + \kappa_6 Y'_{vvv} v'^3 + \kappa_7 Y'_{vvr} v'^2 r' \\ &\quad + \kappa_8 Y'_\delta \delta_R + \kappa_9 Y'_{v\delta\delta} v'^2 \delta_R + \kappa_{10} Y'_{v\delta\delta} v' \delta_R^2 + \kappa_{11} Y'_{\delta\delta\delta} \delta_R^3, \\ N'_H &= N'_0 \kappa_{12} N'_v v' + \kappa_{13} N'_r r' + \kappa_{14} N'_{vvv} v'^3 \\ &\quad + \kappa_{15} N'_{vvr} v'^2 r' + \kappa_{16} N'_\delta \delta_R + \kappa_{17} N'_{vv\delta} v'^2 \delta_R \\ &\quad + \kappa_{18} N'_{v\delta\delta} v' \delta_R^2 + \kappa_{19} N'_{\delta\delta\delta} \delta_R^3, \end{aligned} \quad (7)$$

where $u'^2 = 1 - v'^2$, $\kappa_1, \ldots, \kappa_{19}$ are the adjustable parameters, and $X'_{uu}, \ldots, N'_{\delta\delta\delta}$ are the a priori values of the regression coefficients. In the present study, these values for the *Mariner* ship (Crane et al. 1989) were assumed.

3 IDENTIFICATION PROCEDURE

The "clean" training time histories $\tilde{u}(t), \tilde{v}(t), \tilde{r}(t), \tilde{\delta}_R(t)$ are obtained simulating the $30° - 30°$ zigzag manoeuvre with the mathematical model described in the previous section at $\kappa_1 = \ldots = \kappa_{19} = 1$. The "polluted" training responses are obtained by adding a high-level white Gauss noise, see (Sutulo & Guedes Soares (2014) for details. The resulting time histories are used for test identification in the present study.

While a more detailed description of the identification algorithm can be found in the previous cited publications of the authors, its brief outline looks as follows:

1. Initial values for all correction factors κ_i are set as random variables uniformly distributed within the interval $[0.5, 1.5]$.
2. The optimization process is launched in the factor space i.e. for κ_i aiming at minimizing the weighted distance

$$\rho_w = w_u\rho[u(t), \tilde{u}(t)] + w_v\rho[v(t), \tilde{v}(t)] + w_r\rho[r(t), \tilde{r}(t)] + w_\delta\rho[\delta_R(t), \tilde{\delta}_R(t)], \quad (8)$$

where w_u, w_v, w_r, w_δ are the weights.

1. The reached "optimum" values of the factors κ_i are used for simulating three standard manoeuvres: the $30° - 30°$ zigzag, the $35°$ helm turn, and the Dieudonné spiral with further comparing the resulting time histories with "exact" ones obtained at $\kappa_i = 1$, $i = 1, \ldots, 19$.

The distance ρ can be defined in various metrics of which the following ones are used in the present study:

$$\rho_2(y, \tilde{y}) \triangleq \|y - \tilde{y}\|_{L_2} = \left[\int_0^T (y(t) - \tilde{y}(t))^2 dt\right]^{1/2} \quad (9)$$

—the Euclidean metric;

$$\rho_\infty(y, \tilde{y}) \triangleq \|y - \tilde{y}\|_{L_\infty} = \max_{t \in [0,T]} |y(t) - \tilde{y}(t)| \quad (10)$$

—the uniform or L_∞-metric;

$$\rho_H(\{t, y(t)\}, \{t, \tilde{y}(t)\}) \equiv \rho_H(y, \tilde{y})$$
$$\triangleq \max\left\{\begin{array}{l}\sup_{t_1 \in [0,T]} \inf_{t_2 \in [0,T]} r(y(t_1), \tilde{y}(t_2)), \\ \sup_{t_2 \in [0,T]} \inf_{t_1 \in [0,T]} r(y(t_1), \tilde{y}(t_2))\end{array}\right\} \quad (11)$$

—the Hausdorff metric.

In eqs. (9)–(11): $y(t)$ and $\tilde{y}(t)$ are some functions of time, T is the length of the time interval, $r()$ is the auxiliary sub-metric which in the present study is taken either in the Euclidean form

$$r(y(t_1), \tilde{y}(t_2)) \triangleq \sqrt{(t_1 - t_2)^2 + (y(t_1) - \tilde{y}(t_2))^2} \quad (12)$$

or as

$$r(y(t_1), \tilde{y}(t_2)) \triangleq \max\left\{\tfrac{1}{a}|t_1 - t_2|, |y(t_1) - \tilde{y}(t_2)|\right\}, \quad (13)$$

where it was assumed $a = 1$ in this study.

In earlier studies all weights had been set to unity but, to make the problem more "isotropic", here each of them was set proportional to the inverse of the corresponding partial Hausdorff distance averaged over the optimization domain $[0.5, 1.5]^{\times 19}$ using 10,000 quasi-random points and keeping their sum equal to 4. This resulted in the following values: $w_u = 1.28$, $w_v = 0.424$, $w_r = w_\delta = 1.148$. Alternatively, these weights could be defined to reflect subjective importance of each response.

Inclusion of the rudder angle time histories into (8) is essential because any adequate model presumes that instantaneous values of kinematic parameters must be reproduced at certain values of the rudder angle. There is no need to include the responses for the heading angle and the trajectory as these characteristics are linked to quasi-velocities with accurate equations (5) containing no unknown parameters.

Success of the identification process depends substantially on the applied optimization method. As it was known from the previous studies that the response surface in most ship manoeuvring identification problem is not convex, the authors have never tried to apply any local search method. The following global optimization methods are envisaged by the identification program:

1. The quasi-random search with 10,000 shots.
2. The binary genetic algorithm with 100 individuals, crossover rate 0.6, mutation rate 0.003, maximum number of generations 5000, non-improvement base 2000. Two selection schemes were applied: deterministic and tournament.
3. The ABC algorithm with 100 sources, 30 source improvement attempts, and 3000 iterations.

4 NUMERICAL RESULTS

4.1 Training time histories

The training responses $u(t)$, $v(t)$ and $r(t)$ for the $30° - 30°$ zigzag manoeuvre are shown in Figure 1: clean responses—with the lines while the symbols represent the same responses with the added noise. The corresponding time history for the rudder angle is not shown to avoid congestion of the plot. All details concerning generation of the noise are presented in (Sutulo & Guedes Soares 2014). As indisputably good results had already been obtained with the clean responses in (Sutulo & Guedes Soares 2018), most identifications in the present study were performed with the polluted time histories. Although

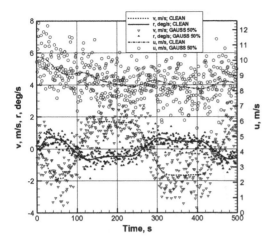

Figure 1. Training responses in the 30° − 30° zigzag.

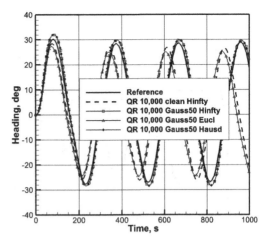

Figure 2. Heading responses in 20° − 20° zigzag: identification with quasi-random search.

pseudo-random sequences could be more efficient in generating highly informative inputs, they are less convenient in implementation especially when it goes about full-scale trials and a strong zigzag manoeuvre seems to be a reasonable compromise.

In the following subsections the responses obtained with the values of the correction factors κ_i estimated with the algorithm described above with various optimization methods activated are presented. It is important that no one simulated manoeuvre is identical to the manoeuvre used for creating training responses.

4.2 General remarks

On all plots representing results corresponding to the identified models are also presented with the thick solid lines the reference responses obtained with $\kappa_i = 1 \ \forall i$. The following abbreviations and acronyms are used in the legends: Hinfty stands for the uniform L_∞-metric, Eucl—for the Euclidean metric, Hausd—for the Hausdorff metric; QR means the quasi-random search, GA—genetic algorithm, t—tournament selection, d—deterministic selection. Finally, the combination GAd+ corresponds to the enhanced configuration of the genetic algorithm with deterministic selection, 300 individuals, maximum number of generations 15,000, and the non-improvement base 5000 generations. The mutation rate was in this case reduced to 0.001. For the Hausdorff metric the submetric (13) was in this case used instead of (12).

4.3 Zigzag outputs

Time histories for the heading angle corresponding to the results obtained by the quasi-random search with 10,000 tries are presented in Figure 2 together with the reference response which must be reproduced exactly in case of absolutely accurate restored model. Of course, in practice this can never be reached and more or less significant differences are visible. Here the best (and identical) results were reached with the uniform and Hausdorff metrics.

The worst model is that obtained with the Euclidean metric. Remarkable is that results obtained with the uniform metric from clean training responses are also poor. This is not surprising as the quasi-random search presumes no feedback and all trial points were identical for all metrics. The quality of resulting models at moderate number of trials is partly a matter of luck. However, augmentation of the number of trials to 100,000 i.e. by the order of magnitude resulted for the Hausdorff metric in absolutely identical values of the parameters let alone responses. It indicates to poor efficiency of the quasi-random search in comparison with other algorithms.

The genetic and ABC methods lead to substantially better results (Figures 3,4) and all identified models look acceptable: a slight advantage of the genetic algorithm with tournament selection is not significant.

4.4 Time histories in turning manoeuvre

Transient responses in the 35° helm turning manoeuvre are presented in Figures 5–10. The best results were here obtained with the quasi-random search on the basis of clean training records. As to identification from polluted data, the genetic algorithm in general performed the best although the steady turn values are somewhat overestimated for all three kinematic parameters. Although the behaviour of the response $V(t)$ is better reproduced with the quasi-random search using the uniform and Hausdorff metrics, the observed initial speed rise (Figure 9) is not physically justified and is never observed in real world.

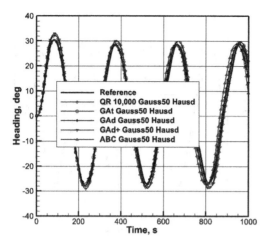

Figure 3. Heading responses in 20° – 20° zigzag: identification with genetic and ABC algorithms.

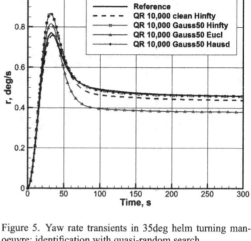

Figure 5. Yaw rate transients in 35deg helm turning manoeuvre: identification with quasi-random search.

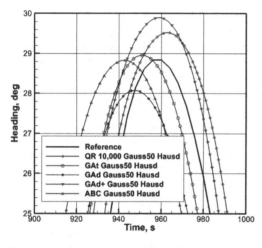

Figure 4. Heading responses in 20° – 20° zigzag: identification with genetic and ABC algorithms (zoomed).

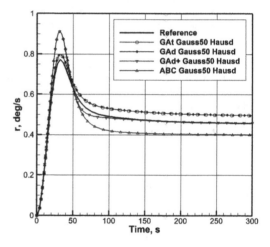

Figure 6. Yaw rate transients in 35deg helm turning manoeuvre: identification with genetic and ABC algorithms.

In this case, however, it is more difficult to conclude definitely which configuration of the genetic algorithm is the best. The enhanced configuration of the genetic algorithm did not demonstrate definite superiority although a very good reproduction of the steady turn values of the rate of turn and of the drift angle (Figures 6, 8) is remarkable.

But the same configuration showed an unnatural overshoot in the speed drop curve (Figure 10). The same happened with the ABC algorithm although in general its performance was competitive.

4.5 *Spiral curves*

As could be expected, the spiral curves, i.e. dependencies of kinematical parameters, especially of the dimensionless rate of yaw, on the rudder angle turned out to be the most difficult for reproduction with identified models as is evident from Figures 11–12. In particular, it is seen that the reference model corresponds to a slightly unstable ship with a very narrow hysteresis loop. In no one case did the quasi-random search produce good results. The results obtained with the genetic algorithm—especially with the deterministic selection and 100 individuals—look definitely better although the width of the hysteresis loop is somewhat overestimated. Contrary to expectations, enhancing the genetic algorithm failed to produce a better model although the reached Hausdorff distance became smaller: 6.03 vs 6.15.

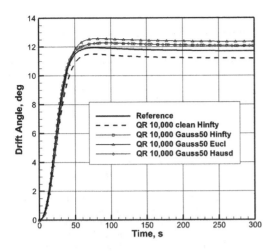

Figure 7. Drift angle transients in 35deg helm turning manoeuvre: identification with quasi-random search.

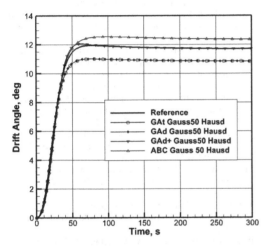

Figure 8. Drift angle transients in 35deg helm turning manoeuvre: identification with genetic and ABC algorithms.

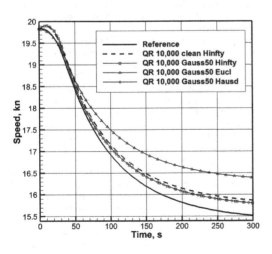

Figure 9. Speed drop in 35deg helm turning manoeuvre: identification with quasi-random search.

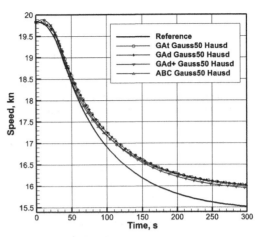

Figure 10. Speed drop in 35deg helm turning manoeuvre: identification with genetic and ABC algorithms.

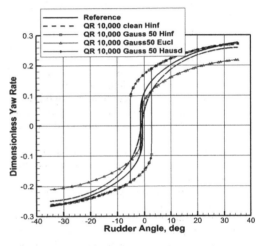

Figure 11. Spiral curve: identification with quasi-random search.

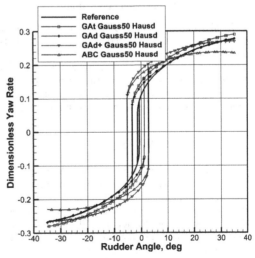

Figure 12. Spiral curves: identification with genetic and ABC algorithms.

5 CONCLUSIONS

An improved version of the system identification algorithm for ship manoeuvring mathematical models has been developed and tested on artificial data, mostly polluted with high-level Gaussian white noise. Analysis of the obtained data resulted in the following conclusions:

1. Although the quasi-random search optimization method is absolutely free of danger of premature convergence and is relatively fast at moderate number of trials, in general it is less efficient than evolutionary algorithms.
2. A somewhat poorer performance of the ABC algorithm in this application was confirmed.
3. Reproduction of the spiral curve turned out to be the most difficult task and the Dieudonné spiral should be considered as a critical validation manoeuvre although its execution in real world may be difficult.
4. With most optimization methods activated the developed identification program is not fast: a single run can take from several hours to several days. Although this is not critical for offline identification, detailed exploration of multiple parameters configuring optimization methods and their combinations is problematic, let alone organization of any kind of meta-optimization.
5. Superiority of the Hausdorff metric has been confirmed although its computation is the most time-consuming.
6. Inferiority of the most popular Euclidean metric was also confirmed.
7. Remembering that most tests described in the present paper were carried out on heavily polluted training records, the method can be assessed as sufficiently robust and reliable for being applied to real experimental data which is planned as the next step in this study.

In addition, it must be emphasized that although the manoeuvring mathematical model used in this study is linear with respect to all its parameters, this is not a condition sine qua non: the method can be used with parametric models of any kind. This property and also possibility of using various metrics determines superiority of the method over some alternative approaches.

ACKNOWLEDGMENTS

The work was performed within the NAVAD project "Simulation of manoeuvrability of ships in adverse weather conditions" which is co-funded by the European Regional Development Fund (Fundo Europeu de Desenvolvimento Regional - FEDER) and by the Portuguese Foundation for Science and Technology (Fundação para a Ciência e a Tecnologia - FCT) under contract 02/SAICT/032037/2017. This work contributes to the Strategic Research Plan of the Centre for Marine Technology and Ocean Engineering (CENTEC), which is financed by the Portuguese Foundation for Science and Technology (Fundação para a Ciência e Tecnologia - FCT) under contract UIDB/UIDP/00134/2020.

REFERENCES

Cooley, D.A. 1999. *An introduction to genetic algorithms for scientists and engineers*, Singapore: World Scientific.

Crane, C. L., H. Eda, and A. C. Landsburg 1989. Controllability. In E. V. Lewis (Ed.), *Principles of Naval Architecture*, Volume 3: 191–422. Jersey City, NJ: SNAME.

Dai, Y., Cheng, R., Yao, X., Liu, L. 2019. Hydrodynamic coefficients identification of pitch and heave using multi-objective evolutionary algorithm, *Ocean Engineering* 171: 33–48.

Haupt, R.L. & Haupt, S.E. 2004. *Practical genetic algorithms*, Hoboken, NJ: Wiley-Interscience.

Jang, J.-N. & Phan, M.Q. 2004. *Identification and control of mechanical systems*, Cambridge, UK: Cambridge University Press.

Kang, F., Li, J., Ma, Z., Li, H. 2011. Artificial bee colony algorithm with local search for numerical optimization. *Journal of Software* 6(3): 490–497.

Liu, B., Jin, Y., Magee, A.R., Yiew, L.J., Zhang, S. 2019. System identification of Abkowitz model for ship maneuvering motion based on ε-support vector regression, *Proceedings of the ASME 2019 38th International Conference on Ocean, Offshore & Arctic Engineering OMAE2019*, June 9 –14,2019,Glasgow, Scoyland, UK. Paper OMAE2019-96699, 10p.

Luo. W. & Cong, H. 2016. Control for ship course-keeping using optimized support vector machines, *Algorithms* 9 (52): 1–15.

Mitsuo, G. & Runwei, C. 2000. *Genetic algorithms and engineering optimization*, New York: Johm Wiley & Sons, Inc.

Press, W.H., Teukolsky, S.A., Vetterling, W.T., Flannery, B. P. 1992. *Numerical recipes in C*, Cambridge University Press.

Reeves, C.R. & Rowe, J.E. 2002. *Genetic algorithms: principles and perspectives*, New York: Kluwer Academic Publishers.

Sutulo, S. & Guedes Soares, C. 2004. Synthesis of experimental designs of maneuvering captive-model tests with a large number of factors. *J Mar Sci Technol* 9: 32–42.

Sutulo, S. & Guedes Soares, C. 2006. Development of a Multi-Factor Regression Model of Ship Maneuvering Forces Based on Optimized Captive Model Tests. *J. Ship Research* 50(4): 311–333.

Sutulo, S. & Guedes Soares, C. 2007a. Contribution of Higher-Order Harmonics for Estimating Manoeuvring Derivatives from Oscillatory Tests. *International Shipbuilding Progress* 54: 1–24.

Sutulo, S. & Guedes Soares, C. 2007b. An algorithm for consistent linearization of ship manoeuvring mathematical models, *Proceedings of the IFAC Conference on Control Applications in Marine Systems, CAMS2007, Bol, Croatia*, 19–21 September 2007, paper No. 25, 6p.

Sutulo, S., Guedes Soares, C. 2011. Mathematical Models for Simulation of Manoeuvring Performance of Ships, In:

C. Guedes Soares et al. (eds.) *Marine Technology and Engineering:* 661–698, London: Taylor & Francis Group.

Sutulo, S. & Guedes Soares, C. 2014. An algorithm for offline identification of ship manoeuvring mathematical models from free-running tests. *Ocean Engineering*: 79: 10–25.

Sutulo, S. & Guedes Soares, C. 2015a. Offline system identification of ship manoeuvring mathematical models with a global optimization algorithm, *MARSIM 2015: International Conference on Ship Manoeuvrability and Maritime Simulation, Newcastle University, United Kingdom,* 8–11 September 2015, Paper 1-2-1, 16p.

Sutulo, S. & Guedes Soares, C. 2015b. Development of a core mathematical model for arbitrary maneuvers of a shuttle tanker, *Applied Ocean Research*: 51. 293–308

Sutulo, S. & Guedes Soares, C. 2018. Comparative testing of an identification method based on the genetic and ABC algorithms, *MARSIM 2018: International Conference on Ship Manoeuvrability and Maritime Simulation, Halifax, Nova Scotia, Canada,* 12–16 August 2018, Paper 2, pp. 1–12.

Sutulo, S., Guedes Soares, C. 2019. On the application of empiric methods for prediction of ship manoeuvring properties and associated uncertainties, Ocean Engineering, 186: article 106111, 23p. https://doi.org/10.1016/j.oceaneng.2019. 106111.

Wang, Z., Zou, Z., Guedes Soares, C. 2019. Identification of ship manoeuvring motion based on nu-support vector machines, *Ocean Engineering* 183: 270–281.

Wang, Z., Guedes Soares, C., Zou, Z., 2020. Optimal design of excitation signal for identification of nonlinear ship manoeuvring model, *Ocean Engineering* 196 (106778): 1–10.

Zhu, M, Hahn, A., Wen, Y.-Q., Sun, W.-Q. 2019. Optimized support vector regression algorithm-base modelling of ship dynamics, *Applied Ocean Research*, 68: 101842.

Ship hydrodynamics – Seakeeping

Development of a three-dimensional frequency domain seakeeping code

A. Abbasnia, S. Sutulo, B. Callewaert & C. Guedes Soares
Centre for Marine Technology and Ocean Engineering (CENTEC), Instituto Superior Técnico, Universidade de Lisboa, Lisbon, Portugal

ABSTRACT: The paper presents results of primary validation of the 3D linear seakeeping code now under development. The code is written in C++ language and is based on a double-body potential code for studying hydrodynamic interaction between ships maneuvering at close proximity. The free surface effects are accounted for by means of a pulsing source Green function. The validation was performed for a standalone Green function, for a hemisphere and then the code was applied to the compute the added masses and damping coefficients of the KVLCC2 ship.

1 INTRODUCTION

Historically, the linear frequency-domain seakeeping analysis was the first approach to appear and has been remaining a unique available tool during several decades. Later, more sophisticated and accurate methods like those based on nonlinear time-domain formulations were developed but frequency domain codes still keep their significance thanks to their unparalleled efficiency permitting extensive parametric studies. At the same time, the accuracy remains satisfactory for many naval architecture and ocean engineering applications.

Many seakeeping codes are based on the strip theory which is applicable in the case of typical slender ship hulls including the case of considerable speed of advance but in the case of floating structures whose shape cannot be characterized as slender the strip theory is no longer applicable and three-dimensional formulations like those described in Newman (1979), Nakos et al. (1991), Bingham & Korsmeyer (1994); Xia et al. (1998) are required.

Nowadays, a number of commercial seakeeping codes such as WAMIT, ANSYS AQWA, MAXSURF, DELFRAC, HydroD are available and, as a rule, a practicing design-oriented analyst does not need to develop in-house seakeeping codes. However, the acquired experience demonstrated some limitations and inconveniencies of using such codes without access to source files when it went about less standard applications and a decision to develop an in-house linear three-dimensional seakeeping code was taken in particular because certain prerequisites for such development already existed.

Some years ago, a double-body panel code had been developed for predicting interaction forces for ships maneuvering at close proximity (Sutulo et al. 2012). The code was based on the known method developed by Hess & Smith (1964) and initially, it was written in Fortran 90 language. However, a desire to avoid mixing functions written in different languages within one code when the interaction module was to be combined with the ship maneuvering simulation program inspired the development of a C++ version whose code named as HYDINTER.

Thanks to natural advantages of the C++ language, this version turned out more elegant, transparent and more suitable for various modifications and developments, see e.g. Sutulo & Guedes Soares (2016). That is why this version of the panel code was selected for its transformation into a three-dimensional seakeeping program.

To realize such transformation, it was necessary to lift the double-body limitation which excluded account for free-surface effects which in seakeeping are of primary importance. For this purpose either it was necessary to include distribution of additional panels on the free surface in order to implement the Rankine source boundary integral method proposed first by Yeung (1973) or to implement an algorithm for computing the pulsing source Green function (Wehausen & Laitone 1960, Newman 1985).

An efficient Fortran 77 subroutine FGREEN package for computing such Green function for infinite as well as for finite fluid depth had been developed as part of the WAMIT project (Lee 1986). This subroutine and some auxiliary subroutines and Fortran functions constituted the package FINFINGREEN. The present development has benefited from this rather valuable asset, translating the Fortran code into C++. This translation was carried out manually and the resulting Green function was thoroughly validated

DOI: 10.1201/9781003216599-27

using, in particular, control points provided by the manual (Newman & Sclavounos 1986).

After that, the function FinGreen was fused with the modified double-body panel code and the resulting program denoted as SEAKIST was subject to verification performed through comparisons with independent numerical data. Results of such comparisons constitute a considerable part of the present paper preceded by brief exposure of a rather standard underlying theory and followed by application of the code for computing inertial and damping characteristics of the KVLCC2 benchmark vessel.

2 MATHEMATICAL FORMULATION

2.1 Main integral equation

The key point of most three-dimensional seakeeping codes consists in solving the following integral equation with respect to the source density function $\sigma(P)$, where $P(x',y',z')$ is a point on the body surface S:

$$2\pi\sigma(M) + \int_S \sigma(P) \frac{\partial G(M,P)}{\partial n_M} dS(P) = f(M) \quad (1)$$

where the point $M(x,y,z)$ also belongs to the body surface, **n** is the external unity normal, and $G()$ is the Green function of the problem defined as

$$G(x,y,z,x',y',z',\omega) = \frac{1}{r} + \frac{1}{\tilde{r}} + \tilde{G}(x,y,z,x',y',z',\omega), \quad (2)$$

and

$$r = \sqrt{(x-x') + (y-y') + (z-z')},$$
$$\tilde{r} = \sqrt{(x-x') + (y-y') + (z+z')}, \quad (3)$$

$\tilde{G}()$ is the regular part of the Green function responsible for free-surface effects and depending on the oscillation frequency ω. The function $G()$ is complex, so complex and frequency-dependent will be also the source density σ.

The excitation function $f()$ in Equation 1 is specified depending on what kind of hydrodynamic forces must be computed. For inertial-and-radiation forces (the only case considered here) this function is defined as

$$f = N^\kappa, \; \kappa = 1,2,...,6 \quad (4)$$

where κ corresponds to a degree of freedom of the rigid body and

$$N^\kappa = n_\kappa, \; \kappa = 1,2,3$$
$$N^\kappa = (\vec{r} \times \vec{n})_{\kappa-3}, \; \kappa = 4,5,6 \quad (5)$$

where $\vec{r}(M)$ is the position vector from the origin of the body-fixed frame.

Once the Equation 1 is solved and the source density distribution is defined, the complex potential ϕ at each point can be computed as

$$\phi(M) = \int_S \sigma(P) G(M,P) dS(P) \quad (6)$$

If the excitation function is defined by Equation 4 and Equation 5, six radiation functions ϕ^κ will be obtained and the complex added masses $f^{\kappa\ell}$ are then defined as:

$$f^{\kappa\ell} = -\rho \iint_S \frac{\partial \phi^\kappa}{\partial n} \phi^\ell dS, \quad \kappa,\ell = 1,2,...,6 \quad (7)$$

where ρ is the fluid density, and the usual real added mass and damping coefficients are

$$A^{\kappa\ell} = \text{Re}(f^{\kappa\ell}), \quad D^{\kappa\ell} = \frac{-\text{Im}(f^{\kappa\ell})}{\omega} \quad (8)$$

2.2 Numerical implementation

According to the Hess and Smith method, the wetted surface of the body is approximated by a set of M flat quadrilateral panels with constant source density on each. The body boundary condition expressed by the excitation function $f()$ is satisfied at the centroid of each element. The integral Equation 1 is then reduced to a set of M linear algebraic equations with respect to M unknown source densities. Specifics of the developed code SEAKIST is that while the singular part of the Green function is applied to the source density uniformly distributed over the panel. The regular part is always calculated for a point source located at the centroid. The latter is also the point at which the potential is computed.

As the primary Fredholm equation (Equation 1) is of the second kind. The approximating set of algebraic equations is well conditioned and in theory, an economical iterative Gauss-Seidel method could be applied. However, the authors still have not developed a complex version of the corresponding solver and the direct Gauss–Jordan method is currently used. The corresponding C++ function was obtained as the adaptation of the real-value solver provided by Press et al. (1992).

3 COMPUTATIONAL RESULTS

The three-dimensional panel code that resulted from incorporating FinGreen into HYDINTER was verified through the computation of the added mass and damping coefficient on a floating hemisphere, and, finally, the code was applied to study the radiation of a real ship form.

3.1 *Verification of the function FinGreen*

The C++ function FinGreen was used in a standalone mode for predicting values of the induced potential and horizontal component of the induced velocity for two values of the pulsation frequency ω as function of the parameter R/h, where $R = \sqrt{(x-x') + (y-y')}$ is the horizontal distance from the pulsating source and h is the fluid depth, which was chosen different for each frequency as were also set the submergence z of the field point and the submergence z' of the source while always $x' \equiv y' \equiv 0$. The results of computations are shown on the plots in Figures 1 and 2 where they are compared with the results from Newman (1985) and Liu et al. (2015) demonstrating perfect agreement of all data.

3.2 *Validation of the code on a hemisphere*

The code SEAKIST was first tested on a floating hemisphere with the radius a performing infinitesimal heave motions with varying frequency ω. The hemisphere was approximated with a set of 684 panels distributed uniformly with the step $\pi/20$ both along parallels and meridians (Figure 3). The results are presented in Figure 4 as dependencies of the dimensionless added mass and damping coefficients on the parameter Ka, where $K = \omega^2/g$ is the wave number.

The added mass coefficients were nondimensionalized by ρV and the damping coefficients by $\omega \rho V$, where V is the volume of the hemisphere. The values obtained with the newly developed code are compared with those from Hulme (1982) demonstrating very good agreement especially for the damping coefficients. Somewhat higher differences observed for some points are most likely caused by presence of irregular frequencies. In general, however, there are reasons to be confident in the consistency of the program.

3.3 *Application to a real ship form*

Finally, the code was applied for computing hydrodynamic characteristics of the popular KVLCC2 virtual benchmark ship (Figure 5). A relatively coarse mesh contained 228 panels. The CPU time required for solving the problem at each frequency for the ship with the number of panels indicated above was 2.25 s on the Intel Core i7 @ 3.40 GHz 16 GB RAM laptop computer.

Some selected plots for the dimensionless added mass and damping coefficients are presented in Figure 6. The added mass coefficients were nondimensionalized by ρV for the translation motions and $\rho V \Re^2$ for rotational ones where V and $\Re$ are the displacement and its radius of Gyration for the ship's wetted surface respectively. The coupling added mass coefficient was nondimensionalized by $\rho V \Re$. Non dimensionalizing of the damping coefficients presumed additional division by ω. In this case the authors failed to trace independent data in the literature but qualitatively the behaviour of most coefficients looks correct. The plots for the surge–surge coefficients show some unexpected "waves".

However, the absolute value of these coefficients are small for relatively slender bodies and a coarse meshing could introduce some numerical errors.

4 CONCLUSIONS

Activities related to the first stage of development of the C++ seakeeping code SEAKIST are briefly described in the present paper. Also, numerical results related to the verification and validation of the code were discussed and analyzed. At present state, the code is only solving the radiation problem i.e. the added mass and damping coefficient can be computed for any three-dimensional body or a set of bodies in infinite or finite fluid depth. The natural limitation of the code stemming from original limitations of the Green function formulation is that it is only valid for zero speed of advance. Extension to a non-zero speed requires substitution of the algorithm for computing the Green function.

However, next planned steps are to complete the code with options to compute the excitation forces in linear approximation, both Froude–Krylov and diffraction ones. After that, it will be possible to compute frequency transfer functions which will make the code SEAKIST fit for practical applications. It is also planned to perform modifications aimed at elimination of irregular frequencies using methodologies outlined by Newman & Sclavounos (1986).

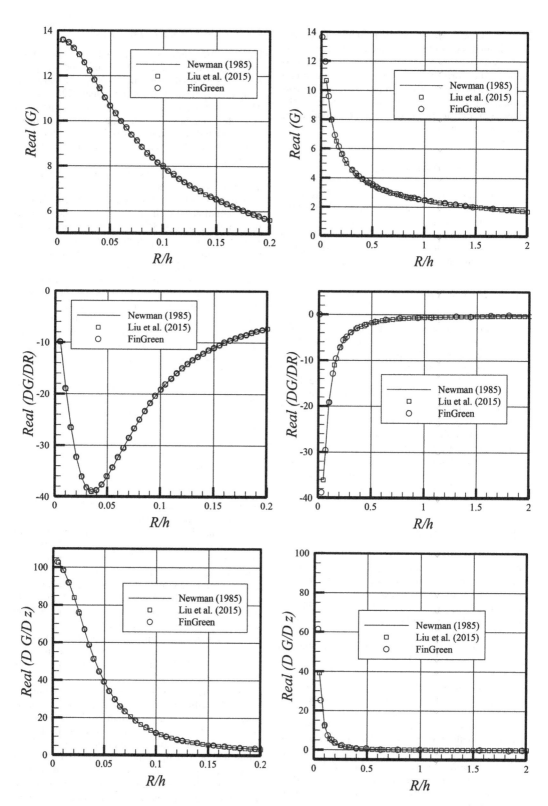

Figure 1. Real parts of the induced potential and of induced velocities from a unity strength pulsing source: $\omega = 0.22\,\text{rad/s}$, $h = 2.0\,\text{m}$, $z = 0.3\,\text{m}$, $z' = 0.2\,\text{m}$.

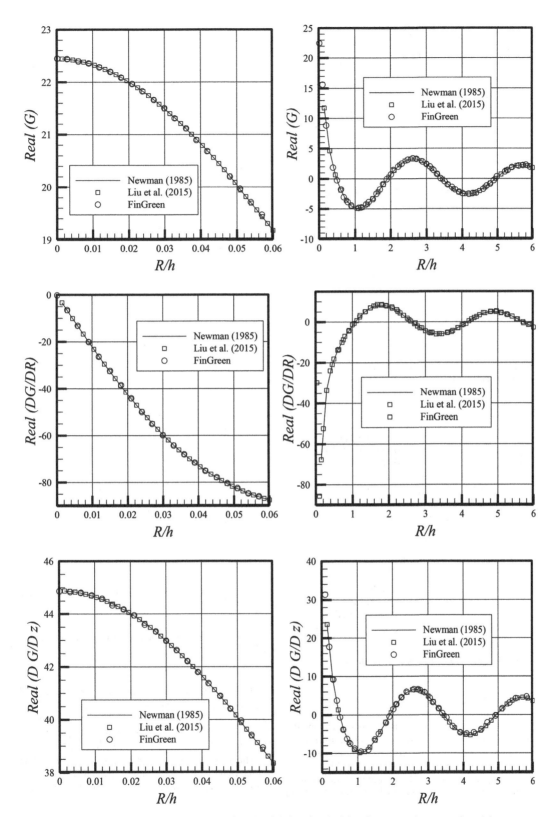

Figure 2. Real parts of the induced potential and of induced velocities from a unity strength pulsing source: $\omega = 4.43\,\text{rad/s}$, $h = 1.0\,\text{m}$, $z = 0.0\,\text{m}$, $z' = 0.1\,\text{m}$.

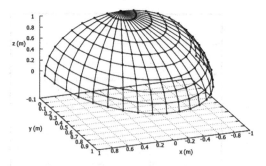

Figure 3. Quadrilateral panels over a hemisphere.

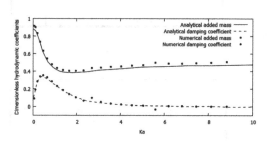

Figure 4. Dimensionless hydrodynamic coefficients for a hemisphere in heave.

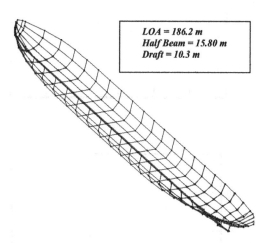

Figure 5. Quadrilateral panels over the ship hull.

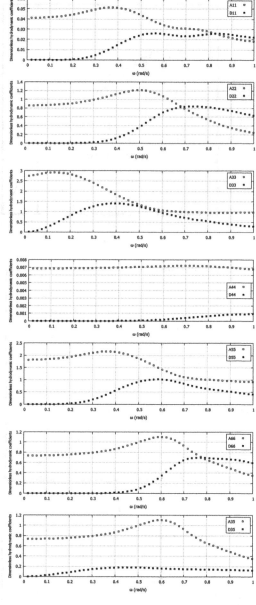

Figure 6. Hydrodynamic coefficients for the KVLCC2 ship hull.

ACKNOWLEDGMENTS

The work was partially performed within the NAVAD project "Simulation of manoeuvrability of ships in adverse weather conditions" which is co-funded under contract 02/SAICT/032037/2017 by the European Regional Development Fund (Fundo Europeu de Desenvolvimento Regional - FEDER) and by the Portuguese Foundation for Science and Technology (Fundação para a Ciência e a Tecnologia - FCT). Most of work related to conversion of the FinGreen function was performed by the third author supported by the ERASMUS programme.

This work contributes to the Strategic Research Plan of the Centre for Marine Technology and Ocean Engineering (CENTEC), which is financed by the Portuguese

Foundation for Science and Technology (Fundação para a Ciência e Tecnologia - FCT) under contract UIDB/UIDP/00134/2020.

REFERENCES

Bingham, H.B. & Korsmeyer, F.T. 1994. The simulation of ship motions. In: *6th International Conference of Numerical Ship Hydrodynamics:* 561. Iowa: National Academy Press.

Hess, J.L. & Smith, A.M.O. 1964. Calculation of nonlifting potential flow about arbitrary three-dimensional bodies. *Journal of Ship Research Research* 8(4): 22–44.

Hulme, A. 1982. The wave forces acting on a floating hemisphere undergoing forced periodic oscillations. *Journal of Fluid Mechanics*. 121(57):443–463.

Jafaryeganeh, H. & Guedes Soares C. 2016. Comparison of two approaches for prediction of wave induced loads in damaged ships. In: Guedes Soares C, A.P. Teixeira, editors. *Maritime Transportation Harvest Sea Resources:* 473–481. Vol. 1. London: Taylor & Francis Group.

Jafaryeganeh, H., Rodrigues, J.M. & Guedes Soares C. 2015. Influence of mesh refinement on the motions predicted by a panel code. In: Guedes Soares C, Santos TA, editors. *Maritime Technology Engineering:* 1029–1038. London: Taylor & Francis Group.

John, F. 1950. On the motion of floating bodies II. Simple harmonic motions. *Communications on Pure and Applied Mathematics*.3(1):45–101.

Lee, C.H. 1995. WAMIT theory manual, *Massachusets Institute of Technology, Report* No. 95-2.

Liu, Y., Iwashita, H. & Hu C. 2015. A calculation method for finite depth Free-Surface Green function. *International Journal of Naval Architecture and Ocean Engineering*. 7(2):375–389.

Nakos, D.E., Nestegard. A., ULstein. T. & Sclavounos, P.D. 1991. Seakeeping analysis of surface effect ships. *FAST 91 Conference*. Trondheim.

Newman, J.N. 1979. The Theory of Ship Motions. *Advances in Applied Mechanics*. 18(C):221–283.

Newman, J.N. 1985. Algorithms for the free-surface Green function. *Journal of Engineering Mathematics*. 19 (1):57–67.

Newman, J.N. 1992. Panel methods in marine hydrodynamics. *In: 11th Australian Fluid Mechanics Conference:* 123–129, University of Tasmani, Harbart Australia.

Newman, J.N. & Sklavounos P.D. 1986. User manual for FINGREEN, Massachusets Institute of Technology.

Press, W.H., Teukolsky, S.A., Vetterling, W.T. & Flannery B.P. 1992. Numerical recipes in C, Cambridge University Press.

Sutulo, S. & Guedes Soares C. 2016. Parametric study of a modified panel method in application to the ship-to-ship hydrodynamic interaction, *Proceedings 4th MASHCON: International Conference on Ship Manoeuvring in Shallow and Confined Water:* 177–185, Hamburg, Germany.

Sutulo, S., Guedes Soares C. & Otzen, J. 2012. Validation of potential-flow estimation of interaction forces acting upon ship hulls in parallel motion, *Journal of Ship Research*, 56(3): 129–145.

Wehausen, J.V. & Laitone, E.V. 1960. Surface waves. Berlin: Springer.

Xia, J., Wang, Z. & Jensen, J.J. 1998. Non-linear wave loads and ship responses by a time-domain strip theory. *Marine Structures*. 11(3):101–123.

Yeung, R.W.C. 1973. A singularity distribution method for free-surface flow problems with an oscillating body, *PhD Thesis*, University of California, Berkeley.

An operational investigation of wave slamming detection

J.C. Bossau & A. Bekker
Stellenbosch University, Stellenbosch, South Africa

ABSTRACT: The SA Agulhas II is a polar supply and research vessel. The extended transom design predisposes the vessel to stern slamming. A systematic operational study was conducted to detect the wave slamming encountered whilst the relative direction at which waves approach the vessel was regulated in different ocean conditions. With a focus on specific case studies, associated with the dedicated open water maneuvers, slamming events are extracted from the full-scale acceleration time signals using three different signal-processing techniques. The hypothetical slam impact location and corresponding peak acceleration value are investigated. It is shown that stern slamming gives rise to higher vibration levels. Moreover, the slamming severity increases with following waves and waves that approach the vessel from the aft quarter, since the slamming count per minute as well as the magnitude of slamming is recorded to be higher for such instances.

1 INTRODUCTION

Full-scale, long-term measurements of ship responses on polar research vessels, in combination with measurements of the environmental conditions encountered, present an opportunity to influence future ship design and aid operational decision-making (Bekker et al. 2018b, Erikstad 2018). Reliably detecting slamming can validate which conditions humans perceive to be worse for slamming and objectively quantify the slamming severity. This paper provides insight into the operational conditions that contribute to excessive slamming as well as the vibration response of the vessel due to wave impacts.

1.1 Slamming and whipping

Wave slamming is described as sudden, high amplitude acceleration forces, due to waves impacting the stern, bow or hull bottom for a short period of time (Kapsenberg 2011). Wave slamming produces an impulsive signal with a high acceleration amplitude at the time of impact. The response to an impulsive event is experienced throughout the vessel structure as large oscillations, which diminish over time. The global transient vibration response of the vessel is called whipping (Dessi 2014).

Slamming is a random, non-stationary and non-linear event, which is known to cause damage to ships. The global response results in the vessel being subject to large shearing forces and bending moments. The local response of the exterior of the vessel, which is subject to repeated impacts, results in localized buckling and plastic deformation (Constantinescu et al. n.d., Henry & Bailey 1970). The location of impact on the vessel structure is used to classify slamming as bottom slamming, bow-flare slamming, breaking wave impacts and wet-deck slamming (Bertram 2012). Stern slamming, in combination with whipping induced vertical bending moments leads to structural fatigue and increases maintenance and repair costs (Henry & Bailey 1970).

1.2 The SA Agulhas II

The SA Agulhas II (SAA II) is a Polar Supply and Research Vessel (PSRV), which operates in Antarctica and the Southern Ocean. The main vessel specifications are conveyed in Table 1. The vessel was designed to navigate in pack ice as well as in open water. The SAA II has a PC-5 ice rating, which enables it to operate in medium first year ice (0.7 to 1.2 m thick) that may contain old ice inclusions year-round (International Association of Classification Societies 2016). The vessel has a raised, flat, extended transom design at the stern. This creates additional deck space for cargo storage or installing scientific container laboratories. The raised, flat stern aids the maneuverability of the vessel in ice and minimizes propeller ice impacts by providing ample propeller clearance (Omer & Bekker 2016). Bow slamming is expected, to a certain degree, in head seas for ships with ice-going hull shapes, due to the increased bow flare angle required for successful ice passage (Kapsenberg 2011). However, the SAA II is pre-disposed to problematic stern slamming. Vessels with flat aft designs and comparatively small immersion often experience stern slamming, even with wave heights less than 1m (Carlton & Vlašić 2005).

DOI: 10.1201/9781003216599-28

Table 1. SAA II specifications (van Zijl & Bekker 2018).

Gross tonnage	12 897 tons
Length	134 m
Breadth	22 m
Motor speed at MCR*	140 rpm
Motor power at MCR *	4500 kW
Nominal torque	307 kNm

* MCR - Mean Continuous Rating

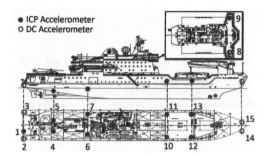

Figure 1. Layout of sensors used for slamming identification.

Previous research on the SAA II has shown that vibration caused by wave slamming has a significant impact on human factors such as sleep, damage to equipment, interference with motor skills and research activities. Moreover, the effects of slamming are exacerbated when the vessel is held stationary during oceanographic activities (Omer 2016). Stern slamming, in contrast to bow slamming, often occurs less frequently as the ship speed increases. The ship's entrained wave system increases at higher speeds and interrupts the environmental wave system, which protects the aft hull (Carlton & Vlašić 2005).

2 FULL SCALE MEASUREMENTS

Real-time ship vibration responses, due to wave slamming, were recorded on board the SAA II during the Southern oCean seAsonaL Experiment (SCALE) winter and spring cruises in 2019. Accelerometers were placed throughout the vessel structure and vertical acceleration measurements from five DC and ten ICP accelerometers, are used in the present analysis. The measurement locations and sensors considered are presented in Table 2 with reference to Figure 1.

An LMS SCADAS master-slave system, in conjunction with LMS Turbine Testing acquisition software, was employed to record data at a sampling frequency of 2048 Hz, with recording lengths of 5 minutes. Fiber optic cables connected the master and slaves through cable trays. The software initiated and stored the continually generated data.

Table 2. Accelerometers used for slamming detection.

Point				
Starboard	Port	Description	Deck	Type
1		Steering Gear	2	ICP
2	3	Steering Gear	2	DC
4	5	Stern Thruster	2	ICP
6	7	Engine store	2	ICP
8	9	Bridge	9	DC, ICP
10	11	Cargo hold aft	3	ICP
12	13	Cargo hold fore	3	ICP
14	15	Bow foxhole	4	DC

The sensors are mounted on structural girders to record the global structural response of the vessel to wave slamming. Sensors were placed close to the expected slamming locations in the stern and bow of the vessel structure. Sensors were additionally placed at regular intervals along the length of the vessel, as close to the waterline as possible (Omer & Bekker 2016). Additionally, two sensors located in the bridge are considered. The operational parameters encountered during both voyages were logged hourly in the bridge, by using the automated meteorological and navigational control systems on board as well as visual observations.

The winter cruise consisted of a 25 day voyage, which took place between 18 July and 12 August. During this cruise a set of open water maneuvers were conducted to regulate the heading and speed of the vessel. The environmental conditions encountered were recorded. The spring cruise comprised of 38 days, from 12 October to 20 November, with more time allocated for dedicated ship maneuvers to be performed in different sea states. During the winter cruise, an additional ICP accelerometer measured the vertical vibration in the starboard steering gear room. Due to module restrictions of the LMS SCADAS Mobile Data Acquisition Units, fewer channels could be connected during the spring cruise. Therefore, it was decided to remove the superfluous measurement location (Point 1). Moreover, during the open water maneuvers performed on 19 October, the portside DC accelerometer (Point 3) was inadvertently disconnected from its power supply by crewmembers. As a result, the vibration response to slamming was not measured for this location during the aforementioned set of maneuvers.

3 SIGNAL PROCESSING TECHNIQUES

Three different methods were used to extract slamming events from the acceleration time signal as illustrated in Figure 2. All three methods aim to extract the peak acceleration amplitude at the time of a wave impact. Figure 2a shows an impulsive signal indicating a slam event, with a high acceleration amplitude at the time of impact, which is followed by transient oscillations known as whipping. The MATLAB function findpeaks is used to extract local maxima in a signal. The minimum peak prominence, a measure of how much the peak protrudes from the rest of the signal due to its relative proximity to other peaks and its inherent height, is set so that only peaks which are considered to be statistical outliers of the signal are extracted. An outlier is defined as a value that is further than three scaled median absolute deviations away from the median value (MathWorks 2017).

Spectrograms and the continuous Morlet wavelet transform, presented in Figure 2b and Figure 2c respectively, show a color plot the signal with combined time and frequency information. Wave slamming results in broadband excitation and excites a range of frequencies, which appears as a vertical line at the time of impact (Omer & Bekker 2016). The whipping presents lower frequency signal content with a smaller magnitude. For longer analysis time periods the impulsive slamming line features are finer and more distinct. These lines can then be detected across higher frequencies due to abrupt changes in pixel brightness.

The frequency domain component of the spectrogram is generated using the short-time Fourier transform (STFT), presented in Equation 1. It applies a window function $\psi(t)$ at time τ, and calculates the Fourier transform of the windowed signal. The parameters w and τ control the modulation and translation of the window function respectively (Kıymıka et al. 2005). To achieve a good time resolution, the frequency resolution needs to be sacrificed due to the fixed time window length (Loughlin et al. 1992).

$$F(w, \tau) = \int_{-\infty}^{\infty} x(t)\psi^*(t-\tau)e^{-jwt}dt \quad (1)$$

The continuous Morlet wavelet transform of a signal is defined in Equation 2, where $WT_x(a,b)$ characterizes the wavelet transforming coefficient derived from the signal. The asterisk, *, denotes a complex conjugate. The mother wavelet is defined as $\psi(t)$. The daughter wavelets $\psi_{a,b}(t)$ are scaled by the factor a, shifted in time by the factor b and compared with the original signal. At instances where the wavelet corresponds to original signal, the transform outputs a higher value. The complex Morlet wavelet function is given in Equation 3. The β parameter controls the geometric shape of the wavelet. A large β is advised for the extraction of impulsive events, as β approaches infinity the function tends to an impulsive function with fine time resolution (Yang & Ren 2004).

$$WT_x(a,b) = \frac{1}{\sqrt{a}} \int_{-\infty}^{\infty} x(t)\psi^* \frac{(t-b)}{a} dt \quad (2)$$

$$\psi(t) = \frac{1}{\sqrt{2\pi}} e^{-\left(\frac{t}{2}\right)\beta^2} e^{j\omega t} \quad (3)$$

However, empirical mode decomposition (EMD) is first used to decompose the signal into its oscillatory modes, called intrinsic mode functions (Huang et al. 1998). The input signal can be represented by Equation 4. The first IMF c_1 is obtained through a sifting process and generally contains the highest frequency component of the signal. The residue r_n contains information of longer period components (Susanto et al. 2018). The continuous Morlet wavelet transform is applied to the first IMF component to generate a clearer image of the high frequency signal content, with more distinct lines which represent slam events.

$$x(t) = \sum_{i=1}^{n} c_i + r_n \quad (4)$$

The image processing and line detection procedure is the same for both spectrogram and Morlet wavelet scalogram images. Bekker et al. (2018a) explores using the Morlet wavelet to detect slamming features presented as vertical lines and presents the procedure and background as a stepwise discussion. A similar procedure is implemented for the present analysis, as summarized in the following three steps:

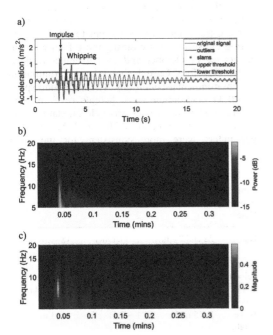

Figure 2. Signal processing techniques used to extract slam events: a) findpeaks, b) spectrogram, c) continuous Morlet wavelet transform.

1. The image is converted to a greyscale intensity image, which is converted to a black and white image.
2. The Hough transform is applied to detect vertical lines (Duda & Hart 1972). The MATLAB function houghpeaks determines peak values in the pixel intensity of binary images, which represent potential lines. The lines associated with the peak values are established using the houghlines function.
3. The peaks detected by the Hough transform are scaled from the image, which consists of pixels, to the original signal in the time domain. The absolute maximum acceleration amplitude of the signal, in the vicinity of the located time interval which corresponds to the pixel width of a detected line, is then extracted.

4 STATIONARY MANEUVRES

4.1 Design for experiment

To investigate the orientation of the vessel and the resulting slamming incidence, a set of open water maneuvers was conducted. Consequently, the vessel was held on station in similar environmental conditions and the relative direction of waves approaching the vessel was regulated. This is demonstrated in Figure 3, where the red arrows labelled A-E indicate different situations, with the waves approaching the vessel at 0°, 45°, 90°, 135° and 180° respectively. Position A indicates head on waves, approaching at the bow. Position E indicates following waves, approaching at the stern.

The ship was kept in a stationary position for 15 minutes at each angle, or the respective mirror image angle (with waves approaching on the portside). This procedure was repeated a total of three times for each angle during the winter and spring cruise for different sea states. However, during the winter cruise no data was recorded for beam waves, which approach the vessel at 90°. Table 3 shows the operational conditions for three different case studies that are considered in the present analysis.

The wave height is defined as the vertical distance between the trough and crest of a wave and is presented in Table 3 as the average range. The wave period is the average time between two successive wave crests that move past a fixed point. The wavelength is defined as the horizontal distance between two successive wave crests and is calculated with Equation 5, which is valid for deep water cases (Bertram 2012, World Meteorological Organization 2010). Where λ represents the wavelength and T_W represents the wave period. The wavelength should be considered with respect to the length of the vessel, which is 134 m. Therefore, the wavelength was generally recorded as being shorter than the vessel length.

$$\lambda = 1.56 T_W^2 \qquad (5)$$

Case 1 consists of the stationary maneuvers conducted throughout the winter cruise. To accommodate the demanding scientific agenda the experiment was conducted on three separate occasions. Case 2 and Case 3 present results recorded during the spring cruise during more focused maneuvers on 19 October and 18 November respectively. Therefore, Case 1 shows large variations in the environmental conditions. The high wind speed of 40 kn and larger wave heights of 5 m were recorded when the vessel was held on station with a relative wave direction of 0° on 4 August. The parameters were more consistent for the other

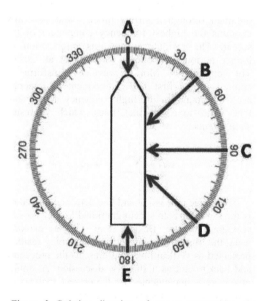

Figure 3. Relative direction of waves approaching the vessel: (A) 0°, (B) 45°, (C) 90°, (D) 135° and (E) 180°.

Table 3. Operational maneuvers.

Case	1	2	3
Dates	22 and 24 July, 4 August	19 October	18 November
Ship velocity	0	0	0
Wind speed	16 – 40 kn	13 – 27 kn	20 – 24 kn
Wave height	2 – 5 m	1 – 2 m	1 – 3 m
Wave period	9 – 12 s	7 s	9 s
Wave length	126 – 225 m	82 m	55 m

angles considered (45°, 135° and 180°), with wind speeds of 16 kn and wave heights between 2 to 3 m. Nevertheless, Case 2 was recorded sequentially over a period of approximately 90 minutes, and during this time the wind speed also increased drastically to 27 kn.

Furthermore, the severity of bow slamming compared to stern slamming is investigated for the different orientations. The hypothesis was that an accelerometer placed closer to the site of an impact would show a peak in the acceleration amplitude at an earlier time compared to the peak recorded by accelerometers placed further away (Bekker et al. 2018a). Identifying the sensor closest to the site of impact will establish whether bow slams or stern slams are more prevalent. Moreover, the peak acceleration amplitudes extracted will reflect the severity of bow and stern slams encountered.

4.2 Results

4.2.1 Site of impact

The three signal processing techniques were applied to the case studies to extract the peak acceleration amplitudes, which correspond to the time of wave slamming events. The data from the 15 accelerometer channels presented in Table 2 is processed for each case and compared. The time of the earliest acceleration peak corresponding to a slamming event was determined across the accelerometer channels to locate the sensor closest to the site of impact. Thus, a single slamming event that is detected across multiple channels is reduced to reflect only one peak acceleration amplitude at the earliest extracted time. A slamming event results in a global vibration response and should be detected by at least two sensors. Therefore, the total number of slams detected across the length of the vessel and the approximate impact location is determined.

Table 4 presents the site of impact extracted by the findpeak, spectrogram and Morlet wavelet methods respectively, for each case study. Table 5 presents the acceleration amplitude extracted from the sensor with the earliest peak in the acceleration-time signal, at the site of impact, for the respective signal processing methods. The port side and starboard side accelerometers are distinguished as left and right of the centerline respectively.

It can be seen in Table 4 that the methods give different results for the site of impact. The methods also show slightly different results in Table 5, however the range of acceleration magnitudes extracted at the site of impact for the different methods is very similar. Therefore, the three methods concur for the magnitude of slams extracted, but differ in determining the frequency of slamming occurrences.

With reference to Table 4, on average more stern slams are detected than bow slams. The corresponding acceleration amplitude extracted is also much higher at the stern, as shown in Table 5. The largest acceleration values occur at location 2 under the transom, close to the hull transition at the stern. This is where waves rush in under the hull as the hull structure emerges and re-enters the water. This corroborates the fact that the SAA II is predisposed to stern slamming. With waves approaching the vessel at a relative angle of 45°, 90° and 135°, higher acceleration amplitudes typically appear to be extracted at the stern, on the side of the approaching waves (port or starboard). The exception to this is Case 3, with waves approaching at a relative angle of 45°. For Case 2, only the sensors between the bow and the stern thrusters, location 8 and 3 respectively, should be considered for this, due to the portside stern accelerometer being switched off during the maneuvers.

4.2.2 Observed and extracted slams

Observers, situated in the bridge during the maneuvers, noted how often slamming was encountered. A slam event was identified by observers experiencing the global response of the vessel structure following an impulsive event, which is often felt as vibrations that propagate throughout the vessel structure, and is known as whipping. Figure 4 shows the total number of slams detected per minute by an observer as well as the total number of slams extracted per minute across the length of the vessel by the spectrogram, Morlet wavelet and findpeak methods respectively. Therefore, it presents the sum of the number of slams recorded across all sensors in Table 4 as an average

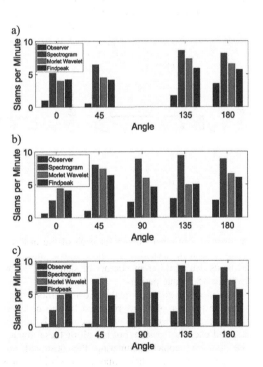

Figure 4. Number of slams detected per minute for a) case 1, b) case 2 and c) case 3, at each of the angles representing the relative direction of approaching waves.

Table 4. Number of slams extracted per minute at the site of impact for a period of 15 minutes.

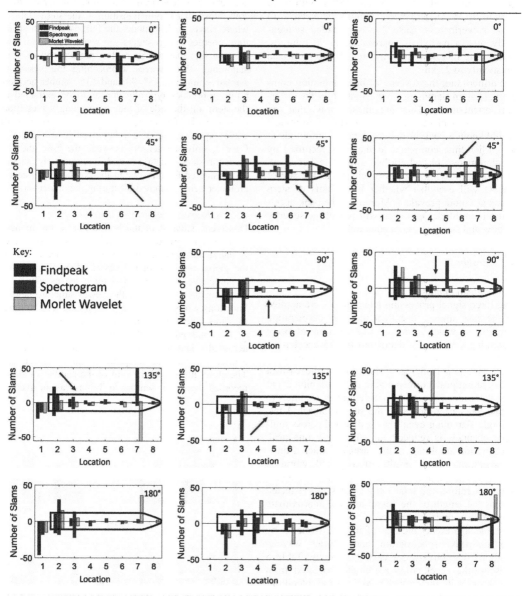

number of slams per minute for each of the different cases. It can be seen that the three signal processing methods extract different number of slamming events over the 15-minute periods.

Additionally, all three methods extract more slams than the number of slams recorded by the observer. This is expected because waves are constantly impacting and exciting the ship, but not all of these impacts are felt by people. Comparing the observed and extracted slams can help find a threshold, below which people do not experience slams. Observers reported that slamming could occur as often as 5 times per minute, whereas the spectrogram method extracted up to 9 slams per minute. The maximum number of slams recorded by the Morlet wavelet and findpeak methods were 8 and 6 slams per minute, respectively.

For Case 1 and Case 3, shown in Figure 4a and Figure 4c respectively, the three methods follow a similar trend to the observed slam rating. The following results are true for both cases. The largest number of slams is extracted for waves approaching at 135°, which is succeeded by 180°. However, the largest number of observed slams is recorded at 180°. Moreover, the lowest number of slams is recorded for waves approaching at 0° and 45° respectively, using the spectrogram and Morlet wavelet methods.

Table 5. Absolute peak acceleration amplitude at the site of impact extracted for a period of 15 minutes.

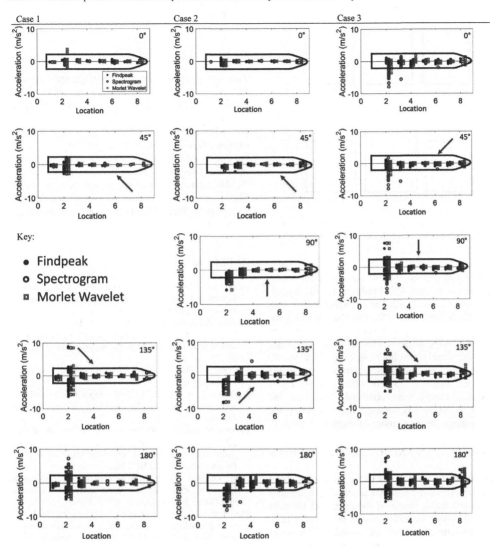

However, the findpeak method extracted a slightly lower number of slams at 45° than at 0°, which is more in accordance with the observed slam rating.

For Case 2, presented in Figure 4b, all three methods and the observed number of slams coincide for the lowest number of slams recorded with waves approaching at 0°. The observer and the spectrogram method detect the largest number of slams at a relative angle of 135°. However, the Morlet wavelet and findpeak method incorrectly detect a large number of slams at a relative angle of 45°. The second highest number of slams extracted by all three methods is for waves approaching at 180°.

Figure 5a presents a summary of the total number of slams extracted by the different methods, as presented in Figure 4. The average of the extracted peak acceleration amplitudes was determined for each accelerometer channel and the channel with the maximum mean value is presented in Figure 5b for each method. The different signal processing techniques are presented in Figure 5 from left to right as the spectrogram, Morlet wavelet and findpeak methods respectively for each case. As stated earlier, the methods show similar results for the number of slams encountered for each case. The number of slams does generally follow the same trend of fewer slams detected with head on waves and more slams detected with following waves and waves approaching the vessel from the aft quarter, with a few exceptions.

By comparing Figure 5a and Figure 5b, the figures indicate that the frequency and magnitude of slams generally show similar results. The magnitude of

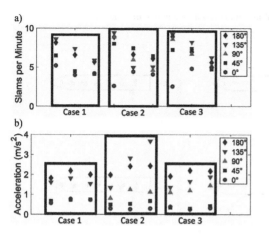

Figure 5. Extracted a) frequency and b) maximum average magnitude of slamming events for the different methods.

slams is recorded to be significantly lower for waves approaching at 0° and 45°. Furthermore, the magnitude of slamming is recorded to be higher with waves approaching at 180° and 135°. For Case 1 and 3 the magnitude of slamming was shown to be dominant for a relative wave angle of 180°. Moreover, in Case 2 the Morlet wavelet and findpeak methods were able to extract the largest acceleration amplitudes for the relative wave angle of 135°, for which a high number of slamming events were observed. Therefore, the magnitude of slams encountered may influence the observer ratings for the number of slams that are felt.

5 CONCLUSIONS AND RECOMMENDATIONS

Due to the large discrepancies in the number of slams extracted by the different signal processing techniques it is proposed that a threshold should be set for each sensor so that only slamming events with higher peak acceleration amplitudes may be considered for slamming detection. This may help to better correlate the number of extracted slams to the number of observed slams.

Nevertheless, the results concur that the frequency and magnitude of slamming is perceived to be higher for following waves and waves approaching the vessel from the aft quarter. The number of slams extracted by the three signal processing techniques, and the corresponding acceleration amplitudes corroborates these results. Moreover, on average more stern slams are detected than bow slams and the corresponding acceleration amplitude extracted is much higher at the stern.

Furthermore, full-scale measurements on future expeditions can further monitor the structural response of the vessel and provide insight into the operational conditions that contribute to excessive slamming. This can aid decision making to mitigate the occurrence of slamming by altering the ship speed and heading. Future research will investigate open water maneuvers where the vessel operates at different velocities.

ACKNOWLEDGEMENTS

The authors gratefully acknowledge the support of the National Research Foundation (NRF), grant number 110737, and Department of Science and Technology under the South African National Antarctic Programme for financial assistance. Opinions expressed and conclusions arrived at, are those of the author and are not necessarily to be attributed to the NRF. Moreover, the authors would like to thank the Department of Environmental Affairs, African Marine Solutions, Captain K. Bengu and the crewmembers for their collaboration in the measurements on board the SAA II.

REFERENCES

Bekker, A., Van Zijl, C.M. & Saunders, C.F.W. 2018a. The detection of wave slamming from vibration measurements on a polar supply and research vessel.

Bekker, A., Suominen, M., Kujala, P., De Waal, R.J.O. & Soal, K.I. 2018b. From data to insight for a polar supply and research vessel. Ship Technology Research. 66(1): 57–73.

Bertram, V. (2nd ed.) 2012. Practical ship hydrodynamics. Oxford: Elsevier.

Carlton, J.S. & Vlašić, D. 2005. Ship vibration and noise: some topical aspects. *1st Int. Conf. on Ship Noise and Vibration*

Constantinescu, A., Alaoui, A., Nême, A. & Rigo, P. (2011). Numerical and experimental studies of simple geometries in slamming. Int. J. of Offshore and Polar Engineering. 21(3): 216–224.

Dessi, D. 2014. Whipping-based criterion for the identification of slamming events. *Int. J. of Naval Architecture and Ocean Engineering*. 6: 1082–1095.

Devleker, K. n.d. Understanding wavelets. [Online], Available: https://www.mathworks.com/videos/series/understanding-wavelets-121287.html [2019, December 07].

Duda, R. O. & Hart, P. E. 1972. Use of the Hough Transformation to detect lines and curves in pictures. Communications of the Association for Computing Machinery. 15(1): 11–15.

Erikstad, S.O. 2018. Designing ship digital services. 458–469.

Henry, J.R. & Bailey, F.C. 1970. Slamming of ships: a critical review of the current state of knowledge.

Huang, N., Zheng, Q. & Tung, C. 1998. The empirical mode decomposition and the Hilbert spectrum for nonlinear and non-stationary time series analysis. *Proc. of the Royal Society A Mathematical Physical and Engineering Sciences*.

International Association of Classification Societies. 2016. Requirements concerning polar class.

Kapsenberg, G.K. 2011. Slamming of ships: where are we now? *Philos. Trans. of the Royal Society* 369: 2892–2919.

Kıymıka, M.K., Güler, İ., Dizibüyük, A. & Akın, M. 2005. Comparison of STFT and wavelet transform methods in determining epileptic seizure activity in EEG signals for real-time application. Computers in Biology and Medicine. 35:603–616.

Loughlin, P.J., Pitton, J.W. & Atlas, L.E. 1992. Proper time-frequency energy distributions and the Heisenberg uncertainty principle. *Proc. IEEE-SP Int. Symp. on Time-Frequency and Time-Scale Analysis.* 6–9.

MathWorks. 2017. isoutlier. [Online], Available: https://www.mathworks.com/help/matlab/ref/isoutlier.html [2019, December 04].

Omer, H. 2016. The impact of wave slamming induced vibration on human factors and equipment on-board the S.A. Agulhas II. Stellenbosch University.

Susanto, A., Liu, C.H., Yamada, K., Hwang, Y.R., Tanaka, R. & Sekiya, K. 2018. Application of Hilbert–Huang transform for vibration signal analysis in end-milling. Precision Engineering. 53:263–277.

Yang, W.X. & Ren, X.M. 2004. Detecting impulses in mechanical signals by wavelets. *EURASIP J. on Applied Signal Processing.* 1156–1162

Van Zijl, C.M. & Bekker, A. 2018. Variations in vibration responses of an ice-going vessel during wave slamming. 31stConf. on Condition Monitoring and Diagnostic Engineering Management. 1–9.

World Meteorological Organization. 2010. Guide to meteorological instruments and methods of observation. Geneva

The measurement and analysis of human comfort as a result of wave slamming on an ice-going vessel

M. Engelbrecht, A. Bekker & J. Muiyser
Department of Mechanical and Mechatronic Engineering, Stellenbosch University, Stellenbosch, Western Cape, South Africa

ABSTRACT: Ships are designed to operate in harsh conditions, during voyages that can last up to several months. During which passengers are confined to the ship. Consequently, human comfort needs to play a vital role in ship design. However, knowledge in this field is limited in research surrounding human comfort, especially impulsive wave slamming, which is the random impact of waves against the ship hull. The study aims to identify human activities that are most disrupted due to slamming and to statistically determine which metric according to ISO 2631-1 is the most suitable in quantifying human response. Data was obtained by correlating daily surveys of passenger experiences to human vibration metrics from on-board measurements. Results show that sleeping was the activity most affected. There was a strong correlation between the root-mean-square value and 'daily slam rating' as well as 'discomfort incidences' and a moderate correlation with reports of 'sleep disturbance'.

1 INTRODUCTION

There has been an increase in navigation in ice infested waters which result in scientific research (Oceanography expeditions) and tourism voyages (Bekker et al. 2017). Crew, researchers and passengers are exposed to constant random vibration and noise at all times, including hours of relaxation and sleep, which repeatedly persist during the entire voyage (Gibbons et al. 1975). Calhoun (2006) claim that the random long-term low-intensity vibration exposure disrupts the human sleep pattern and sleeping cycles which is the effect of the human body when experiencing a constant random state of aggravation. When human sleep patterns and sleeping cycles are disrupted it degrades the required sleep to prevent fatigue, resulting in a decline in productivity and alertness (Calhoun 2006).

Whole-body vibration (WBV) in the occupational environment is important in sectors involving human exposure to vibration and are expected to encourage improvements in the health of the exposed workers (Directive 2002/44/EC of the European Parliament 2002). Health risk assessment limits for an 8-hour working day are defined in the Directive 2002/44/ECof the European Parliament (2002). However it is stated that in case of sea transport it is not possible to comply in all circumstances with the exposure limit values of WBV (Directive 2002/44/EC of the European Parliament, 2002). The International Association of Classification Societies (IACS) only consider the polar class descriptions, application, structural requirements and machinery requirements for steel polar ships and not the health or comfort limits regarding vibration or noise exposure in human environments (International Association of Classification Societies, 2011). While ISO standards provide guidelines for the measurement of vibration due to on-board machinery during sea trials. The sea state must be smaller than 3 and do not include external vibration sources such as wave and ice loads (BS ISO 20283-5:2016).

During recent years researchers have been gathering knowledge on this topic. A previous study by Bekker et al. (2017) observed that occupants are exposed to a degree of perceivable vibration levels due to slamming and ice for most time during a voyage, and are likely to experience vibration levels that are considered 'not uncomfortable'. Due to high crest factors it was concluded that the root-mean-square ($r.m.s.$) metric is not a robust method of quantifying in-service shipborne vibration (Bekker et al. 2017) Considering that vibration levels have been noted as 'not uncomfortable' there still have been complaints about vibration interference with sleep, research, equipment use and equipment damage on the SA Agulhas II (Omer & Bekker 2018). Which leads to research question: How does wave slamming induced vibration affect comfort, sleep and task performance?

Omer & Bekker (2018) investigated this during a 75 day summer voyage between Cape Town and Antarctica. Full-scale vibration measurements were performed and wave slamming events were subsequently identified (Omer & Bekker 2018). Vibration measurements were conducted on Deck 2 at the stern and on Deck 4 at the bow. Slamming events were identified based on the assumption that the crest factor is a likely indicator of slamming. The authors made a subjective choice by only analysing vibration data with a crest factor of 6 and greater, to exclude minor slamming events. Human responses were gathered through daily diary surveys. The Kendall correlation coefficient were computed by correlating ISO 2631-1 WBV metrics with daily diary responses and concluded that VDV is the best metric to represent human response to slamming. It was also noticed that more than 50% of responses relate to sleep when the daily VDV ranged between 8.0 m/s$^{1.75}$ to 10.0 m/s$^{1.75}$ as measured on Deck 2 at the stern (Omer & Bekker 2018). However, to date the vibration exposure limit where discomfort is experienced and perceived are still unknown. As complaints of activity disturbance and discomfort continue to be received, it was the aim of the authors to do further investigation. This study was performed specifically during winter, when the Southern Ocean is at its roughest, the ice at its thickest and is far more extensive. This results in challenging navigation during winter months and is why most polar ships only travel during summer. This paper aims to determine what activities are most disrupted as a result of wave slamming. This was determined through human feedback via human daily diary surveys. The possibility of applying WBV metrics as defined in ISO 2631-1 to quantify discomfort was investigated by correlating it with full-scale vibration measurements.

2 OCEANOGRAPHY RESEARCH EXPEDITION JUNE/JULY 2017

2.1 The SA Agulhas II

The SA Agulhas II is a polar supply and research vessel (PSRV) built by STX Finland at Rauma shipyard with main dimensions and specifications as provided in Table 1. She is Polar Class ice rated PC-5 and provides intermediate comfort (COMF-V(2)) according to the Det Norske Veritas (DNV) comfort class notation (Det Norske Veritas 2014). With the capability to accommodate 44 crew members and 100 passengers, along with cargo, bunker oil and helicopter fuel. She is equipped with laboratories, a moon pool and drop keel to perform scientific research in the Southern Ocean on annual research voyages to South African bases on Antarctica, Gough Island and Marion Island. It is reported that the SA Agulhas II is very susceptible and exposed to wave slamming due to its unique design (Omer&Bekker 2018). It has been determined that the flat stern pre-disposes the ship to wave slamming (Omer & Bekker 2016). Therefore, making her the perfect platform to do in situ research on human response and comfort as a result of impulsive wave slamming.

2.2 Full-scale measurements

On 28 June 2017, the SA Agulhas II departed from Cape Town on a 16-day oceanography research voyage in the Southern Ocean to the Antarctic marginal ice zone (MIZ) with 44 crew members and 67 passengers on board. The following coordinates 61°58.1′S 30°16.1′E indicate the turning point of the voyage due to limited time and unfavourable weather conditions.

The comfort class notation of the Norwegian classification society Det Norske Veritas (DNV) and the ship Classification Rules (Det Norske Veritas 2014) made use of guidelines as provided by ISO 6954:2000. To date ISO 2954:2000 have been withdrawn and revised by ISO 20283-5:2016 which was intended for use during sea trials in sea states below 3. With perceived vibration as a result of on-board machinery and not external sources (BS ISO 20283-5:2016). ISO 20283-5:2016 refer to ISO 2631-1 and 2631-2 as bases for the calculating of metrics and frequency weighting respectively. Therefore ISO 2631-1 was selected as the preferred standard to perform the WBV measurements for the voyage (BS ISO 2631-1:1997 1997). Further reasoning is that ISO 2631-1 provides a generic method which includes dealing with impulsive vibration and applies to public transport applications. In accordance to this standard, a basicentric coordinate system is required, which implies an axis system that follows the body. This coordinate system was applied at the location of the acceleration measurements which were measured at the supporting surface of where the vibration was assumed to enter the feet of a passenger.

The WBV comfort measurements comprised of two accelerometers, both ICP accelerometers (100 mV/g, Model: PCB333B32). These ICP accelerometers were calibrated with a SVANTEK mobile vibration calibrator (Model: SV 111) prior to the voyage to obtain the exact sensitivity values. Measurement locations (see Figure 1) were selected to be on the Bridge (permanently occupied because it is the command platform of the vessel) and Deck 4 (next to chef's cabin and close to some of the accommodation areas). Both accelerometers were mounted with super glue on structural girders (in the Bridge

Table 1. Main dimensions and specifications of the SA Agulhas II.

Length (between perpendiculars)	121.8 m
Width	21.7 m
Draught, design	7.65 m
Deadweight at design displacement	5000 t
Speed, service	14.0 kn
Power supply	4 x 3 MW Wartsila diesel generators
Propulsion	2 x 4.5 MW diesel electric Convert Team motors

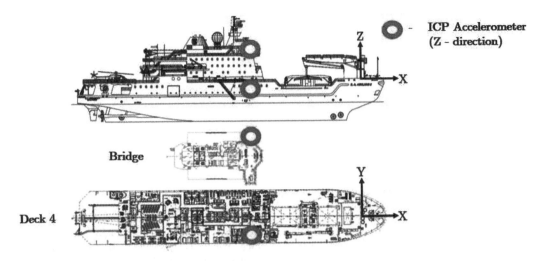

Figure 1. Measurement locations on the SA Agulhas II for Winter Cruise 2017.

to structure under the carpet) on the floor at the respective locations. The floor is flat, rigid and was therefore the reference for vibrations that propagate through the structure. The measurement direction for both ICP accelerometers was selected to be in the vertical direction. This would map to the z-axis for standing or seated vessel occupants since most occupants stand or sit for the largest part of the day. Furthermore, this assumption is based on the results by Bekker (2013) that found the vertical direction to be dominant for most vessel operations in ice and open water (Bekker 2013, Mcmahon 2014).

LMS Test.Lab Turbine Testing software was used as an interface with the LMS SCADAS mobile data acquisition (DAQ) unit to continually record measurements and data was organised in 5-minute files. ISO 2361-1 recommends a measurement duration of 227 seconds for frequencies lower than 0.5 Hz and satisfy the requirement of a 90% confidence level for random stationary signals (BS ISO 2631-1:1997 1997). The structural vibration measurements that form part of a different study was the determining factor for a sample rate of 2048 Hz to avoid aliasing. This sample rate was higher than needed for the present study and did not pose any inconvenience.

2.3 *Surveys - Human response*

Antarctic research institutions and scientists depend on PSRV such as the SA Agulhas II to serve as a mobile laboratory in the Southern Ocean and to supply goods to the research bases on Antarctica which is one of the worlds most remote places. Research from this region offers conclusive and alarming evidence that the world's climate is changing rapidly, and the need for continuous monitoring is thus critical (Skelton et al. 2017). These passengers are often scientists and land-based personnel and are not natural sea born, they work in laboratories, and they use the vessel to get to remote locations and islands to do the required research and construction work.

Polar vessels are exposed to different open water and a variety of ice conditions which excites the ship. Due to this random impact of different excitation mechanisms, it is difficult to determine the effect of it on human health and comfort. Therefore, surveys are implemented to provide further insight into subjective human perceptions of comfort, thus using humans as sensors. Although frequency weighted filters are applied to measurements to compensate for human sensitivity to different frequencies of vibration. It is still necessary to use human feedback to develop methods for quantifying human comfort as a result of impulsive vibration.

At the start of the voyage, a short presentation was delivered to inform passengers about the issue of wave slamming, and everyone that was willing to participate in the daily diary survey received a booklet. The booklets were distributed to 43 willing participants. Figure 2 illustrate the daily diary entry from the survey booklet which is similar to the survey used by (Omer & Bekker 2018). The objective of the questions in the survey was to determine: how often slamming was encountered; the rating of the worst slamming incident; activities disturbed by slamming (sleeping, typing/writing, visual tasks, equipment use, equipment damage) and whether slamming was perceived to be uncomfortable.

2.4 *Methodology and analysis*

Figure 3 illustrate the methodology and analysis that were followed to generate the objective and subjective data. The continuously recorded vibration data are stored in 5-minute files. The 5-minute acceleration time signal recordings from the Bridge and Deck 4

Encountered slamming	No			Occasionally				Regularly		
Worst slamming incident rating (1 = nothing, 3 = slight, 10 = severe)	1	2	3	4	5	6	7	8	9	10
Activity/equipment affected by slamming (tick the appropriate boxes)	No			Typing/writing				Visual tasks (reading/TV)		
	Equipment Use			Equip. Damage				Sleeping		
Did you find slamming to be uncomfortable?	Yes			No						
Comments:										

Figure 2. An example from the booklet of the daily diary questions for Winter Cruise 2017.

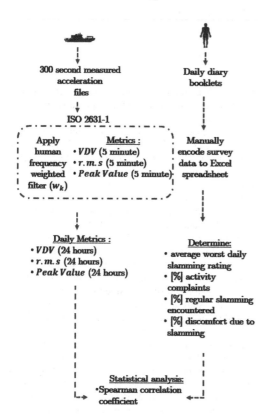

Figure 3. A diagram explaining the methodology and analysis of the objective and subjective data.

frequency weighted acceleration, $a_w(t)$, as shown in Eq 1. Where, T, represent the duration, which is 300 seconds in this case. The *r.m.s.* will increase if the number of slams increase in a 5-minute measurement.

$$a_w = [\frac{1}{T}\int_0^T a_w(t)^2 dt]^{\frac{1}{2}} \quad [m/s^2] \quad (1)$$

It has been shown that cumulative measures have a more reliable means of quantifying vibration severity and are applicable to single shocks or mixtures of shocks and vibration or to different types of vibration in a period of a day (Griffin 1990). The vibration dose value (VDV). The vibration dose value (VDV) is a method of such a cumulative measure and provides a way of quantifying WBV for shock or transient shock and vibration. The VDV can be calculated as shown in Eq 2.

$$VDV = [\int_0^T a_w(t)^4 dt]^{\frac{1}{4}} \quad [m/s^{1.75}] \quad (2)$$

The *Peak value* is the best to capture the magnitude of the most severe slamming incident in a 5-minute measurement and can be obtained by using Eq 3.

$$Peak\ value = max|a_w(t)| \quad [m/s^2] \quad (3)$$

The Spearman correlation coefficient was used in order to evaluate how well these metrics quantify the human response to wave slamming. There was a difference in the resolution of the objective response and the resolution of the subjective response. The human response rate has a time resolution of 24 hours consequently these metrics were transformed to a daily (24 hour) resolution. Thus, the daily *r.m.s.*, *VDV* and *Peak value* (both

were frequency-weighted, in the z-direction by applying the w_k human frequency weighted filter for vertical (BS ISO 2631-1:1997 1997). The frequency weighting was performed in the time domain by implementing the methodology as recommended by Rimell and Mansfield (2007).

Subsequently, the weighted root-mean-square (*r.m.s.*) acceleration, a_w, was calculated for each 5-minutes measurement by using the instantaneous calculated from 00:00 to 24:00) were computed according to Eq 1, 2 and 3 as expressed in ISO 2631-1.

The human response surveys were manually encoded by using MS Excel spreadsheets. During the encoding of the daily diary surveys it was observed that some participants did not complete the surveys or individual questions on a daily basis. Therefore, the sample size changed per question on a specific day and daily during the voyage.

The following assumption was made during the analysis of the vibration data: Since the ship was navigating in the marginal ice zone (MIZ), which is semi ice conditions with thin ice and large polynyas (large open water patches) with swells, all vibration data were assumed to be as a result of slamming. Thin ice will not cause a lot of vibrations. The complete 5-minute vibration signal files were analysed, the magnitude of each slamming event was not extracted and solely applied to the WBV metrics. This simplification was done since it is complicated to extract the slam as well as the whipping, which is the rapid propagation of vibration through the ship structure a result of impulsive wave impact on the hull. Both the slamming and whipping are therefore considered since it is not just the initial slamming magnitude that will cause discomfort but also the vibration that propagates through the structure.

3 RESULTS

The daily *r.m.s.* and *VDV* at the two measurement locations are represented in Figures 4 and 5. Average *r.m.s.* and *VDV* values were recorded in the Bridge (0.14 m/s^2, 4.63 $m/s^{1.75}$) and Deck 4 (0.10 m/s^2, 3.57 $m/s^{1.75}$). The following maximum *r.m.s.* and *VDV* values were measured in the Bridge (0.26 m/s^2, 8.70 $m/s^{1.75}$) and Deck 4 (0.20 m/s^2, 6.59 $m/s^{1.75}$) respectively.

Figure 6 illustrate the average of the daily slam ratings with a 95% confidence interval superimposed with box plots representing participants individual daily slam ratings. Each box plot show the distribution of participants individual slam ratings for a day during the voyage. Neither the average nor the

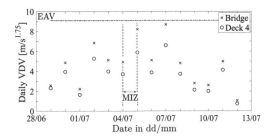

Figure 5. Daily weighted VDV during Winter Cruise 2017.

median (Q2) reach a value below 3 excluding the last day of the voyage which can be as a result of a calmer sea state close to the port. The median (Q2) clearly indicate that the ratings are not always symmetric around the median which is an indication that the subjective data is not normally distributed.

Figure 7 portray the different reported activity disturbances that participants encountered with a 95% binomial confidence interval. It is shown that sleeping was the activity most disturbed.

The percentage of participants that experienced discomfort are illustrated in Figure 7 with a 95% binomial confidence interval. It is revealed that on one specific day 56.76% of participants felt uncomfortable by the slamming induced vibration and on average 29.67% during the duration of the voyage.

Figure 8 display the Spearman correlation coefficients of VDV, *r.m.s.* and *Peak value* at different locations on the ship with respect to the subjective response from participants. The box plots in Figure 6 illustrate that the individual daily slam rating distribution of the participants have outliers and is skew. Therefore, the Spearman correlation is the preferred correlation method since it is more robust to skewness and outliers (Field et al, 2016).

4 DISCUSSION

Figures 4 and 5 show that vibration levels are higher in the Bridge than on Deck 4. ISO 2631-1 states that a weighted *r.m.s.* value of less than 0.315 m/s^2 is perceive to be 'not uncomfortable' (BS ISO 2631-1:1997). It is observed that the weighted *r.m.s.* during the entire duration of the voyage did not exceed this approximated value as given in ISO 2631-1, yet on average 29.67% of passengers indicated that slamming, which is an impulsive transient nature of vibration caused them to feel uncomfortable. A maximum VDV of 8.70 $m/s^{1.75}$ as recorded in the Bridge is near the exposure action value (EAV) of 9.1 $m/s^{1.75}$ as defined in the Directive 2002/44/EC of the European Parliament. The EAV is an indication that measures must be enforced to reduce the vibration exposure to occupants (Directive 2002/44/EC of the European Parliament 2002).

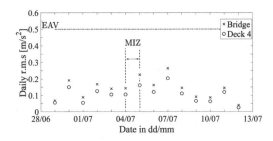

Figure 4. Daily weighted *r.m.s.* during Winter Cruise 2017.

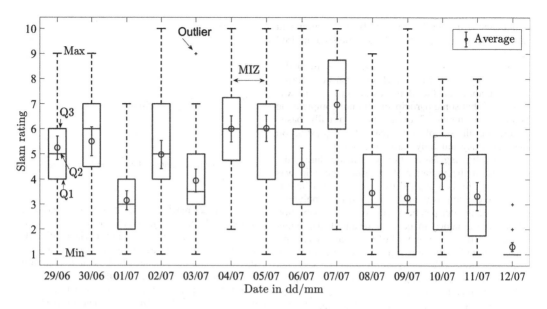

Figure 6. Average daily slam rating and the box plots of individual participant daily slam ratings during Winter Cruise 2017.

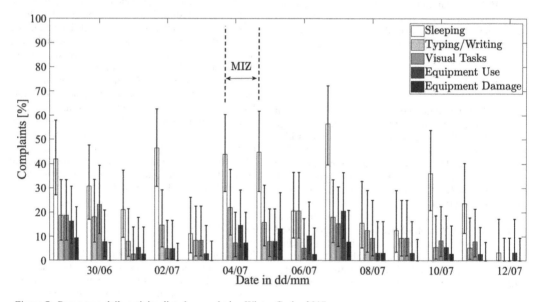

Figure 7. Percentage daily activity disturbances during Winter Cruise 2017.

A varying width of the daily average slam rating confidence interval in Figure 4 can be observed. This can be due to numerous reasons such as: The sample size changes every day and it is not the same participants daily meaning the sample population changes, thus causing more variability.

Sleeping is the activity with the most reported complaints, with an average disturbance of 29.14% for the voyage. On 7 July 2017, both the subjective responses (slam rating, activity disturbance and discomfort incidences) and the objective metrics reached maximum values when compared to the other days of the voyage. This was attributed by an open water storm.

Correlations with Deck 4 vibration measurements give a stronger correlation than the Bridge. This can be due to passengers not spending any time in the Bridge, but rather Deck 4, since it is close to the accommodation and living areas where participants spent relaxation and rest time. The Bridge might

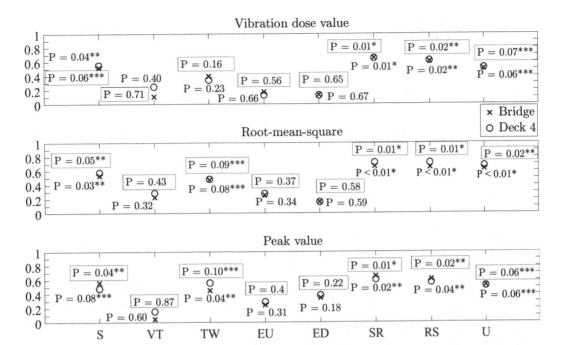

Figure 8. Spearman correlation coefficient - The P-value with the frame (Bridge) and no frame (Deck 4) (*P ≤ 0.01, **P ≤ 0.05 and ***P ≤ 0.1) The following letters represent S-Sleeping, VT-Visual tasks, TW-Typing or writing, EU - Equipment use, ED- Equipment damage, SR-Slam rating, RS-Regular slamming and U-Uncomfortable.

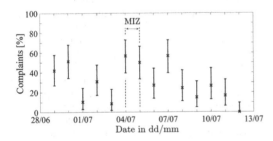

Figure 9. Percentage daily uncomfortable complaints (with a 95% binomial confidence interval) during Winter Cruise 2017.

give better results if the crew were to participate in the surveys. This will be useful when investigating activity disturbance in an operational environment of the crew.

Incidences of regular slamming events have a strong positive linear relationship with the *r.m.s.* (0.71, P ≤ 0.01) and moderate with *VDV* (0.61, P <0.05).

The *r.m.s.* has a 0.70 (P <0.01) correlation coefficient compared to *VDV* (0.64, P ≤ 0.01) and *Peak value* (0.61, P <0.05) which would be better at quantifying slam ratings and possibly the severity of daily slamming as experienced by passengers. There is not a noticeable difference in the correlation coefficient between *VDV* at the two different locations. Only the *r.m.s.* and peak value correlation coefficient changes with location in this case. Which might make *VDV* location independent as a quantifying metric.

Passenger discomfort have a moderate relationship with *r.m.s.* (0.669, ≤ 0.01), *Peak value* (0.515, <0.1) and *VDV* (0.495, <0.1). Location seem to play an important role in the correlation coefficient with the *r.m.s.* value.

When evaluating activity disturbance, sleep disturbance has a moderate positive linear relationship with *r.m.s.* (0.578, P <0.05) and *VDV* (0.552, P <0.05). Sleep disturbance can be quantified by both *r.m.s* and *VDV* since the correlation is similar. Both the VDV and *r.m.s.* correlation changes with location. Visual tasks, equipment use and equipment damage have correlation coefficients of lower than 0.5 for all metrics being investigated. Thus, having a weak linear relationship with the metrics under evaluation. This can be because there was no measurement location in the laboratories where participant would be performing these tasks. Typing and/or writing have a moderate correlation of 0.559 (P <0.05) with the *Peak value*. The correlation of the *Peak value* changes with location.

5 CONCLUSIONS

It is revealed that sleeping is the activity most disturbed by slamming and is similar to what Omer & Bekker (2018) observed. Sleeping is a very important activity that nobody can go without, humans cannot function optimally especially the crew, and it can have catastrophic consequences.

The Spearman correlation indicate that *r.m.s.* show potential as a quantifying metric for regular slamming encounters, slam rating, discomfort associated with slamming and sleep disturbance. The Peak value can be used as a quantifying metric for typing and writing disturbance incidences. This finding does not agree with Omer & Bekker (2018) which concluded that the daily *VDV* presents the strongest correlation for average daily slam ratings of 0.538 and it is a promising metric to represent human response to slamming – this can be due to a number of reasons: A different measurement location on Deck 2 at the stern of the ship were used for the correlation; only recordings with crest factors exceeding 6 were considered. For this study the crest factor criterion were not implemented since it would not be possible to differentiate between a crest factor of 6 in open water and in the MIZ, therefore all the data was used. Omer & Bekker (2018) computed the Kendall correlation coefficient between the subjective responses and objective measurement, reasons for this particular correlation method were not provided. Different assumptions might have been implemented during the encoding of the surveys. For example in this study it can be seen that the median is more robust than the average slam rating. The reasoning for this is that the outliers can change the average very easily while the median will be unchanged.

Bekker, Soal, & McMahon (2017) reasoned that *r.m.s.* is not a robust method of quantifying in-service ship borne vibration. This assumption was made by applying ISO 2631-1 and noticing that *r.m.s.* falls within the basic evaluation method for WBV and since the crest factor was high the additional method should be used which recommended the use of *VDV*. This conclusion was made by comparing the measured values to what is specified in ISO 2631-1 and not by correlation actual human response to the measured vibration. It is thus important to keep in mind that the ISO 2631-1 serves as an approximate indication of human reactions to different levels in WBV and is not specific to human comfort in the shipping industry but it is the best possible starting point in trying to understand human-wave and human-ice response on-board ships.

VDV is not omitted since it shows some likelihood as a quantifying metric for sleep disturbance because the correlation coefficients were very similar to *r.m.s.*. The correlation coefficient of *VDV* does not change a lot with location. The accommodation area such as the measurement location on Deck 4 has a stronger correlation with human responses. This could be because that section is always occupied by most passengers and since passengers are not allowed in the Bridge, only crew and officers. Location where the measurements are conducted play an important role because it need to be in close proximity to where passengers spent their time.

It would be advisable to duplicate all methods from previous SA Agulhas II studies on the current data, since all researchers have different methods and assumptions when doing the encoding of the subjective responses. An interesting case study would be to see how the correlation coefficient would change when the median slam rating are used instead of the average. However, this does not imply that the data from this study cannot be used. Figure 4 shows that on 12 July 2017 and 7 July 2017 when vibration levels were at its lowest and highest respectively all subjective responses matched the lowest and highest as well, indicating some matching trends. When participants experience slamming as indicated by the increase in the average daily slamming rating. Figure 4 show that the confidence band gets larger indicating that passengers are responding differently to the vibrations demonstrating that individual perception is very much present, thus causing more variability in the data. In theory the 95% confidence interval imply that any passengers on this ship during a winter voyage should give responses within these band. Due to different weather conditions and human perception results might change with voyage and population.

From this research, it can be concluded that sleeping is the activity most affected during a voyage and knowing that slamming is contributing to it in one form or the other. Whether it is the impulsive sound, impulsive initial vibration or the after effect of the slamming event call whipping. With regards to finding a suitable metric to quantify human comfort more studies will have to be conducted. In which the sample size of the subjective response should be increase the as well as having voyages during different seasons. This study serves as a stepping stone to do vibration measurements on a ship and be able to have human comfort metrics at hand that can be used to get a sense of the comfort and activity disturbance passengers would typically experience. The shipping industry can benefit by measuring vibration at strategic locations on a vessel. By implementing human comfort metrics in a digital service, the captain can get an instantaneous indication of passenger comfort on a specific route and adjust the route accordingly to ensure maximum passenger comfort.

ACKNOWLEDGEMENTS

The authors would like to thank the South African Department of Environmental Affairs (DEA), the crew and officers of the SA Agulhas II represented by African Marine Solutions (AMSOL) for their hospitality and allowing us to perform measurement on their ship, the National Research Foundation (NRF) and the South African National Antarctic Programme (SANAP) for their support in this research. Opinions expressed and conclusions arrived at, are those of the authors and not necessarily to be attributed to the NRF. (ORCID: 0000-0003-4498-0867)

REFERENCES

Bekker, A. (2013). Whole-body vibration comfort on the bridge of the S.A. Agulhas II polar supply and research vessel during ice-breaking. Number September, pp. 16–18.

Bekker, A., K. I. Soal, & K. J. McMahon (2017). Whole-body vibration exposure on board a Polar Supply and Research Vessel in open water and in ice. *Cold Regions Science and Technology 141*, 188–200.

BS ISO 20283-5:2016. BS ISO 20283-5:2016.

BS ISO 2631-1:1997 (1997). Mechanical vibration and shock - Evaluation of human exposure to whole body vibration Part 1: General Requirements.

Calhoun, S. R. (2006). Human Factors in Ship Design: Preventing and Reducing Shipboard Operator Fatigue. Technical report, University of Michigan, United States.

Det Norske Veritas (2014). Comfort Class.

Directive 2002/44/EC of the European Parliament (2002). Directive 2002/44/EC of the European Parliament and of the Council of 25 June 2002 on the minimum health and safety requirements regarding the exposure of workers to the risks arising from physical agents (vibration).

Gibbons, S. L., A. B. Lewis, & P. Lord (1975). Noise and Vibration on Board Ship. *Journal of Sound and Vibration 43*, 253–261.

Griffin, M. (1990). *Handbook of human vibration*. London: Elsevier Academic Press.

Mcmahon, K. (2014). *Whole-body vibration comfort measurement aboard the S.A. Agulhas II and just noticeable difference threshold testing in the laboratory*. Ph. D. thesis.

Omer, H. & A. Bekker (2016). Detection of wave slamming sites from ship deflections. *Research and Development Journal of South Africa 32*(October), 50–57.

Omer, H. & A. Bekker (2018). Human responses to wave slamming vibration on a polar supply and research vessel. *Applied Ergonomics 67*(September), 71–82.

Rimell, A. N. & N. J. Mansfield (2007). Design of Digital Filters for Frequency Weightings Required for Risk Assessments of Workers Exposed to Vibration. *Industrial Health 45*(4), 512–519.

Skelton, P., D. Butterworth, P. Cilliers, J. Cooper, D. A. Cowan, & R. Dorrington (2017). Exploring South Africa 's southern frontier: A 20-year vision for polar research through the South African National Antarctic Programme. *South African Journal of Science 113*(5), 1–7.

Experimental and numerical investigations of whipping responses of a 20,000TEU ultra large container carrier

Q.D. Feng & L.J. Wen
China Ship Scientific Research Center, Wuxi, China

J.M. Wu
Marine Design and Research Institute of China, Shanghai, China

S. Wang & C. Guedes Soares
Centre for Marine Technology and Ocean Engineering (CENTEC), Instituto Superior Técnico, Universidade de Lisboa, Lisbon, Portugal

ABSTRACT: An accurate determination of global load effects in a ship is vital for the design of the vessel. A ship sailing in severe sea conditions will not only experience large amplitude motions but also suffer nonlinear wave loads including whipping and green water. The coupling effects of several kinds of nonlinear wave loads, especially whipping, may make the hull produce high-frequency and large-amplitude moments and forces, which threaten the safety of ships' structure. Based on a newly designed 20,000 TEU ultra large container ship, the whipping responses of the ship hull subjected to regular waves are analyzed experimentally and numerically in this paper. Model tests of a flexible 20,000TEU containership have been carried out in the seakeeping tank at China Ship Scientific Center, to assess nonlinear wave load on the hull subjected to several regular and irregular sea states. Whipping responses of the hull are predicted using a 2D body nonlinear time domain code based on the potential theory. Some features of whipping loads are discussed by comparing the numerical and experimental results.

1 INTRODUCTION

The container carriers have been built in larger and large size with the strong commercial demand in recent years and the largest ones have the capacity of more than 23,000 TEU. However, the huge hulls tend to be more flexible and show the characteristic of elasticity in severe sea states and its big opening structure feature makes the vertical and torsional wave loads easier to have hydroelastic effects. Besides, the ultra large container carriers usually own obvious bow flares and flat stern bottoms, and slamming often happen in these areas and whipping phenomenon is triggered then.

Whipping, which is related to the hull's structure stiffness, hydrodynamic surface forms and encountering sea states could make the wave loads becomes much larger in a very short time. Moreover, severe whipping is able to thread the structure's ultimate strength and contribute to the fatigue problem. As a result, whipping is the one of the most important problems in developing the ultra large container carriers. ISSC and ITTC formed a joint work group in 2014 aimed at studying ultra large ships' hydroelasticity issues.

The nonlinear wave loads problem has been one of research hotspots in academic and industrial sector and research has been carried out in recent years, such as Wu & Cui (2009), Malenia (2012), Watanabe & Guedes Soares (1999) and Wang (1996), Fonseca and Guedes Soares (1998, 2004), Rajendran et al. (2015, 2016a) and Rajendran and Guedes Soares (2016), with increasing demands for huge-size and high-speed ships whose structure is more likely to be threatened by whipping problem. Some of them applied the hydroelastic theory, considering the coupling effects of elasticity effect and wave loads, which is able to predict the motion and structure deformation. Rajendran and Guedes Soares (2016) performed a study by analysing predictions of nonlinear and nonlinear time-domain computer codes for determining the vertical wave-induced bending moment in a containership in waves of different steepness. Rajendran et al. (2015, 2016a) have concluded that the body nonlinear radiation forces, which is associated with the geometry of ships, plays a significant role in the estimation of the vertical bending moment amidships for ships with large bow flare angle, like containerships.

Model tests were carried out by many researchers using different hull girders to investigate the whipping effects on hydroelastic responses of ships. Zhu et al. (2011) and Zhu and Moan (2014) used flexible joints to connect four rigid segments in the 13000-TEU model. Kim et al. (2014), Houtani et al. (2018), Jiao et al. (2018) and Lin et al. (2020) designed the U shape backbone to consider the warp effects of open section.

Based on a newly designed 20,000 TEU ultra large container ship, the VBM amidships in regular waves are analyzed experimentally, as described in this paper. Whipping responses of the hull are predicted by a 2D nonlinear code based on the potential theory in time domain. Some features of whipping loads are discussed by comparing the numerical and experimental results. The main objective of this paper is to study the springing and whipping effects on vertical bending moment of the ultra large container ship, and the simulation results could be verified by the model test carried out in CSSRC. Meanwhile, the phenomenon and characteristics of multiple frequencies in hull's wave loads can be analyzed based on the experimental measurement and numerical calculations.

2 MODEL TEST

Flexible Model tests of a 20,000TEU container carrier's hull girder's whipping loads including several regular and irregular wave cases have been recently carried out in the seakeeping tank of China Ship Scientific Center (CSSRC) with a model scale of 1:77 in the April of 2019. The basin is 69m long, 4m deep and its width is 46m. Two wave generators are arranged at the long and short side of the basin and oblique waves can be generated by both sides.

The ship model is 5.2m long, 0.76m wide and its displacement is 555kg. The model hull's wave loads in large amplitude wave were measured in several cases with varied speeds, wave height and directions. Main particulars of the model are showed in Table 1 and cross sections are showed in Figure 1. Table 2 lists the test's regular sea states considered in this study.

The ship model is installed with an electrically driven motor and propelled by a propeller and the navigation direction is automatically controlled by a rudder linked with a steering engine, which is operated by software. Figure 2 shows the model in the basin.

Table 1. Main particulars of the 20000TEU container carrier.

Parameters	Full scale	Model scale
Loa (m)	400.0	5.20
Lpp (m)	386.0	5.01
Breath (m)	58.6	0.76
Depth (m)	35.4	0.46
Draft (m)	15.9	0.21
Displacement (t)	259630.6	0.56

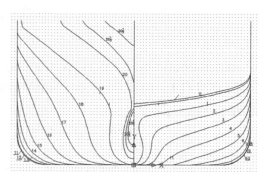

Figure 1. Body plan of the 20000TEU container carrier.

Table 2. Regular sea states considered in this study.

Regular sea states β=180°

Case	Speed (Kn)	H(m) Model scale	Prototype	λ/L
B01	20	0.156	12	0.6,0.8,1.0,1.1,1,1.4
B02	20	0.117	9	0.6,0.8,1.0,1.1,1,1.4

Figure 2. Model of the 20000TEU container carrier in regular waves.

3 NUMERICAL APPROACH

Fonseca and Guedes Soares (1998) calculated nonlinear ship responses using a partially nonlinear time domain code based on strip theory. Rajendran et al. (2016c) improved the method and calculated the rigid body response of a cruise vessel in large amplitude waves and extreme irregular seas by taking account of the geometrical nonlinearity of the wetted hull.

This method was further extended by Rajendran et al. (2016b), to analyze the hydroelastic load acting on an ULCS in severe head seas. The hull structural characteristics are represented by a Timoshenko beam and the global mass and stiffness matrix are calculated using the finite element method. The modal analysis is carried out to calculate the structural natural frequency and the modal matrix. The hydrodynamic and hydrostatic forces were calculated at each time step taking account of the geometrical nonlinearity of the wetted hull. The radiation forces were represented by convolution of the memory functions. Similar formulations are used in this paper for calculation of the VMB of the 20,000TEU container carrier in regular waves due to springing and whipping. Detailed mathematical formulations can be found in Rajendran et al. (2015). Here, the fundamental equations will be presented briefly.

A coordinate system fixed with respect to mean position of the ship is defined for the hydrodynamic problem. The origin is in the plane of the undisturbed free surface. Considering a ship advancing in waves and oscillating as an unrestrained rigid body, the oscillatory motions will consist of three translations and three rotations.

The equation of motion of a structure can be expressed as:

$$[M]\{\ddot{u}\} + [B]\{\dot{u}\} + [K]\{u\} = \{F(x,t)\} \quad (1)$$

where $[M]$=the mass matrix, $[B]$=the damping matrix, $[K]$=stiffness matrix, $\{u\}$=displacement vector, $\{F(x,t)\}$=distributed forced on the ship wet surface. According to the principle of modal superposition, which is valid for linear responses, the distortion of structure can be expressed as a sum of the distortion in the principal modes:

$$u(x,y,z,t) = \sum_{r=0}^{m}\{u_r(x,z,y)\}p_r(t) = [D]\{p\} \quad (2)$$

where $p_r(t)$=the principal coordinate response, u_r=r th principal mode, $[D]$= modal matrix. Eq. (1) can be expressed as below using the principal coordinate response to describe the motion responses of a hydroelastic floating ship:

$$[m]\{\ddot{p}\} + [b]\{\dot{p}\} + [k]\{p\} = \{F_k(t)\} \quad (3)$$

where $[m]$= generalized mass, $[b]$= generalized damping matrix, $[k]$= generalized stiffness matrix, $\{F_k(t)\}$ is the hydrodynamic force vector, which is given as:

$$\{F_k\} = \{F_k^R\} + \{F_k^{FK}\} + \{F_k^D\} + \{F_k^H\} + \{F_k^{GW}\} + \{F_k^{slam}\} \quad (4)$$

where $\{F_k^R\}$ is radiation force, $\{F_k^{FK}\}$ is Froude-Krylov, $\{F_k^D\}$ is diffraction force, $\{F_k^H\}$ is restoring forces, $\{F_k^{GW}\}$ is green water forces, and $\{F_k^{slam}\}$ is slamming forces.

In this study, slamming force is calculated based on 'momentum' equations:

$$F_k^{Slam}(x,t) = \int_L f^{slam} w_k(x) dx \quad (5)$$

$$f^{slam} = \frac{(x)Dw_{rel}}{\partial t}\frac{Dw_{rel}}{Dt} - U\frac{(x)}{\partial x}\frac{Dw_{rel}}{Dt} \quad (6)$$

The vertical force per unit length due to presence of green water is given by:

$$F_k^{GW}(x,t) = \int_L F^{gw} u_k dx \quad (7)$$

$$F^{gw}(x,t) = (\frac{\partial m_{gw}}{dt})w + (g\cos\xi_5 + \frac{\partial w}{dt})m_{gw} \quad (8)$$

where w=velocity of the deck, m_{gw}=the mass the water on the deck, The second term denotes the hydrostatic component and the third term denotes the acceleration of the deck.

4 RESULTS AND DISCUSSION

4.1 Hull modal analysis

As whipping response is a harmonic vibration of the hull, it is very important that the model is able to simulate the real ship's harmonic vibration. Natural frequency of vertical vibration was measured by hammering the hull girder in the still water. The time-domain curve of the stress signal is showed in Figure 3 and frequency-domain curve is showed in Figure 4 by Fast Fourier Transformation (FFT) method. The comparison of results is showed in Table 3. The tested 1st and 2nd vertical natural frequencies are 3.7 Hz and 8.3 Hz, while the numerical simulation results are 3.6 Hz and 8.12Hz.

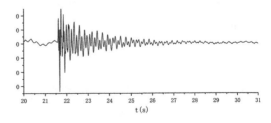

Figure 3. Time-domain of stress of hull girder by hammering.

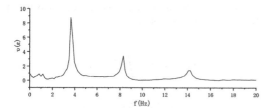

Figure 4. Vertical vibration in frequency domain.

Table 3. Comparison of numerical and tested natural frequency of vertical vibration.

Natural frequency of vertical vibration	Numerical (Hz)	Model test (Hz)	Error (%)
1st order	3.6	3.7	2.7
2nd order	8.1	8.3	2.4

4.2 Model test's results

Whipping is triggered by the slamming phenomenon which is usually observed in severe sea states (Wang and Guedes Soares, 2017). The obvious process of slamming happened in these regular waves as shown in Figure 5-7. The bow of the hull meets the wave crest and then it comes out the water due to the arrival of the wave trough, and finally the bottom of the bow hits the water.

Only bow slamming was observed in the initial tests, which contrasts with the tests of a chemical tanker where bow and stern slamming were identified (Wang and Guedes Soares 2016a,b).

Figure 8 shows the time-recording signal of wave height and VBM midship in case B01. The wavelength

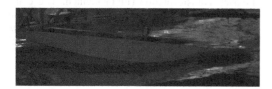

Figure 5. Stage1: Bow into the wave.

Figure 6. Stage2: Bow out the wave.

Figure 7. Stage3: The occurrence of slamming.

is about 5m, which equals the ship length. It is clearly observed that sagging VBM is larger than hogging VBM. The average hogging peak is 15KN.cm while the average sagging peak is 31KN.cm in model scale. Figure 9 presents the separated components of the whole wave loads, where "CM", "WM" and "HM" present combined wave loads, low-frequency component, and nonlinear high-frequency component of wave loads, respectively. Nonlinear high-frequency component, which is mainly caused by slamming accounts for a large proportion in the whole wave loads and the results of spectrum of VBM in Figure 10 also imply this phenomenon.

Figures 11-13 illustrates the measured results of case B02, where the wave height is 9m. Similar to the consequences of B01, whipping phenomenon of

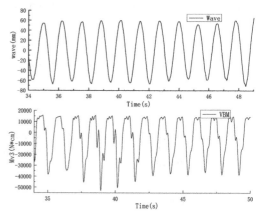

Figure 8. Measured VBM midship in heading sea in case B01 (wave height=12m in full scale), sagging VBM is larger than hogging VBM.

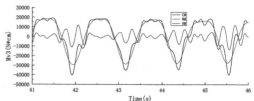

Figure 9. Separated VBM midship in heading sea in case B01 (wave height=12m in full scale), obvious whipping responses are captured.

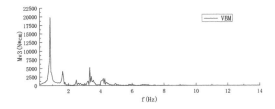

Figure 10. Measured VBM midship spectrum in heading sea in case B01(wave height=12m in full scale).

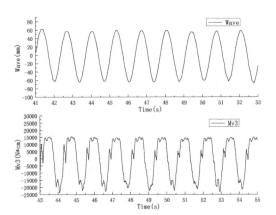

Figure 11. Measured VBM midship in heading sea in case B02 (wave height=9m in full scale).

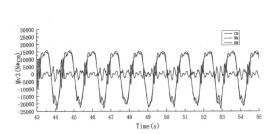

Figure 12. Separated VBM midship in heading sea in case B02 (wave height=9m in full scale).

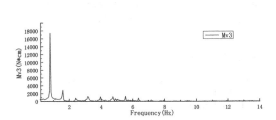

Figure 13. Measured VBM midship spectrum in heading sea in case B02 (wave height=9m in full scale).

the VBM is clear and high-frequency wave loads of first-order harmonic responses are relatively large. The ratio of sagging VBM to hogging VBM equals 1.47 which is lower than that of case B02. It reveals that whipping responses are more important in severe sea states and the proportion of high-frequency wave loads will change with the wave amplitude.

4.3 Comparisons of measured and calculated wave loads

For the 20,000 TEU ultra large container ship, non-linear hydroelastic VBM response in steep regular waves is calculated by the body nonlinear time domain solution mentioned above. This section shows comparison of some results of VBM in both time and frequency domain. It can be found that calculation results reflect the nonlinear feature of wave loads quite well when the hull is in the steep wave.

Figures 14-15 show the comparison of results in case 1 when the wave height is 12m in full scale. Calculation and tests' results are generally agreed. Both time serial results show the asymmetry of the amplitude of hogging and sagging VBM. In the comparison of response spectra, calculation result presents the similar peak distribution in frequency domain. The first order harmonic responses are smaller compared with the amplitude of wave exciting loads.

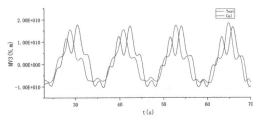

Figure 14. Comparison of time series of VBM midship in heading sea between calculation's and tests' results in Case1 (H=12m, λ/L=1.1). The red line represents the numerical results and the black line represents the test's results.

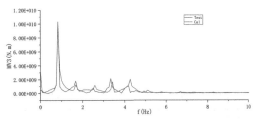

Figure 15. Comparison of response spectra of VBM midship in heading sea in Case 1 (H=12m, λ/L=1.1). The red line represents the numerical results and the black line represents the test's results.

Comparison of results in case 2 is demonstrated in Figures 16-19. The results agree generally well except some small differences. The numerical results indicate that the linear component agrees better with experimental measurements than nonlinear components. It seems that the deviation is cause by the vibration damping which is hard to determine in simulation.

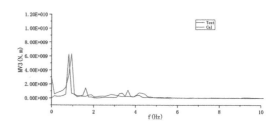

Figure 19. Comparison of response spectra of VBM midship in heading sea in Case 2 (H=9m, λ/L=0.8).

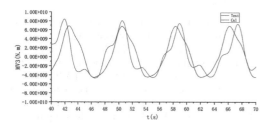

Figure 16. Comparison of time series of VBM between calculation's and tests' results in Case 2(H=9m, λ/L =0.6).

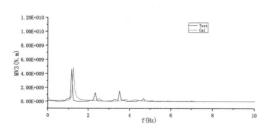

Figure 17. Comparison of response spectra of VBM midship in heading sea in Case 2 (H=9m, λ/L=0.6).

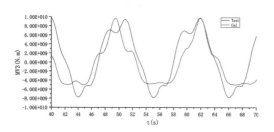

Figure 18. Comparison of time series of VBM between calculation's and tests' results in Case 2(H=9m, λ/L =0.8).

5 CONCLUSIONS

This paper describes the model tests and numerical calculation for the whipping responses of a newly designed 20,000 TEU ultra large container ship. Based on the work, some conclusions can be drawn:

a) As the huge hull's size, the whipping responses of the model of 20,000 TEU ultra large container ship are clearly observed in head sea. With contributions of slamming, the amplitude of sagging VBM is larger than that of hogging VBM.
b) Tests' spectrum results of VBM show that first order and second-order harmonics responses contribute the total wave loads and the second-order components are unobvious.
c) Compared with test results, numerical results' linear component which is the linear wave load agrees with tests better than nonlinear components in frequency domain.

This study is limited to the hull's responses in head sea and oblique waves are suggested to be added in the further work. In addition, it is recommended to further study the effects of hull's vibration damping, which contributes to accuracy of nonlinear wave loads.

ACKNOWLEDGEMENTS

The tests were carried out in the seakeeping tank in China Ship Research Center in Wuxi and gratitude is expressed to those colleagues there for their technical supports and managements. The authors also acknowledge the financial support from Ministry of industry and information technology of China.

REFERENCES

Fonseca, N., Guedes Soares, C., 1998. Time-domain analysis of large-amplitude vertical ship motions and wave loads. J. Ship Res.42 (2), 139–153.

Fonseca, N., Guedes Soares, C., 2004. Validation of a time-domain strip method to calculate the motions and loads on a fast monohull. Appl. Ocean Res. 26, 256–273.

Houtani, H., Komoriyama, Y., Matsui, S., Oka, M., Sawada, H., Tanaka, Y., & Tanizawa, K. (2018). Designing a Hydro-Structural Ship Model to Experimentally Measure its Vertical Bending and Torsional Vibrations. Journal of Advanced Research in Ocean Engineering, 4 (4),174–184.

Jiao, J., Yu, H., Chen, C., & Ren, H. (2019). Time-domain numerical and segmented model experimental study on ship hydroelastic responses and whipping loads in harsh irregular seaways. Ocean Engineering, 185, 59–81.

Kim B.W., Kim K.H., 2014. Torsional Moment Conversion Methods in Model Test With U-shape Backbone. Proceeding of the 24th International Ocean and Polar Engineering Conference. Busan Korea.

Lin, Y., Ma, N., Gu, X., Wang, D. (2020). Experimental study on the asymmetric impact loads and hydroelastic responses of a very large container ship. International Journal of Naval Architecture and Ocean Engineering, 12, 226–240.

Rajendran S., Fonseca N., Guedes Soares C. 2015. Simplified body nonlinear time domai
n calculation of vertical ship motions and wave loads in large amplitude waves, Ocean Engineering, 107, 157–177.

Rajendran, S., Fonseca, N., Guedes Soares, C., 2016a. Body nonlinear time domain calculation of vertical ship responses in extreme seas using a 2nd order Froude–Krylov pressure. Appl. Ocean Res. 54, 39–52.

Rajendran, S.; Fonseca, N., and Guedes Soares, C. 2016b; A numerical investigation of the flexible vertical response of an Ultra Large Containership in high seas compared with experiments. Ocean Engineering. 122:293–310.

Rajendran, S.; Fonseca, N., and Guedes Soares, C. 2016c; Prediction of extreme motions and vertical bending moments on a cruise ship and comparison with experimental data. Ocean Engineering. 127:368–386

Rajendran S., Guedes Soares C. 2016. Numerical investigation of the vertical response of a containership in large amplitude waves, Ocean Engineering,123,440–451.

Wang D.Y. 1996. Three-dimensional hydroelastic analysis of ship in time domain. Ph.D Thesis, China Ship Scientific Research Center, Wuxi, China.

Wang, S. and Guedes Soares, C. 2016a. Experimental and numerical study of the slamming load on the bow of a chemical tanker in irregular waves. Ocean Engineering. 111:369–383.

Wang, S. and Guedes Soares, C. 2016b. Stern slamming of a chemical tanker in irregular head waves. Ocean Engineering. 122:322–332.

Wang, S. and Guedes Soares, C. 2017. Review of ship slamming loads and responses. Journal of Marine Science and Application. 16(4):427–445.

Watanabe, I. and Guedes Soares, C. 1999. Comparative Study on Time Domain Analysis of Non-Linear Ship Motions and Loads. Marine Structures. 12(3):153–170.

Wu Y.S., Cui W.C. 2012. Advances in the three-dimensional hydroelasticity of ships. Special Issue on Fluid-structure, Journal of Engineering for the Maritime Environment, 226 (2).

Zhu S.J., Wu M.K., Moan T., 2011.Experimental and Numerical Study of Wave-Induced Load Effects of Open Ships in Oblique Seas.55,100–123.

Zhu, S.J., Moan, T., 2014. Nonlinear effects from wave-induced maximum vertical bending moment on a flexible ultra-large containership model in severe head and oblique seas. Marine Structures, 35, 1–25.

Improvement of ship hulls for comfort in passenger vessels

J. Gil Rosa, Shan Wang & C. Guedes Soares
Centre for Marine Technology and Ocean Engineering (CENTEC), Instituto Superior Tecnico, Universidade de Lisboa, Lisbon, Portugal

ABSTRACT: In this work the comfort of two different passenger vessels is improved by minimizing the Overall Motion Sickness Index (OMSI). Various hull transformations are considered for both vessels to investigate their influence on passenger's comfort. These are categorized into two groups: geometric and hull from transformations. The transformations are performed using MaxSurf Modeler developed by Bentley systems, based on the Lackenby Method. Seakeeping analysis is performed for each new hull using an in-house strip theory code, accounting for various heading angles and a specific operating scenario described by the JONSWAP Spectrum. The improved hulls based on the study of OMSI are compared to their parent hulls regarding their RAOs plots. A similar comparison is performed regarding the absolute vertical accelerations, at strategic locations on the main deck and the hull resistance. Finally, the improved hull forms are compared to their parent hulls regarding their operability index based on comfort criteria.

1 INTRODUCTION

For naval architects it is crucial to consider the performance of a ship, at an early design stage. One of its parameters is the seakeeping performance, which has been widely used since the development of practical strip theories. From which different tools can be used to check and optimize a certain ship's operability, regarding its motions as an example.

The seakeeping qualities depend not only on the expected seaway, but also on the ship's mission, that is, the type of service and topology. Particularly in passenger or cargo vessels the wellness and comfort on board, crew and passengers safety are the primary elements to be optimized. These qualities become even more important for passengers ships, when considering the collateral effect of seakeeping, the seasickness. These ship motions increase the amount of energy required form the crew. In addition it increases the level of fatigue and drowsiness on passengers, particularly in long journeys. It becomes a defining factor for certain passenger ships and ferries, where passengers can opt between different types of transportation. In terms of comfort, the seasickness produced by the ship's motion also effects the earnings obtained aboard the ship, since nauseate passengers are less likely to show interest on the extra services, such as shops, restaurants, etc. When it comes to safety, seasickness and motions also have harmful effects, particularly in emergency situations. In such conditions both crew and costumers have worsened performances. Even though seakeeping qualities are not the only leading aspect on the design process, it is reasonable to work on possible improvements, despite certain fixed parameters. On passengers ships seakeeping optimization for habitability and operability has been continuously researched in past decades.

Kukner & Sariöz (1995) studied the application of seakeeping analysis into early stages of ship design. A methodology for consistently generate new hull forms, based on Lackenby Method (Lackenby 1950) was proposed. This work was further investigated by Özüm et al. (2011). Cepowski (2010) studied the influence of variations in form coefficients, on the seakeeping behaviour of a passenger-car ferry. Scamardella & Piscopo (2013) used parametric modelling to generate several hull forms, that were used to compare the differences in passenger comfort level, on passenger ship, at various locations and sea-sates. Overall Motion Sickness Index (OMSI) was introduced as the parameter to be minimized in this optimization procedures. More recently Belga et al. (2018) optimized the hull form of a catamaran based on the Motion Sickness Index (MSI), to operate for an offshore platform at the Alentejo basin. The objective of the present work is to optimize hulls from passenger ships for comfort. Overall Motion Sickness Index (OMSI) studied along the main deck was used as a parameter to be minimized in the optimization procedure. OMSI is an average value of Motion Sickness Index (MSI) that is based on absolute vertical accelerations. These are calculated for multiple locations along the deck, for different headings and sea-state. Two different passenger ships are considered (SHIP1 and SHIP2) accounting for both their operating scenario (Operating Scenario 1 and Operating Scenario 2) respectively. SHIP1 is design to operate on

DOI: 10.1201/9781003216599-31

calm conditions, such as river and coastal waters. SHIP2 is to operate on ocean conditions. Various alternative hulls have been generated based on these parent ships. These derived hulls are obtained based on geometric and hull form transformations. The geometric transformations consist on the variation of the length at waterline L_WL and the breath at waterline B_WL. Hull form transformations are obtained using the Lackenby Method (Lackenby 1950), where some hull form parameters such as the block coefficient (C_B), the midship section coefficient C_M) and the longitudinal center of buoyancy (LCB) position are varied. In order to compare the effect of each transformation on the seakeeping performance the Froude number of each parent ship is kept constant regarding the parent hull. Various headings are considered based on the probability distribution. The significant wave height and zero-crossing periods, based on a statistical analysis of the seaway are also considered in order to calculate OMSI. A hull resistance analysis is performed to all hull variations. The optimized hulls are finally compared to the parent hull regarding response amplitude operators (RAOs) peak, absolute vertical accelerations at relevant locations along the deck and on their operability index.

2 BACKGROUND

2.1 Wave spectra theory

The formulation for the wave spectrum here presented is based on *MAXSURF* Motions user manual (Bentley Systems 2017a) and is a generalised spectrum formulation used by DNV, based on JONSWAP spectrum original developed by the Joint North Sea Wave Project. This spectrum has been widely used in the offshore industry and was seen as suitable to be used in the work. In the formulation presented $H_{1/3}$ corresponds to the wave height and T_P is the peak period. The spectrum is defined as follows:

$$1S_\zeta(\omega_0) = \frac{\alpha}{\omega_0} e^{\frac{-\beta}{\omega_0^4}} \gamma^{e^{-\frac{1}{2\sigma^2}\left[\frac{\omega_0}{\omega_p}-1\right]^2}} \quad (1)$$

where,

$$1\alpha = 5\pi^4(1 - 0.287\ln(\gamma))\frac{H_{\frac{1}{3}}^2}{T_p^4} \quad (2)$$

$$\beta = \frac{20\pi^4}{T_p^4} \quad (3)$$

$$\gamma = 5.0 \quad for \quad \frac{T_p}{\sqrt{H_{\frac{1}{3}}}} \leq 3.6$$

$$\gamma = e^{5.75 - \frac{1.15 T_p}{\sqrt{H_{\frac{1}{3}}}}} \quad for \quad 3.6 < \frac{T_p}{\sqrt{H_{\frac{1}{3}}}} \leq 5.0 \quad (4)$$

$$\gamma = 1.0 \quad for \quad 5.0 < \frac{T_p}{\sqrt{H_{\frac{1}{3}}}}$$

$$\sigma = 0.07 \quad for \quad \omega_0 < \omega_p$$
$$\sigma = 0.09 \quad for \quad \omega_0 > \omega_p \quad , \quad 1\omega_p = \frac{2\pi}{T_p} \quad (5)$$

2.2 RMS vertical accelerations

The absolute vertical displacement (ξ_z) at a remote location (x', y',z') is given by Equation (6) assuming motions of generally small amplitude:

$$\xi_z(x',y',\omega) = \Re\{[\xi_3^A(\omega) - x'\xi_5^A(\omega) + y'\xi_4^A(\omega)]e^{i\omega t}\} \quad (6)$$

here ξ_j^A with j = 3,4,5 is the complex amplitude of the harmonic heave, roll and pitch motion, respectively. Let $\omega = \omega\_0$, then the ship vertical responses on a given sea spectrum S_z is given by:

$$S_z(x',y',\omega_0) = |\xi_z(x',y',\omega_0)|^2 S_\zeta(\omega_0) \quad (7)$$

The spectral moment m_{2z} and m_{4z} are given by:

$$m_{2z} = \int_0^\infty \omega_e^2 \cdot S_z(\omega_e) \cdot d\omega_e$$
$$= \int_0^\infty \omega_e^2 \cdot S_z(\omega_0) \cdot d\omega_0 \quad (8)$$

$$m_{4z} = \int_0^\infty \omega_e^4 \cdot S_z(\omega_e) \cdot d\omega_e$$
$$= \int_0^\infty \omega_e^4 \cdot S_z(\omega_0) \cdot d\omega_0 \quad (9)$$

These formulation are proposed by Journée and Massie (2011) as a means to avoid numerical errors for headings from quartering and following seas.

2.3 Motion Sickness Index (MSI)

Many proposals on how to predict motion sickness have been developed over the years, but Motion Sickness Index (MSI) is still one of the most famous and used today. The original model was originally developed by O'Hanlon and McCauley (1974) and it assessed the number of passengers that vomit after two hours. This model was further developed by Mc-Cauley et al. (1976) to include a variable time domain. The formulation here presented to obtain MSI is based on this second iteration of the model and is the same one used by *MAXSURF* Motions (Bentley Systems 2017b). It was described by Colwell (1989) and depends on the average RMS vertical acceleration $|RMSaz|$, the average peak frequency of the vertical motions of the ship $|fe|$ and the voyage time (or period to which MSI is being tested) in minutes (t).

$$MSI\% = 100 \times \Phi(Z_a)\Phi(Z_t) \quad (10)$$

where $\Phi(Z)$ is the standard normal distribution function:

$$\Phi(Z) = \frac{1}{\sqrt{2\pi}} e^{-\frac{z^2}{2}} \quad (11)$$

$$Z_a = 2.128 \log_{10}(a) - 9.277 \log_{10}(f_e) \\ - 5.809[\log_{10}(f_e)]^2 - 1.851 \quad (12)$$

$$Z_t = 1.134 Z_a + 1.989 \log_{10}(t) - 2.904 \quad (13)$$

$$a = \frac{|RMSaz|}{g} = \frac{0.798\sqrt{m_{4z}}}{g} \quad 1|f_e| = \frac{\sqrt{\frac{m_{4z}}{m_{2z}}}}{2\pi} \quad (14)$$

2.4 Overall Motion Sickness Index (OMSI)

On classical seakeeping analysis the procedures to compare the parent hull with ship variation discard the operating scenarios and sea spectra. The classic rule of thumb is selecting the best hull as the one who minimizes heave and pitch RAOs. Head regular waves are usually considered, since they are considered to be the worst case scenario. However it is more reliable, to consider multiple sea-states that the ship may encounter during its life time compared to one single sea-sates. Also considering head seas as the worst case scenario is not always true, since MSI peaks may also occur at transverse headings depending on the wave peak period. Overall Motion Sickness Index (OMSI) developed by Scamardella and Piscopo (2013) was considered as the ideal parameter to be minimized, on ship variations that seek to improve comfort on passenger ships. The optimized hulls are the solutions with smallest values of OMSI. Here MSI is considered on multiple locations along the deck, heading angles and sea states and averaged into a single factor, the OMSI. OMSI is defined as the mean MSI over the deck for any assigned sea-state and heading angle, as:

$$OMSI_{(H_{1/3},T_p)_j,\beta_k} = \frac{\int_{A_{deck}} MSI_{(H_{1/3},T_p)_j,\beta_k,(x',y',z'_{deck})} dA}{A_{deck}} \quad (15)$$

The notation (x',y',z'_{deck}) is used to denote the coordinates of the ith of Nc remote control location points on the main deck area (Adeck) and β as the heading. OMSI is then defined for any assigned sea-state and heading angles:

$$OMSI_{(H_{1/3},T_p)_j,\beta_k} = \frac{1}{N_c}\sum_{i=1}^{N_c} MSI_{(H_{1/3},T_p)_j,\beta_k,(x',y',z'_{deck})_i} \quad (16)$$

Finally, accounting for all heading angles and peak periods:

$$OMSI = \frac{1}{N_c}\sum_{j=1}^{N_s} p_j \sum_{k=1}^{N_\beta} p_\beta \{\sum_{i=1}^{N_c} \\ OMSI_{(H_{1/3},T_p)_j,\beta_k,(x',y',z'_{deck})_i}\} \quad (17)$$

where Nc, Ns and N_β denote the number of remote control location points on the main deck, sea states and heading angles, respectively. Both the sea-states and heading angles have a certain probability of occurrence p_j and p_β, respectively.

3 PROGRAMS VALIDATION

Strip theory was selected as the tool to perform the seakeeping analysis. It is to be embedded on hull optimization procedures, for passengers comfort, of two different types of passenger ships. Programs using the strip theory, must be time efficient while maintaining good level of accuracy. Motivating the comparison of two available code alternatives, **CENTEC-SK** and *MAXSURF* Motions, at different headings and for a fixed Froude number. Belga et al. (2018) made a similar comparison on the same programs but only for head waves and multiple Froude numbers instead. Both codes perform the computations in the frequency domain, following the common method of Salvesen et al. (1970).

3.1 Overview of seakeeping program, CENTEC-SK

CENTEC-SK was developed at CENTEC (Center for Marine Technology and Ocean Engineering) at Instituto Superior Técnico (IST), Lisbon. It is a frequency domain strip-theory code or the linear version of Fonseca and Soares (1994). The available documentation was used, however many of its features were not documented. It is known that it follows the frequency domain formulation of Salvesen et al. (1970) without transom terms in the equations. According to Belga et al. (2018) the numerical solution for the 2-D radiation potential in forced harmonic motions, which allows to determine the sectional added masses, damping coefficients and diffraction force is obtained, via multi-parameter conformal mapping (Ramos and Soares 1997). The linear potential flow theory requires the correction for viscous damping for the case of roll motions.

3.1.1 Overview Of Seakeeping Program Maxsurf Motions

MAXSURF Motions is one module within *MAXSURF* Connected Edition V21 which is a commercially available software developed by Bentley Systems (2017b). This software is very well documented. The configuration set for comparison uses the linear strip theory of Salvesen et al. (1970) and without transom corrections. The numerical solution for 2-D radiation potential is also obtained via multi-parameter conformal mapping. The roll response is calculated using linear roll damping theory. This program is very user friendly and the modules are easy to integrate between each other, making it simple to perform changes on the input file. However the running time can be very long and it is difficult to perform multiple tests.

3.2 *Program Validation*

The comparison process is simplified for the present study. It is done by analyzing the accuracy of the RAOs, from the programs with experimental results available in the literature. Since neither one of the two ships at study have available experimental results, it was selected an alternative ship for the comparison with similar characteristics and very well know to the industry, the S-175 containership.

The validation is performed by comparing the measure data and the calculations for the responses in regular waves for the S-175 containership with a forward speed corresponding to a Froud number of Fn=0.275. This comparison focuses on the transfer functions for heave, roll and pitch at six different heading angles (β =180°, β =150°, β =120°, β =90°, β =60° and β =30°). β =180° is head seas, β =90° is beam seas and β =0° is following seas, following International Towing Tank Conference ITTC standard definitions. The results are plotted against the non-dimensional wave frequency $\omega\sqrt{L/g}$ with a 31 evenly spaced frequencies in regular waves. The responses have been measured at a wave height of 1/50 of Lpp. The non-dimensional parameters, such as heave per wave amplitude, pitch and roll per wave slope are presented in the results.

The validation for the above modes of motion for the S-175 container ship in regular waves, based on the transfer function of the motion, is carried out by comparing the computational results from the numerical code with experimental date available in the literature. The experimental data used in the validation process is from three organizations Ishikawajima-Harima Heavy Industries (IHI), Sumitomo Heavy Industry (SHI) and Ship Research Institute (SRI), presented in the summery report of the seakeeping committee of the 15th and 16th International Towing Tank Conferences, (ITTC 1983). Three different institutions were selected because there were no consistent experimental results for all headings of interest thus becoming the best solution to validate both programs. In this extended summary only some meaningful results were selected and are presented on Figures 1 - 3. It should be noticed that the experimental data was not enough on the measured roll transfer function, specially, at the resonance frequency. For that reason such results can not be confirmed with the same accuracy as heave and pitch.

For the S-175 containership, the comparisons show that both programs predict consistent results regarding heave and pitch motions. Particularly in heave motions, no noticeable differences were found between the two programs at any of the 6 headings studied. On pitch motions *MAXSURF* Motions over predicted the results, for headings between the beam and following seas. Regarding roll motions, the results were not confirmed by the experimental results, since the frequency region for the resonance peak, the one of most interest, was not within the region of the experimental results. However it is clear that *MAXSURF* Motions over predicts the resonance peak of roll motions compared to *CENTEC-SK*. It is easier to include roll damping corrections on the later one, showing clear effect on the results. Thus concluding that *CENTEC-SK* code is the most suitable tool for this dissertation and *CENTEC-SK* is used to obtain all seakeeping results. Its fast computation and flexibility to integrate with with *MATLAB*, makes it the best tool for multiple and reliable seakeeping calculations. Its drawbacks are the lack of official documentation and laborious input files.

4 CHARACTERIZATION OF THE SEAKEEPING OPTIMIZATION PROCESS

4.1 *Parent ships characteristics*

Two different ships were selected to be optimized. The first ship is characteristics of river and coastal waters and is here refereed as **SHIP1**. This ship hull has simple lines that make it easy to manipulate as shown on Figure 4. Its main dimensions are presented on Table 1. The passengers comfort was analysed along the length of its deck, meaning that a large area with points is considered when calculating OMSI, as shown on Figure 5. The second ship is to operate on ocean going routs and is here refereed as **SHIP2**. Its lines are also simple and easy to manipulate as shown on Figure 6. Its main dimensions are presented on Table 2. Unlike on SHIP1, in this second ship a specific area with points is now considered when calculating the OMSI, as shown on Figure 7.

4.1.1 *Operating sites*

4.2 *Coast of Algarve [Operating Scenario 1]*

SHIP1 operates on the basin of Algarve, for touristic trips along the coast, called **Operating Scenario 1**. The characterization of the sea is done using a scatter diagram presented on Table 3. It was constructed based on data collected by CENTEC (Center for Marine Technology and Ocean Engineering) at Instituto Superior Técnico (IST). This data was gathered in one point near the coast of Algarve [37°N, L -8.5°W], for a period between 1958 and 2001. There are 10 different intervals of wave height (H1/3) to 22 different peak periods (TP). The wave spectrum for each sea state Sz(w0) is calculated based on these data.

Statistical information of sea direction is also available and considering a trip from West to East the ship

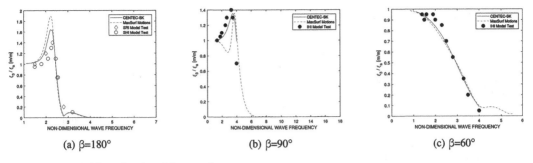

(a) β=180°   (b) β=90°   (c) β=60°

Figure 1. Heave RAOs as function of the wave frequency.

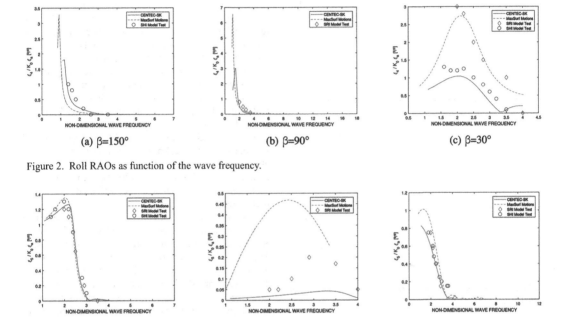

(a) β=150°   (b) β=90°   (c) β=30°

Figure 2. Roll RAOs as function of the wave frequency.

(a) β=180°   (b) β=90°   (c) β=30°

Figure 3. Pitch RAOs as function of the wave frequency.

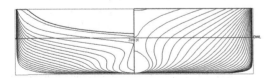

Figure 4. Parent hull forms from *MAXSURF* Modeler [SHIP1].

faces the worst scenario of encountering waves. Figure 8 presents the probability distribution of the ship-wave headings for SHIP1. It is mainly constituted by head and bow seas. It means that for this type of operation: beam, quartering and following seas will have little influence on the OMSI. The best results should be on hull variations that mainly improve comfort on head seas, which correspond to around 62% on encountered seas.

4.3 *Atlantic Ocean region between Algarve and Madeira [Operating Scenario 2]*

SHIP2 operates on the Atlantic Ocean connecting Algarve to Madeira, transporting passengers between the two regions. This operating scenario is called **Operating Scenario 2**. The characterization of the sea is done using a scatter diagram presented in Table 8. It is constructed based on data collected by the European Centre for Medium-Range Weather Forecasts (ECMWF). This data is representative of one point in the middle of the route [ϕ35° N, L 15° W], for a period between 1979 and 2013. There are 10 different intervals of wave height (H1/3) to 20 different peak periods (TP). The wave spectrum for

Table 1. Parent hull main dimensions and form parameters [SHIP1].

Displacement	Δ	960.5	[t]
Draft to baseline	T	1.6	[m]
Waterline length	L_{WL}	75	[m]
Waterline beam	B_{WL}	11	[m]
Prismatic coefficient	C_P	0.717	[-]
Block Coefficient	C_B	0.71	[-]
Midship section coefficient	C_M	0.99	[-]
Waterplane area coefficient	C_{WP}	0.841	[-]
LCB=LCG from MS (-ve aft)	LCB =LCG	-1.5	[m]
Vertical center of buoyancy	KB	0.859	[m]
Vertical center of gravity	KG	3.58	[m]
Speed (Maximum)	V	16	[kn]

Figure 5. Distribution of points along the deck [SHIP1].

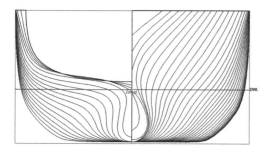

Figure 6. Parent hull forms from *MAXSURF* Modeler [SHIP2].

Table 2. Parent hull main dimensions and form parameters [SHIP2].

Displacement	Δ	5085	[t]
Draft to baseline	T	4.5	[m]
Waterline length	L_{WL}	98	[m]
Waterline beam	B_{WL}	20	[m]
Prismatic coefficient	C_P	0.642	[-]
Block Coefficient	C_B	0.563	[-]
Midship section coefficient	C_M	0.877	[-]
Waterplane area coefficient	C_{WP}	0.719	[-]
LCB=LCG from MS (-ve aft)	LCB =LCG	-2.9	[m]
Vertical center of buoyancy	KB	2.5	[m]
Vertical center of gravity	KG	6.5	[m]
Speed (Service)	V	21	[kn]

each sea state Sz(w0) is calculated for these sea-states. Statistical information of sea direction is also available and a trip from Northeast to Southwest is considered. For this trip it is expected to encounter

Figure 7. Distribution of points along the deck [SHIP2].

mainly head and bow seas and sometimes beam seas as show in Figure 9.

4.4 *Derivation of new hull forms*

Several hull variations were obtained from both parent hulls. Such variations were divided into two categories. The first category is focused on the systematical variation of form parameters such as the longitudinal center of buoyancy (LCB), the block coefficient (CB) and the midship section coefficient (CM), using the Lackenby Method (Lackenby 1950). The second type of systematical variations only depended on main dimensions, such as the length at waterline (LWL), beam at waterline (BWL) and draft (T). This methodology for developing new hull forms is based on the work of Grigoropoulos and Loukakis (1988), Kukner and Sariöz (1995), Özüm et al. (2011), Cepowski (2010), Scamardella and Piscopo (2013) and Belga et al. (2018), who proved that seakeeping performances are affected by these parameters.

Six different types of hull variations were tested in this dissertation. All six on SHIP1 and four on SHIP2. Each hull variation was performed using *MAXSURF* Modeler from *Bentley Systems* (Bentley Systems 2017a), where all the transformations were easily accomplished for a large number of hulls. In order to make the discussion as clear as possible, each type of hull transformations was called **Set n**. With *n* being a number between 1-6 that corresponds to each method of transformation. Set 1-3 corresponds to transformations of block coefficient (CB) and longitudinal center of buoyancy (LCB) differing on which parameters were free to change when the parent hull was being manipulated on *MAXSURF* Modeler. On **Set 1** only the displacement was free to change. On **Set 2** only draft was free to to change. On **Set 3** both beam and draft were free to change while maintaining the same B/T ratio. The goal on this three sets was to see if there would be any clear differences on OMSI if the coefficients were obtained by the manipulation of different variables. **Set 4** corresponds to hull transformations based on the midship section coefficient (CM). **Set 5** corresponds to geometrical hull transformations based on the length at waterline (LWL). **Set 6** corresponds to geometrical hull transformations based on the beam at waterline (BWL). In the following tables the data refereeing to each hull variation is presented. Tables 5-10 are referent to SHIP1. Tables 11-14 are referent to SHIP2. On these tables is clear how each coefficient is varied and which parameters were fixed for

288

Table 3. Joint frequency of significant wave height and spectral peak period. Representative data for the coast of Algarve.

Significant wave height [m]	Spectral peak period (s)																				Sum
	3	4	5	6	7	8	9	10	11	12	13	14	15	16	17	18	19	20	21	22	
1	508	9992	18888	6858	2900	2871	4174	4963	5661	5847	4854	3171	1651	0	676	356	0	65	0	13	73448
2	0	101	5072	8450	6026	1332	1609	1913	2443	2838	3692	3582	2688	0	1419	899	0	111	0	34	42209
3	0	0	2	251	1971	1251	828	735	649	552	727	661	562	0	377	374	0	32	0	6	8978
4	0	0	0	2	38	223	500	427	378	199	212	197	217	0	83	134	0	2	0	0	2612
5	0	0	0	0	0	5	42	142	215	182	83	50	56	0	59	55	0	1	0	0	890
6	0	0	0	0	0	0	0	11	60	99	35	26	21	0	27	15	0	1	0	0	295
7	0	0	0	0	0	0	0	0	6	25	24	14	14	0	8	15	0	0	0	0	106
8	0	0	0	0	0	0	0	0	1	2	2	2	0	0	2	12	0	0	0	0	22
9	0	0	0	0	0	0	0	0	0	1	1	1	0	0	0	1	0	0	0	0	4
10	0	0	0	0	0	0	0	0	0	0	1	2	0	0	0	0	0	0	0	0	3
Sum	508	10093	23962	15561	10935	5682	7153	8191	9413	9745	9631	7706	5210	0	2651	1861	0	212	0	53	128567

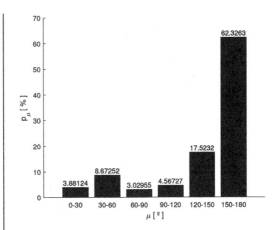

Figure 8. Probable fractions of time at various ship-wave headings [SHIP1].

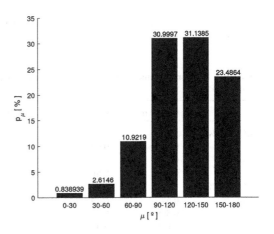

Figure 9. Probable fractions of time at various ship-wave headings [SHIP2].

each **Set n**, where the data in bold is refer to the parent hull/ship.

5 RESULTS

5.1 Results from OMSI analysis

The Overall Motion Sickness Index (OMSI) is analysed for all types of hull variation, at their respective sea environment and for six different headings. The maximum service speed is considered, which for SHIP1 is 16kn and for SHIP2 is 21kn. These following results are obtained from a program developed in MATLAB MathWorks.

5.1.1 OMSI results for hull variation based on SHIP1

Hull variations derived from changing the CB and shifting the LCB position indicate that OMSI is

Table 4. Joint frequency of significant wave height and spectral peak period. Representative data for the Atlantic Ocean (Region between Algarve and Madeira).

Significant wave height [m]	Spectral peak period (s) 5	6	7	8	9	10	11	12	13	14	15	16	17	18	19	20	Sum
1	6	38	244	238	241	128	58	42	17	26	4	0	4	0	0	0	1046
2	7	360	2235	2160	3094	3318	3638	4125	2870	1007	239	8	26	3	0	0	23090
3	0	11	570	1183	1583	1237	1290	2380	4150	4008	1505	59	258	38	0	2	18274
4	0	0	0	77	278	426	477	526	809	1502	1529	89	447	69	0	2	6231
5	0	0	0	2	8	64	130	216	218	298	404	36	358	71	0	2	1807
6	0	0	0	0	1	3	15	54	73	69	115	12	108	39	1	5	495
7	0	0	0	0	0	0	0	4	14	20	37	5	52	15	0	0	147
8	0	0	0	0	0	0	0	0	1	5	21	1	6	3	0	0	37
9	0	0	0	0	0	0	0	0	0	1	3	0	1	3	0	0	8
10	0	0	0	0	0	0	0	0	0	0	1	0	0	0	0	0	1
Sum	13	409	3049	3660	5205	5176	5608	7347	8152	6936	3858	210	1260	241	1	11	51136

Table 5. Hull form parameters for Set 1 of variations. Fixed $C_M = 0.99$, $L_{WL} = 75$ m, $B_{WL} = 11$ m and $T = 1.6$ m. Parent ship: SHIP1.

	$C_B = 0.66$	$C_B = 0.68$	$C_B = 0.70$	$C_B = 0.71$	$C_B = 072$	$C_B = 0.74$	$C_B = 0.76$
LCB=50%							
C_P	0.67	0.69	0.707	-	0.727	0.748	0.780
C_{WP}	0.817	0.828	0.843		0.857	0.871	0.885
Δ	901 t	920 t	948 t		974 t	1001 t	1028 t
LCB=52%							
C_P	0.67	0.69	0.707	**0.717**	0.727	0.748	0.78
C_{WP}	0.809	0.818	0.833	**0.841**	0.848	0.862	0.876
Δ	901 t	920 t	948 t	**960.5 t**	974 t	1001 t	1028 t
LCB=54%							
C_P	0.67	0.69	0.707	-	0.727	0.748	0.78
C_{WP}	0.801	0.809	0.824		0.838	0.853	0.867
Δ	901 t	920 t	948 t		974 t	1001 t	1028 t

Table 6. Hull form parameters for Set 2 of variations. Fixed $C_M = 0.99$, $L_{WL} = 75$ m, $B_{WL} = 11$ m and = 960.5 t. Parent ship: SHIP1.

	$C_B = 0.66$	$C_B = 0.68$	$C_B = 0.70$	$C_B = 0.71$	$C_B = 072$	$C_B = 0.74$	$C_B = 0.76$
LCB=50%							
C_P	0.667	0.687	0.707	-	0.727	0.748	0.768
C_{WP}	0.809	0.825	0.84		0.855	0.869	0.883
T	1.721 m	1.671 m	1.623 m		1.578 m	1.535 m	1.495 m
LCB=52%							
C_P	0.667	0.687	0.707	**0.717**	0.727	0.748	0.768
C_{WP}	0.803	0.818	0.833	**0.841**	0.848	0.862	0.876
T	1.721 m	1.671 m	1.623 m	**1.6 m**	1.578 m	1.535 m	1.495 m
LCB=54%							
C_P	0.667	0.687	0.707	-	0.727	0.748	0.768
C_{WP}	0.794	0.810	0.825		0.839	0.853	0.867
T	1.721 m	1.671 m	1.623 m		1.578 m	1.535 m	1.495 m

Table 7. Hull form parameters for Set 3 of variations. Fixed $C_M = 0.99$, $L_{WL} = 75$ m, $B_{WL}/T = 6.9$ and $\Delta = 960.5$ t. Parent ship: SHIP1.

	$C_B = 0.66$	$C_B = 0.68$	$C_B = 0.70$	$C_B = 0.71$	$C_B = 072$	$C_B = 0.74$	$C_B = 0.76$
LCB=50%							
C_P	0.666	0.687	0.707	-	0.728	0.748	0.768
C_{WP}	0.813	0.828	0.843		0.857	0.871	0.885
T	1.659 m	1.635 m	1.611 m		1.589 m	1.567 m	1.546 m
B_{WL}	11.41 m	11.24 m	11.078 m		10.923 m	10.775 m	10.632 m
LCB=52%							
C_P	0.666	0.687	0.707	**0.717**	0.728	0.748	0.768
C_{WP}	0.803	0.818	0.833	**0.841**	0.848	0.862	0.876
T	1.659 m	1.635 m	1.611 m	**1.6 m**	1.589 m	1.567 m	1.546 m
B_{WL}	11.41 m	11.24 m	11.078 m	**11 m**	10.923 m	10.775 m	10.632 m
LCB=54%							
C_P	0.666	0.687	0.707	-	0.728	0.748	0.768
C_{WP}	0.794	0.809	0.824		0.838	0.853	0.867
T	1.659 m	1.635 m	1.611 m		1.589 m	1.567 m	1.546 m
B_{WL}	11.41 m	11.24 m	11.078 m		10.923 m	10.775 m	10.632 m

Table 8. Hull form parameters for Set 4 of variations. Fixed $C_B = 0.71$, $B_{WL} = 11$ m, $T = 1.6$ m and $\Delta = 960.5$ t. Parent ship: SHIP1.

	$C_M = 0.99$	$C_M = 0.98$	$C_M = 0.97$	$C_M = 0.96$	$C_M = 0.95$
LCB = 52%					
C_P	**0.717**	0.725	0.733	0.742	0.75
C_{WP}	**0.841**	0.845	0.847	0.852	0.855

Table 9. Hull form parameters for Set 5 of variations. Fixed $C_B = 0.71$, $C_P = 0.717$, $C_M = 0.99$, $B_{WL}/T = 6.87$ and $\Delta = 960.5$ t. Parent ship: SHIP1.

	$L_{WL} = 90\%$	$L_{WL} = 95\%$	$L_{WL} = 100\%$	$L_{WL} = 105\%$	$L_{WL} = 110\%$
LCB = 52%					
L_{WL}	67.5 m	71.25 m	**75 m**	78.75 m	82.5 m
B_{WL}	11.60 m	11.30 m	**11 m**	10.74 m	10.50 m
T	1.69 m	1.64 m	**1.6 m**	1.561 m	1.53 m

Table 10. Hull form parameters for Set 6 of variations. Fixed $C_B = 0.71$, $C_P = 0.717$, $C_M = 0.99$, $L_{WL} = 75$ m and $\Delta = 960.5$ t. Parent ship: SHIP1.

	$B_{WL}/T=5.2$	$B_{WL}/T=5.8$	$B_{WL}/T=6.87$	$B_{WL}/T=7.9$	$B_{WL}/T=8.6$
LCB=52%					
B_{WL}	9.5 m	10.15 m	**11 m**	11.8 m	12.3 m
T	1.852 m	1.734 m	**1.6 m**	1.491 m	1.431 m

Table 11. Hull form parameters for Set 2 of variations. Fixed $C_M = 0.877$, $B_{WL} = 20$ m and $\Delta = 5085$ t. Parent ship: SHIP2.

	$C_B = 0.50$	$C_B = 0.53$	$C_B = 0.56$	$C_B = 0.58$	$C_B = 0.60$
LCB=50%					
C_P	0.57	0.604	-	0.661	0.684
C_{WP}	0.652	0.688		0.745	0.768
T	5.07 m	4.78 m		4.37 m	4.23 m
LCB=53%					
C_P	0.57	0.604	**0.642**	0.661	0.684
C_{WP}	0.644	0.680	**0.719**	0.738	0.76
T	5.07 m	4.78 m	**4.5 m**	4.37 m	4.23 m
LCB=56%					
C_P	0.57	0.604	-	0.661	0.684
C_{WP}	0.636	0.672		0.730	0.752
T	5.07 m	4.78 m		4.37 m	4.23 m

Table 12. Hull form parameters for Set 4 of variations. Fixed $C_B = 0.563$, $B_{WL} = 20$ m, $T = 4.5$ m and $\Delta = 5085$ t. Parent ship: SHIP2.

	$C_M = 0.79$	$C_M = 0.83$	$C_M = 0.87$	$C_M = 0.92$	$C_M = 0.96$
LCB = 53%					
C_P	0.714	0.679	**0.642**	0.612	0.587
C_{WP}	0.758	0.738	**0.719**	0.71	0.702

reduced by both increasing CB and moving LCB forward, as seen in Tables 15, 16 and 17. For SHIP1 the effect off shifting LCB is not as clear as of changing CB. This can be explain by the type of points distribution along the deck, see Figure 5. Since the points are equally distributed along the ship deck any improvements on one extremity of the ship will degrade the other and vice versa. Nevertheless the method still gives an optimized solution, based on the configurations that have smaller MSI values overall. In this dissertation an optimized solution is considered

Table 13. Hull form parameters for Set 5 of variations. Fixed $C_B = 0.563$, $C_P = 0.642$, $C_M = 0.877$, $B_{WL}/T = 4.4$ and $\Delta = 5085$ t. Parent ship: SHIP2.

	L_{WL} = 90%	L_{WL} = 95%	L_{WL} = 100%	L_{WL} = 105%	L_{WL} = 110%
LCB = 53%					
L_{WL}	93 m	96 m	**98 m**	100 m	19.50 m
B_{WL}	20.52 m	20.20 m	**20 m**	19.69 m	4.39 m
T	4.62 m	4.54 m	**4.5 m**	3.362 m	3.310 m

Table 14. Hull form parameters for Set 6 of variations. Fixed $C_B = 0.563$, $C_P = 0.642$, $C_M = 0.877$, L_{WL} = 98m and $\Delta = 5085$ t. Parent ship: SHIP2.

	B_{WL}/T = 3.33	B_{WL}/T = 3.77	B_{WL}/T = 4.44	B_{WL}/T = 5.10	B_{WL}/T = 5.55
LCB = 53%					
B_{WL}	17.4 m	18.5 m	**20 m**	21.5 m	22.35 m
T	5.17 m	4.87 m	**4.5 m**	4.20 m	4.03 m

when OMSI is reduced. It is also important to notice that the improvements on OMSI are consistent in all three tables. That is, regardless of the method used to change CB and LCB. Either using Set 1, Set 2 or Set 3, the OMSI was smaller on the highest CB and lowest LCB. In all three cases the increase of CB at a constant CM will always benefit OMSI.

The variations performed using a CB = 0.76 together with a shift of LCB to the midship gives the most comfortable hull. When CB is transformed using the Set 1 for hull variations (variable displacement), the reduction of OMSI was in the order of 12.9% compared to the parent hull. Using Set 2 for hull variation (variable T do change the CB), the reduction on OMSI was in the order of 17.7% compared to the parent hull. On the Set 3 of hull variations (variable T and BWL) the reduction on OMSI was in the order of 12.4%. The results variations presented in Table 14 seem to consistently give slightly smaller results of OMSI. Such differences are explained by the fact that the BWL/T is different for each new CB, and an increase in this ratio is beneficial for the OMSI. Nevertheless, the goal of using three different sets to change CB and LCB was achieved. The results were consistent on all three sets, showing that the results are not affect by how each coefficient was obtained. Still, it was possible to select a solution that least affect the original design of the hull. For SHIP1 it is best to only change the draft of the ship, instead of changing the displacement (Set 1) or even the beam and draft simultaneously (Set 3).

The form variation obtained by reducing CM (Set 4) is beneficial to OMSI. As shown in Table 18, such reductions consistently give smaller values of OMSI. The smallest of all is for a CM = 0.95, where OMSI is reduced by 7.2% compared to the parent hull. This reductions may not seem as significant, but it is worth noticing that a CM = 0.95 is less than 5% difference compared to CM = 0.99. This is an interesting result, because not only the seakeeping is improved, while no major changes in the hull were introduced to do so.

Table 15. Values of OMSI on each hull variation based on Set 1 [SHIP1].

	CB=0.66	CB=0.68	CB=0.70	CB=0.71	CB=0.72	CB=0.74	CB=0.76
LCB=50%	4.637	4.487	4.280	-	4.089	3.942	3.787
LCB=52%	4.761	4.630	4.438	4.349	4.228	4.048	3.854
LCB=54%	4.869	4.758	4.511	-	4.032	4.078	3.863

Table 16. Values of OMSI on each hull variation based on Set 2 [SHIP1].

	CB=0.66	CB=0.68	CB = 0.70	CB = 0.71	CB = 0.72	CB=0.74	CB=0.76
LCB = 50%	4.727	4.538	4.383	-	4.102	3.862	3.581
LCB = 52%	4.855	4.612	4.489	4.349	4.386	4.018	3.652
LCB = 54%	4.985	4.662	4.535	-	4.281	3.987	3.725

Table 17. Values of OMSI on each hull variation based on Set 3 [SHIP1].

	CB = 0.66	CB = 0.68	CB = 0.70	CB = 0.71	CB = 0.72	CB=0.74	CB=0.76
LCB = 50%	4.728	4.055	4.261	-	4.101	3.975	3.808
LCB = 52%	4.870	4.294	4.483	4.349	4.254	4.051	3.863
LCB = 54%	4.818	4.367	4.572	-	4.365	4.158	3.900

Table 18. Values of OMSI on each hull variation based on Set 4 [SHIP1].

	CM = 0.99	CM = 0.98	CM = 0.97	CM = 0.96	CM = 0.95
LCB = 52%	4.349	4.213	4.147	4.157	4.038

Table 19. Values of OMSI on each hull variation based on Set 5 [SHIP1].

	L_{WL} = 90%	L_{WL} = 95%	L_{WL} = 100%	L_{WL} = 105%	L_{WL} = 110%
LCB = 52%	5.378	4.836	4.349	3.808	3.109

Table 20. Values of OMSI on each hull variation based on Set 6 [SHIP1].

	B_{WL}/T = 75%	B_{WL}/T = 85%	B_{WL}/T = 100%	B_{WL}/T = 115%	B_{WL}/T = 125%
LCB = 52%	4.553	4.440	4.349	4.042	3.992

Table 21. Values of OMSI on each hull variation based on Set 2 [SHIP2].

	CB = 0.50	CB = 0.53	CB = 0.56	CB=0.58	CB=0.60
LCB = 50%	18.137	17.987	-	16.915	15.552
LCB = 53%	16.588	16.332	16.106	15.025	15.098
LCB = 56%	15.938	15.739	-	14.678	13.267

Table 22. Values of OMSI on each hull variation based on Set 4 [SHIP2].

	CM = 0.79	CM = 0.83	CM = 0.87	CM = 0.92	CM = 0.96
LCB = 53%	13.775	15.654	16.106	14.756	14.591

Table 23. Values of OMSI on each hull variation based on Set 5 [SHIP2].

	L_{WL} = 90%	L_{WL} = 95%	L_{WL} = 100%	L_{WL} = 105%	L_{WL} = 110%
LCB = 53%	16.553	16.569	16.106	14.892	14.625

Table 24. Values of OMSI on each hull variation based on Set 6 [SHIP2].

	B_{WL}/T = 75%	B_{WL}/T = 85%	B_{WL}/T = 100%	B_{WL}/T = 115%	B_{WL}/T = 125%
LCB = 53%	18.122	16.802	16.106	14.369	14.435

The first geometrical variation in study or Set 5 of hull variations, was the variation of LWL. Looking at Table 19 the increase in LWL clearly reduces OMSI. Particularly an increase by 10% reduced OMSI by 28.5% compared to the parent hull. Making it the lowest OMSI from all the transformations performed to SHIP1.

Finally, the results for the second type geometrical variation or Set 6 of hull variations, were also obtained. Increasing the BWL/T ratio reduces OMSI, as shown in Table 18. The change in ratio already seemed to give the advantage to the transformations of CB by only changing T, as shown in Table 16. The increase in ratio by 25% reduced OMSI by 8.2%, which is not as significant as changes in LWL.

5.1.2 *OMSI results for hull variation based on SHIP2*

The OMSI on various hull variations was also studied on SHIP2. This is a different ship but still with the same type of hull transformations, namely: Set 2, Set 4, Set 5 and Set 6. By using another ship with the same type of transformations the performance of OMSI from different ships, sea-state conditions and studied locations can be studied. The first thing to be noticed is that OMSI on SHIP2 is much higher than before. Now the parent hull [SHIP2] has an OMSI = 16.106. This value is considerably higher than an OMSI = 4.349 from SHIP1. It can be explained by the harsher sea conditions and by the smaller area on the aft region, where points are distributed.

For SHIP2 only Set 2 was used to perform hull variations of CB and LCB. According to Table 21, increasing CB still contributes to reduce OMSI. In fact OMSI reduced by 17.6% when comparing the parent hull with the hull variation with the lowest OMSI, as expected from the previous results. On the other hand the best hull variation is now the one where LCB = 56%, which is the one further away from the midship. An interesting but predictable result, that shows how reducing the distance between the area where comfort is to be improved and the center of buoyancy is clearly valid. However it should be clear that the opposite is also true and some areas of the ship will degrade by such actions.

Reductions of CM once again proved to be effective on reducing OMSI, as shown in Table 22. With a reduction of 14.5% from the parent hull. Yet the increase of CM also improved the OMSI, which is not to be expected. A possible reason for this unexpected results may be due to a distortion on the hull transformations, particularly on the bulb region. This distortion improved OMSI in the order of 9.4%. Its validity however can not be confirmed, since the distortions on the bulb may too be influencing it.

More in line with previous results are the geometrical hull variations. As shown in Table 21 the increase in LWL reduced once again the OMSI. The reduction is in the order of 9.2% compared to the parent hull. The increase in ratio BWL/T also proved beneficial to the OMSI, as shown on Table 24. This reduction was of 10.4% compared to the parent hull.

The difference between the two types of geometrical variations is in this case very similar unlike it was on SHIP1. It means that each variation does not influence every hull types exactly the same way, depending on the type of ship, the operating scenario and the significant type of headings. An optimization is then affected by both the type of hull, the method in use, together with sea environments and deck locations being improved.

5.2 Comparison between heave, roll and pitch motions

The optimized results from the OMSI analysis for each ship at each Set n where compared to the parent ship, regarding the heave, pitch and roll RAOs. Each type of RAO was plotted at four different headings (180°, 120°, 90° and 60°). In this extended summary only the plots comparing the optimized hull obtained from Set 2, CB = 0.76 and LCB = 50%, 52% and 54% with the parent hull CB = 0.71 and LCB = 52% are presented, due to lack of space. These can be found on Figures 10 - 12.

The RAOs comparison proved that the reductions on OMSI were directly linked to reductions on ship motions for both SHIP1 and SHIP2.

5.3 Absolute vertical accelerations

Absolute vertical accelerations responses as function of encounter frequency are compared in this section. Since so many sea-states, headings and deck locations were used it would be impractical to compare every single one of them. For that reason a sea-state with H1/3 = 1 m and TP = 9 s is selected for comparison and the same headings used to compare RAOs are used to compare absolute vertical accelerations. Different points were selected to be studied on both ships and their locations are found on Table 25 and Table 26. Figures 12-13 correspond to such comparison between the parent hull SHIP1 and the optimized hull CB = 0.76, LCB = 50% obtained from Set 2. By comparing the vertical accelerations it is confirmed that the optimized hull based on OMSI also reduced its absolute vertical accelerations. However it is worth noticing that not all locations see its vertical accelerations being reduced, as shown in Figures 14(b) and 14(c). In such headings

the hull transformations seem to be less desirable, noticing that by using a parameter such as OMSI, the overall results are being improved instead of only some particular conditions.

5.4 Resistance analysis

The main focus of the present work has been on improving the seakeeping performance of passengers ships for comfort purposes. However such transformations my influence other performance parameter of a ship, as is the case of hull resistance. Therefore the hull resistance was assessed for each

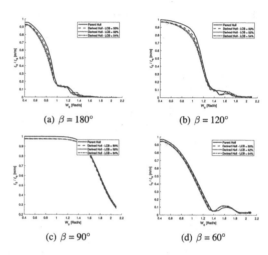

Figure 10. Heave RAOs. Parent Ship: SHIP1 with C_B = 0.71. Derived Hulls: Set 2 with C_B = 0.76.

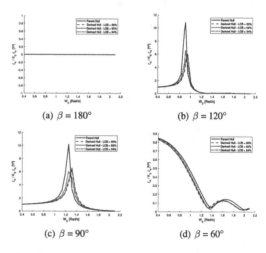

Figure 11. Roll RAOs. Parent Ship: SHIP1 with C_B = 0.71. Derived Hulls: Set 2 with C_B = 0.76.

Table 25. Remote location points on SHIP1.

Description	Units	1	2	3	4	5	6
Longitudinal Position (+ fwd MS)	m	29	0	-35	29	0	-35
Offset from center line	m	0	0	0	-5	-5	-5

Table 26. Remote location points on SHIP2.

Description	Units	1	2	3
Longitudinal Position (+ fwd MS)	m	-36	-36	-36
Offset from center line	m	-6	0	

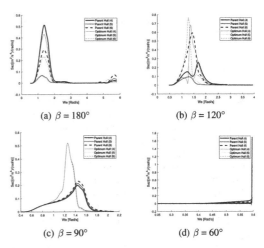

(a) $\beta = 180°$ (b) $\beta = 120°$

(c) $\beta = 90°$ (d) $\beta = 60°$

Figure 14. Absolute vertical acceleration. Parent hull: SHIP1 ($C_B = 0.71$, LCB = 52%) Optimum hull: Set2 ($C_B = 0.76$, LCB = 50%), at points 4, 5 and 6.

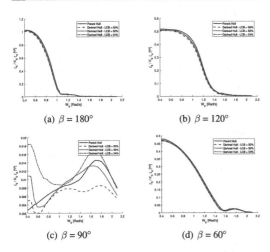

(a) $\beta = 180°$ (b) $\beta = 120°$

(c) $\beta = 90°$ (d) $\beta = 60°$

Figure 12. Pitch RAOs. Parent Ship: SHIP1 with $C_B = 0.71$. Derived Hulls: Set 2 with $C_B = 0.76$.

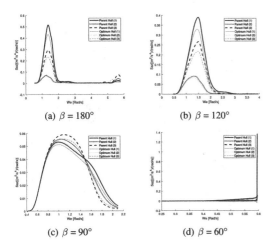

(a) $\beta = 180°$ (b) $\beta = 120°$

(c) $\beta = 90°$ (d) $\beta = 60°$

Figure 13. Absolute vertical acceleration. Parent hull: SHIP1 ($C_B = 0.71$, LCB = 52%) Optimum hull: Set2 ($C_B = 0.76$, LCB = 50%), at points 1, 2 and 3.

Set n of hull transformations. In this study it was concluded that the reductions in OMSI are generally associated with an increase in ship resistance. Only hull transformations using Set 5, increasing length at waterline LWL are associated with both reductions on OMSI and hull resistance. It is then up to the naval architect to consider the priority of each parameter in a ships performance before performing any hull transformation.

5.5 Operability assessment of various hull variations with reduced OMSI

The operability index is a ratio, between the number of sea-sates (for all available peak periods) with significant wave heights, that do not exceed the maximum significant wave height (based on the seakeeping criteria), over the total number of sates (N) in a certain wave scatter diagram.

Two different criteria are selected namely, vertical accelerations and MSI. The criteria for vertical accelerations is that the maximum vertical acceleration during an exposure of 2 hours at any point should be smaller than **0.05*g** (g being the gravitational acceleration). While for MSI is that the maximum MSI during an exposure of 2 hours at any point should be less than **35%**. Both criteria are based on Tezdogan et al. (). From the operability analysis it was confirmed that the optimized hulls based on the OMSI analysis are associated with an increase of ship operability based on the same comfort criteria that were minimized. It was also concluded that using a operability index that is based on pass/fail that discards any progress out of the criteria range is a less efficient approach compared to using a parameter like OMSI.

6 CONCLUSIONS

Two different passenger ships were used to study the comfort of passenger on the deck. The first ship (SHIP1) was set to operate on calm waters near the coast of Algarve (Operating Scenario 1) had multiple points of interest along the deck. The second ship (SHIP2) was set to operate on the Atlantic Ocean (Operating Scenario 2), connecting Algarve to Madeira and it only had a single area of interest. Six different sets of hull transformations were performed using *MAXSURF* Modeler (Bentley Systems 2017a). For every new hull the parameter OMSI, was calculated using *MATLAB*, based on the results from *CENTEC-SK*. OMSI was used to compare the differences in passenger's comfort on each new hull transformation. Based on this analysis the following steps may be take to obtain an optimized hull for passenger's comfort:

• Increase block coefficient (C_B) by reducing draft (T) for a fixed midship coefficient (C_M), displacement, breath and waterline length.

• Shift the longitudinal center of buoyancy (LCB), depending on locations of interest, equilibrium and trim considerations.

• Decrease midship coefficient (C_M), while increasing prismatic coefficient (C_P) and waterplane coefficient (C_{WP}.)

• Increase waterline length (L_{WL}) for fixed B_{WL}/T ratio, displacement and form coefficients.

• Increase B_{WL}/T ratio for fixed waterline length (L_{WL}), displacement and form coefficients.

REFERENCES

Belga, F., S. Sutulo, & C. G. Soares (2018). Comparative study of various strip-theory seakeeping codes in predicting heave and pitch motions of fast displacement ships in head seas. *C. Guedes Soares and T. A. Santos (Eds). Progress in Maritime Engineering and Technology, London, UK:Taylor & Francis*.

Belga, F., M. Ventura, & C. G. Soares (2018). Seakeeping optimization of a catamaran to operate as fast crew supplier at the alentejo basin. *C. Guedes Soares and T. A. Santos(Eds). Progress in Maritime Engineering and Technology, London, UK:Taylor & Francis*.

Bentley Systems, I. (2017a). *Maxsurf Modeler, Windows Version 21, User Manual*. Bentley Systems, Incorporated.

Bentley Systems, I. (2017b). *Maxsurf Motions, Windows Version 21, User Manual*. Bentley Systems, Incorporated.

Cepowski, T. (2010). Influence analysis of changes of design parameters of passenger-car ferries on their selected sea-keeping qualities. *POLISH MARITIME RESEARCH 1(64) Vol 17;* pp. 25–32.

Colwell, J. L. (1989). Human factors in the naval environment: a review of motion sickness and biodynamic problems. *Technical Report DREA-TM-89-220, Defence Research Establishment Atlantic, Dartmouth, Nova Scotio, Canada*.

Fonseca, N. & C. G. Soares (1994). Time domain analysis of vertical ship motions. *Transaction on the Built Environment vol 5, WIT Press, ISSN 1743–3509*.

Grigoropoulos, G. J. & T. A. Loukakis (1988). A new method for developing hull forms with superior seakeeping qualities. *Department of Na val Architecture and Marine Engineering, National Technical University of Athens, 42 October 28th, Athens, Greece*.

ITTC (1983). Summary of results obtained with computer programs to predict ship motions in six degree of freedom and related responses: comparative study on ship motion program. *15th & 16th ITTC seakeeping committee, Japan*.

Journée, J. & W. Massie (January 2011). *OFFSHORE HYDROMECHANICS, First Edition*. Delft University of Technology.

Kukner, A. & K. Sariöz (1995). High speed hull form optimization for seakeeping. *Advances in Engineering Software, 22(3):*179–189.

Lackenby, H. (1950). On systematic geometrical variation of ship forms. *RINA Transactions, Vol.92*.

McCauley, M. E., J. W. Royal, C. D. Wylie, J. F. O'Hanlon, & R. R. Mackie (1976). Motion sickness incidence: Exploratory studies of habituation, pitch and roll, and the refinement of a mathematical model. *Technical Report 1733-2, Human Factors Research Inc., Goleta, California*.

O'Hanlon, J. F. & M. E. McCauley (1974). Motion sickness incidence as a funtion of the frequancy and acceleration of vertical sinusoidal motion. *Aerospace Medicine, vol.45(4)*, pp. 366–369.

Özüm, S., B. Sener, & H. Yilmaz (2011). A parametric study on seakeeping assessment of fast ships in conceptual design stage. *Ocean Engineering 38* 1439–1447.

Ramos, J. & C. G. Soares (1997). On the assessment of hydrodynamic coefficients of cylinders in heaving. *Ocean Engineering, 24(8):*743–763.

Salvesen, N., E. O. Tuck, & O. Faltinsen (1970). Ship motions and sea loads. *In Transactions of the Society of Naval Architects and Marine Engineers, SNAME, vol. 78* , pp. 250–287.

Scamardella, A. & V. Piscopo (2013). Passenger ship seakeeping optimization by the overall motion sickness incidence. *Ocean Engineering 76 (2014)* 86–97.

Tezdogan, T., A. Incecik, & O. Turan (-). Operability assessment of high speed passenger ships based on human comfort criteria. *Department of Naval Architecture, Ocean and Marine Engineering, University of Strathclyde, 100 Montrose Street, Glasgow, G4 0LZ, UK*.

Experimental study on the wave loads including springing response of a very large crude carrier in regular head waves

Y. Lin, N. Ma, D. Wang & X. Gu
State Key Laboratory of Ocean Engineering, School of Naval architecture, Ocean and Civil Engineering, Collaborative Innovation Center for Advanced Ship and Deep-Sea Exploration, Shanghai Jiao Tong University, Shanghai, China

ABSTRACT: This paper presents an experimental investigation of hydroelastic responses in heading regular wave. A 1:55 scaled segmented ship model is made to meet elastic similarity condition by using ten segments and two backbones. The vertical bending moments and shearing forces are measured by using load cells located on several sections. Furthermore, pitch and heave motions are measured by gyroscope situated at the center of gravity. Band-pass filter and power spectral density method is adopted to analyze hydroelasic responses. In conclusion, the influences of wave length and hull girder stiffness on hydroelastic responses are discussed. Springing phenomena occur in the small wavelength. In addition, the reduction of hull girder stiffness leads to the occurrence of springing easily.

1 INTRODUCTION

With the development of global trade, ship size increases every year. However, some maritime accidents also occurred, such as MSC Napoli and MOL Comfort. The major cause of accidents is that the natural frequency of hull girder is similar to the wave encounter frequency with the increasing ship size. Accordingly, the emphasis on the dynamic responses of large-scale ship should be placed and hydroelastic responses and its influence on structural damage should be discussed.

Since the end of 70s in last century, two-dimensional and three dimensional classic hydroelasicity theories were developed (Bishop and Price, 1979; Newman, 1979; Wu, 1984; Faltinsen et al., 1991). On the other hand, hybrid hydroelasitcity theory has been also proposed. Wang et al. (1997) combined the 2-D strip method with the 3-D FEM for floating structures. Lin et al. (2017) proposed a hybrid hydroelasitc approach to analyze the responses of large-scale ship.

In addition, experimental technology is regarded as an essential approach to reflect the hydroelastic responses of real ship. At present, springing and whipping are usually discussed in these experiments. And segmented ship model is usually adopted in tests and was described by Jiao et al. (2016) or Maron and Kapsenberg (2014). Springing is regarded as the steady-state resonant vibration, whereas whipping is a transient vibration caused by slamming. Linear springing often occurs when the encounter frequency is similar to wet natural frequency. At the same time, nonlinear springing occurs when the encounter frequency is double or multifold wet natural frequency. Slamming often causes both local and global effects. The global effect is often called whipping (Faltinsen, 2005).

The previous researches mainly paid attention to the vertical bending moment. Li et al. (2016) introduced the segmental model test and compared the three-dimensional numerical simulations with the springing test results for a 550,000DWT ore carrier. The model was divided into nine segments and a backbone system which was made up by connecting four beams with every segment. Ren et al. (2016) simulated the container ship's springing and whipping response. They focused on the fatigue analysis due to springing and whipping. Jiao et al. (2019) conducted large-scale ship model test on hydroelastic responses and whipping loads in harsh irregular seaways.

The participants of the WILS JIP (Wave-Induced Loads on Ships) have systematically studied the hydroelastic responses. Their experimental study was conducted as a joint industry project. In the WILS JIP-I project (Kim and Yu, 2010), a ship model of 10,000 TEU container ship was equally divided into six segments with backbone system and the backbone was made of steel with a thin walled open channel section. Nonlinear vertical bending and torsional moments in extreme wave conditions were measured and studied. Furthermore, an H-shaped backbone was used in WILS JIP-II because of the advantages afforded by its symmetric section shape (Hong et al., 2012). They focused on the research of torsional springing and

DOI: 10.1201/9781003216599-32

whipping. Moreover, a U-shape backbone was utilized in WILS JIP-III project (Hong et al., 2014). The influence of slamming loads on hydroelastic responses was investigated.

In this paper, a ship model of the 350,000 DWT VLCC is divided into ten segments and is connected by the backbone system which consists of two circular steel tubes. Three investigated cases are adopted. Furthermore, hydroelastic responses in heading waves are analyzed by band-pass filter and power spectral density method. In conclusion, the influences of wave lengths and hull girder stiffness on hydroelastic responses are discussed.

2 EXPERIMENTAL SETUP

2.1 Test model and measurement system

The model experiments in heading waves are conducted in the towing tank of China Ship Scientific Research Center (CSSRC), which is 474m long, 14m wide and 7m deep and a towing carriage is utilized. A segmented ship model of the 350,000 DWT Very Large Crude Carrier (VLCC) is adopted to study hydroelastic responses. The ship model has a scale ratio of 1/55. Main particulars of full-scale VLCC are shown in Table 1. Mass distribution of full-scale ship is listed in Figure 1.

The model hull is made of FRP (Fiber Reinforced Plastics) and wood. The model segments are connected by the backbone with varying section, which can satisfy the request of natural frequency and stiffness distribution. Moreover, the backbone is consisted of two circular sectional beams. The backbone is made of steel. As shown in Table 2, variable circular sections are chosen to simulate the real stiffness of ship. No. 1~19 stations are abbreviated as ST. 1~19.

As illustrated in Figure 2, the 350,000 VLCC model is composed of ten rigid segments connected by nine flexible joints. There are 17 measure points. Cross-sectional load effects, such as the vertical bending moment, are measured at 0.1Lpp, 0.2Lpp, 0.3Lpp, 0.4Lpp, 0.5Lpp, 0.6Lpp, 0.7Lpp, 0.8Lpp and 0.9Lpp before aft perpendicular (AP). The measurement

Table 1. Main particulars of 350,000 DWT VLCC. (Full-scale ship size)

Parameters	Full load	Ballast
Length between perpendiculars, L_{PP}(m)	320	320
Breath, B(m)	60	60
Depth, D(m)	29.80	29.80
Fore Draft, T_f(m)	21.63	11.16
Aft Draft, T_a(m)	21.97	7.63
Displacement, Δ(t)	354329.7	139337.2
Radius of inertia moment	0.243 L_{PP}	0.258 L_{PP}
Service speed, V(kn)	15.7	15.7

Table 2. Transformation of vertical bending stiffness.

Station	Full-scale ship I_v (m^4)	Circular steel tube: diameter×thickness (mm×mm)	Error
St.1~3	809.73	76×6	1.20%
St.3~5	1162.49	89×5	1.12%
St.5~7	1369.18	89×6	0.44%
St.7~15	1417.26	89×7	8.43%
St.15~19	928.82	83×5	1.39%

points of vertical bending moments are marked as VBM$_1$-VBM$_9$ in Figure 2. Then heave and pitch motions are measured at the center of gravity. In addition, vertical accelerations are measured at 0.1Lpp, 0.3Lpp, 0.5Lpp, 0.7Lpp and 0.9Lpp. The wave height is measured at the front of the bow. Furthermore, the arrangement of steel tubes and base of measurement device are presented in Figure 3. As shown in Figure 3, the ten segmented parts are connected to the two non-uniform steel tubes. As shown in Figure 4, The flexible joints are rubber sealing strip.

2.2 Test conditions

For the model test, two loading conditions are suggested: full load condition and ballast condition. At the same time, two backbones stiffnesses are set: original hull girder stiffness and 70% of original hull girder stiffness.

Therefore, three cases are discussed in the model tests: ballast condition with original hull girder stiffness (abbreviated as ballast condition in the following paper), full load condition with original hull

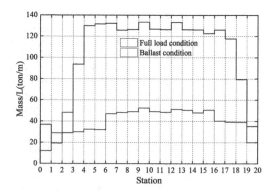

Figure 1. Mass distribution of the full-scale ship.

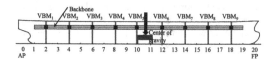

Figure 2. The arrangement of the segmented model.

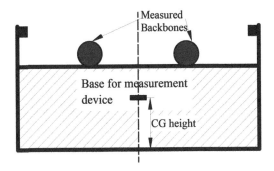

Figure 3. Arrangement of measuring backbones.

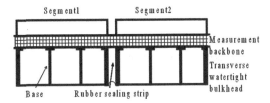

Figure 4. Longitudinal plan of the segmented model.

girder stiffness (abbreviated as full load condition in the following paper) and full load condition with 70% of original hull girder stiffness (abbreviated as reduced stiffness condition in the following paper).

The ratio of wave-length and ship-length is listed in Table 3.

3 EXPERIMENTAL RESULTS

3.1 *Hammering test in calm water*

Wet hammering test is utilized to measure the natural frequencies of ship model. It is believed as the most effective approach. Through knocking the backbone by a hammer, the decay curve of vertical bending moment (VBM) of mid-ship section is obtained. Then the natural frequencies would be gained by Fast Fourier Transform (FFT). The natural frequencies of three investigated cases are listed in Table 4.

In addition, the prediction of structural damping is necessary to distinguish hydroelastic responses. Therefore, the calculation method of log decrement of hull girder is shown in the equation (1).

$$\delta = \frac{1}{N} \ln \frac{x_m}{x_{m+N}} \qquad (1)$$

Where δ = log decrement.

Through analyzing time records of hammering tests of three investigated cases, log decrement of ship model is calculated and listed in Table 5.

3.2 *Regular wave test results*

3.2.1 *Full load condition*

For the full load condition, the first order natural frequency is 3.712 Hz and the second order natural frequency is 7.863 Hz. The natural frequency is essential to judge springing or whipping responses.

As it is well-known, linear springing often occurs when the encounter frequency is similar to wet natural frequency. At the same time, nonlinear springing occurs when the encounter frequency is double or multifold wet natural frequency.

Therefore, nonlinear springing response could be found in small wave-length conditions through the comparisons of natural frequency and wave encounter frequency. The comparisons are also listed in Table 6. When the ratio of wave-length and ship-length is equal to 0.24 or 0.3, the ratio of first order

Table 3. Test conditions: ratio of wave length and ship length.

	Full load condition	Ballast condition	Reduced stiffness condition
1	0.24	0.20	0.20
2	0.30	0.24	0.28
3	0.42	0.30	0.32
4	0.55	0.34	0.40
5	0.65	0.43	0.51
6	0.80	0.52	0.60
7	0.92	0.61	0.79
8	1.10	0.80	1.00
9	1.22	1.00	1.12
10	1.57	1.20	1.50
11	1.96	1.60	1.98
12		2.00	2.41

Table 4. Natural frequencies of ship model (Hz).

Investigated cases	First Order	Second Order
Full load	3.712	7.863
Ballast	4.881	9.361
Reduced Stiffness	3.3	6.9

Table 5. Dimensionless damping coefficient of ship model.

Investigated cases	Log decrement
Full load	0.0651
Ballast	0.1404
Reduced Stiffness	0.0696

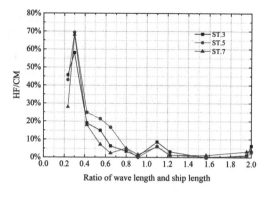

Figure 5. Ratio of high frequency vertical bending moment and total vertical bending moment (HF/CM) in full load condition.

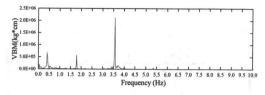

Figure 6. Power spectral density of VBM in full load condition. (wavelength/ship-length =0.30).

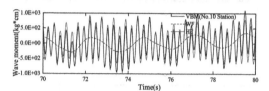

Figure 7. VBM time series at mid-ship section. (wavelength/ship-length =0.30).

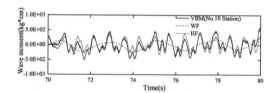

Figure 8. VBM time series at mid-ship section. (wave-length/ship-length =0.42).

natural frequency and wave encounter frequency is near to 2.0 or 3.0 (1.99 or 2.93). The wave encounter frequency is double or multifold wet natural frequency and nonlinear springing phenomena occur.

Then high frequency vertical bending moment (HF) accounts for 30~70% of the total vertical bending moment (CM) in small wavelength. The relationship could be presented in Figure 5. As a result, high frequency bending moment often occurs in small wave-length because wave encounter frequency is double or multifold wet natural frequency. Through Fast Fourier Transform (FFT), the vertical bending moment of mid-ship section presents slight springing responses in Figure 6. High frequency component accounts for large part in small wavelength.

Furthermore, the time-series of VBM in waves with short wave-lengths are shown in Figures 7-8. The HF bending moment is periodic. Therefore, only the springing phenomena are found and whipping are not founded.

Table 6. Relationship between natural frequency and wave encounter frequency. (Full load condition).

Wave-length/ ship-length	Wave encounter frequency ω_e (Hz)	1st natural frequency/ω_e	2nd natural frequency/ω_e
0.24	1.87	**1.99**	4.22
0.30	1.27	**2.93**	6.21
0.42	1.03	3.61	7.66
0.55	0.87	4.25	9.00
0.65	0.79	4.69	9.93
0.80	0.70	5.31	11.24
0.92	0.65	5.74	12.16
1.10	0.58	6.38	13.52
1.22	0.55	6.78	14.37
1.57	0.47	7.82	16.56
1.96	0.42	8.85	18.74

3.2.2 Ballast condition

For the ballast condition, natural frequencies increase: the first order natural frequency is 4.881 Hz and the second order natural frequency is 9.361 Hz.

As shown in Table 7, nonlinear springing response could be founded in small and middle wave-length conditions through the comparisons of natural frequency and wave encounter frequency. When the ratio of wave-length and ship-length is equal to 0.3 or 0.44, the ratio of first order natural frequency and wave encounter frequency is near to 3.0 or 4.0. For the sake of completeness, encounter-frequency load (WF) caused by waves and the total bending moments (CM) are separated by use of band-pass filter and are presented in Figure 9. Then high frequency vertical bending moment (HF) accounts for 30~80% of the total vertical bending moment (CM). The relationship could be presented in Figure 9. Compared with Figure 6, the part of high frequency component of the vertical bending moment of mid-ship section increases in Figure 10.

Table 7. Relationship between natural frequency and wave encounter frequency. (Ballast condition).

Wave-length/ship-length	Wave encounter frequency ω_e (Hz)	1st natural frequency/ω_e	2nd natural frequency/ω_e
0.20	2.12	2.31	4.42
0.24	1.82	2.69	5.16
0.30	1.58	**3.08**	5.91
0.34	1.44	3.40	6.52
0.44	1.21	**4.03**	7.74
0.52	1.08	4.54	8.70
0.61	0.97	**5.01**	9.61
0.80	0.81	**6.00**	11.51
1.00	0.71	6.92	13.27
1.20	0.63	7.76	14.89
1.60	0.53	9.27	17.78
2.00	0.46	10.61	20.36

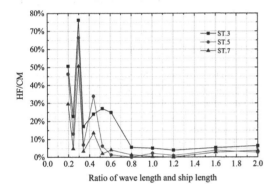

Figure 9. Ratio of high frequency vertical bending moment and total vertical bending moment (HF/CM) in ballast condition.

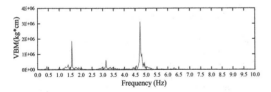

Figure 10. Power spectral density of VBM in ballast condtion. (wavelength/ship-length =0.30)

As shown in Figure 11, HF components are obtained and presented through band-pass filter when the ratio of wave-length and ship-length are equal to 0.30 and 0.43. HF components present periodic trend. Therefore, whipping responses do not happen.

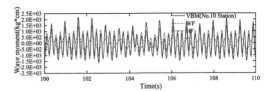

Figure 11. VBM time series at mid-ship section. (wavelength/ship-length =0.30).

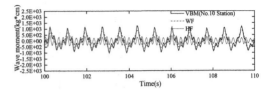

Figure 12. VBM time series at mid-ship section. (wavelength/ship-length =0.43).

3.2.3 *Reduced stiffness condition*

For the reduced stiffness condition, the first order natural frequency is 3.3 Hz and the second order natural frequency is 6.9 Hz. Because of reducing the hull girder stiffness, the natural frequency decreases.

As shown in Table 8, nonlinear springing response could be easily founded. The reason is the reduced stiffness. Compared with the full load condition, the percentage of high frequency vertical bending moment (HF) in reduced stiffness condition increases. The relationship is presented in Figure 13. Through Fast Fourier Transform (FFT), the vertical bending moment of mid-ship section presents wave encounter component and high frequency component in Figure 14.

As shown in Figures 15-16, HF components are obtained and presented through band-pass filter when the ratio of wave-length and ship-length are equal to 0.20 and 1.12. HF components present periodic trend. Therefore, whipping responses do not happen.

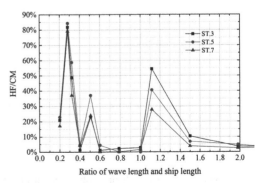

Figure 13. Ratio of high frequency vertical bending moment and total vertical bending moment (HF/CM) in reduced stiffness condition.

Table 8. Relationship between natural frequency and wave encounter frequency. (Reduced stiffness condition).

Wave-length/ship-length	Wave encounter frequency ω_e (Hz)	1st natural frequency/ω_e	2nd natural frequency/ω_e
0.20	2.09	1.58	3.29
0.28	1.64	**2.01**	4.20
0.32	1.50	2.20	4.60
0.40	1.29	2.56	5.36
0.51	1.10	**3.01**	6.29
0.60	0.98	3.36	7.04
0.79	0.82	**4.02**	8.40
1.00	0.71	4.68	9.78
1.12	0.66	**5.02**	10.49
1.50	0.55	**6.02**	12.60
1.98	0.46	7.13	14.92
2.41	0.41	**8.03**	16.79

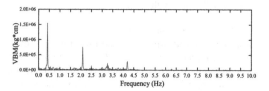

Figure 14. Power spectral density of VBM in reduced stiffness condition. (wavelength/ship-length =0.20).

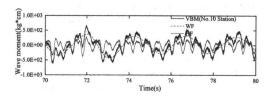

Figure 15. VBM time series at mid-ship section. (wavelength/ship-length =0.20).

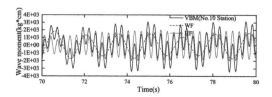

Figure 16. VBM time series at mid-ship section. (wavelength/ship-length =1.12).

4 CONCLUSIONS

This article introduces the hydroelastic experiments of a 350,000 DWT VLCC in heading regular wave. Nonlinear springing phenomena are found in three investigated cases. At the same time, whipping does not occur. Band-pass filter and FFT technologies are adopted to deal with test records. Through the analyses of test results, the following conclusions could be obtained:

(1) For full load and ballast conditions, springing responses easily occur in small wave-length condition. For reduced stiffness condition, springing occurs in small and middle wave-length conditions. The wave encounter frequency decreases as the wave-length increases. At the same time, the natural frequency decreases as hull girder stiffness decreases. Therefore, springing responses easily occur in the reduced stiffness condition.

(2) The percentage of high frequency vertical bending moment in ballast condition is higher than that in full load condition. High frequency component presents periodic trend and whipping responses do not happen,

(3) Reducing hull girder stiffness would lead to the easy occurrence of springing phenomena. The high-frequency load caused by springing may be much larger than wave-frequency load in certain frequency region.

ACKNOWLEDGMENTS

This study is supported by the China Ministry of Education Key Research Project "KSHIP-II Project" (Knowledge-based Ship Design Hyper-Integrated Platform): No. GKZY010004. Authors are also grateful to Mr. Jiajun Hu, Mr. Yanchao Geng, Mr. Jun Ding and Mr. Haibo Dong of China Ship Scientific Research Center (CSSRC) for their help in the model tests.

REFERENCES

Bishop, R.E.D. & Price, W.G. 1979. Hydroelasticity of ships. Cambridge University Press.
Faltinsen, O., Zhao, R. & Umeda, N. 1991. Numerical Predictions of Ship Motions at High Forward Speed. Philosophical Transactions of the Royal Society of London A: Mathematical, Physical and Engineering Sciences 334(1634): 241–252.
Faltinsen, O.M. 2005. Hydrodynamics of high-speed marine vehicles. Cambridge University Press.
Hong, S.Y., Kim, B.W. & Kim, Y.S. 2014. Experimental Study on the Bow-Flare Slamming of a 10,000 TEU Containership. Proceedings of the Twenty-fourth International Offshore and Polar Engineering Conference.
Hong, S.Y., Kim, B.W. & Nam, B.W. 2012. Experimental study on torsion springing and whipping of large container ship. International Journal of Offshore and Polar Engineering. 22(2): 97–107.
Jiao, J., Yu, H., Chen, C. & Ren, H. 2019. Time-domain numerical and segmented model experimental study on ship hydroelastic responses and whipping loads in harsh irregular seaways. Ocean Engineering, 185:59–81.
Jiao, J., Ren, H., Sun, S., Liu, N., Li, H. & Adenya, C. A. 2016. A state of the art large scale model testing technique for ship hydrodynamics at sea, Ocean Engineering, 123:174–190.

Kim, S. & Yu, H. 2010. Segmented model testing and numerical analysis of wave-induced extreme and springing loads on large container carriers. Proceedings of the Twentieth International Offshore and Polar Engineering Conference.

Li, H., Wang, D., Zhou, C., Zhang, K. & Ren, H. 2016. Springing Responses Analysis and Segmented Model Testing on a 550,000 DWT Ore Carrier. ASME 2016 35th International Conference on Ocean, Offshore and Arctic Engineering. American Society of Mechanical Engineers.

Lin, Y., Ma, N., Wang, D., & Gu, X. 2017. Hydroelastic Analysis and Experimental Validation of a 350,000 DWT Very Large Crude Carrier. ASME 2017 36th International Conference on Ocean, Offshore and Arctic Engineering.

Maron, A. & Kapsenberg, G. 2014. Design of a ship model for hydroelastic experiments in waves. International Journal of Naval Architecture and Ocean Engineering, 6:1130–1147.

Newman, J.N. 1979. The theory of ship motions. Advances in applied mechanics 18: 221–283.

Ren, H., Zhang, K., Li, H. & Wang, D. 2016. Large Containerships' Fatigue Analysis due to Springing and Whipping. ASME 2016 35th International Conference on Ocean, Offshore and Arctic Engineering. American Society of Mechanical Engineers.

Wang, S., Ertekin, R.C. & Riggs, H.R. 1997. Computationally efficient techniques in the hydroelasticity analysis of very large floating structures. Computers & structures, 62(4): 603–610.

Wu, Y. 1984. Hydroelasticity of floating bodies. University of Brunel.

On the water entry problem of 2D wedges and bow flare section

Pravallika Peddamallu, Aravind K Menon & Suresh Rajendran
Department of Ocean engineering, Indian Institute of technology Madras, India

ABSTRACT: Slamming is a phenomenon that results from the relative motion between a ship hull and water surface in rough seas. It is associated with high impact loads and whipping which may result in structural failure. Hence accurate estimation of slamming loads is important during the structural design of ships, particularly containerships with pronounced bow flare. This paper presents the numerical analysis of the slamming loads acting on triangular wedge sections by the application of Computational Fluid Dynamic (CFD) techniques using a commercial software. The water entry of 2D sections are simulated by modelling a free surface using Eulerian multiphase and VOF method. The body is kept stationary and the free surface is moved relative to the body by solving the flow equations using unsteady implicit time marching scheme. The phenomenon is numerically simulated in in-viscid, laminar, and turbulent flow regimes by solving Euler equations, Navier-Stokes equations, and Reynolds Average Navier-Stokes equations respectively using a commercial CFD tool star-CCM+ . This methodology is applied to 2D wedge sections and bow flare section and results are compared with existing literature. The effect of viscosity on the water entry of wedge sections with various dead rise angles and bow flare section is analyzed.

1 INTRODUCTION

Ships operating in rough seas are prone to the phenomenon of slamming, where in aft and fore end portions of the ship exit out of the water and impacts the water surface with high velocities. In the context of assessing the effects of slamming, it is important to study the water entry of ship shaped geometries.

Earlier studies were done based on analytical methods and used drop test to validate the results. von Karman (1929) has presented a derivation of an impact formula for wedge entry into water based on momentum theory while neglecting the water pileup. Wagner (1932) extended the theory by accounting for the spray during the impact. Dobrovol'skaya (1969) presented an similarity solution based on Wagner function and applied the method to study the free surface behavior during the uniform symmetrical entry of wedge into half-plane of incompressible fluid by neglecting gravity. Cointe & Armand (1987) applied the method of matched asymptotic expansions to solve the boundary value problem pertaining to vertical entry of rigid horizontal cylinder into an incompressible, inviscid fluid. An expression for impact force is derived and the results are compared with reviewed literature.

The initial development of BEM for two dimensional water entry problems was formulated by Greenhow & Lin (1985). It was developed and used to model the fluid domain during water entry of two dimensional and three dimensional bodies by various literature. A simple asymptotic solution for small deadrise angles α based. Zhao & Faltinsen (1993) presented similarity solution and nonlinear boundary element method with jet flow approximation to investigate water entry of wedges with constant velocity for a broad range of dead rise angles. The two methods were compared with simple asymptotic solution based on Wagner solution. Zhao et al (1997) established a fully nonlinear numerical solution method which incorporate flow separation from knuckle and he developed one more method by extending Wagner solution (1932) which does not include flow separation. The numerical methods show agreement with the experimental drop test results of ship cross sections. Faltinsen (2002) extended matched asymptotic expansions to study the water entry of a rigid wedge with finite dead rise angles where Cointe & Armand (1987) done it for very small dead rise angles. Faltinsen et al. (2004) reviewed the state of the art pertaining to research in water entry on an initially calm free surface, wet deck slamming, green water, and sloshing. It is indicated that the slamming should be dealt as a global phenomenon integrating the structural dynamic response and fluid flow around the ship. This paper also studied slamming of very large floating structures (VLFS) with shallow draft. Hermunstad & Moan (2005) and Tuitman (2010) extended BEM method validated by Zhao et al. (1997) to three dimension problems.

Later works applied CFD techniques to investigate the phenomenon of slamming. Muzaferiza et al (1998) used free surface capturing CFD technique to analyses the water entry of 2D and 3D wedges and compared

DOI: 10.1201/9781003216599-33

the results with Zhao et al (1997). Algarin (2011) studied water impact phenomenon for 2D boat sections and critical conditions for flow separation from the keel are also mentioned. Wang & Guedes Soares (2012, 2013, and 2014) conducted studies on slamming based on Arbitrary Lagrangian- Eulerian (ALE) algorithm. This section presents the various analysis used in water impact problems. Aquelet et al. (2006) developed the Euler –Lagrangian coupling algorithm for application to fluid structure interaction problems. LS DYNA uses explicit finite element method (FEM) to solve the coupling algorithm which has been shown by Stenius et al. (2006 and 2007). Wang & Guedes Soares (2012) studied slamming loads on 2D bodies using an explicit finite element code which is based on a multi material arbitrary Lagrangian Eulerian formulation and penalty coupling method. Furthermore, the effects of the roll angle on the slamming loads are investigated through the calculations for the bow flare section with different roll angles.

1.1 Outline of the paper

In the initial sections of the paper presents the methodology and background of CFD techniques applied to water entry of 2D sections. Various discretization schemes, meshing parameters, physics models, boundary and initial conditions, and solver parameters used for analysis are described.

The following cases are studied by applying the described techniques.

- Water entry of triangular prismatic Wedges at constant velocities
- Water entry of Ship Bow Sections at constant velocities

A time independent study and grid independent study is performed in each case.

A study of effect of flow regime, impact velocity is performed and, results and inferences are presented. Based on the inferences study on the effect of dead rise angle of wedges is performed and compared with Zhao & Faltinsen (1993).

Entry of bow flare section in various flow regimes are simulated for significant time span after impact and the flow separation is studied.

The description of case, and discussion of results is presented in later sections. Conclusions are drawn and ideas for further work are presented.

2 METHODOLGY

The flow problem is mathematically modeled based on assumptions, the equations are discretized in time and space using a suitable scheme to apply on the domain. The mathematical conditions that the flow is supposed to satisfy are implemented in the domain and boundaries. "SIMPLE" algorithm is used to solve the flow algebraically and solve the discretized equations and predict the pressure field and velocity field in the flow region at discrete nodal points.

The pressure distribution over the wetted surface of the impact body is plotted in space at various time instances. The predicted pressure field on the surface of the impact body is integrated to obtain the impact force on the body.

3 NUMERICAL SETUP

Analysis of 2D sections are proceeded using following assumptions. The main idea starts with considering the body as fixed and giving relative velocity to the free surface. As gravity will not play significant effect in initial impact phase, gravity can be neglected. Fluid is incompressible and Fluid flow is solved considering implicit unsteady scheme. There are 3 types of flow regimes namely Inviscid, laminar and turbulent flow regimes which are solved using Euler, Navier Stokes and Reynolds Average Navier Stokes Equations respectively. K-ε and K-ω models are the main turbulence models where K-ε model is used for complex geometries by using fine mesh close to the wall and K-ω model is used when the wall boundary conditions are predominant. Law of the wall is given by the equation $u^+ = (1/\kappa)\ ln(Ey^+)$, where u$^+$ is the average turbulent velocity, y$^+$ is the function of the distance of the first grid point from the wall, κ is von Karman constant and E is the log law offset. The default values were used for parameters in turbulence models. A smooth wall surface specification is applied at the wedge/section surface. A blended wall function condition is applied at the wall surface with the log law offset, E=9 and von Karman constant, κ =0.42.

An Eulerian multiphase technique is used to model the multiphase flow constituting of two phases, water and air. Volume of Fluids (VOF) Model is used for capturing the air water interface, which predicts the distribution and movement of the interface of immiscible phases.

Volume of fluids is an Eulerian model used for continuous phase interactions. In present work, the free surface is an interface created between air and water. The distribution of phases and the position of the interface are described by volume fraction.

3.1 Volume Fraction Transport equation

The CFD software application used for the simulation of the water entry phenomenon solves the following volume fraction transport equation.
Ref.StarCCM+ (2018).

$$\frac{\partial}{\partial t}\int_v \alpha_i dV + \oint_A \alpha_i \vec{v}.da = \int_v \left(S_{\alpha_i} - \frac{\alpha_i}{\rho_i}\frac{D\rho_i}{Dt}\right)dV$$
$$- \int_v \frac{1}{\rho}\nabla.(\alpha_i\rho_i\vec{v}_{dr,i})dV + \int_A \frac{\mu_t}{\sigma_{t}\rho}\nabla\alpha_i.da$$

Where,
a = surface area vector
v = mass averaged velocity
$\vec{v}_{dr,i}$ = diffusion velocity
S_{α_i} = user-defined source term of phase i
μ_t = turbulent dynamic viscosity
σ_t = turbulent Schmitdt number
$\frac{D\rho_i}{Dt}$ = material or Lagrangian derivative of the phase densities ρ_i
α_i is the volume fraction
The volume fraction of phase i is defined as

$$\alpha_i = \frac{V_i}{V}$$

Where,
V_i = volume of phase i in the cell
V = volume of the cell
The volume fractions of all phases in a cell must sum up to one:

$$\sum_{i=1}^{N} \alpha_i = 1$$

Where,
N = total number of phases.
Depending on the value of the volume fraction, the presence of different phases or fluids in a cell can be distinguished:

- $\alpha_i = 0$ – the cell is completely void of phase i.
- $\alpha_i = 1$ – the cell is completely filled with phase i.
- $0 < \alpha_i < 1$ – values between the two limits indicate the presence of an interface between phases.

3.2 High-resolution interface capturing (HRIC)

High-Resolution Interface Capturing (HRIC) scheme is used for tracking sharp interfaces.

Table 1 Shows the volume of fluid properties which are used for interface tracking in HRIC scheme. CFL_l and CFL_u are the lower and upper courant number limit in HRIC scheme.

Table 1. VOF Properties.

Convection scheme	2nd order
Sharpening factor	0.0
Angle factor	0.05
CFL_l	0.5
CFL_u	1.0

3.3 Geometry and domain

2D water entry analysis is performed on wedges with dead rise angles 7.5°, 45°, 81° and DTC bow flare section to study the effects of slamming. Analysis is done for only half of the domain by taking the advantage of symmetry and to reduce the computational time.

In Figure 1, the triangular wedge is the demonstrative of the body under analysis. The wedge section can be replaced by bow flare section for water entry analysis.

Coordinate axis for wedges is placed at the undisturbed free surface to validate the results with published results. Unlike the wedge section, coordinate axis for bow flare section is located at the keel of the section.

3.4 Meshing

Figure 2 shows the combination of polygonal and prism layer mesh are used for better capturing of sharp pressure peaks. Prism layers are placed near the wall boundaries as they allow cells of higher aspect ratio. Far from the boundaries coarser mesh is given to reduce the computational time.

Table 2 Gives an overview of the mesh model given in Figure 2. It consists number of cells, interior faces and vertices present in domain.

3.5 Boundary conditions

The domain being two dimensional region is bounded by the wedge surface and the enclosing

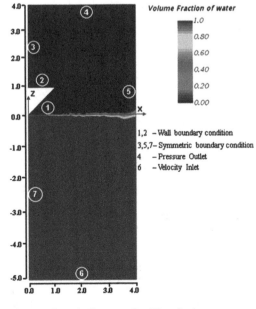

Figure 1. Domain Geometry for 45° wedge impact.

sides, top and bottom edges as shown in Figure 1. The following boundary conditions were applied

- **Body/Wall boundary condition**: Boundaries 1 and 2 are the sections where water entry analysis is conducting and no slip is applied.
- **Symmetric Boundary condition**: This boundary conditions is applied to boundaries 3, 5 and 7.
- **Pressure outlet**: This condition is applied to boundary 4 where pressure is specified.
- **Velocity inlet Boundary condition**: This condition is applied to boundary 6 where velocity is predefined.

3.6 *Solver parameters*

Consistency, stability, convergence, conservation and accuracy are vital properties which should be taken into account for CFD to be effective. The choice of optimized time step and grid sizes are important to get converged and stability solution.

3.7 *Brief summary of test sections*

Water entry analysis is done for wedge sections of 7.5°, 45° and 81° of deadrise angles and a bow flare section of DTC container ship.

3.7.1 *Triangular wedge sections*
The geometry of the wedge test sections is shown in Figure 3.

3.7.2 *Bow Flare section*
The geometry of the bow flare section is shown in Figure 4.

3.8 *Velocity profile*

Water entry analysis for wedge sections is done with constant velocities of 1 m/s and 2 m/s. The wedge section water entry cases are simulated assuming a constant velocity for two reasons. Firstly to validate with Zhao & Faltinsen (1993,) which present results for constant velocity water entry cases. Secondly because only the early stage water entry of wedges is studied which occurs in a very short interval of time, during which the change in velocity, gravity can be neglected.

Bow flare section is impacted using velocity profile in order to validate with the entry case results presented in Zhao et al. (1997). The velocity profile is presented in the following section.

4 RESULTS AND DISCUSSIONS

The above-mentioned methodology is applied to study the effect of various parameters during the entry of triangular wedges, ship bow flare section.

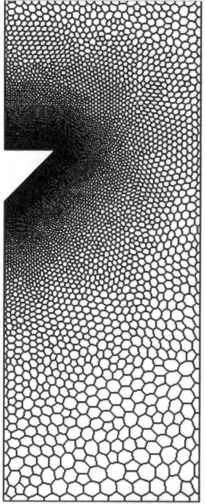
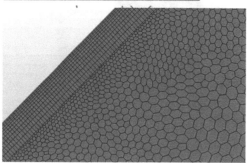

Figure 2. The meshed domain for 45° Wedge impact analysis [prism layers in the inset].

Table 2. Properties of volume mesh for 45° wedge.

Cells	67170
Interior Faces	176616
Vertices	111985

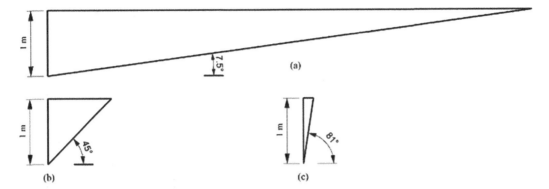

Figure 3. The geometry of 2D wedge sections.

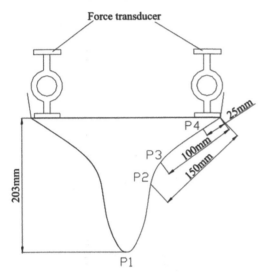

Figure 4. Geometry of DTC Bow flare section as given in Zhao et al. (1997).

The results are presented using the non-dimensional parameters, Coefficient of pressure, C_P and relative height from instantaneous draft level, Z_{Rel}. These parameters are defined by the following expressions.

$$C_P = \frac{P_{abs} - P_{atm}}{0.5 \times \rho \times V^2}$$

For, the wedge sections,

$$Z_{Rel} = \frac{Z}{V \times t} - 1$$

For the bow flare sections,
$Z_{Rel} = \frac{Z}{V \times t}$
Where,
P_{abs} is absolute pressure at any location
P_{atm} is atmospheric pressure
ρ is density of water
V is velocity of entry

4.1 Water entry of triangular wedge

The water entry of symmetric wedges with various dead rise angles is studied by varying the impact velocity, and flow regimes. The peak pressure coefficient on the wetted surface of the symmetric wedges are evaluated.

Firstly grid and time independent studies were conducted to study the sensitivity of results with grid size and time step. The estimated pressure distribution and peak pressure coefficients are validated with Zhao & Faltinsen (1993). A study on effect of flow regime, and impact velocity for various dead rise angle is performed.

4.1.1 Time and grid independent study

Initially several trials were performed on wedges with various deadrise angles, grid sizes and time steps. Systematic spatial and temporal uncertainty for both C_p and Z_{Rel} is done for 7.5° wedge and presented in Table 3 and 4. For the grid independence study, the grid size is varied by keeping the time step fixed at 5E-5s. For the time independence study, the time step is varied by keeping the minimum grid size at 0.5mm.

In order to find an optimum solution between the computation time and accuracy of the solution, grid size of 0.5mm was chosen. Time step of 5E-5s was chosen to give best performance from Table 3 and 4.

The uncertainty analysis was performed based on Generalized Richardson extrapolation described in ITTC (2017). The following are the definitions of the parameters presented in the paper.
Δx is mesh size
Δt is time step
Refinement ratio,

$$r_i = \Delta x_{i,m} / \Delta x_{i,m-1}$$

Table 3. Grid independent study for 7.5° wedge using laminar model.

Peak Pressure - Grid independent Study

S. NO	Grade	Δx (mm)	r_i	C_p (Si)	$\varepsilon_{i,m}$	R_i	P_i	δ
1	Fine	0.50	1.41	148.87				
2	Medium	0.71	1.41	146.19	-2.68	**0.100**	6.632	-0.299
3	Coarse	1.00	↑	119.52	-26.67			
	0< R_i<1			(Monotonic Convergence)				

Z_{Rel} - Grid independent Study

Z_{Rel} (Si)	$\varepsilon_{i,m}$	R_i	P_i	δ
0.5576				
0.5534	-0.0042	**0.424**	2.474	-0.003
0.5435	-0.0099			
(Monotonic Convergence)				

Table 4. Time independent study for 7.5° wedge using laminar model.

Peak Pressure - Time independent Study

S.NO (m)	Grade	Δt (s)	r_i	C_p (Si)	$\varepsilon_{i,m}$	R_i	P_i	δ
1	Fine	5.00E-05	1.41	148.87				
2	Medium	7.07E-05	1.41	145.48	-3.39	**0.225**	4.307	-0.983
3	Coarse	1.00E-04	↑	130.40	-15.08			
	0< R_i<1			(Monotonic Convergence)				

Z_{Rel} - Time independent Study

Z_{Rel} (Si)	$\varepsilon_{i,m}$	R_i	P_i	δ
0.5376				
0.5352	-0.0024	**0.229**	4.259	-0.0007
0.5247	-0.0105			
(Monotonic Convergence)				

$$r_i = \Delta t_{i,m}/\Delta t_{i,m-1}$$

Simulation value = $(\widehat{S}_{i,m})$
Changes between simulation values,
$\varepsilon_{i,(m)(m-1)} = \widehat{S}_{i,m} - \widehat{S}_{i,m-1}$
Convergence ratio, $R_i = \varepsilon_{i,21}$
Order of accuracy, $p_i = \frac{\ln(\varepsilon_{i,32}/\varepsilon_{i,21})}{\ln(r_i)}$
Uncertainty, $\delta_{i,1} = \frac{\varepsilon_{i,21}}{r_i^{p_i}-1}$

Grid and time independent study conducted using refinement ratio of 1.414. Convergence ratio of both C_p and Z_{Rel} for grid and time independent study is in between 0 to 1, which means monotonic convergence. Uncertainty has very less value in all cases.

Peak pressure coefficient obtained using optimum mesh size and time step for 7.5° wedge is close to the peak pressure coefficient of 147.33 which is taken from BEM results of Zhao & Faltinsen (1993).

Similarly grid and time independent study for 45° wedge was also conducted and found that it has monotonic convergence. Optimum grid size and time step considered are 1mm and 1E-3s.

4.1.2 Validation

Figure 5 (a)-(c) show that the pressure distribution on wedges with dead rise angles of 7.5°, 45° and 81° predicted using laminar CFD model are in well agreement with the BEM results of Zhao & Faltinsen (1993). It can also be noticed that the effect of impact velocities on the pressure coefficient is minimal.

4.13 Deadrise angle effect

Figure 6 shows the effect of dead rise angle on pressure coefficient using laminar model. As the dead rise angle decreases below 45°, coefficient of pressure increases drastically due to the fluid entrapment between water surface and wedge bottom wall.

This entrapment is attributed to lack of clearance for the air/flash to escape from below the wedge bottom wall during impact. Wedges with higher dead rise angles illustrate the lesser pressure coefficient values.

Figure 7 shows the movement of position of coefficient of pressure as the dead rise angle increases using laminar model. Peak pressure is moving along with the free surface for lower dead rise angles and for higher dead rise angles, it is located at the keel of the wedge.

4.1.4 Study on effect of flow regime

The effect of modelling the flow regime as inviscid, laminar and turbulent (K-ε) during the impact of symmetric wedges in to water is studied. Wedges of dead rise angles 7.5°, 45°and 81° impacting with velocities of 1m/s and 2 m/s are simulated and the variation of pressure distribution in space during the early impact stage are recorded.

Peak pressure coefficient values are more or less matching in all the three regimes. Aimed at 7.5° wedge, variation in peak pressure values for three flow regimes has less than 6%. From Figure 8 and 9, it can

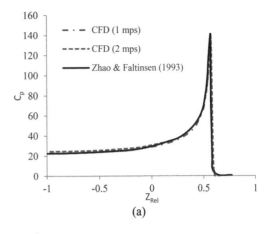

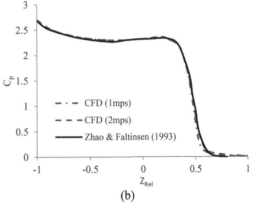

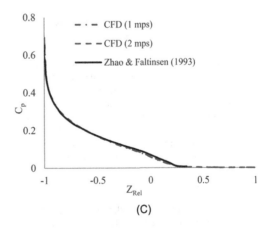

Figure 5. Pressure distribution on wedge side at 0.06s during water entry with constant velocity of 1m/s and 2m/s, CFD results compared with Zhao & Faltinsen (1993) results for dead rise angles of (a) 7.5° (b) 45° (c) 81°.

be observed that there is no considerable flow regime effect on simple geometries like wedges with large dead rise angles and also coefficient of pressure variation for various velocities are not showing significant effect during impact stage. This can be observed from Table 4. Hence, it is inferred that slamming problem is dominated by inertia rather than viscosity.

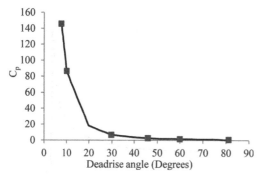

Figure 6. This shows the relationship between deadrise angle and the coefficient of maximum pressure.

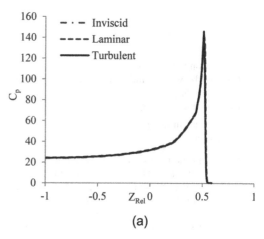

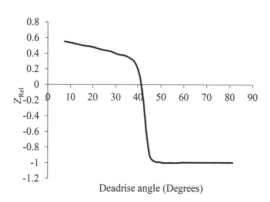

Figure 7. This shows the relationship between deadrise angle and position of coefficient of maximum pressure.

Table 5 Shows the data of various dead rise angles pressure coefficient at 0.06s for three flow regimes and 1& 2 m/s. The percentage difference in the predicted Cp values between laminar and turbulent regimes for each deadrise angle and velocity is also presented. The difference is comparatively high for 7.5° wedge impacting with 2 m/s whereas it is relatively insignificant for remaining cases.

4.2 Bow flare section

Water entry of a DTC Bow flare section is studied to analyses the effect of time step, grid size, and flow regime. A series of simulations are performed and the corresponding results are presented in the following sub sections.

According to the drop tests of the two dimensional bodies Zhao et al. (1997), slamming force, and pressure distributions during water impact are predicted. The present bow flare section has

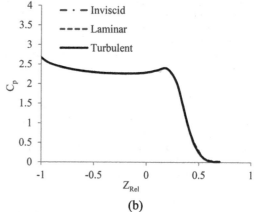

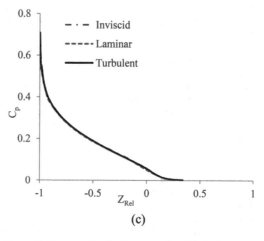

Figure 8. Pressure distribution on wedge side during water entry with constant velocity of 1m/s at 0.06 sec after impact for dead rise angles of (a) 7.5° (b) 45° (c) 81°.

312

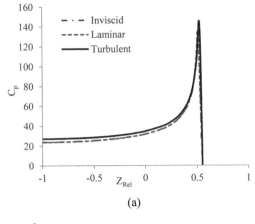

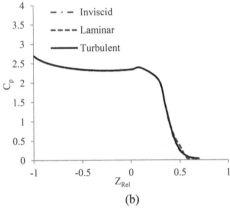

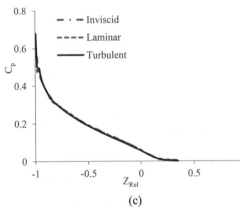

Figure 9. Pressure distribution on wedge side during water entry with constant velocity of 2m/s at 0.06 sec after impact for dead rise angles of (a) 7.5° (b) 45° (c) 81°.

a varying curvature with inflections which during the water entry will result in flow separation and possible air entrapment. Hence, a turbulent (K-ε) model is used for grid and time independent study. Predicted values are showing good agreement with the published results.

Table 5. Peak Values of Pressure Coefficients.

α	V (m/s)	Flow Regime	C_P	%diff	Z_{Rel}
7.5°	1	I	146.41		0.515
		L	148.87	-1.52%	0.515
		T	146.64		0.512
	2	I	150.41		0.526
		L	137.05	5.71%	0.512
		T	145.35		0.525
45°	1	I	2.69		-0.997
		L	2.69	0.00%	-0.997
		T	2.69		-0.997
	2	I	2.66		-0.997
		L	2.67	-0.38%	-0.997
		T	2.66		-0.997
81°	1	I	0.66		-0.996
		L	0.68	0.00%	-0.996
		T	0.68		-0.996
	2	I	0.7		-0.996
		L	0.7	1.41%	-0.996
		T	0.71		-0.996

I = Inviscid
L = Laminar
T = Turbulent K-ε Model
Cp = Coefficient of pressure
Z_{Rel} = Relative position
$\%diff = \frac{(C_{pT} - C_{pL}) \times 100}{C_{pT}}$

4.2.1 Time and grid independent study

Water entry in bow flare section is bit complicated because of the complexity in shape. Grid and time independent study for such bodies is necessary to improve the accuracy and to reduce computational time.

Without compromising the resolution and computational time, minimum grid size of 0.1mm and time step of 0.0001s is chosen from Table 6 and Table 7.

4.2.2 Validation

4.2.2.1 Slamming force

Figure 10 (a) shows the force time history of the bow flare section. The slamming force and its instant of occurrence predicted by the CFD using inviscid, laminar, turbulent K-ε and K-ω models is in good

Table 6. Grid independent study using Turbulent (K-ε) Model.

Size (mm)	Cp	Position (z = mm)	Computation Time (hrs.)
0.5	1.55	0	0.53
0.1	1.582	0	1.56
0.05	1.582	0	6.12

Table 7. Time Independent Study using Turbulent (K-ε) Model.

Time Step (s)	Cp	Position (z=mm)	Computation Time (hrs.)
0.005	1.520	0	0.62
0.0001	1.582	0	1.56
0.00005	1.583	0	7.85

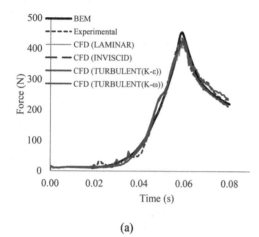

(a)

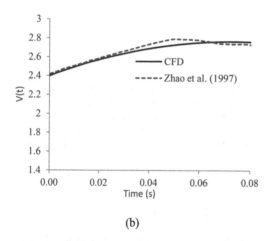

(b)

Figure 10. The water entry of bow flare section: CFD results compared with Zhao et al. (1997), t is time variable. t=0 corresponds to the keel touches the water surface. (a) Vertical slamming force (b) V (t), Vertical drop velocity.

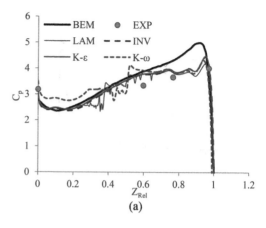

(a)

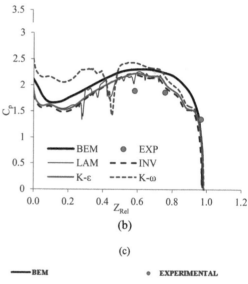

(b)

(c)

Figure 11. The pressure distribution during water entry of bow flare section at (a) 0.06 s; (b) 0.07 s; (c) 0.08 s.

agreement with the experimental and boundary element method results of Zhao et al. (1997).

Velocity profile used in the CFD is obtained from Zhao et al. (1997) as shown in Figure 10 (b).

4.2.2.2 Pressure distribution
Pressure coefficient distribution along the wetted surface of the bow flare section at time instants of 0.06s, 0.07s and 0.08s are plotted and compared with the experimental and BEM results from Zhao et al. (1997) in Figure 11. The figure shows the predicted pressure distribution using inviscid, laminar, turbulent K-ε and K-ω regime models compared with literature.

Predicted results are showing good agreement with the literature. The BEM results of Zhao et al. (1997) over predicts both the CFD and experimental results except in turbulent K-ω flow. The predicted CFD pressure distribution is found to be in good agreement with the experimental results.

The pressure distribution from the laminar and turbulent K-ω cases is having fluctuations compared with the smooth distribution in case of inviscid and turbulent K-ε cases. These variations in pressure along wetted surface can be attributed to the air

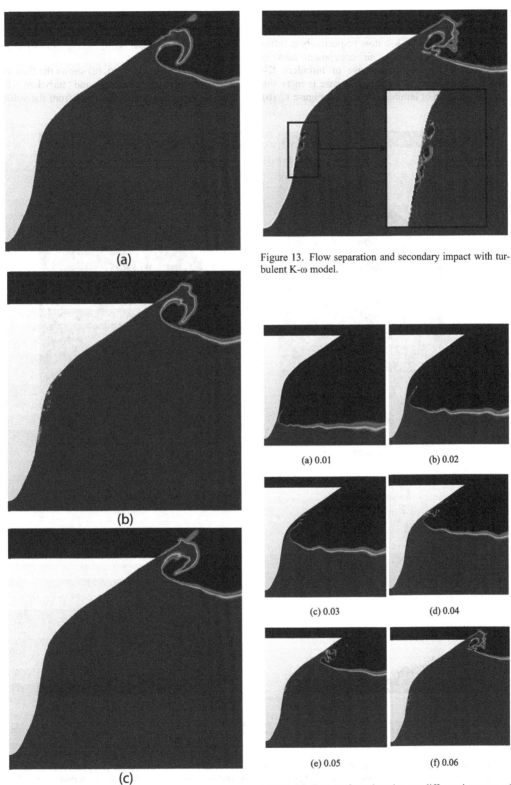

Figure 12. (a)-(c) Free surface elevations for bow flare section at 0.06s for inviscid, laminar and turbulent respectively.

Figure 13. Flow separation and secondary impact with turbulent K-ω model.

Figure 14. Free surface elevations at different instances of time from 0.01 to 0.06s for the case of turbulent K-ω model.

entrapment. Figure 12 (a)-(c) show the free surface elevation around the bow flare section for inviscid, laminar and turbulent K-ε flow respectively at 0.06s.

The Figure 13 shows air entrapment near the inflexion which occurs in case of turbulent K-ω model. The air entrapment in this case is more than that of the case of laminar flow model Figure 12 (b).

Figure 14 shows the free surface elevations around the bow flare section from 0.01s to 0.06s in the case of water entry using turbulent K-ω model.

Figure 15 (a), (c) and (b), (d) shows the flow variation between the laminar and turbulent (K-ε) models respectively. It is depicted from the velocity

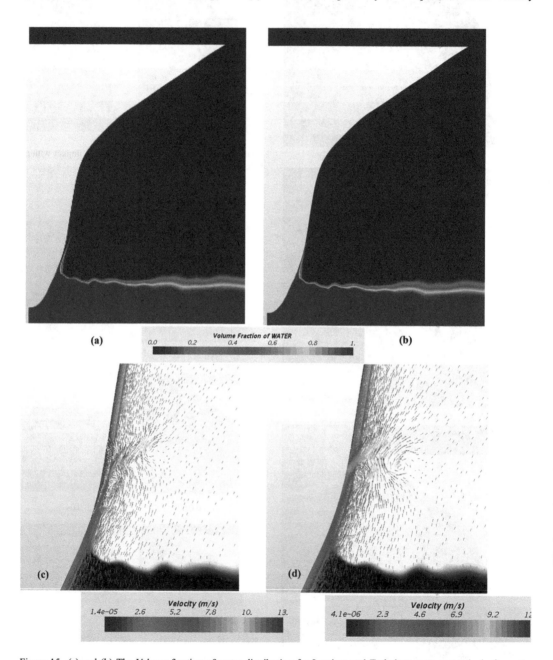

Figure 15. (a) and (b) The Volume fraction of water distribution for Laminar and Turbulent cases respectively for water entry of DTC ship section; (c) and (d) are the velocity vectors near the spray zone in laminar and turbulent (K- ε) cases respectively.

vector figures that the laminar flow is detaching from the surface at spray zone while turbulent (K-ε) flow is moving along with the surface.

5 CONCLUSIONS

The water entry of 2D rigid wedges with different deadrise angles and a bow flare section is investigated using CFD. The effect of grid size, time step and flow regime for two impact velocities (1 m/s and 2 m/s) are studied while predicting the pressure distribution, peak impact pressure.

For the wedge entry the effect of flow regime models namely in-viscid, laminar, and turbulent (K-ε) is studied. It is found that the early impact stage is dominated by inertia instead of viscosity. Laminar model is chosen for grid and time independent study on wedges of dead rise angles 7.5°, 45°. A time step of 0.001 s and grid size of 1mm is found to be optimum for 45° wedge. For 7.5° wedge a higher resolution of grid size 0.5 mm and smaller time step of 5E-5 s is required to predict peak impact pressure more accurately. The water entry of wedges with varying dead rise angles is studied with chosen optimum simulation parameters. The predicted peak pressures coefficient and distribution of pressure coefficient is validated with Zhao & Faltinsen (1993) and found to be in good match. Peak pressure coefficient increases as the deadrise angle decreases and it is moving along with the wetted surface for lower deadrise angles whereas for higher deadrise angles, it is located at the keel of the wedge. It can also be concluded that the effect of impact velocities on the early impact problem is not significant.

The water entry of bow flare section of the DTC container ship model is studied. A grid and time independent study using a turbulent (K-ε) model is presented. A time step of 1E-4 s and a grid size of 0.1 mm is found to be optimum. A study on effect of inviscid, laminar, and turbulent flow regime models is performed. Comparison between K-ε and K-ω turbulent models is carried out. K-ε model better predicts the pressure distribution while K-ω over predicts in comparison with BEM results. The chosen simulation model parameters are used to recreate the water entry of the same section as given in Zhao et al. (1997). The pressure distribution and the forces are found to be in accordance with the literature.

ACKNOWLEDGEMENTS

This work is supported by Naval Research Board (NRB) under the grant number: NRB/4003/PG/439.

REFERENCES

Algarín, R., Bula, A., & Tascón, O. (2011). CFD modeling of 2D asymmetric entry impact along with horizontal velocity. *Ciencia y Tecnología de Buques*, 5(9), 99. http://dx.doi.org/10.25043/19098642.54

Aquelet, N., Souli, M., & Olovsson, L. (2006). Euler-Lagrange coupling with damping effects: Application to slamming problems. *Computer Methods in Applied Mechanics and Engineering*, 195(1–3), 110–132. http://dx.doi.org/10.1016/j.cma.2005.01.010

Cointe, R., & Armand, J. L. (1987). Hydrodynamic impact analysis of a cylinder. *Journal of Offshore Mechanics and Arctic Engineering*, 109(3), 237–243. http://dx.doi.org/10.1115/1.3257015

Commerce, U. S. D. (2019). *National Technical Information Service*.

Dobrovol'skaya, Z. N. (1969). On some problems of similarity flow of fluid with a free surface. *Journal of Fluid Mechanics*, 36(4), 805–829. http://dx.doi.org/10.1017/S0022112069001996

Faltinsen, O. (2002). Water Entry of a Wedge with Finite Deadrise Angle. *Journal of Ship Research*, 46(1), 39–51.

Faltinsen, O. M., Landrini, M. & Greco, M. (2004). Slamming in marine applications. *Journal of Engineering Mathematics*, 48(3–4), 187–217. http://dx.doi.org/10.1023/b:engi.0000018188.68304.ae

Hermundstad, O. A., & Moan, T. (2005). Numerical and experimental analysis of bow flare slamming on a Ro-Ro vessel in regular oblique waves. *Journal of Marine Science and Technology*, 10(3), 105–122. http://dx.doi.org/10.1007/s00773-005-0192-3

ITTC Quality System Manual Recommended procedures and Guidelines, 7.5-03-01-01: Uncertainty analysis in CFD Verification and validation, methodology and procedures. (2017).

M Greenhow, W. L. (1985). Numerical simulation of non-linear free surface flows generated by wedge entry and wavemaker motion. *International Conference on Numerical Ship Hydrodynamics, 4th*, 13.

StarCCM+ Documentation Version 13.02, SIEMENS PLM Software (2018).

Stenius, I., Rosén, A., & Kuttenkeuler, J. (2006). Explicit FE-modelling of fluid-structure interaction in hull-water impacts. *International Shipbuilding Progress*, 53(2), 103–121.

Stenius, I., Rosén, A., & Kuttenkeuler, J. (2007). Explicit FE-modelling of hydroelasticity in panel-water impacts. *International Shipbuilding Progress*, 54(2–3), 111–127.

Tuitman, J. T. (2010). *Hydro-elastic response of ship structures to slamming induced whipping*. Retrieved from https://repository.tudelft.nl/islandora/object/uuid%3Af9aa0204-650d-493f-b1e9-43e91c0f4993

von Karman, T. (1929). The impact on seaplane floats during landing. In *National Advisory Committee for Aeronautics Technical Notes*. Retrieved from http://authors.library.caltech.edu/47898/%5Cnhttp://naca.central.cranfield.ac.uk/report.php?NID=766

Wagner, H. (1931). *Landing of seaplanes*. 32. Retrieved from http://ntrs.nasa.gov/search.jsp?R=19930094794

Wang, S. (2011). *Assessment of slam induced loads on two dimensional wedges and ship sections*. 113 pages.

Wang, S., & Guedes Soares, C. (2012). Analysis of the water impact of symmetric wedges with a multi-material Eulerian formulation. *The Transactions of The Royal Institution of Naval Architects, Volume 154, Part A4, International Journal of Maritime Engineering, Paper: T2012-4 Transactions.*, (September 2014). http://dx.doi.org/10.3940/rina.ijme.2012.a4.249

Wang, S., & Guedes Soares, C. (2014). Numerical study on the water impact of 3D bodies by an explicit finite element method. *Ocean Engineering*, *78*, 73–88. http://dx.doi.org/10.1016/j.oceaneng.2013.12.008

Wang, S., & Guedes Soares, C. (2013). Slam induced loads on bow-flared sections with various roll angles. *Ocean Engineering*, *67*, 45–57. http://dx.doi.org/10.1016/j.oceaneng.2013.04.009

Zhao, R., Faltinsen, O. & Aarsnes, J. (1997). Water Entry of Arbitrary Two-Dimensional Sections with and Without Flow Separation. *Proc. 21th Symp. Naval Hydrodynamics*, 408–423.

Zhao, R., & Faltinsen, F. O. (1993). Water entry of two-dimensional bodies. *Journal of Fluid Mechanics*, *246*(4), 593–612. http://dx.doi.org/10.1017/S002211209300028X

Assessment of ship motion responses to multi-peaked spectral models

L.Z.M. Silva, R. Vettor & C. Guedes Soares
Centre for Marine Technology and Ocean Engineering (CENTEC), Instituto Superior Técnico, Universidade de Lisboa, Lisbon, Portugal

ABSTRACT: Spectral parametric models are used to describe the energy distribution of both swell and wind sea wave components, into the frequency and directional domains and to assess the ship motions by means of transfer functions computed by linear strip theory. The objective is investigating the influence of the spectral models on the ship responses, studying the significance of the wave climate on such differences, so that more suited spectral models can be recommended according to the areas the vessels are designed to operate at. It is shown that traditional approaches are acceptable for the evaluation of extreme events, while in milder conditions larger differences are found, suggesting to consider the adoption of more complete models for estimating operability and voyage planning. Generally, more marked variability is observed in roll, pointing out the need of a more accurate description of the wave energy in this case.

1 INTRODUCTION

The operating life of any marine structure is dramatically influenced by its responses to environmental loads. A major design concern is related with the wave induced structural stresses, but the operations can also be strongly limited by other responses such as roll motion, accelerations, slamming and green water occurrences, due to their effect on the safety of people and cargo on-board.

The description of the wave field energy is crucial part of the ship response computations. The wave energy spectrum is largely used for describing the wave energy distribution into both the frequency and directional domains. Full representation of the energy spectrum is, in most of the cases, impractical, so that parametric models have been proposed in the literature and are usually adopted to fit the energy distribution. Integral parameters required to describe the wave field main characteristics are, for instance: significant wave height (H_s), mean wave period (T_m) and mean wave direction (θ_m). The wave energy spectrum can be expressed by different parametric models, such as uni- or multi-directional, single- or double-peaked ones, reflecting the presence of multiple wave systems. Nevertheless, more often than not, the simplest unidirectional single peaked model is used. This model is, however, only expected to be adequate in case the sea-state is characterized by a single long-crested wave system.

Depending on the sea-state characteristics, the variability on the ship response estimations by changing the parametric model can be more or less significant, in such way that the importance of selecting a suitable model to avoid eventual under-estimations on the calculation of motions is highlighted in this article,.

The influence of selecting either a parametric spectra formulation or the full spectrum on both the ship responses and weather routing has been investigated showing that they can result in different decisions on route planning (Spentza, et al. 2018). Detailed and reliable estimates of vertical bending moment, shear stresses and accelerations could be derived thanks to wave spectra partitioning into wave components (Lawford, et al. 2008), where the marked relevance of wind-sea in the response estimations was highlighted.. Further investigations have shown that the directional dispersion function can significantly influence estimations of roll motions, although less marked effect is verified regarding vertical motions such as heave, pitch and bow vertical acceleration (Jiao et al. 2019). Uncertainties related to the sea state spectra shape and transfer functions have been shown to also produce uncertainties in the ship response short-term predictions (Guedes Soares 1990; 1991a). Uncertainties are also reflected in the long-term distributions (Guedes Soares & Trovao, 1992). Although this paper and the previous discussion addresses ship motions, similar formulations have been made for wave induced loads (Teixeira & Guedes Soares, 2009). The relevance of spectral models and wave climate on the ship response estimations is, therefore, a known issue, although it has not yet been explored deeply by the scientific community.

This work aims at covering the gap, starting from the study of the fundamental motions, which in turn, affect the other relevant responses. The influence of the spectra model on the ship responses is analyzed, deriving the relevance of the wave climate on the

DOI: 10.1201/9781003216599-34

differences between the models. The study allows identifying the cases when the simplest approach can be reliable as those when a more complete description of the wave field energy distribution is suggested. The selection of a suited model shows to be crucial for the response estimations, being important for both the design and operational purposes.

2 SHIP SEAKEEPING

2.1 Seakeeping problem and strip theory

To compute the ship responses, both the wave energy spectrum and the ship transfer functions are needed. The response spectrum, $S_r(\omega, \theta)$, associated to a given response r, as a function of the wave frequency ω and direction θ can be found as (Journée & Massie 2001):

$$S_r(\omega, \theta) = |\Phi_r(\omega, \theta)|^2 \times S_w(\omega, \theta) \quad (1)$$

where the term $|\Phi_r(\omega,\theta)|$ is the Response Amplitude Operator (RAO), $S_w(\omega,\theta)$ holds for the wave energy spectrum and r is the response which, in this work, includes heave (ξ_3) and roll (ξ_4).

The ship transfer functions are usually obtained either experimentally from tests in model basins or can be determined computationally, by solving the seakeeping problem with numerical methods such as Strip Theory. The latter is the most commonly used in ship response analysis, and the one applied in this work which makes use of the linear version of an in-house seakeeping code developed by (Fonseca & Guedes Soares 1998), in which Salvesen, Tuck and Faltinsen method (Salvesen, et al. 1970) is implemented to solve the seakeeping problem. Accurate estimations of the RAOs, *heave* and *pitch*, specifically, were found to be derived from the code, by undertaking a comparative investigation between three codes (the in-house developed one, PDStrip and MaxSurf) and experimental data from two fast displacement hulls in head waves obtained from model testing (Belga et al.2018). Additionally, for a realistic computation of the roll transfer function, the evaluation of the viscous-damping is required, which is estimated by making use of the Miller method (Miller 1974).

2.2 Ship description

The ship selected is the S-175 container ship, for which a considerable volume of published material can be found in the literature undertaking investigations towards seakeeping analysis and loads assessment, where nonlinear responses are compared to published experimental data (Fonseca & Guedes Soares 2002, 2004).

In Table 1 are presented the ship main particulars while the hull bodylines are displayed in Figure 1. The ship forward speed is hereafter considered to be such that the Froude number is $F_n = 0.2$, yielding

Table 1. S175 Container Ship main particulars.

Name	Symbol	Value
Length between perpendiculars	L_{pp} [m]	175
Breadth	B [m]	25.4
Depth	D [m]	15.4
Draft	T [m]	9.5
Displacement	Δ [ton]	24742

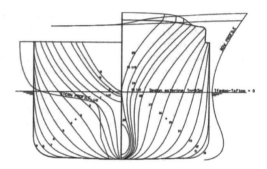

Figure 1. S175 Container Ship hull bodylines.

approximately 16 knots. Ship courses in a range with step of 10 degrees from 0° to 180° are implemented to obtain the RAOs.

3 WAVE SPECTRA MODELS AND SHIP RESPONSE

3.1 The JONSWAP Spectrum

In 1964, Pierson and Moskowitz presented the unidirectional wave energy spectrum (P-M Spectrum) for a fully developed sea-state (Pierson & Moskowitz 1964). Developing seas, however, were found to have a more peaked shape, which came to be better described by the JONSWAP Spectrum, where the dependency on the wind speed and fetch was introduced (Hasselmann, et al. 1973). This latter is considered to be a generalization of the P-M Spectrum through the introduction of the mentioned parameters, and particularly when the so-called peak enhancement factor equals 1, it simplifies into the P-M Spectrum formulation.

In 1976, the parametrization of the former JONSWAP spectrum was proposed in terms of H_s and T_m (Hogben, et al. 1976). Such expression is used in this work to describe the wave energy distribution into the frequency domain.

3.2 Double-peaked parametric model

Single-peaked wave energy spectrum can eventually be inadequate to represent the wave field energy, as it describes the energy distribution of a combined wave system, so that the separate contribution of each component (swell and wind-sea) is not, consequently, considered. Depending on the wave climate, different wave components can be equally relevant on the total wave field energy in such way that a simpler representation may lead to inaccurate estimations of the ship response (Guedes Soares, 1991b).

The double-peaked spectral modeling can be expressed by the sum of two JONSWAP spectra models. Considering swell (S_w^S) and wind-sea waves (S_w^w) as the major wave components of the wave field system, where the upper case W refers to wind-sea waves and S refers to swell, the total spectrum can be expressed as shown in (Guedes Soares 1984):

$$S_w(\omega) = S_w^S(\omega) + S_w^S(\omega) \qquad (2)$$

The JONSWAP parametric formulation is used, in this work, for the representation of both the swell and wind-sea energy spectra, regarding the correspondents H_s, T_m and θ_m.

More recent results have confirmed the adequacy of this model and of the procedure to adjust it to measured data (Ewans et al. 2006; Lucas & Guedes Soares, 2015).

3.3 Directional spreading function

The wave energy distribution into the directional domain can be performed by weighting $S_w(\omega)$ with a probability distribution function (Guedes Soares 2003), as shown in

$$S_w(\omega, \theta) = D(\theta|s, \theta_m).S_w(\omega) \qquad (3)$$

The term $D(\theta|s,\theta_m)$ is defined as the *directional spreading function*. It represents the wave energy distribution at a given frequency into the direction domain around θ_m, as expressed by Equation 4:

$$D(\theta|s, \theta_m) = \left[2^{2s-1}\Gamma(s+1)\Gamma(s)/\pi\Gamma(2s)\right] \times \cos^{2s}(\theta - \theta_m) \qquad (4)$$

where:

- s is the factor of the dispersion function, in this work, considered to be 1;
- θ_m is the dominant wave propagation direction (mean wave direction);
- $\Gamma(s)$ is the Gamma Function.

The factor of the dispersion function, s, may assume different values for swell and wind-sea, as these two components can present different directionality, which is inherently associated to their generation mechanisms (Lucas & Guedes Soares 2009). Wind-sea is commonly to be found propagating towards different directions while more marked regularity is found when assessing swell waves propagation. In this work, the ship responses are to be computed over a grid of points on the North Atlantic, thus the definition of suited dispersion factors at each point shows to be impractical, and the same value for both components is assumed. Further investigations on the influence of the dispersion factor on the ship responses may be, nevertheless, required.

3.4 Parametric models

Four parametric models varying in terms of number of wave components and energy distribution are implemented. The frequency (uni-directional) single-peaked model (1D1P) represents the wave energy spectrum of a combined wave system and energy directionality is not considered. The frequency double-peaked model (1D2P) holds for representation of the energy spectrum considering both the swell and wind-sea components separately. The directional single-peaked model (2D1P) constitutes the energy distribution in both the frequency and directional domain of the combined wave system while the directional double-peaked one (2D2P) holds for the separate representation of swell and wind-sea.

3.5 Ocean wave data

The integral parameters H_s, T_m and θ_m of both the combined wave system and wave components are needed for the implementation of the models described. In this work, such data is retrieved from the ERA-Interim database, which is an ocean atmospheric reanalysis provided by the European Centre of Medium-Range Weather Forecasts (ECMWF) (Dee, et al. 2011). The evolution of two-dimensional wave spectrum at the sea surface, considering the contribution of swell and wind-sea, is obtained by the WAM model, covering the whole globe, including a combination of data assimilated and prior information from forecast models. A 6-hourly global ocean-wave data from 2017 is used in this work.

4 RESPONSE TO DIFFERENT SPECTRAL MODELS

In this section, two examples of the differences between the outputs of the parametric models on heave and roll motions are highlighted considering characteristic sea-state conditions for which energy distribution in the frequency and directional domains are strongly affected by the selected model. A location in the North Atlantic near the Azores archipelago (GPS coordinates: 40° N, 26° W) is considered. The ships course is 45 degrees, North-East direction. Due to space constraints, the discussion is

Table 2. Main wave data for the assessment of the relevance of frequency distribution.

	H_s [m]			T_m [s]			θ_m [deg]		
	Combined Wave System	Swell Waves	Wind Sea Waves	Combined Wave System	Swell Waves	Wind Sea Waves	Combined Wave System	Swell Waves	Wind Sea Waves
Date	H_S	(H_S^S)	(H_S^W)	(T_m)	(T_m^S)	(T_m^W)	(θ_m)	(θ_m^S)	(θ_m^W)
7/1/2017 18:00	2.68	2.47	1.04	7.46	8.76	4.06	123	142	100

here limited to two cases, for deeper analysis and other relevant examples, the reader can refer to (Silva, 2019).

To characterize the double-peaked sea-states, hereafter a wave component is considered *negligible* if the ratio between the energy carried by that component is lower than 10% of the total spectral energy as shown in

$$\left(\frac{H_S^W}{H_S}\right)^2 < 0.1 \quad (5)$$

for the case of wind-sea.

4.1 Effect of frequency distribution

In this example, the wave characteristics are those shown in Table 2. It can be noticed that wind-sea is considered to be relevant, as $\left(H_S^W/H_S\right)^2 = 0.15$. The RAO of heave ($|\Phi_{\zeta 3}|$) and the wave energy spectra of the frequency models are displayed in Figure 2 (in the text box, θ_H represents the relative wave direction).

The mean period of wind-sea waves (4.06 [s]) is in this case less than half of the swell period (8.76 [s]). As shown in Figure 2, the energy peak associated to wind-sea is not represented (see the red line), as in this case it has relatively short wave length compared with the ship size, resulting in negligible excitations. Nevertheless, the combined wave system (see the green line) is strongly affected by the wind-sea contribution, shifting the wave energy peak towards frequencies where the amplification of the motion is higher.

The result is a higher response assessed by the 1D1P, with significant heave amplitude $\zeta_{3s,1D1P} = 1.56$ m, compared with the 1D2P model ($\zeta_{3s,1D2P} = 1.39$ m), as shown in Figure 3, with a difference of approximately 11%. Moreover, the peak of the response spectrum moves from lower to higher frequencies.

In sight of that, even a wave system which motion excitation is not marked can play a fundamental role on the evaluation of the combined parametric wave spectrum, significantly affecting the response estimation.

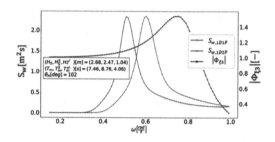

Figure 2. Wave energy spectra and heave RAO for the frequency models.

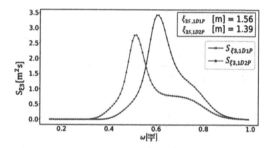

Figure 3. Heave response spectra for the frequency models.

4.2 Effect of directional distribution

In this second example, the considered wave characteristics are provided in Table 3. It can be noticed that the energy content of wind-sea waves is relevant, as $\left(H_S^W/H_S\right)^2 = 0.67$. The mean wave direction of the combined wave system (123 [deg]) and the ship course resulted in a relative wave direction of 2 degrees, which lays within the range of low amplification directions. Thus, if one considers long-crested waves, as those represented by 1D1P spectral models, the expected roll significant amplitude would be almost negligible as ($\zeta_{4s} = 0.43$ deg).

On the other hand, as shown in Figure 4, the amplification reaches its maximum for relative directions

Table 3. Main wave data for the assessment of the relevance of directional distribution.

	H_s [m]			T_m [s]			θ_m [deg]		
	Combined Wave System	Swell Waves	Wind Sea Waves	Combined Wave System	Swell Waves	Wind Sea Waves	Combined Wave System	Swell Waves	Wind Sea Waves
Date	H_S	(H_S^S)	(H_S^W)	(T_m)	(T_m^S)	(T_m^W)	(θ_m)	(θ_m^S)	(θ_m^W)
24/1/2017 18:00	3.71	2.09	3.05	7.27	9.43	6.55	223	263	207

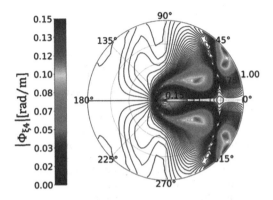

Figure 4. RAO of roll. Range of frequencies on the radial axis from 0.15 to 1.0 rad/s.

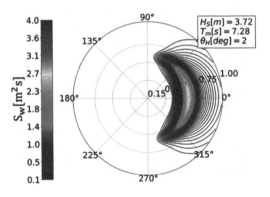

Figure 5. Wave energy spectrum for the 2D1P model.

of about 30 degrees, which are excited when 2D models are considered (see Figure 5).

In such cases, even considering one peak models, the response spectrum in roll is strongly amplified at +30 and -30 degrees, presenting two sharp peaks as shown in Figure 6, with a resultant roll significant amplitude growth of more than 10 times (ξ_{4s} = 5.6 deg), better reflecting the expectable behavior of the ship in short-crested seas.

Roll is shown to be highly sensitive to minor variations in the directional distribution of the wave energy content.

5 SHIP RESPONSES ON THE NORTH ATLANTIC

Heave and roll responses computed over a grid representing the North Atlantic are shown in this section. Visual evidences of the differences between the models over the grid are displayed and assessed in sight of the general wave climate expectable on the North Atlantic.

In order to take into account all possible courses that the ships can assume in each location, a discrete probability distribution function has been calculated (Vettor & Guedes Soares 2015) for each considered grid point by analyzing the reports provided within the Voluntary Observing Ships (VOS) scheme (Fletcher 2008) by vessels navigating in these areas.

The dependency of ship responses on the course is accounted by weighting the responses at each direction by the correspondent course probability of occurrence, providing a map of the expectable behavior of the ship. As a reference, in Figure 7, the significant heave amplitude weighted averages for 1D1P model are presented.

Figure 8 shows the relative differences between the single and double-peaked frequency models. These plots allow verifying that the differences tend to decrease towards the extratropical area, where, the probability of encountering wave fields dominated by one single component (see Eq. 5) is higher, as discussed in the next section. Since dominated wave field is expected there, the spectra obtained by single and double-peaked models almost coincide, explaining the agreement verified in this area. Single-peaked models could be chosen over double-peaked ones in these cases, based on the modeling simplicity and lower computational effort.

Single and double-peaked models tend to be strongly correlated, especially in more severe seastates, as seen in Figure 9. Even though these models tend to produce agreeing responses under the occurrence of dominated wave fields, this is not necessarily true when comparing frequency and directional models for which marked differences can often be expected.

Figure 10 displays the algebraic difference between the frequency single- and double-peaked models and its relation with the part from the total

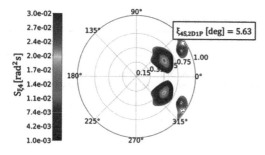

Figure 6. Roll response spectrum for the 2D1P model.

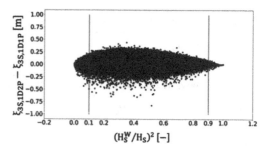

Figure 10. Relation between the significant heave amplitude algebraic difference and the part of wind-sea energy with respect to the total one, 1D1P vs 1D2P.

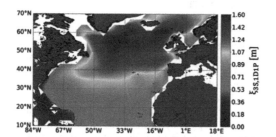

Figure 7. Weighted average mappings for the North Atlantic on the Heave Response, 1D1P model.

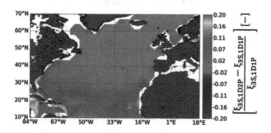

Figure 8. Heave relative difference mapping for the North Atlantic on the Heave Response, 1D2P vs 1D1P.

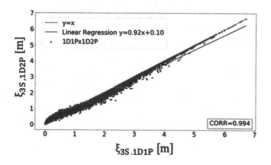

Figure 9. Correlation between the models, 1D1PX1D2P.

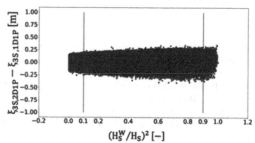

Figure 11. Same as Figure 10, but for 1D1P vs 2D1P.

wave field energy carried by the wind-sea component. It shows that the difference tends to increase as wind-sea becomes relevant, $\left(H_S^W/H_S\right)^2 > 0.1$, and tend to vanish when swell becomes negligible, $\left(H_S^W/H_S\right)^2 > 0.9$.

The relation between Figure 9 and Figure 10 can be found by analyzing the results shown in (Lucas, et al. 2011), where the wind-sea dominated seastates are shown to be predominant in severe conditions. It is found that, in general, for heave responses higher than 5 meters, the model comparison method adheres the $y = x$ line quite strongly. This is true even from the comparison between frequency and directional models (not shown here), although in this case the adherence was found to be less marked.

When comparing frequency and directional models (see Figure 11 for 1D1P and 2D1P), the same pattern as observed in Figure 10 is not verified. Clearly, even in dominated wave fields, not necessarily the decreasing of the difference between frequency and directional models is derived, showing that a more complete description of the energy field in terms of directionality for the response estimation can be suggested.

As general rule, the higher the responses, the stronger the correlation between the models. These findings allow to draw some important conclusions about the usage of different models for design or operational purposes. At the design stage when the behavior under extreme weather conditions is often a concern, the selection of simpler models is not expected to lead to substantial disagreements compared to results from more complete ones. Thus, the traditional and simpler 1D1P model can be recommended.

On the other hand, the general findings in less severe sea-states, $H_S \leq 5.0\ m$, are not conclusive, as a marked disagreement about the ideal line is observed. In sight of that, when considering the performance in milder climate, the parametric model to be used should be accurately selected. In this case, it is suggested to gather more information about the sea-ways the ship is supposed to sail through, as to determine if they are likely to be dominated by one wave component, or rather composed by multiple wave systems, possibly from different directions. This allows, eventually, the selection of the most suited model. It must be noted that these less severe sea-states are the ones that occur more frequently and are dealt with in weather routing systems (Vettor & Guedes Soares 2016).

6 SEA STATE CLASSIFICATIONS

It becomes then vital to know beforehand if the wave field is expected to be dominated, as in this case single-peaked models are sufficiently accurate to compute the desired responses. Pursing this objective, wave fields have been classified according to pre-defined parameters and statistical analysis are performed in order to determine the probability of occurrence of each class.

The classification procedure used in this work follows a straightforward parametric methodology based on the wave field main characteristics. Three parameters are used to distinguish the further presented classes. They are:

$$\tilde{H} = \left(\frac{H_S^W}{H_S}\right)^2 \quad (6)$$

$$\tilde{T} = abs\left(T_m^S - T_m^W\right) \quad (7)$$

$$\tilde{\theta} = abs\left(\theta_m^S - \theta_m^W\right) \quad (8)$$

The classes whose nomenclature is described below, are assigned to the specific sea-state according to the conditions defined in Table 4.

- One-peaked swell dominated – OPS;
- One-peaked wind sea dominated – OPWS;
- Two-peaked, no crossing-seas occurrence – TPNCS;
- Two-peaked, with crossing-seas occurrence – TPCS;
- Undefined Mixed Condition – UMC.

Table 4. Mathematical description of the classes.

Class	Description
OPS	$\tilde{H} \leq 0.1$
OPWS	$\tilde{H} \geq 0.9$
TPNCS	$0.1 < \tilde{H} < 0.9$ $\tilde{T} > 4.0\ s$ $\tilde{\theta} \leq 30°$
TPCS	$0.1 < \tilde{H} < 0.9$ $\tilde{\theta} > 30°$
UMC	$0.1 < \tilde{H} < 0.9$ $\tilde{T} \leq 4.0\ s$ $\tilde{\theta} \leq 30°$

According with the defined classification, the probability of occurrence of single-peaked events is computed over the North Atlantic, as shown in Figure 12. The sum of both the swell (OPS) and wind-sea (OPWS) probability of occurrences is represented, meaning when the wave field is likely to be dominated by a single component.

The direct influence of the classified sea states upon the differences between the models can be verified by conditioning the statistical analysis of the wave field to the specific classes. It is expected that OPS and OPWS classes would be fairly represented by 1D1P or 2D1P models, TPNCS class would require at least 1D2P model, whereas TPCS would include both double peak and directionality in the spectral model as to catch the real physics of the wave field. In Figure 13 are shown the relative differences conditioned to single-peaked wave field for heave (a) and roll (b) motions.

Accordingly, the differences between single and double-peaked models in heave are not relevant on the North Atlantic when the wave climate is conditioned to dominated wave field only, except in marginal seas such as the Caribbean one. The same agreement is verified regarding roll responses, although the 1D1P model slightly over-estimated the responses around parallel 50°N. This is due to the fact that roll amplification is typically restricted to a relatively narrow range of frequencies, thus minor

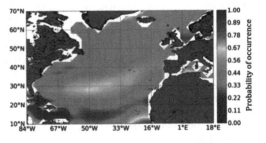

Figure 12. Probability of occurrence of single-peaked events.

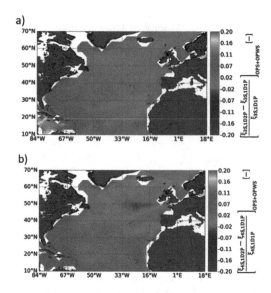

Figure 13. Relative difference conditioned to single-peaked classes for the North Atlantic on the (a) heave and (b) roll response.

variations in the estimation of the wave peak period may have a significant effect in the estimated roll.

Strong variability on the differences between frequency and directional models in roll motion was further observed (figures not shown here), even in dominated wave field. Predicting the behavior of these models for roll in not dominated climate shows to be a difficult task as no pattern can be directly derived. For heave, on the other hand, the differences showed equally to decrease towards more violent response locations, even though it became clear that more complete models in terms of wave components and energy directionality would be suggested as the simpler frequency approach appeared to strongly under-estimate the responses about the intertropical area.

7 CONCLUSIONS

It was found that when both swell and wind-sea are energetically relevant, the responses to the models tend to diverge more. The differences between single and double-peaked models tend to decrease as the relevance of one of the components decreases. The representations of the wave field energy show to be coincident, in these cases. The differences between frequency and directional models, even considering dominated wave field, vary according to the relative wave direction. Frequency models can provide similar, significantly higher or lower results compared to the directions ones, depending whether range of higher amplification is close to the relative wave direction or not.

The sea state classification procedure demonstrated that the differences between the models could be analyzed regarding similar wave fields recorded in each classification. For heave, when responses are conditioned to single-peaked events, similar results can be expected from different models in open waters.

A higher variability is verified when comparing frequency and directional models. For sea conditions characterized by two distinct wave systems, it was found that single-peaked models tend to underestimate the responses compared to those from the double-peaked ones. For roll, even though single- and double-peaked models presented significant agreement in dominated wave field, a general higher variability on the estimated responses between the models was observed. In this case, it was not possible to identify a general rule to predict whether the error is conservative or not and the comparison between frequency and directional models showed quite high variability in all conditioned seas.

It is clear that different parametric models can provide different responses, depending on the wave climate. The prior knowledge of the climate of the sea-ways the structures are designed to operate at can be fundamental for the selection of a suitable model, as in some cases, simpler models can present fairly reliable results compared to those from more complete ones. In general, in dominated sea-states, the single-peaked directional model can be used, especially in severe weather conditions. In locations where both the swell and wind-sea components are relevant, more complete models should be taken into consideration. Moreover, directional models are always to be preferred, except in case of long-crested swells, however further researches are necessary to appropriately tune the directional spreading function for a realistic short crest representation.

The findings of the present work allow to provide some important recommendation for the selection of the most appropriate spectral model:

– for design purposes, when limit state values are to be evaluated, the traditional approach to single-peak model can be accepted, however taking into account directional spreading is recommendable, especially when roll motion is considered.
– In case of design parameter influenced by frequent events of lower intensity, such as fatigue, more complex models may be needed, however further research on structural loads should be carried out to better investigate these aspects;
– for operational purposes, the expected sea-state should be carefully categorized and guided towards the model that better reflects the physics of such a wave field.

ACKNOWLEDGEMENTS

This work contributes to the project ROUTING research project (MARTERA-/ROUTING/3/2018) which is supported by the Portuguese Foundation for

Science and Technology (Fundação para a Ciência e Tecnologia - FCT) under grants on in EU ERA-NET COFUND MarTERA-1 programme (2018-2021). This work contributes to the scope of the Strategic Research Plan of the Centre for Marine Technology and Ocean Engineering (CENTEC), which is financed by the Portuguese Foundation for Science and Technology (Fundação para a Ciência e Tecnologia-FCT) under contract UIDB/UIDP/ 00134/2020.

REFERENCES

Belga, F., S. Sutulo & C. Guedes Soares. 2018. Comparative Study of Various Strip-Theory Seakeeping Codes in Predicting Heave and Pitch Motions of Fast Displacement Ships in Head Seas. *Progress in Maritime Technology and Engineering*, Guedes Soares, C. & Santos T. A., (Eds.). London, UK: Taylor and Francis; 599–610.

Dee, D. P. et al. 2011. The ERA-Interim Reanalysis: Configuration and Performance of the Data Assimilation System. *Quarterly Journal of the Royal Meteorological Society* 137 (656): 553–97.

Ewans, K. C.; Bitner-Gregersen, E., and Guedes Soares, C. 2006. Estimation of Wind-Sea and Swell Components in a Bimodal Sea State. *Journal of Offshore Mechanics and Arctic Engineering.* 128(4): 265–270.

Fletcher, J. 2008. Meteorological Observations from Ships. *Seaways - The Nautical Institute*, 2008.

Fonseca, N. & Guedes Soares, C. 1998. Time-Domain Analysis of Large-Amplitude Vertical Ship Motions and Wave Loads. *Journal of Ship Research.* 42(2): 139–153.

Fonseca, N. & C. Guedes Soares. 2002. Comparison of Numerical and Experimental Results of Nonlinear Wave-Induced Vertical Ship Motions and Loads. *Journal of Marine Science and Technology* 6 (4): 193–204.

Fonseca, N. & Guedes Soares, C. 2004; Experimental Investigation of the Nonlinear Effects on the Statistics of Vertical Motions and Loads of a Containership in Irregular Waves. *Journal of Ship Research.* 48(2): 148–167.

Guedes Soares, C. 1984. Representation of Double-Peaked Sea Wave Spectra. *Ocean Engineering* 11 (2): 185–207.

Guedes Soares, C. 1990. Effect of Spectral Shape Uncertainty in the Short-Term Wave Induced Ship Resposnes. *Applied Ocean Research*, 12: 54–69.

Guedes Soares, C. 1991a. Effect of Transfer Function Uncertainty on Short-Term Ship Responses. *Ocean Engineering* 18 (4): 329–62.

Guedes Soares, C. 1991b. On the Occurrence of Double Peaked Wave Spectra. Ocean Engineering. 18(1-2): 167–171.

Guedes Soares, C. 2003. Probabilistic Models of Waves in the Coastal Zone. Lakan, V. C., (Ed.). *Advances in Coastal Modelling.* The Netherlands: Elsevier; pp. 159–187

Guedes Soares, C. & Trovao, M. F. S. 1992. Sensitivity of Ship Motion Predictions to Wave Climate Descriptions. *International Shipbuilding Progress.* 39(418): 135–155.

Hasselmann, K. et al. 1973. Measurements of Wind-Wave Growth and Swell Deacy during the Joint North Sea Wave Project (JONSWAP). *German Hydrographic Journal* 8 (12): 1–95.

Hogben, N. et al. 1976. Environmental Conditions. *Report of Committee I.1-6th International Ship Structures Congress.* Boston.

Jiao, J., C. Chen & H. Ren. 2019. A Comprehensive Study on Ship Motion and Load Responses in Short-Crested Irregular Waves. *International Journal of Naval Architecture and Ocean Engineering*, 11: 364–79.

Journée, J.M.J & W.W. Massie. 2001. *Offshore Hydromechanics.* 1st ed. Delft Univeristy of Technology.

Lawford, R. et al. 2008. Directional Wave Partitioning and Its Applications to the Structural Analysis of an FPSO. *Proceedings of the 27th International Conference on Offshore Mechanics and Arctic Engineering.* pp. 333–341. Estoril, Portugal. June 15–20, 2008

Lucas, C. & Guedes Soares, C. 2015; On the modelling of swell spectra. *Ocean Engineering.* 108: 749–759.

Lucas, C., A. Boukhanovsky & C. Guedes Soares. 2011. Modeling the Climatic Variability of Directional Wave Spectra. *Ocean Engineering*, 38:1283–90.

Lucas, C. & C. Guedes Soares. 2009. Directional Distribution of Components in Combined Sea States. *Proceedings of the 6th Seminar on Coastal and Port Engineering.* Funchal.

Miller, E. R. 1974. Roll Damping, Technical Report 6136-74-280, NAVSPEC.

Pierson, W. J. & L. Moskowitz. 1964. A Proposed Spectral Form for Fully Developed Wind Seas Based on the Similarity Theory of S. A. Kitaigorodskii. *Journal of Geophysical Research*, 69: 5181–90.

Salvesen, N., E. O. Tuck & O. M. Faltinsen. 1970. Ship Motions and Sea Loads. *The Society of Naval Architects and Marine Engineers*, 6:1–30.

Silva, L.M.Z. 2019. Influence of Spectra Model on the Ship Response. MSc Thesis, Instituto Superior Técnico - Universidade de Lisboa.

Spentza, E. et al. 2018. A Ship Weather-Routing Tool for Route Evaluation and Selection: Influence of the Wave Spectrum. *Maritime Transportation and Harvesting of Sea Resources*, Guedes Soares, C. & Teixeira A. P., (Eds.). London, UK: Taylor and Francis; 453–62.

Teixeira, A. P. & Guedes Soares, C. 2009. Reliability Analysis of a Tanker Subjected to Combined Sea States. *Probabilistic Engineering Mechanics.* 24(4): 493–503.

Vettor, R. & C. Guedes Soares. 2015. Detection and Analysis of the Main Routes of Voluntary Observing Ships in the North Atlantic. *Journal of Navigation* 68 (2): 397–410.

Vettor, R. & Guedes Soares, C. 2016. Development of a ship weather routing system. *Ocean Engineering.* 123: 1–14.

Numerical analysis of water impact of spheres using mesh-free and mesh-based methods

S. Wang & C. Guedes Soares
Centre for Marine Technology and Engineering (CENTEC), Instituto Superior Técnico, Universidade de Lisboa, Lisbon, Portugal

J. González-Cao, J.M. Domínguez & M. Gómez-Gesteira
Environmental Physics Laboratory (EphysLab), CIM-UVIGO Universidade de Vigo, Orense, Spain

ABSTRACT: The accuracy of the numerical models DualSPHysics (mesh-less model) and OpenFOAM (mesh-based model) to reproduce the impact of a solid sphere onto a still water tank is analysed by different metrics (normalized standard deviation, correlation coefficient and root-mean square error) using Taylor diagrams. These metrics were applied to the total force exerted on the sphere during the impact. The results of both numerical models converge to reference data when increasing the resolution, being the accuracy similar for both models at high spatial resolution. Therefore, this analysis suggests that mesh-less models have attained the level of maturity required to provide results with an accuracy similar to mesh-based models for this kind of problem.

1 INTRODUCTION

Coastal and marine engineering studies often require a detailed analysis of the physical processes that characterize wave formation, propagation or wave-structure interaction. For this purpose, either physical or numerical modelling are employed. In general, physical model tests constitute the most used approach for analysis purposes despite being costly, time consuming and strongly dependent on the accuracy of the measurement equipment. Numerical models can be a useful alternative to be used in coastal and marine engineering for practical purposes. One of the main advantages of numerical modelling is their capability to simulate any scenario with reduced costs. Moreover, numerical models do not suffer from scale effects and can provide information on physical quantities that could be difficult to measure in scaled models or in prototypes. There are two main types of numerical models to analyse flow fields: Eulerian and Lagrangian. Traditional Computational Fluid Dynamics (CFD) techniques use the Eulerian approach. These mesh-based models analyse the flow field at a fixed position of the domain, hence they might require the definition of fine meshes to discretize the domain to study, for example, the wave-structure interaction (Kleefsman et al. 2005, Higuera et al. 2013). The mesh-based methods require, in some cases, expensive mesh generation and have severe technical challenges associated with implementing conservative multi-phase schemes. Free surface elevation is obtained by using volume of fluid methods (VOF). The Lagrangian methods, also called mesh-free methods, analyse the flow by following the movement of the fluid particles. These methods allow overcoming part of the drawbacks of the mesh-based schemes, although they usually have a higher computational cost. Methods such as Smoothed Particle Hydrodynamics (SPH) (Violeau, 2012) and the particle finite element method (PFEM) (Oñate et al. 2011) are examples of mesh-free schemes. In SPH no special tracking is used to detect the free surface and the domain is multiply-connected due to the Lagrangian nature the method. Consequently, large deformations can be efficiently treated since there is no mesh distortion, making SPH an ideal technique to study highly non-linear phenomena.

Only a few comparisons between mesh-based and mesh-free methods can be found in the literature. For example, Neves et al. (2016) compared the time series of free-surface elevation and horizontal velocity of two types of breaking waves using IHFOAM and DualSPHysics. The authors concluded that both numerical models provide similar results but the mesh-free method was three times faster (on GPU) than the mesh-based method (on CPU). However, the authors analysed the results with only one spatial resolution and the geometries defined for each numerical model were not equivalent. Kas et al. (2009) analysed two types of tsunami wave generation by using FLOW-3D (Flow Sciences, 2006) and a SPH code. The authors defined different geometries and resolutions for each type of wave generation concluding that both numerical methods were in a good agreement with the reference data but no information about runtimes was provided. Koukouvinis et al. (2010) and Koukouvinis et al. (2011) compared the modelling of a Turgo turbine using the mesh-based code Fluent® and SPH. They defined different resolutions to compare both models to conclude that mesh-free method provide similar results in much less time than the mesh-based method. The work of Zidonis & Aggidis (2015) presented the benefits and drawbacks of different mesh-based and mesh-free codes in the numerical modelling of Pelton turbines. More recently a complete comparison between DualSPHysics and IHFOAM to analyse violent impacts of wave on marine structures was carried out by González-Cao et al. (2019).

This paper contributes to fill the gap of comparison studies by using two popular non-commercial CFD codes DualSPHysics and OpenFOAM to analyse the impact of a sphere on a still water tank. This problem is directly linked to wave energy converters where, under some wave conditions, floaters mechanisms can experiment high vertical displacements due to resonance phenomena (De Backer et al. 2008). The problem of a sphere impacting on water was first studied more than fifty years ago when May (1951) analysed the cavity that forms when the sphere enters the water. A complete description of the experimental methodology carried out to analyse the problem was presented in Nisewanger (1961). Moghisi & Squire (1980) conducted a series of experimental tests to analyse the effect of the viscosity of the liquids and also the variation of the initial velocity of the sphere on the drag coefficient. Kuwabar et al. (1987) analysed the splash formation when a smooth spheres of different materials impacted to liquid surface with different viscosities. More recently De Backer et al. (2009) carried out experiments using several types of asymmetric bodies to analyse the effect of the shape in the force exerted onto these bodies. They also compare the results with the asymptotic theory of rigid bodies with constant entry velocity. From a numerical point of view there are some interesting works related with this kind of problem. For example, Maruzewski et al. (2010) showed the capability of SPH models to reproduce water entry problems, Ahmadzadeh et al. (2014) analysed the hydrodynamic of the sphere water entry problem using a coupled Eulerian-Lagrangian (CEL) formulation implemented in the code ABAQUS. Also, Wang & Guedes Soares (2014) developed a numerical methodology based on explicit finite element method to analyse the water impact of 3D bodies. More recently, an interesting study on the effect of the impact velocity, the radius of the sphere and also the mass of free-falling spheres on the force exerted onto the sphere was carried out by Yu et al. (2019), and the motion of a freely falling horizontal cylinder into water was investigated by Xiang et al. (2020).

The paper is structured as follows: first, a brief description of the numerical models is shown in section 2; next, in section 3, a description of the physical model and the numerical set-up is shown along with a description of the statistic parameters used to compare both numerical models; section 4 shows the numerical results of several variables associated to this case along with some reference solutions (experimental and theoretical) and a convergence analysis of the numerical displacements, velocities and forces exerted onto the sphere by means of Taylor diagrams (Taylor, 2001); finally, section 5 shows the conclusions of the work.

2 NUMERICAL MODELS

2.1 *DualSPHysics model*

DualSPHysics is a numerical model based on the Smoothed Particle Hydrodynamics (SPH) method. DualSPHysics was conceived to use SPH for real engineering problems. This model is open source and can be freely downloaded from http://www.dual.sphysics.org. DualSPHysics includes a software that can be run on either CPUs or GPUs (graphics cards with powerful parallel computing). GPUs offer greater computing power than CPUs, and they are an affordable option to accelerate SPH modelling. This software also includes pre-processing and post-processing tools. A complete description of DualSPHysics can be found in Crespo et al. (2015).

SPH is a Lagrangian and mesh-less method where the fluid is discretised into a set of particles that are nodal points where physical quantities (such as position, velocity, density, pressure) are computed as an interpolation of the values of the neighbouring particles. The contribution of these neighbours is weighted using a kernel function (W) that measures that contribution from the rest of the particle in terms of the particle spacing. This distance between particles is normalized using the smoothing length (h_{SPH}), which is the characteristic length that defines the area of influence of the kernel. The kernel presents compact support, so that the contribution of particles beyond a cut-off distance (here $2h_{SPH}$) is not considered.

The mathematical fundamentals of SPH are based on integral interpolants. Any function F can be computed by the integral approximation.

$$F(r) = \int F(r')W(r-r', h_{S}PH)dr' \quad (1)$$

This function F can be expressed in discrete form based on particles. Thus, the approximation of the function is interpolated at particle a and the summation is performed over all the particles within the region of compact support of the kernel:

$$F(r_a) \approx \sum_b F(r_b) W(r_a - r_b, h_{SPH}) \frac{m_b}{\rho_b} \quad (2)$$

where the volume associated to the neighbouring particle b is m_b/ρ_b, being m and ρ mass and density respectively.

The discrete SPH system of equations of a weakly compressible fluid is, according to Monaghan (1992):

$$\begin{cases} \frac{d\rho_a}{dt} = \sum_b m_b (v_a - v_b + \Psi_{ab}) \nabla_a W_{ab} \\ \frac{dv_a}{dt} = -\sum_b m_b \left(\frac{P_b + P_a}{\rho_b \rho_a} + \Pi_{ab} \right) \nabla_a W_{ab} + g \\ \frac{dr_a}{dt} = v \end{cases} \quad (3)$$

where t is time, r position, v velocity, P pressure, ρ density, m mass, g gravitational acceleration and W_{ab} the kernel function that depends on the distance between particles a and b. One option is the Quintic kernel (Wendland, 1995) where the weighting function vanishes for a particle spacing greater than $2h_{SPH}$. Π_{ab} is the viscous term according to the artificial viscosity proposed in Monaghan (1992). Ψ_{ab} is the diffusion term introduced in the so called delta SPH approach proposed by Molteni & Colagrossi (2009).

The system is closed with the Tait's equation of state that allows computing pressure from density values

$$P = B \left[\left(\frac{\rho}{\rho_0} \right)^\gamma - 1 \right] \quad (4)$$

where $\gamma=7$ is the polytropic constant and $B=c_0^2 \rho_0/\gamma$, ρ_0 the reference density and c_0 the numerical speed of sound.

2.2 OpenFOAM model

The OpenFOAM (Open Source Field Operation and Manipulation) version applied in this study is 2.4.0 and maintained by the OpenFOAM foundation. It provides the solution to the unsteady incompressible Reynolds-Average Navier-Stokes (RANS) equations discretized using the finite volume method. The Navier-Stokes equations for an incompressible flow of a Newtonian fluid in vector form are:

$$\rho \left(\frac{\partial v}{\partial t} + v \cdot \nabla v \right) = -\nabla p + \mu \nabla^2 v + \rho g \quad (5)$$

where v is the velocity, p is the pressure, g is the acceleration of gravity, μ is the dynamic viscosity and t represents the time. The continuity equation is:

$$\nabla \cdot v = 0 \quad (6)$$

The volume of fluid (VOF) method is used to track the free surface position. This method determines the fraction of the fluid that exists in each cell. The equation for the volume fraction is:

$$\frac{\partial \alpha}{\partial t} + \nabla \cdot (\alpha U) = 0 \quad (7)$$

where U is the velocity field, α is the volume fraction of water in the cell that varies from 0 to 1, full of air to full of water, respectively.

Time integration is performed by a semi-implicit second-order, two-point, backward-differencing scheme and pressure velocity coupling is provided by the PIMPLE algorithm. A detailed description of the solver may be found in the publications by Jasak (1996, 2009).

For mesh generation, blockMesh and snappyHexMesh tools are applied. To resolve the motion of the mesh (mesh morphing) around the geometry, OpenFOAM's dynamicMotionSolverFvMesh solver is utilized. sixDoFRigidBodyMotion function is used to capture the free movement of the wedges. To capture the moving interface boundaries as well as model mesh motions and topology changes, the interDyMFoam solver is applied.

Turbulence was modelled with a Reynolds averaged stress (RAS) k-ω two equation model.

3 CASE OF STUDY

3.1 Physical model

The physical model consists of a $H \times H$ rectangular water tank with a water depth equal to D. A sphere with radius equal to R_e falls into the tank with initial velocity V_0. In this work R_e is equal to 0.15 m, V_0 is 4 ms^{-1}, D is equal to 0.5 m and H is greater than 1 m to avoid reflection in the lateral walls of the numerical tank. Figure 1 shows a sketch of the physical model.

During the physical tests, the displacement, velocity and acceleration of the sphere were measured using two different methodologies. A high speed camera (HSC) recording the movement of the and an accelerometer (Acc) installed on the surface of the sphere. The experimental results were obtained from De Backer et al. (2009). In addition to these experimental data different theories were applied to obtain more reference data. The added mass (AM) and the pressure integration (PI) method were used to obtain those reference data (Miloh 1991).

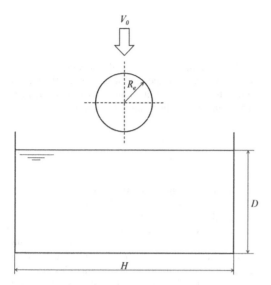

Figure 1. Sketch of the physical water tank.

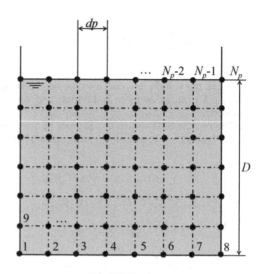

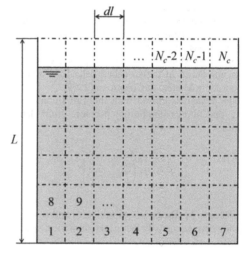

Figure 2. Discretization of a square domain of size L with a water height of D using DualSPHysics and OpenFOAM.

3.2 *Numerical setup*

In DualSPHysics, the numerical tank was created with a pre-processing tool that allows generating particles starting from any type of complex geometry. This tool employs a 3-D Cartesian lattice to locate particles. The idea is to build any object using particles. These particles are created at the nodes of the 3-D Cartesian lattice. First, the lattice nodes around the object are defined and then particles are created only at the nodes needed to draw the desired geometry. Only the initial size of the lattice needs to be defined which will be the initial inter-particle spacing, dp.

OpenFOAM is a mesh-based method where the numerical domain is initially meshed by using a mesh generator tool as, for example, Gmsh (Geuzaine & Remacle, 2009) or the blockMesh utility implemented in OpenFOAM. The defined mesh will be a set of cells with a characteristic length equal to dl.

Figure 2 shows an example of the discretisation of a square box of size L with a water depth equal to D using DualSPHysics and the Block-Mesh utility of OpenFOAM. The initial inter-particle spacing defined with DualSPHysics is equal to dp leading to Np particles of water and the characteristic length of the mesh cells of OpenFOAM is equal to dl leading to Nc cells. Most of them correspond to the water phase and only a few to the air phase.

Table 1 and 2 show the different resolutions defined for both numerical models along with the number of particles/elements and the characteristic length (dp and dl).

The physical time simulated with both numerical models was equal to 0.012 s and the sampling frequency was equal to 1000 Hz.

The convergence analysis of the numerical results is carried out in terms of their normalised standard deviation (σ_n), centred root-mean-square difference (E_n) and correlation (R).

$$\sigma_{n,A} = \frac{\sqrt{\frac{\sum_{i=n}^{N}(A_i - \bar{A})^2}{N}}}{\sigma_B} \qquad (8)$$

Table 1. Parameters of the discretization of DualSPHyiscs.

Resolution	dp (mm)	Num. of particles (millions)
Reference	2.0	11
Fine	2.5	5
Medium	3.0	2
Coarse	3.5	2

Table 2. Parameters of the discretization of OpenFOAM.

Resolution	dl (mm)	Num. of particles (millions)
Reference	0.7	3.6
Fine	1.5	3.0
Medium	6.0	2.8
Coarse	8.3	2.2

$$E_{n,A} = \frac{\sqrt{\frac{\sum_{i=n}^{N}[(A_i-\bar{A})-(B_i-\bar{B})]^2}{N}}}{\sigma_B} \quad (9)$$

$$R_A = \frac{\sum_{i=n}^{N}[(A_i-\bar{A})(B_i-\bar{B})]}{N \sigma_A \sigma_B} \quad (10)$$

where A is a generic variable and B a reference variable. The subscript i refers to the different samples, N is the number of samples, barred variables refer to mean values and σ is the standard deviation calculated as

$$\sigma_B = \sqrt{\frac{\sum_{i=n}^{N}(B_i-\bar{B})^2}{N}} \quad (11)$$

These variables will be grouped together in Taylor's diagrams (Taylor, 2001). The accuracy of the numerical results is computed by means of the centred root-mean-square difference (E_n). Note that E_n represents the distance, measured in the Taylor diagram, from results calculated with the reference resolution to those obtained with the Fine, Medium and Coarse resolutions. Therefore, small values of E_n (~0) mean a good accuracy.

4 RESULTS AND DISCUSSION

The numerical results of displacement and velocity obtained with the reference resolution, along with reference data are depicted in Figures 3 and 4, respectively.

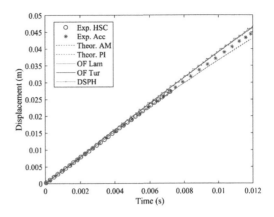

Figure 3. Displacement of the sphere obtained with DualSPHysics (yellow) and OpenFOAM (laminar: blue; turbulent: purple) using the reference resolution. The experimental data (circle: using High Speed Camera; asterisk: using accelerometer) and theoretical data (green: using Added Mass method; red: using Pressure Integration method) are also depicted.

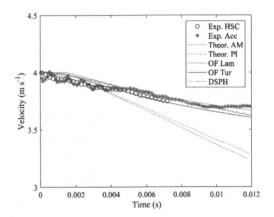

Figure 4. Velocity of the sphere obtained with DualSPHysics (yellow) and OpenFOAM (laminar: blue; turbulent: purple) using the reference resolution. The experimental data (circle: using High Speed Camera; asterisk: using accelerometer) and theoretical data (green: using Added Mass method; red: using Pressure Integration method) are also depicted.

On the one hand, the numerical displacements obtained with DualSPHysics and OpenFOAM have a very good agreement with both the experimental and theoretical ones (Figure 3). The numerical velocities show a good agreement with the experimental values but show a deviation from the theoretical ones for t greater than 0.004 s (Figure 4). This deviation is also observed for the experimental ones.

Another interesting variable of this kind of experiments is the evolution of the force exerted onto the sphere vs. the time. Figure 5 shows the numerical

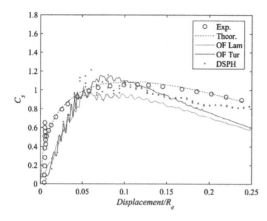

Figure 5. Impact coefficient obtained with DualSPHysics (yellow), OpenFOAM (laminar: blue; turbulent: purple) using the reference resolution. The experimental data (circle) and theoretical data (green dashed line) versus relative displacement (Displacement/R_e) are also depicted.

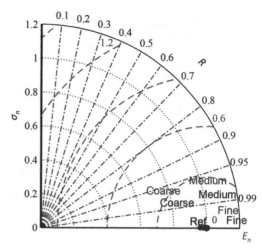

Figure 6. Taylor diagram of displacement obtained with DualSPHysics (red circles) and OpenFOAM (blue circles) using four different resolutions.

results of the slamming coefficient (C_s) along with the experimental and theoretical data. The C_s is defined as

$$C_s = \frac{F_e}{0.5 \rho \pi V_0^2 R_e^2} \quad (12)$$

where F_e is the force exerted on the sphere. The slamming coefficient is plotted vs. a relative displacement of the sphere defined as displacement/R_e.

Figure 5 shows that in general, the numerical results obtained using the reference resolution show an acceptable agreement with the reference data. For values of the relative displacement less than 0.06 (pre-peak stage), the numerical results show a very a good agreement. For relative displacements between 0.05 and 0.11 (peak stage) the numerical results show some deviation from each other and for values of relative displacement greater than 0.11 (post-peak stage) Open-FOAM C_s values tend to 0.6 while DualSPHysics values tends to 0.8.

In order to analyse the convergence of both numerical models, computations were made for the accuracy of the numerical results of displacement, velocity and force by means of Taylor diagrams using four spatial resolutions: Reference, Fine, Medium and Coarse. The reference solution for each model was those obtained with the Reference resolution. Figures 6, 7 and 8 show the Taylor diagrams of displacement, velocity and force obtained with DualSPHysics and OpenFOAM, respectively.

Figure 6 shows that for both numerical models the results of displacement are very accurate. E_n of the Fine resolution to Reference one is near 0 for Dual-SPHysics and OpenFOAM (0.003 and 0.002,

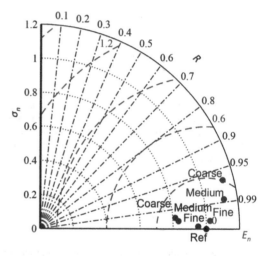

Figure 7. Taylor diagram of velocity obtained with Dual-SPHysics (red circles) and OpenFOAM (blue circles) using four different resolutions.

respectively). The values of E_n obtained with Dual-SPHyisc using Medium and Coarse resolutions are 0.019 and 0.037 and, with OpenFOAM, are 0.003 and 0.003. In the case of DualSPHysics the tendency of the results is quasilinear whilst for OpenFOAM E_n remains constant for Medium and Coarse resolutions.

Figure 7 shows the results of velocity obtained with DualSPHysics and OpenFOAM. In general, the accuracy of both numerical models increases with the spatial resolution. The value of E_n obtained with the Fine resolution is near 0.05 both for DualSPHysics

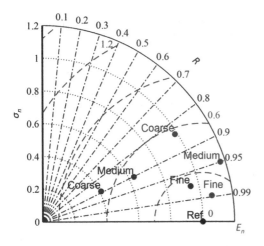

Figure 8. Taylor diagram of velocity obtained with DualSPHysics (red circles) and OpenFOAM (blue circles) using four different values of resolutions.

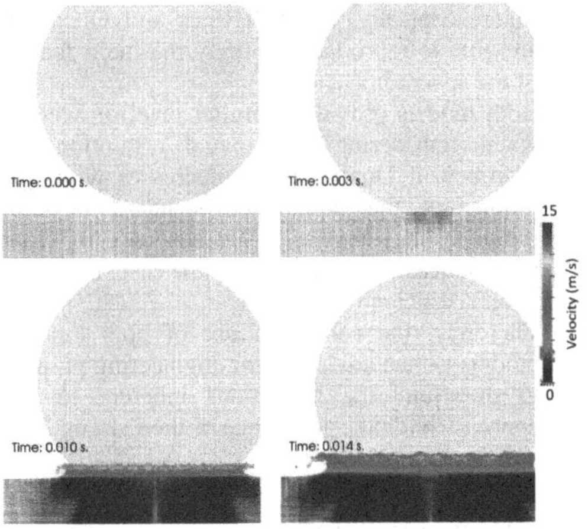

Figure 9. Different snapshots of the DualSPHysics simulation.

and OpenFOAM. For the Medium resolution the value of E_n using OpenFOAM is 0.174 and for DualSPHysics.is equal to 0.20 The values of E_n obtained with DualSPHysics and OpenFOAM for the Coarse resolution are 0.20 and 0.30, respectively. The values of E_n of both numerical models show a quasi-linear behaviour on the characteristic length.

Figure 8 clearly shows that the accuracy of the F_e obtained with both numerical models increases as the resolution increases (dp or dl decreases). The values of E_n obtained with the Fine resolution are 0.17 and 0.23 for DualSPHysics and OpenFOAM. For the Medium resolution E_n is equal to 0.38 for DualSPHysics and 0.51 for OpenFOAM and for the Coarse resolution, E_n is equal to 0.56 and 0.66 for DualSPHysics and OpenFOAM, respectively. This tendency is quasi-linear for the range of resolutions analysed in this work. Figure 8 also shows that for DualSPHysics, the normalized standard deviation remains quasi-constant and the correlation and RMSD get worse as resolution decreases. For OpenFOAM, the correlation remains quasi-constant and the normalized standard deviation get worse as the resolution decreases.

Figures 9 and 10 show some snapshots of the simulation carried out with DualSPHysics and OpenFOAM using the Reference resolution. The magnitude of velocity obtained with both numerical models during the impact are similar (~ 7 ms^{-1}) but the behaviour of the water shows some differences. In DualSPHysics the water splashes back and goes downwards after the impact while the water phase in OpenFOAM remains stuck to the sphere. These differences are related to the different approaches to define the boundary conditions in both numerical models.

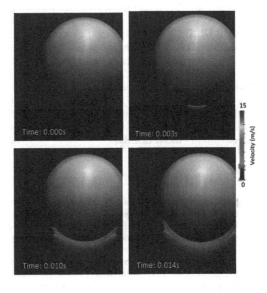

Figure 10. Different snapshots of the OpenFOAM simulation.

5 CONCLUSIONS

The accuracy and performance of the mesh-less model DualSPHysics and mesh-based OpenFOAM have been studied for a case involving an impact of a sphere on a still water tank. OpenFOAM is selected here as a state-of-the art mesh-based and DualSPHysics is selected to be one of the most popular mesh-less SPH models.

The main conclusions of the study are:

- Macroscopically, DualSPHysics and OpenFoam are able to reproduce properly the main features of the sphere impact.
- Both models provide a similar level of accuracy when considering fine spatial resolution. The accuracy of DualSPHysics decreases with resolution but the normalised standard deviation remains quasi-constant. The accuracy of OpenFOAM also decreases but, in this case, the correlation coefficient is constant.
- Therefore, the combined use of both kinds of models is then advisable for engineering purposes to overcome the limitations inherent to each approach and take advantage of their strengths.

ACKNOWLEDGMENTS

This work was performed within the Strategic Research Plan of the Centre for Marine Technology and Ocean Engineering (CENTEC), which is financed by Portuguese Foundation for Science and Technology (Fundação para a Ciência e Tecnologia-FCT) under contract UIDB/UIDP/00134/2020. This work was also funded by Ministry of Economy and Competitiveness of the Government of Spain under project WELCOME ENE2016-75074-C2-1-R and by Xunta de Galicia (Spain) under project ED431C 2017/64 "Programa de Consolidación e Estructuración de Unidades de Investigación Competitivas (Grupos de Referencia Competitiva)" cofunded by EUropean Regional Development Fund (FEDER).

REFERENCES

Ahmadzadeh, M., Saranjam, B., Hoseini Fard, A., Binesh, A.R. 2014. Numerical simulation of sphere water entry problem using Eulerian-Lagrangian method. Applied Mathematical Modelling, 38 (5-6): 1673–1684. DOI: 10.1016/j.apm.2013.09.005.

Altomare, C., Suzuki, T., Domínguez, J., Barreiro, A., Crespo, A., Gómez-Gesteira, M. 2015. Numerical wave dynamics using Lagrangian approach: wave generation and passive & active wave absorption. Proceedings of the 10th SPHERIC International Workshop, Parma, Italy.

Canelas, R.B., Domínguez, J.M., Crespo, A.J.C., Gómez-Gesteira, M., Ferreira, R.M.L. 2015. A Smooth Particle Hydrodynamics discretization for the modelling of free surface flows and rigid body dynamics. International Journal for Numerical Methods in Fluids, 78(9): 581–593. DOI: 10.1002/fld.4031

Crespo, A.J.C., Gómez-Gesteira, M., Dalrymple, R.A. 2007. Boundary conditions generated by dynamic particles in SPH methods. Computers, Materials and Continua, 5 (3): 173–184.

Crespo, A.J.C., Domínguez, J.M., Rogers, B.D., Gómez-Gesteira, M., Longshaw, S., Canelas, R., Vacondio, R., Barreiro, A., García-Feal, O. 2015. DualSPHysics: Open-source parallel CFD solver based on Smoothed Particle Hydrodynamics (SPH). Computer Physics Communications, 187: 204–216. DOI: 10.1016/j.cpc.2014.10.004.

Das, K., Janetzke, R., Basu, D., Green, S., Stamatakos, J. 2009. Numerical simulations of tsunami wave generation by submarine and aerial landslides using RANS and SPH models. Proceedings of the International Conference on Offshore Mechanics and Arctic Engineering - OMAE, 5: 581–594. DOI: 10.1115/OMAE2009-79596.

De Backer, G., Vantorre, M., Victor, S., De Rouck, J., Beels, C. 2008. Investigation of vertical slamming on point absorbers. Proceedings of the International Conference on Offshore Mechanics and Arctic Engineering - OMAE, 6: 851–859. DOI: 10.1115/OMAE2008-57962.

De Backer, G., Vantorre, M., Beels, C., De Pré, J., Victor, S., De Rouck, J., Blommaert, C., Van Paepegem, W. 2009. Experimental investigation of water impact on axisymmetric bodies. Applied Ocean Research, 31 (3): 143–156. DOI: 10.1016/j.apor.2009.07.003.

Flow Sciences, Incorporated, "Flow3D Users Manual", Flow Sciences, Incorporated, Santa Fe, New Mexico (2006).

Geuzaine, C. and Remacle, J.-F. 2009. Gmsh: a three-dimensional finite element mesh generator with built-in pre- and post-processing facilities. International Journal for Numerical Methods in Engineering, 79(11): 1309–1331.

González-Cao, J., Altomare, C., Crespo, A.J.C., Domínguez, J.M., Gómez-Gesteira, M., Kisacik, 2019. D. On the accuracy of DualSPHysics to assess violent collisions with coastal structures. Computers and Fluids, 179: 604–612. DOI: 10.1016/j.compfluid.2018.11.021.

Jasak, H., 1996. Error Analysis and Estimation for the Finite Volume Method with Applications to Fluid Flows, Ph.D. thesis, Imperial College of Science, Technology & Medicine, London, 1996.

Jasak, H. 2009. OpenFOAM: Open source CFD in research and industry. International Journal of Naval Architecture and Ocean Engineering, 1 (2): 89–94. DOI: 10.3744/JNAOE.2009.1.2.089.

Higuera, P., Lara, J.L., Losada, I.J. 2013. Realistic wave generation and active wave absorption for Navier-Stokes models. Application to OpenFOAM®. Coastal Engineering, 71: 102–118. DOI: 10.1016/j.coastaleng.2012.07.002.

Higuera, P., Lara, J.L., Losada, I.J. 2014. Three-dimensional interaction of waves and porous coastal structures using OpenFOAM®. Part I: Formulation and validation. Coastal Engineering, 83: 243–258. DOI: 10.1016/j.coastaleng.2013.08.010.

Kleefsman, K.M.T., Fekken, G., Veldman, A.E.P., Iwanowski, B., Buchner, B. 2005. A Volume-of-Fluid based simulation method for wave impact problems. Journal of Computational Physics, 206 (1): 363–393. DOI: 10.1016/j.jcp.2004.12.007.

Koukouvinis P.K., Anagnostopoulos J.S. and Papantonis D. E. 2010. Flow modeling in a Turgo turbine using SPH. 5th International Smoothed Particle Hydrodynamics European Research Interest Community Workshop, SPHERIC '10, Manchester, U.K., June 22–25.

Koukouvinis, P.K., Anagnostopoulos, J.S., Papantonis, D. E. 2011. SPH method used for flow predictions at a Turgo impulse turbine: Comparison with fluent. World Academy of Science, Engineering and Technology, 79: 659–666.

Kuwabara, G., Tanba, H., Kono, K. 1987. Splash Produced by a Smooth Sphere or Circular Cylinder Striking a Liquid Surface. Journal of the Physical Society of Japan, 56 (8): 2733–2743. DOI: 10.1143/JPSJ.56.2733.

Maruzewski, P., Le Touzé, D., Oger, G., Avellan, F. 2010. SPH high-performance computing simulations of rigid solids impacting the free-surface of water. Journal of Hydraulic Research, 48 (SUPPL. 1): 126–134. DOI: 10.1080/00221686.2010.9641253.

May, A. 1951. Effect of surface condition of a sphere on its water-entry cavity. Journal of Applied Physics, 22 (10): 1219–1222. DOI: 10.1063/1.1699831.

Miloh, T. 1991. On the initial-stage slamming of a rigid sphere in a vertical water entry. Applied Ocean Research, 13 (1): 43–48. DOI: 10.1016/S0141-1187(05)80039-2.

Moghisi, M., Squire, P.T. 1981. An experimental investigation of the initial force of impact on a sphere striking a liquid surface. Journal of Fluid Mechanics, 108: 133–146. DOI: 10.1017/S0022112081002036.

Molteni, D., Colagrossi, A. 2009. A simple procedure to improve the pressure evaluation in hydrodynamic context using the SPH. Computer Physics Communications, 180 (6): 861–872. DOI: 10.1016/j.cpc.2008.12.004.

Monaghan, J.J. 1992. Smoothed particle hydrodynamics. Annual Review of Astronomy and Astrophysics, 30 (1): 543–574. DOI: 10.1146/annurev.aa.30.090192.002551.

Monaghan, J.J., Kos, A., Issa, N. 2003. Fluid motion generated by impact. Journal of Waterway, Port, Coastal and Ocean Engineering, 129 (6): 250–259. DOI: 10.1061/(ASCE)0733-950X(2003)129:6(250).

Monaghan, J.J. 2005. Smoothed particle hydrodynamics. Reports on Progress in Physics, 68 (8): 1703–1759. DOI: 10.1088/0034-4885/68/8/R01.

Neves, D.R.C.B., Pires-Silva, A.A., Fortes, C.J.E.M., Matos, J.J.G. 2016. A comparison of wave breaking with RANS and SPH numerical models. Proceedings of the International Offshore and Polar Engineering Conference, 2016-January: 1182–1189.

Nisewanger, C. 1961 Experimental Determination of Pressure Distribution on a Sphere During Water Entry. Naval Ordnance Test Station: China Lake, CA, USA

Oñate, E., Celigueta, M.A., Idelsohn, S.R., Salazar, F., Suárez, B. 2011. Possibilities of the particle finite element method for fluid-soil-structure interaction problems. Computational Mechanics, 48 (3): 307–318. DOI: 10.1007/s00466-011-0617-2.

Ren, B., He, M., Dong, P., Wen, H. 2015. Nonlinear simulations of wave-induced motions of a freely floating body using WCSPH method. Applied Ocean Research, 50: 1–12. DOI: 10.1016/j.apor.2014.12.003.

Taylor, K.E. 2001. Summarizing multiple aspects of model performance in a single diagram. Journal of Geophysical Research Atmospheres, 106 (D7), art. no. 2000JD900719: 7183–7192. DOI: 10.1029/2000JD90071.

Violeau, D. 2015. Fluid Mechanics and the SPH Method: Theory and Applications. Oxford University Press.

Wang, S., Guedes Soares, C. 2014. Numerical study on the water impact of 3D bodies by an explicit finite element method. Ocean Engineering, 78: 73–88. DOI: 10.1016/j.oceaneng.2013.12.008.

Wendland, H. 1995. Piecewise polynomial, positive definite and compactly supported radial functions of minimal degree. Advances in Computational Mathematics, 4 (1): 389–396. DOI: 10.1007/BF02123482.

Xiang, G., Wang, S., Guedes Soares, C. 2020. Study on the motion of a freely falling horizontal cylinder into water using OpenFOAM. Ocean Engineering, 196; 106811. https://doi.org/10.1016/j.oceaneng.2019.106811

Yu, P., Shen, C., Zhen, C., Tang, H., Wang, T. 2019. Parametric study on the free-fall water entry of a sphere by using the RANS method. Journal of Marine Science and Engineering, 7 (5), art. no. 122, . DOI: 10.3390/jmse7050122.

Židonis, A., Aggidis, G.A. 2015. State of the art in numerical modelling of Pelton turbines. Renewable and Sustainable Energy Reviews, 45: 135–144. DOI: 10.1016/j.rser.2015.01.037.

Ship hydrodynamics - Moorings

Experimental and numerical study of wave-induced ship motions and mooring loads of a tanker moored in Leixões port

H.S. Abdelwahab & C. Guedes Soares
Centre for Marine Technology and Ocean Engineering (CENTEC), Instituto Superior Técnico, Universidade de Lisboa, Lisbon, Portugal

L.V. Pinheiro & C.J.E.M. Fortes
National Laboratory for Civil Engineering, Portugal

J.A. Santos
Instituto Superior de Engenharia de Lisboa, Lisbon, Portugal
Centre for Marine Technology and Ocean Engineering (CENTEC), Instituto Superior Técnico, Universidade de Lisboa, Lisbon, Portugal

ABSTRACT: This paper presents experimental and numerical analyses for ship motions and mooring loads of the Esso Osaka model moored at berth A in Leixões port. The physical model tests are carried out at the Portuguese Civil Engineering Laboratory, the port layout and bathymetry are constructed at 1:80 scale including the future 300 m extension of Leixões' outer breakwater. In this paper, the first objective is to evaluate the performance of the non-linear spring systems that simulate fenders and mooring lines. The second objective is to evaluate the validity of the existing numerical method to estimate the mooring loads and ship motions inside port. The numerical simulations are carried out in time-domain at constant water depth including non-linear mooring system, quay wall and viscous damping. The experimental time series of the measured wave at berth location are inputted in the numerical model as long-crested waves. Finally, numerical results are compared with statistical results obtained from physical modelling.

1 INTRODUCTION

Large tankers and LNG carriers tend to be moored at cargo-handling facilities near the port entrance or at jetties and buoys that are built close to deep water. As a result, berth locations for these ships can be exposed to severe incident wave conditions combined with the action of some other effects such as wind, currents, tides, passing ship effects, swells and seiches. Mooring system generally consists of ropes, wires and fenders that should have an appropriate arrangement and give adequate strength that helps the ship to be moored safely. Excessive ship motions at the berth location can breakdown the cargo loading and offloading and reduce the berth efficiency. In other situations, it can cause failure in the mooring system that may end in a serious accident for crew or damage for the infrastructures and environment.

Ship motions and loads on each element of the mooring system are the main design criterion to ensure operational and safety conditions at berth location. The motions of the moored body must be within the required operational limits while the mooring loads must maintain acceptable levels. For berthed tankers, the cargo manifolds are the limiting factor for safe operation, it allows 3m in surge and sway (PIANC 1995). While the load failure criteria are defined by OCIMF (2018) to be 50% of the minimum breaking load MBL for each mooring line and 100% of the fender maximum reaction.

The estimation of moored ship behaviour requires detailed investigation for not only wave heights at berth location but also wave period, direction, details of berthing structure, bathymetry and characteristics of moored body and mooring system (Taveira-Pinto et al. 2008), so that the combined interactions between ship, mooring elements and environmental conditions at a specific berth location are a sophisticated problem and require a combination between physical and numerical models.

During the last decades, numerical methods became available due to powerful computers. Van Oortmerssen (1976) developed the first numerical model (DIFFRAC) that can estimate the behaviour of a moored tanker in irregular waves. Abdelwahab & Guedes Soares (2018) presented a simple frequency domain model including the second-order effect to study motions and mooring loads at an open jetty with the application of a linearized mooring system.

DOI: 10.1201/9781003216599-36

Other advanced hybrid numerical models proposed by Bingham (2000), Van der Molen (2006) and Pinheiro et al. (2015) are developed to incorporate the effect of complex port geometry and bathymetry at berth location. These hybrid numerical models are based on the application of Boussinesq-type wave propagation models to account for different wave transformation effects such as wave refraction, shoaling, reflection, diffraction and sometimes wave breaking. Then, Cummins (1962) equation is applied to obtain the radiation forces and solve the equation of motion in the time domain to account for other nonlinear effects of the mooring system.

However, numerical models still have limitations due to the complex nature of the hydrodynamic problem in form of viscous effects, turbulence and high order interactions (Rosa-Santos & Taveira-Pinto 2013). The numerical models need yet to be calibrated with results obtained from physical models or prototype measurements. In the context of DOLPHIN project, Taveira-Pinto et al. (2008) proposed a methodology that integrates the application of numerical models, physical modelling and prototype measurements to estimate the ship motions and mooring loads for ships moored in Leixões port. Weiler et al. (2009) used a combination of a time-domain numerical model with physical modelling to study the effect of gusting wind on LNG carrier moored at a jetty.

As mentioned above, severe ship motions at berth location may increase the downtime of operations in ports. This is the case of berth A at the oil terminal in the port of Leixões in Portugal, where the average downtime may reach about 20% of the days per year due to extreme wave conditions (Veloso-Gomes et al. 2005). To improve the berth efficiency, several studies are presented by Rosa-Santos et al. (2008) and Rosa-Santos et al. (2010) based on physical modelling. Those studies focused on applying minor interventions at the location of berth A. To enable the berthing of larger ships (up to 300 m long), other studies presented by Neves et al. (2017) and Santos et al. (2019) were carried out based on major modifications at berth A by increasing the existing breakwater length and water depth.

In this paper, physical model results are presented for the motions and mooring loads of the Esso Osaka tanker moored at berth A in the port of Leixões. The tests were carried out at the Portuguese Civil Engineering Laboratory (LNEC), where the port layout and bathymetry were constructed at 1:80 in model scale and include the future 300 m extension of Leixões' outer breakwater.

The fenders and mooring lines were simulated in the physical model with a different non-linear spring system. The applied spring system is evaluated for each mooring element based on the experimental results. Then, the measured wave time series obtained from physical model results are used as an input for the numerical model.

The numerical simulations were carried out in the time domain based on potential flow software ANSYS® AQWA. The calculations are carried at constant shallow water depth taking into account the representation of nonlinear behaviour of fenders and mooring lines, quay wall effects and viscous damping. Finally, the numerical results for motions and mooring loads are compared with the statistical experimental data obtained from the physical model.

2 LEIXÕES OIL TERMINAL

Leixões port is one of the major Portuguese ports that can receive several types of ships, located 4 km north of the Douro River, near the city of Porto. The port has an oil terminal that consists of three berth locations as shown in Figure 1. Berth A is located at the port entrance to receive large tankers; it consists of two breasting dolphins and a loading platform. The water depth along the berth is -16 m from the zero hydrographical levels (ZHL). The height of tide varies between 2 to 4 m. Berth A is protected by the North breakwater which is 700 m long and has a height of 15 m above the seawater level; however, it is exposed to severe ocean waves that reach the Portuguese coast from directions between west and northwest. During storms, the offshore significant wave heights H_s may exceed 8 m and wave periods T_p can be around 16-18 s. Studies show that it is possible to have waves with 2.5 m significant wave height around berth A at a certain sea state.

Veloso-Gomes et al. (2005) showed that operation at berth A is affected by several factors such as breakwater overtopping, wave diffraction, current and sediment transmission, mooring and longwave effects. Minor modifications were investigated by Rosa-Santos & Taveira-Pinto (2013) to provide safe motions and mooring loads for the tankers at the berth. The proposed modifications are summarized as increasing the stability of the breakwater layer, applying higher pretension, modifying mooring configurations, changing water depth and finally slight modification of breakwater configurations. To provide protection for the oil terminal by increasing its shelter conditions, and to allow the entrance of large ships up to 300 m, the North breakwater is supposed to be extended in the future with 300 m length with an opening angle of 20° relative to the alignment of the existing breakwater. Also, the access channel

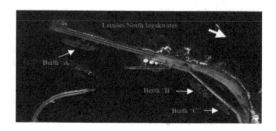

Figure 1. Leixões Oil Terminal(Rosa-Santos et al. 2010).

alongside berth A is supposed to be dredged to 16.85 m (ZHL) water depth.

3 PHYSICAL MODEL STUDY

This section presents the details of the physical model to study the motions and mooring loads of the Osaka tanker moored at berth A in the port of Leixões including the future developments.

The full test campaign investigates the effects of different parameters on waves, motions and mooring loads at berth A such as tide level, mooring pretension and sea state condition H_s and T_p. Some results from the test campaign have been presented by Santos et al. (2019). In the current paper, certain test conditions were repeated to evaluate the performance of the instrumentation, so that the results are presented for one sea state condition.

3.1 Experimental facility and model layout

The scaled model tests were carried out in a basin at LNEC. The basin is 23 m long and 22 m wide and is equipped with a mobile piston wave generator board that can generate regular and irregular long-crested waves at a water depth up to 50 cm.

The three-dimensional model of berth A and surrounding geometry were built at a geometric scale of 1:80. The waves were generated following Froude law of similarity, so the model represents the whole basin of the port of Leixões up to the entrance of Leça river as shown in Figure 2. Also, it includes accurate reproduction for the bathymetry, nearby beaches, the South and North breakwaters, in addition to 300 m as a future extension of the existing North breakwater. The model includes the interior basin of port, a new port configuration and the new dredging depth of the entrance channel to 16.85 m (ZHL) and of the rotating basin to -15.5 m (ZHL).

The selected ship model for the study is the Esso Osaka oil tanker shown at Figure 3, the model is constructed in fibreglass reinforced plastic and covered with 18 mm wooden deck to facilitate the installation of mooring equipment. It is assumed that the scaling of the vessel is 1:80. Before the moored ship test, the ship model is calibrated to achieve the

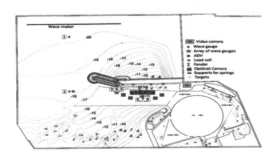

Figure 2. Physical model layout in the tank.

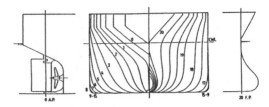

Figure 3. Esso Osaka hull form (Schellin & Östergaard 1995).

Table 1. Main dimensions of Esso Osaka model.

Main dimensions	Tanker
Length between perpendiculars (m)	3.250
Beam (m)	0.530
Depth (m)	0.347
Draft (m)	0.132
Displacement (kg)	186.8
Longitudinal centre of gravity (m)*	0.135
Block coefficient	0.800
Prismatic coefficient	0.807
Mid-ship section coefficient	0.997
Vertical centre of gravity (m)	0.155
Metacentric height (m)	0.078
Pitch radius of gyration (m)	0.812
Roll radius of gyration (m)	0.185

* measured from the mid-ship section.

characteristics shown in Table 1. Concrete weights were used to ballast the model and then the inclination test is carried out to estimate the metacentric height GM. Decay tests were performed to evaluate the vessel's natural periods and damping ratios.

3.2 Waves and ship motion measurements

The Osaka model is settled in the tank at berth A against two breasting dolphins and a loading platform. The wavemaker generates irregular waves that propagate in a perpendicular direction to the new extension of North breakwater. The tests were carried out to simulate a storm of 1200s in model scale (3 hours in real scale). The wavemaker generates irregular waves that follow JONSWAP spectrum with a significant wave height $H_s = 7.5$ cm and peak period $T_p = 1.79$ s (respectively, 6 m and 16 s in real scale) and peak enhancement factor $\gamma = 3.3$. The approximate water depth near the berth location is 26 cm including a simulated tide level of 5 cm in model scale (respectively, 20.85 and 4 m in real scale).

Wave conditions at four different locations in the basin were measured with 8 resistive wave gauges and Acoustic Doppler Velocimetry (ADV) at a sampling frequency of 25 Hz. The wave gauges were divided into four main groups as shown in Figure 1. One wave gauge (1) was located near the wave maker to check the incident wave condition; another wave gauge (2) near the ADV at the port entrance to characterize the wave height and direction; group three that combine three of wave gauges (3, 4, and 5) in front of the moored ship and finally group four that combine gauges (6, 7 and 8) alongside the centre of gravity of the moored ship. The recorded signals of different wave gauges are synchronized together.

The accuracy of the obtained results is evaluated by repeating the test at the above-mentioned conditions for 6 times. The spectral analysis of the recorded free surface elevation using Fourier analysis provides the information about the significant wave heights, peak periods and maximum amplitudes as shown in Table 2 in model scale.

An array of three wave probes is used to estimate the two-dimensional spectrum, the calculations are carried out with the directional wave spectra toolbox DIWASP proposed by Johnson (2017) and based on the extended maximum likelihood method presented by Isobe et al. (1984). By integration of the 2D directional spectrum in a heading, one obtains one-dimensional spectrum whose moments estimate the significant wave height and mean energy period. On the other side, the integration in frequency side provides the directional spectrum from which the mean direction can be estimated. The obtained signals of a combined three of wave gauges are used to determine the wave elevation and direction around the ship as shown in Table 2. Figure 4 shows the 2D directional spectrum for combined wave gauges array (3, 4 and 5) that is in front of the ship's bow. Zero incident angle means following waves propagate from stern to bow. The analysis of the obtained directional spectrum classifies waves according to their directions so that the waves could be identified as an incident or reflected waves. The dominant wave direction of the measured waves near the bow of the model is 225°, while the reflected waves have a direction of 55°.

The motions of the Esso Osaka model are evaluated in the six degrees of freedom using the OptiTrack™ motion capture system. The system composed of 4 digital cameras that can capture the motions of the moored ship using 5 target

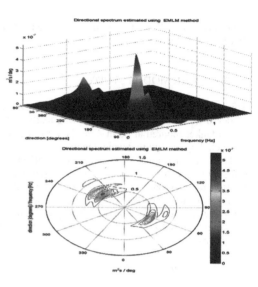

Figure 4. 2D directional spectrum in front of the ship's bow.

markers installed onboard the wooden deck. However, the results are obtained at the centre of gravity of the scaled vessel at a sampling frequency of 120 Hz.

3.3 Mooring system

The Esso Osaka model is moored at berth A, against two breasting dolphins and loading platform. All mooring equipment was manufactured in the workshop of LNEC and was installed in the tank on the exact locations after the calibration of each element in the mooring system. The prototype characteristics of the mooring system were obtained from a similar case presented by Rosa-Santos & Taveira-Pinto (2013). However, only four lines and two fenders are used in the presented physical model of the current study as shown in Figure 5.

The installed fenders on the dolphins were simulated using rocking arms, to which nonlinear spring systems were connected. The arm has a rubber end that touches the moored model. The nonlinear spring system for fender is attached to a force transducer to measure the applied loads on the fender. The mooring lines were simulated as a nonlinear spring system, installed on the wooden deck, attached by a wire to a force transducer installed on the quay. Fairleads were installed on the deck and quay to guide the mooring lines to the connection

Table 2. Recorded wave condition at wave gauges.

Wave Gauge	Hs(cm)	Tp(s)	A_{max}(cm)	Direction (°)
WG1	6.40	1.74	6.79	-
WG2	4.27	1.74	4.85	112*
WG3	1.10	1.74	1.46	225
WG4	1.16	1.74	1.29	225
WG5	1.23	1.74	1.34	225
WG6	1.18	1.39	1.09	231
WG7	1.21	1.39	1.09	231
WG8	1.15	1.39	1.05	231

* The wave direction at gauge 2 is evaluated by ADV.

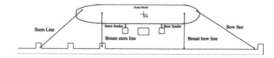

Figure 5. Mooring configurations of Esso Osaka model.

points. The complete set-up of the mooring equipment is shown in Figure 6. The stiffness of the mooring elements is simulated by a nonlinear spring system proposed by Marcos-Rita (1984). The system is made of a steel blade installed in support where screws can be adjusted in a way that their length can limit the blade deflection as cantilever support, and hence during the calibration process, the screw lengths were carefully selected to fulfil the appropriate elasticity of each mooring element using several known weights. Six force transducers are used to measure both loads in mooring lines and fenders at a sampling frequency of 50 Hz. Prior testing, the target pretensions in each mooring element are controlled by adjusting screws attached to the force transducers. Table 3 show the characteristics of the mooring system in model scale.

The applied spring system is evaluated by repeating the same testing conditions 6 times. It must be noted that the mooring system is asymmetric so that some differences in the applied pretensions are expected. However, to satisfy the same equilibrium condition for the moored model at each test, the applied pretensions were compared before and after each test. The analysis of the time series of the recorded load signals at each mooring element provides the information about the maximum load in each element, Table 4 show the mean and standard error of the maximum loads at the 6 repetitions.

Figure 6. Moored model at berth A with full mooring system.

Table 3. Characteristics of the mooring system.

Element	length (m)	T_{Before}^*(kgf)	T_{After}^*(kgf)
Bow line	1.90	0.058	0.056
Breast bow line	0.95	0.077	0.078
Bow fender	-	0.115	0.114
Stern fender	-	0.105	0.101
Breast Stern line	0.87	0.082	0.081
Stern line	1.50	0.061	0.065

* Pretensions before and after the tests in model scale.

Table 4. Analysis of loads at six repetitions.

Element	$\bar{F}_{max}$(kN)	SE(kN)	Criteria*(kN)
Bow line	636	9.7	640
Breast bow line	1307	24.2	640
Bow fender	2357	71.5	2450
Stern fender	2893	50.4	2450
Breast Stern line	1329	47.5	640
Stern line	728	14.1	640

* OCIMF load failure criteria in prototype scale.

4 NUMERICAL SIMULATIONS

Compared to physical modelling, numerical modelling is an inexpensive tool and has reasonable time consumption. In this paper, the numerical simulations, are carried out in the time-domain using the potential flow software ANSYS® AQWA. The main target is to calculate the motions and mooring loads on the moored Osaka model. The bathymetry of the port layout is complex, however, the access channel along with berth A location has nearly constant water depth. So that hydrodynamic problem is solved assuming constant water depth of 26 cm in model scale. The North breakwater and the new extension of the breakwater are included in the numerical simulations as simplified fixed bodies that influence the hydrodynamic forces on the moored ship. The mooring system with detailed characteristics is included in the time-domain simulations. The theory for the numerical calculation has been thoroughly presented and discussed by many authors and is widely available in the literature. It can be found for instance in AQWA's theory manual ANSYS (2016). In this section, only a brief explanation is presented for the formulation of the hydrodynamic problem in frequency and time domain.

4.1 Frequency domain diffraction/radiation model

Before the time-domain simulations for the moored vessel, linear diffraction and radiation calculations were carried out in AQWA to determine the free-floating hydrodynamic coefficients such as added mass and damping, as well as the first and second-order wave exciting loads. A fixed Cartesian coordinate system is defined with the vertical z-axis pointing upwards, and zero incidences of the waves when they propagate along the direction of the positive x-axis. The fluid is assumed to be inviscid, incompressible and the flow is irrotational so that the flow can be described by a velocity potential within the domain enclosed by the boundaries defined for the problem. These include the wetted body surface, the free surface, walls of the North breakwater and the sea bottom. The velocity potentials are obtained using Green's function approach. Each submerged body surface is discretized into small panels, and a pulsating source is located on each panel. The combinations of source strengths required to diffract an incoming regular wave of a given frequency and to allow body oscillation in each degree of freedom are then calculated. Then, the incident forces, diffraction forces, added mass $a_{kj}(\omega)$, and radiation damping $b_{kj}(\omega)$ on the body are calculated.

The second-order problem is due to interactions between two waves with different frequencies and the oscillating body. This study considers only the effect of mean and difference frequency components of the second-order effect. The second-order wave forces are calculated using the pressure integration method proposed by Pinkster (1980). The simulations in the frequency domain for the free-floating vessel were carried out for 50 frequencies. The range of frequencies is selected with care to have accurate time-domain calculations. Additional external lid surface is applied to the gap between the two structures to damp the overestimation in standing waves between the ship and quay as shown in Figure 7.

4.2 Time-domain simulation model

The time-domain simulations were carried out using the AQWA time-domain module to calculate the motions and mooring load on the vessel in irregular waves. In this paper, the behaviour of the mooring lines and fenders are studied with realistic nonlinear elasticity, thus the equations of motion are solved at each time step and the obtained results from the diffraction/radiation potential in the frequency domain are converted to the time domain using the retardation function approach for the hydrodynamic forces. According to Cummins (1962), the equation reads:

$$\sum_{j=1}^{6} \left[[M_{kj} + A_{kj}]\ddot{x}(t) + \int_{-\infty}^{t} K_{kj}(t-\tau)\dot{x}(\tau)d\tau + C_{kj}x(t) \right] \\ = F_k^1(t) + F_k^2(t) + F_k^m(t) \quad (1)$$

where $F_k^1(t)$ is the total first-order wave exciting forces including incident and diffraction forces, $F_k^2(t)$ is the second-order wave exciting forces. These forces can be obtained in a time domain based on the first order and second-order wave loads obtained from the frequency domain solution. $F_k^m(t)$ are the mooring system forces for lines and fenders, C_{kj} is the hydrostatic restoring matrix, A_{kj} is the added mass at an infinite frequency and $K_{kj}(t)$ is the retardation function that describes the time of the generalized force k after an impulsive motion along each of the generalized coordinates j. The retardation functions $K(t)$ are the Fourier transform of the frequency-dependent damping coefficients $b_{kj}(\omega)$ obtained from the frequency domain solution as:

$$K_{kj}(t) = \frac{2}{\pi}\int_0^\infty b_{kj}(\omega)\cos(\omega t)d\omega \quad (2)$$

The frequency-independent added mass can be calculated based on the frequency dependant added mass and retardation functions as follow:

$$A_{kj} = a_{kj} + \frac{1}{\omega}\int_0^\infty K_{kj}(t)\sin(\omega t)d\omega \quad (3)$$

The simulations in time domain were carried out at constant water depth of 26 cm in model scale that represents the future dredged water depth at port entrance 16.85 m plus a tide level of 4 m (real scale). As the bathymetry was oversimplified in the applied numerical model based on constant water depth assumption, wave effects such as shoaling could not be simulated. Therefore, to achieve a reasonable similarity between the physical model results and numerical simulation results, the wave spectrum data collected from the physical model, near the bow of the moored tanker, are used as an input in the time domain numerical simulations. The time history of the irregular waves obtained from wave gauge 3 of $(\omega)H_s = 1.1$cm and $T_p = 1.74$s is used as an input in the numerical simulations. The total simulation time is selected to be like physical model 1200 s. The input wave spectrum in the numerical simulations is assumed to be long-crested waves.

4.3 Viscous damping

The potential flow assumptions neglect the viscous damping forces, while the transverse plan motions of a moored ship in the surge, sway and yaw modes are usually influenced by the natural periods of the mooring system and, as the ship mass is relatively high compared to the stiffness of the mooring system, the natural periods of such modes is very high. The potential wave radiation damping is very small at the long periods, and other damping sources become valuable such as viscous fluid forces for roll motion and mechanical friction with the fender surface. The roll damping in the numerical simulations is tuned with viscous damping obtained from the roll decay tests during the physical modelling as shown

Figure 7. Applied mesh in AQWA numerical simulations.

in Figure 8. The fender friction forces are integrated into the numerical simulations with 0.25 friction coefficient at the fender contact surface.

4.4 Mooring simulation

Four mooring lines and two fenders are represented in the numerical simulation with lines and fenders that has a nonlinear stiffness as shown in Figure 9. The load elongation curve that is obtained during the calibration of the spring system in the physical model is fitted with a fifth-order polynomial function. Five polynomial coefficients are obtained and then represented in the numerical modal according to Equation 4. Figure 10 shows an example of the load elongation curve of the bowline. The applied pretension in each mooring element is tuned with the obtained pretension from physical modelling. Before starting the time domain simulation, stability analysis is carried out to make sure that the moored Osaka model starts the simulation at an equilibrium position like that in physical modelling.

$$Load = k_1(\delta L) + k_2(\delta L)^2 + k_3(\delta L)^3 + k_4(\delta L)^4 + k_5(\delta L)^5 \quad (4)$$

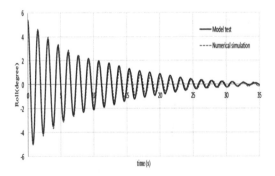

Figure 8. Roll decay test at 26 cm water depth in model scale.

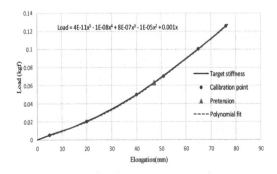

Figure 9. Load-elongation curve for bowline in model scale.

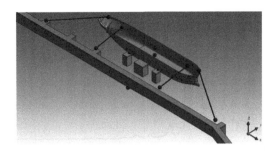

Figure 10. Simulation of the mooring system in AQWA.

5 COMPUTATIONAL AND EXPERIMENTAL RESULTS

In the present study, the validity of the existing numerical method, to estimate the motions and mooring loads of the moored ship inside the port, is evaluated by comparison with statistical results obtained from the physical model.

The selected case study is the Esso Osaka tanker moored at berth A at water depth= 20.85 m including tide level of 4m in prototype scale. The existing North breakwater and its future extension are included in the case study. The offshore sea state condition fit the JONSWAP spectrum of H_s=6 m and T_p=16 s in prototype scale with a peak enhancement factor of 3.3. The obtained numerical results for motions and mooring loads are calculated with the assumption of long-crested bow quartering waves 225° like the dominant direction of the measured incident wave in the physical model.

The variance spectra for the motions and mooring loads are calculated from the times series of the experimental results and vessel's response spectra are presented for surge, sway and yaw in Figures 11-13. The experimental load spectra for all mooring lines and fenders are shown in Figures 14-16. Besides spectra, the numerical model is evaluated based on comparison with the statistical parameters obtained from the physical model. Table 5 presents a comparison between the numerical and experimental statistical quantity RMS value of the variance spectrum in long-crested wave bow quartering 225°.

6 DISCUSSION OF RESULTS

It is important to analyse the wave conditions at the berth location around the moored model, The analysis of physical model wave records in Table 2 and Figure 4 show that as the wave propagates to the port entrance, it diffracts around the new breakwater extension, then move to berth location with a dominant heading angle of 225° to the moored

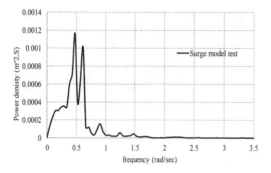

Figure 11. Experimental surge motion in long-crested bow quartering wave 225° at model scale.

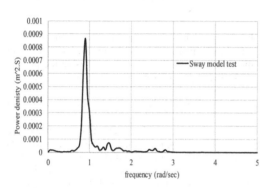

Figure 12. Experimental sway motion in long-crested bow quartering wave 225° at model scale.

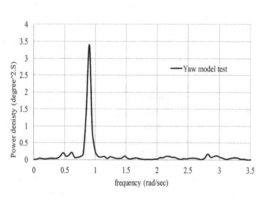

Figure 13. Experimental yaw motion in long-crested bow quartering wave 225° at model scale.

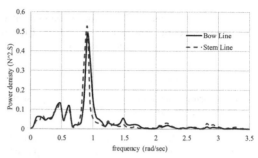

Figure 14. Experimental mooring loads in the bow and stern line at model scale.

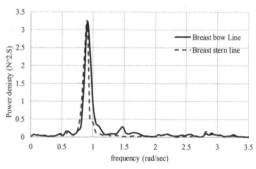

Figure 15. Experimental Mooring loads in the bow and stern breast lines at model scale.

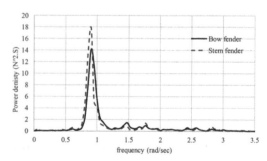

Figure 16. Experimental Mooring loads in the bow and stern fenders at model scale.

model. When the wave reaches the South breakwater and quay wall, it starts to reflect in the opposite direction and travel back to berth location with a heading angle of about 55°. The wave condition around berth A might increase the importance of modelling the waves with a directional spectrum, during numerical simulations, to account for all possible interactions. The analysis of wave heights around the moored model shows that the wave amplitudes decay as the waves propagate inside the port. The incorporation of the new extension of North breakwater results in a significant wave height less than 1 m at berth A in prototype scale. This is considered as a remarkable decrease in wave height compared to results without the new extension in other publications. However, the breakwater is still not effective for problems of the resonance due to the long period of oscillation.

One of the main targets of this work is to evaluate the applied nonlinear spring system that is used to simulate physical mooring system. The analysis of results obtained from 6 repetitions in Table 4 shows that the applied nonlinear spring system has good accuracy to measure the maximum loads and the error is acceptable. Regardless of the symmetry in the mooring system, the pretension values should be evaluated before and after each test to assure similar equilibrium conditions. The application of 4 mooring lines other than 6 results in high loads in the mooring lines that exceed the failure criteria. Study with the full 6 mooring line would give better results with respect to the failure criteria.

The calibration of the numerical model with the physical model results is carried out to include the roll viscous damping and to evaluate the natural roll period at 1.5 s in model scale. The representation of nonlinear stiffness for fenders and mooring lines with 5 polynomial coefficients is convenient to fit the load elongation relationship accurately. The experimental results shown in Figures 11-16 show that the motions of the moored model and loads in mooring lines and fenders can be captured in the physical model with reasonable accuracy. The peak periods for surge sway and yaw motions are affected by low frequencies other than the wave exciting frequency. This means that it is important to include the second-order low-frequency motion for the problem of moored bodies in waves. The mooring system is asymmetrical; however, the experimental data show similar behaviour for fenders together, the two breast lines together and for bow and stern lines, the peak period of the loads in mooring lines and fenders corresponding to the same low-frequency.

Statistical comparison for the motions and mooring loads shown in Table 5 show that the numerical model has a good agreement with the experimental results. The numerical results for the RMS variance of loads are slightly higher than the experimental results. However, this is expected due to the long-created waves assumption as it might have higher exciting energy than the real short-crested waves for certain modes of motion. Also, the assumption of constant water depth and simplified surrounding structures could affect the hydrodynamic forces on the moored vessel. The interactions with the North and South breakwater are important and complex, it requires special care such as lid surfaces to overcome some numerical limitations.

7 CONCLUSIONS

From the above discussion, it can be concluded that the main objectives of the presented study have been accomplished. As a general conclusion, one may say that the presented physical model study can represent reasonably well the motion responses and mooring loads for a moored ship in irregular sea states inside the port. The applied nonlinear spring system has good accuracy and results can be reproduced easily. The applied numerical method has some limitations regarding the constant water depth assumption, however, if the berthing condition is reproduced accurately in the numerical model and water depth around the moored model do not have a large variation, the applied numerical model is suitable to solve the problem of moored ships inside ports. The assumption of long-crested waves may give a good indication for the loads and motions inside closed boundaries, however, the representation of short-crested waves with a two-dimensional spectrum would give better accurate results. The combination of numerical modelling and physical modelling still important to calibrate the numerical model and fill the gaps due to numerical limitations such as roll viscous damping and fender friction forces. The account of second-order low-frequency forces is important for the analysis of dynamics of a moored body inside ports.

ACKNOWLEDGEMENTS

This work is a contribution to the M&M SHIPS project "Manoeuvring & Moored Ships in ports" (PTDC/EMSTRA/5628/2014) funded by the Portuguese Foundation for Science and Technology. The authors are grateful with F.G.L. Pedro, M.A. Hinostroza and R. Ramachandran for their help during the model tests.

REFERENCES

Abdelwahab, H. S. & Guedes Soares, C. 2018. Motions and mooring loads of a tanker moored at open jetty in long-crested irregular waves including second order effects. *Progress in Maritime Technology and Engineering*, Guedes Soares, C. & Santos T.A. (Eds.), London, UK: Taylor & Francis. pp. 557–567.

ANSYS 2016. *AQWA theory manual - Release 17.2*. ANSYS, Inc., Canonsburg, pp. 112.

Bingham, H. B. 2000. A hybrid Boussinesq-panel method for predicting the motion of a moored ship. *Coastal Engineering*, 40, 21–38.

Cummins, W. E. 1962. The impulse response function and ship motions. *Schiffstechnik*, 9, 101–109.

Isobe, M., Kondo, K. & Horikawa, K. 1984. Extension of MLM for estimating directional wave spectrum.

Table 5. Comparison between numerical and experimental RMS variance in bow quartering wave 225°.

Signal	Experimental	Numerical
Surge (m)	0.007	0.004
Sway (m)	0.005	0.004
Yaw (degree)	0.278	0.356
Bow line(N)	0.148	0.127
Stern line(N)	0.145	0.176
Breast bow line(N)	0.323	0.331
Breast stern Line(N)	0.289	0.273
Bow fender (N)	0.708	0.820
Stern fender (N)	0.730	0.889

Proceedings of Symposium on Description and Modeling of Directional Seas. Lyngby, Denmark.

Johnson, D. 2017. *A directional wave spectra toolbox for MATLAB®: User Manual.* Coastal Oceanography Group, Centre for Water Research,University of Western Australia.

Marcos-Rita, M. 1984. *On the behaviour of moored ships in harbors: theory,practice and model tests.* PhD, LNEC, Lisbon.

Neves, M. G., Fortes, C. J. E. M. & Lemos, R. 2017. Estudos em modelo físico e numérico do prolongamento do quebra-mar exterior e das acessibilidades marítimas do porto de Leixões. estudo I - ensaios tridimensionais de agitação marítima. Relatório 315/2017 - DHA/NPE, LNEC. (in portuguese).

OCIMF 2018. *Mooring equipment guidelines: (MEG4)*, Livingston, Witherby Seamanship International Ltd.

PIANC 1995. *Criteria for movements of moored ships in harbours: a practical guide*, Report of working group PTC II-24.

Pinheiro, L. V., Fortes, C. J. E. M., Abecassis Jalles, B. M. & Santos, J. A. 2015. Simulation of wave action on a moored container carrier inside Sines' harbour. *Maritime Technology and Engineering*, Guedes Soares, C. & Santos T.A. (Eds.), London, UK: Taylor & Francis. pp. 1113–1121.

Pinkster, J. A. 1980. *Low frequency second order wave exciting forces on floating structures.* PhD, Delft University of Technology.

Rosa-Santos, P. & Taveira-Pinto, F. 2013. Experimental study of solutions to reduce downtime problems in ocean facing ports: the port of Leixões, Portugal, case study. *Journal of Applied Water Engineering and Research*, 1, 80–90.

Rosa-Santos, P., Veloso-Gomes, F., Taveira-Pinto, F. & Bròguiera-Dias, E. 2010. Physical modelling of Leixões oil terminal – Portugal. *Port Infrastructure Seminar.* Delft, Netherlands.

Rosa-Santos, P., Veloso-Gomes, F., Taveira-Pinto, F., Bròguiera-Dias, E. & Guedes-Lopes, H. 2008. Improving operational conditions at Leixões oil terminal – Portugal. *the 7th International Conference on Coastal and Port Engineering in Developing Countries (COPEDEC VII).* Dubai, United Arab Emirates.

Santos, J. A., Pinheiro, L. V., Abdelwahab, H. S., Fortes, C. J. E. M., Pedro, F. G. L., Capitão, R. P., Hinostroza, M. A. & Guedes Soares, C. 2019. Physical modelling of motions and forces on a moored ship at the leixões port. *Defect and Diffusion Forum*, 396, 60–69.

Schellin, T. E. & Östergaard, C. 1995. The vessel in port: Mooring problems. *Marine Structures*, 8, 451–479.

Taveira-Pinto, F., Veloso-Gomes, F., Rosa-Santos, P., Guedes Soares, C., Fonseca, N., Santos, J. A., Moreira, A. & Costa, P. 2008. Analysis of the behavior of moored tankers. *Proceedings of the International Conference on Offshore Mechanics and Arctic Engineering - OMAE.* Estoril, Portugal. Paper no. OMAE2008-58013.

Van der Molen, W. 2006. *Behaviour of moored ships in harbours.* PhD, Delft University of Technology.

Van Oortmerssen, G. 1976. *The motions of a moored ship in waves.* NSMB publication No. 510, Delft University of Technology.

Veloso-Gomes, F., Taveira-Pinto, F., Rosa-Santos, P., Bròguiera-Dias, E. & Guedes-Lopes, H. 2005. Berthing characteristics and the behaviour of the oil terminal of Leixões harbour, Portugal. *Maritime Heritage and Modern Ports.* WIT Press. pp. 481–492.

Weiler, O., Cozijn, H., Wijdeven, B., Le-Guennec, S. & Fontaliran, F. 2009. Motions and mooring loads of an LNG-Carrier moored at a jetty in a complex bathymetry. *Proceedings of the ASME 28th International Conference on Ocean, Offshore and Arctic Engineering.* Honolulu, Hawaii. Paper no. OMAE2009-79420.

Wind safety limits on ships docked with two different mooring systems

E. Díaz-Ruiz-Navamuel, A. Ortega-Piris, C.A. Pérez-Labajos & M.A. Andrés
Ocean and Coastal Planning and Management R&D Group, University of Cantabria, School of Maritime Engineering, Department Sciences and Techniques of Navigation and Shipbuilding, Santander, Spain

ABSTRACT: The efficiency of mooring systems will have an impact on the productivity of maritime transport, under the generally accepted assumption that the time of the ship in port is unproductive. At present, new commercial mooring systems for merchant ships are being implemented in several commercial ports around the world, but several technical questions arise as to the reasons why such AMS1 might be installed in a commercial port. The objective of this work is to verify how the AMS performs in relation to TMS2 for different vessels and wind conditions. The study aims to ascertain whether the presence of wind has a greater impact on those vessels moored with the TMS than those moored with the AMS. From the results obtained, it can be stated that, in general terms, the vessels have been moored with greater safety and less movement with the automatic mooring system than with the traditional system.

1 INTRODUCTION

Until the Second World War, the management and organization of maritime traffic did not undergo any major changes. The loading and unloading operations were slow and laborious. Thus, in the post-war era, with an expansion of the market and a rapid rise in labor costs, the system was put under tremendous stress. Congestion in ports increased and the ingenuity had to be sharpened to seek a response to these problems through innovation in both technology and in processes.

The maritime industry responded to the new challenges with two "revolutions" in the two subsectors of maritime transport: in non-scheduled traffic through the development of integrated transport systems (bulk carriers) and in regular lines by grouping together the general cargo by means of the phenomenon of containerization, all of which led to profound changes being made in commercial seaports in order to respond to these challenges.

As a consequence of these revolutions, new innovations have taken place in the technological as well as the organizational sphere, with the appearance of new means of traffic, new equipment and new methods. The main aim of all these changes is to reduce the time spent by the vessel in port, as this is considered unproductive.

However, although there has been innovation in all areas of the maritime sector, in the case of the mooring of vessels these changes would seem to be less extensive, as traditional systems are still used in most commercial ports around the world.

We understand that every study on mooring systems must be considered within the context of sea transport because it is about a direct part of it. Efficiency of the mooring systems affects the productivity of the sea transport according to the general accepted theory that time of ship in port is unproductive.

Currently, traditional systems coexist together with new mooring systems. There is an extensive bibliography on the traditional mooring system, most of the authors focusing their analysis on the different conventional mooring elements on board and on land, and on the factors that condition them from a technical point of view. (Barbudo Escobar, 2004; Gaythwaite, 2004; Schelfn & Östergaard, 1995).

Up to the present, these studies have focused on analyzing the reliability and risk of berthing, mooring and defense systems. Studying the behavior of mooring ropes using computer programs (Banfield & Flory, 2010) and the movement of moored ships by simulation (Fang & Blanke, 2011); as well as port structures (Thoresen, 2014) and the environmental loads supported by mooring systems (Díaz et al., 2016; Fang et al., 2015).

Several authors analyze security factors in navigation that affects the docking of the ships in port. Among them, we can find those that focus on work and fatigue (Hetherington et al., 2006; Hsu, 2015, 2012; Iskeragolec et al., 1996; Josten et al., 2003) lack of experience of crew, wear and tear of machinery and mooring elements (Hsu et al., 2015; Kokotos & Smirlis, 2005) and also climatic factors (Uğurlu et al., 2015).

It was in 1914 that the research into the possibility of developing different mooring systems, with different mechanisms from the traditional ones, began. In order to differentiate these systems, it would seem appropriate now to formalize the concept of

DOI: 10.1201/9781003216599-37

automatic mooring system for the purposes of this work: we understand by automatic mooring system any mooring device applied to moored ships, which adapts, totally or partially, without external help, to the weather conditions of the environment (tide, wind and current). It is now generally established in the literature that TMS refers to the mooring of the vessel to the dock by means of cables or traditional systems while AMS refers to an automated mooring system with vacuum suction cups.

The difference between smooth and uneven surfaces is that the new mooring system vacuum pump will run more. On a smooth surface the pump after having created the vacuum only turns on when needed i.e. when a vacuum drop is sensed. In case the hull has different layers of paint, it is possible that the paint is removed by vacuum, but this does not affect the suction of the hull of the ship and its security docked.

The research carried out so far has culminated in an AMS that is being implemented in different ports around the world (USA, Canada, UK, Denmark, Norway, Finland, Holland, Australia, New Zealand, South Africa and Lebanon). Despite the apparent increasing acceptance of the new mooring system, several technical questions arise as to why the AMS might be installed in a commercial port: Can this system be applied to any type of vessel? Is this mooring system more effective for a particular type of vessel? To what extent do the prevailing wind conditions in the port affect the system? Are there any conditions that make the use of the system optimum? To what extent is the automatic mooring system more effective than the conventional one? The need to find answers to these questions has motivated the development of this work.

In this context, we aim to verify how the automatic mooring system behaves in relation to the traditional system for different vessels and wind conditions (direction and speed). In order to reach the proposed objective, the present work has been formalized in the following sections: Section 2 addresses the methodology, Section 3 establishes the formalization of scenarios for the simulation and describes the mooring maneuver simulations performed in the simulator, Section 4 outlines the results obtained with the simulations and finally in Section 5 the conclusions are presented.

2 METHODOLOGY

The applied methodology basically consists of a technical analysis to demonstrate if under the same meteorological conditions, the AMS responds more safely than the traditional TMS system

For this purpose, a real-time maneuver simulator was used following the Methodology for Recommendations on Maritime Works (Costas., 2000), devised by the Group of experts of the General Direction of Ports and Coasts of the Spanish Ministry of Development in 2000 (currently State Ports). These recommendations are formalized for studies performed with a real-time maneuver simulator. In the present work, a "Polaris" simulator developed by "Kongsberg Norcontrol Simulations" (Norway), located in the Technical School of Nautical of the University of Cantabria, was used to carry out the maneuvers.

The purpose of this system is to reproduce the behavior of specific vessels in real time, in our case during the stay of ships berthed under the action of wind, waves and current and aided by tugs. The simulator includes a mathematical model that calculates the trajectory of the vessels and the evolution of their respective courses with two important characteristics: interactivity and operation in real time.

In order to carry out the study, we selected vessels of different sizes that correspond to actual ships that are currently sailing, but to analyze the results we have denominated them as follows: number type of vessel (example:1_RORO).

The methodology was adapted to the study of moored ships and the following procedure was established to the design of maneuvers performed for the proposed cases:

I. In order to reach the objectives clearly, the study was carried out in a model port, with ships docked at the dock, establishing the most unfavorable wind (direction and intensity) conditions. Other determinants that were taken into account in the simulation are: the type of ship, the mooring system used (AMS or TMS), and the number of robots required in the case of the AMS or the number of ropes in the case of TMS.
II. A series of maneuvers were carried out, with the vessel moored, using first the TMS and then with the AMS. The maneuvers with the TMS began with a type of ship and with calm wind, then wind that increased in a determined direction of ten in ten knots, until obtaining the extreme conditions from which the ropes began to break.

The maneuvers with the AMS were carried out following the same guidelines until the ship was no longer fully moored, thus obtaining a wind force that represents the safety limit of one for each mooring system, type of vessel and direction of the wind.

To make a comparative study, a table was made combining the mooring systems, the different types of ship and the different wind directions.

3 FORMALIZATION OF SCENARIOS FOR THE SIMULATION

For the formalization of the simulation scenarios of mooring maneuvers in real time, the following aspects are studied and defined.

a) *Vessels used:*
Four different types of vessels were used: Type 1 Ro-Ro, type 2 bulkcarrier, type 3 cruise Ship and type 4 container Ship, the Table 1 shows the characteristics.

Table 1. Characteristics of vessels used in the study.

Type of vessel N°	LENGTH m.	BREADTH m.	DRAUGHT m.	LATERAL WINDAGE AREA m^2	BLOCK COEFFICIENT	DISPLACEMENT Tons.	Tons. Stretch breaking stress
1_RORO	198.0	32.3	7.5	5,564	0.56	26,500	71.4
2_BULKC	215.4	31.8	11.5	1,852	0.79	60,920	71.4
3_CRUIS	260.7	31.5	7.8	7,550	0.62	34,710	92
4_CONT	285.0	40.0	12.7	6,799	0.63	87,400	71.4

Source: Author with the data of the specifications of the ships used in simulator for the study.

b) Wind Directions:
The three most unfavorable wind directions were selected for a ship docked port to the dock as are the wind through the port quarter, port side and port bow.

Illustrations 1 and 2 show the wind directions selected for all the types of vessels and each mooring system.

c) Mooring systems used:
As mentioned above, the mooring systems selected for the study are the traditional system TMS, using ropes and the automatic system, AMS, using vacuum suction cups.

Throughout history, ships have been docking in different ports using the traditional mooring method by means of ropes, both of vegetable or synthetic origin and of steel cables, depending on the type of vessel and tonnage, and using for its handling on board the mooring equipment consisting of fenders, bits fairleads and winches.

On the land side, the vessel rests against the dock on fenders so as not to damage the dock or hull, securing the ropes with the help of the port dockers.

The risks of a breakage of the rope in TMS may involve material or human damages.

Illustration 1 shows the ship moored with traditional mooring system (TMS) the ship is moored with ropes.

Illustration 2 shows the vessel moored with AMS, through vacuum cups.

Material damages may occur in the docks, in the load and unload infrastructure or in the vessel itself. Human damages may occur either in the crew or in the port staff.

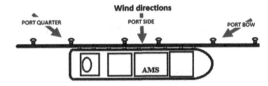

Illustration 2. AMS and wind directions.
Source: Author

In case of failure, using the AMS, the risks are alike but in a minor quantity. According to the manufacturer and user`s information, since this system is in use, no failure has been reported.

The ropes used in the simulator are synthetic 60 mm in diameter and weighing 200 kg/m. which have a breaking tension (Tr) of 71.4 tonnes. (700.2 kN.) for vessels of options 1, 2 and 4 (ro-ro, bulkcarriers and container carriers), and for the vessel of option 3 (cruiser) the breaking tension was of 92 tonnes. (886.6 kN.).

The efficiency of the ropes were a function of the angle they form with the horizontal and the vertical (Villa Caro, 2015) and the distance. As the angle decreases, the efficiency increases (Thoresen, 2014; Yamase & Ueda, 2007; Zendrera, 1994). In our case, the height of the cables is set at zero; being the distances perpendicular from the chocks to the lines and springs to the pier of 18 and 8 m. respectively.

The number of ropes that were used in the simulations for both bow and stern are two lengths and two springs, which gives a total retention capacity of 531 tons for ship with a tensile strength of 71.4 tons. (see Table 2) and 656 tones. for the ship with cables with a breaking strength of 92 tons (see Table 3).

The traditional mooring system not only depends on the meteorology, but also on the distribution of the mooring posts along the dock. Thus, for the simulations, the mooring posts were distributed at a distance of 25 meters from each other.

In the simulations of the stays of ships moored with AMS, it was verified that the movements of the ships were reduced to a minimum and that it was not necessary to use tugboats or to reinforce with cables to support the ship docked in any extreme wind conditions.

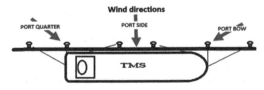

Illustration 1. TMS and wind directions.
Source: Author

Table 2. Number of the rope and its length when T_L=71.4 tons option Ships 1, 2 and 4. $T_T=T_L$*sen α, sen α=d/L.

	Rope length L (m)	Distance to the pier d (m)	sin α	α	Date: TL (tons)	Tt (tons) $T_T=T_L$ *sen α
2 Head line	47	18	0.38	0.39	71.40	27.34
2 Stern spring	32	8	0.25	0.25	71.40	17.85
2 Forward line	49	18	0.37	0.38	71.40	26.23
2 Aft spring	56	8	0.14	0.14	71.40	10.20

Source: Author

Table 3. Number of the rope and its length when TL=TBroken = 92 tons. Ship 3.

	Rope length L (m)	Distance to the pier d (m)	sin α	α	Date: T_L (tons)	T_T (tons)
2 Head line	75	18	0.24	0.24	92	22.08
2 Sternspring	25	8	0.32	0.33	92	29.44
2 Forward line	75	18	0.24	0.24	92	22.08
2 Aft spring	25	8	0.32	0.33	92	29.44

Source: Author

The system that has been selected to make the study was Cavotec's MoorMaster Ltd. (Cavotec, 2015) Model "MoormasterTM 40010" which has the ability to keep the vessel moored by absorbing motions on the three linear axes of motion (x, y, z). (See Illustration 3.)

The AMS consists of an automatic mooring technology based on a vacuum which secures all kinds of vessels safely to the dock, eliminating the need for conventional mooring lines (ropes and cables).

The system consists of some mooring robots equipped with vacuum pads, remote-controlled, which can be installed on the edge of the dock or on it and which are fitted on arms which are hydraulically activated, and which stretch out, thus connecting the vacuum pads with the ship's hull in a matter of seconds.

The performance of the automatic mooring units (robots) is conditioned, in addition to the size of the vessel, by the following factors: wind, current, wave action, variation of tide height and interaction of the vessel with the fenders. In our study, we considered only the wind (direction and intensity) as well as the type and size of the ships.

The interconnecting areas between the mooring robot and the ship's hull must be sufficiently strong to withstand a force of 200 kN (22.5 Ton) of vacuum on a surface of 1.9 x 1.4 m (size of the vacuum pad) and the hull of the vessel must be clear of obstructions. The system to be installed consists of robots composed of two pads each, which makes a total of 400 kN (45 Ton) of vacuum force per robot.

The vacuum units manufacturer have undertaken theoretical wind loading analyses for four design vessels: RoRo/RoPax, Bulk, Cruise and Container vessels using industry standard wind drag coefficients and the characteristics of vacuum mooring.

Indicative vessel geometry has been employed to represent design vessels having the approximate lateral windage area as detailed below.

To carry out the study, the manufacturer of AMS was provided with all data of the vessels where simulations took part and they determined the number of necessary robots for every vessel and the recommended wind speed limits.

Data shown on Table 4 are theorical data given by manufacturer and indicate the approximate number of vacuum pads required at the worst-case wind incident direction for each ship used. The worst-case wind direction is application specific and dependent upon ship hull geometry and MoorMaster™ layout.

Therefore, according to the manufacturer, starting from these winds it will be necessary to reinforce with mooring lines.

The system has been dimensioned in the simulator according to the manufacturer's specifications with 10 robots for vessels up to 250 m in length and winds up to 48 knots and the same for ships up to 285 meters in length and winds of 38 knots.

In the simulations, the 10 AMS robots of 45 tons (441.3 kN) retention per unit have been simulated with 6 tugs of 75 tons distributed along the length of the boat pushing perpendicular towards the dock.

As can be seen in Table 5, the displacement perpendicular to the robot spring oscillates between a minimum of 700 mm. (sufficient to position the ship ahead of the line of fenders and to keep it at a safe distance both, for mooring and to release the

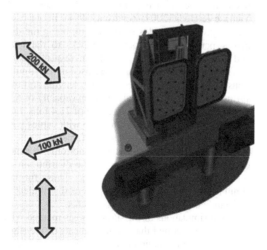

Illustration 3. MoorMasterTM400 Retention Force.
Source: Cavotec

Table 4. Number of robot units to install based on ship size and wind speed. Each vacuum pad has a nominal holding capacity of 400kN. (*LOA: Length overall).

Design Vessel	LOA*(m)	Beam(m)	Draft(m)	Lateral Windage (m2)	Frontal Windage (m2)	Nº Vacuum Pads req for: Knots 29	39	48
Ro/Pax	212	30.6	7.5	5,517	898	4	7	12
Bulk	215	32.2	11.5	2,051	767	2	4	6
Cruise	260	31.5	7.8	7,543	1,658	8	14	22
Container (6k TEU)	285	40.0	12.7	6,795	1,492	4	12	19

Source: Cavotec

Table 5. Characteristics of the AMS used.

Dimensions/ Features	mm	kg	Kw	kN
Maximum holding force				400 - 475
Maxima force of securing by pad				200
Power Consumption (Peak)			17	
Unit Weight: approx.		10,000		
Vertical displacement	2,000			
Lateral displacement	800			
Length	960			
Height of unit	4,000			
Unit Width	3,060			
Width of base	2,150			
Depth Unity	3,050			
Depth of base	2,000			
Max Range	960			
Minimum Reach	700			
Maximum lateral movement	800			
Vertical movement	2,000			

Source: Author

ship in the departure maneuver) and 960 mm. The vessel in the resting position, that is, once moored remains supported on the fenders and attached to the suction cups.

Today, AMS is a widely accepted technology that has made 69,916 mooring operations per year, with a security ratio of one hundred percent, and is installed on all types of docks and used by different types of ships such as ferries, bulk carriers, and RoRo and container carriers.

The system is used by ships of different characteristics, ages, hull forms, types of painting and state of the same (Díaz, 2016: Diaz et al., 2017).

The condition and type of hull paint does not influence the suction capacity of the suction cups. The suction cups work the same on new or newly painted ships as on those with many uneven paint layers on the hull.

The difference between smooth and uneven surfaces is that the vacuum pump will run more. On a smooth surface the pump after having created the vacuum only turns on when needed i.e. when a vacuum drop is sensed. In case the hull has different layers of paint, it is possible that the paint is removed by vacuum, but this does not affect to the suction of the hull of the ship and its security docked.

Year 2017 saw the highest number of installations undertaken per year, fifteen in total, and also the largest increase in the number of mooring maneuvers, reaching 1,852 per week (see Table 6).

Table 7 shows the relation between the different types of terminals in which this type of automatic mooring system is installed with the number of docks, number of robots and number of mooring maneuvers per year and per day. This automatic mooring system is present at Sixty-five quays, and there are currently plans scheduled to install it in a further six ports.

3.1 *Maneuvers performed in the simulator*

For the study of the influence of the wind on the TMS and AMS of merchant ships, 24 simulations were made, 12 with the TMS and another 12 with the AMS. The simulations were performed in the simulator in real time for the different mooring systems, types of vessel and wind directions.

The formalization of the enumeration of the maneuvers is described in Table 8.

The numbers shown in Table 8 indicate the characteristics of each simulation. For example:

Number 22 refers to the simulation performed for a container ship (type 4) using the AMS and with port side wind. (22_AMS_PORT SIDE_4).

Table 6. Relationship between annual AMS facilities, number of weekly maneuvers, robots installed per year and type of dock.

Year	N° installations per year.	N° Robot installed per year	Moorings per week	Type of terminal
1999	1	2	7	Ferry/RoRo
2001	1	1	7	Ferry/RoRo
2003	2	8	14	Ferry/RoRo
2005	2	3	22	Ferry/RoRo
2007	3	45	59	Container/locks
2009	4	18	112	Ferry/RoRo/container/locks
2010	2	22	6	Bulk/liquid
2011	2	14	25	Bulk/Ferry/RoRo
2012	2	2	224	Ferry/RoRo
2013	1	3	50	Locks
2014	6	61	280	Ferry/RoRo/cont/locks/dredging
2015	13	60	614	Ferry/RoRo/Cont/Locks/STS
2016	5	35	156	Bulk/Container/lock
2017	15	48	1,852	Ferry/RoRo/container/locks
2018	6	7	683	Ferry/RoRo/STS

Source: Author with data from the manufacturer of the AMS

Number 6 refers to the simulation performed for a bulkcarrier (type 2) using the TMS and with port quarter wind. (6_TMS_PORT_QUARTER_2).

3.2 Procedure for performing the simulations

The simulations undertaken started in both cases with the vessel moored port side to the dock. These simulations were repeated four times for each type of ship, and wind direction.

Table 7. Terminals where the AMS is installed and its use.

Terminal Type	Number of terminals	Number of Robot	Mooring per year	Moorings per week
Ferry & RoRo	32	54	16,5932	3,191
Container	7	116	1,404	27
Bulk Load & liquid	4	52	624	12
Locks & Others	22	107	45,812	881
Total	65	329	213,772	4,111

Source: Author with data from the manufacturer of the AMS

With both systems in each mooring maneuver, it started with the calm wind and it increased in intensity until the lines broke or until the safety in the dock was threatened and the ship separated from the pier, obtaining the limit of wind for case.

Table 6, 4.22 of ROM 2.0-11 (Recommendations of Maritime Works. Spanish normative in port projects) (Llorca et al., 2012) specifies the recommended values for the maximum permissible displacements and turns and the amplitudes of the moored vessel which are compatible with loading and unloading operations and passenger loading and unloading, with TMS and in safe conditions.

In the case of container ships, these values are: Surge: ± 0.5 m, Sway: 0.6 m.

In the simulations it was checked if the ship exceeded any of these values, monitoring the lateral movement (Sway) and the longitudinal movement of forward or reverse (Surge), as well as the tensions of the cables.

In addition, data of time, heading, direction of the bow, location, wind strength, wind direction, and speed were all recorded.

To ensure that the vessel was always in the same moored position, fixed lengths of the moorings lines and a constant tension of winches were defined, which allows us to easily verify if there was any change in the position of the ship.

Table 8. Simulations: Combination of Mooring system, type of vessel and wind direction.

Mooring system	Wind direction	Simulations RoRo	BULK	CRUISE	CONTAINER
TMS (Traditional)	Port Side	1	4	7	10
	Port Bow	2	5	8	11
	Port Quarter	3	6	9	12
AMS (Automatic)	Port Side	13	16	19	22
	Port Bow	14	17	20	23
	Port Quarter	15	18	21	24

Source: Author

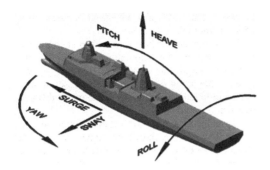

Illustration 4. Movement of vessel.
Source: (González, 2006)

4 RESULTS OF THE SIMULATION

Tables 9 and 10 show the results obtained for the simulations of the 24 maneuvers, detailing the winds limits obtained and the movements made by the vessels during the performance of the simulations both with the use of TMS and with AMS.

In general terms, the vessels have remained moored with greater safety and less movement with the AMS than with the TMS.

All the simulations have been safer with the AMS than with the TMS and the wind limits in all cases were higher.

Table 9. Wind limits and movements with TMS, each mooring maneuver started with the calm wind and it increased in intensity until the lines broke.

Simulations	Mooring System	Wind Direction PORT=P Quarter=Q	Vessel type	Security wind limit (knots)	Max Surge 0.5 (m)	Max Sway 0.6 (m/s)
1	TMS	P SIDE	1_RORO	45	0.2	0.07
2	TMS	P BOW	1_RORO	45	0.3	0.15
3	TMS	P Q	1_RORO	35	0.2	0.25
4	TMS	P SIDE	2_BULKCARRIER	90	0.3	0.3
5	TMS	P BOW	2_BULKCARRIER	95	0.01	0.2
6	TMS	P Q	2_BULKCARRIER	80	0.32	0.25
7	TMS	P SIDE	3_CRUIS	40	0.38	0.4
8	TMS	P BOW	3_CRUIS	40	0.02	0.3
9	TMS	P Q	3_CRUIS	40	0.05	0.2
10	TMS	P SIDE	4_CONTAINER	45	0.03	0.1
11	TMS	P BOW	4_CONTAINER	50	0.03	0.05
12	TMS	P Q	4_CONTAINER	50	0.02	0.04

Source: Author

Table 10. Wind limits and movements with AMS each mooring maneuver started with the calm wind and it increased in intensity until the safety in the dock was threatened and the ship separated from the pier.

Simulations	Mooring System	Wind Direction PORT=P Quarter=Q	Vessel type	Security wind limit (knots)	Max Surge 0.5 (m/s)	Max Sway 0.6 (m/s)
13	AMS	P SIDE	1_RORO	70	0.1	0.1
14	AMS	P BOW	1_RORO	75	0.04	0.2
15	AMS	P Q	1_RORO	70	0.07	0.1
16	AMS	P SIDE	2_BULKCARRIER	140	0.01	0.1
17	AMS	P BOW	2_BULKCARRIER	110	0.01	0.04
18	AMS	P Q	2_BULKCARRIER	120	0.05	0.03
19	AMS	P SIDE	3_CRUIS	70	0.03	0.4
20	AMS	P BOW	3_CRUIS	60	0.02	0.2
21	AMS	P Q	3_CRUIS	60	0.04	0.2
22	AMS	P SIDE	4_CONTAINER	60	0.03	0.1
23	AMS	P BOW	4_CONTAINER	70	0.02	0.1
24	AMS	P Q	4_CONTAINER	60	0.03	0.1

Source: Author

The results obtained are shown in summary form in Table 11. For example, the wind limit with conventional mooring system obtained for a RO-RO vessel with wind for port bow was 45 knots, while with the AMS system was 75 knots. As can be seen, for this type of ships that have large windage, the AMS keeps the ship safely moored even with higher speed of wind than with the TMS, up to 30 knots more of wind.

In the case of the bulkcarrier, the results of the simulations reveal, with the TMS, that the breaking limit was at least 80 knots, well above the limit of the rest of the ships, and with the AMS, the minimum limit is 110 knots, also far higher than the rest. This is because the bulkcarrier has a smaller sail area. In the case of this type of vessel, the AMS resists between 15 and 50 knots of wind more than the TMS.

In the case of the cruise ship, also with a large sail area, the breaking limit with the TMS was 40 knots, while with the AMS this increased to 60 and 70 knots, holding between 20 and 30 knots more than with the TMS.

In the case of the container ship, also with a large sail area, with the TMS it resisted up to 50 knots of wind, both for bow and quarter winds and 45 knots of side wind, while with the AMS this limit increased to 60 and 70 knots of wind. For this type of vessel, the AMS also withstood between 20 and 25 knots more than the TMS.

As for the sail surface assigned to each model of vessel used in the simulations, the bulk carrier 215 m in length had a sail area of 1,852 m2 compared to the 5,564 m2 of the Ro-Ro vessel of almost 200 m in length, which gives 3,712 m^2 of difference between one and another.

The bulkcarrier had 8.61 m^2 of sail area per meter of length while the other three types of ships have 28.10 m^2, 29 m^2 and 23 m^2. As verified with the maneuvers, the vessel with the lowest sail area withstood more wind intensity when moored than the rest of the ships.

As can be seen in Table 12, the smallest difference between the wind limits when using the TMS and the AMS was recorded for the container ship, this being due to the irregularity of the surface exposed to the wind that depends on the number of containers loaded.

On the other hand, the biggest difference is for the Ro-Ro, for which the AMS allows it to hold at least 35 knots more wind than the TMS.

If the recommendations for use given by the AMS supplier (see Table 13) are followed, the cases where the AMS resists the most are those of the container ship and the bulk carrier.

Table 11. Results: Security wind limit.

Wind direction	RORO TMS	RORO AMS	BULKC TMS	BULKC AMS	CRUISE TMS	CRUISE AMS	CONTAINER TMS	CONTAINER AMS
Port Side	45	70	90	140	40	70	45	60
Port Bow	**45**	**75**	95	110	40	60	50	70
Port Quarter	35	70	80	120	40	60	50	60

Source: Author

Table 12. Lateral windage.

Type of vessel N°	LENGTH m.	Security wind limit TMS	Security wind limit AMS	Average wind limit AMS-TMS	LATERAL WINDAGE AREA m^2
1_RORO	198.0	35	70	35	5,564
2_BULKC	215.4	80	110	30	1,852
3_CRUIS	260.7	40	60	20	7,550
4_CONT	285.0	45	60	15	6,799

Source: Author

Table 13. Comparative table of the wind limits of use recommended by the manufacturer of the AMS and the data resulting from the mooring maneuvers carried out with the AMS in the simulator.

Type of vessel N°	LENGTH m.	Manufacturer recommendations WIND SPEED knots	Simulation results. Security wind limit AMS
1_RORO	198,0	48	70
2_BULKC	215,4	48	110
3_CRUIS	260,7	48	60
4_CONT	285,0	38	60

Source: Author

5 CONCLUSIONS

1. In all simulations, the wind limit capable of supporting a ship berthed safely was always higher for ships moored with the AMS than with the TMS.
2. The vessels with a smaller sail area withstood the wind better at berth than the rest of the vessels studied, no matter which mooring system used.
3. Wind is one of the factors in the final decision as to whether or not to install an AMS in docks dedicated exclusively to bulk carriers.
4. The manufacturer of AMS recommends a wind limit of 38 knots for vessels of a length of up to 285 meters and 48 knots for vessels of up to 250 meters in length, in all cases for installations made up of 10 robots of 45 tonnes of retention each. The wind recommended for the use of the AMS is greater than the breaking point of the cables defined in the study for the RoRo vessels and cruise ships.
5. The wind limit from which the TMS ceases to be safe is lower compared to the AMS. In all cases, the AMS withstands stronger winds than the TMS, as long as vacuum is preserved in the suction cups.
6. The sail area of the vessels affects the safety limit at berth. In the case studied, the bulkcarrier is the vessel with the lowest sail area and the breaking point both of the cables and of the AMS is far greater than that of the rest of the vessels.
7. The use of the AMS is beneficial for vessels with a large sail area as it has been verified that vessels with a lower sail area can be moored with a lower area can be moored safely with both the AMS and the TMS with over 80 knots of wind, a highly unlikely wind speed. It has also been verified that the AMS is more safely than the TMS for vessels with a large sail area, such as container ships, cruise ships and RoRo vessels.

As a final consideration the installation of AMS does not require any changes in the structure of the docks. This mooring system compared to the old one is not less secure because the movement of the vessel is automatically reduced while in the dock.

The AMS has advantages from the point of view of security thus reducing the risk of accidents in port, minimizing the movements of the vessel while moored and environmentally it reduces CO_2 emissions because the docking maneuver time is shorter both on board and in the dock and the mooring systems have a low electricity demand and hardly any energy consumption once the vessel is docked. The system guarantees the operating even in situations of loss of control signals and power cuts.

REFERENCES

Banfield, S., Flory, J., 2010. Effects of fiber rope complex stiffness behavior on mooring line tensions with large vessels moored in waves, in: OCEANS 2010. IEEE, pp. 1–11. https://doi.org/10.1109/OCEANS.2010.5663801

Barbudo Escobar, I., 2004. Fundamentos de Maniobra, 1a, Volume. ed. Fragata Libros Naúticos., Barcelona.

Cavotec, 2015. Cavotec [WWW Document]. URL http://www.cavotec.com/

Costas., G. de expertos de la dirección general de puertos y, 2000. ROM 3.1-99 Proyecto de la configuracion maritima de los puertos; canales de acceso y areas de flotacion, 1a. ed. Puertos del Estado, Madrid.

Diaz, E., 2016. Innovación en el sistema de amarre de los puertos marítimos comerciales. Universidad de cantabria.

Diaz, E., Ortega, A., Perez_Labajos, C., 2017. Commercial maritime ports with innovative mooring technology., *Maritime Transportation and Harvesting of Sea Resources*, C. Guedes Soares & A. P. Teixeira (Eds), Taylor and Francis Group. Vol. 1, pp 137–146.

Díaz, E., Ortega, A., Pérez, C., Blanco, B., Ruiz, L., Oria, J., 2016. Empirical analysis of the implantation of an automatic mooring system in a commercial port. Application to the port of santander (Spain), *Maritime Technology and Engineering 3*, C. Guedes Soares & T. A. Santos (Eds), Taylor and Francis Group. pp 193–200,.

Fang, S., Blanke, M., 2011. Fault monitoring and fault recovery control for position-moored vessels. International Journal of Applied Mathematics and Computer Science 21, 467–478.

Fang, S., Blanke, M., Leira, B.J., 2015. Mooring system diagnosis and structural reliability control for position moored vessels. Control Engineering Practice 36, 12–26. https://doi.org/10.1016/j.conengprac.2014.11.009

Gaythwaite, J.W., 2004. Design of Marine Facilities for Berthing, Mooring, and Repair of Vessels., 2a. ed. American Society of Civil Engineers., Reston, Virginia.

González, D.D.C., 2006. Estudio parametrico de las fuerzas en sistemas de amarre para buques amarrados en puerto. Estudio paramétrico de las fuerzas en sistemas de amarre para buques amarrados en puertos. Universidade do Porto.

Hetherington, C., Flin, R., Mearns, K., 2006. Safety in shipping: The human element. Journal of Safety

Research 37, 401–411. https://doi.org/10.1016/j.jsr.2006.04.007

Hsu, W.K.K., 2015. Assessing the safety factors of ship berthing operations. Journal of Navigation 68, 576–588. https://doi.org/10.1017/S0373463314000 861

Hsu, W.K.K., 2012. Ports' service attributes for ship navigation safety. Safety Science 50, 244–252. https://doi.org/10.1016/j.ssci.2011.08.057

Hsu, W.K.K., Yu, H.F., Huang, S.H.S., 2012. 2015. Evaluating the service requirements of dedicated container terminals: a revised IPA model with fuzzy AHP. Maritime Policy and Management 42, 789–805. https://doi.org/10.1080/03088839.2015.1043 750

Iskera-golec, I., Folkard, S., Marek, T., Noworol, C., 1996. Health, well-being and burnout of ICU nurses on 12- and 8-h shifts. Work & Stress 10, 251–256. https://doi.org/10.1080/02678379608256804

Josten, E.J.C., Ng-A-Tham, J.E.E., Thierry, H., 2003. The effects of extended workdays on fatigue, health, performance and satisfaction in nursing. Journal of advanced nursing 44, 643–52. https://doi.org/10.1046/j.0309-2402. 2003.02854.x

Kokotos, D.X., Smirlis, Y.G., 2005. A classification tree application to predict total ship loss. Journal of Transportation and Statistics 8, 31.

Llorca, J., González Herrero, J.M., Ametller, S., Piñeiro Díaz, E., 2012. ROM 2.0-11: Recomendaciones para el proyecto y ejecución en Obras de Atraque y Amarre. Puertos del Estado, Madrid

Schelfn, T.E., Östergaard, C., 1995. The vessel in port: Mooring problems. Marine Structures 8, 451–479.

Thoresen, C.A., 2014. Port Designer's Handbook, 3a. ed. ICE Publishing, Londres.

Uğurlu, Ö., Köse, E., Yıldırım, U., Yüksekyıldız, E., 2015. Marine accident analysis for collision and grounding in oil tanker using FTA method. Maritime Policy and Management 42, 163–185. https://doi.org/10.1080/03088839.2013.856524

Villa Caro, R., 2015. Sistemas de amarre en buques: situación actual y evolución futura.

Yamase, S., Ueda, S., 2007. Reliability of design methods of fender systems for very large container vessels. Energy 9, 10.

Zendrera, J., 1994. Amarres y fondeos, 4a. ed. Noray, Barcelona.

Optimal mooring system deployment in line breakage condition

Mingxiao Liang, Shengwen Xu, Xuefeng Wang & Aibing Ding
School of Naval Architecture, Ocean and Civil Engineering, Shanghai Jiao Tong University, Shanghai, China

ABSTRACT: The mooring system safety and the floating structure motion response in the survival condition are the main criteria in mooring system design. The safety factor of mooring system should be examined in the situation that the mooring system is intact and one mooring chain is broken. However, the previous researches mainly focus on the safety of the intact mooring system or the safety of the damaged mooring system in the steady stage. In this context, the safety of the damaged mooring system in the transient stage is investigated on a VLFS's mooring system comprising 20 mooring lines. It is found that the effect of the breakage of the mooring chain in the transient stage is equivalent to an impact load, which will significantly reduce the safety factor of the mooring system while increasing the motion response of the VLFS. The optimal mooring system deployment in line breakage condition is further investigated by establishing a multi-objective optimization problem using NSGA-II. It can be found from the numerical results that the proposed optimal mooring system deployment technique can effectively improve the safety of mooring system while suppress motion response of the VLFS.

1 INTRODUCTION

To examine the safety of floating structures and their mooring system under the survival condition is an important part of the design of mooring systems. The API (API 2005), DNV ((DNV 2008), (DNV 2010)) and other international standardization organizations issued a series of detailed specifications for the safety of mooring systems. These specifications clearly require that, in the process of mooring system design, the safety factor of the mooring system must be checked in the survival condition, where the safety factor is the ratio of mooring chain tension to its minimum breaking load (MBL). It is also necessary to examine the safety of the mooring system and the motion response of the floating structure under the intact condition and damaged condition (one-chain damaged).

The dynamic response of the floating structure and its mooring system under the damaged condition can be divided into two stages, which are transient stage and steady stage. Transient stage refers to the process that the floating structure and its mooring system move from the initial position to the new position after one mooring chain is damaged. The steady stage refers to the process after the floating structure and its mooring system moving to the new position when one mooring chain is damaged. The transient process of a floating structure changes with different inputs, it is usually difficult to be evaluate with a set of prevailing standards. Therefore, the relevant specifications mainly regulate the safety of floating structure and its mooring system in the steady state process, while the safety in the transient process needs to be specifically evaluated according to the inputs such as environment condition, characteristics of floating structure and mooring system.

2 SAFETY AND DYNAMIC RESPONSES UNDER INTACT CONDITION

2.1 Overview

The safety factor, which is the ratio of mooring chain tension to the MBL, is the index of the mooring system safety. The safety factors for both intact and damaged condition (API 2005) are listed in Table 1, where the tension limit is the reciprocal of the safety factor. The commercial software Orcaflex (Orcina 2015) is used in this paper to simulate the dynamic response of floating structure-mooring coupled system, thus the corresponding lower limit of the safety factor is 1.67.

A very large floating structure (VLFS) is utilized in this paper, and the properties of the VLFS and its mooring system are listed in Table 2. The structure of the VLFS is shown in Figure 1.

The survival condition of the VLFS is used to investigate the safety of mooring system. The corresponding parameters are listed in Table 3. Figure 2 gives the coordinate system and the layout of the mooring system, where the OXYZ is the global coordinate system and the $O_b X_b Y_b Z_b$ is body-fixed coordinate system.

DOI: 10.1201/9781003216599-38

Table 1. Safety factor of mooring system.

	Analysis Method	Tension Limit	Safety Factor
Intact	Quasi-static	0.5	2
Intact	Dynamic	0.6	1.67
Damaged	Quasi-static	0.7	1.43
Damaged	Dynamic	0.8	1.25

Table 2. Properties of the VLFS and mooring system.

VLFS		Mooring system		Upper-segment	Bottom-segment
Draught (m)	12	Length(m)		208	300
Displacement (ton)	93247	Diameter (mm)		200	170
COG (m)	20	Mass (kg/m)		876	633
Rolling inertia radius (m)	28.47	EA (kN)		4040000	2918900
Pitch inertia radius (m)	86.31	MBL (kN)		35840	28114
Yaw inertia radius (m)	89.66	Grade		R5	R5

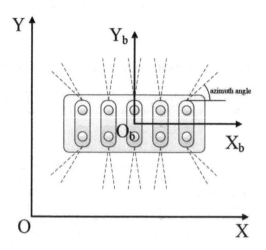

Figure 2. Illustration of the coordinate system and the mooring system layout.

Figure 1. The sketch of the VLFS module.

Table 3. The environmental condition.

Type	Hs (m)	Tp (s)	γ(-)	Direction (deg)
Jonswap	8	11.35	2	225

2.2 Mooring system safety and VLFS motion response

The dynamic response of the VLFS and its mooring system is simulated by the Orcaflex (Orcina 2015), where the simulation time is 10800 seconds with a time step of 0.2 seconds. The obtained mooring chain tension and the corresponding safety factor are listed in Table 4.

As shown in Table 4, the maximum tension in the mooring system appears on the No. 4 mooring chain. The maximum tension of No. 4 mooring chain is 13497kN in the upper-segment and 13312kN in the bottom-segment. The corresponding safety factors are 2.66 and 2.11, respectively. Meanwhile, the No.

16 mooring chain has the lowest maximum tension under the survival condition. The maximum tension in the upper- and bottom-segment is 3311kN and 3021kN, respectively, and the corresponding safety factors are 10.82 and 9.31, respectively.

Comparing the mean tension of each mooring chain, it can be found that the chains on the wave side have the larger mean tension than those on the lee side. This phenomenon indicates that in the survival condition, the restoring force of the mooring system is mainly provided by the No. 1 to No. 7 mooring chain and the No. 19 to the No. 20 mooring chain. The No. 2 mooring chain has the largest mean tension which are 2550kN and 2350kN for upper- and bottom-segment, respectively. It is also should be pointed out that the occurrence of the maximum tension has a certain randomness. The maximum tension and the largest mean tension do not necessarily appear on the same mooring chain, but the mooring chain with a larger mean tension has a larger maximum tension.

According to the results listed in Table 4, the safety factor of each mooring chain in the mooring system is greater than the lower limit, which is 1.67. Therefore, the intact mooring system is safe under the survival condition.

The statistical values of the VLFS motion response are listed in Table 5. It can be found from the table that the VLFS six-degree-of-freedom motions have a small mean value while the corresponding standard deviations are relatively larger. That indicates the equilibrium position of the VLFS in the survival condition is not far from its initial position, while the VLFS has a large amplitude near the equilibrium position under the excitation of environmental force.

The results in Table 5 show that the mean value of the heave motion is not zero. The VLFS has a trim and heel under the action of environmental

Table 4. The tension and safety factor for each mooring chain.

	Upper- segment			Bottom- segment		
Number	Mean tension (kN)	Maximum tension (kN)	safety factor	Mean tension (kN)	Maximum tension (kN)	safety factor
1	2470	9371	3.82	2265	9103	3.09
2	2550	10134	3.54	2350	9884	2.84
3	2445	11604	3.09	2267	11404	2.47
4	2486	13497	2.66	2313	13312	2.11
5	2126	5529	6.48	1935	5267	5.34
6	2110	5370	6.67	1921	5099	5.51
7	2222	12706	2.82	2057	12554	2.24
8	2157	10493	3.42	1989	10320	2.72
9	2047	7496	4.78	1875	7267	3.87
10	1981	6006	5.97	1803	5758	4.88
11	1779	7069	5.07	1611	6837	4.11
12	1829	8077	4.44	1668	7858	3.58
13	1823	7492	4.78	1672	7266	3.87
14	1870	8674	4.13	1724	8462	3.32
15	1729	3528	10.16	1551	3227	8.71
16	1742	3311	10.82	1569	3021	9.31
17	1978	8930	4.01	1819	8705	3.23
18	1959	7369	4.86	1795	7118	3.95
19	2177	8548	4.19	1998	8317	3.38
20	2148	7360	4.87	1964	7117	3.95

Table 5. The statistics of the VLFS motion response.

	Max	Mean	Std. Dev.
Surge (m)	4.99	-0.46	1.47
Sway (m)	4.08	-0.43	0.91
Heave (m)	4.63	0.81	0.85
Roll (deg)	10.03	0.43	1.95
Pitch (deg)	4.01	-0.15	0.62
Yaw (deg)	6.79	-0.06	2.16

force. As a result, the average vertical position of its center of gravity increases relative to the initial position. Meanwhile, due to the large difference between the lateral and longitudinal dimensions of the VLFS, the restoring moment of the mooring system in roll direction is small. Thus, the maximum roll motion of the VLFS exceeds 10 degrees.

The maximum surge and sway displacement of the VLFS are 4.99 meters and 4.08 meters, respectively, and the corresponding standard deviations are 1.47 meters and 0.91 meters. The maximum yaw amplitude of the VLFS is 6.79 degrees, and the standard deviation is 2.16 degrees. In general, the mooring system has sufficient station-keeping ability to constrain the motion of the VLFS under the survival condition.

The power spectral density (PSD) of the VLFS motion responses are shown in Figure 3. It can be found in the figure that low frequency motion dominates the VLFS motion response. The PSD of the sway, surge and sway has only one peak, which occurs at frequencies of 0.13 rad/s, 0.21 rad/s and 0.14 rad/s, respectively. The PSD peak of roll and pitch occurs at frequencies of 0.17 rad/s and 0.2 rad/s, respectively. However, except the peak at the frequencies of 0.2 rad/s, another obvious peak can be found near 0.01 rad/s in heave motion. In general, with the coupling of the mooring system, the motion response of the VLFS in the survival condition is dominate by low frequency motion.

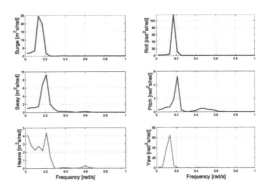

Figure 3. The power spectral density of the VLFS motion response.

3 SAFETY AND DYNAMIC RESPONSES UNDER DAMAGED CONDITION

The mooring chain may be damaged due to corrosion, collision, fatigue, structural defects and other factors. It is necessary to investigate the safety of mooring system and the motion response of the VLFS with one mooring chain damaged.

3.1 Overview

The damage of the mooring chain may be caused by corrosion, collision, fatigue, structural defects and excessive tension. It is usually difficult to determine the actual breaking process, breaking moment and breaking position of a mooring chain. Instead of the breaking process, the aim of this paper is to investigate the mooring system safety and the VLFS motion response. Therefore, it is stipulated that the mooring chain breaks at the time that the mooring chain tension reaches its maximum value; the mooring chain breaking point is the fairlead and the breaking is instantaneously completed; the interaction of the VLFS and the mooring chain is relieved immediately when the chain is broken. The time when the tension of each mooring chain reaches the maximum value are listed in Table 6.

With one mooring chain damaged, the safety and the station-keeping ability of the mooring system will be reduced. Thus, the most dangerous situation of the VLFS and its mooring system will occur in the survival condition. The parameters of environmental condition, VLFS and its mooring system are listed in Tables 2 and 3. The dynamic response of the VLFS and its mooring system is simulated by the Orcaflex (Orcina 2015), where the simulation time is 10800 seconds with a time step of 0.2 seconds.

3.2 Mooring system safety

The number of the most dangerous mooring chain and the corresponding safety factor for each damaged condition are listed in Table 7.

As shown in Table 7, the mooring chain with the smallest safety factor appears near the damaged

Table 6. The Breaking moment of each mooring chain.

Number	Breaking moment (s)	Number	Breaking moment (s)
1	2410	11	9030
2	2410	12	9030
3	650	13	696
4	650	14	696
5	400	15	9745
6	400	16	9745
7	9730	17	414
8	9731	18	413
9	670	19	9006
10	7000	20	9007

mooring chain if the damaged mooring chain is located on the wave side. While the No. 4 mooring chain has the smallest safety factor if the damaged mooring chain is located on the lee side. In general, the No. 3 and No. 4 mooring chain are most dangerous in the damaged condition. The minimum safety factor appears in the bottom-segment of the two mooring chains, which are 1.47 and 1.58, respectively. The results in Table 7 show that the minimum safety factor of the mooring system is larger than the lower limit value of 1.25, thus the mooring system is safe under the survival condition with one mooring chain damaged.

Comparing the result listed in Table 4 and Table 7, the maximum tension of the most dangerous mooring chain is significantly increased relative to the intact mooring system if the damaged mooring chain is located on the wave side of the VLFS. Taking the No. 4 mooring chain as an example, the maximum tension of its upper- and bottom-segment is 19305kN and 19163kN on the condition that No. 3 mooring chain is damaged. That is 42% and 44% compared with 13497kN and 13312kN when the mooring system is intact. However, if the damaged mooring chain is on the lee side of the VLFS, the maximum tension of the most dangerous mooring chain is not significantly affected or even slightly reduced. For example, the tension range of the No. 4 mooring chain is 12424kN-13446kN for the upper-segment and 12243kN-13260kN bottom segment when the No. 10 to No. 20 is broken. On this condition, the maximum tension of the No. 4 mooring chain is slightly lower than that of the intact mooring system. This result shows that the safety of the mooring system is significantly reduced with one mooring chain damaged on the wave side of the VLFS, while the damage of the mooring chain on the lee side has limited impact on the safety of the mooring system.

The time histories of the tension of the NO. 4 mooring chain on the damaged condition of No. 3 and No. 10 mooring chain are shown in Figures 4 and 5 respectively to investigate the transient and steady stage of the damaged condition.

As shown in Figure 4, the tension of No. 4 mooring chain rises rapidly to the maximum value after No. 3 mooring chain breaks at 650 seconds. Then, the tension of the No. 4 mooring chain has a significant fluctuation from 664 to 672 seconds and reaches a new steady state after 672 seconds. Therefore, after the breaking of the No. 3 mooring chain, the transient stage of the No. 4 mooring chain is the duration from 650 to 672 seconds, and the steady stage is the duration after 672 seconds. At the transient stage, the tension of the No. 4 mooring chain increases sharply, which can be regard as a result of an impact load. In this case, the safety of the No. 4 mooring chain is determined to some extent by the transient stage. In the steady stage, the mean tension of the No. 4 mooring chain increased from 2488kN to 3061kN. It should be pointed out that the maximum tension of the No. 4 mooring chain does not

Table 7. The number of most dangerous mooring chain and safety factor.

Number of broken chain	Number of most danger chain	Upper-segment Maximum tension (kN)	Safety factor	Bottom-segment Maximum tension (kN)	Safety factor
1	2	14085	2.54	13880	2.03
2	4	14673	2.44	14495	1.94
3	4	19305	1.86	19163	1.47
4	3	17907	2.00	17763	1.58
5	4	14783	2.42	14620	1.92
6	4	14972	2.39	14810	1.90
7	8	15313	2.34	15169	1.85
8	7	16879	2.12	16751	1.68
9	7	13467	2.66	13305	2.11
10	4	13446	2.67	13260	2.12
11	4	13443	2.67	13257	2.12
12	4	13444	2.67	13257	2.12
13	4	13444	2.67	13257	2.12
14	4	13444	2.67	13258	2.12
15	4	13444	2.67	13258	2.12
16	4	13444	2.67	13258	2.12
17	4	12424	2.88	12243	2.30
18	4	12557	2.85	12371	2.27
19	4	13445	2.67	13259	2.12
20	4	13445	2.67	13258	2.12

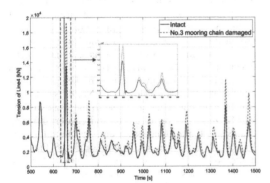

Figure 4. Time history of tension of No.4 mooring chain when No.3 mooring chain breaks.

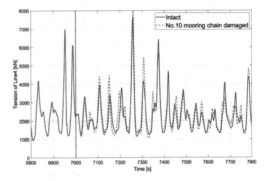

Figure 5. Time history of tension of No.4 mooring chain when No.10 mooring chain breaks.

necessarily appear in the transient stage. Since the performance of the mooring system declines after one chain is damaged, the maximum tension may occur during the steady stage. Therefore, the transient or steady stage cannot be considered separately when investigating the safety of the mooring system at the damaged condition.

As shown in Figure 5, on the damaged condition of No. 10 mooring chain, no obvious transient stage is observed in the time history of tension of the No. 4 mooring chain. In the steady stage, the phase of tension time history of No.4 mooring chain is basically the same as that of the intact mooring system, while the amplitude of tension is slightly different. The difference of tension amplitude is mainly caused by the change of mooring system performance after one mooring chain damaged. The results in Figure 5 show that the damage of the lee side mooring chain has a limited impact on the safety of the mooring system, which may not necessarily produce an impact load on the mooring system.

3.3 VLFS motion response

The statistics of the VLFS motion response at different damaged condition are listed in Table 8.

Comparing the results listed in Tables 5 and 8, the mean position of the surge motion of the VLFS is shifted in the positive direction, with an offset of 0.03m-0.57m (the difference between the mean value of the surge motion at the intact and damaged condition), which is 7%-124% of the mean value of the intact mooring system. Meanwhile, the maximum value of the surge motion is 3.18m-5.04m, which is the 64%-101% of the intact mooring system.

However, if the damaged mooring chain are No. 1 to No. 6 or No. 16 to No. 20, the maximum and mean value of the surge motion is increased. The corresponding maximum and mean value are 5.15m-6.38m and 0.46m-1.18m respectively, which is 103%-130% and 100%-256% of the intact mooring system. This result shows that if the mooring chain close to the bow of the VLFS breaks, the VLFS will have a more significant surge motion. On the contrary, if the broken mooring chain is close to the stern of the VLFS, the surge motion will be reduced to some extent. Since the force that the VLFS receives in the negative direction of its longitudinal axis includes the environmental force and the mooring force provided by the mooring chain located on the stern of the VLFS, the restoring force of the mooring system in the positive direction of the longitudinal axis is actually increased if the mooring chain located on the stern of the VLFS is broken. Thus, the surge motion response of the VLFS will be reduced to some extent. Conversely, if the broken mooring chain is located on the bow of the VLFS, the restoring force of the mooring system in the positive direction actually reduced, which leads to an increase of the VLFS motion response. Similarly, when the broken mooring chain is on the wave side of the VLFS (one of the No. 1 to No. 10 mooring chain is broken), the maximum and mean value of the sway motion are 3.91m-4.76m and 0.57m-0.60m, which is the 96%-117% and 133%-140% of that in the intact mooring system. While the maximum and mean value of the sway motion reduce to 3.52m-4.12m and 0.10m-0.31m if the broken mooring chain is on the lee side of the VLFS (one of the No. 11 to No. 20 mooring chain is broken), which is the 86%-101% and 23%-72% of that in intact mooring system.

As listed in Table 8, the mean value the yaw motion of the VLFS is negative if one of the No. 1 to No. 4 or No. 11 to No. 14 mooring chain is broken. On that condition, the absolute value of the mean value of the yaw motion is 0.19°-0.54°, which is equivalent to 317% - 900% of that in the intact mooring system. However, if one of the No. 7 to No. 10 or No. 17 to No. 20 mooring chain is broken, the mean value of the sway motion is positive, which is 0.05°-0.48° and is the 83% - 800% of that in the intact mooring system. Since the restoring moment in the positive direction of yaw motion is mainly provided by the No. 7 to No. 10 and No. 7 to No. 10 mooring chain, the VLFS will have a large mean deviation along the positive direction of yaw motion if one of those mooring chain is broken. The locations of the fairlead of the No. 5, No. 6, No. 15 and No. 16 mooring chain are close to the Z-axis of the VLFS, thus the breakage of those four mooring chains has limited impact on the yaw motion of the VLFS. In particular, the mean value of the yaw motion of the VLFS is 0.02°-0.07° if one of the four mooring chains is broken and is not significantly larger than that of the intact mooring system.

The motion response of the VLFS in surge, sway and yaw direction on the damaged condition of No. 3 and No. 10 mooring chain is shown in Figures 6 and 7. As shown in Figure 6, the fluctuation can be found in the low-frequency motion of the VLFS in surge, sway and yaw direction from 650 to 2000 seconds. After 2000 seconds, the low frequency motion in these three degrees of freedom tends to be stable. Therefore, after the No. 3 mooring chain is broken, the duration of 650 to 2000 seconds is the transient stage of the VLFS motion response and the steady stage is the duration after 2000 seconds. Further, the mean position of the sway motion gradually shifts to -0.7m to -0.8m form its initial position -0.5m. However, the mean position of the surge and yaw motion are not significantly changed. As shown in Figure 6, the maximum values of the VLFS motion in surge, sway and yaw direction do not

Table 8. Statistics of the VLFS motion response.

Number of broken chain	Surge Max (m)	Mean (m)	Sway Max (m)	Mean (m)	Yaw Max (deg)	Mean (deg)
1	6.38	-1.18	3.91	-0.60	6.90	-0.19
2	6.15	-1.16	4.21	-0.61	7.03	-0.34
3	5.15	-0.65	4.57	-0.78	7.18	-0.44
4	5.24	-0.55	4.69	-0.82	7.32	-0.54
5	5.48	-0.46	4.74	-0.77	6.55	-0.02
6	5.53	-0.40	4.76	-0.77	6.53	-0.07
7	4.54	-0.34	4.07	-0.77	6.60	0.48
8	4.27	-0.25	4.04	-0.73	6.38	0.37
9	4.88	0.10	4.40	-0.59	7.43	0.17
10	5.07	0.11	4.07	-0.57	6.49	0.05
11	5.02	0.00	3.64	-0.31	6.24	-0.23
12	5.04	0.00	3.61	-0.29	6.46	-0.34
13	4.92	-0.27	3.98	-0.14	6.45	-0.38
14	4.88	-0.33	3.83	-0.11	6.26	-0.46
15	3.18	-0.43	3.52	-0.11	5.71	-0.02
16	3.20	-0.48	3.53	-0.10	5.71	-0.05
17	5.20	-0.58	4.12	-0.11	7.20	0.33
18	5.23	-0.64	4.01	-0.14	7.17	0.26
19	5.64	-1.12	3.76	-0.26	6.39	0.24
20	5.72	-1.15	3.74	-0.27	6.24	0.11

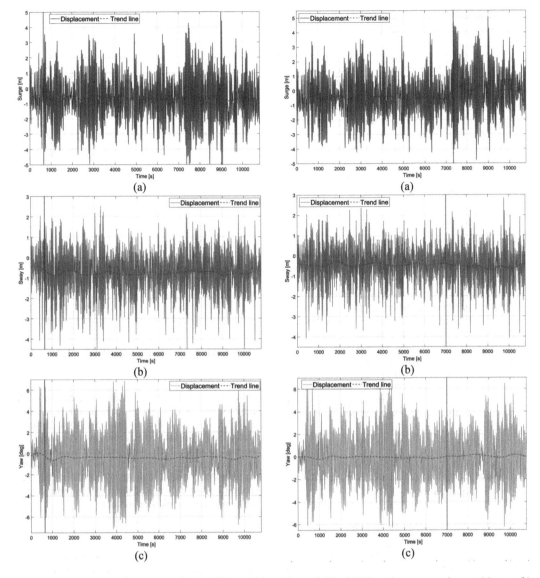

Figure 6. The VLFS motion response in surge(a), sway(b) and yaw(c) direction.

Figure 7. The VLFS motion response in surge(a), sway(b) and yaw(c) direction.

occur in the transient stage, but occur in the steady stage. The increasing of the VLFS motion response is caused by decreasing of the mooring system performance and the mooring system has sufficient redundancy to withstand the impact load cause by the damaging of one mooring chain.

As shown in Figure 7, with the breaking of No. 10 mooring chain, the equilibrium position of the surge motion is shifted from its initial position -0.45m to the 0.2m at the duration of 7000 to 8000 seconds and stabilized at around 0.2m at the duration after 8000 seconds. However, the breakage of the No. 10 mooring chain does not significant affect the motion in sway and yaw direction.

In general, the effect of the mooring chain damage on the VLFS motion response is mainly composed of two parts: the impact load caused by the breaking of the mooring chain in the transient stage and the effect caused by the reducing of the mooring system performance in the steady stage. The station-keeping ability of the mooring system will be weakened at the damaged condition, but the damaging of mooring chain will improve the mooring system performance in some specific direction under specific environmental condition.

4 OPERATION STRATEGY ON THE DAMAGED CONDITION

The result presented before shows that the mooring system is safe on both intact and damaged condition. However, the software cannot simulate all the possible outcomes and it is necessary to develop a safe operation strategy for the mooring system to ensure the safety of the VLFS and the mooring system. Due to the difficult of estimating the breaking moment of a mooring chain and predict the duration of the transient stage after that, the operation strategy of the mooring system is developed for steady stage at the damaged condition.

4.1 Mathematical model

The essence of the operation strategy for the mooring system on the damaged condition is to improve the safety of mooring system and reduce the motion response of the VLFS by adjusting the parameters of mooring system. For the mooring system which has been used in actual engineering, the upper-segment length is only parameter available for adjustment on the damaged condition. The safety of the mooring system at the steady stage is characterized by the safety factor. The motion response of the VLFS is characterized by the maximum horizontal displacement and the amplitude of the yaw motion. Thus, the mathematical model of the mooring chain length optimization at the steady stage can be established as follows:

$$\text{minimize}: F(L_i) = [\emptyset_H, \emptyset_Y, \emptyset_S],$$
$$\text{subject to}: L_i \in \Omega, \ i = 1, 2, 3, \ldots, 20, \quad (1)$$
$$\text{constrained to}: \emptyset_S > 1.25,$$

where: L_i is length of the i-th mooring chain; $\emptyset_H$, $\emptyset_Y$, and $\emptyset_S$ are the corresponding objective function for VLFS horizontal displacement, yaw motion and mooring system safety factor, respectively; Ω is the feasible range of the chain length. As shown in Table 1, the safety factor of the mooring system on the damaged condition must larger than 1.25.

Several methods such as NSGA-II(Deb, Pratap, Agarwal, & Meyarivan 2002), PESA-II((Zitzler & Thiele 1999), (Zitzler, Laumanns, & Thiele 2001)) and SPEA-II(Corne, Knowles, & Oates 2000) can be used to solve the Problem 1. Since the NSGA-II method is more efficient than the other two methods, a MATLAB program is developed based on the NSGA-II and coupled with the Orcaflex (Orcina 2015) to solve the Problem 1. Figure 8 illustrates a schematic diagram of the NSGA-II. The initial random parents are the input. Then the corresponding parameters of the input are transmitted to the Orcaflex to calculate the vessel motion response and mooring force. Based on the results obtained by the Orcaflex, the

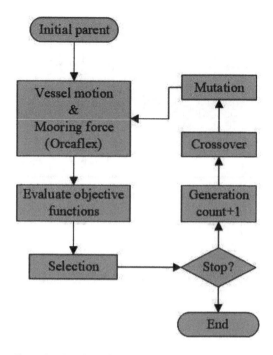

Figure 8. The schematic diagram of NSGA-II.

value of the objective function for each set of the input (which is also called as individual) is calculated. Then, sort the individuals into different fronts and estimate the crowding distances for them. The individuals with higher rank and larger crowding distance are selected as the new parents for crossover and mutation to generate the new generations of children. Continue the process until the termination condition is met.

4.2 Operating strategy

As listed in Tables 7 and 8, the VLFS and its mooring system in the most dangerous condition if the damaged mooring chain located on the wave side of the VLFS. Since the safety of the mooring system is most concerned if one mooring chain is damaged, the damaged condition of No. 3 mooring chain is selected to develop the operating strategy.

The environmental condition and the properties of the VLFS and the mooring system are listed in Tables 2 and 3. It is specified that length of the two mooring chains on the same fairlead are the same, thus there are 10 groups of mooring chain lengths to be optimized. The population and generation of the NSGA-II are 50 and 100, respectively. The simulation time in the Orcaflex (Orcina 2015) is 10800 seconds with a time step of 0.2 seconds.

With the accomplishment of the calculation, 50 sets of the solution are obtained which can be divided into 11 groups and listed in Table 9. As mentioned before, the safety of the mooring system is

Table 9. The horizontal displacement and yaw of the optimal solutions.

Set	horizontal displacement (m)	Yaw (deg)	Safety factor Upper-segment	Bottom-segment
1	5.14	3.76	3.00	2.40
2	5.37	3.53	2.95	2.40
3	5.28	3.72	2.92	2.38
4	5.59	3.52	2.81	2.38
5	5.88	3.43	2.79	2.30
6	5.08	5.62	2.77	2.30
7	4.19	3.01	2.75	2.22
8	4.31	2.76	2.66	2.10
9	4.21	2.42	2.64	2.15
10	4.00	3.54	2.52	2.00
11	3.96	3.20	2.14	1.60

the decisive factor in developing the operation strategy in the damaged condition. Therefore, the set 1, which has the largest safety factor, are selected as the desired solution for the damaged condition.

The mooring chain length corresponding to the set 1 optimal solution is listed in Table 10. In general, the optimized mooring chain length is shorter than the initial one, especially for the No. 9 to No. 12 and No. 15 to No. 20 mooring chains. The length of these mooring chains is reduced by 2-3 m. For the No. 1 to No. 4 mooring chains, which are located on the wave side, their length is not changed after the optimization. Thus, for the mooring system investigated in this paper, increasing the safety factor of the mooring system with one chain breaking requires tightening some of the mooring chains. Moreover, the additional advantage brought by tightening the mooring chains is to increase the station-keeping ability of the mooring system, thereby reducing the motion response of the VLFS. Specifically,

Table 10. The corresponding length of the set 1 optimal solution.

Number	Length of upper-segment (m)	Number	Length of upper-segment (m)
1	208	11	205
2	208	12	205
3	(Broken)	13	208
4	208	14	208
5	207	15	205
6	207	16	205
7	206	17	206
8	206	18	206
9	205	19	205
10	205	20	205

comparing the results listed in Tables 8 and 9, the maximum amplitude of VLFS sway motion is reduced from 7.18° to 3.72° and the safety factor of the mooring system is increased from 1.47 to 2.40.

The maximum tension and corresponding safety factor of the set 1 optimal solution are listed in Table 11. The safety factor of the No. 1 to No. 4 mooring chain is relatively smaller than other mooring chains, the safety factors of the four mooring chains are close to 3.0 at the upper-segment and close to 2.4 at the bottom-segment, since the restoring force of the mooring system is mainly provided by the mooring chains located on the wave side of the VLFS. With the optimized chain length, the No. 4 mooring chain is still the most dangerous mooring chain, but its safety factor has increased by 63% compared to the initial length. For the No. 10 to No. 18 mooring chain, which located on the lee side of the VLFS, their safety factor is significantly increased compared to the initial mooring system. The safety factors of the upper- and bottom-segment of these mooring chains are 4.26-9.18 and 3.44-7.93, respectively. In general, compared the initial mooring system, the safety factor of the damaged mooring system with the optimized mooring chain length is significantly improved, but the No. 1 to No. 4 mooring chains are still the most dangerous mooring chain in the damaged condition.

Table 11. The safety factor of the optimized mooring system.

	Upper-segment		Bottom-segment	
Number	Maximum tension (kN)	Safety factor	Maximum tension (kN)	Safety factor
1	11644	3.08	11357	2.48
2	11930	3.00	11643	2.41
3	(Broken)	(-)	(Broken)	(-)
4	11983	2.99	11698	2.40
5	10503	3.41	10230	2.75
6	10209	3.51	9936	2.83
7	7952	4.51	7663	3.67
8	7651	4.68	7341	3.83
9	7556	4.74	7322	3.84
10	7484	4.79	7245	3.88
11	6157	5.82	5879	4.78
12	7181	4.99	6925	4.06
13	3904	9.18	3545	7.93
14	4216	8.50	3885	7.24
15	7571	4.73	7327	3.84
16	8409	4.26	8174	3.44
17	5310	6.75	5048	5.57
18	5723	6.26	5462	5.15
19	9726	3.69	9483	2.96
20	11320	3.17	11093	2.53

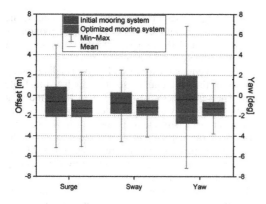

Figure 9. The statistics of the VLFS motion in surge, sway and yaw direction.

The statistics of the VLFS surge, sway and yaw motion are shown in Figure 9. It can be found that the maximum value and the standard deviation of the VLFS motion responses in surge, sway and yaw direction are obviously reduced while the mean value of motion response in those three directions are slightly increased. Taking the yaw motion as an example, the maximum value and the standard deviation of the VLFS yaw motion with optimized mooring system are 53% and 28% of that before optimization, while the mean value increases by about 0.88°.

5 CONCLUSIONS

The safety of mooring system in the survival condition are the main criteria in mooring system design, which should be examined in the situations that the mooring system is intact and one mooring chain is broken. In this paper, the safety of the damaged mooring system in the transient stage is investigated on a VLFS's mooring system comprising 20 mooring lines.

The effect of the breakage of the mooring chain in the transient stage is equivalent to an impact load, which will significantly reduce the safety factor of the mooring system while increasing the motion response of the VLFS. However, the maximum value of the mooring chain tension and the VLFS motion response do not necessarily appear in the transient stage, they may occur during the steady stage since the performance of the mooring system declines with one chain damaged.

The optimal mooring system deployment in damaged condition is further investigated and the multi-objective optimization problem is established and solved by NSGA-II. The numerical results show that tightening the mooring chains in the damaged mooring system can effectively increase the safety factor of the mooring system and reducing the motion response of the VLFS.

REFERENCES

API. 2005. Recommended practice for design and analysis of stationkeeping systems for floating structures: API RP 2SK. *American Petroleum Institution* (API).

Corne, D. W., J. D. Knowles, & M. J. Oates. 2000. The pareto envelope-based selection algorithm for multiobjective optimization. *In International conference on parallel problem solving from nature*, pp. 839–848. Springer.

Deb, K., A. Pratap, S. Agarwal, & T. Meyarivan. 2002. A fast and elitist multi-objective genetic algorithm: NSGA-II. *IEEE transactions on evolutionary computation* 6(2), 182–197.

DNV. 2008. Offshore mooring chain. *Offshore Standard DNVOS-E302*.

DNV. 2010. Position mooring. *Offshore standard DNV-OSE301*.

Orcina. 2015. *OcraFlex Manual (Version 10.0e)*.

Zitzler, E., M. Laumanns, & L. Thiele. 2001. SPEA-II: Improving the strength pareto evolutionary algorithm. *TIK report 103*.

Zitzler, E. & L. Thiele. 1999. Multiobjective evolutionary algorithms: a comparative case study and the strength pareto approach. *IEEE transactions on Evolutionary Computation* 3(4), 257–271.

Investigation of long-term extreme mooring tensions by fully coupled dynamic analysis

Sheng Xu & C. Guedes Soares
Centre for Marine Technology and Ocean Engineering (CENTEC), Instituto Superior Técnico, Universidade de Lisboa, Lisbon, Portugal

Chunyan Ji
School of Naval Architecture and Ocean Engineering, Jiangsu University of Science and Technology, Zhenjiang, Jiangsu, China

ABSTRACT: A numerical model, which has been validated by the experimental data is used to simulate a semi-submersible taut mooring dynamic responses in a specified site of South China Sea. In order to take the random wave elevations into consideration, the short term analysis with different random wave seeds are carried to study the system dynamics. The mooring tension distributions in different significant wave heights and peak periods are fitted by Weibull distributions. Different methods including the global maximum method, peak-over-threshold method and short-term peaks method are applied to investigate the long term extreme mooring tension. The estimated long-term extreme mooring tensions are compared, and the accuracy of these methods are discussed.

1 INTRODUCTION

The floating structures, such as offshore platforms, wave energy converters and floating wind turbines are subject to different environmental loads. The mooring system, whose main role is to keep the floating structure on station is a crucial component of the floating system. The mooring is closely related to system safety as well as economy. This means that the mooring system needs to be strong enough to withstand the combinations of environmental loads, while it should not be over-designed, which would increase costs. This suggests that the dynamic responses of floating system need to be predicted precisely during the mooring design process.

Numerical methods and hydrodynamic model tests are two approaches used in predicting floating system dynamic responses. However, the experimental research is rarely used in the initial design due to its high cost, and the numerical simulation provides an alternative solution. The fre.tifuency domain and time domain are two generally used method in calculating the responses. Without any doubt, the linear fre.tifuency domain method is the most efficient one since the nonlinearities are neglected. As a conse.tifuence, it may fail in predicting dynamic responses precisely, especially for mooring line dynamic analysis.

Since 2000s, the fully coupled dynamic method are studied extensively in solving floating structure-mooring-riser system dynamic responses (Garrett, 2005; Low &Langley, 2006; Ormberg & Larsen, 1998; Yang et al., 2012; Ran, 2000). By taking coupled effects between floating structure-mooring-riser system and nonlinearities into consideration, the fully coupled simulations are recognized as the most reliable numerical results. However, it should be noticed that the fully coupled dynamic analysis is cumbersome. In view of this, Low & Langley (2008) developed a hybrid time-fre.tifuency domain approach for analyzing the coupled problem of vessel-mooring-riser. This method presents accurate estimations of motion responses of floating structure and mooring tensions. Besides, it is much more efficient than the fully coupled dynamic approach.

The full long-term analysis is recognized as the most accurate approach to estimate extreme response of offshore structures under the effects of random sea environmental loads (Guedes Soares & Scotto, 2011; Xu et al., 2019c). Basically, the full-long term extreme analysis takes all the possible sea states and the dynamic response probability distributions conditional on corresponding sea states into consideration. As a conse.tifuence, the direct integration is inefficient, since a large number of combinations of environmental parameters need to be considered. Thus, some numerical methods are developed to reduce the burden of calculation of full-long term integration.

Sagrilo et al. (2011) discussed five models for estimating long-term extreme response of a linear single degree of freedom system. The performances

DOI: 10.1201/9781003216599-39

of different models, including all short-term peaks, all extreme short-term peaks and all short-term upcrossing rates were studied. It was shown that the approach by combing the inverse first order reliability (I-FORM) and importance sampling Monte Carlo Simulation presented precise estimations of long term extreme value. Low & Huang (2017) proposed a combination of subset simulation and importance sampling techni.tifue to study the long-term extreme responses of offshore structures. It was validated that this approach shows both high efficiency and accuracy. Besides, the long-term integration problem can also be efficiently solved by I-FORM (Giske et al., 2017) and inverse second order reliability method (I-SORM) (Giske et al., 2018).

In addition to the full long-term integration approach, the environmental contour line method (ECM) is an efficient method in the application of long-term extreme response analysis of offshore structures (Haver & Kleiven, 2004; Haver & Winterstein, 2009, Karmakar et al. 2016). By applying ECM, the environmental contour line with the prescribed return period is constructed. The long-term extreme response is determined by searching the greatest short-term extreme response along the environmental contour line.

Generally, the environmental contour line is generated based on I-FORM (Winterstein et al., 1993), while the I-SORM (Chai & Leira, 2018) and direct Monte Carlo simulations (Huseby et al., 2013) are also available. The comparisons of applying different ECMs to estimate long-term extreme responses of a semi-submersible were conducted by Raed et al. (2020). The original ECM is not feasible in predicting long-term extreme responses of wind turbine due to their non-monotonic behavior under wind loads. By noticing this, Li et al. (2016) developed a modified ECM method, which has applied successfully in long-term extreme response of offshore wind turbine analysis. Despite that the ECM has high efficiency, it may present poor estimation of long-term extreme response due to the fact that it omits response variability. In order to solve this problem, a 3-D I-FORM was developed to analyze long-term extreme response of offshore wind turbine (Agarwal & Manuel, 2009; Rendon & Manuel, 2014). It was observed that the 3-D I-FORM presented close estimations of long-term extreme response to the full long-term integration results.

It is seen that the different method for analyzing long–term extreme responses of offshore structures have been developed. However, the study of long-term extreme mooring tension is limited. In this work, the short-term and long-term extreme mooring tension of a semi-submersible is numerically studied, and the fully coupled numerical model has been validated. Three different methods, including all peaks method, POT method and all short-term extreme peaks are discussed. Besides, the influence of significant wave height, wave peak period and the number of numerical simulations on extreme mooring tension is discussed. The uncertainties of estimated short-term extreme mooring tensions are evaluated by the bootstrap techni.tifue. Then, the long-term extreme mooring tensions with different return periods are calculated, and the results of different methods are compared.

2 METHODOLOGY

2.1 Statistic distributions

2.1.1 Gumbel distribution

The Gumbel distribution is generally used to fit the extreme peaks, and the cumulative distribution function is defined as:

$$F(x; \mu_l, \beta_l) = \exp\{-\exp(-\frac{x-\mu_l}{\sigma_l})\} \quad (1)$$

where μ_l is the location factor, σ_l is the scale factor.

In this study, the L-moments method is applied to fit the parameters of Gumbel distributions (Bílková, 2014):

$$\sigma_l = \frac{l_2}{\ln 2} \quad \mu_l = l_1 - \gamma \sigma_l \quad (2)$$

where l_i is referred to as the *ith* order l moment, the details for calculating l moment can be checked in (Xu et al., 2019a). γ is the Euler's constant.

The most probable maximum extreme (MPME) value, which is defined as the mode value has a 63.2% chance to be exceeded (Cheng & Kuang, 2016). Then, the MPME value is determined according to the Gumbel distribution:

$$x_{mp} = \mu - \beta \ln\{-\ln(F(1-0.632)))\} = \mu_l \quad (3)$$

2.1.2 The peak-over-threshold method and Generalized Pareto distribution

The POT method is one of the most popular methods for extreme value analysis. It is assumed that the parent distribution belongs to one of the extreme value distributions, and then multiple important crests over threshold are fitted by the Generalized Pareto distribution (GPD). Based on the assumptions that the selected peaks are Poisson distributed, and the exceedances are approximately independent, the POT method shows good performance in predicting extreme responses.

One of the crucial steps in applying POT method is to select suitable threshold (Ferreira & Guedes Soares, 1998, Guedes Soares & Scotto, 2001). In this work, the optimum threshold is determined by searching suitable dispersion index in conjunction with declustering algorithm (Brodtkorb et al., 2000).

The GPD was proposed by Pickands (1975), and its CDF is defined as:

$$F(x;\mu_g,\sigma_g,\xi_g) = \begin{cases} 1-\left(1+\xi_g\frac{x-\mu_g}{\sigma}\right)^{-1/\xi_g} & \xi \neq 0 \\ 1-\exp\left(-\frac{x-\mu_g}{\sigma_g}\right) & \xi = 0 \end{cases} \quad (4)$$

where the parameters μ_g, σ_g and ξ_g are the location, scale and shape factor, respectively. These parameters are fitted by efficient L-moments method (Pandey et al., 2001):

$$\xi_g = \frac{3t_3-1}{t_3+1} \quad \sigma_g = (1-\xi_g)(2-\xi_g)l_2 \quad (5)$$
$$\mu_g = l_1 - (2-\xi_g)l_2$$

2.1.3 Weibull distribution

The Weibull distribution is widely used in ships and offshore structures dynamic responses analysis (Guedes Soares & Moan, 1991; Xu et al., 2019a, 2019c). The CDF of three parameters Weibull distribution is defined as:

$$F(x;\mu_w,\sigma_w,\xi_w) = 1 - \exp\left[-\left(\frac{x-\mu_w}{\sigma_w}\right)^{\xi_w}\right] \quad (6)$$

where the parameters μ_w, σ_w and ξ_w are the location, scale and shape factor, respectively.

Again, the L-moments approach is applied to estimate the parameters of Weibull distribution (Goda et al., 2010):

$$\xi_w = 285.3t_3^6 - 658.6t_3^5 + 622.8t_3^4 - 317.2t_3^3$$
$$+ 98.52t_3^2 - 21.256t_3 + 3.516 \quad (7)$$

$$\sigma_w = \frac{l_2}{(1-2^{-1/\xi_w})\Gamma(1+1/\xi_w)} \quad (8)$$

$$\mu_w = l_1 - \sigma_w\Gamma(1+1/\xi_w) \quad (9)$$

where $\Gamma(\cdot)$ denotes the Gamma function.

2.2 Long-term response modelling

2.2.1 Models based on all short-term peaks

Assuming that the response peaks and environmental parameters are statistically independent, the long-term probability distribution is given by:

$$F_R(r) = \int^{F_{R|S}}(r|\mathbf{s})f_\mathbf{S}(\mathbf{s})d\mathbf{s} \quad (10)$$

where $f_\mathbf{s}(\mathbf{s})$ is the joint probability density function of the environmental parameters. In this study, $\mathbf{S}$ includes significant wave height and wave peak period, i.e., $\mathbf{S} = (H_s, T_p)$. $F_{R|S}(r|\mathbf{s})$ is the cumulative distribution of global peaks conditional on short term sea state, which is approximated by the Weibull distribution.

By assuming that the short-term sea states are mutually exclusive, Eq. (10) can then be discretized as (Sagrilo et al., 2011):

$$F_R(r) = \sum F_{R|s_i}(r|s_i)P(s_i) \quad (11)$$

where $P(s_i)$ is the probability of the occurrence of ith sea state.

2.2.2 Models based on POT

The POT method concerns the peak loads exceed the defined threshold. The long-term response probability distribution of POT is given as:

$$F_{R_p}(r) = \int^{F_{R_p|S}}(r|\mathbf{s})f_\mathbf{S}(\mathbf{s})d\mathbf{s} \quad (12)$$

where $F_{Rp|\mathbf{S}}(r|\mathbf{s})$ is the cumulative distribution of POT, which is modelled by the GPD and conditional on sea states $\mathbf{S}$.

Again, the integral representation in Eq. (12) can be given as the discrete form:

$$F_{R_p}(r) = \sum F_{R_p|s_i}(r|s_i)P(s_i) \quad (13)$$

2.2.3 Formulations based all short term extreme peaks

The above two approaches deal with the probability distribution of all peaks and POT in each sea state. An alternative and accurate method is the global maximum approach, which adopts the maximum peak of each individual response. The sample of maximum response for each individual environmental condition should large enough to obtain convergent result.

The long term extreme peak distribution is defined as:

$$F_{R_e}(r) = \int^{F_{Re|S}}(r|\mathbf{s})f_\mathbf{S}(\mathbf{s})d\mathbf{s} \quad (14)$$

where the $F_{Re|\mathbf{S}}(r|\mathbf{s})$ is the short term extreme peak distribution which is fitted by the Gumbel distribution. Similar to Eqs. (11) and (13), the Eq. (14) can also be discretized.

2.3 Long-term extreme value analysis

The probability distribution of long-term extreme peaks can be obtained by assuming the short-term extreme peaks are independent:

$$F_{R_{e,L}}(r) = (F_{R_e}(r))^N \qquad (15)$$

where N is the number of short term sea states in a given long term period. Typically, the long period is 1 year, and short term period is 3-hour, where the environmental conditions are considered as roughly constant. Then, $N = 365.25*8 = 2922$.

If the return period is M year, the exceedance probability per year is $1/M$:

$$F_{R_{e,L}}(r) = 1 - \frac{1}{M} \qquad (16)$$

By invoking Eq. (16) into Eq. (15), the M year extreme response can be obtained by solving the following equation:

$$F_{R_{e,L}}(r_M) = \left(1 - \frac{1}{M}\right)^{1/N} \approx 1 - \frac{1}{MN} \qquad (17)$$

The relation between short-term peaks and short-term extreme peaks cumulative distribution is:

$$F_{R_{e|s}}(r|s) = \left[F_{R_{|s}}(r|s)\right]^{n(s)} \qquad (18)$$

where $n(s)$ is the expected number of peaks in the corresponding sea state (3-hour).

By combing Eq. (18) and Eq. (14) The long term extreme peak distribution is then written as:

$$F_{R_e}(r) = \int \left[F_{R_{|s}}(r|s)\right]^{n(s)} f_S(s)ds \qquad (19)$$

Similar to Eq. (18), the cumulative distribution of extreme peaks can be calculated from POT extremes:

$$F_{R_{e|s}}(r|s) = \left[F_{R_{p|r}}(r|s)\right]^{n_p(s)} \qquad (20)$$

where $n_p(s)$ is the expected number of exceedances above threshold in each corresponding sea state (3-hour).

3 MODEL DESCRIPTIONS

A semi-submersible moored by twelve taut moorings in 200m water depth is investigated in this work. The fully coupled dynamic analysis is implemented to study mooring extreme tensions when the platform operates in Nanhai S4 area of China. For simplification of analysis, only the wave load is considered and the wave direction is in head sea.

3.1 Semi-Submersible

The sixth generation semi-submersible HYSY 981 is acted as the research target. The dynamic responses of this platform when it operates in 100-year wave condition South China Sea have been studied extensive by numerical and experimental methods (Ji & Xu, 2014; Xu et al., 2019a, 2019b, 2018a, 2018b).

The crucial parameters of this floating structure is given in Table 1. The panel model of semi-submersible is shown in Figure 1.

3.2 Mooring system

The mooring system is composed by twelve taut wires, which are symmetrically arranged. The azimuth angle between two adjacent mooring is 20 degrees, the detail of mooring arrangement is shown in Figure 2.

The main parameters of mooring wire are displayed in Table 2, where D denotes the nominal

Table 1. Main parameters of the semi-submersible.

Parameters	Unit	Quantities
Length	m	114.07
Width	m	78.68
H	m	8.6
Cy	m	58.5
Cx	m	58.5
Draft	m	16
Displacement	t	48196.6
Cgz	m	25.98
Cgx	m	57
Rxx	m	29.79
Ryy	m	31
Rzz	m	36.58

Figure 1. The hydrodynamic model of semi-submersible.

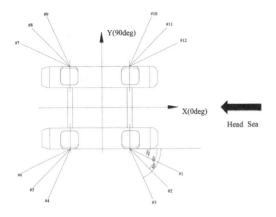

Figure 2. The plan view of mooring system.

Table 2. Main parameters of the semi-submersible.

	D(mm)	Length(m)	EA(KN)	W(KN/m)
Wire	300	340	55093.75	4.51

diameter, W is the submerged weight per unit length. The pretension of mooring is 1620 KN.

The fairlead coordinates are shown in Table 3, where the origin coordinate of X-Y plan is shown in Figure 2 and the baseline of Z axis is on the bottom of platform. Since the fairlead are symmetrically arranged, only the coordinates of #1~#3 fairleads are listed.

3.3 Environmental conditions

The long-term environmental condition in the zone of Nanhai S4 of China is discretized by 64 short-term sea conditions (Huang et al., 2011). Only the wave conditions are considered in this study, the random waves are simulated by the Jonswap spectra. The main wave parameters are shown in Table 4, where Hs and Tp means significant wave height and peak period respectively, and the peak enhancement factor is set as 3 for all sea states.

Table 3. Main parameters of the semi-submersible.

Fairlead	X(m)	Y(m)	Z(m)
F1	34.785	-38.735	18.49
F2	30.035	-38.735	18.49
F3	25.285	-38.735	18.49

Table 4. Wave parameters in Nanhai S4 area of China.

Sea	H_s(m)	T_p(s)	P(%)	Sea	H_s(m)	T_p(s)	P(%)
1	0.25	3.5	0.1	33	1.05	8	1.3
2	0.25	4	1	34	1.55	8	2.5
3	0.675	4	0.8	35	2.175	8	3
4	1.05	4	0.7	36	2.875	8	3.1
5	1.55	4	0.5	37	3.625	8	2.2
6	2.175	4	0.2	38	4.5	8	1.7
7	0.25	5	2.9	39	5.5	8	0.6
8	0.675	5	3.1	40	6.75	8	0.2
9	1.05	5	3.4	41	0.25	9	0.1
10	1.55	5	3.7	42	0.675	9	0.2
11	2.175	5	1.9	43	1.05	9	0.4
12	2.875	5	0.7	44	1.55	9	0.8
13	3.625	5	0.1	45	2.175	9	1
14	0.25	6	2.9	46	2.875	9	1.2
15	0.675	6	3.7	47	3.625	9	1
16	1.05	6	5	48	4.5	9	1
17	1.55	6	7.2	49	5.5	9	0.6
18	2.175	6	5.5	50	6.75	9	0.4
19	2.875	6	3.2	51	0.675	10	0.1
20	3.625	6	1.1	52	1.05	10	0.1
21	4.5	6	0.2	53	1.55	10	0.2
22	0.25	7	1.5	54	2.175	10	0.2
23	0.675	7	2.1	55	2.875	10	0.3
24	1.05	7	3.3	56	3.625	10	0.3
25	1.55	7	5.7	57	4.5	10	0.3
26	2.175	7	5.7	58	5.5	10	0.2
27	2.875	7	4.6	59	6.75	10	0.3
28	3.625	7	2.4	60	2.875	11	0.1
29	4.5	7	1.3	61	3.625	11	0.1
30	5.5	7	0.3	62	4.5	11	0.1
31	0.25	8	0.5	63	5.5	11	0.2
32	0.675	8	0.8	64	3.625	12	0.1

4 RESULTS AND DISCUSSION

The fully coupled dynamic analysis are carried out by SESAM DeepC package (DNVGL, 2017), and the accuracy of numerical model has been validated in (Xu et al., 2018a).

Only the head sea condition is considered, the #1 mooring line is the most loaded one in this case. In the following study, the short-term and long-term extreme load of #1 mooring will be discussed. The all peaks method, POT method and all extreme peaks method for predicting extreme response are discussed. The optimal POT method is implemented by applying the declustering algorithm in WAFO (Brodtkorb et al., 2000).

4.1 Short-term extreme responses

The 3-h fully coupled dynamic simulations are carried out 30 times to take the random wave elevations into considerations. The maximum loads of each individual simulation are extracted and fitted by the Gumbel distribution, besides, the probability distributions of all peaks and POT are approximated by the Weibull distribution and GPD respectively.

The results of three typical sea states, including the calm sea condition (#7), most fre.tifuently happen sea condition (#17) and the severe sea condition (#50) are shown in Figures 3-5. It is seen that the exceedance probabilities of short term extreme peaks are well fitted for all discussed sea states, which indicates that the global maximum method is able to present good estimations of extreme mooring tensions. Besides, it is observed that the performance of Weibull distribution and GPD is related to the sea state. For instance, the empirical exceedance probabilities of peak tensions in #50 sea state are in good

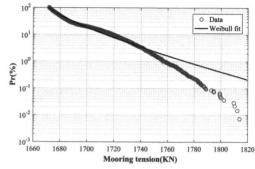

(a) Exceedance probability of all short-term peaks

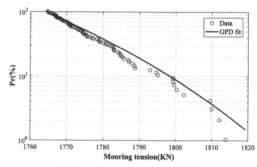

(b) Exceedance probability of POT

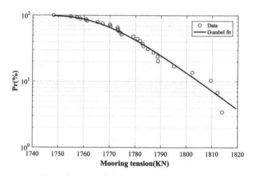

(c) Exceedance probability of all short-term peaks

Figure 4. The exceedance probability of #1 mooring line in #17 sea state (H_s = 1.55m, T_p = 6s).

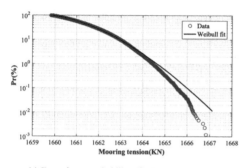

(a) Exceedance probability of all short-term peaks

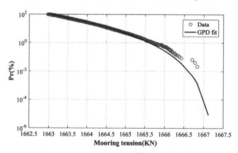

(b) Exceedance probability of POT

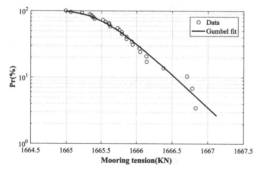

(c) Exceedance probability of all short-term peaks

Figure 3. The exceedance probability of #1 mooring line in #7 sea state (H_s = 0.25m, T_p = 5s).

agreement with the Weibull model. However, it makes poor estimations of peak tensions exceedance probabilities in other two sea states, especially for the tail data. It illustrates that the extreme mooring tensions are overestimated by Weibull model. It could be the reason that the peak tensions are not mutual independent, which leads to the difficulties for the Weibull model to fit well the empirical probability distributions. The differences between empirical POT distributions and GPD model can be seen. However, the discrepancies are small. This could be the reason that the declustering procedure is applied during the conduction of POT method. It indicates that the optimal POT approach is capable of

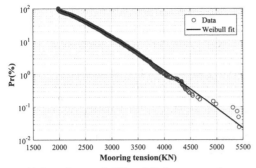

(a) Exceedance probability of all short-term peaks

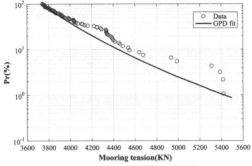

(b) Exceedance probability of POT

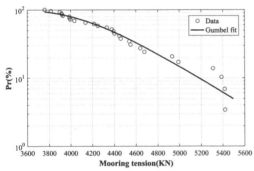

(c) Exceedance probability of all short-term peaks

Figure 5. The exceedance probability of #1 mooring line in #50 sea state ($H_s = 6.75m$, $T_p = 9s$).

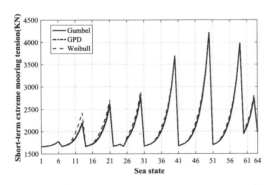

Figure 6. Shor-term extreme mooring tensions in all sea states.

presenting reasonable estimations of extreme mooring tensions.

The MPME mooring tensions predicted by different methods in all sea states are plotted in Figure 6. It is observed that the POT results are in good agreement with the Gumbel ones for all sea states, which illustrates that the optimal POT method performs well in predicting short-term extreme mooring tension. While, the all peaks method (Weibull) overestimate the extreme tension slightly for most of the sea states, especially for sea states with $T_p = 5s$, 6s and 7s. Fortunately, the largest three extreme tensions are well represented by the Weibull distribution.

The convergence analysis of estimated extreme mooring tension is then conducted, and the convergence criterion is similar to the study of Agarwal & Manuel (2009):

$$NCI = \frac{r_e^{CI+} - r_e^{CI-}}{r_e} < \frac{q}{100} \qquad (21)$$

where r_e^{CI} is the 90% confidence interval, which is calculated by the bootstrap techni.tifue within 10,000 resamplings, and q is set as 10% in this study.

To show the influence of significant wave height on the convergence of predicted short-term extreme mooring tension, the results in the sea states with the same T_p ($T_p = 9s$) but different H_s are concluded in Table 5. From where it is seen that 30 simulations are enough to obtain good estimations of short-term extreme result, the maximum error is around 6% for all discussed cases. Besides, it is observed that results of global maximum method have the largest uncertainties compared to other two methods. This is because the Gumbel distribution only has 30 samples. The significant wave height has notable influence on extreme mooring tension, both the MPME

Table 5. Estimated short-term extreme mooring tensions and their normalized 90% confidence intervals under sea states with different H_s, $T_p = 9s$.

H_s (m)	GUM Exe (KN)	GUM NCI (%)	POT Exe (KN)	POT NCI (%)	WEB Exe (KN)	WEB NCI (%)
0.25	1675	0.0	1676	0.0	1676	0.0
0.675	1703	0.2	1704	0.1	1705	0.1
1.05	1738	0.4	1742	0.2	1740	0.1
1.55	1803	0.8	1812	0.5	1818	0.3
2.175	1915	1.4	1932	1.0	1975	0.7
2.875	2092	2.3	2122	1.6	2195	1.1
3.625	2354	3.2	2395	2.3	2465	1.6
4.5	2751	4.5	2808	3.0	2836	2.3
5.5	3332	5.2	3380	4.1	3357	3.0
6.75	4204	6.0	4226	5.0	4197	3.6

and its corresponding NCI are increasing with the H_s. A comparison between the extreme mooring tensions predicted by different methods indicate that both the POT method and all peaks method give satisfied predictions to the extreme mooring tensions.

The discussion of the influence of T_p on simulation convergence is conducted, and the results are displayed in Table 6. It is seen that the T_p has limited influence on extreme responses as well as their confidence intervals. The NCIs on the MPME load of all discussed cases are smaller than the convergence criterion. If check the results carefully, it can be found that the extreme mooring tension in sea state when the T_p = 9s is the greatest one.

To discuss the influence of number of simulations it is necessary to get the convergent results, the MPME and its 90% confidence intervals for the severest environmental state condition is shown in Table 7, where Ns is the number of simulation. It is seen that the numerical simulations should repeat more than 20 to obtain acceptable result. The confidence interval is getting narrow with the number of simulation increasing. Besides, it is seen that the extreme tension predicted by the all peaks method agrees well with the global maximum one. It is explained that the probability distribution of peak tensions is well fitted by the Weibull distribution, which can be validated in Figure 5(a).

Table 6. Estimated short-term extreme mooring tensions and their normalized 90% confidence intervals under sea states with different T_p, H_s = 4.5m.

T_p (s)	GUM Exe (KN)	NCI (%)	POT Exe (KN)	NCI (%)	WEB Exe (KN)	NCI (%)
6	2571	3.7	2641	2.7	2712	2.0
7	2381	3.0	2420	2.1	2498	1.6
8	2519	3.0	2555	2.2	2609	1.8
9	2751	4.5	2808	3.0	2836	2.3
10	2639	4.1	2675	2.9	2707	2.1
11	2362	3.2	2385	2.7	2436	1.6

Table 7. Estimated short-term extreme mooring tensions and their normalized 90% confidence intervals by different number of simulations (in sea state, H_s = 6.75m, T_p = 9s).

Ns	GUM Exe (KN)	NCI (%)	POT Exe (KN)	NCI (%)	WEB Exe (KN)	NCI (%)
10	4291	14.0	4167	7.8	4294	6.1
20	4185	8.7	4111	6.0	4177	4.3
30	4204	6.0	4226	5.0	4197	3.6
40	4131	5.3	4188	4.0	4166	3.0

4.2 Long-term extreme results

The long-term extreme tensions of #1 mooring under different return periods are investigated. Figure 7 shows the long-term exceedance probability of #1 mooring tension based on 30 simulations of each sea state. It is seen that there is some difference between the exceedance probability curve approximated by different models, especially for the tail zone. It indicates that the predicted long-term extreme mooring tensions are different, and the differences are increased with the return period.

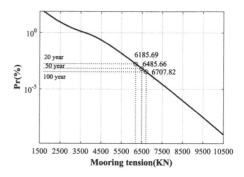

(a) Fitted exceedance probability based on all short-term peaks

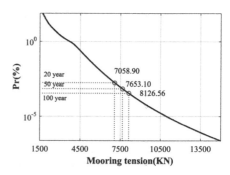

(b) Fitted exceedance probability based on POT

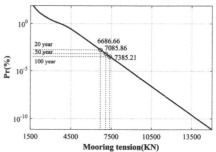

(c) Fitted exceedance probability based on all short-term extreme peaks

Figure 7. The long-term exceedance probability of #1 mooring line tension.

Table 8. Estimated long-term extreme mooring tensions by different methods.

Return Period (year)	Ns	GUM Exe (KN)	POT Exe (KN)	POT Diff (%)	WEB Exe (KN)	WEB Diff (%)
20	10	7544	9627	28	6407	15
	20	6994	9058	30	6159	12
	30	6687	7059	6	6186	7
	40	6555	7058	8	6070	7
50	10	8061	11441	42	6727	17
	20	7444	10665	43	6457	13
	30	7086	7653	8	6486	8
	40	6945	7704	11	6356	8
100	10	8449	13101	55	6964	18
	20	7782	12126	56	6678	14
	30	7385	8127	10	6708	9
	40	7237	8228	14	6567	9

To better study the influence of the number of simulations and different analysis methods on long-term extreme mooring tensions, the results are shown in Table 8.

By checking the approximated long-term extreme values of global maximum method are varied significantly with the increase of simulation number, until the Ns is greater than 30. It indicates that the number of numerical simulations should be greater than 30 to obtain good estimation of extreme mooring tension. Besides, it is seen the POT results are very sensitive to the Ns, the long-term extreme mooring tension would be overestimated significant when Ns less than 30. It is understood that in the application of POT method for long-term extreme response analysis, the result is closely related to the expected number of POTs.

The limited number of simulations could give riser to incorrect estimations of number of POTs, which induce the great errors of predicted long-term extreme mooring tensions. However, the POT approach is able to give reasonable approach when the Ns is greater than 30, the errors are below 15% for all discussed return values. It is observed that the long-term extreme responses given by the all peaks approach are comparatively stable to the variation of simulation number. The return values are seen to be insensitive to the variation of Ns. This is explained that the number of peaks are great for each individual simulation, and the expected number of peaks is not sensitivity to the Ns. It is observed that the Ns should be greater than 30, in order to make difference induced by the Weibull model lower than 10%.

5 CONCLUSIONS

The fully coupled dynamic analysis is carried out to study the short-term and long-term extreme mooring tension of a semi-submersible when it operates in the South China Sea.

The exceedance probability of all extreme peaks and POTs are fitted well by the Gumbel distribution and GPD. The all probability distribution of all mooring tension peaks are approximated by the Weibull model based on the sea state. In some certain sea states, the Weibull distribution shows poor performance in estimating the exceedance probability, especially for the tail data.

The POT model present good estimations of short-term extreme mooring tension, which are close to the MPMEs from global maximum method. While, the Weibull would overestimate the short-term extreme mooring tension in some specific sea states.

The influence of significant wave height on short-term extreme response and its corresponding confidence interval is significant. The predicted extreme tension increases greatly with the significant wave height. On the other hand, the influence of wave peak period on mooring tension is limited. For the sea states have the same period, the one with Tp = 9s causes to the greatest system response. The global maximum method induces the greatest uncertainties in the estimation of short-term extreme mooring tension.

The number of numerical simulations on long-term extreme mooring tensions can be clearly seen, at least 30 simulations are needed in order to get accurate estimation of long-term return values. Once the number of simulation less than 30, the POT method fails to present reasonable long-term extreme mooring tension. The performance of all short-term peaks is less sensitive to the number of simulation compared with the other two approaches. The 20-year, 50-year and 100-year extreme mooring tensions are around 6600 KN, 7000 KN and 7300 KN respectively.

ACKNOWLEDGEMENTS

The work of the first author has been funded by the the Strategic Research Plan of the Centre for Marine Technology and Ocean Engineering (CENTEC), which is financed by the Portuguese Foundation for Science and Technology (Fundação para a Ciência e Tecnologia) under contract UIDB/UIDP/00134/2020. The third author gratefully acknowledges the financial support from the National Natural Science Foundation of China (Grant No.51622902).

REFERENCES

Agarwal, P., Manuel, L. 2009. Simulation of offshore wind turbine response for long-term extreme load prediction. *Eng. Struct.* 31, 2236–2246.

Bílková, D. 2014. Robust Parameter Estimations Using L-Moments, TL-Moments and the Order Statistics. *Am. J. Appl. Math.* 2, 36.

Brodtkorb, P. a., Johannesson, P., Lindgren, G., Rychlik, I., Ryden, J., Sjö, E. 2000. WAFO—a Matlab toolbox for analysis of random waves and loads. *Proc. 10th Int. Offshore Polar Eng. Conf.* 3, 343–350.

Chai, W., & Leira, B.J. 2018. Environmental contours based on inverse SORM. *Mar. Struct.* 60, 34–51.

Cheng, Z., & Kuang, J., 2016. Extreme Response Predictions for Deepwater Mooring System, *in: Offshore Technology Conference Asia*, OTC-26423-MS, Kuala Lumpur, Malaysia.

DNVGL, 2017. DeepC User Manual.

Ferreira, J. A. and Guedes Soares, C. 1998. An Application of the Peaks Over Threshold Method to Predict Extremes of Significant Wave Height. *Journal of Offshore Mechanics and Arctic Engineering.* 120 (3):165–176.

Garrett, D.L. 2005. Coupled analysis of floating production systems. *Ocean Eng.* 32, 802–816.

Giske, F.-I.G., Kvåle, K.A., Leira, B.J., & Øiseth, O. 2018. Long-term extreme response analysis of a long-span pontoon bridge. *Mar. Struct.* 58, 154–171.

Giske, F.-I.G., Leira, B.J., & Øiseth, O. 2017. Full long-term extreme response analysis of marine structures using inverse FORM. *Probabilistic Eng. Mech.* 50, 1–8.

Goda, Y., Kudaka, M., & Kawai, H. 2010. Incorporating of Weibull distribution in L-moments method for Regional Fre.tifuency Analysis of Peak Over Threshold wave heights, *in: 32nd International Conference on Coastal Engineering.* pp. 2–6.

Guedes Soares, C., & Moan, T. 1991. Model uncertainty in the long-term distribution of wave-induced bending moments for fatigue design of ship structures. *Mar. Struct.* 4, 295–315.

Guedes Soares, C. & Scotto, M. G. 2001. Modelling Uncertainty in Long-Term Predictions of Significant Wave Height. *Ocean Engineering.* 28(3):329–342.

Guedes Soares, C. and Scotto, M. G. 2011. Long Term and Extreme Value Models of Wave Data. Guedes Soares, C. Garbatov Y. Fonseca N. & Teixeira A. P., (Eds.). *Marine Technology and Engineering.* London, UK: Taylor & Francis Group; pp. 97–108

Haver, S., & Kleiven, G. 2004. Environmental Contour Lines for Design Purposes: Why and When?, *in: 23rd International Conference on Offshore Mechanics and Arctic Engineering*, Volume 1, Parts A and B. ASME, pp. 337–345.

Haver, S., & Winterstein, S.R. 2009. Environmental contour lines: A method for estimating long term extremes by a short term analysis. *Trans. Soc. Nav. Archit. Mar. Eng.* 116, 116–127.

Huang, W., Liu, H., Shan, G., & Hu, C. 2011. Fatigue analysis of the taut-wire mooring system applied for deep waters. *China Ocean Eng.* 25, 413–426.

Huseby, A.B., Vanem, E., & Natvig, B. 2013. A new approach to environmental contours for ocean engineering applications based on direct Monte Carlo simulations. *Ocean Eng.* 60, 124–135.

Karmakar, D.; Bagbanci, H., & Guedes Soares, C. 2016. Long-term extreme load prediction of spar and semisubmersible floating wind turbines using the Environmental Contour Method. *Journal of Offshore Mechanics and Arctic Engineering.* 138 (2):021601.

Ji, C., & Xu, S. 2014. Verification of a hybrid model test method for a deep water floating system with large truncation factor. *Ocean Eng.* 92, 245–254.

Li, .tif., Gao, Z., & Moan, T. 2016. Modified environmental contour method for predicting long-term extreme responses of bottom-fixed offshore wind turbines. *Mar. Struct.* 48, 15–32.

Low, Y.M., & Huang, X. 2017. Long-term extreme response analysis of offshore structures by combining importance sampling with subset simulation. *Struct. Saf.* 69, 79–95.

Low, Y.M., & Langley, R.S. 2008. A hybrid time/fre.tifuency domain approach for efficient coupled analysis of vessel/mooring/riser dynamics. *Ocean Eng.* 35, 433–446.

Low, Y.M., & Langley, R.S. 2006. Time and fre.tifuency domain coupled analysis of deepwater floating production systems. *Appl. Ocean Res.* 28, 371–385.

Ormberg, H., & Larsen, K. 1998. Coupled analysis of floater motion and mooring dynamics for a turret-moored ship. *Appl. Ocean Res.* 20, 55–67.

Pandey, M.D., Van Gelder, P.H.A.J.M., & Vrijling, J.K. 2001. The estimation of extreme .tifuantiles of wind velocity using L-moments in the peaks-over-threshold approach. *Struct. Saf.* 23, 179–192.

Pickands, J. 1975. Statistical Inference Using Extreme Order Statistics. *Ann. Stat.* 3, 119–131.

Raed, K., Teixeira, A.P., & Guedes Soares, C. 2020. Uncertainty assessment for the extreme hydrodynamic responses of a wind turbine semi-submersible platform using different environmental contour approaches. *Ocean Eng.* 195, 106719.

Ran, Z.H. 2000. *Coupled Dynamic Analysis of Floating Structures in Waves and Currents*. Ph.D. thesis. Texas A&M University.

Rendon, E.A., & Manuel, L. 2014. Long-term loads for a monopile-supported offshore wind turbine. *Wind Energy* 17, 209–223.

Sagrilo, L.V.S., Naess, A., & Doria, A.S. 2011. On the long-term response of marine structures. *Appl. Ocean Res.* 33, 208–214.

Winterstein, S., Ude, T., Cornell, C., Bjerager, P., & Haver, S. 1993. Environmental parameters for extreme response: inverse form with omission factors., *in: 6th International Conference on Structural Safety and Reliability.* Innsbruck, Austria.

Xu, S., Ji, C., & Guedes Soares, C. 2019a. Estimation of short-term extreme responses of a semi-submersible moored by two hybrid mooring systems. *Ocean Eng.* 190, 106388.

Xu, S., Ji, C., & Guedes Soares, C. 2019b. Experimental study on effect of side-mooring lines on dynamics of a catenary moored semi-submersible system. *Proc. Inst. Mech. Eng. Part M J. Eng. Marit. Environ.* 234(1), pp.127–142.

Xu, S., Ji, C., & Guedes Soares, C. 2018a. Experimental and numerical investigation a semi-submersible moored by hybrid mooring systems. *Ocean Eng.* 163, 641–678.

Xu, S., Ji, C., & Guedes Soares, C. 2018b. Experimental study on taut and hybrid moorings damping and their relation with system dynamics. *Ocean Eng.* 154, 322–340.

Xu, S., Wang, S., & Guedes Soares, C. 2019c. Review of mooring design for floating wave energy converters. *Renew. Sustain. Energy Rev.* 111, 595–621.

Yang, M., Teng, B., Ning, D., & Shi, Z. 2012. Coupled dynamic analysis for wave interaction with a truss spar and its mooring line/riser system in time domain. *Ocean Eng.* 39, 72–87.

Ship hydrodynamics - Resistance

Predicting head wave resistance for a KVLCC2 model using OpenFOAM

H. Islam & C. Guedes Soares
Centre for Marine Technology and Ocean Engineering (CENTEC), Instituto Superior Técnico, Universidade de Lisboa, Lisbon, Portugal

ABSTRACT: The paper discusses calm water and added resistance simulation of a tanker ship model using OpenFOAM. Initially, calm water simulations are performed for a KVLCC2 model, for varying Froude numbers, with heave and pitch free motion, after verification and validation study. The uncertainty estimation for the verification study is discussed extensively, including studies with multiple uncertainty estimation methods. The target of the uncertainty study is to provide a relative comparison among the popular uncertainty estimation methods used in CFD simulations and also discuss their advantages and limitations. Next, head wave simulations are attempted with heave and pitch free motion, and the results are compared with experimental data. The paper comments on the findings from the uncertainty study and conclude that the OpenFOAM solver is well capable of predicting ship resistance in sea conditions.

1 INTRODUCTION

Prediction of ship hull resistance and motion using Computational Fluid Dynamics (CFD) has become very common these days. Numerous commercial and in-house codes are available that can produce reliable predictions for both total drag in calm water and added resistance in waves for different type of ship hulls. However, when it comes to open source CFD tools, like OpenFOAM, although many examples are available for total drag prediction (Islam & Guedes Soares, 2019a,b), added resistance prediction results are limited. Most of the available added resistance prediction results using OpenFOAM are from extended versions of OpenFOAM (Wang and Wan, 2018; Gatin et al, 2019) which are not openly available. This paper aims at demonstrating the capabilities of OpenFOAM in predicting added resistance in head waves for a very large crude carrier (KVLCC2), with heave and pitch free motion. It also presents calm water simulation results for the ship model and also provides a discussion on uncertainty analysis in CFD studies.

2 METHOD

A KRISO Very Large Crude Carrier (KVLCC2) ship model was simulated for the case study using Open-FOAM versions 2.4.0 and version 6. The calm water simulations, including the mesh dependency study, was performed using version 2.4.0, whereas, the head wave simulations were performed using version 6. All simulations were performed with heave and pitch free motion. The dynamic simulations were performed using mesh morphing technique together with sixDoFRigidBodyMotion and rigidBodyMesh-Motion libraries. Simulations were performed at high Reynolds number with turbulent flows. Details on the solver, ship model, simulation setup and resources are given in following subsections.

2.1 The solver

OpenFOAM is an open source library that numerically solves a wide range of problems in fluid dynamics from laminar to turbulent flows, with single and multi-phases. It contains an extensive range of solvers to perform different types of CFD simulations. The solver has several packages to perform multiphase turbulent flow simulation for floating objects. The solver has been elaborately described by Jasak (2009).

The module used to perform ship hydrodynamic simulations in OpenFOAM simulates incompressible, two-phase flow. The solver follows earth and body-fixed Cartesian coordinate system, with z-axis upward positive. The governing equation is based on continuity and Reynolds averaged Navier-Stokes equation. The Volume of Fluid (VOF) method is used to model fluid as one continuum of mixed properties. Finite Volume Method (FVM) is used to discretize the governing equations. Pressure-velocity coupling is obtained through PIMPLE algorithm. Mesh morphing technique was used to accommodate the dynamic simulations. OpenFOAM incorporates several turbulence models, and for the present paper, the SST k-ω model was used. The wave simulations were performed using the built-in wave generation model of OpenFOAM version 6. The waves were generated using Stokes second order formulation. Unfortunately, detail regarding the wave generation model is missing in the documentations of the version.

2.2 Ship model

The KRISO Very Large Crude Carrier 2 (KVLCC2) is a large oil tanker model developed solely for research purpose and was first introduced to researchers in SIMMAN 2008 (Larsson et al., 2011). Table 1 provides the specifications of the KVLCC2 model and Figure 1 shows its side view and body planes. All the simulations have been performed in model scale.

2.3 Mesh

In the paper, five different meshes were used. Four for grid dependency study in calm water and one for added resistance simulations in waves. All simulations were run for model scale ship with heave and pitch free motion. In this section, the principal two meshes using for calm water and added resistance simulations are described. Meshes used in the grid uncertainty study are described in the results section.

For calm water simulations, the domain size (blockMesh) for simulations was set mostly following ITTC (2011) guidelines; the inlet was placed two ship length windward the bow, the outlet four ship length downstream the stern, each lateral boundary was two ship lengths away from the ship's symmetry plane, the depth or bottom of domain was set at one ship length and the atmosphere was at half ship length from free surface.

The hull form was integrated to the blockMesh by using snappyHexMesh utility, which creates a "body fitted" hexahedral mesh around the hull surface from the specified STL file. The domain area near the free surface and hull form was refined multiple times using toposet and refinement, then snappyHexMesh was applied. For calm water simulations, full hull (both starboard and port side) was simulated and a mesh resolution of 1.6 million was used. The general mesh assembly is shown in Figure 2.

For head wave simulations, domain length was set according to the applied wave length. Roughly 1.5 wave length was kept from inlet to the model and 3 wave length was kept from model to outlet. To save computational resource, for added resistance prediction, only half domain (starboard side) was simulated. Similar to calm water mesh, the mesh for added resistance simulation was generated using blockMesh and snappyHexMesh.

Initially block mesh was generated with was further refined several times using toposet to ensure both proper propagation of incoming waves and force prediction near the hull surface. After that snappyHexMesh was used to incorporate the hull form to the initial domain. The average mesh resolution used for the half hull simulation was 3.1 million. The general mesh assembly for added resistance simulation is shown in Figure 3.

2.4 Computational resources

Simulations were performed in multiple computers with Intel Core i-9, 2.90GHz, 12 core processors, 64GB RAM and 1TB SSD disk for data writing. On average, the calm water simulation cases presented in the results section took around 24 hours. Higher mesh resolutions used for grid dependency study took longer hours. As for head wave simulation cases, each case was ran for different periods depending on the wave length and the time required to reach stability. On average, the head wave

Table 1. Specifications of the oil tanker ship model KVLCC2.

Specification		KVLCC2 (full scale)	KVLCC2 (model scale)
Length between perpendicular	Lpp (m)	320.0	7.00
Breadth	B (m)	58.0	1.2688
Depth	D (m)	30.0	0.6563
Draft	T (m)	20.8	0.4550
Wetted surface area	S (m^2)	27194.0	13.0129
Displacement volume	V (m^3)	312622	3.2724
LCB from midship	LCB (m)	11.136	0.2436
Kyy	Kyy (m)	0.25 Lpp	0.25 Lpp

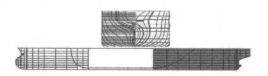

Figure 1. Body planes and side view of the KVLCC2 ship model.

Figure 2. General mesh assembly for calm water simulations.

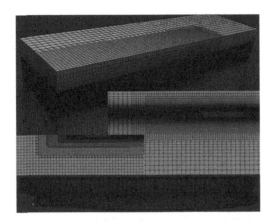

Figure 3. General mesh assembly for head wave simulations.

simulations were ran for 50 seconds, and each simulation took roughly 130 hours.

3 RESULTS

The paper mainly presents calm water and added resistance simulation results for a KVLCC2 hull model. Initially, an extended verification and validation study is performed for two calm water simulation cases. Next, calm water simulations are performed for a range of Froude numbers and the total drag, sinkage and trim results are compared with experimental data. Finally, head wave simulations are performed for different wave lengths and wave amplitudes, and the added resistance, heave and pitch motion results are compared with experimental data.

3.1 Verification and validation study

Uncertainty analysis is a systematic study performed to assess the consistency and accuracy of a CFD solver in solving the intended problem. Uncertainty analysis is sub-divided into two processes, verification and validation. Verification assesses the consistency of the solver, whereas, validation evaluates its accuracy.

According to ITTC (2008) guidelines, uncertainty in CFD studies may be expressed as a summation of modelling error δ_{SM} and numerical error δ_{SN} of CFD. However, in CFD studies, modelling errors are mostly ignored and only numerical errors are estimated. Thus, verification of numerical data involves assessing simulation numerical uncertainty, and determining the error sign and magnitude, when conditions permit. It also involves assessing the uncertainty in the error estimation, U_{ScN}. For uncorrected simulation approach, numerical errors are decomposed into iterative errors δ_I, grid size errors δ_G, time step errors δ_T, and other parameters related errors δ_P. In this case, the simulation numerical uncertainty is provided as,

$$U_{SN}^2 = U_I^2 + U_G^2 + U_T^2 + U_P^2. \quad (1)$$

For the corrected simulation approach, the solution is corrected to produce a numerical benchmark S_C and the estimated simulation numerical error δ_{sn}^* and corrected uncertainty U_{ScN} are given by,

$$\delta_{SN}^* = \delta_I^* + \delta_G^* + \delta_T^* + \delta_P^* \quad (2)$$

$$U_{ScN}^2 = U_{I_C}^2 + U_{G_C}^2 + U_{T_C}^2 + U_{P_C}^2 \quad (3)$$

In general, it is assumed that CFD simulations are steady, thus iterative errors are ignored. Also, there are no defined ways to determine other parameter related errors. Thus, uncertainty determination mostly comes to grid and time step dependency.

According to ITTC recommendation, grid and time step uncertainty studies are done independently, and then combined together to determine total uncertainty. However, in CFD, time step is closely related to mesh size. If the grid size is reduced, the time step should be reduced as well, to ensure that the Courant–Friedrichs–Lewy (CFL) condition is met. As such, Oberhagemann & el Moctar (2017) proposed the used of constant CFL number for uncertainty study, rather than independent time and grid study. This process requires fewer simulations and provides better convergence. To provide a relative comparison between the traditional time and grid dependency study and constant CFL study, both the methods are followed in this paper.

For the uncertainty analysis, three different methods are approached. Two of the most popular uncertainty estimation methods are based on Richardson extrapolation, namely the Correction Factor (Cf) based approach proposed by Celik et al. (2008) and Factor of Safety (Fs) based approach proposed by Stern et al. (2001). The third method used is based on a fit curve approach using least square estimation for error (Ls) propose by Eça & Hoekstra (2014). Further explanations on uncertainty study and these methods can be found at Islam & Guedes Soares (2019b).

For the uncertainty study, four different mesh resolutions were used, along with four different time steps. Initially, simulations were performed keeping constant CFL, thus, time steps were reduced keeping the same refinement ratio at that of the grid. Next, independent time and grid studies were performed. The mesh and time resolutions used for the studies are shown in Table 2.

For the study, simulations were run for two Froude numbers 0.1423 and 0.1194, and total drag, sinkage and trim results are compared. The simulation results for constant CFL, independent Grid and Time study are shown in Table 3, 4 and 5.

Table 2. Mesh resolution used for constant CFL and independent grid study.

Mesh No.	Minimum Grid Resolution			Total mesh Resolution (mil)
	X	Y	Z	
1	0.019	0.019	0.006	3.7
2	0.024	0.024	0.0075	2.0
3	0.031	0.031	0.010	1.6
4	0.040	0.040	0.012	0.9

Table 3. Calm water simulation results for constant CFL study for uncertainty analysis.

Mesh (mil)	Time step, dT	Total Drag, Ct (x e-3)		Sinkage (mm)		Trim (deg)	
		0.1423	0.1194	0.1423	0.1194	0.1423	0.1194
3.7	0.011	3.87	4.00	-8.07	-5.83	0.137	0.097
2.0	0.014	3.78	3.84	-8.33	-5.96	0.140	0.098
1.6	0.018	3.96	4.09	-8.03	-5.82	0.137	0.097
0.9	0.023	3.83	3.89	-8.07	-5.80	0.136	0.096

Table 4. Calm water simulation results for grid dependency (constant time step) study for uncertainty analysis.

Mesh (mil)	dT	Ct (x e-3)		Sinkage (mm)		Trim (deg)	
		0.1423	0.1194	0.1423	0.1194	0.1423	0.1194
3.7	0.011	3.87	4.00	-8.07	-5.83	0.137	0.097
2.0	0.011	3.73	3.84	-8.17	-5.90	0.138	0.098
1.6	0.011	3.95	4.05	-7.99	-5.74	0.136	0.097
0.9	0.011	3.83	3.89	-8.07	-5.80	0.136	0.096

Table 5. Calm water simulation results for time step dependency (constant grid) study for uncertainty analysis.

Mesh (mil)	dT	Ct (x e-3)		Sinkage (mm)		Trim (deg)	
		0.1423	0.1194	0.1423	0.1194	0.1423	0.1194
1.6	0.011	3.95	4.05	-7.99	-5.74	0.136	0.096
1.6	0.018	3.96	4.09	-8.03	-5.82	0.137	0.097
1.6	0.03	4.00	4.01	-8.05	-6.47	0.139	0.091
1.6	0.04	4.00	3.37	-8.00	-6.47	0.139	0.091

As can be seen from the tables, the simulations mostly show oscillatory results for both constant CFL and independent time and grid study. Nevertheless, the results do not show significant difference among each other.

Next, uncertainty analysis was performed for both the constant CFL and independent time and grid study results using factor of safety, correction factor and least square method. The summarized results are shown in Table 6 and 7, respectively. However, results for only the first three meshes are shown for the Cf and Fs method.

The comparative results for the three methods are also provided in Figure 4 and 5 for easier comparison. Figure 4 shows result comparison for constant CFL cases and Figure 5 shows that for combined grid and time study.

The results show that for the constant CFL cases, the Fs method shows relatively low uncertainty. However, most of the constant CFL cases presented here showed oscillatory convergence, thus, the uncertainty predictions shown here for Fs method were gained simply by taking the percentage of average deviation between the maximum and minimum prediction. For the Cf method, uncertainties were predicted using Richardson extrapolation. Whereas, Ls method used curve fitting for uncertainty prediction. For most of the cases, Ls method shows the highest level of uncertainty.

As for the comparison between constant CFL and independent grid and time step study, both the Cf and Fs method show lower uncertainty prediction for independent study, which makes validation study difficult. In case of the Ls method, it shows less uncertainty for constant CFL cases comparing to the other.

Overall, although both the studies show somewhat similar results, the constant CFL cases significantly reduce the number of total simulations required for uncertainty study. Furthermore, the relative high prediction of uncertainty also ensures easier validation of simulation results.

Next, for validation study, results from the finest mesh resolution were compared with the experimental data (Larson et al., 2013). The results were taken from the 2010 Gothenburg Workshop, that reported an uncertainty of just 1% for the resistance prediction and around 7% uncertainty for sinkage and trim prediction. The results are shown in Table 8.

As can be seen from the results, only resistance prediction results could be validated for the Ls method. As for other methods, none of the results could be validated.

3.2 *Calm water simulation results*

Following the uncertainty study, calm water simulations were performed for a range of Froude and Reynolds number following the cases presented in the Gothenburg 2010 workshop (Larson et el, 2013).

The grid dependency results showed that mesh 3 with 1.6 million cells showed better results. Thus, this mesh resolution was chosen to run further simulations. For conversion of resistance, results to total drag coefficient, was used.

Table 6. Grid uncertainty analysis summary for constant CFL cases using three uncertainty analysis methods.

Fr. number		Total drag coefficient $C_{t\,(e-3)}$ 0.1423	0.1194	Sinkage (mm) 0.1423	0.1194	Trim (deg) 0.1423	0.1194
Factor of Safety based approach, Cf							
Grid convergence index (GCI)	GCI^{21}_{fine}	0.0261	0.0805	-0.2011	-0.3504	-0.1944	-0.0159
Uncertainty	$U1$	2.61%	8.05%	20.11%	35.04%	19.44%	1.59%
Corrected Uncertainty	$U1c$	0.52%	1.61%	4.02%	7.01%	3.89%	0.32%
Normalized Correction Factor based Approach, Fs							
Uncertainty	$U1$	2.35%	3.13%	1.89%	1.20%	1.24%	0.67%
Corrected Uncertainty	$U1c$	2.11%	0.16%	1.25%	1.04%	0.94%	0.07%
Least square-root approach, Ls							
uloc	U	0.95	1.22	0.04	0.03	0.00	0.00
uloc(%)	U(%)	24.48	30.50	0.48	0.53	0.98	0.45

Table 7. Grid uncertainty analysis summary for combined results from the independent time and grid dependency study using three uncertainty analysis methods.

Fr. number		Total drag coefficient $C_{t\,(e-3)}$ 0.1423	0.1194	Sinkage (mm) 0.1423	0.1194	Trim (deg) 0.1423	0.1194
Factor of Safety based approach, Cf							
Grid convergence index (GCI)	GCI^{21}_{fine}	0.0813	0.1426	0.0216	0.0123	0.0131	0.0121
Uncertainty	$U1$	8.13%	14.26%	2.16%	1.23%	1.31%	1.21%
Corrected Uncertainty	$U1c$	1.63%	2.85%	0.43%	0.25%	0.26%	0.24%
Normalized Correction Factor based Approach, Fs							
Uncertainty	$U1$	3.63%	2.81%	1.14%	1.58%	2.22%	3.19%
Corrected Uncertainty	$U1c$	0.71%	1.24%	0.48%	1.79%	1.01%	4.47%
Least square-root, Ls							
uloc	U	2.27	1.68	0.63	0.73	0.01	0.01
uloc(%)	U(%)	16.95	41.67	7.76	12.64	4.70	14.78

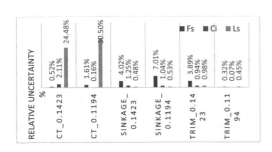

Figure 4. Comparative analysis of different uncertainty estimation methods for constant CFL cases.

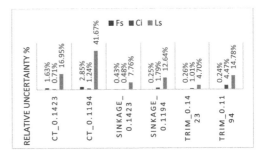

Figure 5. Comparative analysis of different uncertainty estimation methods for combined grid and time uncertainty study cases.

Table 8. Validation of results for KVLCC2 calm water simulation.

Fr		0.1423			0.1194		
Rn		4.9 x e6			4.1 x e6		
		CFD	EFD	Deviation	CFD	EFD	Deviation
Drag	$C_T \times 10^3$	3.87	4.056	5%	4.00	4.146	4%
Sinkage	$\sigma \times 10^{2\,(m)}$	-8.07	-0.437	-1747%	-5.83	-0.281	-1975%
Trim	τ°	0.137	-0.132	4%	0.097	-0.100	3%

Table 9. Calm water simulation results for the KVLCC2 model.

	$C_T \times 10^3$			$\sigma \times 10^{2(m)}$		τ°	
Fr	EFD	CFD	Dev. (%)	EFD	CFD	EFD	CFD
0.1010	4.237	4.237	0.000	-0.147	-0.430	-0.075	-0.071
0.1194	4.146	4.090	1.351	-0.281	-0.580	-0.100	-0.100
0.1377	4.071	3.980	2.235	-0.409	-0.758	-0.124	-0.125
0.1423	4.056	4.000	1.381	-0.437	-0.805	-0.132	-0.135
0.1469	4.046	3.972	1.829	-0.472	-0.860	-0.138	-0.141
0.1515	4.037	3.940	2.403	-0.499	-0.908	-0.154	-0.153

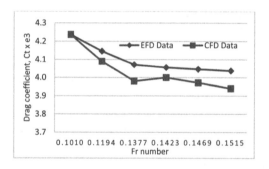

Figure 6. Comparison between experimental and simulation results for the total drag coefficient for the KVLCC2 model.

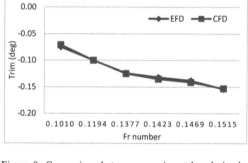

Figure 8. Comparison between experimental and simulation results for trim for the KVLCC2 model.

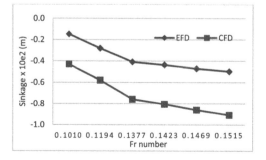

Figure 7. Comparison between experimental and simulation results for sinkage for the KVLCC2 model.

$$C_T = {R_T}/{0.5\rho U^2 S_{WS}}$$

The results are shown in Table 9. The results are further illustrated through Figure 6, 7 and 8.

As can be seen from the results, the resistance results agree very well with the experimental data, with slight under prediction, which might be attributed to the missing rudder in the CFD simulations. Both the total drag and trim results show every good agreement with experimental data. However, the sinkage results show a large deviation, although the trend is well followed.

Possible reasons behind the deviation might be the difference in the consideration of center of gravity (COG) in the experimental and CFD study, towing point in the experiments, and uncertainties in both experiments (reported as around 7%) and CFD simulations (calculated as around 8%). Nevertheless, the actual deviation here is in the millimeter scale, which is very minor. As such, it may be concluded that calm water results are well predicted.

3.3 Head wave simulation results

After calm water simulations, head wave simulations were performed with heave and pitch free motion to predict ship added resistance, and heave and pitch response amplitude operator (RAO). However, to reduce the computational cost, head wave simulations were performed using only half of the hull (starboard side). Furthermore, the deck of the ship was also extended slightly to avoid the green water problem. All simulations were performed at ship design speed (Fr 0.1423). However, considering that this is an initial study for added resistance simulations, no fixed wave steepness was considered. Nevertheless, in most cases, wave amplitude is 1/100 of the wave length. For each case, four to five steady wave encounters were considered for results extraction. This was done since after an initial set of waves, an artificial pressure region develops at the inlet due to the "nut" value of the turbulence model at the flow inlet, which starts to dissipate the incoming waves. The issue might be partly encountered by incorporating the stable SST-kOmega model, however, it wasn't attempted for the present cases.

Added resistance is mainly the additional resistance a ship encounters during its voyage in waves. This additional resistance is created due to loss of energy to both, radiated waves caused by the ship motion and diffraction of the incident waves on the ship hull. However, energy distribution between these two components depends on the ration of the incident wave length to ship length (λ/L).

To validate the simulation results, experimental data from KRISO and Osaka University were used, reported by Kim et al., 2013. For conversion of the results, following equations were used.

Added resistance coefficient,

$$C_{AW} = \overline{F_X} - \overline{F_{X-calm}}/\rho g A^2 B^2/L.$$

Heave RAO, $Z/A = {}^{Z/L}/_{A/L}$.

Pitch RAO, $\theta/Ak = {}^{\theta \times \lambda/L}/_{A/L \times 360}$.

Results for the added resistance prediction, heave, and pitch RAO are shown in Figure 9, 10 and 11, respectively.

The results show relatively good agreement for short wave length cases, whereas, the deviation

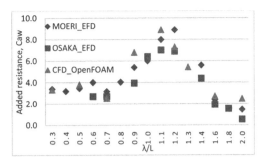

Figure 9. Comparison between experimental and simulation results for added resistance coefficient for the KVLCC2 model.

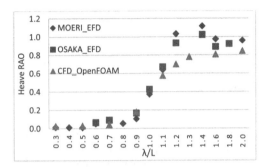

Figure 10. Comparison between experimental and simulation results for Heave RAO for the KVLCC2 model.

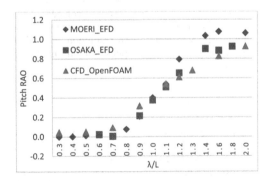

Figure 11. Comparison between experimental and simulation results for Pitch RAO for the KVLCC2 model.

increases with increasing wave length. In general, the results show better agreement with Osaka results, which might be due to the ship model size. KRISO used slightly shorter ship model during experiments.

To further illustrate the results, pressure distribution on the hull form while encountering a wave length of 1.6 λ/L and wave height of 0.05m, is shown in Figure 12.

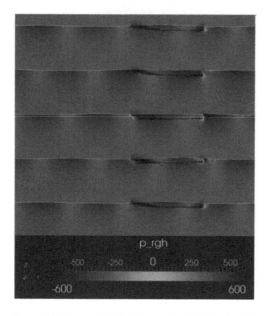

Figure 12. Pressure distribution at the side for the hull encountering wave length 1.6 λ/L.

The added resistance results show relatively acceptable agreement except for a few cases, especially close to the resonance area (around 1.2 λ/L). As for heave and pitch results, both show under prediction after 1.1 λ/L. The over prediction of resistance and under prediction of motions are mostly related to mesh resolution and the results should improve with improved resolution. At the same time, the effect of wave steepness was not considered with also affects the motion prediction. Thus, further simulations with better mesh resolution and following experimental wave steepness should improve the results.

4 CONCLUSIONS

Calm water and added resistance simulations have been performed for a KVLCC2 model, after verification and validation study. Verification or uncertainty analysis was performed using three different popular methods and their results were compared. The calm water simulation results showed good agreement with experimental data, whereas, head wave simulation results have room for improvement.

The uncertainty study showed that while both the correction factor and factor of safety based approach provide close results, least-square error method estimates relatively large uncertainty. Nevertheless, Ls is the only method that allows uncertainty estimation for divergent cases, whereas, the other two are limited to convergent cases. Almost all the studied cases showed monotonous or oscillatory convergence, and very few divergent cases were observed.

Due to larger deviation from experimental data comparing to uncertainty, none of the cases studied could be validated.

The calm water results showed very good agreement with experimental data and confirmed that CFD and especially, OpenFOAM is well capable in estimating calm water towing test results with sufficient reliability and accuracy.

As for head wave simulations, the predictions show promising results, with room for much improvement. The results somewhat capture the overall trend of the results. However, further studies are needed to improve accuracy and reliability.

Nevertheless, the study shows that OpenFOAM is well capable in delivering seakeeping results with sufficient accuracy and reliability, in an economically viable way.

ACKNOWLEDGEMENTS

This work was performed within the scope of the Strategic Research Plan of the Centre for Marine Technology and Ocean Engineering (CENTEC), which is financed by the Portuguese Foundation for Science and Technology (Fundação para a Ciência e Tecnologia) under contract UIDB/UIDP/00134/2020.

REFERENCES

Celik, I. B., Ghia, U.; Roache, P. J., Coleman, H., Raad, P. E., 2008. Procedure for Estimation and Reporting of Uncertainty Due to Discretization in CFD Application. *ASME J. Fluid Eng.*, 130 (7), pp. 078001–4. doi: 10.1115/1.2960953.

Eça, L., and Hoekstra, M., 2014. A procedure for the estimation of the numerical uncertainty of CFD calculations based on grid refinement studies. *Journal of Computational Physics* 262, pp. 104–130. doi: 10.1016/j.jcp.2014.01.006.

Oberhagemann, J., and el Moctar, O., 2017. *On prediction of Wave-Induced Loads and Vibration of Ship Structures with Finite Volume Fluid Dynamics Method*. PhD Thesis, University of Duisburg-Essen.

Islam, H. and Guedes Soares, C. 2019a. Effect of trim on container ship resistance at different ship speeds and drafts. *Ocean Engineering*. 183: 106–115. doi.org/10.1016/j.oceaneng.2019.03.058.

Islam, H., Guedes Soares, C., 2019b. Uncertainty analysis in ship resistance prediction using OpenFOAM. *Ocean Engineering*, 191: 105805 doi.org/10.1016/j.oceaneng.2019.02.033.

ITTC, 2008. *Recommended Procedures and Guidelines, 2008. "Uncertainty Analysis in CFD Verification and Validation Methodology and Procedures."* ITTC – 7.5-03-01-01.

Jasak, H., 2009. OpenFOAM: Open Source CFD in research and industry. *International Journal of Naval Architecture and Ocean Engineering*, 1(2), pp. 89–94.

Kim J, Park I-R, Kim K-S, Kim Y-C, Kim Y-S and Van S-H, 2013. Numerical Towing Tank Application to the Prediction of Added Resistance Performance of

KVLCC2 in Regular Waves. *Proceedings of the Twenty-third International Offshore and Polar Engineering (ISOPE)*, 2.

Larsson L., Stern, F. & Visonneau, M. 2011. "CFD in Ship Hydrodynamics—Results of the Gothenburg 2010 Workshop". *MARINE 2011, IV International Conference on Computational Methods in Marine Engineering*, pp 237–259.

Stern, F., Wilson, R. V., Coleman, H. W., and Paterson, E. G., 2001. Comprehensive Approach to Verification and validation of CFD Simulations—Part 1: Methodology and Procedures. *ASME J. Fluids Eng.*, vol. 123 (4), pp. 793–802. doi:10.1115/1.1412235.

Wang J, Wan D, 2018. CFD investigation of ship manoeuvring in waves using NAOE-FOAM-SJTU solver. *Journal of Marine Science and Application*. doi.org/10.1007/s11804-018-0042-4.

Gatin I, Vladimir N, Malenica S, Jasak H, 2019. Green sea loads in irregular waves with Finite Volume Method. *Ocean Engineering* 171:554–564. doi: 10.1016/j.oceaneng.2018.10.061.

Investigation of the hydrodynamic properties of an inland container vessel

H. Islam & C. Guedes Soares
Centre for Marine Technology and Ocean Engineering (CENTEC), Instituto Superior Técnico, Universidade de Lisboa, Lisbon, Portugal

J. Kan
School of Transportation, Wuhan University of Technology, Wuhan, P. R. China

J. Liu & X. Wang
Intelligent Transportation Systems Research Center, Wuhan University of Technology, Wuhan, P. R. China
National Engineering Research Center for Water Transport Safety, Wuhan, P. R. China

ABSTRACT: The paper investigates hydrodynamic properties of an inland container vessel using computational fluid dynamics (CFD) and compares the results with experimental data. A newly designed container vessel for inland waterways of China is investigated using the open source CFD toolkit, OpenFOAM, and the commercial software StarCCM+. OpenFOAM was mostly used for the investigation, while, StarCCM+ was used to validate some cases. Simulations were performed for different ship drafts and different ship speeds, with heave and pitch free motion. An uncertainty study was performed to verify the simulation outputs. Validation of the results was attempted by comparing some of the results with experimental and StarCCM+ simulation results.

1 INTRODUCTION

Investigation of vessel hydrodynamic and maneuvering properties during the design stage is essential to ensure an efficient and optimal design. Hydrodynamic analysis during the design stage is nothing new in the maritime industry. Historically, most of such studies were done through model experiments. However, with the recent development in numerical tools, such studies are mostly performed using a combination of experimental and numerical studies. With the development of computational resources, CFD has taken a central stage in such investigations, especially because of its economy comparing to experimental cost.

Although a lot of research is done to investigate the seakeeping and maneuvering capabilities of sea-going vessels (Tokyo 2015, SIMMAN 2014, Islam & Guedes Soares (2018), Shigunov et al. (2018)), interest in inland vessels has remained limited. Inland vessels being relatively small and low budget, shipbuilders are rarely interested in thoroughly investigating such vessels (Liu et. al, 2015). However, with the increasing environmental concern, several countries with inland waterways are investigating options of shipping goods through inland waterways.

With a view to reducing carbon footprint generated due to goods transportation in China, RESET project was initiated to develop a smart and efficient inland vessel that will transport containers between Huzhou and Shanghai, with minimum human intervention. This paper attempts an initial hydrodynamic assessment of the vessel at varying operating conditions. The aim is to investigate the total resistance of the vessel at varying vessel speeds and draft conditions. The paper concludes that the open-source CFD solver, OpenFOAM is well capable of providing sufficient insight into the vessel hydrodynamics with reasonable reliability.

2 METHOD

2.1 *The numerical solver*

The open-source CFD toolkit, OpenFOAM was used for most of the study. The solver is based on Reynolds averaged Navier-Stokes (RANS) and continuity equation, which solves incompressible, two-phase, Newtonian fluid. The Volume of Fluid (VOF) method is used for the multiphase solution that traces each fluid that exists in each cell, thus tracking the free surface elevation. The unstructured collocated finite volume method (FVM) is used to discretize the governing equations, and pressure-velocity coupling is done using PIMPLE algorithm. For the presented simulations, spatial discretization was performed using second-order schemes, whereas, temporal discretization was done using the first-order method. Turbulence was modeled using SST-kOmega turbulence mode, and the dynamic motion was accommodated using the mesh-morphing technique. A detailed description of the OpenFOAM solver can be found in Jasak (2009).

For confirming the results, another commercial CFD solver, StarCCM+ was also used. The solver is also based on RANS and continuity equation, which performs multiphase flow simulations and uses VOF method for free surface tracking. The discretization is done using FVM, and for turbulence k-ω model was used. For dynamic simulation, DFBI motion was activated. The experimental data was taken from an internal towing tank test report, which unfortunately is not available to the public.

2.2 The ship model and the mesh

The simulations and experiments were performed for a 2.065 m long 64 twenty feet equivalent unit (TEU) inland container ship model, with a bare hull and no appendages. The vessel follows a novel design aiming at a smart inland vessel with multiple advanced technologies, intended to be operated between Huzhou to Shanghai. Apart from a blunt bow, the vessel features a rim-driven thruster propulsion system, containerized batteries and ship-shore coordination assisted navigation. The ship's principal dimensions (for both full scale and model scale) and a representative hull diagram are shown in Table 1 and Figure 1.

For OpenFOAM simulations, the mesh was generated using the mesh generation utility of Open-FOAM. The blockMeshDict was used to generate the initial simulation domain, which was then refined six times using topoSetDict and refineMeshDict. Next, snappyHexMeshDict was used to incorporate the hull form into the blockMesh. Four layers were added around the hull for proper capturing of the viscous force. All simulations were run for the half-hull (port side). The simulation conditions are shown in Table 2, and the general mesh configuration is shown in Figure 2. The mesh used for the studies (3.0 million) had an average non-dimensional wall distance (y+) value of around 50. Further detail on the mesh is provided in the grid dependency study. The mesh resolution varied depending on the drift angle and the resolution was higher for larger drift angles.

For StarCCM+, the mesh was generated following the StarCCM+ mesh generation utility. The mesh generator automatically generates unstructured, hexahedral mesh, with refinement near the curved surfaces. For the presented simulations, three sets of refinements were applied at the free surface to properly capture the Kelvin pattern, and refinement was also performed around the hull form to properly capture the pressure and viscous forces. Eight layers were added near the hull surface with the first cell near the hull at the size of y+ 20. The total resolution of the mesh was 2.4 million (half hull). Mesh distribution on the free surface is shown in Figure 3.

2.3 Computational resource

The OpenFOAM simulations were performed on intel Xenon processors (2.2 Gz) with 24 threads, and 16 GB of RAM. Each simulation was run for 50 s (simulation

Table 1. Principal dimensions of the 64TEU vessel, for both full scale and model scale.

	Full-scale	Model-scale
Scale	1:1	1:34.5
Lpp (m)	69.00	2.00
Lwl (m)	71.26	2.065
Bwl (m)	12.60	0.365
D (m)	3.45	0.1
T (m)	2.60	0.0754
Displacement (m^3)	2040300	49.69
S w/o rudder (m^2)	1154.8	0.9702
CB	0.0.869	0.651
CM	0.991	0.985

Table 2. Simulation conditions.

Parameters	
Fr number	0.111, 0.155, 0.200
DoF	2 (heave and pitch)
Mesh resolution	3.0 mil
Draft (m)	0.0435, 0.0580, 0.0754, 0.0870
Displacement (m^2)	0.7884, 0.8839, 0.9702, 1.0239
Velocity (m/s)	0.5, 0.7, 0.9

Figure 1. Simplified representation of the 64TEU hull form used in simulations.

Figure 2. Simulation mesh for OpenFOAM; overall simulation domain (half-hull), mesh distribution at the side, on the free surface, and on the hull form.

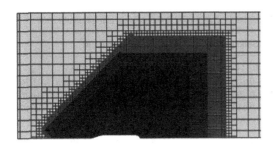

Figure 3. Mesh distribution at the free surface, generated using StarCCM+ mesh generation tool.

time), with an average time step of 0.01s, and took a physical time of 50 hours (on average).

For StarCCM+, a similar processor was used (intel Xenon processors (2.2 Gz)) with 64 GB ram. The simulations were run for 70 s with an average time step of 0.04 s, which took 18.5 physical hours.

3 RESULTS

The paper mostly focuses on simulations performed using OpenFOAM. OpenFOAM was used to perform calm water simulations for the container vessel with heave-free and pitch-free motions, for four different ship drafts, and at three different cruising speeds. Initially, a verification study was performed for the OpenFOAM simulations, using three different mesh resolutions. Later, a validation study was performed by comparing some of the results with experimental and StarCCM+ results.

3.1 Verification study

For the verification study of the OpenFOAM solutions, three different mesh resolutions were used to perform a systematic uncertainty study. The mesh resolutions used for the study are shown in Table 3.

For uncertainty study, three simulations were performed at three different Froude numbers, all at ship design draft. For uncertainty analysis or verification study, the ITTC-2008 procedure was followed and uncertainty was quantified following both the factor of safety (Celik et al., 2008) and correction factor-based approach (Stern et al., 2001). A summary of the analysis is shown in Table 4.

The analysis shows monotonous convergence for most cases, with two oscillatory convergences and one divergent case. The exceptions are observed for one resistance, one sinkage, and one trim case. The estimated order of accuracies is also close to the theoretical value of 2, except a few.

As for the estimated uncertainty, the factor of safety based approach shows reasonably low uncertainty for most of the cases, except for a sinkage case. Comparatively, the correction factor based approach shows higher uncertainty for most of the cases, especially for the sinkage at Froude 0.111. The predicted resistance at Froude 0.2 also shows higher uncertainty in both methods. Although the sinkage estimation shows very high uncertainty, the difference in their physical values is very small. Furthermore, at low-speed condition, sinkage is relatively low. As such, mesh size may not be enough in some cases to properly capture the slight difference in the vertical position of the vessel. As for the variation in resistance prediction at Froude 0.2, the high uncertainty mostly comes because of the estimation at the low mesh resolution. The mesh 3 shows a significantly different trim comparing to the other two cases, as such, resistance prediction also came out different. The estimated uncertainty suggests that the low mesh resolution might have been too low for this particular hull form.

3.2 Validation Study

For the validation study, the OpenFOAM simulation results were compared with available experimental data and StarCCM+ simulation results. However, comparison data was made available only for a limited number of cases. Experimental data was made available only for two draft conditions at design speed. The StarCCM+ results included simulation results for three different Froude numbers, for the same two draft conditions. The comparative results are shown in Table 5 and Figures 4 and 5.

The comparison shows a significant deviation among the results. However, according to the experimental report, the results obtained in the experiments contain high uncertainty, due to measurement-related issues. As such, it was recommended that the obtained values should be taken as a reference, and not as an exact result. Furthermore, the sinkage and

Table 3. Mesh resolutions used for the uncertainty study.

Mesh	Resolution (million)	Cell size (X x Y x Z; before Layers)	Refinement Ratio	Min Thickness	y+ (0.111, 0.155, 0.2)
1	1.55	0.00703 x 0.0067 x 0.00375	1	0.0017	35, 50, 65
2	0.6	0.009375 x 0.009375 x 0.005	1.35	0.0023	50, 70, 85
3	0.245	0.014 x 0.0117 x 0.0075	1.417	0.003	65, 90,110

Table 4. Summary of the uncertainty analysis for the 64TEU container vessel model simulations using OpenFOAM.

		Total Resistance Coefficient, Ct			Sinkage (cm)			Trim (deg)		
Froude Num.		0.111	0.155	0.200	0.111	0.155	0.200	0.111	0.155	0.200
	$\emptyset_1$ (M1)	5.94E-03	5.35E-03	6.29E-03	-0.100	-0.200	-0.330	-0.0794	-0.0415	0.02673
Output values	$\emptyset_2$ (M2)	5.68E-03	5.57E-03	6.61E-03	-0.106	-0.190	-0.330	-0.0778	-0.0414	0.0257
	$\emptyset_3$ (M3)	6.13E-03	6.00E-03	7.02E-03	-0.113	-0.203	-0.343	-0.074	-0.04134	0.0175
Convergence	$\epsilon_{21/\epsilon 32}$	-0.58	0.50	0.75	0.86	-0.77	0.03	0.42	1.67	0.13
Order of accuracy	p	1.64	1.64	0.36	0.02	0.80	9.94	2.17	2.46	5.66
Grid convergence index (GCI)	GCI^{21}_{fine}	0.086	0.080	0.546	14.082	0.232	0.000	0.027	0.003	0.011
Uncertainty	U_1	8.60%	8.00%	54.56%	1408.19%	23.20%	0.01%	2.75%	0.28%	1.08%
Corrected Uncertainty	U_{1c}	1.72%	1.60%	10.91%	281.64%	4.64%	0.00%	0.55%	0.06%	0.22%
Normalized Correction Factor-based Approach											
Correction factor	C1	0.7731	0.7731	0.1387	0.0065	0.3276	22.7936	1.1146	1.3280	5.4301
Error estimate	$\delta^*_{i,1}$	0.0532	-0.0495	-0.0605	-0.0729	0.0608	-0.0015	0.0245	0.0029	0.0468
Uncertainty	U_1	0.02%	9.31%	118.83%	3365.07%	0.65%	0.29%	2.70%	NA	8.51%
Corrected Uncertainty	U_{1c}	0.02%	1.43%	37.59%	1119.26%	0.65%	0.14%	0.25%	NA	3.82%

Table 5. Comparative results among CFD and EFD estimation for total drag estimation for a 64TEU inland vessel.

Draft:	0.0435m			0.0754m		
Velocity (m/s)	EFD	CFD_StarCCM+	CFD_OpenFOAM	EFD	CFD_StarCCM+	CFD_OpenFOAM
0.50	-	5.69E-03	6.21E-03	-	6.27E-03	5.94E-03
0.70	-	5.88E-03	5.74E-03	-	6.45E-03	5.35E-03
0.90	5.14E-03	6.49E-03	6.36E-03	5.47E-03	6.85E-03	6.29E-03

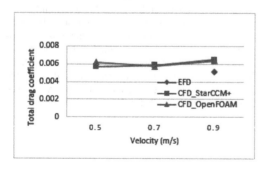

Figure 4. Comparative results for the total drag coefficient for 64TEU inland vessel at draft 0.0435m.

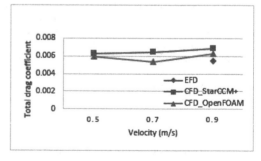

Figure 5. Comparative results for the total drag coefficient for 64TEU inland vessel at draft 0.0754m.

trim data were not recorded during the experiments either. As for the CFD result from StarCCM+, for some reason, the CFD simulations in StarCCM+ was showing a trim towards the bow at the relatively high-speed cases, instead of showing a trim by stern.

As such, relatively higher resistance was recorded in the StarCCM+ simulations. The StarCCM+ simulations show higher frictional resistance prediction comparing to OpenFOAM results.

For the 0.0435m draft, the relative difference between OpenFOAM and experimental results in 23%, and the relative difference between OpenFOAM and StarCCM+ results is 2%, at Froude 0.2. For the design draft of 0.0754m, the difference with experimental data is 15%, and with SSStarCCM+ is 8%. The estimated corrected uncertainties at the design draft are 11% and 37% for the factor of safety based approach, and for the correction factor-based approach, respectively. Thus, the results stand validated for the correction factor-based approach.

3.3 Simulation results

To understand the hydrodynamic behavior of the vessel, calm water simulations were performed using OpenFOAM at four different drafts, at three different ship speeds. However, for the first draft (lowest draft condition), only static simulations were performed. For other cases, the vessel had free sinkage and trim motion. The simulation results for the different draft conditions are shown in Table 6.

The results indicate that for all the draft conditions, the Froude 0.155 indicates the optimal operation condition, resistance wise. The sinkage and trim also show expected response, with sinkage increasing with increasing speed, and trim changing from bow trim to stern trim with increasing speed. The results also show maximum trim of 4% relative to ship height, and also very small trim, indicating almost even keel condition, which is optimal for container carrying vessels.

Surprisingly, at the lowest draft, the vessel shows relatively high resistance. Initially, simulations were performed for this draft with heave-free and pitch-free motions. However, the ship, in that case, showed positive sinkage, indicating a possible error in the calculation of the vessel mass at that condition.

However, the data came from experiments, thus, instead of adjusting the mass, simulations were run at the fixed conditions. Furthermore, at such low draft, shrinkage, and trim should be very low, thus, ignoring it should not have altered the results much. As such, further experiments and CFD simulations might be needed to explain the results.

To further illustrate the results, free surface elevation along the hull form is shown for all draft conditions in Figure 6. As expected, the figure shows a relatively higher deformation of the free surface at higher Froude number cases. The figure also shows a stable operating condition with a very small trim.

Table 6. OpenFOAM simulation results for the 64TEU inland container vessel at different draft conditions.

Froude Number	Velocity (m/s)	Total draft coefficient, Ct	Sinkage (cm)	Trim (deg)
Draft 1: 0.0435 (m)				
0.111	0.5	6.21E-03	-	-
0.155	0.7	5.74E-03	-	-
0.200	0.9	6.36E-03	-	-
Draft 2: 0.0580 (m)				
0.111	0.5	5.71E-03	-0.065	-0.1786
0.155	0.7	5.09E-03	-0.140	-0.15
0.200	0.9	5.93E-03	-0.240	-0.1036
Draft 3: 0.0754 (m)				
0.111	0.5	5.94E-03	-0.100	-0.0794
0.155	0.7	5.35E-03	-0.200	-0.0415
0.200	0.9	6.36E-03	-0.321	0.0233
Draft 4: 0.0870 (m)				
0.111	0.5	6.32E-03	-0.12	-0.0155
0.155	0.7	5.65E-03	-0.23	0.031785
0.200	0.9	6.71E-03	-0.39	0.1206

Figure 6. Waterline along with the hull form for different draft conditions, at different Froude numbers (0.111, 0.155, and 0.2 respectively).

The free surface elevation for the design draft condition (draft 3) and pressure distribution at the side of the vessel is also shown in Figures 7 and 8.

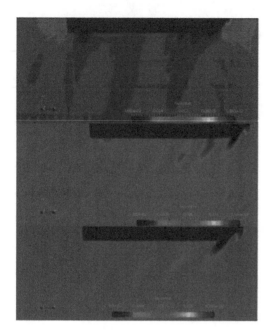

Figure 7. Free surface elevation for varying Froude numbers (0.111, 0.155, 0.2) at draft 0.0754m.

Figure 8. Pressure distribution at the side of the hull for varying Froude numbers (0.111, 0.155, 0.2) at draft 0.0754m.

The free surface elevation and the pressure distribution shows higher distortion in a free surface and higher pressure distribution for high-speed cases. The full form shows high pressure at the bow front, and relatively small distortion or pressure at the stern or the flow separation region.

Overall, the simulation results provide a reasonably reliable prediction of the vessel's possible behavior at operating conditions. The data would also be useful in determining the propulsion power requirement of the vessel for safe and optimal operation.

4 CONCLUSIONS

The paper investigates the hydrodynamic properties of a novel energy-efficient hull form designed for inland container transportation. Simulations were performed mainly with OpenFOAM, and comparison was made with StarCCM+ and experimental results. A systematic verification and validation study was performed. Finally, simulations were performed at different operating conditions to predict the vessel's hydrodynamic behavior.

The validation study shows a significant discrepancy among the experimental and CFD results, which was contributed to the uncertainties related to the experimental study. The StarCCM+ and OpenFOAM also disagree for certain result points. Overall, it might be stated that, although the simulations provide a reference regarding the vessel's performance, more simulations and experimental studies are needed with a larger model to confirm the results with good confidence.

ACKNOWLEDGMENTS

This work was performed within the Reliability and Safety Engineering and Technology for large maritime engineering systems (RESET), which is financed by EU H2020 Marie Curie RISE Project under the grant agreement No. 73088 RESET. It was also supported by National Key R&D Program of China (2018YFB1601505), Research on Intelligent Ship Testing and Verification (2018473), National Natural Science Foundation of China (51709217). This work contributes to the Strategic Research Plan of the Centre for Marine Technology and Ocean Engineering (CENTEC), which is financed by the Portuguese Foundation for Science and Technology (Fundação para a Ciência e Tecnologia - FCT) under contract UIDB/UIDP/00134/2020.

REFERENCES

Celik, I. B., Ghia, U.; Roache, P. J., Coleman, H., Raad, P. E., 2008. Procedure for Estimation and Reporting of Uncertainty Due to Discretization in CFD Application. *ASME J. Fluid Eng.*, 130(7), pp. 078001–4.

Islam, H., Guedes Soares, C., 2019. Uncertainty analysis in ship resistance prediction using OpenFOAM. *Ocean Engineering*, 191 (105805).

ITTC 2008. Recommended Procedures and Guidelines. "Uncertainty Analysis in CFD Verification and Validation Methodology and Procedures." ITTC – 7.5–03–01–01.

Liu J., Hekkenberg R., Rotteveel E., Hopman H., 2015. Literature review on evaluation and prediction methods of inland vessel manoeuvrability. *Ocean Engineering* 106 (2015) 458–471.

Jasak, H., 2009. OpenFOAM: Open Source CFD in research and industry. *International Journal of Naval Architecture and Ocean Engineering*, 1(2), pp. 89–94.

Shigunov, V., El-Moctar, O., Papanikolaou, A., Potthoff, R., & Liu, S., 2018. International Benchmark Study on Numerical Simulation Methods for Prediction of Manoeuvrability of Ships in Waves. *Ocean Engineering*. 165:365–385.

SIMMAN *Workshop, 2014*. [Online]. Available: http://www.simman2014.dk/.[Accessed 2020].

Tokyo 2015 *Workshop, 2015*. [Online]. Available: https://t2015.nmri.go.jp/. [Accessed 2020].

Stern, F., Wilson, R. V., Coleman, H. W., and Paterson, E. G., 2001. Comprehensive Approach to Verification and validation of CFD Simulations—Part 1: Methodology and Procedures. *ASME J. Fluids Eng.*, vol. 123 (4).

Fast ferry design – a case for the Gulf of Cádiz

M.J. Legaz, A. Querol, B. Flethes & M. Avalos
Department of Sciences and Techniques of Navigation and Naval Construction, University of Cádiz, Spain

M.I Ibrahim
Faculty of Engineering, Department of Naval Architecture and Marine Engineering, Alexandria University, Egypt

ABSTRACT: ESPOmar is a European Interreg POCTEP Project in which several Spanish, Portuguese universities, research groups and public organizations collaborated to examine the potential of establishing a competitive regular passenger maritime transport system in the Gulf of Cadiz. An important aspect of this competition is the reduction of resistance. This reduction implies also a reduction in fuel consumption and the emission of CO2. Two catamaran configurations have been analyzed by ANSYS FLUENT and Maxsurf Resistance to establish the best catamaran configuration for the ESPOmar project.

1 INTRODUCTION

ESPOmar is the short form of the project name "España and Portugal unidos por el mar (Spain and Portugal connected by sea)". This project has been gained in the framework of European Interreg Projects (POCTEP 2014-2020). The objective of ESPOmar project is to study the possibility of establishing a competitive regular maritime passenger line between Spain and Portugal within the Gulf of Cadiz. Partners of ESPOmar Project are the Spanish Universities of Cadiz and Huelva, Portuguese University of Algarve and Andalusian Agency of Public Ports.

The Gulf of Cadiz can be found in the southwest part of Iberian Peninsula and is surrounded by the Spanish provinces of Cadiz and Huelva and the Portuguese region of Algarve. In Figure 1, the interest area and maritime connections can be seen. This territory has peculiar characteristics because of the existence of the Guadalquivir River and Doñana National Park. The previous one carries out the route by road much longer than the potential route by sea. Specifically, the distance by sea between Cadiz and Faro is 156 kilometres shorter than the distance by road. By road, you have to travel north and pass throw out Seville. This is would not happen in waterborne transport, so this leads us to the idea that maritime transport, could be a more sustainable transport option. The main idea is to establish lines between Cadiz, Huelva and Algarve with the possibility to establish other fluvial lines within river Guadiana, which is a natural border between the two countries.

One of the ambits of the project is the design of the ships optimized for each of the defined lines. The new ship designs have to be able to compete with the existing land transport based on the private car and public buses to accomplish the regulations and to follow the European Union transportation trends. Two distinctive new concepts vessels could be possible for the ESPOmar project. The first is a passenger ferry for coastal routes, which has to compete with road transport both speed and CO2 emissions. The ferry has to meet the requirements for the sustainable propulsion system; lightweight structure and hydrodynamic optimized hull. The second vessel is a medium-size ferry specifically designed for nautical tourism. The aim of the vessel is not only transportation but also an entertainment centre. This paper has focused on the first one.

Section 2 shows a brief description of the regular navigational line established and the main particulars of the two catamaran configurations selected for the ESPOmar project. Section 3 presents a revision of the bibliography regarding hydrodynamic behaviour. Resistance and its components are defined in section 4. An explanation about the different ways of analysing the resistance is shown in section 5. In section 6, an explanation of the two methods used to calculate the resistance of the two configurations of the catamaran for ESPOmar project. Section 7 shows the results obtained from ANSYS Fluent. And finally, the results from slender body and Fluent are compared.

2 REGULAR TRANSPORT FERRY DESIGN

In order to establish a regular maritime transport, sixteen maritime lines have been analysed between different destinations in the Gulf of Cádiz. The study of the lines concluded that the maritime connection between Chipiona and Mazagón is the line that can offer more

DOI: 10.1201/9781003216599-42

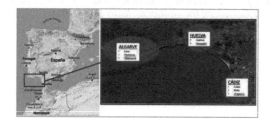

Figure 1. Area of interest.

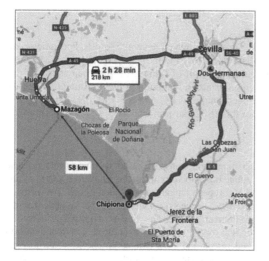

Figure 2. Connection Chipiona-Mazagón.

advantages versus land transportation. The distance between Chipiona and Mazagón is 218 km by road and the maritime connection would be 58 km, approximately 31 nautical miles (see Figure 2).

In the scope of the ESPOmar project, a demand study has been developed between the possible customers of the maritime regular transport. This demand study concluded that the maritime connection should be done in 1.7 hours. This means a reduction of more than 1.1 hours regarding land transport. Another aspect that demand study concluded is the line capacity requirement of 200 passengers. To achieve the previous one, the required service speed of the ferry should be between 20-24 knots (maximum speed of 28 knots).

Nowadays, the trend in fast ferries designs is catamarans and monohulls. Around 60% of the high-speed ferry market belong to catamarans (Legaz et al. 2019). Following this market numbers, the design team decided to select a catamaran, specifically a wave-piercing catamaran for the maritime line between Chipiona and Mazagón ports. After studying the two ports of destinations Chipiona and Mazagón it is observed that, there is a dimensional restriction at the ports regarding maximum length. For this reason, the maximum length of the vessel is restricted to 30 meters.

A database of more than two hundred vessels has been collected for the ESPOmar project. From this database using regression functions and after giving the first turns to the design spiral. Two possible configurations of catamaran hull design have been selected for the maritime line. One configuration of 30 meters length, 9 meters beam (see Figure 3 and Table 1) and the other of 30 meters length, 12 meters beam (see Figure 3 and Table 2). For both configurations, the pontoon has a beam of 1.55 m to ensure that the main engine could be fitted inside.

The two pontoons have the same length with two different spacing values making this study highlights the impact of using different spacing values between the pontoons on the total resistance of the catamaran.

A reduction of resistance leads to a reduction of consumption of combustible or energy and therefore a reduction of the amount of CO_2 released to the atmosphere. With the aim of reducing the emission of CO_2, the total resistance of the two catamaran configurations have been estimated in this paper.

3 BACKGROUND

Regarding hydrodynamic behaviour and focusing on the studies of resistance whose purpose is to minimize the resistance by optimizing the different affecting

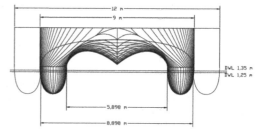

Figure 3. Frontal view of two hulls ESPOmar catamaran configurations.

Table 1. Principal Particulars of 9 meters beam catamaran.

Principal Particulars	Specifications	Unit
Length	30	m
Breadth	9	m
Draft	1,25	m
Displacement	70,07	ton

Table 2. Principal Particulars of 12 meters beam catamaran.

Principal Particulars	Specifications	Unit
Length	30	m
Breadth	12	m
Draft	1,35	m
Displacement	77,57	ton

parameters. Some papers evaluate the importance of the different components of the resistance in multihulls in which the interference resistance is included (Tuner and Taplin 1968, Insel and Molland 1991).

The majority of the research consider high speed (Fr>5) typical condition of this vessels (Molland et al. 1996, Migali et al. 2001, Moraes et al. 2004, Sahoo et al. 2004). The navigation in shallow water is another aspect analysed, this is a relevant aspect due to the small draft of the multihulls (Insel and Doctors 1995, Jiankang et al. 2001, Tarafder and Suzuki 2008a, Aubault and Yeung 2012). Some researches combine both conditions assessment the behaviour in shallow waters and high speed (Chen et al. 2003b, Chen et al. 2003a, Molland et al. 2004) even adding the effect of navigation by narrow channels (Chen and Sharma 1997).

There are few pieces of research about the real size of the vessels, the majority of then consists of numerical methods or model basin tests. It can be highlighted the work of Davis et al. (2005), where the behaviour at the sea of a wave-piercing catamaran is analysed. Others works are the paper of Macfariane (2009) in which tests are done using a recreational catamaran and the work of Lee et al. (2007) regarding a small catamaran.

From a theoretical point of view, most of the researches use the linear theory for the prediction of wave resistance (Insel et al. 1994, Yeung et al. 2004, Yeung 2005). Under the assumption of slender bodies, which is appropriate for multihulls, the flow around the hull can be calculated as a distribution of sources or sinks about the centre plan whose intensity is proportional to the horizontal slope of the average surface of the hull. The Michell integral (Michell 1898) can be used to obtain the resistance, as it is shown in the works of Tuck (1987) and Tuck et al. (2002). Doctors (2006) extends this theory to hulls with sterns of the transom. Pérez Arribas (2000) applied to SWATH type catamarans. Lunde (1951), Yeung (1978) and Liu and Yue (1996) consider its utilization in nonstationary conditions.

On the other hand, Miller et al. (2006), Broglia et al. (2011), Zaghi et al. (2011) and He et al. (2015) use numerical approximation to approximate the solution for some form of Reynold- averaged Navier Stokes equations, being able to estimate the values of resistance and predicts the effect of interference to high Froude numbers.

Respect to the separation between hulls can be found several pieces of research that analyse its effect in the resistance (Insel et al. 1994, Tarafder and Suzuki 2007). Sarles et al. (2011) analyse the interference resistance with different hulls of semi-elliptical.

The main aspect about the effect of the interference is the annulation of the wave trains of each hull, which reduces the wave resistance (Chen and Sharma 1997, Chen et al. 2003a, Tuck 2005). Most of the researches took the assumption of fixed model and linear theory, which reduces the computational demands and allows to be implemented in the initial phases of the project (Tuck and Lazaukas 1998, Moraes et al. 2007, Yeung and Wan 2008).

4 RESISTANCE

Inertia is defined as a property of matter by which it continues in its existing state of rest or uniform motion in a straight line unless that state is changed by an external force. Therefore, when a ship starts to navigate has to overcome her resistance to reach her operational conditions. To do this, the ship needs to use energy but the environment will oppose the changes in states. Some environment effects:

- Movement of the flow particles around the ship (air and water) because of the effects of viscous friction.
- Effects of the pressure (normal forces on the hull and the superstructure, deformation of the free surface)
- Turbulence, both air and water
- Spray
- Break waves

All the previous ones form a component almost constant the ship has to overcome, this is named resistance. Optimizing the resistance has the significance of reducing ship impact on the environment.

4.1 *Components of the resistance*

The subdivision of the physical phenomena provoked by the forward movement of the ship lead to the subdivision of total resistance of the ship in several components (SNAME 1941). All the components have a relation between them. These relations have complex modelling, so they are usually considered independent for practical purposes.

William Froude (Froude 1868, Froude 1874) was the first to subdivide the total resistance into a friction component and a residual component that includes the rest of the factors. Later, Hughes (1954) identified the wave resistance, which is a consequence of the normal component of the forces on the hull.

The viscosity effect is difficult to model. The classic point of view follows the approach proposed by Prandtl (1904) considering the viscous effect only in a thin area in contact with the hull surface named boundary layer. This simplification allows for obtaining results close to reality. The difficulty is to delimit this zone, which analytical solution only can be found in a few cases (Schlichting et al. 2000).

Focusing on multihulls, it is clear that interference exists between the individual hulls. So, considering that the hulls are independent leads to inaccurate results. In the case of catamarans, the interaction of the two hulls is quite complex and difficult to analyse. In the works of Insel (1990) and Insel and Molland (1991), deep research about the interference between the components on hulls was presented.

5 PREDICTION OF RESISTANCE TECHNIQUES

The resistance is one of the main operating expenses of a ship, and for that reason, its minimization is an important aspect of the design.

In order to estimate the resistance, it would be necessary to solve the Navier-Stokes equations. Exact solutions of these equations are unknown, it is necessary to make assumptions that allow obtaining approximated solutions. In the beginning, the test with the scaled model was performed. In the latest years, there has been an increment on the use of numerical methods, because of the increase of the capacity to calculate.

5.1 Empirical methods

The utilization of scaled models to predict the resistance is based on the similitude laws that allow extrapolating the resistance measurement to the real scale of the ship. To establish a correlation, it's necessary to obtain a dynamic similitude, which implies geometric and cinematic similitude.

William Froude (Froude 1868, Froude 1874) was the pioneer in measuring the resistance in tank basin and subdivided the resistance into two components; friction resistance and residual resistance. Following Froude, the friction resistance component is equivalent to the flat-plate with the same wet surface. The residual resistance component encompasses the rest of the factors. Following this hypothesis, several experiments about flat-planes were developed, resulting in the improved formulation to obtain friction resistance component, some references can be found in Schoenherr (1932), Hughes (1954) and Hughes (1966).

In 1957, the ITTC proposed a new formulation for friction curve known as ITTC-57 (ITTC 1957) and it's currently used. These formulations of the friction coefficient equate the wet surface of the ship to a flat plate without taking into account the hull forms. Hughes (1954) tried to include this fact into the resistance. The friction resistance due to the forms can be considered as an increment of the friction resistance of the flat plate. This increment is considered into the formulations as a form factor. Further research in this regard, Prohaska (1966). In the conferences ITTC of 1978 (ITTC 1978) and ITTC of 2011 (ITTC 2011), recommendations were included in the formulation of the coefficient of total resistance.

5.1.1 Catamaran particularization

For an individual hull of a catamaran, the previous method could be used. However, the interference between the two hulls should be taken into account. Insel (1990) presented a detailed analysis of the modifications to introduce in the formulations to include the effects of the interference. Insel and Molland (1991) describe the total resistance of a catamaran as:

$$C_T = (1 + \phi)\sigma C_F + \tau C_w \qquad (1)$$

where C_F is derived from the ITTC1957 correlation line, $(1 + k)$ is the form factor for a demihull in isolation, ϕ is introduced to take account of the pressure field change around the hull, σ takes account the velocity augmentation between the two hulls and would be calculated from an integration of local frictional resistance over the wetted surface, C_w is the wave resistance coefficient for a demihull in isolation and τ is the wave resistance interference factor.

For practical purposes, ϕ and σ were combined into a viscous interference factor β, where $(1 + \phi k)\sigma C_F$ is replaced by $(1 + \beta k)C_F$.
where

$$C_T = (1 + \beta k)C_F + \tau C_w \qquad (2)$$

Noting that, for a demihull (monohull) in isolation, $\beta = 1$ and $\tau = 1$.

One of the main causes of the reduction of the resistance of interference is the annulment of waves.

5.2 Analytical methods

Michell (1898) devised a thin-body method to predict the wave resistance of a ship moving in shallow water. The fundamental assumption behind the Michell (1898) method is that the ship's beam is small compared to its length. As a consequence of this, the waves generated are also of small amplitude, which allows the linearization of the free water surface. Later Joukvski (1903) derived a similar formulation of the problem independently. Havelock (1908) investigated the wave pattern created by the propagation of a point source in shallow water. His work led to the introduction of the non-dimensional depth Froude number.

Tuck (1966) reproduced Michell's linearized Slender-body theory using matched asymptotic expansions to solve for the hydrodynamic forces in shallow water. In his paper, Tuck (1966) explored the scenario where a ship is travelling in shallow waters of constant infinite width. He used the vertical forces and moments acting on the ship to successfully compute the sinkage and trim for subcritical and supercritical speeds and validated the results with model-scale experiments.

5.3 Numerical techniques

Although the tank basin test with models give important information, the prediction of resistance is not resolved. There have been a lot of efforts to find an approximation solution to Navier-Stokes equations applies to the flow around a ship. Because of the complex hull geometry and the existence of free surface, it is only possible to obtain solutions to the discretized equations. This leads to the use of computational tools, CFD (computational fluid dynamics).

The variables which characterise a flow are; density, pressure, velocity and temperature. All of them are a function of the position and the time and they are related by the Navier-Stokes equations. These equations are based on the conservation laws, mass conservation (3), movement quantity conservation (4), and energy conservation (5).

$$\frac{d}{dt}\int_{V(t)} \rho dV = 0 \qquad (3)$$

$$\frac{d}{dt}\int_{V(t)} \rho \vec{f} dV + \int_{s(t)} \bar{\bar{\sigma}} d\vec{S} \qquad (4)$$

$$\frac{d}{dt}\int_{V(t)} \rho\left(e + \tfrac{1}{2}|\vec{v}|^2\right) dV = \int_{V(t)} \rho \vec{f} \cdot \vec{v} dV \\ + \int_{s(t)} (\bar{\bar{\sigma}}\vec{v}) \cdot d\vec{S} + \int_{s(t)} -\vec{q} \cdot d\vec{S} + \int_{V(t)} \rho Q dV \qquad (5)$$

Where V represents a fluid domain, S the limit of the previous domain, $\bar{\bar{\sigma}}$ efforts tensor of Cauchy, $\vec{f}$ volumetric forces, e internal energy, $\vec{v}$ velocity vector, $\vec{q}$ heat conduction vector and Q is the source of volumetric heat. The previous expression has to fulfil for any domain and make the assumption that there are no discontinuities, these equations can be manipulated to obtain the differential formulation (Kundu et al. 2012).

$$\frac{\partial \rho}{\partial t} + div(\rho \vec{v}) = 0 \qquad (6)$$

$$\rho \frac{\partial \vec{v}}{\partial t} + \rho(grad\,\vec{v})\vec{v} = div\bar{\bar{\sigma}} + \rho \vec{f} \qquad (7)$$

$$\rho \frac{\partial e}{\partial t} + \rho(grad\,e)\cdot \vec{v} = \bar{\bar{\sigma}} \cdot grad\,\vec{v} + div(-\vec{q}) + \rho Q \qquad (8)$$

There are six state variables and there are only five equations, so another linearly independent equation is needed. This equation is the state equation of the thermodynamic variables of the flow (9).

$$\rho = f(p, T) \qquad (9)$$

In order to complete the formulation of the problem is necessary to define the initial and boundary conditions. The first one depends on the navigation conditions to simulate. The second one depends on the assumption made on the hull, on the free surface, on the bottom and far away from the ship.

As it is said previously the exact solution of this system of nonlinear partial derivate equation is unknown. So, it is necessary to used approximation method to solve them. Sometimes assumptions are made in order to simplify these equations. Some of them are; the stationary problem, incompressible flow, potential flow.

On the other hand, experimental measurements have shown that aleatory oscillation of the state variables appears, which is known as turbulent flow. They are not a function of time or space, so they are taken as stochastic values.

6 THE TOOLS USED TO PREDICT THE RESISTANCE OF ESPOMAR CATAMARAN

In this section, two different resistance calculations approaches will be discussed and presented. Later on, the total resistance calculated by each method will be compared and validated.

6.1 *Maxsurf resistance*

MAXSURF Resistance is essentially a resistance prediction program. It has some regression-based methods and one analytical method that are used to predict the resistance of the hull form (Maxsurf Resistance, 2018).

In the framework of naval architecture, the resistance is broken down into components which scale according to different laws. MAXSURF Resistance calculates the resistance components by the coefficient.

Total resistance is normally divided into a Froude number dependent component – wave resistance (residuary resistance) and a Reynolds number dependent component – viscous resistance (friction resistance). The resistance can be also divided as:

Total resistance = Wave + Viscous = Residuary + Friction

Normally, the friction resistance is predicted by the ITTC57 ship-model correlation line or some similar formulation. Viscous resistance includes a form effect applied to the friction resistance thus:

Viscous resistance = (1 + k) Friction resistance; where (1 + k) is the form factor.

In MAXSURF Resistance, slender body method can be used, this method is based on the work of Tuck et al. (1998) and Couser et al. (1996). The method utilizes a Michell (1898) approach to compute the wave resistance of a port/starboard symmetrical monohull.

The slender body method is available for many different hull forms including multihulls. Nevertheless, every individual hull has to be slender (have narrow beam compared to their length) and has to be symmetrical about their local centreline. This method predicts only the wave pattern resistance component. To calculate the total resistance, MAXSURF Resistance calculates and adds the viscous resistance component using the ITTC'57 friction coefficient calculation method and the specified form factor. The form factor can be specified in MAXSURF Resistance dialogue. For catamarans the Molland algorithm is available. (Maxsurf resistance, 2018).

The Molland method uses the demihull slenderness ratio, $L/\nabla^{1/3}$ to determine the form factor according to the following equation:

$$(1 + \beta k) = 3.03 \left(L/\nabla^{1/3}\right)^{-0.40} \quad (10)$$

The previous form factor, $(1 + \beta k)$ of the complete catamaran include viscous interaction effects between the demihulls.

The wave pattern is calculated using a Michell/Slender Body type approach. This free surface wave pattern calculation ignores the effects of viscosity and wave breaking. The speed field in the free surface calculation parameters dialogue allows you to specify the vessel speed at which you wish to calculate the wave pattern. This can either be specified directly as speed or as a Froude Number.

6.2 ANSYS Fluent (CFD)

ANSYS Fluent make modelling capabilities available for a broad range of incompressible, compressible, laminar and turbulent fluid flow problems. It is possible to carry out both steady-state or transient analyses.

ANSYS fluent offers also a set of models for free surface and multiphase. It is possible to use these models for the analysis of gas-liquid, gas-solid, liquid-solid, and gas-liquid-solid flows. Regarding previous problems, ANSYS Fluent provides the volume-of-fluid (VOF), mixture, and Eulerian models, as well as, the discrete phase model (DPM). The software also has a set of robust and accurate turbulence models. These turbulence models can be adopted to a wide range of cases, such as; buoyancy and compressibility.

ANSYS Fluent resolves conservation equations for mass and momentum and for all type of flows. For flows involving heat transfer or compressibility, an additional equation for energy conservation is solved. Additional transport equations are also solved when the flow is turbulent (ANSYS Fluent, 2017).

7 CFD MODEL

In this work, ANSYS FLUENT 18.1 was used. FLUENT is one of the most famous and widely used CFD numerical code in the research industry.

Although two different hull configurations have been simulated, both of them present dimensions relatively similar. This allowed homogenizing the calculus parameter and comparing the results obtained by each hull configuration, minimizing the purely numerical deviations.

The first step to carry out the simulations is defining the computational domain, which should be a close volume. In this case, a prismatic volume has been used, see Figure 4. This domain is formed by four faces plus the hull surface. The four faces are; A (inlet), B (outlet), D (symmetry) and E (wall). One of the characteristics of the problem is its symmetry with respect central plane, which allows modelling only half of the domain reducing the computational needs.

The domain limits have been considered by the following dimensions. The length of the domain is 1.5 L (length) forward and 3L aft. A total length of 4.5 L. The width is 3B (beam). Total width of 4B. The total height is 12.6 T (draft). See Figure 4.

The monohull is less computational demanding than the catamaran, the flow is solved only around one hull.

Adequate mesh is really important to obtain accurate results (Figure 5). For the catamaran, there have been used 1.464.600 tetrahedron elements. The minimum edge length is 0.1075 m. In the hull surface, the size of elements is 0.1 m. In the rest of the domain, the element size is 1 m.

A pressure inlet boundary condition is imposed at the inlet (blue colored face) while, a pressure outlet boundary condition is imposed at the outlet (green colored face) of the computational domain. Wall boundary conditions are applied at the side, upper and, lower

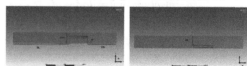

Figure 4. On the top, domain for the two configurations of the ESPOmar catamaran. On the left and right, dimensions of the domain.

Figure 5. Mesh.

faces (cyan colored faces) of the computational domain with a No-slip boundary condition imposed on them.

The two equations Standard k-ε turbulence model is well known for its robustness, reasonable accuracy and reasonable computational time for a wide range of turbulent flows therefore; it has been selected for the work presented here within. The coupled scheme pressure-velocity coupling method is used in all simulations with a Second-order Upwind spatial discretization algorithm used for all equations including pressure, momentum and turbulence.

The maximum number of iterations for convergence is set to 1000.

8 RESULTS AND DISCUSSIONS

In this section, the total resistance (R_T) resulting from using Fluent and slender body with Molland form factor from the Maxsurf Resistance module are presented and discussed. In addition, the fields of pressure and velocities contours are visualised and shown for the two geometric configurations. The variations of ESPOmar catamaran velocity of service in this research are 20 knots, 24 knots and a maximum velocity of 28 knots. The total resistance coefficient (C_T) obtained from CFD simulations and Maxsurf for both configurations are shown in Figure 6 and Figure 7. The different pressure and velocities contours for the two configurations with the three service speeds are shown in Figure 8 and Figure 9.

The previous graphs can be tabulated to calculate the RPE (Relative Percentage Error) between the two methods used. Table 3 and Table 4 shows the values of the total resistance coefficient (C_T), total resistance (R_T) and RPE from CFD simulations and Maxsurf for both configurations.

In Figure 8, the pressure and velocity contours of the first configuration (30 m length and 9m beam) are shown. At 20 knots velocity of service, the magnitude of velocity ranged from 9.2 m/sec to 11 m/s

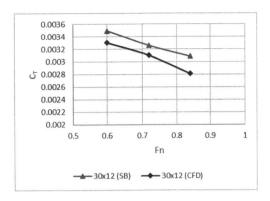

Figure 7. Validation of Total Resistance Coefficient (C_T) based on Fluent simulations and Slender Body for ESPOmar catamaran configuration (L=30m, B=12m).

while, the magnitude of pressure ranged from 1500 Pa to 7000 Pa. Total resistance (Rt) resulting from the simulation is 39.74 kN. At 24 knots velocity of service, the magnitude of velocity ranged from 11.82 m/sec to 12.4 m/sec. While the magnitude of pressure ranged from 2500 Pa to 5500 Pa. Total resistance (Rt) resulting from the simulation is 49.07 kN. At 28 knots, the magnitude of velocity ranged from 13.92 m/sec to 14.6 m/sec. While the magnitude of pressure ranged from 2000 Pa to 5000 Pa. Total resistance (Rt) resulting from the simulation is 56.92 kN.

Figure 9 shows the pressure and velocity contours of the second configuration (30 m length and 12 m beam). At 20 knots velocity of service, the magnitude of velocity ranged from 9.2 m/sec to 11 m/s while, the magnitude of pressure ranged from 3000 Pa to 6000 Pa. Total resistance (Rt) resulting from the simulation is 33.89 kN. At 24 knots velocity of service, the magnitude of velocity ranged from 11.82 m/sec to 12.4 m/sec. While the magnitude of pressure ranged from 2500 Pa to 5000 Pa. Total resistance (Rt) resulting from the simulation is 45.84 kN. At 28 knots, the magnitude of velocity ranged from 13.92 m/sec to 14.6 m/sec. While the magnitude of pressure ranged from 2600 to 4500 Pa. Total resistance (Rt) resulting from the simulation is 56.56 kN.

The CFD results obtained from ANSYS Fluent show a good agreement with slender body method form Maxsurf resistance with a max error percentage of 9.03%, and this can be due to many reasons related to the differences and assumptions of the abovementioned methods used in calculating the total resistance (R_T) like; effect of viscosity and wave interference between the two pontoons. From the results, it can be said that the parameters used in CFD are valid.

As a conclusion, the catamaran configuration which better meets the requirements of the regular line Chipiona-Mazagón of ESPOmar project is the catamaran of the 30 m length and 12 m beam. With this configuration, the lowest values of total resistance are obtained. Another advantage of this

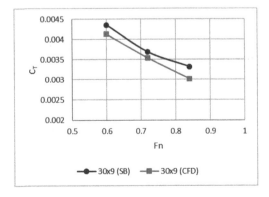

Figure 6. Validation of Total Resistance Coefficient (C_T) based on Fluent simulations and Slender Body for ESPOmar catamaran configuration (L=30m, B=9m).

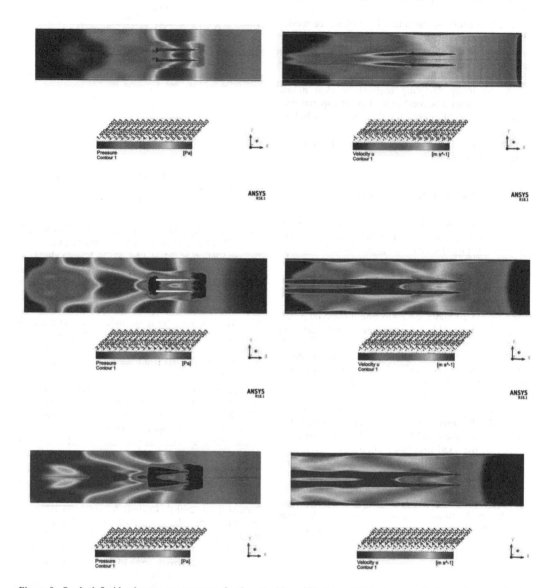

Figure 8. On the left side, the pressure contours for the velocities of 20, 24 and 28 knots respectively can be seen. On the right side, the velocity contours of 20, 24 and 28 knots respectively are shown. Both for the 30 m. length and 9 m. beam ESPOmar catamaran configuration.

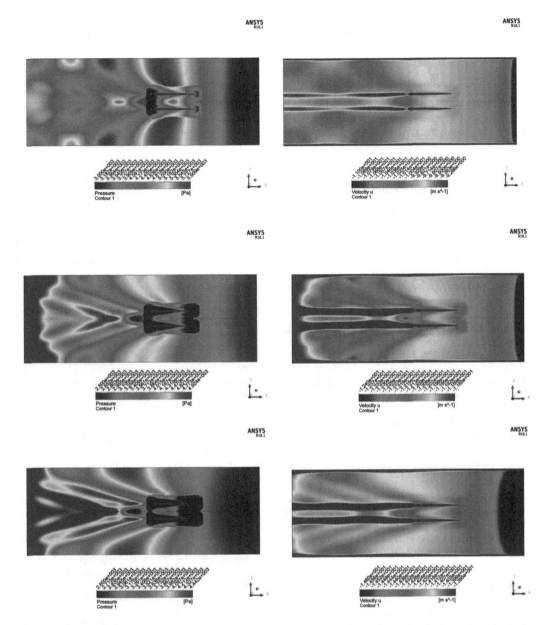

Figure 9. On the left side, the pressure contours for the velocities of 20, 24 and 28 knots respectively can be seen. On the right side, the velocity contours of 20, 24 and 28 knots respectively are shown. Both for the 30 m. length and 12 m. beam ESPOmar catamaran configuration.

Table 3. Validation of Total Resistance (R_T) based on Fluent simulations and Slender Body for ESPOmar catamaran configuration (L=30m, B=9m).

V (knots)	$C_{T(Fluent)}$	$C_{T(SB)}$	$R_{T(Fluent)}$ (kN)	$R_{T(SB)}$ (kN)	Error (%)
20	4.13E-03	4.35E-03	39.74	41.87	5.14
24	3.54E-03	3.69E-03	49.07	51.05	3.99
28	3.02E-03	3.32E-03	56.92	62.57	9.03

Table 4. Validation of Total Resistance (R_T) based on Fluent simulations and Slender Body for ESPOmar catamaran configuration (L=30m, B=12m).

V (knots)	$C_{T(Fluent)}$	$C_{T(SB)}$	$R_{T(Fluent)}$ (kN)	$R_{T(SB)}$ (kN)	Error (%)
20	3.30E-03	3.49E-03	33.89	35.84	5.44
24	3.10E-03	3.26E-03	45.84	48.17	4.82
28	2.81E-03	3.09E-03	56.56	62.10	8.91

configuration is the larger deck area of 377.3 m^2 compared to the other configuration which has an approximate value 279.5 m^2.

Obtained results will be a preamble for conducting more extensive studies on the current design of the selected configuration. The study will cover more important aspects related to the operation of the catamaran like; seaworthiness, manoeuvrability and structural strength.

ACKNOWLEDGEMENTS

This research was supported by the ESPOmar project. This project belongs to program POCTEP 2014-2020, from European Regional Development Fund (ERDF) of the European Union (EU) for co-financing under the Interreg Projects (2014-2020) program.

REFERENCES

ANSYS Fluent. 2017. Tutorial guide. ANSYS, Inc.
Aubault A, Yeung RW. 2012. Interference resistance of multihull vessels in finite depth waters. OMAE 2012, Rio de Janeiro. ASME
Broglia R, Zaghi S, Di Mascio A. 2011. Numerical simulation of interference effects for high-speed catamaran. Journal of Marine Science and Technology, 16(3): 254–269.
Chen XN, Sharma SD, Stuntz, N. 2003a. Zero wave resistance for ships moving in shallow channels at supercritical speeds. Part 2. Journal of fluid mechanics, 478: 111–124.
Chen XN, Sharma SD, Stuntz, N. 2003b. Wave reduction by S-catamaran at supercritical speeds. Journal of ship research, 47(2): 145–154.
Chen XN, Sharma SD. 1997. Zero wave resistance for ships moving in shallow channels at supercritical speeds. Journal of fluid mechanics, 335: 305–312.
Couser P. 1996. An investigation into the performance of high-speed catamarans in calm water and waves. PhD thesis. Department of Ship Science. University of Southampton.
Davis MR, Watson NL, Holloway DS. 2005. Measurement of response amplitude operators for an 86 m high-speed catamaran. Journal of ship research, 49(2): 121–143.
Doctors LJ. 2006. A numerical study of the resistance of transom-stern monohulls. Proceedings 5th International Conference on High performance marine vehicles, Australia.
Froude W. 1868. Observations and suggestions of determining by experiments the resistance of ships. Correspondence with Admiralty. Reprinted in "The papers of William Froude", INA, 1955.
Froude W. 1874. Experiments for the determination of the frictional resistance of water on a surface under various conditions. Report to admiralty and British association for the advancement of Science. Reprinted in "The papers of William Froude", INA, 1955.
Havelock TH. 1908. The propagation of groups of waves in dispersive media, with application to water waves produced by a travelling disturbance. Proceedings of Royal Society London. 81(A): 398–430.
He W, Castiglione T, Kandasamy M, Stern F. 2015. Numerical analysis of the interference effects on resistance, sinkage and trim of a fast catamaran. Journal of Marine Science and Technology, 20(2): 292–308.
Hughes G. 1954. Friction and form resistance in turbulent flow, and a proposed formulation for use in model and ship correlation. Transactions of RINA, 96.
Hughes G. 1966. An analysis of ship model resistance int viscous and wave components. Transactions of RINA, 108.
Insel M, Doctors LJ. 1995. Wave pattern prediction on monohulls and catamarans in shallow water canal by Linearised Theory. 12th AFMC, 259–262.
Insel M, Molland AF, Wellicome JF.1994. Wave resistance prediction of a catamaran by linearised theory. CAMO'94: the built environment, 5: 59–67.
Insel M, Molland AF. 1991. An investigation into the resistance components of high speed displacement catamarans. RINA, 134: 1–20.
Insel M. 1990. An investigation into the resistance components of high speed displacement catamarans. PhD. University of Southampton. United Kingdom.
ITTC. 1957. Proceedings of 8th International Towing Tank, Madrid, Spain.
ITTC. 1978. Proceedings of 15th International Towing Tank, Hague, Netherlands.
ITTC. 2011. Proceedings of 26th International Towing Tank, Rio de Janeiro, Brazil.
Jiankang W, Lee TS, Shu, C. 2001. Numerical study of wave interaction generated by two ships moving parallely in shallow water. Computer methods in applied mechanics and engineering, 190(15): 2099–2110.
Jones N. 1975. On the shakedown limit of a ship's hull girder. Journal of Ship Research. 19(2): 118–121.
Joukovski N. 1903. On the wave of translation. Complete Works 4.
Kundu PJ, Cohen IM, Dowling DR. 2012. Fluid Mechanics. Academic Press: Elsevier.
Lee SH, Lee YG, Kim SH. 2007. On the development of a small catamaran boat. Ocean Engineering, 34: 2061–2073.
Legaz MJ, Querol A, Flethes B. 2019. Ship design challenges for ESPOMAR project: A review of available

methods. Advances in marine navigation and safety of sea transportation. CRC Press: Taylor and Francis.

Liu Y, Yue DK. 1996. On time dependence of the wave resistance of a body accelerating from rest. Journal of Fluid Mecahnics,310: 337–364.

Lunde JK. 1951. On the linearized theory of wave resistance for displacement ships in steady and accelerated motion. Society of Naval Architects and Marine Engineers.

Macfarlane GJ. 2009. Correlation of prototype and model-scale wave wake characteristics of a catamaran. Marine Technology, 46(1): 1–15.

Maxsurf Resistance. 2018. User manual. Bentley Systems.

Michel JH. 1898. The wave-resistance of a ship. The London, Edinburgh, and Dublin Philosophical Magazine and Journal of Science,45(272): 106–123.

Migali A, Miranda S, Pensa C. 2001. Experimental study on the efficiency of trimaran configuration for high-speed very large ships. FAST, RINA. 4–6.

Miller R, Gorski J, Xing T, Carrica P, Stern F. 2006. Resistance predictions of high speed mono and multihull ships with and without water jet propulsors using URANS. 26th symposium on naval hydrodynamics.

Molland AF, Wellicome JF, Couser PR. 1996. Resistance experiments on a systematic series of high speed displacement catamaran forms: variation of length-displacement ratio and breadth-draught. RINA, 138: 55–71.

Molland AF, Wilson PA, Taunton DJ, Chandrapabha S, Ghani, PA. 2004. Resistance and wash wave measurements on a series of high speed displacement monohull and catamaran forms in shallow water. RINA, 146(A2): 19–38.

Moraes HB, Vasconcellos JM, Latorre RG. 2004. Wave resistance for high speed catamarans. *Ocean Engineering*, 31: 2253–2282.

Pérez Arribas FL. 2000. Estudio hidrodinámico de un catamaran tipo SWATH. Tesis doctoral, Universidad Politécnica de Madrid, España.

Prandtl L. 1904. Über Flüssigkeitsbewegung bei sehr Kleiner Reibung. Verh III. Intern. Math. Kongr., Heidelberg, 484-491.

Prohaska CW. 1966. An analysis of ship model resistance into viscous and wave components. Transactions of RINA, Londres.

Sahoo PK, Browne NA, Salas M. 2004. Experimental and CFD study of wave resistance of high-speed round bilge catamaran hull forms. Proceedings of 4 th International Conference on High Performance Marine Vehicle, Rome, Italy.

Sarles C, Gelles B, Malarkey A. 2011. An investigation into the effect of section shape on the interference resistance of catamarans. In proceedings 11th International Conference on Fast Sea Transportation, 335–362.

Schlichting H, Gersten K, Gersten K. 2000. Boundary-layer theory. Springer Science & Business Media.

Schoenherr KE. 1932. Resistance of flat surfaces moving through a fluid. SNAME transactions. 40: 279–313.

SNAME.1941. Principles of naval architecture, Vol II: Resistance. Society of naval architects and marine engineers. Henry Eastin Rossell, L.B. Chapman.

Tarafder S, Suzuki K. 2007. Computation of a wave-making resistance of a catamaran in deep water using a potential-based panel method. Ocean Engineering, 34: 1892–1900.

Tarafder S, Suzuki K. 2008a. Wave-making resistance of a catamaran hull in shallow water using a potential-based panel method. Journal of ship research, 52(1): 16–29.

Tuck E. 1966. Shallow-water flows past slender bodies. Journal of Fluid Mechanic. 26: 81–95.

Tuck EO, Lazaukas L. 1998. Optimum hull spacing of a family of multihulls. Ship Technology Research-Schiffstechnik, 45(4).

Tuck EO, Scullen DC, Lazauskas L. 2002. Wave patterns and minimum wave resistance for high-speed vessels. Proceedings 24th Symposium on Naval Hydrodynamics, Fukuoka, Japan.

Tuck EO. 2005. Can lateral asymmetry of the hulls reduce catamaran wave resistance?. Proceedings 20th International workshop on water waves and floating bodies, Spitzbergen, Norway.

Tuck EO. 1987. Wave resistance of thin ships and catamaran. International report T8701.Adelaide: Applied Mathematics Department of the University of Adelaide, Adelaide.

Tuner H, Taplin A. 1968. The resistance of large powered catamarans. SNAME, 76: 180–213.

Yeung RW, Poupard G, Toilliez JO. 2004. Interference-resistance prediction and its applications to optimal multi-hull configuration design. Transactions of the society of naval architects and marine engineers. SNAME, 112: 142–168.

Yeung RW, Wan H. 2008. Multihull and surface-effect ship configuration design: a framework for powering minimization. Journal Offshore Mechanic an Artic Engineering, 130(3).

Yeung RW. 2005. Interference resistance of multi-hulls per thin-ship theory. In 20th international workshop on water waves and floating bodies, Longyearbyen, Spitsbergen.

Yeung RW.1978. On the interactions of slender ships in shallow water. Journal of Marine Science and Technology, 11(1): 39–51.

Zaghi S, Broglia R, Di Mascio A. 2011. Analysis of the interference effects for high-speed catamarans by model tests and numerical simulations. *Ocean Engineering*, 38 (17): 2110–2122.

Dowling NE. 2007. Mechanical Behavior of Materials. New Jersey, USA: Pearson International Edition. pp. 612–705.

Hughes OF, Paik JK. 2013. Ship structural analysis and design. Alexandria, USA: The Society of Naval Architects and Marine Engineers.

Hodge PG. 1959. Plastic analysis of structures. New York: McGraw-Hill Series in Engineering Sciences. 1–139.

ISO. 2007. Ships and marine technology – Ship structures, Part 1: General requirements for their limit state assessment. *International standard ISO 18072-1*, Geneva: International Organization for Standardization.

Jones N. 1975. On the shakedown limit of a ship's hull girder. *Journal of Ship Research*. 19(2): 118–121.

Jones N. 1976. Plastic Behavior of Ship Structures. *Transactions, Society of Naval Architects and Marine Engineers*. 84: 115–145.

Jones N. 1973. Slamming Damage. *Journal of Ship Research*. 17(2): 80–86.

Paik JK. 2016. Test database of mechanical properties on carbon steels, aluminum alloy and stainless steel associated with cold temperatures and strain rates. Proceedings of International Conference on Ships and Offshore Structures, 31 August – 2 September, Hamburg, Germany.

An experimental investigation on the resistance and added resistance of two series 60 models with block coefficient 0.6 and 0.7 respectively

D.E. Liarokapis, G.P. Trachanas & G.D. Tzabiras
National Technical University of Athens, LSMH, Athens, Greece

ABSTRACT: In the present work the resistance and the dynamic behavior of two series 60 models with block coefficient of 0.6 and 0.7, has been extensively tested in the towing tank of the Laboratory for Ship and Marine Hydrodynamics (LSMH) of the National Technical University of Athens (NTUA). The resistance tests concerned two loading conditions for a range of speed from 0.492 m/s to 1.912 m/s which corresponded to Froude Number of 0.089 to 0.356. Regular wave testing were conducted for two speeds (1.367 m/s and 1.804 m/s which corresponds to Fr of 0.25 and 0.33) and for nine frequencies with different altitude covering extreme realistic conditions. Results, referring to the resistance, the CG rise, the dynamic trim, the added resistance and the RAO coefficients are presented in detailed. Useful conclusions are drawn following the discussion of the experimental results.

1 INTRODUCTION

Nowadays, ship owners tend to use cargo ships with higher block coefficient in order to maximize the cargo capacity. However, ships with higher block coefficient, present higher resistance at the same cruising speed, thus increasing fuel cost. In addition, fuel saving is related to environmental benefits since it is related to the reduction and quality of the exhaust gases. Consequently, the ship owners must decide when these kinds of ships are cost effective for a certain route. Moreover, according to the latest changes of the relevant IMO resolution (IMO regulations), particular criteria on the Energy Efficiency Design Index (E.E.D.I.) of ships, must be fulfilled.

The calculation of the added resistance of ships in wave can be investigated by two methods: By conducting experiments on ship models or by using analytical codes (Bing-jie & Sverre 2011). To experimentally investigate this phenomenon, the models are towed with steady speed facing random or sine heading waves. Experiments in random waves provide fairly accurate results for a certain sea state. On the other hand by conducting experiments on sine waves provides accurate results that with the proper analysis, an estimation of the added resistance of the ship in waves is feasible.

In this work, we recent an experimental study on the effect of the block coefficient on the calm water and sine wave resistance and the dynamic behavior of the classical series 60 ship model. Two loading conditions were used to obtain the resistance curve and one loading condition at two speeds for the dynamic behavior.

To experimentally estimate the added resistance, the model was towed through the towing tank with a constant speed both in calm water and in sine waves (Arribas 2007).

Nine frequencies were tested (0.3 to 1.1 Hz) covering the frequency range that a ship can actually encounter. The tests concerned one loading conditions (T = 0.163 m) and two cruising speeds of 1.367 m/s and 1.804 m/s. The difference between the mean resistance in rough water and the calm water resistance is defined as added resistance (Figure 1). From the above we note that $R_{aw} = R_w - R_{sw}$. RAO coefficients for heave, pitch and resistance were calculated.

2 EXPERIMENTAL SETUP

All the experiments were carried out in the Towing Tank of the Laboratory for Ship and Marine Hydrodynamics of the National Technical University of Athens, which has a length of 91 m, a width of 4.55 m and a water depth of 3.00 m (Figure 2). The towing tank is equipped with a running carriage that can achieve a maximum speed of 5.5 m/s or 10.5 knots.

The tank is also equipped with a wave generating paddle (wave maker), located at one end of the flume. It is a single direction wave maker, capable of producing random and sine head waves with frequency between 0.3 and 1.2 Hz, and maximum amplitude of 35 cm (Figure 3). At the opposite end there is a properly shaped inclined shore, for the absorption of the waves.

The model was attached to the resistance dynamometer on the towing carriage via a trim pivot configuration located longitudinally at the corresponding LCG and transversely at the center line (Figure 4).

DOI: 10.1201/9781003216599-43

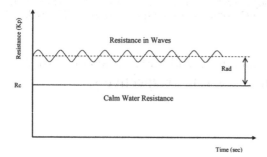

Figure 1. Added Resistance in Waves versus Time.

Figure 2. The towing tank of NTUA.

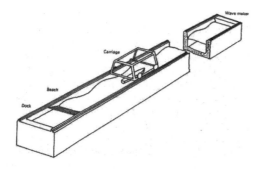

Figure 3. Wave maker representation.

This type of attachment allows the vertical motion of the model (heave) and the rotation around the lateral axis of the attaching point (pitch), while the rest degrees of freedom are restrained. At the axle of the pivot, a pitch sensor was attached allowing the measurement of the dynamic trim. Moreover, the cg rise of the center of gravity was measured.

Figure 4. NTUA classic dynamometer.

3 TEST CONDITIONS

All the tests were performed in fresh water and covered a speed range corresponding to full scale speeds. A time of 12 min for the calm water testing and 25 minutes for the dynamic behavior was kept between every experiment. Throughout the test series, the water temperature was measured and recorded. During the tests, the model's resistance, the rise of the center of gravity (c.g.) at the point of attachment to the dynamometer, the dynamic trim and the towing speed of the model were recorded.

In this study, trim is defined as the signed rotation about the transverse axis passing through the c.g. and is considered positive when the bow of the model sinks.

The models hull was made of wood to ensure precise representation of the hull form. The models were measured without the rudder, hub and propeller fitted. The length of the models is about 3m. A turbulence stimulator was fitted to the model, to compensate for the violation of Reynolds similarity and enforce laminar-turbulent transition in the model roughly at the same location as in full scale.

Turbulence stimulator dimensions were chosen accordantly to the ITTC standards. Extra weights were distributed in the model to achieve the desired displacement at an even keel condition and in a manner that the inertia radius is equal to the ¼ of the Lwl.

By using the software Rhinoceros5 to produce the hull form, the hydrostatic parameters (draft, LCG) were calculated. Its main particulars at full scale, along with the form of the hull can be seen in Table 1 and in Figure 5. It can be noticed that by keeping the same

Table 1. Main particulars of the series 60 model.

Condition		Heavy Ballast		Full Load	
C_B		0.6	0.7	0.6	0.7
L_{WL}	m	2.941m	2.992m	3.048m	3.099m
B_{WL}	m	0.406m	0.469m	0.406m	0.469m
T_M	m	0.127m	0.127m	0.163m	0.163m
Δ	t	89.55kg	123.3kg	120kg	163.3kg
LCB,	m	1.431m	1.567m	1.447m	1.581m
LCF	m	1.466m	1.602m	1.512m	1.650m
Trim	Deg	Even keel		Even keel	
WS	m2	1.221m^2	1.620m^2	1.579m^2	1.869m^2

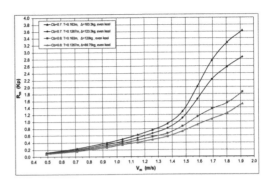

Figure 6. Resistance against speed for both models at two loading conditions.

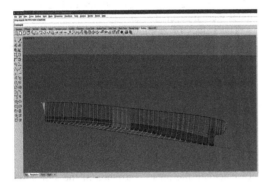

Figure 5. Sections of series 60 model, $C_b = 0.7$.

draft, the cargo weight increases at about 27% for both drafts.

4 ANALYSIS AND PRESENTATION OF THE RESULTS

Graphical representation of the resistance curves as well as the Heave and Pitch spectrum for both loading conditions are presented in the paragraph 2.1. In the paragraph 2.2 the added resistance in sine head waves for two speeds is presented. Finally, the last paragraph consists of the RAO responses.

4.1 Calm water testing

To evaluate the models resistance for the calm water testing, the models were measured for a range of speeds from 0,492 m/s to 1.914 m/s, which correspond to Fr of 0.089 to 0.356 (Figure 6). Two drafts were measured, the full load and heavy ballast conditions. In the following graph the resistance is plotted against the velocity for the two models concerning the two loadings. All tests conducted at even keel condition. Evidently the resistance obtained for the higher block coefficient (C_b 0.7) is significantly bigger than the C_b of 0.6, especially at higher Reynolds number. Small differences are observed at the intermediate speeds.

Moreover, the percentage change of the total resistance for the two loading conditions against the velocity is presented at the above figure (Figure 7). At the higher speeds of 1,568 m/s to 1,914 m/s we notice an increase of about 50% for both loading condition. Both loading conditions present the same percentage increase except from the speed of 1.039m/s.

Additionally, to validate the data, older experiment values concerning the model with the smaller block coefficient (C_b of 0.6) and the draft of 0.163m were added to the measure data (Figure 8). The older experiments (blue dots) are in great accordance with the new results (Garofallidis, 1996).

At Figure 9 the dynamic pitch versus speed is presented. In all cases, the maximum deviations of the dynamic pitch in all speeds are about 0.15 degrees which can be assumed as negligible; hence it doesn't affect the total resistance. At the figure below, the CG rise versus speed is presented (Figure 10).

In all cases we notice a drought of about 1.5 cm. The above behavior was expected as it is typical for such type of vessels. Heavier loading doesn't seem to affect the model with the smaller block coefficient while we notice a small change for the model with the C_B of 0.7 at higher speeds.

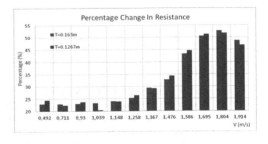

Figure 7. Percentage changes of the resistance for the two loading conditions versus the velocity.

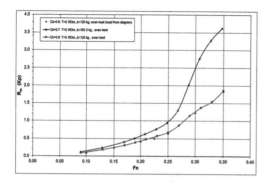

Figure 8. Resistance against speed for both models at two loading conditions.

Table 2. Amplitude and frequencies of the head sine waves encountered.

Frequency (Hz)	Amplitude (cm)
0.3	5
0.4	5
0.5	5
0.6	4
0.7	4
0.8	4
0.9	3
1.0	3
1.1	2

Moreover, nine frequencies with the different amplitudes were measured (Table 2).

The values of amplitude were selected the maximum allowable, without getting deck watering. However, at the frequency of 0.6Hz, at the speed of 1.367 m/s, the bow of the model with block coefficient of 0.6 dived underwater. Thus, a superstructure was added to the model and the tests were repeated. Moreover, similar problems were faced at the frequency of 0.7 Hz for the higher speed (1.804 m/s).

4.3 Added resistance in waves

To calculate the mean resistance of the ship model over a sine wave, the encounter frequency was calculated via the Doppler Effect. Then the wave resistance is the mean value of the measured resistance over a sine period.

It can be notice from the Figures 11 and 12 (green marks), the huge effect of deck watering to the added resistance.

At the smaller speed of 1.367 m/s, the higher block coefficient doesn't affect significantly the resistance component (Figure 11 and 13). On the other hand, at the higher speed of 1.804 m/s there is a huge increase on the resistance (Figure 12 and 14), especially in the frequency region of 0.4 Hz to 0.8. At the smaller and higher frequencies there is not a significant change in the resistance compared to the calm

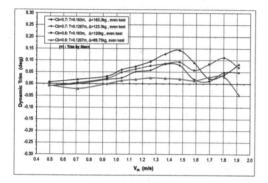

Figure 9. Dynamic Trim versus speed.

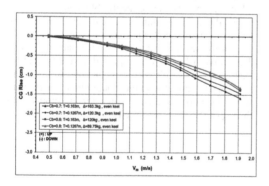

Figure 10. CG rise versus speed.

4.2 Sine head waves

The two models were tested at two indicative speeds of 1.367m/s (Fr=0.25) and 1.904 m/s (Fr=0.32) encountering head sine waves. The scope of the tests was to investigate the dynamic behavior of the two models at rough conditions (Walter, 1999). Thus, the heavier loading condition was selected (T=0.163 m).

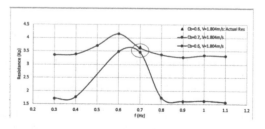

Figure 11. Total resistance against speed, V = 1.367 m/s.

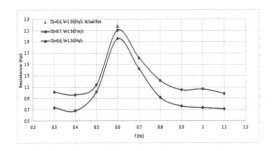

Figure 12. Total resistance against speed, V = 1.804 m/s.

water. Added resistance can be calculated by analytical prediction but compared to motion predictions give weaker predictions (Grigoropoulos 1999).

In addition, the added resistance for the two speeds is presented at the following graphs (Figure 13 and 14).

4.4 *Response amplitude operator*

Response amplitude refers to the degree of movement induced in a floating vessel due to a passing hydrodynamic wave. It is used experimentally to indicate the dynamic behavior of ship vessels. By measuring the response of a model in regular waves, a set of response amplitude operators can be used to predict the performance in actual sea conditions (Liarokapis 2015). Moreover, in a previous work the authors proposed a new method to predict the added resistance in random waves by measuring the resistance in sine waves, based on the work of Shukui (Shukui, et. al. 2011). The RAO for the heave and pitch of the models at the speed of 1.367 m/s are illustrated at Figures 15 and 16.

As it was noticed from the added resistance, for the small speed there are not significant differences between the two block coefficients. The behavior for the heave motion is almost identical, while for the pitch motion small differences appear at the frequencies of 0.5 Hz to 0.8 Hz. Impressively, probably due to the higher displacement the pitch motion of the C_B 0.7 is smaller except from the frequency of 0.6 Hz where resonance occur.

Again, for the higher speed there are significant differences in the pitch variations especially at the middle frequencies (0.5 Hz to 0.8 Hz). Greater heave and pitch motion dissipates more energy that partly explains the higher added resistance needed. The RAO for the heave and pitch of the models at the speed of 1.804 m/s are illustrated at Figures 17 and 18.

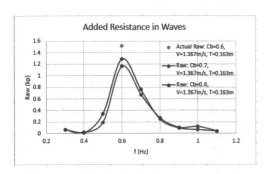

Figure 13. Added resistance against freq., V = 1.367 m/s.

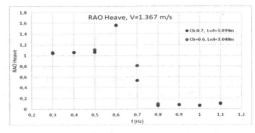

Figure 15. RAO Heave against frequency, V = 1.367 m/s.

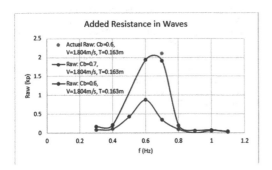

Figure 14. Added resistance against freq., V = 1.804 m/s.

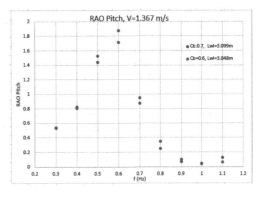

Figure 16. RAO Pitch against frequency, V = 1.367 m/s.

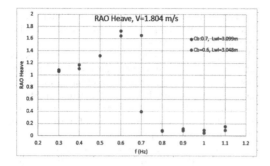

Figure 17. RAO Heave against frequency, V = 1.804 m/s.

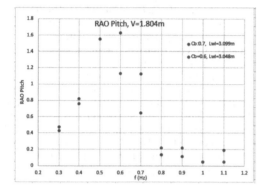

Figure 18. RAO Pitch against frequency, V = 1.804 m/s.

5 CONCLUSIONS

The scope of this work was to experimentally investigate the effect of the block coefficient on the resistance of a series 60 ship model in waves and on calm water. For the calm water resistance, the model with the higher block coefficient presented increased resistance as it was expected. For the lower Fr from 0.089 to 0.210, the percentage of the resistance difference was up to 25%, while for the higher Fr (0.210 to 0.330) the percentage difference was about 50%. Similar results obtained for the two drafts tested. In both case, the cargo weight increased by about 27%.

The added resistance in waves was evaluated by conducting experiments in nine sine waves at two characteristic speeds with Fr of 0.25 and 0.33. For the relative small speed (Fr = 0.25) there was no significant change for the added resistance in wave in all frequencies. For the higher speed, higher alternations were noticeable at the middle frequencies, between 0.4 and 0.8 Hz. Similar results were obtained for the response amplitude coefficients. Especially for the higher speed, the pitch motion seems to be the one to be affected mostly, increasing the resistance. The results led to the conclusion that by reducing the ships speed, the two models with different block coefficient present the same behavior.

It must be noted, that in case of a power prediction, self-propulsion tests are needed to establish the self-propulsion parameters (the thrust deduction fraction (t), the wake fraction (w) and the relative rotative efficiency (n_R)). The propellers efficiency is greatly affected by the shape of the stern of the ship.

Moreover, more sophisticated methods must be included to the experimental methods to increase the accuracy of the experiments. Even better, improved evaluation methods for free-sailing model tests can take the small unwanted model accelerations into account that almost always occur during "real life" testing (Kjellberg, 2019).

In general, by knowing the ships route, the fuel prices and the cargo value, the ship companies can use experimental data of their vessels to optimize their profit.

ACKNOWLEDGEMENTS

It must be mentioned that this work was part of the undergraduate thesis of the second author. Acknowledgements must also be given to the laboratory faculty who did their best to get this work completed.

REFERENCES

Arribas, P. 2007. Some methods to obtain the added resistance of a ship advancing in waves. Ocean Engineering 34: 946–955.

Bing-jie, G. & Sverre, S. 2011. Evaluation of added resistance of KVLCC2 in short waves. Journal of Hydrodynamics, 23(6): 709–722.

Garofallidis, D., 1996, "Experimental and Numerical Investigation of the flow around a Ship model at various Froude Numbers. Ph.D Thesis.

Grigoropoulos, G., Loukakis, T. & Perakis, A., 1999, Seakeeping standard series for oblique seas, Ocean Engineering 27(2): 111–126.

Kjellberg, M., Frederik G, 2019, Improved methods for the experimental Determination of Added Resistance in Waves, AMT19, Rome, Italy.

Liarokapis, D., Tsami, I., Trahanas J. & Tzabiras, G. 2015, An experimental study on the added resistance of a bulk carrier model. Towards Green Marine Technology and Transport, pp.121–126.

Shukui, L., S. Papanikolaou A. & Zaraphonitis G. 2011, Prediction of added resistance in waves, Ocean Engineering, Ocean Engineering 38: 641–650

Walter M. 1999. Sea spectra revisited, Marine Technology, 36(4): 211–227.

A review of FUNWAVE model applications in the propagation of waves generated by vessels

G.O. Mattosinho
IFMG – Federal Institute of Minas Gerais, Piumhi, Minas Gerais, Brazil

G.F. Maciel & F.O. Ferreira
Unesp - São Paulo State University, Ilha Solteira, São Paulo, Brazil

J.A. Santos
ISEL – Instituto Superior de Engenharia de Lisboa, Instituto Politécnico de Lisboa and CENTEC – Centre for Marine Technology and Ocean Engineering, Lisboa, Portugal

C.J.E.M. Fortes
LNEC - National Laboratory of Civil Engineering, Lisboa, Portugal

ABSTRACT: This work revisits and updates the literature on ship-wave actions and its hydrodynamic description based on the Boussinesq Equations and more specifically the FUNWAVE model (Fully Nonlinear Model) to study the propagation of those waves in coastal and port regions. For that, classic and current works of literature that complement and advance knowledge in this field are reviewed. Among those stand out the contributions of Nascimento (2007) and Rodrigues (2018). This communication focuses on the classification of wake waves, on the general formulation of the problem and on wake waves effects on the banks of channels or reservoirs. Furthermore, some results on FUNWAVE model validation for wake waves produced by a vessel moving through shallow water are discussed. Finally, the advances, limitations and possibilities of application of the model are explained, as well as the need for its validation with the largest possible number of data, namely from field measurements.

1 STUDIES ON WAVES AND ENVIRONMENT PROTECTION

The protection of riverbanks, waterways and coastal areas is a topic of great interest to companies and governments worldwide, given the economic impacts that silting up, for example, can cause. In this regard, Coops et al. (1996) stated that the development of emergent vegetation, wave extinction and soil erosion are strongly interrelated processes in exposed riverside areas.

These authors observed in a three-year field study that emerging vegetation influenced the erosive impact of the waves, which had been confirmed by the sediment transport. Furthermore, this phenomenon reflected the observed standing wave patterns. At that time, the measured data showed less erosion in areas protected by vegetation when compared to those without protection, and that the greatest wave attenuation occurred in the vegetated field.

In the Brazilian context, it is observed that waterway transport and reservoir navigation has generated environmental concern regarding bank preservation.

Nascimento et al. (2010) stated that environmental agencies seek to limit the speed of navigation, as a way to limit the impact of ship wake waves. For waterways, it is observed that the passage of vessels through narrow stretches does intensify the ship wake waves erosive action.

Ship wake waves and their impacts on the banks and bottom of shallow water bodies have been studied for years. However, such work has focused mainly on specific and current studies. Nascimento et al. (2010) make an extensive bibliographic review on the theme:

"… reported by Blume (2002) cases that occurred on the Parramatta River, Australia; Marlborough Sound, New Zealand; San Francisco Bay and James River, United States. Verheij & Knaap (1995) carried out studies on erosion caused by vessel waves in Sarawak, Malaysia. Currently, the Quebec Department of Transportation (2003) has studied the erosion problem on the Saint Lawrence River, Canada, where 86% of the erosion has been attributed to the action of vessel waves. Studies by Brebner

DOI: 10.1201/9781003216599-44

et al. (1966) also on the Saint Lawrence River revealed that, at that time, the percentage of erosion caused by the action of vessel waves was only 1 to 2%. The comparison between these percentages reveals that the increase in vessel traffic aggravates the current erosion problem of the river." (Nascimento et al., p. 5, 2010).

Other relevant information can be found in Oliveira et al. (2001), who studied the waterway stretch of the Paraguay River and highlighted the effects of waves generated by speedboats and pushers (when sailing alone), the effects of the former being due to the high frequency and the latter by the associated high waves that attacked the unprotected banks with no plant coverage. They conclude that the effect of ship wake waves in that region should be the subject of further studies. However, more recent studies on the Paraguay-Paraná waterway did not evaluate the generation, propagation and incidence of wind or ship waves.

Still in the Brazilian context, there is the recent work of Trombetta et al. (2019) which studied wind-wave action along the Santa Catarina coast and analyzed and characterized the most energetic zone using the Tomawac numerical model. To protect the study zone, the authors propose the use of a ramp to mitigate wave action in the Cabo de Santa Marta region in Santa Catarina state, as it is the most energetic area. The simulation showed that it was possible to reduce 98% of the wave height that approaches the coast and approximately 90% of the energy potential. They conclude that this solution is feasible for solving the problem of coastal erosion in the study area.

Despite this communication focusing on the FUNWAVE model, the model used by Trombetta et al. (2019), is briefly presented here to highlight some of its differences to the first one. Tomawac is a scientific software to model changes in the time and space domains of the sea-waves energy spectrum for applications in oceanic and coastal areas (Awk, 2017).

This is a so-called third generation spectral model and calculates sea-state characteristics by solving the Wave Action Density Conservation Equation in the discretized domain, both in Cartesian coordinates (x, y) and in spherical coordinates (λ, φ) that is, longitude and latitude, through the Finite Element Method (Trombetta et al., 2019). It differs from FUNWAVE because, among other aspects, it does not consider wave diffraction and reflection.

In this aspect, there is still the work of Kurdistani et al. (2019) who proposed a new equation for the design of bank protection against the combined action of ship wake waves and river flows. Among the results, it must be pointed out:

"Results show that not only the maximum wave height and river bank slope but also the water depth, flow velocity, wave length, wave obliquity, and wave period are important parameters for predicting the mean diameter of the armor units, highlighting the multivariate behavior of protecting the river bank in the presence of ship-induced waves and river flow velocity." (Kurdistani et al., p. 129, 2019).

The authors validated the proposed equation and the dimensionless variables used aim to make applications easier. Given the correct prediction of the average particle diameter, which depends on the maximum wave height and bank characteristics as well as on the river depth, wave length and period and direction of travel of the vessel, it is possible to predict the average diameter of the armor layer unit in a wide variety of river conditions and waves induced by wind or boats.

2 CLASSIFICATION OF SHIP WAKE WAVES

Nascimento et al. (2010) make a succinct and precise classification about vessel waves, that is transcribed almost entirely in the course of this topic. It is worth mentioning that a similar description is found in Rodrigues (2018).

Ship-wake waves are classified, according to the relative depth (h/λ), in deep water waves (h/λ ≥ 0.5) or shallow water (h/λ <0.04), where h is the depth of the water column where the vessel moves and λ is the wave length.

2.1 Deep water

In deep water, as Stoker (1957) reports, ship-wake waves have a very peculiar behavior: the generated disturbance follows the object in motion without changing its shape, confined in a region behind it, in such a way that it always presents a V-shape, regardless of the object being a duck swimming in a pond or a large aircraft carrier.

The first explanation and theoretical treatment of this phenomenon was given by Thompson (1887a, 1887b). This author was knighted in 1866 becoming Lord Kelvin, and, for this reason, it is also known as Kelvin Theory of Ship Waves or Kelvin Waves. This researcher concluded that, in deep waters, a ship (or any object) that moves with constant velocity always generates waves confined in a V-shaped region, with an approximate 19.5° semi-angle in relation to the imaginary axis of the vessel course and propagate at an angle of approximately 35° also in relation to that axis. In this region, two distinct sets of waves appear, one emanating from the ship bow, called the divergent system, and the other positioned approximately at right angles to the course of the boat, called the transverse system, Figure 1.

A very important parameter to characterize deep-water waves is the Froude number referred to the ship length (F_L). Originally proposed by William Froude (1810-1879), during his research to establish similarity laws for scale-model studies of wave resistance to ship motion, such a number is based on the ratio of the speed to the square root of the length of an object moving in a body of water. The Froude number of the length is given by:

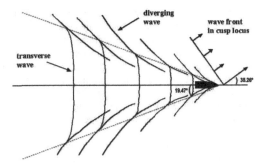

Figure 1. Typical Kelvin wave pattern. (Rodrigues, 2018).

$$F_L = \frac{V}{\sqrt{gL}} \quad (1)$$

where L = ship's length; V = ship's speed; and g = acceleration of gravity.

Depending on this number, the behaviour of transverse and divergent waves is analysed. The velocity of the transverse waves (C_T) is equal to the speed of the ship.

The velocity of the divergent waves (C_D) is also given as a function of the propagation angle. Then, according to Sorensen (1967):

$$C_T = V \quad (2)$$

$$C_D = V \times \cos\theta \quad (3)$$

$$\theta = 35,27\left(1 - e^{12(F_h - 1)}\right) \quad (4)$$

$$F_h = \frac{V}{\sqrt{gh}} \quad (5)$$

Where F_h = depth Froude number; and θ = wave propagation angle.

The velocity of the wave (C) is related to the wave length (λ) and the local depth (h) by the dispersion relation given by the Linear Theory, that is:

$$C^2 = \frac{g\lambda}{2\pi}\tanh\left(\frac{2\pi h}{\lambda}\right) \quad (6)$$

2.2 Shallow water

In shallow water, Havelock (1908) applying an approximation like the Kelvin one deduced equations to define the pattern of divergent and transverse waves for subcritical and supercritical velocities as a function of Froude's depth number, F_h, that is, F_h <1 and F_h> 1. In shallow water, these waves undergo considerable changes in relation to deep water waves. The results of Havelock (1908) showed that, in shallow water, three different wave patterns can appear depending on the F_h value. If the relationship F_h <1 is satisfied (subcritical velocity), the general wave pattern is the same of deep water, and for 0 <F_h <0.7, the envelope angle τ, which is the limit of the V-shape where the divergent and transversal waves are confined, has the same value 19.5° as in deep water. In the range $0.7 \leq F_h$<1, an increase in τ occurs that varies within the range 19.5° <τ <90°. For F_h = 1 (critical velocity), the divergent and transverse waves combine to form a simple wave (like a solitary wave according to Sorensen, 1967) with τ = 90°. For F_h>1 (supercritical velocity), the transverse waves disappear, since the wave velocity cannot exceed the critical speed of the vessel, and only the divergent system is found. In this situation, the opposite occurs, that is, for the interval 1<F_h<3, there is a decrease in τ that varies within the interval 90°<τ<19.5°; for $F_h \geq 3$, τ = 19.5° (a condition similar to the Mach number in aerodynamics). Thus, for F_h>1, the angle τ is given by:

$$\tau = \arcsen\left(\frac{\sqrt{gh}}{V}\right) = \arcsen\left(\frac{1}{F_h}\right) \quad (7)$$

3 VALIDATION OF THE FUNWAVE MODEL AND BOUSSINESQ-TYPE EQUATIONS

This paper focuses on the FUNWAVE model that is known and explored worldwide. However, it is worth emphasizing that it is a shallow-water hydrodynamic model based on fully non-linear Boussinesq equations that considers the coastal phenomena of wave-refraction, shoaling and breaking (Nascimento, 2007).

In 2007, Nascimento proposed the modification of the FUNWAVE model with the addition of a ship-wave generating source function (pressure distribution equation). The functionalities were explored, and it proved to be feasible for simulating ship-wake waves and produced the expected two-dimensional pattern. However, no experiments were performed at the time.

Nascimento et al. (2010), state that the model developed by Nascimento (2007) adequately reproduces the wave patterns observed in the literature. The model was able to simulate wave breaking, but there is still a need for calibration of the wave breaking parameters in the model as well as more experimental results for model validation.

Rodrigues (2018) conducted studies by inserting three other pressure distribution equations, which simulate the passage of the ship, and tried to validate the numerical model with scale-model experiments carried out at the National Civil Engineering Laboratory (LNEC) in Lisbon. For this purpose, a methodology based on Johnson (1957) was used. Tests were carried out with a scale model of a ship that moves at a constant speed across a region with a horizontal bottom.

The author tries to validate the model in limited-depth zones using time series of the free-surface elevation which are compared between the experiment and the numerical simulation. Among the conclusions, it is mentioned that it was possible to validate the shapes and heights of the waves predicted in numerical modelling (Rodrigues, 2018).

Another interesting study was conducted by Bruno et al. (2009). The authors begin the work by stating that the design of structures in regions close to the coast generally requires a study of the effects of local waves, which can be tested experimentally in the laboratory using appropriate scale models.

They draw attention to the simplifications and limitations of each model. They reaffirm the model's capacity and efficiency to accurately simulate all phenomena close to the coast (turbulence, waves, currents, sediment transport and so on).

Some studies aimed at overcoming shallow water restrictions and extended Boussinesq equations were derived by adding terms to varying degrees of precision to represent non-linearity and frequency dispersion (Bruno et al., 2009). To obtain the best possible linear dispersion ratio, Madsen et al. (1991), among others, added new terms to the momentum equations, while Nwogu (1993) used flow velocity at a reference depth as a dependent variable in governing equations. These extended Boussinesq equations are capable of simulating sea-wave propagation from relatively deep water up to shallow water.

Wei et al. (1995) developed a higher-order numerical model based on Nwogu (1993) equations, but did not assume small non-linear effects, thus deriving a new set of Boussinesq equations that include additional nonlinear dispersive terms. In this case, the equations can be applied to simulate the propagation of waves with strong non-linear interaction and to model the wave/current interaction (Bruno et al., 2009).

The FUNWAVE model created by Kirby et al. (1998) was later modified with the changes of Kennedy et al. (2000) to the Boussinesq-type equations of Wei et al. (1995). It must be pointed out that these equations refer to the standard equations of Peregrine (1967) or to the non-linear shallow-water equations or to the Nwogu (1993) extended equations, by defining some basic parameters.

Bruno et al. (2009) innovated at the time, in the first place, by comparing both simulated wave elevations and velocities to regular wave experiments.

The authors used the modified methodologies and base equations, described in Wei et al. (1995) and Nwogu (1993) and carried out laboratory studies to validate their modelling, but, according to the authors, they encountered difficulties due to the lack of validation of existing Boussinesq models, which is due to difficult and time-consuming laboratory experiments and measurements. The authors also claim that, sometimes, the aforementioned reasons lead researchers to compare results from different numerical models without providing a comparison between the results of the analyzed model and the measured data.

On the other hand, more recent works such as that of Rodrigues (2018), show that there is currently an easier access to scale-model experiments whose data can be used to validate various numerical models. However, experimental data for validations are still scarce and further research and experience is needed.

In short, according to Bruno et al. (2009) the FUNWAVE model, based on the extended Boussinesq equation of Nwogu (1993), was validated through laboratory data. The model showed that it was able to predict the flow velocity and free-surface elevation associated to the propagation of regular waves both in deep water and in breaking regions. The innovative element of that research was the investigation on the model's ability to accurately reproduce not only wave elevations, but also velocity parameters. In fact, according to the authors, previous research such as that by Ozanne et al. (2000) and Bosboom et al. (1997) highlighted the scarcity of such comparisons.

Advancing in chronology, the studies of David et al. (2017) bring another model proposal using the local pressure change to simulate the passage of vessels, as explored by Liu and Wu (2004), Dam et al., (2006), Bayraktar and Beji (2013), Dam et al., (2008), Soomere and Rannat (2003), Soomere (2007) and Nascimento et al. (2011).

The "Boussinesq Ocean and Surf Zone" (BOSZ) model developed by Roeber and Cheung (2012) was used in the modeling by David et al. (2017). This model was validated with the classic literature results and with field measurements in irregular bathymetry. The key point in their work was the proposal of a unified tool to simulate and evaluate the ship-wave propagation away from the generation field considering any movement in a straight path with arbitrary angles.

It is worth mentioning that the simplifications used in such modelling, namely not including wind waves and non-linear interaction of any waves (wave breaking, transformation) in close vicinity to the pole where the wave gauge device was mounted, or how complexities in measurements were addressed are also interesting points to be pursued. Furthermore, the work of David et al. (2017) brings several comparisons and validations that prove the applicability of the model. Finally, they suggest using the model for studies related to erosion and eco-hydraulics.

3.1 Applications of FUNWAVE model

Mil-Homens et al (2010) highlight the importance of validating the model when complex bathymetry is involved, since wave breaking, and non-linear interactions may then occur, and they are simulated by FUNWAVE using approximations. The comparison with laboratory data allows to test the FUNWAVE performance in these cases.

The FUNWAVE model is widespread due to low cost of modelling in relation to field verification and more recently one can observe works of greater interest such as those by Rodrigues (2018) and David et al. (2017).

Regarding the work of Nascimento et al. (2010), it can be mentioned that the authors proposed a coastal hydrodynamic Boussinesq-type model (FUNWAVE) for ship-wake wave generation and propagation in shallow water. They emphasize that the application of the model, provided it is properly validated, may help in the analysis of erosive processes resulting from ship-wake waves on the margins of navigation channels, waterways and lakes. Among its main results, it can be mentioned that the model had good agreement with the literature of the time, but still needed physical experiments to confront the simulations, a task performed, in part, by Rodrigues (2018).

As mentioned, another study focused on hydrodynamics to assist in port and waterway infrastructure projects was conducted by David et al. (2017). Among the main work points, it can be highlighted the wide range of applicability of the model, which deals with the evolution of the ship's wedge compared to an analytical solution for subcritical and supercritical velocities and the evaluation of wave patterns over a wide range of pressure terms, including validations and findings in other studies. As a result of interest, there is a set of exclusive field data that highlights the ability of an extended model of the Boussinesq-type to calculate the propagation of ship-wake waves over an irregular bathymetry and which may assist in the validation of other numerical proposals.

It is a well-known fact that ship dimensions have increased due to the demand of the globalized market in which we live and it is extremely important to quantify the impacts they generate on waterways, in general, and on shallow ecosystems in order to assist in management. In contrast to the use of the FUNWAVE model, but still dealing with ship-wake waves, Bellafiore et al. (2018) conducted a case study in Venice using a sequence of numerical models that reproduce the hydrodynamic field near the ship's hull and the ship wake-wave propagation in the surrounding shallow areas (tidal flats). After validating the model, they observed that the deeper the initial depression (near the hull in relation to the average water level), the greater the dissipation in the tidal flat. One of the results that stands out in this work is transcribed in full:

"...In these conditions smaller vessels sailing at higher speed produce smaller waves with low amplitudes compared to larger ships traveling at lower speed. We considered vessels moving at different speeds providing useful information to evaluate impacts and to define criteria for decision support systems for a sustainable management of navigation." (Bellafiore et al. p. 227, 2018).

This work will not be discussed in greater depth on this occasion, given the proposed theme. However, it is worth mentioning the open research topics listed by the authors:

"This analysis suggests that the developed tools could be further refined to introduce other hydrodynamic drivers, like atmospheric forcing and tides, needed to match the complexity of the real case. Moreover, the numerical models could be also used to investigate the effect of ship waves on sediment resuspension and morphodynamics of complex coastal systems such as lagoons or estuaries." (Bellafiore et al. p. 238, 2018).

4 THE FUNWAVE MODEL

FUNWAVE (Kirby et al., 1998; Chen et al., 2000) is a wave propagation model based on Boussinesq extended equations derived by Wei et al. (1995). The approach followed by the authors, which included additional non-linear terms for the Boussisnesq equations developed by Nwogu (1993), extended the original equation to intermediate water depths and allowed the simulation of wave propagation with strong non-linear interactions. The inclusion of total nonlinearity also leads to a correct form of Doppler shift in the equations when an ambient current is present. The model solves the conservation of mass, Equation 8, and the conservation of momentum, Equation 9, equations:

$$\eta_t + \nabla \cdot \left\{ (h+\eta)\left[u_a + \left(z_a + \frac{1}{2}(h-\eta)\right)\nabla(\nabla \cdot (h.u_a)) + \left(\frac{1}{2}z_a^2 - \frac{1}{6}(h^2 - h.\eta + \eta^2)\right)\nabla(\nabla \cdot u_a)\right]\right\} = 0 \quad (8)$$

$$u_{at} + (u_a \cdot \nabla)u_a + g\nabla\eta + z_a\left\{\frac{1}{2}z_a\nabla(\nabla \cdot u_{at}) + \nabla(\nabla \cdot (hu_{at}))\right\}$$
$$+ \nabla\left\{\frac{1}{2}(z_a^2 - \eta^2)(u_a \cdot \nabla)(\nabla \cdot u_a) + \frac{1}{2}[\nabla(hu_a) + \eta\nabla \cdot u_a]^2\right\}$$
$$+ \nabla\left\{(z_a - \eta)(u_a \cdot \nabla)(\nabla(hu_a)) - \eta\left[\frac{1}{2}\eta\nabla \cdot u_{at} + \nabla \cdot (hu_{at})\right]\right\} = 0 \quad (9)$$

where η = free-surface elevation; h = water depth; u_a = horizontal velocity vector in the water depth $z = z_a = -0.531h$; g = gravitational acceleration;

and the index t represents the partial derivative over time. The above equations describe the evolution of the waves on a sloping impermeable bottom, without considering wave breaking (Mil-Homens et al., 2010).

The FUNWAVE model was developed for situations of small depth and contains a simplifying hypothesis that limits it: vertical integration of the equations to define average speed. Wei et al. (1995) included additional dispersive terms in the equations in order for the FUNWAVE model to efficiently simulate the propagation of finite amplitude waves at intermediate depths with strong nonlinear effects.

Another relevant point in the simulation of the hydrodynamics of the surf zone occurs in the dissipation of energy due to the surf, which is dealt with by including terms of turbulent viscosity in the equations of conservation of the amount of movement.

The FUNWAVE model was developed for applications in 1D and 2D, a fact that imposes limitations such as the existence of problems in the generation and propagation of waves with different directions from that defined by the perpendicular to the input boundary of the calculation domain and the impossibility of generating irregular agitation among others. These constraints somewhat limit the applicability of this two-dimensional version to real case studies (Teixeira & Fortes, 2008).

In this work, only the base equations of the model are presented, the other equations in the literature are not listed since they are adapted to each application.

Mil-Homens et al. (2010) also state that FUNWAVE has great potential for simulating waves on an impermeable bottom and on the coastal platform close to the shore. However, they warn of the particularities in the application of the FUNWAVE model, since much attention is needed to adjust the model parameters related to wave breaking, wave generation and growth in the model, for example. The correct selection of these parameters determines the convergence of the model. A sensitivity analysis with these parameters would be necessary to adjust the default values (Mil-Homens et al., 2010).

As an example, we can bring the input data for the FUNWAVE model used by Mil-Homens et al., (2010): bathymetry, synthesized time series of the free-surface elevation in wave maker position and a file with the model control parameters. This file contains, for example, the characteristics of the forcing waves, the domain definitions, the position of the source function and the sponge layers, the time interval and the total calculation time. The results of the model are the time series of the free-surface elevation and the horizontal velocities, which were also studied by Bruno et al., (2009).

In the work of Mil-Homes et al. (2010), it is presented the analyses, both in the time and frequency domains, of results of wave propagation simulations performed by the non-linear FUNWAVE model (Kirby et al., 1998) in a channel with a bar profile, for monochromatic and irregular wave conditions. Special attention was given to the influence on numerical simulations of the variation of the beginning of the wave break, namely on the role of the parameter cbkv, which affects not only the beginning of the wave break, but also the amount of dissipation.

The main conclusion of the authors of that application is that:

"...in general, the one-dimensional version of FUNWAVE simulates well the nonlinear transformation of a wave over a bottom with a bar-tough profile, for both regular and irregular incident conditions. In fact, and in terms of free surface elevation time series, the numerical results reproduce the transformation of the wave shape (skewness and asymmetry) as it propagates along the domain. However, some differences persist after wave breaking. In general, the simulated values are a little higher (between 5% and 20%, depending on cbkv value) than the experimental ones in both tests, which suggest that the wave-breaking formulation is less effective in dissipating energy than the observed on the physical model test." (Mil-Homens et al., p. 250, 2010).

The FUNWAVE model solves Boussinesq's non-linear equations, as deduced by Wei et al. (1995) and reproduces most of the phenomena related to the wave transformation along variable depth regions, namely, frequency dispersion, amplitude dispersion, diffraction, refraction by the bottom and by currents, energy transfer between harmonic components and energy dissipation due to wave breaking and bottom friction (Nascimento et al., 2010).

It is worth mentioning that several numerical models can be used to study waves generated by moving vessels, however, each model has its advantages and limitations. Some of these models can solve the wave field closer to the vessels or more distant in greater detail. Generally, the works that are focused on small scale local interaction, that is, solving the fields close to the vessels (between the hull and water) use models developed based on CFD (Computational Fluid Dynamics) (Ahmed & Guedes Soares, 2009, Ji et al., 2011, Broglia et al., 2015, Dubbioso et al., 2017, Visonneau et al., 2016, Carrica et al., 2016, Volpi et al., 2016, Mousaviraad et al., 2015, Fleit et al., 2016).

The main advantage of CFD-based models is the high resolution and the ability to reproduce small-scale turbulence effects, as well as wave patterns. However, the need for high computational resources for CFD simulations makes it impossible for the CFD to be considered the most suitable for analyzing the waves generated by vessels in distant fields (Rodrigues, 2018).

5 CONCLUSIONS AND PERSPECTIVES

In this work it is possible to observe that numerical models are widespread and there are many references in studies of risks caused by ship wake and wind waves. Thus, it is concluded that such tools are very useful, due to their low cost and quick response, for evaluation of possible environmental impacts. Nascimento et al. (2010) bring a synthesis, which remains actual, on numerical models for wave propagation including those that simulate coastal phenomena, and highlight four models in the literature, namely: Stockstill & Berger (2001) (waves and currents generated by vessels sailing on waterways), Belibassakis (2003) (problem of propagation-refraction-diffraction of waves generated by vessels sailing close to coastal regions), Nwogu & Demirbilek (2004) (waves and currents generated by vessels in restricted channels) and Dam et al. (2006) (problem of wave propagation-refraction-breaking of ship-wake waves in navigation channels).

Nascimento et al. (2010) state that from a hydrodynamic model (Navier-Stokes, shallow water equations or Boussinesq equations) it is possible, with the addition of a convenient source, to make such a model able to reproduce the phenomenon of ship-wake waves and that was the main point that motivated the authors' research. This motivation is also found in more current works and makes clear the need for further study.

Rodrigues (2018) considers that in addition to the models listed by Nascimento et al. (2010), two others stand out, namely, that of Nascimento (2007) and Torsvik et al (2009). Rodrigues (2018) validated the model proposed by Nascimento (2007) and three other pressure distribution function equations. In addition, the models mentioned have been evaluated and applied by several authors in recent years and still further studies are needed due to the phenomenon complexity and simplifications performed by the authors.

This communication brought classic and current works that were complementing and advancing in knowledge. However, there is still a small range of studies and coupled validations, thus there are gaps in knowledge. Thus, the vast field of research on the subject and the need to better understand the phenomena involved and their complex dynamics are evidenced.

REFERENCES

Ahmed, Y., Guedes Soares, C. 2009. Simulation of Free Surface Flow around a VLCC Hull using Viscous and Potential Flow Methods. *Ocean Engineering* 36 (9-10): 691–696.

Awk, T. 2017. Tomawac User Manual Version 7.2, third ed. *The TELEMAC-Mascaret Consortium*, p. 90, URL www.opentelemac.org.

Bayraktar, D. & Beji, S. 2013. Numerical simulation of waves generated by a moving pressure field. *Ocean Engineering* 59: 231–239.

Belibassakis, K.A., 2003. A coupled-mode technique for the transformation of shipgenerated waves over variable bathymetry regions. *Applied Ocean Research* 25: 321–336.

Bellafiore, D., Zaggia, L., Broglia, R., Ferranrin, C., Barbariol, F., Zaghi, Lorenzetti, G., Manfé, G., Pascalis, F., Benetazzo, A. 2018. Modeling ship-induced waves in shallow water systems: The Venice experiment. *Ocean Engineering* 155: 227–239.

Blume, A. 2002. High-speed vessel wake wash. In: Ship Effects Workshop, Gulport, MS.

Bosboom, J., Klopman, G., Roelvink, J.A., Battjes, J.A. 1997. Boussinesq modelling of wave-induced horizontal particle velocities. *Coastal Engineering* 32: 163–180.

Brebner, A., Helwig, P.C., Carruthers, J., 1966. Waves produced by ocean-going vessels: a laboratory and field study. *Proceedings of the 10th Conference on Coastal Engineering*, American Society of Civil Engineers: 455–465.

Broglia, R., Dubbioso, G., Durante, D., Di Mascio, A. 2015. Turning ability analysis of a fully appended twin screw vessel by CFD. Part I: single rudder configuration. *Ocean Engineering* 105: 275–286.

Bruno, D., Serio, F., Mossa, M. 2009. The FUNWAVE model application and its validation using laboratory data. *Costal Engineering* 56: 773–787.

Carrica, P., Kerkvliet, M., Quadvlieg, F., Pontarelli, M., Martin, J. 2016. CFD simulations and experiments of a maneuvering generic submarine and prognosis for simulation of near the surface operation. In: *31st Symposium on Naval Hydrodynamics*, Monterey, California

Chen, Q., Kirby, J.T., Darymple, R.A., Kennedy, A.B., Chawla, A. 2000. Boussinesq modeling of wave transformation, breaking and run-up. II: Two horizontal dimensions. Journal of *Waterway, Port, Coastal and Ocean Engineering* 126: 48–56.

Coops, H.; Geilen, N.; Vereij, H. J.; Boeters, R.; Van der Velde, G.1996. Interactions between waves, bank erosion and emergent vegetation: an experimental study in a wave tank. *Aquatic Botany* 53: 187–198.

Dam, K. T., Tanimoto, K., Nguyen, B. T., Akagawa, Y. 2006. Numerical study of propagation of ship waves on a sloping coast. *Ocean Engineering* 33:350–364.

Dam, K.T., Tanimoto, K., Fatimah, E. 2008. Investigation of ship waves in a narrow channel. *Journal of Marine Science and Technology* 13: 223–230.

David, C. G.; Roeber, V.; Goseberg, N.; Schlurmann, T. 2017. Generation and propagation of ship-borne waves - Solutions from a Boussinesq-type model. *Coastal Engineering* 127: 170–187.

Dubbioso, G., Broglia, R., Zaghi, S. 2017. CFD analysis of maneuvering characteristics of a submarine model. *Ocean Engineering* 129: 459–479.

Fleit, G., Baranya, S., Rüther, N., Bihs, H., Kramer, T., Jozsa, J. 2016. Investigation of the effects of ship induced waves on the littoral zone with field measurements and CFD modeling. Water 8 (7), 300.

Havelock, T.H. 1908. The propagation of groups of waves in dispersive media with application to waves on water produced by a traveling disturbance. *Proceedings of the Royal Society of London* 81 (A):398–430.

Ji C.S., Ouahsine A., Smaoui H., Sergent P. 2011. Numerical Prediction of Ship-Generated Waves in Restricted Channel. Marine 2011 Computational Methods in Marine Engineering IV, Lisbon, Portugal, 146–156.

Johnson, J.W., 1957. Ship waves in navigation channel. *Proceedings of 6th Coastal Engineering Conference* 40: 666–690.

Kennedy, B.A., Chen, Q., Kirby, J.T., Dalrymple, R.A. 2000. Boussinesq modelling of wave transformation, breaking and runup. I: 1D. *Journal of Waterway, Port, Coastal, and Ocean Engineering* 119 (6): 618–638.

Kirby, J.T., Wei, G., Chen, Q., Kennedy, A., Dalrymple, R. A. 1998. FUNWAVE 1.0: Fully Nonlinear Boussinesq Wave Model Documentation and User's Manual, Research Report CACR-98-06. *Center for Applied Coastal Research*, University of Delaware, 1998.

Kurdistani, S. M.; Tomasicchio, G. R.; D'Alessandro, F.; Hassanabadi, L. 2019. River bank protection from ship-induced waves and river flow. *Water Science and Engineering* 12: 129–135.

Liu, P. L. F., Wu, T. R. 2004. Waves generated by moving pressure disturbances in rectangular and trapezoidal channels. *Journal of Hydraulic Research* 42: 163–171.

Madsen, P.A., Murray, R., Sørensen, O.R. 1991. A new form of the Boussinesq equations with improved linear dispersion characteristics. *Coastal Engineering* 15:371–388

Mil-Homens, J., Fortes, C. J. E. M., Pires-Silva, A. A. 2010. An evaluation of wave propagation simulations over a barred beach with a Boussinesq-type model. *Ocean Engineering* 37: 236–251.

Mousaviraad, S.M., Wang, Z., Stern, F. 2015. URANS studies of hydrodynamic performance and slamming loads on high-speed planing hulls in calm water and waves for deep and shallow conditions. *Applied Ocean Research* 51: 222–240.

Nascimento, M. F. 2007. *Estudo numérico da propagação para águas rasas de ondas geradas por embarcações.* 223 p. Thesis (Doctoral in Ocean Engineering) – Federal University of Rio de Janeiro.

Nascimento, M. F.; Neves, C. F.; Maciel, G. F. 2010. Modelo Numérico de Boussinesq Adaptado para a Propagação de Ondas de Embarcação em Águas Rasas. *Brazilian Journal of Water Resources* 15: 5–15.

Nascimento, M.F., Neves, C., Maciel, G. 2011. Waves generated by two or more ships in a channel. *Coastal Engineering Proceedings* 32. DOI: https://doi.org/10.9753/icce. v32. waves.60.

Nwogu, G.O., Demirbilek, Z., 2004. Numerical modeling of ship-induced currents in confined waterways. *Proceedings of the 29th International Conference on Coastal Engineering*: 256–268.

Nwogu, O., 1993. Alternative form of Boussinesq equations for nearshore wave propagation. *Journal of Waterway, Port, Coastal, and Ocean Engineering* 119 (6): 618–638.

Oliveira, C.A., Calheiros, D.F., Salomão, F. X. T., Júnior, G. W., Albrecht, K. J., Neves, M. A. S., Galinkin, M., Guimarães, S. H. 2001. *Retrato da Navegação no Alto Rio Paraguai*. Brasilia, CEBRAC/ICV/WWF.

Ozanne, F., Chadwick, A.J., Huntley, D.A., Simmonds, D. J., Lawrence, J. 2000. Velocity predictions for shoaling and breaking waves with a Boussinesq-type model. *Coastal Engineering* 41:361–397.

Peregrine, D.H. 1967. Long waves on a beach. *Journal of Fluid Mechanics* 27:815–827.

Quebec Department of Transport. 2003. "St-Laurent Centre". In: http://lavoieverte.qc.ec.gc.ca. Accessed in: may/2003.

Rodrigues, S. R. A. 2018. *Propagation of waves generated by a ship navigating in a channel*. 215 p. Thesis (PhD in Naval Architecture and Marine Engineering) – Instituto Superior Técnico, University of Lisbon.

Roeber, V., Cheung, K.F. 2012. Boussinesq-type model for energetic breaking waves in fringing reef environments. *Coastal Engineering* 70: 1–20.

Soomere, T. 2007. Nonlinear components of ship wake waves. *Applied Mechanics Reviews* 60: 120–138.

Soomere, T., Rannat, K. 2003. An experimental study of wind waves and ship wakes in Tallinn Bay. *Proceedings of the Estonian Academy of Sciences, Engineering* 9 (3): 157–184.

Sorensen, R.M. 1967. Investigation of ship-generated waves. *Journal of the Waterways and Harbor Division* 93:85–102.

Stockstill, R.L., Berger, R.C., 2001. Simulating barge drawdown and currents in channel and backwater areas. *Journal of Waterway, Port, Coastal and Ocean Engineering*, ASCE: 290–298.

Stoker, J.J. 1957. *Waves caused by a moving pressure point. Kelvin's theory of the wave pattern created by a moving ship.* Water waves: The mathematical theory with application, chapter 8. New York: Interscience Publishers.

Teixeira, P.R.F., Fortes, C.J.E.M. 2008. Análise comparativa de modelos não-lineares na simulação da propagação de ondas sobre um quebra-mar submerso. *II Seminário e Workshop em Engenharia Oceânica - SEMENGO.*

Thompson, W. (Kelvin, Lord), 1887a. On ship waves. *Proceedings, Institute of Mechanical Engineering.* Reprinted, 1891, in Popular Lectures and Addresses 3: 450–500.

Thompson, W. (Kelvin, Lord), 1887b. On the waves produced by a single impulse inwater of any depth, or in a dispersive medium. *Proceedings, Royal Society of London*, Series A, 42: 80–85.

Torsvik, T., Pedersen, G., Dysthe, K., 2009. Waves generated by a pressure disturbance moving in a channel with a variable cross-sectional topography. *Journal of Waterway, Port, Coastal and Ocean Engineering* 135: 120–123.

Trombetta, T. B.; Oleinik, P. H.; Guimarães, R. C.; Lopes, B. V.; Marques, W. C. Isoldi, L. A. 2019. Wave energy attenuation over a plane slope acting as a coastal protection structure on the southern Brazilian shelf. *Regional Studies in Marine Science* 28, doi.org/10.1016/j.rsma.2019.100582.

Verheij, H.J., Knaap, F.C.M. van der. 1995. Riverbank erosion in Sarawak, Malaysia. In: *PIANC-PCDC*, Third Seminar on Ports and Inland Waterways, Goa, India.

Visonneau, M., Deng, G., Guilmineau, E., Queutey, P., Wackers, J. 2016. Local and global assessment of the flow around the Japan bulk Carrier with and without energy saving devices at model and full scale. In: *31st Symposium on Naval, Hydrodynamics*, Monterey, California.

Volpi, S., Diez, M., Sadat-Hosseini, H., Kim, D.H., Stern, F., Thodal, R.S., Grenestedt, J.L. 2016. Full-scale fluid-structure interaction simulation and experimental validation of high-speed planing-hull slamming with composite panels. In: *31st Symposium on Naval Hydrodynamics*, Monterey, California.

Wei, G., Kirby, J.T., Grilli, S.T., Subramanya, R. 1995. A fully nonlinear Boussinesq model for surface waves. I: highly nonlinear, unsteady waves. *Journal of Fluid Mechanics* 294: 71–92.

Wei., G., Kirby, J.T. 1995. Time-dependent numerical code for extended Boussinesq equations. *Journal of Waterway Port Coastal Ocean Engineering* 121 (5): 251–261.

Experimental and numerical study of added resistance in waves at low forward speeds

H. Orihara, H. Yoshida & K. Takagishi
Japan Marine United Corporation, Yokohama, Japan

ABSTRACT: Added resistance characteristics in waves are studied by means of model experiments and CFD calculations. In the experiments, added resistances are measured in head waves over a range of forward speeds. Forward speed effect on added resistance is thoroughly examined. To assess the side-wall effect on the measured added resistance characteristics, measurements are conducted with changing distance from the basin's side wall to ship model. Significant side-wall effect is observed on added resistance at low forward speeds. It is shown that the distance to the side wall is needed to be larger than 4 ship lengths to avoid the side-wall effect at low forward speeds. CFD results agree well with the experimental results. It is confirmed the accuracy of CFD for predicting added resistance at low forward speeds and its effectiveness in the evaluation of physical mechanism of the added resistance under varying forward speed conditions.

1 INTRODUCTION

In recent years, with the introductions of IMO's guideline for specifying the minimum propulsion power requirement to maintain the maneuverability of ships in adverse conditions (IMO 2017), accurate predictions of added resistance in waves at low forward speeds have become of significant importance in the ship design since a minimum power required by the IMO's guideline are mainly determined from the added resistances in waves at low forward speeds.

It is well known that ship responses in waves changes significantly with ship's forward speeds. As for the added resistance in waves, it is normally evaluated at forward speeds of Froude numbers (Fn) greater than 0.1 corresponding to ship's operating conditions under calm to rough weathers. On the other hand, in the IMO's guideline the evaluation of added resistance in waves is required at low forward speeds around Fn = 0.05. For these low forward speed conditions, the added resistance characteristics have not studied thoroughly and a few studies have published so far.

In response to the IMO's activities, a growing number of studies concerning the added resistance characteristics at low forward speeds have made recently. Among them, a comprehensive test program covering a variety of ship types have conducted within the framework of the EU research project SHOPERA (Sprenger et al 2016). While the SHOPERA project has made significant achievement in the insight into the added resistance characteristics, detailed physical features have not fully elucidated yet.

In the present study, added resistance characteristics in waves at low forward speeds are studied by means of the model experiment and CFD calculations to examine the physical characteristics and evaluate the effectiveness of CFD as a predicting tool. Particular emphasis is placed on the elucidation of forward-speed effects on the added resistance and the side-wall interference effect encountered in the experiment in model basins. As a CFD code, in-house developed WISDAM-X (Orihara & Miyata 2003, Satoh, et al 2006, Orihara 2019, Orihara, et al, 2018) have employed. This code has thoroughly validated for the prediction of the added resistance in waves for normal forward speed conditions (Fn > 0.1)

A brief description of the model experiment conducted is provided including the model testing facilities, ship models and conditions of the experiments in the next section. Then, CFD simulation procedures employed is described mainly on the principal features of the CFD code and the conditions of the CFD simulations. . After that, results of the model experiment and CFD simulations are presented and thoroughly discussed mainly on the relevant issues to the added resistance at low forward speed and the side-wall interference on the measured values in the experiment. Brief conclusions are presented in the final section.

2 MODEL EXPERIMENT DESCRIPTIONS

2.1 Model testing facilities

The model experiments have been conducted in a seakeeping and maneuvering basin of Japan Marine

United Corporation. The principal dimensions of the basin are L×B×D = 70m×30m×3m. Layout of the basin is shown in Figure 1. Origin of the basin's position coordinate system is placed at the south-west corner. Flap-type wave-makers are equipped at both east-side (Y=30m, 70m length) and north-side (X= 70m, 30m length) of the basin and it generates unidirectional waves. A tested model is towed or freely propelled in arbitrary wave directions by changing model's heading angle.

All the experiments have been made with the seakeeping dynamometer as shown in Figure 2. Six degrees of freedom of ship motion in waves are realized in the experiment by towing the model connected to the dynamometer. The dynamometer is consisted of a mount, a nested sliding platform and a heave rod. The nested sliding platform moves smoothly in surge and sway directions on the rails, and is balanced to a mean position by means of soft springs and counter-weights. A heave rod moves smoothly in vertical direction to allow for free heave motion. The yawing motion is balanced with a bar-spring accommodated in the heave rod. Free pitch and roll motions are achieved by connecting a ship model to the bottom of the heave rod at the center of gravity of the model through a gimbal. The resistance and drifting force are measured by means of 3-component load cell placed at the lower end of the heave rod.

2.2 Model description

Two models of bulk carriers (Model A and B) have been employed in the experiment whose dimensions are listed in Table 1. Model B towed in waves is shown in Figure 3. The models have hull forms typical of recent large bulk carrier design. The models have been dynamically balanced so that the weight, the center of gravity, the longitudinal radius of gyration and roll natural period coincide with those of the full load condition.

2.3 Condition of experiment

In the experiment, all the measurements have been conducted in regular head waves with wave length to ship length ratio (λ/L) from 0.4 to 2.0.

For Model A, model towing speed have been set at Froude number (Fn) of 0.05 and 0.14. Wave amplitude to ship length ratio (ζ_A/L) is set at 0.93% for all the wave lengths. To prevent the side-wall reflection effect on the ship responses which is noticeable in low forward speed cases, model is towed along the lateral centerline (X=35m) so that the distance to the side wall (L_{SDWL}, see Figure 1) is greater than 10 model lengths.

For Model B, model towing speed have been set at Froude number (Fn) of 0.05. Wave amplitude to ship length ratio (ζ_A/L) is set at 0.77% for all the wave lengths. To examine the characteristics of side-wall interference effect on the ship responses at low forward speeds, the distance to the side wall (L_{SDWL}) have been varied from 1.3 to 10.0.

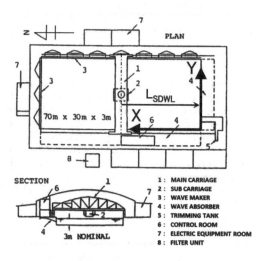

Figure 1. Layout of the seakeeping and maneuvering basin.

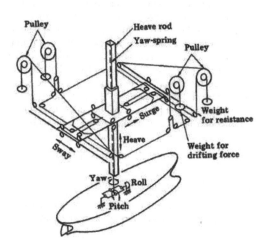

Figure 2. Schematic sketch of the seakeeping dynamometer.

Table 1. Principal dimensions of the models.

Model	Length (L)	Breadth (B)	Draft (d)
Model A	3.00m	0.51m	0.19m
Model B	3.08m	0.56m	0.20m

Figure 3. Model B towed in head waves at low forward speed.

3 CFD SIMULATIONS

3.1 Outline of CFD code

In this study, RANS-code called WISDAM-X has been used. This code employs an overlapping grid system to implement rigorous wave generation, the interactions of ships with incident waves and the resultant ship motions. Since the details of the computational procedure of the WISDAM-X have been explained in Orihara & Miyata (2003), they are described here only briefly in the following.

Reynolds-Averaged Navier-Stokes (RANS) equation and the continuity equation are solved on the overlapping grid system using finite-volume discretization. The RANS and the continuity equations formulated in non-inertial coordinate system. All of the fluid variables are made dimensionless with respect to the constant reference velocity, the ship length and the density of fluid.

For the turbulent closure of the governing equations, eddy-viscosity type Baldwin-Lomax algebraic turbulence model (Baldwin & Lomax, 1978) is employed. The free-surface treatment is based on the density-function method (DFM) developed by Miyata et al. (1988). DFM is a kind of front capturing methods and treats the time-historical evolution of the free surface by solving the transport equation of the scalar variable called density function. Value of the density function is defined as 1 in the fluid region and 0 outside the fluid.

Using DFM, it is not necessary to fit the computational grid to the free surface and the arbitrary three-dimensional free-surface deformation can be treated without re-generation of the grid system.

In order to implement the interaction of a ship with incident waves and the resultant ship motions, an overlapping grid system is employed in the WISDAM-X code. By employing the overlapping grid method, the overall computational domain is divided into two solution domains. The inner solution domain covers the region in the vicinity of the hull. The outer solution domain extends to the outer boundaries, which are placed several ship's lengths away from the hull surface. In each solution domain, the computational grid is generated independently. The generation of the inner grid was made by the GMESH grid generation code developed at the National Maritime Research Institute (Kodama 1988, Kodama 1996).

The treatments of incident waves are made by specifying the fluid velocity components and wave height explicitly at the inflow boundary of the solution domain. The wave height and fluid velocity components are calculated according to the linear wave theory. At the inflow boundary, the values of the density function are determined so that the vertical location of the iso-surface of $\rho m=0.5$ coincides with the wave height.

The motion of the ship is simultaneously solved by combining the equations of motion of the ship body with the flow computation. Since the non-deforming grid is used, the flow computation in the near field is performed on the non-inertia coordinate system fixed to the body of the ship. The effect of the ship motion on the flow solution is taken into account by adding inertia forces as the body force term in the RANS equation.

In WISDAM-X code, a PID (Proportional, Integral and Derivative) control is implemented for keeping a time-averaged ship advancing speed to a specified mean value during surging motion in waves. This control simulates the artificial thrust force needed to keep the determined time-averaged speed in waves. Based on the current and determined time-averaged advancing speeds of the ship, the thrust command is evaluated and added to the surging equation of motion. Similar controls are applied to sway and yaw motions in the simulations in oblique, beam waves.

3.2 Condition of simulation

Simulations have been conducted for Model A. The simulations are conducted on the overlapping grid system consisting of the inner and outer grids. The numbers of grid points allocated for the grids is $183\times30\times89$ and $356\times61\times101$ for the inner and the outer grids, respectively. Since only the head wave condition is considered, half side of the model is modeled in the simulations.

Conditions of a ship model and waves are basically same as those of the experiment. Model speeds are Fn = of 0.05 and 0.14. Regular head waves are considered. Wave amplitude to ship length ratio (ζ_A/L) is set at 0.93% for all the wave lengths. For cases of wave length, $\lambda/L = 0.4, 0.6, 0.8$ and 1.0, are selected. The ship is set free to heave, pitch and surge. The flow is accelerated from the rest to a steady advancing condition during the computational time T=0.0 to T=4.0, where T is the normalized time made dimensionless with respect to (L/U_0, U_0 is mean advancing speed). The wave computations start at T=8.0 and continued until T=24.0. Surge motions is restrained until T=8.0+8Te, where Te is the encounter wave period. Then the model is released free to surge.

4 RESULTS AND DISCUSSIONS

4.1 Forward speed effect on added resistance

In this section, results of CFD and experiment for Model A is presented and examined.

Firstly, time evolutions of simulated surface pressure distributions in head waves of $\lambda/L=0.6, 1.0$ at Fn = 0.05 and 0.14 are examined and shown in Figure 4 and 5, respectively. In the figures, pressure distributions excluding hydrostatic components are shown at an interval of 1/4 of the encounter period (Te). Left sides of the figures are for $\lambda/L=0.6$ and right sides are for $\lambda/L=1.0$. In the figures, t = 1/16Te

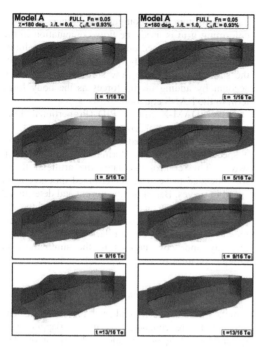

Figure 4. Comparison of time-evolutions of computed pressure contour maps on Model A in regular head waves of $\zeta_A/L=0.93\%$ and $\lambda/L=0.6, 1.0$ at Fn = 0.05.

corresponds to the phase when the crest of incident waves reach at the bow.

As clearly seen in Figures 4 and 5, time-sequential variations of the surface pressure distributions are noticeably changed with the increase in forward speed from Fn = 0.05 to 0.14 in particular in the near bow region. Relative ship motions and surface pressure variations near the bow region increase remarkably at higher speed of Fn = 0.14. It is also noted that the variation in wetted surface area is increased with the forward speed. Thus it can be readily understood that hull surface areas affecting ship motions and wave-induced forces including added resistance are enlarged with increasing forward speed. In other words, this implies that at low forward speeds narrower area close to the still water level has dominant effect on the wave-induced motions and forces. As for the comparison of $\lambda/L=0.6$ and 1.0 cases at Fn = 0.05, distribution pattern and magnitudes of surface pressure variation are similar between the two cases.

Then, to assess the prediction capability of the CFD code, simulated added resistance in waves and ship motions are compared with the experimental data and shown in Figures 6 and 7.

Comparison of simulated added resistance in waves with the experimental results are shown in Figure 6, where simulated and measured added resistances are normalized with $\rho g \zeta_A^2 (B^2/L)$ and shown as a function of λ/L. While the simulated results slightly overestimate the experiment in wave range around the peak of the added resistance,

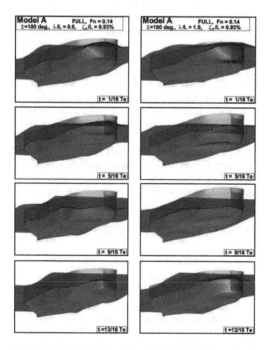

Figure 5. Comparison of time-evolutions of computed pressure contour maps on Model A in regular head waves of $\zeta_A/L=0.93\%$ and $\lambda/L=0.6, 1.0$ at Fn = 0.14.

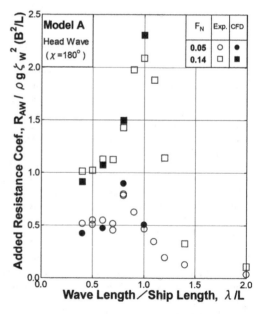

Figure 6. Comparison of normalized added resistance for a Model A in head waves at Fn=0.05 and 0.14, $\zeta_A/L=0.93\%$.

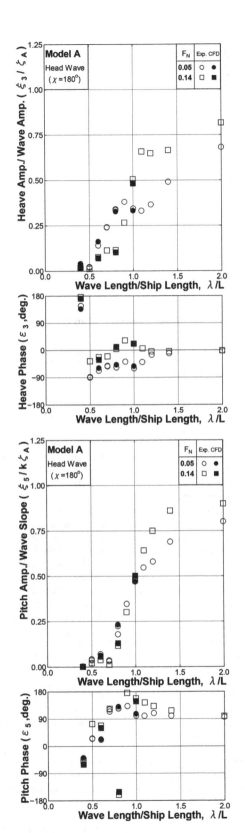

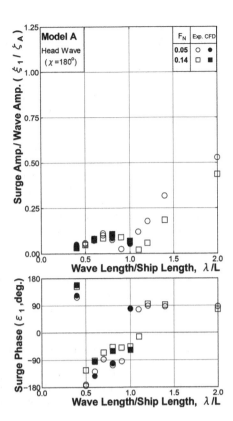

Figure 7. Continued.

simulated results reproduce reasonably well the experimental data for both forward speed cases including the variation in magnitudes and wave lengths correspond to the peak of added resistance. Also noted is that magnitude of added resistance significantly decrease with reducing forward speeds, that is, about 50% reduction in added resistance is shown around $\lambda/L=0.5$ and about 75% reduction around $\lambda/L=1.0$ from Fn = 0.14 to Fn = 0.05.

While the added resistance reduction around $\lambda/L=1.0$ is partly due to the shift of the peak to shorter wave length due to the change in encounter frequency, forward speed effect still plays dominant role as clearly seen in the reduction of the peak values in the added resistance, that is, about 2.1 at Fn = 0.14 at $\lambda/L=1.0$ to about 0.8 at Fn=0.05 at $\lambda/L=0.8$. It is also noted that the reduction in added resistance magnitudes in low forward speed case of Fn = 0.05 is consistent quite well with the hull surface pressure patterns shown in Figures 4 and 5 where variations in pressures show noticeable increase with forward speeds.

Comparisons of simulated ship's surge (ξ_1), heave (ξ_3) and pitch (ξ_5) motions with the experimental results are shown in Figure 7, where surge and heave amplitudes are made dimensionless with respect to incident wave amplitudes (ζ_A), while pitch motion amplitudes are made dimensionless with respect to

Figure 7. Comparison of RAO's of ship motion for a Model A in head waves at Fn=0.05 and 0.14, $\zeta_A/L=0.93\%$.

incident wave slope ($k\zeta_A$), respectively. Phase angles are defined as phase lags with respect to that of incident waves at the ship's center of gravity. As clearly seen in the figures, ship motions are accurately predicted by CFD simulations in terms of both amplitudes and phase angles. It is also noted that the variation in ship motion responses with forward speed is less significant compared to the added resistance characteristics. Amplitudes of ship motions are of similar magnitudes for both speed cases of Fn = 0.05 and 0.14. Although this may seem to contradict the added resistance characteristics as shown earlier since ship motion component is normally predominant around the peak of added resistance and in longer wave lengths, one can readily have understood the physical explanation to this phenom enon by examining the characteristics of phase angles as follows. Atλ/L=1.0, differences between phase angles between the two speed cases are quite large (about 90 degrees), and phase angles for pitch and surge motions at Fn = 0.05 are close to 90 degrees which corresponds to in-phase conditions relative to incident waves.

Under these conditions, ship's relative motions are reduced and the added resistance resulting from the ship's disturbances to the incident waves is reduced accordingly. Attenuation of the relative motions with decreasing forward speed as pointed out above is also seen in the simulated results shown in Figures 4 and 5.

4.2 Tank-wall interference on added resistance in waves

In this section, results of the experiment for Model B in head waves with varying lengths to the side wall of the basin (L_{SDWL}) are presented to examine the side wall interference effects on the added resistance in head waves. In the experiment, Model B is towed in waves in Y direction at constant locations of X corresponding to those of L_{SDWL}/L = 1.3, 2.0, 3.0, 4.0 and 10.0. Since the towing speed is low (about 0.25m/s), measurement of resistance and ship motions for the duration of 20 encounter periods can be made within the relatively short towing distance of 10m including acceleration and deceleration of the model.

Comparison of added resistance in waves with varying L_{SDWL} are shown in Figure 8, where normalization are made with $\rho g \zeta_A^2 (B^2/L)$ and shown as a function of λ/L. Noticeable side-wall interference effects is observed in the figure. That is, added resistance values at the wave lengths changes with varying L_{SDWL} and the variation tends to increase in shorter wave lengths. At λ/L = 0.4, Added resistance increases by about 15% with the reduction in L_{SDWL}/L from 10.0 to 1.3.

Comparisons of simulated ship's surge (ξ_1), heave (ξ_3) and pitch (ξ_5) motions with varying L_{SDWL} are shown in Figure 9, where surge and heave amplitudes are made dimensionless in the same way as

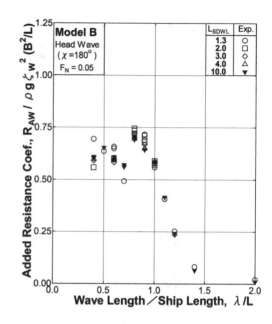

Figure 8. Comparison normalized added resistance for a Model B with a variety of lengths to side wall in head waves at Fn=0.05, ζ_A/L=0.77%.

Figure 7. Definition of phase angles is the same as in Figure 7. As clearly seen in Figure 9, effects of side-wall interference are observed mainly in motion amplitudes in particular in heave and pitch motions. For instance, variations in motion amplitude at λ/L = 1.0 are approximately 30% and 10% for heave and pitch motions, respectively.

From a fluid dynamics point of view, side-wall wave interference in head waves can be considered as a superposition of side-wall reflection waves with the incident waves as schematically shown in Figure 10. Assuming these encountered wave conditions, ship responses can be regarded as a summation of those in incident (head) waves and reflection waves (equivalent to oblique or beam incoming waves). At low forward speeds, encounter frequency of waves can be approximated with wave frequency, one can consider that the length of side-wall reflection waves with same encounter frequency have the length close to those of incident waves. According to these considerations, ship responses in waves with side-wall interference can be evaluated as a summation of responses in multi-directional waves. Based on the hypothesis, responses in waves with side-wall interference shown in Figures 8 and 9 are examined.

As for added resistance, added resistance in the reflection waves having of oblique or beam direction is normally greater than those in incident head waves under shorter wave length conditions mainly due to shift of the peak to shorter wave lengths. In longer waves, on the other hand, added resistance normally smaller in oblique and beam waves relative to those in head waves. Thus, added resistance

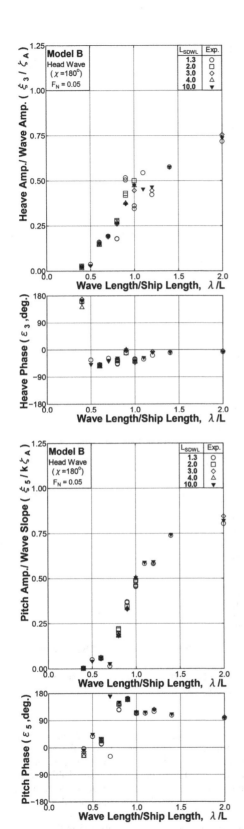

Figure 9. Comparison of RAO's of ship motion for a Model B in head waves at Fn=0.05, ζ_A/L=0.77%.

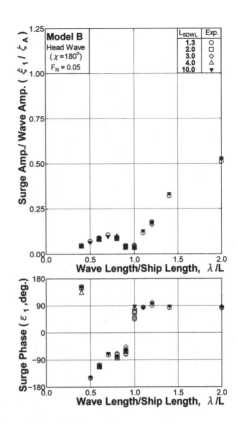

Figure 9. Continued.

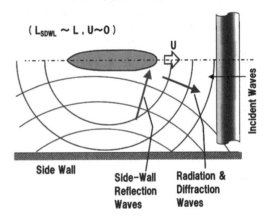

Figure 10. Schematic sketch of side-wall interference in waves at low forward speeds.

variation due to the side-wall interference can be signified in waves of shorter lengths with the contribution from the reflection wave and is reasonably consistent with the experimental results shown in Figure 8.

As for ship motions, side-wall interference effects can be explained in the same way as for the added resistance. In terms of heave motion, its amplitude normally increases from conditions in head wave to oblique and beam waves. On the other hand, pitch and surge motion amplitudes normally tend to reduce in oblique and beam waves. Thus the variation in heave motion amplitude due to side-wall interference can be signified compared to those in pitch and surge motion amplitudes as in quite consistent with the results shown in Figure 9.

To examine the extent of side-wall distance to which the interference affects ship responses in head waves at low forward speed, measured added resistance and ship motion amplitudes are plotted against a distance to side-wall to ship length ratio (L_{SDWL}/L) as shown in Figures 11 and 12. In the figures, variations in the measured values tend to attenuate with the increase in L_{SDWL}/L and converge to constant values around $L_{SDWL}/L = 4$. Thus one can consider that under the conditions of $L_{SDWL}/L \geqq 4$ ship responses in waves at low forward speed (Fn = 0.05) can be evaluated without the effects of the side-wall interference. As a forward speed of Fn = 0.05 corresponds approximately to the conditions specified by the IMO's guideline for evaluating added resistance in waves for the minimum power requirement, these findings can be used as a guide for model basin size employed for the measurement of added resistance for the minimum power evaluation to avoid side-wall interference effects on measured data. From the practical point of view, this finding has a significant meaning since the condition of $L_{SDWL}/L \geqq 4$ cannot be achieved in normal towing tanks who's the tank breadth is around 2L corresponding to $L_{SDWL}/L = 1$. Since the IMO guideline requires added resistance measurement only in head wave conditions, it has been common practice to conduct model experiments at low forward speed in the narrow towing tanks.

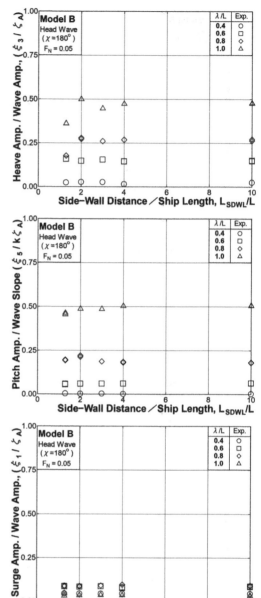

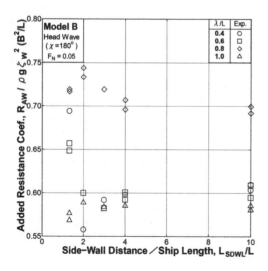

Figure 11. Effects of side-wall interference on normalized added resistance for a Model B in head waves at Fn=0.05, ζ_A/L=0.77%.

Figure 12. Effects of side-wall interference on ship motion amplitudes for a Model B in head waves at Fn=0.05, ζ_A/L=0.77%.

For instance, part of the experiment reported in Sprenger et al (2016) are made in the narrow tanks with $L_{SDWL}/L \leqq 2$. These tests may result in the added resistance data with remarkable side-wall interference effects and significant error in minimum power evaluation. For the operational safety under adverse conditions rigorous examination should be made before these data are utilized in the evaluation of minimum power requirement.

From a quantitative point of view, it may be considered that the variation in the magnitude of added resistance is relatively small as shown in Figures 8 and 11. it must be noted that the present model experiment has conducted under the condition $L_{SDWL}/L \geqq 1.3$ and that side-wall interference effects will magnified under the normal conditions in the towing tank ($L_{SDWL}/L \sim 1$) as the magnitudes of interference increase $L_{SDWL}/L < 2.0$ as shown in Figures 11 and 12. Therefore it can be recommended that the added resistance measurement at low forward speed as required for the minimum power evaluation should be conducted in the basin with a large width free from the effects of side-wall interference on measured ship response data.

5 CONCLUSIONS

This paper deals with added resistance characteristics in waves of two large bulk carrier models at low forward speeds. Its hydro-dynamical characteristics are studied by means of model experiments and CFD calculations to examine the physical mechanism and evaluate the effectiveness of CFD as a predicting tool.

In the model experiment, added resistance characteristics are evaluated in head wave conditions over a range of forward speeds down to Fn = 0.05. Forward speed effect on added resistance is thoroughly examined. Then, to assess the side-wall effect on the measured added resistance characteristics, measurements are conducted with increasing distance from the basin's side wall to the ship model. Significant side-wall effects have been observed on added resistances and ship motions at low forward speeds. It is shown that the distance to the side wall is needed to be larger than 4 ship lengths to avoid the side-wall effect on the measured added resistance for low forward speed cases. Also it can be recommended that the added resistance measurement at low forward speed as required for the minimum power evaluation should be conducted in the basin with a large width free from the effects of side-wall interference on measured ship response data.

In the CFD simulations, calculations are conducted for the same model and under the same condition as the experiment in head waves. CFD results correlate fairly well with the experimental results. It is confirmed the accuracy of CFD for predicting added resistance in waves for low forward speed cases and that the simulated flow field data can aid effectively in understanding the physical mechanism of added resistance in waves.

REFERENCES

Baldwin, B. & Lomax, T (1978). "Thin-layer approximation and algebraic model for separated turbulent flows", AIAA-Paper 78–0257.

IMO (2017). 2013 Interim guidelines for determining minimum power to maintain the manoeuvrability of ships in adverse conditions, as amended (resolution MEPC.232-(65), as amended by resolutions MEPC.255(67) and MEPC.262 (68)), MEPC.1/Circ.850/Rev.2.

ITTC (2017), Seakeeping Experiments, ITTC-Recommended Procedures and Guidelines 7.5-02-07-02.1.

Kashiwagi, M. & Ohkusu, M. (1991). A new theory for side-wall interference effects on forward-speed radiation and diffraction forces. *Schiffstechnik 38*, 33–40.

Kodama Y (1988). "Three-dimensional grid generation around a ship hull using the geometrical method", Journal of Society of Naval Architects, Japan, 164, 1–8.

Kodama Y (1996). "Representation of ship hull form using a multi-block grid", Journal of Kansai Society of Naval Architects, Japan, 226, 85–90(in Japanese).

Miyata, H., Katsumata, M., Lee, Y.G. & Kajitani, H (1988). "A Finite-Difference Simulation Method for Strongly In-teracting Two-Phase Flow", Journal of Society of Naval Architects, Japan, 163, 1–16.

Orihara, H. & Miyata, H (2003). "Evaluation of added re-sistance in regular incident waves by computational fluid dynamics motion simulation using an overlapping grid system", Journal of Marine Science and Technology, 8, 47–60.

Orihara, (2010) Comparison of CFD Simulations with Experimental Data for a Tanker Model Advancing in Waves, International *Journal of Naval Architecture and Ocean engineering*, Vol. 3, No. 1 pp. 1–8, Mar. 2011.

Orihara, H., Yoshida, H., & Takagishi, K. (2018), A validation study of CFD simulations of a tanker in ballast condition advancing in waves, Proc. 28th Int. Ocean and Polar Engineering Conference, Sapporo, JAPAN.

Sato, Y, Orihara, H. & Miyata, H, Practical Application of Two CFD Codes for Ship Motions in Arbitrary Waves, *Proceedings of Twenty-Sixth Symposium on Naval Hydrodynamics*, Rome, Italy, 17–22 September 2006.

Miyata, H., Katsumata, M., Lee, Y.G. & Kajitani, H (1988). "A Finite-Difference Simulation Method for Strongly Interacting Two-Phase Flow", Journal of Society of Naval Architects, Japan, 163, 1–16.

Sprenger, F. et al, (2016), Establishment of a validation and benchmark database for the assessment of ship operation in adverse conditions. Proc. 35th Int. Conf. Ocean, Offshore & Arctic Engineering (OMAE2016), OMAE2016-54865.

Ship machinery

Auxiliary generator of a platform supply vessel based on fuel cell technology

M. Acanfora, T. Coppola, E. Fasano & L. Micoli
University of Naples "Federico II", Naples, Italy

ABSTRACT: The work deals with a preliminary project of a 5000 DWT Platform Supply Vessel (SV), equipped with a Diesel electric propulsion system and 300 kW of an auxiliary power unit based on fuel cell technology. A Proton Exchange Membrane Fuel Cell (PEMFC) is considered for the installation onboard, in order to guarantee low emissions when the ship is berthed in port and uses the auxiliary plant for other services. The system is made by commercial 3x100 kW PEMFC stacks, supplied by Ballard Company, operating with pure hydrogen (H_2) fuel. The H_2 storage system is based on compressed gas cylinders at 350 atm with a volume of about 52 m^3, that are capable to guarantee 48 hours of autonomy. These cylinders are located on the main deck in order to make easier the handling during the refuelling operations and to mitigate hazard to lower levels under all operation conditions.

1 INTRODUCTION

International Maritime Organization (IMO) and other bodies are making growing efforts to impose severe limits on shipping pollution. IMO sets for 2030 the goal of reducing CO_2 emissions from shipping by a minimum of 40% per cargo ton-mile, while for 2050 the reduction is 50% (Mocerino 2018, ABS 2019, EMSA 2019). For this reason, ship-owners are looking for different technologies to be used on board, in order to reduce ship emissions (Miola 2010, Altosole 2014, EU 2012, Embankment 2015).

Clean energy solutions, such as alternative and renewable fuels (Biodiesel, Biogas, Hydrogen, Liquefied Natural Gas (LNG), Methanol and Ethanol), solar and wind energy, Fuel Cells (FCs), and hybrid renewable power systems are being considered as valid options for the emission reduction, taking into account the chance to be integrated for both existing and new ships (Altosole 2012, IMO 2014, DNV GL 2018). In this context, FCs are one of the most promising solutions, as they are zero-emission systems.

Nowadays, FCs are commercially available as energy providers both for the stationary production and for the on-board power supply in the automotive. They are being tested also in other application fields, such as aviation, railway and shipping. The low- and high-temperature FCs, specifically the Proton Exchange Membrane FC (PEMFC) and the Solid Oxide FC (SOFC), are seen as the most promising FCs types for marine applications (Coppola 2014, EMSA 2017, Cordis 2019, Micoli et al. 2019).

The application of PEMFC has been tested successfully under marine environment conditions by several project and studies. For instance, submarines operated with PEM have been developed in the USA and Germany using metal hydride hydrogen stores. In 2005, the first example of the Type 212 submarine come into service with the German navy. In such a king of applications, PEMFCs have shown their particular advantages as low noise emissions, low operating temperatures and air-independent operation (Fonseca 2009).

Other PEMFC applications in ship industry can be reported as samples: in 2000, the 22-passengers Hydra ship was demonstrated (Hydra 2019), in 2003 the Duffy-Herreshoff water-taxi (Duffy 2019), Yacht No. 1 and Hydroxy3000 made their first appearance in 2003 (Hydroxy 2008, H2Yacht 2019). The AUV Deep C and Yacht XV 1 were shown in 2004. In 2006 the 12-person Xperiance was debuted, as well as the Zebotec. The Fuel Cell Boat project started in 2007; it was run by a consortium of Dutch partners, with the aim to develop a hydrogen FC powered vessel operating in the Amsterdam channels to transport around 86 passengers. The FC system provided 65kW for an expected maximum speed of 8 kts (FCBoat 2019). Moreover, in 2007 both the 8-person Tuckerboot and the Canal boat Ross Barlow made its first appearance. In 2008 the ZEMships project Alsterwasser went into service in Hamburg. This project had the objective of developing and testing a ship that features 25.5 m of length, with two PEMFC of 50 kW and a carrying capacity of 100 passengers. The hydrogen was stored on board at a pressure of 350 bar (Zemships 2019). Additional vessels went into service in 2009, such as the Nemo H2 and the Frauscher 600 Riviera HP (Hydrogen 2011) and in 2013, with the Hydrogenesis Passenger Ferry project (Hydrogenesis 2019).

The use of hydrogen-powered FC for ship propulsion, by contrast, is still at beginning design or

DOI: 10.1201/9781003216599-46

prototipal stage, with applications in smaller passenger ships, ferries or recreational craft. However, no FCs have been scaled for and used for bigger ships. Moreover, the impact that volumes and weights have in ship design applications cannot be neglected: indeed, H_2 presents some drawbacks due to its low energy density in the gaseous phase. In the same time, safety aspects have also to match with regulatory rules.

The present study considers a larger scale power application (300 kW) of PEMFC able to provide energy source during berthing for a Supply Vessels (SV). This is a novel project compared to the existing applications in the state of the art. In addition, the design of the energy storage and of the electric power production and distribution is integrated with a careful design of the vessel.

The demand of SVs has increased considerably in the last years, in order to ensure all operations required for drilling and for energy production platforms, both offshore and onshore. SVs often implement cutting-edge technologies to guarantee an increasing number of services and performances. At the same time, SVs must be equipped with ecological propulsion plants to comply with the current environmental regulations, reducing the pollution and increasing the energy efficiency.

The case study considers a particular working ship as the supply vessel, ship specially intended for the carriage or storage of special materials and equipment and used to provide facilities or assistance to offshore installations. This ship is also arranged for fire-fighting operations, personnel transfer, stand by operations as well as first aid and accommodation in state of emergency.

2 METHODS

2.1 *Design requirement and general layout of the SV*

SV main specifications are synthesized in Table 1 as result of statistical analysis of samples derived from most common included in the technical literature.

The ship's electrical system design is compatible with the electrical balance, i.e. with the definition of the powers required by all on-board users in the various operating conditions. The power generation and distribution system meet the load needs referring to the conditions of maximum electrical input of power.

The electrical balance has been developed considering the operational conditions listed below:

- Sea Going (navigation);
- Stand-By (assistance to offshore platforms);
- Cargo Load/Discharge in Harbor (port loading and unloading operations);
- DP2 Mode (second level dynamic positioning mode);
- Fi-Fi Mode (fire-fighting mode in which the ship is involved in firefighting operations);
- Harbor Resting (stay in port).

Table 1. Main characteristics of the SV.

Type of Vessel	Supply Vessel
Navigation	Unrestricted
L_{OA} [m]	88
L_{BP} [m]	81
B [m]	19
D [m]	8.5
T [m]	7.22
DWT [t]	5000
V_{MAX} [kts]	15
$V_{SERVICE}$ [kts]	13
Deck Load Capacity [t]	3000
Clear Deck Area [m^2]	800
Deck Cargo Area [m^2]	1000
Propulsion	Double propeller
Crew	18

The analysis shows that the most demanding condition is relative to the Sea Going operation, when the electrical power demand is 10 MW, while the berthing operation requires approximately 300 kW provided by the auxiliary power unit.

In the present case study, it is assumed that the auxiliary power generation is entirely provided by the PEMFC system.

The choice of a PEMFC technology ensures zero emissions (water is the only by-product) and limited sizes if compared to others FC types. In addition, it has low start-up, low operating temperatures (< 100 °C), it can work in humid environment and starting at low temperatures, it guarantees high versatility and ability to adapt to the customer needs (Bensmail 2015, DNV GL 2017).

2.2 *PEMFC*

The proton exchange membrane fuel cell (PEMFC) uses a water-based, acidic polymer membrane as its electrolyte, with Platinum-based electrodes. PEMFC cells have the advantage of operating at low temperatures (from room temperature to about 100 °C). On the other hand, these temperatures force to use precious metal-based electrodes and to operate on pure hydrogen (H_2).

According to the reactions reported below (Equations 1-3), the H_2 fuel is processed at the anode where electrons are separated from protons on the surface of a platinum-based catalyst. The protons pass through the membrane to the cathode side of the cell while the electrons flow in an external circuit, generating the electrical output of the cell. On the cathode side, protons, electrons and oxygen (from the air) are combined to produce water, which is expelled as the only waste product (Sørensen & Spazzafumo 2018).

Anode reaction: $H_2 \rightarrow 2H^+ + 2e^-$ (1)
Cathode reaction: $2H^+ + 2e^- + \frac{1}{2}O_2 \rightarrow H_2O$ (2)
Global reaction: $H_2 + \frac{1}{2}O_2 \rightarrow H_2O$ (3)

The power output obtained from the PEMFC system is given by:

$$P_{PEMFC} = n \cdot V_{Stack} \cdot I = n \cdot V_{SC} \cdot N \cdot I \quad (4)$$

Where, n is the number of stacks (or independent modules), V_{Stack} is the stack voltage (V), I represents the current (A), V_{SC} is the single cell voltage (V), and N is the number of cells in the stack.

The PEMFC electrical efficiency is:

$$\eta = P/(m_{H2} \cdot HHV_{H2}) \quad (5)$$

Where, HHV_{H2} is the hydrogen higher heating value (120 MJ/kg) and m_{H2} (kg/s) is the H_2 mass flow rate. Equation (5) is used to calculate the amount of fuel required for the SV operations, assuming that the efficiency remains constant during the load variations at 60 % (Ballard 2019).

It is supposed that the power produced by the PEMFC is 300 kW with an autonomy of 48 hours.

The stack module, considered in the present study, is provided by Ballard company (model HD100), and its main specifications are summarized in Table 2 (Ballard 2019).

Table 2. Main PEMFC system specifications.

Characteristic	Value
Net power [kW]	100
Operating voltage range [V]	400 - 580
Rated net current [A]	288
Idle power [kW]	6
Dimensions, L x W x H [m]	1.20 x 0.87 x 0.51
Weight [kg]	285
Supply pressure, nominal [bar$_g$]	8

2.3 Hydrogen storage

Different hydrogen storage approaches include high pressure compressed gas, cryogenic liquid hydrogen storage, solid state and electrochemical.

Solid-state hydrogen storage can be done easily in materials like metal hydrides, complex hydrides, carbon containing materials like carbon nanotubes.

The choice of the optimal storage system should consider the gravimetric capacity, thermodynamics and kinetics criteria (Züttel 2004, Niaz et al. 2015, Manmeet & Kaushik 2019). However, in view of a practical application, the present study focuses on the gravimetric and volumetric capacity and the commercial availability as the preferential criteria for the selection of the optimal H_2 storage system on the SV. Therefore, methods considered for the hydrogen storage are compressed gas cylinders at 200, 350 and 700 atm, and metal hydrides. Among different types of metal hydrides (Rusman & Dahari 2016), the $NaAlH_4$ is taken into account for the comparison. This is one of the most commercial hydrides with a gravimetric density of 4%.

3 RESULTS

3.1 Subdivision and preliminary design of the ship

The longitudinal, transversal and vertical subdivision of the ship is in compliance with the international requirements of the classification societies and design constraints of the ship owner. Compared with similar ships, the main deck arrangement has been chosen among the most common adopted solutions for this type of ship, therefore, it has a large free space aft-wards, in order to load special cargos on deck, and it arranges the superstructures for crew accommodation forwards (see Figure. 1-4).

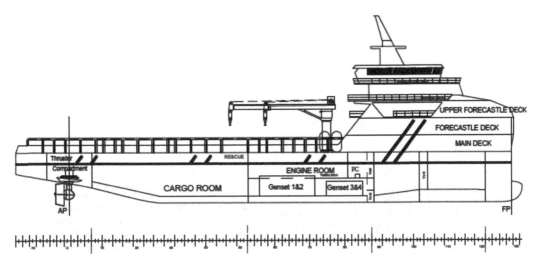

Figure 1. Longitudinal section.

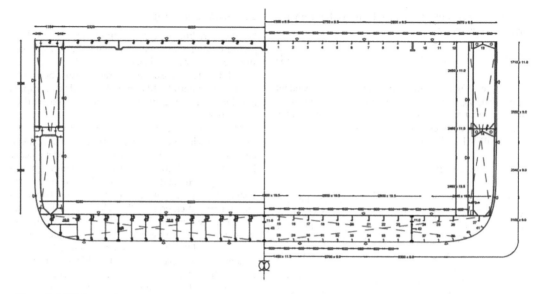

Figure 2. Midships section.

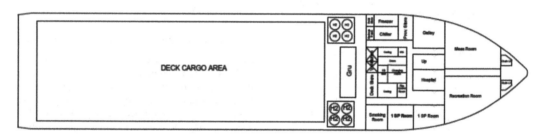

Figure 3. Main deck.

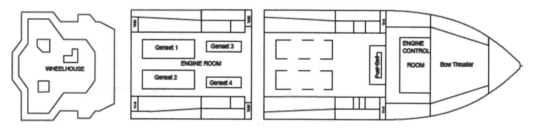

Figure 4. WheelHouse, engine room and tween deck.

The superstructures have been organized into several decks, specifically, spaces have been allocated on the main deck for deposits, warehouses, kitchens, leisure areas for crew, smoking room, pantries and storage of stocks. Proceeding upwards, the forecastle deck provides for housing, laundry, linen stores, etc. (see Figure. 5-7).

3.2 *Propulsion system*

The SV has to accomplish the mission profile, providing a great manoeuvrability and usability for the recovery of shipwrecks at sea. Furthermore, it is characterized by variable service speeds according to the working conditions and equipped with a dynamic

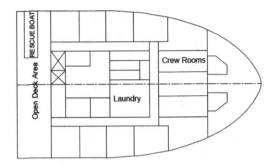

Figure 5. Forecastle deck.

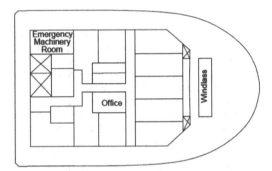

Figure 6. Upper forecastle deck.

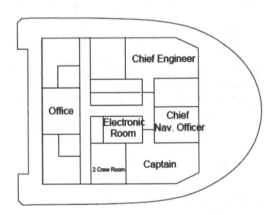

Figure 7. Officer deck.

to the platform (standby vessel). In addition, the ship is equipped with the rescue and the fire-fighting facilities.

The type of propeller is an "Azimuthing Thruster", with a ducted propeller and an electric motor inside the hull. It has been considered a propeller with a high maximum diameter, since this type of propulsion system does not have a large extension in the longitudinal and transverse direction behind the hull. The maximum diameter obtained from the analysis of the

dimensions is 3.5 m, with obvious advantages on the efficiency of the isolated propeller as well as an increase in the performance due to the presence of the nozzle (see Figure 8 and 9).

The ship has an integrated electrical system which consists of some generator sets that provide for the

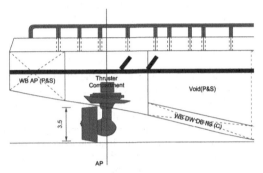

Figure 8. Stern vault of the ship.

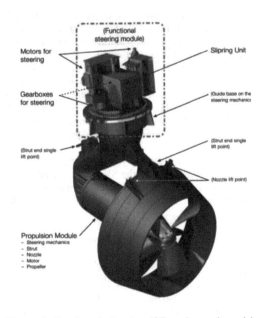

Figure 9. Details of thruster (CZ series and model CZ1400L ABB).

positioning system. Therefore, the more appropriate propulsion system is the Diesel-electric engine. This has the main advantage to guarantee a great ship flexibility in the various service conditions, by making the generating sets able to supply power at the project rotation speed.

The SV is arranged with a large open deck aftwards, required for the transport of cargo to the offshore structures. It must give assistance and monitoring all electrical needs of the ship: propulsion and general services.

The electrical system is based on four main units and one emergency unit working at 415 V and 50 Hz, according to the following subdivisions:

- Main Switchboard Bus-A
- Main Switchboard Bus-B
- Main Switchboard Bus-C
- Main Switchboard Bus-D
- Emergency Switchboard

Considering the actual commercial availability, the following models have been chosen:

1) 2 x 4.5 MW Wartsila Diesel-generators, model 8V31 (Wartsila 2019);
2) 2 x 1.0 Wartsila MW Diesel-generators, model 6L20 (Wartsila 2019);
3) a 100 kW Caterpillar Diesel emergency generator, model C7.1 (Caterpillar 2019);

3.3 PEMFC system and hydrogen storage

The space for the installation of the PEMFC system has been considered as simple as possible and compatible with the available spaces in the engine room.

A parallel connection of the stacks has been expected and arranged on two horizontal planes, in order to reduce the longitudinal dimensions. However, this increases slightly the vertical dimensions, while ensuring the spaces required for the connection of the various elements of the system and their maintenance or handling. The estimated maximum overall dimensions are: 2.3 x 0.76 x 1.0 m (length x width x height).

Equation (5) allows to calculate the amount of H_2 required, that is about 721 kg. As consequence, it is possible to estimate the volumes of the storage systems that are reported in Table 3:

From Table 3, it results that the metal hydride system is less voluminous than others, on the other hand, the weight of such a system is about 1,44 t (excluding the H_2). Gas cylinders add at least 9-12 wt % at the total H_2 weight, meaning that the maximum weight for the compressed gas storage system is about 0.8 t.

In the present case study, it is assumed that critical points for the design of the SV are the weights rather than volumes, therefore, the solution involving the gas cylinders at 350 bar was considered the most suitable

Table 3. H_2 storage systems characteristics.

Storage method	Density [g_{H2}/L]	Volume [m^3]
gas cylinders @ 200 bar	11	65.5
gas cylinders @ 350 bar	14	51.5
gas cylinders @ 700 bar	25	28.8
metal hydride (NaAlH$_4$)	80	18

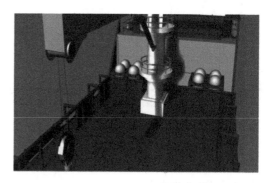

Figure 10. Arrangement of compressed hydrogen cylinders on the main deck.

for implementation on board. According to the IGF Code, the storage of compressed and liquefied gases on an open platform is recommended. Based on these indications, it was decided to place 8 compressed hydrogen cylinders at 350 bars on the main deck.

The arrangement of the H_2 storage system is shown in Figure 10. It is located on the main deck in order to minimize the effect of gas explosions in case of collisions or impacts.

In this way, the probability of gas explosions in the engine apparatus, in which low flashpoint gas or fuel is present for the FC power supply, has been minimized. Moreover, open deck is considered by classification societies as non-hazardous area, that means any explosive atmosphere is not expected to be present at all.

Nevertheless, H_2 cylinders arrangement designed in the paper fulfills register's requirements as regard protection by mechanical damage and by other potential risks. In fact, it is surrounded by coaming in order to collect spills; it is secured to ship structure in order to react at dynamic acceleration loads and it is provided for drip try for leak containment and water spray systems for emergency cooling.

4 CONCLUSIONS

It has been presented a preliminary analysis of a platform SV equipped with an APU system based on a PEMFC fuel cell technology. A preliminary design and investigation of the space's subdivision, compatible with the SOLAS code, has been carried out.

The adoption of a low temperature PEMFC ensures a good compromise between different needs of the ship, such as zero emissions, low start-ups and limited dimensions. Nevertheless, the choice of the optimal H_2 storage system is a critical issue.

The 3 x 100 kW PEMFC stack system supplied by Ballard and compressed gas cylinders at 350 atm have been selected for the installation on board. The H_2 storage system occupies a volume of about 52 m^3 that guarantee a power autonomy of 48 hours and it is located on the main deck in order to minimize the probability of damaged and gas explosions in case of collisions or impacts.

REFERENCES

ABS, 2019. "Setting the course to low carbon shipping".
Altosole, M., Figari, M., Martinelli, L., Raimondi, M. 2012. Hybrid propulsion by gas engines for an ASD harbour tug. In Visconti and Maestro (eds.), 17th NAV International Conference on Ship and Shipping Research, Proc. intern. symp., Naples, 17–19 October 2012.
Altosole, M., Buglioni, G., Figari, M. 2014. Alternative propulsion technologies for fishing vessels: A case study. International Review of Mechanical Engineering, 8(2): 296–301.
Ballard https://www.ballard.com/fuel-cell-solutions/fuel-cell-power-products/fuel-cell-stacks Accessed 2019.
Bensmail, S., Rekioua, D., Azzi, H., 2015, Study of hybrid photovoltaic/fuel cell system for stand-alone applications, Int. J. Hydrogen Energy 40 (39) 13820–13826.
Caterpillar. https://www.cat.com/it_IT/products/new/power-systems/industrial/industrial-diesel-engines/18279748.html. Accessed 2019.
Coppola, T., & Quaranta, F. 2014. Fuel saving and reduction of emissions in ports with cold ironing applications. Naples: High Speed Marine Vehicles.
Cordis https://cordis.europa.eu/article/id/26826-hydrogen-on-the-high-seas Accessed 2019.
DNV GL. 2017. Study on the Use of Fuel Cells in Shipping.
DNV GL. 2018. LNG fuelled vessels - GoLNG.
Duffy water-taxi, http://en.wikipedia.org/wiki/Duffy-Herreshoff_watertaxi. Accessed 2019.
Embankment A., 2015 Third International Martime Organization GHG Study, Published by the international maritime organization 4, London SE1 7SR.
EMSA. http://www.emsa.europa.eu/implementation-tasks/environment.html. Accessed 2019.
EU. 2012. Directive 2016/802/EU of the European Parliament and of the Council. Official Journal of the European Union.
FCBoat, http://www.fuelcellboat.nl/Accessed 2019.
Fonseca N., Tiago Farias, Filipe Duarte, Gonçalo Gonçalves, André Pereira. The Hidrocat Project – An all electric ship with photovoltaic panels and hydrogen fuel cells. World Electric Vehicle Journal Vol. 3 - ISSN 2032-6653–2009.
H2Yacht, http://www.h2yacht.com/Accessed 2019.
Hydra boat, http://www.diebrennstoffzelle.de/h2projekte/mobil/hydra.shtml. Accessed 2019.
Hydroxy 2008. https://web.achive.org/web/20081112061641/http://iese.heig-vd.ch/hydroxy. Accessed 2019.
Hydrogen for Frauscher Riviera 600 Archived 2011-07-22 at the Wayback Machine
Hydrogenesis. https://www.ship-technology.com/projects/hydrogenesis-passenger-ferry/. Accessed 2019
IMO, Third International Martime Organization GHG Study, 2014
Kendall, K., & Kendall, M. 2017. High-Temperature Solid Oxide Fuel Cells for the 21st Century. Academic Press.
Li, J., Wu, B., & Mao, G. 2015. Research on the performance and emission characteristics of the LNG-diesel marine engine. Journal of Natural Gas Science and Engineering: 945–954.
MAN. https://marine.man-es.com/. Accessed 2019.
Manmeet K., Kaushik P., Review on hydrogen storage materials and methods from an electrochemical viewpoint, Journal of Energy Storage, Volume 23, June 2019, Pages 234–249
McPhail, S. J., Kiviaho, J., & Conti, B. 2017. International Status of SOFC deployment 2017. VTT Technical Research Centre of Finland Ltd.
Miola, A., Giovane, B., & Marra, M. 2010. Regulating Air Emissions from Ships the State of Art on Methodologies, Technologies and Policy Options. Luxembourg: Joint Research Centre Reference Report.
Micoli, L., a, T., Turco, M., Application of High Temperature Fuel Cell powered by LNG on a ferry boat: a case study, Proceeding of International Congress of the International Maritime Association of the Mediterranean, 2019
Mocerino, L., Quaranta, F., Rizzuto, E. 2018. Climate changes and maritime transportation: A state of the art. In Alberto Marinò and Vittorio Bucci (eds.), 19th NAV International Conference on Ship and Shipping Research, Proc. intern. symp., Trieste, 20–22 June 2018.
Niaz, S., Manzoor, T., Hussain, A., 2015 Hydrogen storage: materials, Methods Persp., 50, pp. 457–469
Rusman, N.A.A., Dahari, M., 2016, A review on the current progress of metal hydrides material for solid-state hydrogen storage applications, International Journal of Hydrogen Energy, Volume 41, Issue 28, 27 July 2016, Pages 12108–12126
Sørensen, B., & Spazzafumo, G. 2018. 3 - Fuel cells. In Hydrogen and Fuel Cells (Third Edition): 107–220.
Wartsila. https://www.wartsila.com/products/marine-oil-gas/gas-solutions/lng-solutions. Accessed 2019.
Zemships, http://www.zemships.eu/en/. Accessed 2019.
Züttel Andreas, 2004; Hydrogen storage methods, Naturwissenschaften volume 91, pages157–172

Analysis of ship performance data for the evaluation of marine engines emissions in ports

M. Altosole, F. Balsamo, L. Mocerino & F. Quaranta
University of Naples "Federico II", Italy

U. Campora & E. Rizzuto
University of Genoa, Italy

ABSTRACT: A reasonable prediction of the air emissions from ships at port is crucial to evaluate the impact on the surrounding inhabited zones and to evaluate and adopt effective countermeasures. A quantification of the power utilized by ships in port is crucial, since the level of emissions from an engine strictly depends on the power supplied. In order to assess the power profile of a vessel during navigation, maneuvering and docking in the port area, several approaches are possible, although experimental measurements are the most reliable source of data. This paper presents results of the post-processing analysis carried out on a large amount of emission data recorded during the navigation of two small ferries operating in the Gulf of Naples. The research activity aims to identifying the different behavior of the propulsion engine in terms of power and emissions (mainly NO_x, CO_2, Hydrocarbons (HC) in addition to the content of O_2 in the exhausts), during the navigation and maneuvering phases of the vessel in port area. The results are presented by means of numerical tables representing the dependence between emissions patterns and significant engine operational data. The long-term goal is to use such results in connection with the simulation of the engine working conditions to derive a prediction of the emissions.

1 INTRODUCTION

The problem of pollution due to maritime activities in the ports of the so-called "water cities" takes on increasing priority. The worldwide-recognized need to reduce the effects of pollution, both and air, asks for increasingly stringent regulations, especially when ships (together with their noise and exhausts) are close to the people (Coppola et al. 2018; Iodice et al 2015, 2018; Karl et al. 2019, Murena et al. 2018, Mocerino et al. 2020).

The problem, especially as for air pollution, is increasingly felt in the maritime field, which is not always up to date and ready to respond with effective solutions to comply with the regulations issued (Battistelli et al. 2012; Quaranta et al. 2012, Toscano & Murena 2019).

Therefore, it is necessary to characterize, as precisely as possible, the pollutants emission from the engines powering the various types of ships arriving at the harbours, and to carry out, as much as possible, continuous and reliable monitoring of the emissions in the port areas. Many problems arise in setting up a research like this: the main goal should be to monitor and reduce the overall emissions in ports (generally in very inhabited zones) but to this end, first of all a systematic data logging activity should be set with the aim of collecting data about exhaust gas of all ships in ports. Afterwards, by means of robust simulation applications, the diffusion of the noxious substances in the air (NO_x, SO_x, HC, CO_2 and so forth) should be predicted in order to define the scenario created by the presence of many ships in the same port.

Finally, in order to assess/validate the results of the analytic applications; another series of tests on field should reveal the real distribution in the atmosphere of the elements coming from the funnels of the ships. While considering this series of information will involve any single ship entering the port (in the port of Naples the number of ships expected every day is around 100), it is clear that the size of this activity could result very large. Due to the size of this research program, a step-by-step procedure is necessary; in this work a part of this procedure is considered and, specifically, the knowledge of the power produced in port by the ships engines. Indeed, the only way to know the amount of pollutants emitted from any ship is the knowledge of the power rated by engines. Unfortunately, this datum is rarely available, due to the reticence of ship-owners in spreading data about their fleet; therefore it is necessary to resort to analytic methods whose results need

DOI: 10.1201/9781003216599-47

be validated - by experimental tests - in order to be reliable. Of course, the final goal of all this should be the development of a complex tool capable of predicting the air pollution starting from the number of ships in port and their characteristics.

In fact, such tool would be very useful and it could represent a very important tool to regulate the ship traffic, to sanction the emission exceeding the maximum tolerable values, to decide in a reasonable way the distribution of the ships in the available wharves in port.

However, this can be achieved only as a result of the abovementioned procedure, i.e.: a relevant number of campaigns of data logging on site, measurements of the main noxious emissions, a real time elaboration of logged data with the study of their diffusion in the environment with the prediction of the local and global pollution due to the marine activities. Many studies have approached the problem: Corbett et al. (2010) studied the emissions of black carbon and other pollutants into the Artic area presenting a mean term scenario, revealing the influence of the emissions on the local climate and indicating some possible countermeasures. Others (De Melo Rodríguez et al. 2017), starting from the fuel consumption data in port of 30 ships, provided an estimate about the emission of the main pollutants in the air of the port of Barcelona (Spain). Corbett et al. (2009) evaluated whether a reduction in ship speed can lead to a significant decrease in CO_2 emissions and to a potential economic advantage for ships calling US ports. In addition, Peng et al. (2016) carried out tests on site on three cruise ships, in order to measure and analyze the particles emitted by their funnels. The complexity of these investigations, their costs and the enormous size of the research activity involved, could not lead to a common, complete and effective result, forcing the world of the science to the abovementioned step-by-step procedure. All the scientific effort in this field leads more to a contribution on particular aspects of the problem rather than a complete procedure to measure and contain the emissions in port. The problem of monitoring the environment in port areas does not seem to have a final solution at hand In this sense, the present work is to be considered a contribution representing a real scenario of emissions from two different kinds of ships, whose characteristics will be declared later.

2 EXPERIMENTAL CAMPAIGN

The data logging campaigns were carried out on two ships owned by CaReMar, the Company that grants the connection between the port of Naples and the islands of the Neapolitan gulf. The first tests were made in 1995 on the ship *Sibilla (Ship 1*, a slow passengers + cars ferry boat) while the second ones in

Table 1. Ships.

Ships	Ship 1	Ship 2
IMO number	7717250	9086332
Hull type	Monohull	Catamaran
L_{BP}	64.30 m	42.12 m
L_{OA}	69.59 m	44.00 m
B	14.00 m	10.52 m
D	3.61 m	1.83 m
Displacement	2073 t	153 t
Propulsion type	2 x CPPs	2 x Waterjets
Nominal ship speed	16 kn	30 kn
Overall propulsion power	2x1850 kW @1100 rpm	2x2000 kW @2000 rpm
Engines	2x GMT B230.12	2XMTU 16V396

2003 on the cat *Achernar* (S*hip 2*, a passenger high speed vessel) both in the routes to and from the islands Procida, Ischia and Capri.

The main characteristics of the two ships are reported in Table 1.

In both cases, a data logging system was capable to register the main parameters of the propulsion and navigation; in some cases, an exhaust gas analyzer was used in order to log the concentration of the main pollutants in the exhausts.

The main characteristics of the data logging system used for the campaigns are reported in Table 2, while Table 3 shows the timetable for the two ships monitored.

The monitored parameters were torque on the propeller shaft (kNm), power (kW) rpm (g/min), specific fuel consumption (cm^3/s) and exhaust gas temperature (^{O}C).

The pollutants measured are, HC (ppm), CO (% vol), CO_2 (%vol), NO_X (ppm) were measured together with the concentration of O_2 in the air. Since both vessels work with low-sulphured fuels, SO_x was not recorded (Cooper 2001).

The vessels studied are mainly different in hull geometry and propulsion type, being *Ship 1*

Table 2. Data logging system.

Parameter	Sensor	Manufacturer
Torque	Extensimetric torque meter	Binsfeld Eng.
RPM	Magnetic pick-up	
T_{AIR} [^{O}C]	J thermocouples	Tersid
T_{WATER} [^{O}C]	J thermocouples	Tersid
$T_{EXHAUST}$ [^{O}C]	K thermocouples	Tersid
Ship speed	DGPS	
Ship position	DGPS	
NO_X, HC, CO, CO_2, O_2	Gas Analyser	TecnoTest
Data logger		Nat. Instruments

Table 3. Timetable (Na= Naples, Is= Ischia, Pr= Procida).

Ships	Route and departure time	Date
Ship 1-**1**	Na-Pr-Is 04,30	24/06/95
Ship 2-**1**	Is-Na 08,50	26/06/03
Ship 2-**2**	Na-Pr-Is 09,55	"
Ship 2-**3**	Na-Is 13,10	"
Ship 2-**4**	Is-Na 14,10	"
Ship 2-**5**	Na-Is 07,50	27/03/03
Ship 2-**6**	Na-Is 09,50	"
Ship 2-**7**	Is-Na 12,05	"
Ship 2-**8**	Na-Is 13,10	"
Ship 2-**9**	Is-Na 14,10	"

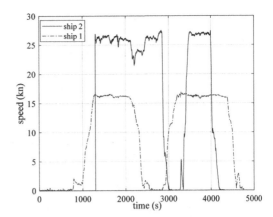

Figure 2. Example of time histories acquisitions for the two ships.

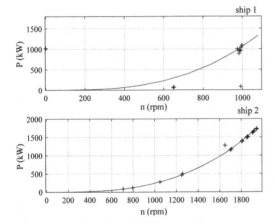

Figure 1. Rpm-power curves and experimental data. On the top *Ship 1*, on the bottom *Ship 2*.

a monohull equipped with controllable pitch propellers (CPPs) while *Ship 2* is a catamaran driven by two waterjet units, but enough similar in the main engines power. Figure 1 illustrates the power vs rpm curves for both ships, where the solid lines indicate the cubic propeller curves, while the cross points represent the average values obtained from the steady state conditions analysis. The figure shows that the data measured for *Ship 2* are perfectly set on the cubic line, thus reproducing the typical behavior of a jet impeller (Altosole et al. 2012). On the contrary, the required power is slightly lower for *Ship 1* at low revolutions, revealing a change in the propeller pitch, being *Ship1* equipped with CPPs.

The time histories of all the measured parameters are similar to the speed curves illustrated in Figure 2.

3 NUMERICAL ANALISYS OF EXPERIMENTAL DATA

Once gathered the raw data, they were post processed to evaluate some specific emissions, especially as regards nitrogen oxides, in view of the use of the same data for the validation of a numerical simulation model reproducing the engine behavior. To this end, it is important to associate NO_x emission values to the engine performance, therefore the results of measurement has been converted from concentration in ppm into specific emission in g/kWh.

In order to obtain this, the NO_x values, measured in ppm by the instruments, have been processed. Four methods have been considered for the conversion.

3.1 *NO_x conversion: Method A*

The first conversion performed is based on the torque and engine data and chemical-physical parameters of the process.

As for nitrogen oxides in g/kWh, the following formula is used:

$$NO_x = \beta \cdot \frac{NO_x \cdot (\mu_{nox}/\mu_{air}) \cdot V_c \cdot \rho_{air} \cdot \eta_m \cdot \eta_v}{|C| \cdot 10^3} \quad (1)$$

where C = propeller shaft torque measured in kNm; NO_x= nitrogen oxides ppm; β = numerical correction equal to 0.000277; μ_{NOx} = nitrogen oxides molecular weights equal to 44.48 g/mol; μ_{air} = air molecular weights equal to 28.962 g/mol.

Table 4 reports the characteristics of the engines.

Table 4. Characteristics of the engines.

	Ship 1	Ship 2
V_c, cylinder capacity [m^3]	0.134	0.063
η_m, mechanical efficiency	0.950	0.950
τ, ratio between propeller and motor	3.85	2.33
η_v, volumetric efficiency	1.20	2.00

3.2 NO_x conversion: Method B

According to Balzani (2014), the specific emissions in g/kWh are obtained by means of equation (2):

$$NO_x = 0.87 \cdot C_s(g/kWh) \cdot NO_x(ppm)/CO_2(ppm) \quad (2)$$

where C_s = specific fuel consumption; and 0.87 is the percentage by mass of Carbon in the fuel.

3.3 NO_x conversion: Method C

By this conversion method, NO_x emission is depending on the airflow rate; the latter can be considered as a function of the air fuel flow ratio (A/F), estimated downstream of the emission measures by Heywood (1988):

$$\frac{A}{F} = 4.773 \cdot \left(\frac{\mu_{air}}{\mu_f}\right) \cdot \frac{(CO_2)+\left(\frac{CO}{2}\right)+\left(\frac{H_2O}{2}\right)+\left(\frac{NO}{2}\right)+(NO_2)+(O_2)}{(HC)+(CO)+(CO_2)} \quad (3)$$

where μ_{air} = air molecular weight; μ_f = fuel molecular weight fixed to 13.89. Between brackets, the measured concentrations of the single chemical compounds.

The concentrations of NO and NO_2 have been neglected, while the molar percent water in the combustion products has been estimated as:

$$H_2O = 0.5y \cdot \frac{(CO_2) + (CO)}{(CO)/K[(CO_2)] + 1} \quad (4)$$

where K = constant value equal to 3.50; and y = H/C ratio of the fuel.

Thus, it is possible to assess the flow rate of air (m_a):

$$m_a = C_S \cdot P \cdot (A/F) \cdot 10^{-3} \quad (5)$$

where C_s = fuel consumption in g/kWh; P = engine power in kW; and A/F = air fuel ratio.
The final relationship for NO_x conversion into g/kWh is:

$$NO_x = (m_a \cdot NO_x \cdot 10^{-6})/(\rho_{air} \cdot P) \quad (6)$$

where m_a= flow rate of air in kg/h; NO_X = the concentration of NO_X in µg/m³; ρ_{air}= the air density in kg/m³; P= engine power in kW.

3.4 NO_x conversion: Method D

In this case, the specific emissions are obtained by fixing a fuel air ratio equal to 35, which, assuming a stechiometric ratio of 14.6, is equivalent to a λ=2.4.

Finally, the airflow rate and NO_x in g/h have been calculated according to method C, by equations (5) and (6).

4 EMISSIONS AND ENGINE BEHAVIOUR

This chapter presents some qualitative and quantitative trends of the results achieved from the experimental campaigns. The temporal acquisitions clearly show peaks in correspondence of the acceleration and deceleration phases of the ships. The first methodology used (method A), although effective, is customized for these types of ships and therefore cannot be generalized.

The method B, fairly simplified, offers values of first attempt and to be obtained in the absence of more detailed information, necessary for the application of the other methods presented.

For all the ship runs analyzed, method B offers the specific emissions lower and far from the classics Emission Factor (EF) (Trozzi C. et al 2016) proposed for these types of vessels (see Figure 3 for *Ship 2*).

Methods C and D, mainly for the navigation phases, return practically coincident results.

Consequently, they have been considered as the two most accredited methods for these types of analysis; method C, in particular, is easy to apply when all the concentrations of pollutants from the engine exhaust gas are known. Method D allows an estimate of the specific emissions once the air fuel ratio is assumed and not calculated by equation (3): therefore the procedure may be usefully followed in case of lack of information about the several chemical compounds.

According to Trozzi (2016), the NOx emission factors for the main engine (high-speed diesel), burning marine gas oil (MGO), are 11.2 g/kWh for cruising condition and 8.9 g/kWh for phase of maneuvering and hotelling.

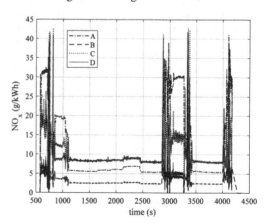

Figure 3. Comparison among the four methods considered for calculating NOx-specific emissions *(Ship 2)*.

Regarding the maneuvering phases, the two methods are opposite: the first, Method C, provides a higher specific emission of NO_x in comparison with the navigation condition; on the contrary, the second one, Method D, provides an average lower specific emission (if peaks due to measurement errors are excluded) during the maneuver. In accordance with the results found by Trozzi (2016) in maneuver condition, the method D is chosen for the comparison in Table 5.

As a general comment, the average values for *Ship 1* and *Ship 2* are lower than EF reported by Trozzi. This should be due to a difference in engine efficiency and fuel characteristics. In addition, the behavior of the two ships for maneuvers in port is similar; while comparing the two phases for each ship, it is also noted that the ratio (b/a in the Table 5) is quite similar to that proposed by Trozzi.

With regard to CO_2 emissions, the data are shown (as % volume) for the two ships in Figure 4.

Figures 5, 6 and 7 respectively show the efficiency of the *Engine 2*, in terms of specific fuel consumption and NO_X and CO_2 emissions measured at the power cubic line of the jet impeller.

Unfortunately, a comparison with *Engine 1* is not possible due to the lack of useful emission data from the experimental campaign of *Ship 1*.

As shown in the figures, a maximum NO_X emission value (Figure 6) is found at the minimum specific fuel consumption (Figure 5).

Table 5. EF comparison between experimental data and literature (Trozzi 2016).

NO_x Specific emissions (g/kWh)	Ship 1	Ship 2	EF Trozzi
Cruise (**a**)	6.38	8.39	11.2
Maneuvering (**b**)	5.50	7.40	8.9
Ratio **b/a**	0.86	0.88	0.79

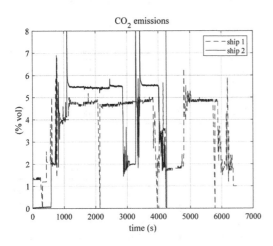

Figure 4. Time history of CO_2 emissions for the two ships.

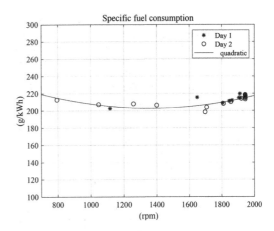

Figure 5. Specific fuel oil consumption (SFOC).

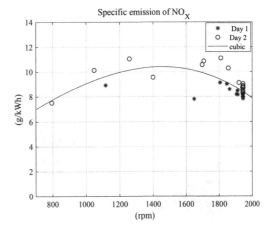

Figure 6. Specific emission of NO_X.

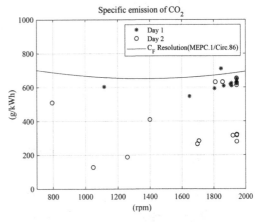

Figure 7. Specific emission of CO_2.

As for CO_2, experimental data in Figure 7 are more scattered (a temporary unavailability of the CO_2 sensor in the campaign of the second day is conceivable), however it is possible to imagine a minimum around 1300÷1500 rpm, as in the case of Figure 5. The latter consideration is supported by the comparison with the solid line represented in Figure 7 and obtained from multiplying the emission factor (C_F = 3.206 t_{CO2}/t_{fuel} for Gas Oil) available in IMO 2014 by the SFOC data reported in Figure 5.

Figures 8 and 9 show the flow rates of NO_X and CO_2 as a function of the load on the engine, including both steady-state and transient conditions.

Table 6 shows the total fuel consumption for *Ship 1* and *Ship 2* (during the first test day), while the total emissions of nitrogen oxides and CO_2 are shown inTable 7.

The last column of the Table 7 indicates the percentage of emissions produced in port during the ship's arrival and departure (i.e. navigation at reduced speed, maneuver and mooring).

Experimental data show that the two ships emit on average the same percentage of pollutants in port, i.e. around 20% in NO_x and around 17% in CO_2, and the remaining percentage during navigation (see Table 7).

As regards the rate of O_2 and HC from the engine exhaust gas, statistical data are illustrated respectively in Table 8 and Table 9.

Unfortunately, some inaccuracies doe to zeroing and/ or spaming phases of the measuring instruments occurred during the experimental campaign and reduced the emissions data useful for the present analysis.

Table 6. Total fuel consumption.

Ship	FC (t)
Ship 1-1	1.65
Ship 2-1	1.22
Ship 2-2	1.28
Ship 2-3	1.27
Ship 2-4	1.27

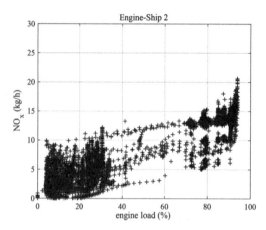

Figure 8. Flow rate of NO_X.

Table 7. Total emission of NO_X and CO_2 and the % emitted during the maneuvering phases.

Ship	NO_x	CO_2	In port NO_x	CO_2
	(kg)	(t)	(%)	
Ship 1-1	37.38	3.81	17.39	17.60
Ship 2-2	49.83	3.67	20.31	17.14
Ship 2-3	48.72	3.58	20.52	14.72
Ship 2-4	47.36	3.62	21.11	18.78

Table 8. Data statistics for O_2 content (%vol) in exhaust gas.

Ship	Min	Max	Mean	Standard deviation
Ship 1-1	12.91	21.1	15.1	1.79
Ship 2-2	2.74	22.37	13.92	2.82
Ship 2-3	4.65	21.04	12.92	2.93
Ship 2-4	4.67	22.6	13.48	3.54

Table 9. Data statistics for the emissions of HC (ppm).

Ship	Min	Max	Mean	Standard deviation
Ship 1-1	0.00	26.9	14.2	3.31
Ship 2-2	0.00	32.6	6.40	6.94
Ship 2-3	0.00	14.8	0.77	2.45

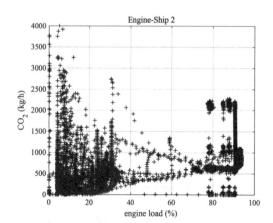

Figure 9. Flow rate of CO_2.

5 CONCLUSIONS AND FUTURE WORK

This work presents the results of a post processing analysis regarding experimental data in pollutants production from marine engines. The main purpose is to draw useful considerations for the numerical modeling of air pollution processes in "water cities". To this end, emissions measurements were carried out for two small ferries operating in the Gulf of Naples. Some methods to associate the emission rates to engine power have been illustrated, identifying the most appropriate one and presenting the most reliable results. Despite the similar power of the two different main high speed diesel engines, some instruments failures have reduced the large initial availability of the recorded data, not allowing a proper comparison between the performance of the two engines (in fact reliable emissions data are available only for one engine type). In addition, the engine efficiency in terms of pollutants emissions has been mainly limited to NO_x and CO_2.

However, two interesting considerations can be outlined from the present analysis:

- from NO_x and CO_2 data, it is possible to suppose an opposite behavior for the considered engine (i.e. at the maximum efficiency in terms of fuel consumption and CO_2 emission corresponds a worse efficiency in NO_x production);
- for the two examined ships, the same mean rate of NO_x and CO_2 is emitted in port.

The obtained database will be used in a future work for the validation of an engine simulation model including also emission aspects. Once developed the engine code, the contribution to air pollution of this kind of vessels in ports can be more easily assessed and then addressed.

ACKNOWLEDGMENTS

The Authors would like to thank all the people who co-operated in the organization and realization of the full-scale tests. In particular, the CaReMar staff.

REFERENCES

Altosole, M., Benvenuto, G., Campora, U., Figari, M. 2012. Dimensionless numerical approaches for the performance prediction of marine waterjet propulsion units. *International Journal of Rotating Machinery*, Volume 2012, Article number 321306: 1–12.

Balzani Lööv, J. M., Alfoldy, B., Gast, L. F. L., Hjorth, J., Lagler, F., Mellqvist, J., Swart, D. P. J. 2014. Field test of available methods to measure remotely SOx and NOx emissions from ships. *Atmospheric Measurement Techniques*, 8, 7, 2597–2613.

Battistelli, L., Fantauzzi, M., Coppola, T., Quaranta, F. 2012. Evaluation of the environmental impact of harbour activities: Problem analysis and possible solutions. In Carlos Guedes Soares and Enrico Rizzuto (eds.), *Sustainable Maritime Transportation and Exploitation of Sea Resources, Proc. intern. Symp.*

Brettschneider, J. 1997. Extension of the equation for calculation of the air-fuel equivalence ratio (No. 972989). *SAE Technical Paper*.

Cooper, D. A. 2001. Exhaust emissions from high speed passenger ferries. *Atmospheric Environment*, 35(24), 4189–4200.

Coppola, T., Mocerino, L., Rizzuto, E., Viscardi, M., Siano, D. 2018. Airborne noise prediction of a Ro/Ro pax ferry in the port of Naples. In Alberto Marinò and Vittorio Bucci (eds.), *NAV International Conference on Ship and Shipping Research, Proc. intern. symp., Trieste.*

Corbett, J. J., Wang, H., Winebrake, J. J. 2009. The effectiveness and costs of speed reductions on emissions from international shipping. *Transportation Research Part D: Transport and Environment*, 14(8), 593–598.

Corbett, J. J., Lack, D. A., Winebrake, J. J., Harder, S., Silberman, J. A., Gold, M. 2010. Arctic shipping emissions inventories and future scenarios. *Atmospheric chemistry & Physics discussions*, 10(4).

Heywood, J. B. 1988. Combustion engine fundamentals. 1ª Edição. Estados Unidos.

IMO 2014, MEPC, Guidelines On The Method Of Calculation Of The Attained Energy Efficiency Design Index (Eedi) For New Ships, As Amended (*Resolution Mepc.245(66), As Amended By Resolutions Mepc.263-(68) And Mepc.281(70)*)

Iodice, P., & Senatore, A. 2015. Industrial and urban sources in Campania, Italy: The air pollution emission inventory. *Energy & Environment*, 26(8), 1305–1317.

Iodice, P., Langella, G., & Amoresano, A. 2017. A numerical approach to assess air pollution by ship engines in manoeuvring mode and fuel switch conditions. *Energy & Environment*, 28(8), 827–845.

Karl, M., Jonson, J. E., Uppstu, A., Aulinger, A., Prank, M., Sofiev, M., ... & Matthias, V. 2019. Effects of ship emissions on air quality in the Baltic Sea region simulated with three different chemistry transport models. *Atmospheric Chemistry and Physics*, 19(10), 7019–7053.

Mocerino, L., Murena, F., Quaranta, F., Toscano, D. 2020. A methodology for the design of an effective air quality monitoring network in port areas. *Scientific Reports*, 10 (1), 1–10.

Murena, F., Mocerino, L., Quaranta, F., Toscano, D. 2018. Impact on air quality of cruise ship emissions in Naples, Italy. *Atmospheric Environment*, 187, 70–83.

Nunes, R. A. O., Alvim-Ferraz, M. C. M., Martins, F. G., & Sousa, S. I. V. (2017). Assessment of shipping emissions on four ports of Portugal. *Environmental Pollution*, 231, 1370–1379.

Peng, Z., Ge, Y., Tan, J., Fu, M., Wang, X., Chen, M., ... & Ji, Z. 2016. Emissions from several in-use ships tested by portable emission measurement system. *Ocean Engineering*, 116, 260–267.

Quaranta, F., Fantauzzi, M., Coppola, T., Battistelli, L. 2012. The environmental impact of cruise ships in the port of Naples: analysis of the pollution level and possible solutions. *Journal of Maritime Research*, 9(3): 81–86.

Rodríguez, G. D. M., Martin-Alcalde, E., Murcia-González, J. C., & Saurí, S. 2017. Evaluating air emission inventories and indicators from cruise vessels at ports. *WMU Journal of Maritime Affairs*, 16(3): 405–420.

Toscano, D., & Murena, F. 2019. Atmospheric ship emissions in ports: A review. Correlation with data of ship traffic. *Atmospheric Environment: X*, 4, 100050.

Trozzi, C., & De Lauretis, R. 2016. EMEP/EEA Air Pollutant Emission Inventory Guidebook 2016 (Technical guidance to prepare national emission inventory), ISBN 978-92-9213-806-6, *European Environment Agency*.

New methodologies for the study of transport phenomena in ship's ballast water

A. Amoresano, P. Iodice, G. Langella, L. Mocerino & F. Quaranta
University of Naples "Federico II", Naples, Italy

ABSTRACT: Anthropic activities alter the normal equilibrium of ecosystems of air and water. The world maritime traffic drastically influences the marine ecosystem. The main harmful effects of ships on the ocean due to shipping sector are the noise irradiated in the water, the pollutants in the atmosphere, the effects of using toxic paint and the displacement of non-indigenous species (NIS). The management of ballast water is a great challenge for the maritime traffic. The maritime sector plays a fundamental role in the climate changes. The ballast sediments provide the breeding ground of living organisms and may affect the weight balance of the ship. The study of the behavior of sediments in ballast tanks plays an important role in understanding the phenomena of transport and sedimentation. Ballast pumps are certainly the most stressed components in the ballast charge/discharge system. This work aims at analyzing a new methodology for the study of transport phenomena in ship's ballast water. The presented results have been reached by using a fastcam device (CMMOS MINI FASTCAM AX100) coupled with a transparent duct and show the behavior of the sediments as a function of the particles size and the liquid flow rate.

1 INTRODUCTION

The maritime sector plays a fundamental role in the climate changes (Mocerino 2018). Anthropogenic activities alter the normal equilibrium of ecosystems of air and water (Mocerino 2020; Murena 2018). The world maritime traffic drastically influence the marine ecosystem due to the noise irradiated in the water, the effects of using toxic paint and the displacement of non-indigenous species (NIS) (Bilgin Güney et al 2018; Ivče et al, 2017).

Normally, the ballast water loaded onboard contains biological organisms and substances (fish larvae, small fish, crustaceans, algae, and invertebrates), sediments and other types of potentially polluting elements such as viruses and bacteria, which escape the incoming filters (Gollasch et al, 2015). If all these organisms survive between a stopover and the following, they will be released in waters other than those in which they originated. Once released into the new environment, they can potentially survive and proliferate at the expense of native species, obviously causing damage to the ecosystem.

The effect on the ecosystem of the NIS transported in the ballast tank of ships is a severe alteration in the equilibrium of the habitat with the rise of new and harmful ecosystems often accompanied by the extinctions of the indigenous species. The phases of discharges of water ballast during the normal operations of a vessel generate a dangerous contamination of the water in port because, generally, the ports of loading and unloading of ballast water are very far from each other, often in different continents. NIS include bacteria, microbes, small invertebrates, eggs, cysts and larvae of various species. The transferred species may survive to establish a new and invasive population in the host environment.

The problem related to the ballast water as a vector for moving NIS species have been studied since the 1970s. In the late 1980s, Canada and Australia experienced particular damage because of invasive species and awekened the attention of IMO's Marine Environment Protection Committee (MEPC) (IMO 2017 and Ivče et al 2017). The increase of global maritime trade, over the last few decades, and the new routes are worsening the situation with new invaded areas and increasing danger.

Only in 2004, did the IMO publish the International Convention for the Control and Management of ship's ballast water and sediments, known as BWM Convention (IMO 2004).

The Convention aims at preventing and minimizing the menace to the environment which arises from the transfer of the so-called HAOP (Harmful Aquatic Organism and Pathogens) in the ships'ballast waters (Ivče et al 2017). The convention consists in five sections (General provisions; Management and control Requirements for Ships; Special Requirements in Certain Areas; Standard for BWM; Survey and Certification requirement for BWM) and two appendices respectively for standard formats and requirements regarding the form of International BWM Certificates

DOI: 10.1201/9781003216599-48

and reporting and verification in a ballast water Record Book (David et al, 2015).

The entry into force of the Convention dates back to 2017, 12 months after the ratification of more than 35% of world merchant shipping tonnage; as of November 2018 the contracting States are 78 and representing 77.2% of world merchant shipping tonnage.

The processes provided for prevention and elimination of the transfer of HAOP according to the Convention are a combination of mechanical, physical, chemical and biological processes.

Several elements influence the accumulation of sediments in a ballast tank such as the flow rate, the structure of the hull, the complex geometry, the longitudinal and transverse structural elements and so forth (Prange, 2013 and Yuan et al, 2017). The geometric complexity also causes a complex flow rate during the loading and unloading of the ballast water. With low loading and unloading speeds, different types of sediment accumulate in the dead spots of the structure (Yuan et al, 2017).

In the ten billion tons of ballast water that are handled worldwide every year, the ten most invasive species that are transported are cholera, Cladoceran, Water Flea, Mitten Crab, Toxic Algae, Round Goby, Zebra Mussel, North American Comb Jelly, North Pacific Seastar, European Green Crab and Asian Klep (Gollasch et al, 2015). This study represent the first step of the study of the transportation of alien elements in a stream with consequences for the ecosystem and for the elements of ballast water system (first of all, pumps).

2 THE EXPERIMENTAL SYSTEM

In order to carry out the first tests, an experimental system, Figure 1 (Amoresano et al, 2015), was used consisting in a tool for the circulation of water in steel pipes and two sections in plexiglass, a water storage and discharge tank, a pump with radial blades, connected via a double cardan joint to an electric engine three-phase two-pole asynchronous.

The motor is placed on a free base support connected to a dynamometric cell. Through the deformations of the elastic cell system, stresses (force and resisting torques) are measured.

From the value of these stresses, it is possible to quantify the energy dissipation phenomena related to the pump.

The hydraulic circuit is equipped with a rolling valve (B in Figure 1) and a by-pass valve (H in Figure 1) which allow the adjustment of the flow passing through the pump.

Finally, there are two strain gauge pressure transducers, G, located respectively in the suction tube, immediately upstream of the impeller and in the upper part of the auger, downstream of the impeller itself.

Plexiglas parts allow you to see and film what happens to the impeller blades and in the duct with the fast camera.

In Figure 2, the scheme of the experimental system and in Table 1 the characteristics of the main component have been represented.

3 THE AVAILABLE DEVICES

CMOS MINI FASTCAM AX100 camera (Figure 3) that offers high imaging performance was used to monitor the setup of this plant. This tool provides a 1.3 megapixel resolution (1280 x 1024 pixels) with frame rates up to 4.000 fps, with recording memory options up to 32 GB that offer extended recording times and activation flexibility.

In order to have an adequate recording, the measurement space was highlighted by using a halogen HLX 64627 - OSRAM 12 V 100 W. A strong light point was required due to the reduction of light because of the speed shutter that decreases by increasing the frame rate of the image acquisition. This choice was made to cut frequencies, especially low frequencies that would alter the distribution of gray tones in the image. This Xenon lamp provides light with a wavelength of approximately 650 nm, where the

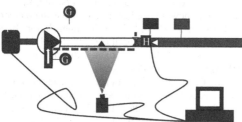

A - Centrifugal Pump.
B - Motorized Valve.
C - Volumetric Flow meter.
D - FAST CMOS Camera.
E - Lap Top.
F - Pump Inverter Device.
G - Pressure Transducer.
H - By Pass Valve.

Figure 1. Experimental scheme and nomenclature.

Figure 2. Transparent inlet of the centrifugal pump.

Table 1. The characteristics of the main component.

Component	Characteristics
Single-phase asynchronous motor	P = 9 [kW]
	n = 2890 [rpm]
	380 [V]
	50 [Hz]
Centrifugal pump	Q_{max} = 15 [m^3/h]
	H_{max} = 19.5 [m]
	n_{max} = 2850 [rpm]
Plexiglass suction tube	L = 500 [mm]
	D = 50 [mm]

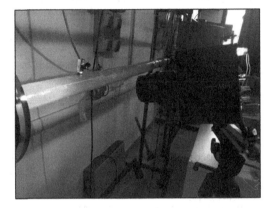

Figure 3. Photron CMOS CAMERA AX-100.

Fastcam Photron UX100 sensor is particularly stable and sensitive. To facilitate the procedure, a standard 50mm Canon lens was used.

This choice does not allow a good magnification ratio but supplies a stable image with a shallow depth of field.

The image sensor used is the active C-MOS, or Active Pixel Sensor, consisting of an integrated circuit, a Bayer filter, a pixel matrix, a digital controller and an A/D converter.

Each of these components contains a light sensor and a signal amplifier. In addition, an analog converter and a digital controller are part of the same integrated circuit.

The light comes through the lens and it is processed by the color filter before reaching the pixel array. Once the filtered light reaches the matrix, each individual pixel converts the light into an amplified voltage, which will be processed by the rest of the sensor.

With the use of this camera and the related software, it was possible to take videos and images monitoring the different phases of motion, up to the sediment transport phase.

The suspensions inserted in the fluid were first sieved to establish the size of the particles (Francis 1973). A particle size analysis to determine the distribution of the particles has been therefore necessary. Calibrated sieves arranged in series have been used: they consist in a woven mesh fabric, whose opening is assumed to be almost graduated, fixed to the base of an open cylindrical container.

Four diametrical classes were identified through the sieving operation (Figure 4) d_1 = *0.8 mm*, d_2 = *0.7 mm*, d_3 = *0.6 mm*, d_4 = *0.4 mm*. Subsequently, Table 2, the granules were weighed on an analytical balance with a capacity of 120 g and sensitivity 0.1 mg. (Gibertini E42 scale was used).

4 TESTS

In order to acquire the behavior of the particles carried by the water stream (Heyman et al. 2016), many dust particles of known dimension were put inside the transparent duct like shown in the Figure 5.

The first tests were carried out starting with the setup of the hydraulic device shown in Table 3. By using the fast camera, the trajectory of the single particles were analyzed and it was possible to characterize the behavior of the particles for different regimes (Moghadasiab et al, 2004).

In order to consider the interaction between the particle and the water stream, two Reynolds numbers were considered. The Re_p and the Re_l defined as follows:

$$Re = \frac{\rho u D}{\mu} \quad (1)$$

While taking into account the volumetric flow rate

$$Q = u \frac{\pi D^2}{4} \quad (2)$$

Figure 4. Calibrated sieves.

Table 2. Average weight.

Diameter (mm)	Average weight (mg)
0.8	0.0022
0.7	0.0017
0.6	0.00094
0.4	0.00069

Figure 5. Dust heap in a transparent duct.

In the Table 3 the fluid dynamic data of the water stream are reported as a function of the rpm of the pump and consequently of the mass flow rate; where Q is the volumetric flow rate, u is the stream velocity, A is the duct section and μ is the kinematic viscosity of the liquid phase.

The data are carried out for two particle diameters $d=0{,}8mm$ $d=0{,}7mm$.

In order to analyze the droplet behavior, the Reynolds number between the water stream and the droplets must be considered:

$$Re = \frac{\rho(|u - u_p|)d}{\mu} \qquad (3)$$

The water stream velocity was fixed by the setup of the centrifugal pump by imposing the rpm.

The velocity u of the formulas 1 and 3 were carried out by reading the digital value on the screen of the magnetic volumetric flow meter (C component of the Figure 1) so that the equation 1 can be solved once the duct diameter (2 inch) and the water properties at the working pressure and temperature are known.

On the other hand, the equation 3, instead can be solved by measuring the u_p term by using the FAST CMOS UX 100 PHOTRON Camera.

The equation 2 takes into account the inertial force of the particle and the viscous force of the liquid phase (Pähtz & Durán, 2017).

Specifically, it was possible to evaluate the speed of movement of a sample particle within the pipeline calculated according to the hourly law:

$$v = \Delta s / \Delta t \qquad (4)$$

To define the time interval Δt, the acquisition frequency of the fast camera was set to 250 fps.

In order to have tangibility of the movement of the particle, not perceptible in a single frame. The measured time interval relating to the i-th movement was acquired after 5 frames (1st column of Tables 4 and 5) so the time interval between two sequential position of the particle is equal to 0.02 s (2nd column of Tables 4 and 5).

For the calculation of the i-th position a software tracking was developed. Taking into account the ratio between the real distance and the pixel dimension above reported:

(681 *(pixels)*): (50.8 *(mm)*) = (number of pixels displayed) : (ΔS *(mm)*).

where the number of considered pixel has been represented in the 3rd column of Tables 4 and 5 and the related conversion in mm in the 4th.

The particles velocity and acceleration are calculated by using respectively equation 3 and 4 and their values have been presented in 5th and 6th column of Tables 4 and 5.

The space shifted by a particle in the given time interval tracking the particle and processing the image by dedicated software (Amoresano 2013 and Couëdel 2019.

By analyzing the trajectory in off line conditions, the particle velocity was measured.

The following tables, Table 4 and Table 5, show the results calculated for the two diameter classes;

The data logged describe the interaction between the liquid stream and the particles; in particular, it is possible to analyze the behavior between speeds and accelerations.

The following figures (Figure 6 and Figure 7) show the diagram of the velocity and acceleration of the particle of *0,8* and *0,7 mm*.

The particles are hit by the current and are transported; their speed tends to increase as shown in the speed diagram. The acceleration diagram shows that initially the acceleration does not increase because the particles are still hindered by the mound. The speed gradient is not negative and the particle has a positive - but decreasing - acceleration.

Table 3. Fluid dynamic data.

rpm	Q (m³/s)	u (m/s)	A (m²)	Re /
900	5.40E-04	2.75E-01	1.96E-03	1.54E+04
990	6.10E-04	3.11E-01	1.96E-03	1.74E+04
1300	7.90E-04	4.03E-01	1.96E-03	2.25E+04

Table 4. Results (*d = 0.8 mm*).

Frame	t (s)	n° Pixel /	Particle shift (mm)	u_p (m/s)	a (m/s²)
601	0.02	46	3.43E+00	1.72E-01	1.86E-01
606	0.04	94	7.01E+00	1.75E-01	6.22E-02
611	0.06	142	1.06E+01	1.77E-01	7.77E-01
616	0.08	206	1.54E+01	1.92E-01	4.66E-01
621	0.1	270	2.01E+01	2.01E-01	3.73E-01
626	0.12	336	2.51E+01	2.09E-01	1.86E-01
631	0.14	399	2.98E+01	2.13E-01	-

Table 5. Results (*d= 0.7 mm*).

Frame	t (s)	n° Pixel /	Movement? (mm)	up (m/s)	a (m/s2)
310	0.02	22	1.64+00	8.21E-02	1.86+00
315	0.04	64	4.77+01	1.19E-01	3.73E-01
320	0.06	102	7.61+01	1.27E-01	3.73E-01
325	0.08	144	1.07E+01	1.34E-01	1.34E+00
330	0.10	216	1.61E+01	1.61E-01	1.52E+00
335	0.12	308	2.30E+01	1.91E-01	-

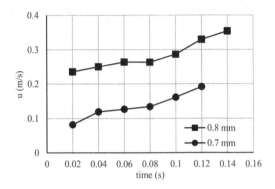

Figure 6. Velocity diagram of the particle in a water stream.

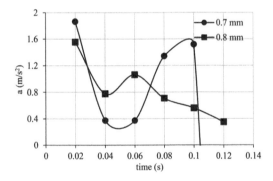

Figure 7. Acceleration diagram of the particle in a water stream.

As the particle is free from the obstacle it begins to feel the speed of the fluid that develops along the axis and it gains speed. This behavior is highlighted by the increase in speed as seen in the Figure 6 and referring to Figure 7 by the positive acceleration gradient. Continuing the analysis of the speeds, notably the particle reaches a maximum speed point. This occurs because it reaches an equilibrium position and then settles under the effect of weight force. This behavior is highlighted by the fact that the acceleration gradient has an opposite sign.

5 CONCLUSIONS

The work highlights that the main behavior of sediments occurs when they are compacted within a liquid stream. Particles behave differently if they occur singly, in the form of clusters or compact sediments. In this paper, sediments of known size have been considered in order to quantify and analyze their behavior in detail. Obviously, what here described does not solve the problem of the transport of sediments but enhances the knowledge of the transport process. In relation to the problem of ballast and therefore of the "Ballast Pump" it is underlined that the only type of fluid dynamic (turbulent) regime is not explanatory of the possible interaction between fluid and particles. Furthermore, the work shows that small particles and weight are not easily dragged by the current. The particles tend to settle and spread on the bottom of the duct and are dragged to the suction mouth of the impeller from where they are difficult to extract. The foregoing highlights that the transport behavior cannot be separated from the presence of the cohesion forces of the agglomeration. In the course of the work, other flow rate and particle size values will be analyzed in order to complete the knowledge of the transport mechanisms and to design pumping systems capable of limiting environmental damage. Further steps will consider other particles with the aims of understanding how the clusters of duplets can be controlled during pumping.

ACKNOWLEDGMENTS

Thanks for the writing of this work to Eng. Miriana Dedes for the definition of the data and to the IMAT center for the scientific collaboration.

REFERENCES

Amoresano, A., Langella, G., Niola, V., & Quaremba, G. 2013. Statistical method to identify the main parameters characterizing a pressure swirl spray. *International Review of Mechanical Engineering (IREME)*, 7(6), 1007–1013.

Amoresano, A., Langella, G., Niola, V., & Quaremba, G. 2014. Advanced image analysis of two-phase flow inside a centrifugal pump. *Advances in Mechanical Engineering*, 6, 958320.

Bilgin Güney, C., Danişman, D. B., Ertürk Bozkurtoğlu, Ş. N., & Yonsel, F. 2018. DETERMINATION OF SEDIMENT ACCUMULATION PATTERN IN A DOUBLE BOTTOM BALLAST TANK MODEL. *Brodogradnja: Teorija i praksa brodogradnje i pomorske tehnike*, 69 (2), 55–67.

Couëdel, L., & Nosenko, V. 2019. Tracking and Linking of Microparticle Trajectories During Mode-Coupling Induced Melting in a Two-Dimensional Complex Plasma Crystal. *Journal of Imaging*, 5(3), 41.

David, M., Gollasch, S., Elliott, B., & Wiley, C. 2015. Ballast water management under the ballast water management convention. In *Global maritime transport and ballast water management* (pp. 89–108). Springer, Dordrecht.

Francis, J. R. D. 1973. Experiments on the motion of solitary grains along the bed of a water-stream. Proceedings of the Royal Society of London. A. *Mathematical and Physical Sciences*, 332(1591), 443–471.

Gollasch, S., Minchin, D., & David, M. 2015. The transfer of harmful aquatic organisms and pathogens with ballast water and their impacts. In *Global maritime transport and ballast water management* (pp. 35–58). Springer, Dordrecht.

Heyman, J., P. Bohorquez, and C. Ancey 2016. Entrainment, motion, and deposition of coarse particles transported by water over a sloping mobile bed, *J. Geophys. Res. Earth Surf.*, 121, 1931–1952, doi:10.1002/2015JF003672.

IMO, International Maritime Organization 2004. *International convention for the control and management of ships' ballast water and sediments*

IMO, International Maritime Organization. 2017. *International Convention for the Control and Management of Ships' Ballast Water and Sediments* (BWM).

Ivče, R., Valčić, S., & Jurdana, I. 2017. Assesment and prediction model of ballast water management. In 2017 International Symposium ELMAR (pp. 275–278). IEEE.

Mocerino, L., & Rizzuto, E. 2018. Climate changes and maritime transportation: A state of the art. In *NAV International Conference on Ship and Shipping Research*, (221499). https://doi. org/10.3233/978-1-61499-870-9-1005.

Mocerino, L., Murena, F., Quaranta, F., & Toscano, D. 2020. A methodology for the design of an effective air quality monitoring network in port areas. *Scientific Reports*, 10(1), 1–10.

Moghadasi, J., Müller-Steinhagen, H., Jamialahmadi, M., & Sharif, A. 2004. Model study on the kinetics of oil field formation damage due to salt precipitation from injection. *Journal of Petroleum Science and Engineering*, 43(3-4), 201–217.

Murena, F., Mocerino, L., Quaranta, F., & Toscano, D. 2018. Impact on air quality of cruise ship emissions in Naples, Italy. *Atmospheric Environment*, 187, 70–83.

Pähtz, T., & Durán, O. 2017. Fluid forces or impacts: What governs the entrainment of soil particles in sediment transport mediated by a Newtonian fluid?. Physical Review *Fluids*, 2(7), 074303.

Prange, G. 2013. Ship ballast tank sediment reduction methods. *Naval Engineers Journal*, 125(2), 127–134.

Yuan, H., Zhou, P., & Mei, N. 2017. Numerical and experimental investigation on the ballast flushing system. Ocean Engineering, 130, 188–198.

Numerical modelling and analysis of the ambient conditions influence on the performance of a marine diesel engine

G. Benvenuto & U. Campora
Polytechnic School, University of Genoa, Genova, Italy

M. Altosole & F. Balsamo
School of Polytechnic and Basic Sciences, University of Naples 'Federico II', Naples, Italy

ABSTRACT: The paper reports the results of a study concerning the influence of ambient conditions on the performance of a marine diesel engine. Starting from the availability of a code previously developed for the thermodynamic simulation of the four-stroke marine engine General Electric 12 V 228, used as prime mover of a marine propulsion system, it was possible to determine the performance of the engine, running in the operating conditions existing in the ship's engine room, for different ambient and seawater temperature values. The correlation between ambient and engine room conditions was assumed on the base of data available in literature. As regards the sea water temperature, which is not strictly dependent on that of the ambient air, in the final part of the paper a sensitivity analysis is reported on the influence of this parameter on engine performance. The analysis carried out allows to obtain the variation of the performance of the engine and its main components (turbocharger compressor and turbine, cylinders, inlet and exhaust manifolds, intercooler, etc.), as function of the ambient conditions and for different engine loads. The results of this investigation are reported in graphical form and discussed in the paper.

1 INTRODUCTION

In the shipping world the diesel engines are currently the most widely used prime movers for ship propulsion and electric energy generation. The manufacturers of these engines usually declare their main operating data (i.e.: efficiency, exhaust emissions) referring to the engine working in standard ambient conditions concerning the ship engine room: temperature of 25° Celsius and 1 bar of total pressure.

In some cases, further data relating to the engine operating in tropical temperature conditions (45° Celsius in the engine room) are provided by the manufacturer, such as in Wärtsilä (2014) and MAN Diesel &Turbo (2015). Comparing the manufacturer working data of a marine engine running at the same load and at the same speed but in different ambient conditions, some differences can be observed with regard to the parameters of both engine and its turbocharger. In literature there are different papers dealing with topics of this type: for instance MAN Diesel & Turbo (2014) and Kahandagamage (2015) refer to two-stroke diesel engines, respectively to an engine for marine propulsion and to an engine of the same type and power but used for electric energy production; Alam et al. (2005) and Akasyah et al. (2015) are pertinent to automotive diesel engines.

This paper investigates, by simulation, the influence of environmental conditions on the performance of a marine four-stroke diesel engine, running in the operative conditions existing in the ship's engine room. The considered engine is an essential part of the propulsion system of a small cruise-ship. The simulation of both engine and propulsion plant was carried using a Matlab©-Simulink© simulation code developed for the purpose.

The environmental conditions considered in this study vary from arctic to equatorial, with a variation of the ambient temperature from -30 to 40 °Celsius.

The engine room temperature is evaluated as a function of the outside environmental temperature by means of a correlation available in literature, while the sea water temperature is determined by data available on-line, always as a function of the environmental temperature.

Because of the higher thermal capacity of sea water compared to air, the temperature of sea water does not strictly depend on the ambient temperature, so it was considered appropriate to include in this study a sensitivity analysis about the influence of this parameter on engine performance.

The present investigation made it possible to obtain the performance of the engine and its main components (turbocharger, cylinders, etc.) as

DOI: 10.1201/9781003216599-49

a function of the environmental conditions and for different ship speeds (i.e. different engine loads). The results presented are adequately discussed.

2 BASIC CONSIDERATIONS

As for marine diesel engines, it is important to identify the most significant parameters that define the environmental conditions, i.e.:

- pressure;
- humidity;
- wind speed;
- temperature.

At the sea level the atmospheric pressure variation is very low, therefore it does not substantially affect the performance of marine diesel engines. Also the air humidity has a negligible influence on the performance of this type of engines (Kahandagamage, 2015). As regards the wind speed, this variable cannot affect, if not indirectly, the behavior of the engine, the latter being confined to the engine room of the vessel.

As a consequence of this, the most important environmental parameter considered in this investigation is the air temperature in the ship's engine room, which is different from the air temperature outside the ship, due to the significant heat developed by the engine.

The relationship between the external air temperature and that inside the engine room will be described hereinafter.

It was decided to consider the engine room air temperature interval of 5÷55 °Celsius, as indicated by the marine engines manufacturers (Wärtsilä, 2014; MAN Diesel & Turbo, 2015). In this study it is assumed that the air temperature at the engine compressor inlet is the same as in the engine room.

Other aspects relating to environmental conditions, so far not explicitly considered, concern the temperature of sea water and the wave motion. The first parameter has influence on the temperature of the fresh water used in the engine intercooler, therefore on the air density introduced into the engine cylinders. This factor has an influence on the engine performance and will be investigated in this work. On the contrary, the wave motion will not be considered and the hypothesis assumed concerns a ship sailing in calm water and in the absence of wind.

3 ENGINE NUMERICAL MODELLING

The engine considered in this study is the General Electric 12V 228 four-stroke marine diesel engine, characterized by a Maximum Continuous Rating (MCR) power of 2289 kW at 1050 rpm.

Table 1 shows the main engine technical data, provided by the manufacturer (General Electric, 2015).

In the table B.m.e.p. is the brake mean effective pressure and B.s.f.c. represents the brake specific fuel consumption.

Table 1. General Electric 12V 228 engine main data.

Engine main data	units	values
Cylinders number	-	12 V
Bore	mm	228.6
Stroke	mm	266.7
Fuel type	-	HFO
Brake power	kW	2289
Speed	rpm	1050
Compression ratio	-	15.7
B.m.e.p	bar	21.9
B.s.f.c	g/kWh	207.9

The analysis of the operation of the engine and the assessment of its performance are carried out by means of a filling and empting thermodynamic simulator, developed in Matlab®-Simulink® language and already presented in previous papers of the authors (Benvenuto et al. 1998; Benvenuto & Campora 2008; Benvenuto et al. 2017). The engine model is organized in modular form as shown in the Simulink scheme of Figure 1.

With reference to the previous figure, the engine model consists of several modules, each representing the following components:

- cylinder;
- engine room;
- intercooler;
- inlet manifold;
- outlet manifold;
- TC_compressor;
- TC_turbine;
- TC_shaft dynamics.

A zero-dimensional approach is used for each block of the simulator referred to the pertinent engine component. The characteristics and performance of the engine components are modeled by algebraic or differential equations and by steady-state performance maps. As regards the fluid model, the ideal gas equation is adopted, while it is assumed that the specific internal energy and enthalpy depend on both temperature and fluid composition.

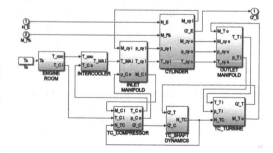

Figure 1. Engine simulation scheme in Simulink® environment.

A synthetic explanation of the engine model is reported below, while for a more detailed description the reader is referred to previous authors' papers (Benvenuto et al. 1998; Benvenuto & Campora 2008; Benvenuto et al. 2017; Altosole et al. 2019).

3.1 Simulation input data

The following main data are required by the engine simulator: geometric data of the engine main components, number of cylinders, intake and exhaust valve data and opening/closing timing logics, compressor and turbine performance maps, engine room ambient conditions, fuel characteristics.

The engine working condition data are defined by: rotational speed, fuel mass percentage introduced in each cylinder and ambient temperature (NE, M_f% and Ta, respectively in Figure 1).

3.2 Cylinder modelling

A single zone approach is used in the 'cylinder' block (Figure 1) to simulate the thermodynamic processes occurring within the cylinder, whose calculation proceeds step by step, according with the crank angle θ value variation (one degree for each step is adopted). The displacement of the piston from the top dead centre (TDC) is calculated as a function of the crank angle value through the equation given by Benvenuto et al. (1998). The equations presented in Whitehouse & Sareen (1974) are used for the convective gas-cylinder wall heat transfer evaluation. The gas-dynamic equations shown in Benvenuto et al. (2013) for the compressible flow through a flow restriction, in case of both subsonic and choked flow, are used to calculate the cylinder inlet and exhaust mass flow rates through the poppet valves.

The release of combustion heat (x_b), as a function of the crank angle, is calculated through the Wiebe equation (Benvenuto et al. 1998):

$$dx_b = 1 - \exp\left[-a\left(\frac{\vartheta - \vartheta_{ign}}{\Delta\vartheta}\right)^m\right] \quad (1)$$

where a and m = numerical constants; θ_{ign} = the combustion start crank angle (the ignition delay angle is determined as reported in Benvenuto et al. 1998); and $\Delta\theta$ = the combustion crank angle interval. It is possible to determine the pressure (p) variation inside the cylinder as a function of the crank angle, by integrating the differential equation (2) (Benvenuto et al. 2017):

$$\frac{dp}{dt} = \frac{k-1}{V_c}\frac{dQ}{dt} - \frac{k}{V_c}p\frac{dV}{dt} + \frac{k-1}{V_c}\left[\left(\frac{dm_i}{dt}\right)H_i - \left(\frac{dm_o}{dt}\right)H_o\right] \quad (2)$$

where t = the time; k = the ratio of specific heats; V_c = the cylinder volume; Q = the heat generated by fuel combustion and exchanged with the walls of the cylinder (see Benvenuto et al. 1998 for more details); m_i = cylinder inlet fluid mass; m_o = the cylinder outlet fluid mass; H_i = fluid inlet specific enthalpy; and H_o = outlet specific enthalpy.

The engine brake torque, representing the output of the engine model (named Q'_E in Figure 1), is obtained as reported in Benvenuto et al. (1998), from the evaluation of the net indicated mean effective pressure (i.m.e.p.), the friction mean effective pressure (f.m.e.p.), determined as indicated in Benvenuto & Campora (1996), and the cylinder displaced volume (V).

3.3 Engine room

The typical trend of the temperature in the ship's engine room versus the ambient air temperature (T_{Ci} and Ta in Figure 1) is modeled in the Engine Room simulator block of Figure 1, by means of a correlation available in literature (MAN Diesel & Turbo, 2015) and shown as a red curve in Figure 2.

The same block is used to determine the sea water temperature as a function of the ambient air one, by the relationship illustrated as a blue curve in Figure 2. This correlation is taken from a web site (www.climieviaggi.it), reporting for a great number of world coastal locations the minimum and maximum atmospheric and sea water temperatures, referred to the twelve months of the year. In this study, the average between maximum and minimum values was considered as the ambient temperature for each month of the year. In order to take into account most of the possible different ambient temperatures that a ship can encounter during its operational life, the data considered were chosen with reference to the following

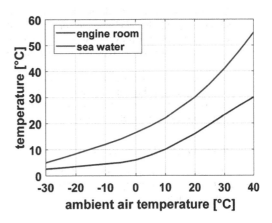

Figure 2. Air temperature in the ship's engine room and seawater temperature, depending on the ambient air temperature.

locations: North Cap and Bergen (Norway), Genova (Italy) and Nassau (Bahamas).

As suggested by MAN Diesel & Turbo (2014), the inlet temperature of the cooling water (T_{coo}), i.e. an output of the engine room block represented in Figure 1, is determined by increasing by 5° Celsius the sea water temperature, in turn calculated as a function of the ambient temperature through the correlation shown in Figure 2.

3.4 Intercooler

In the 'intercooler' module of the simulator, the air temperature at the intercooler outlet is computed by using the heat exchanger efficiency (assumed constant) (Benvenuto et al. 1998).

3.5 Inlet and outlet manifolds

The main equations of the 'inlet manifold' and 'outlet manifold' blocks of Figure 1 are the mass and energy dynamic equations:

$$\frac{d(\rho V)}{dt} = (m_i - m_o) \quad (3)$$

$$\frac{d(\rho V U)}{dt} = (m_i H_i - m_o H_o) \quad (4)$$

where ρ = gas density; V = manifold volume; m_i = inlet gas mass flow rate; m_o = outlet gas mass flow rate; U = specific internal energy; H_i = inlet enthalpy; and H_o = outlet enthalpy.

The total pressure loss is determined as function of the quadratic volumetric flow rate (Benvenuto & Campora, 2008).

3.6 Turbocharger compressor and turbine

Two 2D matrices are used to define the steady state compressor map in the 'TC_compressor' block of Figure 1. The compressor pressure ratio and isentropic efficiency are determined as reported in (Benvenuto et al. 1998).

The turbocharger turbine is simulated in the 'TC_turbine' block of Figure 1 by adopting the typical representation of the turbine steady state performance map (Benvenuto et al. 1998).

3.7 Turbocharger shaft dynamics

The turbocharger shaft dynamics is calculated in the pertinent simulator block by time integration of the following equation:

$$\frac{d\omega}{dt} = \frac{1}{J}(Q'_T - Q'_C) \quad (5)$$

where ω = shaft speed; J = rotor inertia; Q'_T = turbine torque; and Q'_C = compressor torque.

4 ENGINE SIMULATOR VALIDATION

The engine simulator model, after calibration, was applied to the simulation of the General Electric 12V 228 engine. To validate the model, the simulator results in term of brake specific fuel consumption were compared with manufacturer data (General Electric, 2015) for different steady state engine load and speed conditions.

Figure 3 reports the good agreement between reference and calculated values.

In a previous authors' paper (Benvenuto & Campora, 2008) the above described diesel engine model was applied to the simulation of the Wärtsilä 8L46A diesel engine, a medium speed four stroke engine for ship propulsion applications, characterized by 7240 kW of brake power at 500 rpm. In this case more engine data were available from the manufacturer and the mismatches between simulation and reference values, reported in Table 2, are generally low for all of the monitored parameters, particularly at high engine load and speed.

The results obtained for the validation of the engine simulator, shown in Figure 3 and Table 2, show its suitability to be used for the prediction of the engine performance variations due to ambient conditions changes.

5 SHIP PROPULSION SYSTEM SIMULATOR

The engine simulation model is used as an essential part in the propulsion system simulator of the cruise ship "Spirit of Oceanus", whose main characteristics

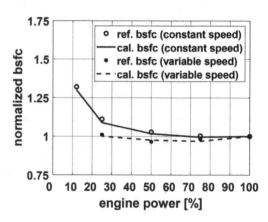

Figure 3. General Electric 12V 228 engine: comparison between reference and calculated brake specific fuel consumption data.

Table 2. Comparison between reference and simulation results in steady state conditions of the engine.

Propulsion data		Engine loads				
Engine power (% MCR)	100	90	85	75	50	25
Engine speed (% MCR)	100	96.6	94.8	90.8	79.4	66
		mismatches (%)				
B.s.f.c.	-0.1	0.3	0.3	0.7	1.9	3.1
Turbocharger speed	0.7	-1.4	-1.3	-2.7	-4.6	-6.4
Outlet compressor temp.	1.8	-2.7	-2.9	-3.3	-4.9	-3.7
Inlet cylinder temperature	1.0	0.6	0.7	0.1	-1.1	-25
Inlet turbine temperature	-0.8	-0.4	0.9	1.9	2.2	-1.4
Outlet turbine temperature	0.3	1.9	2.9	3.1	3.4	2.4
		mismatches (bar)				
Inlet cylinder pressure	0.15	0.15	0.21	0.23	0.32	0.41
Maximum cylinder pressure	-0.08	-2.2	-3.1	-3.4	-4.6	-3.6
Inlet turbine pressure	-0.05	0.01	0.11	0.22	0.32	0.39

are reported in Table 3. The ship's propulsion plant consists of two controllable pitch propellers, each one driven by a GE 12V 228 marine diesel engine through a shaft line and a gearbox. During the navigation the electric power is produced by two electric shaft generators (one for each propeller shaft), while two diesel generators are used in port or in case of emergency.

Figure 4 shows the Simulink scheme of the ship's propulsion model, developed in modular form, like the engine model. In the figure only the modules of the port side components of the propulsion system are shown, these being the same as those of the starboard side. The ship speed (Vs) is determined in the 'ship dynamics' module of the propulsion plant model.

A short description of the ship propulsion model is given below, while more details on the modules and their validity can be found in Altosole et al. (2012).

5.1 Engine governor

A PID type governor is adopted in the 'port governor' block of Figure 4. The governor senses the actual engine speed (N_E) and controls the engine fuel flow percentage (M_f%) in order to maintain the required engine speed (Req_N_E), as commanded by the 'telegraph' block. PID gains are selected through a "trial and error method" procedure, to avoid engine overloads in standard ship manoeuvres (in case of heavy accelerations and crash stop a more complex control logic should be adopted). This simple assumption is considered acceptable, since the whole simulation model is used for a steady state analysis in the present study.

5.2 Shaftline dynamics with electric generator

In this module ('port shaft with eg' of Figure 4) the propeller shaft speed is determined by the dynamic equation:

$$\frac{dN\_P}{dt} = \frac{1}{2\pi J_{PS}} (Q'_{E\_P} - Q'_P - Q'_{EG}) \quad (6)$$

where N_P = propeller shaft speed; J_{PS} = total inertia; Q'_{E_P} = engine torque; Q'_P = propeller torque; and Q'_{EG} = electric generator torque.

5.3 Propeller

In the 'port propeller' block of Figure 4, the Wageningen series open water propeller data (Kuiper, 1992) have been used to find thrust and torque coefficients, needed to simulate propeller thrust and torque.

Table 3. Main ship characteristics.

Ship data	units	values
Overall length	m	80.7
Length between perpendiculars	m	78.8
Breadth	m	15.3
Draught	m	3.9
Displacement	t	3000
Main engines	kW	2 x 2289
Shaft generators	kWe	2 x 800
Diesel generators	kWe	2 x 1050
Summer electric load	kWe	984
Winter electric load	kWe	728
Maximum speed	kn	18.5
Passengers	-	120
Crew	-	72

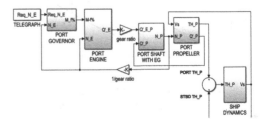

Figure 4. Simulink scheme of the port side propulsion shaftline model.

5.4 Ship dynamics

The ship speed V_S is calculated in the 'ship dynamics' module of Figure 4, by solving the differential equation representing the vessel surge motion:

$$\frac{dV_S}{dt} = \frac{1}{m_S + m_{ad}} \left(z\, TH_{\_P} - \frac{R_T}{1 - t_P} \right) \quad (7)$$

where m_S = ship mass; m_{ad} = added water mass; z = number of working propellers; $TH_{\_P}$ = propeller thrust; t_p = thrust deduction factor; and R_T = total ship resistance.

6 SHIP POWER REQUIREMENT

During navigation, the ship has a mechanical power requirement both for propulsion and for electric loads. In this study three ship speeds are considered: 15, 17 and 18 knots, corresponding to a brake power of the two main engines equal to 603.2, 1214.7 and 1625.1 kW. These values are reported in the propulsion power curve (black) of Figure 5.

As mentioned above, the ship electric loads during the navigation, whose different values depending on the season (winter or summer) are shown in Table 3, are satisfied by a shaft electric generator for each of the two propeller lines.

Assuming that the overall efficiency of electric generator and frequency converter is equal to 0.94, the mechanical power required by this system is obtained by dividing the ship's winter and summer electric loads by this value. The obtained mechanical powers are 387.1 and 523.4 kW, for each of the two shaft generators during winter and summer respectively. These power values have to be added to the power curve of each propulsion engine (black curve in Figure 5) in order to obtain the single engine total delivered power as function of its rotational speed.

By this way the blue curve is obtained in case of winter navigation and the red curve in case of summer navigation, as shown in Figure 5. It has to be noted that all the power curves represented in the figure do not depend on the ambient temperature.

7 SIMULATION RESULTS AND DISCUSSION

This section presents the results of simulations concerning the performance of the engine and its main components for the three ship speeds examined and with temperature variations in the engine room between 5 and 55 °Celsius, in correspondence with changes of the ambient air temperature between -30 and 40 °Celsius. This correspondence is shown in the red curve of Figure 2, while the blue curve of the same figure represents the sea water temperature variation with the ambient air temperature.

As regards the electric loads, with an engine room temperature less than 35 °Celsius, a winter electric load value is considered, while the summer value is considered when this temperature is greater than 35 °Celsius. With a temperature in the engine room equal to 35 °Celsius, both the electric power values (winter and summer) are considered.

The main results of the analysis carried out are presented from Figure 6 to Figure 12. The data shown in the figures are normalized by dividing each datum by the corresponding value referred to the MCR condition of the engine and at a temperature of 25 °Celsius in the engine room.

Figure 6 shows that the compression ratio of the turbocharger compressor decreases as the temperature of the engine room increases, with a discontinuity in correspondence of 35 °Celsius, due the winter-summer electric load variation (in summer condition the required engine power increases, as mentioned above).

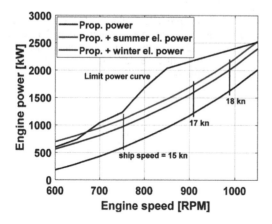

Figure 5. Propulsion power and electric loads of a single engine depending on the engine rotational speed.

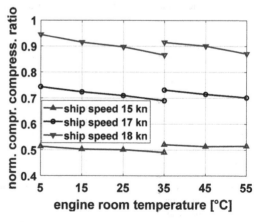

Figure 6. Compression ratio of the turbocharger compressor depending on the engine room temperature, for different ship speeds.

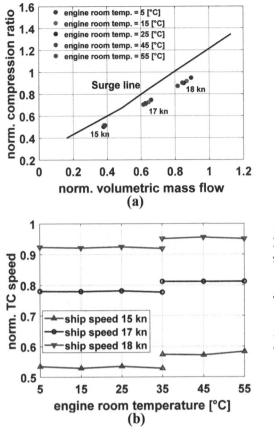

Figure 7. Working points in the compressor map (a) and turbocharger speed (b) for different ship speeds and engine room temperatures.

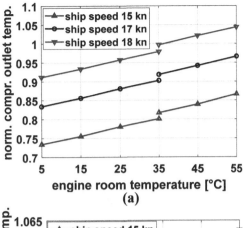

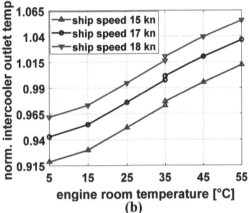

Figure 8. Air temperature at the compressor outlet (a) and at the intercooler outlet (b), depending on the engine room temperature for different ship speeds.

From the same figure it is clear that the compression ratio of the compressor increases with the speed of the ship, due to the consequent increase of the engine load.

Similar considerations can be made regarding the mass flow rate at the inlet of the cylinders. The considerations on the results reported in Figure 6 are confirmed by the data presented in Figure 7 (a), where the same working points are shown in the compressor map. Figure 7 (b) shows that the speed of the turbocharger presents only small variations when the engine room temperature changes; obviously the value of this parameter increases when the engine load (i.e. the ship speed) increases.

Contrary to what happens for the compression ratio of Figure 6, the temperature at the compressor outlet increases with the temperature of the engine room, as shown in Figure 8 (a); this is due to the fact that the temperature at the compressor inlet is the same as in the engine room.

A similar trend is observed in Figure 8 (b), with regard to the air temperature at the intercooler outlet, with a minor variation in comparison to the compressor.

Figure 9 (a) shows that the cylinder equivalence ratio (i.e. the ratio between the stoichiometric air fuel ratio and the effective air fuel ratio) increases as the engine room temperature increases and obviously decreases as the engine load (ship speed) increases. Consequently the in cylinder maximum pressure varies in the opposite way to the cylinder equivalence ratio, as in Figure 9 (b). For obvious reasons the turbocharger turbine inlet pressure varies with a trend similar to that of the maximum cylinder pressure (Figure 9 (b)).

On the contrary, as reported in Figure 10, the temperature at the turbine inlet as a function of the temperature in the engine room and of the engine load (ship speed) presents a significant trend variation compared to the other variables examined so far, as this variable depends on different parameters of the thermodynamic cycle.

As far as fuel consumption parameters are concerned, Figure 11 (a) shows that the fuel mass flow

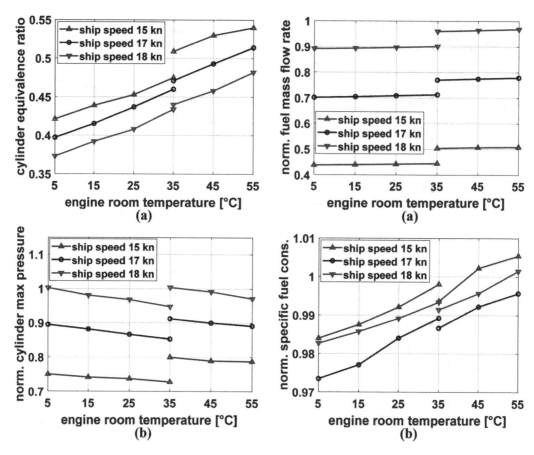

Figure 9. Cylinder equivalence ratio (a) and maximum pressure (b) for different ship speeds and engine room temperatures.

Figure 11. Cylinder fuel mass flow rate (a) and engine fuel consumption (b) for different engine room temperatures and ship speeds.

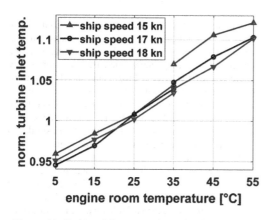

Figure 10. Turbine inlet temperature depending on the engine room temperature for different ship speeds.

rate slightly decreases as the engine room temperature decreases (at the same engine load).

Figure 11 (b) shows the trend of the specific fuel consumption, which increases with the temperature in the engine room. It can also be noted that the lowest specific consumption occurs at an intermediate value of the engine load, this confirming a typical characteristic of the marine diesel engines.

In order to have a concise and immediate indication of the engine's performance, Figure 12 shows the trend of a parameter representing the percentage difference of the specific fuel consumption, defined according to the following equation:

$$\Delta sfc/sfc\% = \frac{sfc_{ER\ T} - sfc_{T\ ref}}{sfc_{T\ ref}} 100\ [\%] \qquad (8)$$

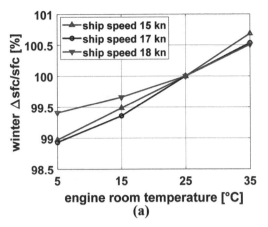

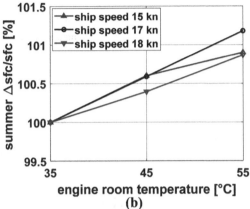

Figure 12. Percentage differences of the engine specific fuel consumption in case of winter conditions (a) and summer conditions (b), for different engine room temperatures and ship speeds.

where $sfc_{ER\ T}$ = fuel consumption corresponding to the actual temperature of the engine room; and $sfc_{T\ ref}$ = fuel consumption referred to the reference temperature of the engine room: 25 °Celsius for winter conditions and 35 ° Celsius for summer conditions.

The data of Figure 12 (a) show a specific fuel consumption increase of about 1.5% (about 1% in case of ship speed of 18 kn) in the winter engine room temperature range.

The data of Figure 12 (b) show a similar increase of the specific fuel consumption (just under 1% in case of ship speed of 15 and 18 kn and just over 1% in case of ship speed of 17 kn) in the summer engine room temperature range.

8 SENSITIVITY ANALYSIS ON SEA WATER TEMPERATURE

The analysis on the influence of ambient conditions on the performance of a marine diesel engine was developed in the previous sections considering a close correlation between the temperature of the engine room and that of the sea water, both depending on the ambient air temperature according to the curves illustrated in Figure 2.

However, the greater thermal capacity of the sea water compared to the air suggests that the correlation used may be adequate for the temperature in the engine room, but not for the sea water temperature. For example, in the passage between day and night the ambient air temperature can normally present variations of several degrees Celsius, while the sea water temperature remains substantially constant. This means that the use of the aforementioned correlation for sea water temperature may not be fully correct.

For this reason, a sensitivity analysis is presented, aimed at assessing the influence of sea water temperature errors on the engine performance.

To this purpose, the ship propulsion plant simulations are repeated, always for different values of the ambient air temperature in the range of variation considered above, with the difference that in this case the sea water temperature is kept constant, with a value of 12 °Celsius in winter conditions and of 24 °Celsius in summer conditions.

From Figure 13 to Figure 15, the characteristics of the engine and its components (previously calculated with the water temperature depending on the ambient air temperature according to the correlation of Figure 2) are compared with those obtained maintaining the temperature of the sea water at a constant value of 12 ° Celsius or 15 ° Celsius in some cases (red lines in the figures). The data shown in the figures refer to a ship speed of 17 knots in winter conditions.

The comparison of the data reported in Figure 13-15 show that the values determined by the engine simulator considering the sea water temperature constant or variable with the ambient temperature do not show significant differences. A similar result is obtained also for a ship speed of 15 and 18 knots. Similar results are obtained considering the ship navigation in summer conditions (in this case 24 °Celsius of sea water temperature is assumed), for all the three here investigated vessel speeds.

The conclusions that can be drawn from the sensitivity analysis is that the sea water temperature value does not have a significant influence on the engine performance, provided that this value does not deviate excessively from the value calculated from the correlation of Figure 2.

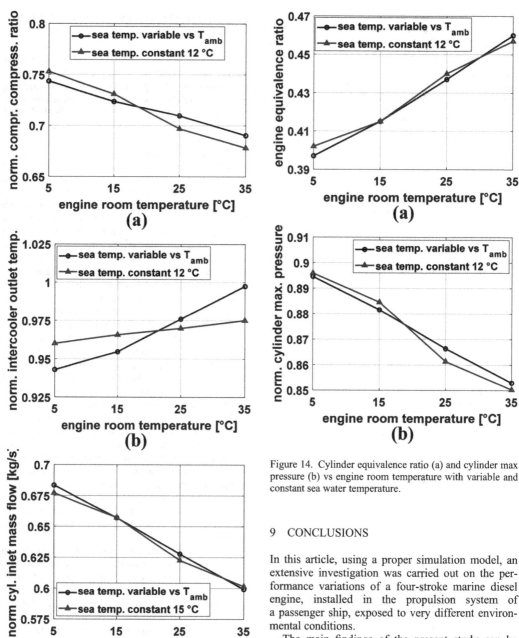

Figure 13. Compressor pressure ratio (a), intercooler outlet air temperature (b) and cylinder inlet mass flow rate (c) versus engine room temperature with variable and constant sea water temperature.

Figure 14. Cylinder equivalence ratio (a) and cylinder max pressure (b) vs engine room temperature with variable and constant sea water temperature.

9 CONCLUSIONS

In this article, using a proper simulation model, an extensive investigation was carried out on the performance variations of a four-stroke marine diesel engine, installed in the propulsion system of a passenger ship, exposed to very different environmental conditions.

The main findings of the present study can be summarized as follows:

– the humidity of the air and the variation of the pressure at sea level do not have substantial consequences on the parameters of the engine. This consideration derives from the bibliographic analysis carried out;

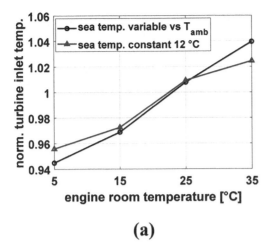

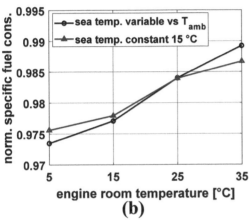

Figure 15. Turbine inltet temperature (a) and specific fuel consumption (b) vs engine room temperature with variable and constant sea water temperature.

− the sea surface water temperature, not strictly dependent on the ambient air temperature, has a negligible influence on the engine operating parameters, as verified by the sensitivity analysis reported in the study;
− the ambient air temperature, which can vary considerably in the various possible climatic conditions in which the ship operates and has a strong influence on the air temperature in the engine room, is the variable that has the greatest influence on the performance of the engine.

As further considerations emerging from the simulation analysis, it can be stated that in the three conditions of ship speeds (or engine loads) examined, there were no surge risks for the compressor of the turbocharger. Moreover, the simulated variation in fuel consumption between summer and winter condition shows a percentage increase of about 2.5% of this parameter between the minimum and maximum temperature of the engine room considered in the investigation.

From a practical point of view, the main conclusion is that for the propulsion engines and diesel generators a 0.5÷0.8% efficiency increase, mainly in the summer-tropical ambient conditions, can be obtained by improving the ship engine room ventilation.

REFERENCES

Akasyah, M. K., Mamat, R., Abdullah, A., Aziz, A., Yassin, H.M. 2015. Effect of ambient temperature on diesel-engine combustion characteristics operating with alcohol fuel. *International Journal of Automotive and Mechanical Engineering*, Vol. 11, pp. 2373–2382.

Alam, M., Song, K.H., Boehman, A. 2005. Effects of inlet air temperature on performance and emissions of a direct injection diesel engine operated with ultra-low sulfur diesel fuel. International Conference on Mechanical Engineering, *(ICME2005-TH-35; Proc. intern. symp, Dhaka, Bangladesh*, 28–30 December 2005.

Altosole, M., Figari M., Martelli, M. 2012. Time domain simulation for marine propulsion applications. *The 44th Summer Computer Simulation Conference; Proc. intern. symp., Genoa, Italy,* 8–11 July 2012.

Altosole, M., Campora, U., Figari, M., Laviola, M., Martelli, M. 2019. A diesel engine modelling approach for ship propulsion real-time simulators. *Journal of Marine Science and Engineering*, 7(5), 138, pp. 1–19.

Benvenuto, G. & Campora, U. 1996. A computer model for, the dynamic simulation of turbocharged diesel engine. *1st International Conference on Control and Diagnostics in Automotive Applications; Proc. intern. symp, Genoa, Italy*, 3–4 October 1996.

Benvenuto, G., Campora, U., Carrera, G., Casoli, P. 1998. A two-zone diesel engine model for the simulation of marine propulsion plant transients. *MARIND 98, 2nd International Conference on Marine Industry; Proc. intern. symp, Varna, Bulgaria*, September 28 – October 2, 1998.

Benvenuto, G. & Campora, U. 2008. Simulation and performance analysis of a faulty marine diesel engine running in realistic operating conditions. *INEC 2008, 9th International Naval Engineering Conference, Hamburg, Germany*, 1–3 April 2008.

Benvenuto, G., Campora, U., Laviola, M. 2013. Simulation model of a methane-fuelled four stroke marine engine for studies on low emission propulsion systems. *IMAM 2013, 15th International Congress on maritime association of the Mediterranean, A Coruna, Spain, 14–17 October 2013.*

Benvenuto, G., Campora, U., Laviola, M., Terlizzi, G. 2017. Simulation model of a Dual-Fuel four stroke engine for low emission ship propulsion applications. *International Review of Mechanical Engineering*, Vol. 11, N. 11, November 2017, pp. 817–824.

General Electric, 2015. GE-Marine-228-250 4T Engines. *Product Selection Guide.*

Kahandagamage, G. 2015. Analysis of the effect of charge air temperature and humidity on the combustion process of diesel engines at Heladhanavi Power Plant-Puttalam-Sri Lanka. *Master of Science Thesis, KTH School of Industrial Engineering and Management Energy Technology-Division of Heat & Power, Stocholm, Sweden.*

Kuiper, G. 1992. The Wageningen propeller series. MARIN Publication 92–001.

MAN Diesel & Turbo, 2014. Influence of ambient temperature conditions - main engine operation of MAN B&W Two-Stroke Engines. *Internal report, Copenhagen, Denmark*

MAN Diesel & Turbo, 2015. MAN 51/60 DF IMO TIER II/IMO TIER III. *Project Guide*.

Wartsila, 2014. Wartsila 46 DF Product Guide. *Marine, Wartsila, Vaasa, October 2014.*

Whitehouse, N.D., Sareen, B.K. 1974. Prediction of release in a quiescent chamber diesel engine allowing for fuel/air mixing. *Automotive Engineering Congress; Proc. SAE 740084, Detroit, Michigan, February 25 - March 1, 1974.*

# Condition analysis of air conditioning cooling water pumps

S. Lampreia, V. Vairinhos & V. Lobo
Portuguese Naval Academy & Centro de Investigação Naval (CINAV), Alfeite, Almada, Portugal

T. Morgado
Laboratório Nacional de Engenharia Civil (LNEC), Instituto Politécnico de Tomar e UNIDEMI da FCT-UNL

ABSTRACT: In a ship, the operation of air conditioning system plays a prominent role in maintaining the operation of various electronic systems. Air conditioning system cooling water electropumps are rotating equipment that may be subject to degrading operating conditions. The electropump condition monitoring is a premise for maintaining the performance of air conditioning. For this, vibration measure is done on the electropumps. The objective of this paper was to define a statistic methodology to detect eventual anomaly in early stages. In phase I the collected data was analyzed and processed with Statistica and Matlab software. To obtain the functioning parameters, mean and standard deviation, the univariate Shewhart control charts: individual observation and moving range, were applied. In phase II, the monitoring phase, it was applied the Re-Modified CUSUM control chart. The application of statistic techniques can allow the knowledge of data tendency, and eventually define a future intervention.

1 INTRODUCTION

Cooling electro pumps from a ship air condition system are one important equipment for its properly functioning and for the ship itself. If it has a low performance the ship mission can be compromised.

A cooling electro pump maintenance plan can be preventive systematic by substituting some components (ex: sealing components) based on functioning time, or condition based on others (ex: bearings). The maintenance strategies will always depend on the electro pump lifecycle and the owner's financial capacity and its objectives for the systems. For example, considering owner in a bad financial context or if the system is on the end of life cycle, the implemented maintenance system can be a Risk Based Maintenance (RBM). A RBM system can be based on the results of equipment condition monitoring applied statistical methodologies.

On condition monitoring many non-destructives techniques may be use, for these electro pumps it is suggested to choose vibration monitoring with data registration and treatment.

Many statistical methodologies may be used, like modified control charts (Dias *et al*, 2009) and biplots, in this case and because of the results a re-modified CUSUM Control Chart will be used.

The main objective on this study is to predict, on time and continuously, the instant where a repairable equipment monitoring chosen parameter reaches a value of a failure.

2 STATISTICAL METHODS

2.1 *Phase I*

If there is a significate (200 or more) sample of the functioning parameters from an equipment, the Shewhart control charts will be applied, considering individual observations (X) and moving range (MR) control charts. With those charts, the parameters: mean and standard deviation will be estimated. If the data was not independent the ARIMA are suggested model (Lampreia *et al*, 2018a). The variables/parameters under study are considered continuous and independent (proven in the results), so the ARIMA models in this article will not be developed.

When the charts are design on phase I it should show under control variables, and if there are outliers it should applied statistical techniques to eliminate or integrate it.

Although the use of vibration monitoring, where the maximum values are controlled, and not the minimum, on Table 1 for phase I the equations for the upper control limit (*UCL*), the lower control limit (*LCL*) and the center line (*CL*) for the Shewhart charts, are presented. This limits are calculated based on the *m* (or m − 1) sample statistics, with the next equations:

$$\bar{X} = \sum_{i=1}^{m} X_i / m \qquad (1)$$

DOI: 10.1201/9781003216599-50

Table 1. – Shewhart Control Charts Limits - phase I (Requeijo & Pereira, 2012).

Chart	LCL	CL	UCL
X	$\bar{X} - 3\sigma_X$	$\bar{X}$	$\bar{X} + 3\sigma_X$
MR	$D_3 \overline{MR}$	$\overline{MR}$	$D_4 \overline{MR}$

$$\overline{MR} = \sum_{i=1}^{m-1} MR_i/(m-1) \quad (2)$$

$$MR_i = |X_i - X_{i-1}| \quad (3)$$

If the process is under statistical control with all the observations between the control limits, its parameters should be estimated based on $\hat{\mu} = \bar{X}$ and $\hat{\sigma} = \overline{MR}/d_2$. The constants on Table 1, D_3, D_4 and d_2 depend exclusively on the sample dimension and its values are defined on factors tables for variables traditional control charts defined by Shewhart. (Requeijo et al, 2012)

2.2 Phase I – Modified CUSUM chart

The CUSUM control charts are based on "memory" statistics using the early results to calculate the present, it has high sensitivity to detect small shifts (Perry & Pignatiello, 2011). The analysis of an out of control in this charts must consider the values at present time and the values at the previous time. (Pereira and Requeijo, 2012).

For phase II it was tested the application of the modified CUSUM control chart for online condition monitoring, (Lampreia et al, 2016a), but accordingly the obtained results, it is proposed a re-modification of this charts.

A "Modified CUSUM" control chart is built on cumulative sum – C – (Lampreia et al, 2018b) like in the original CUSUM control chart (Sibanda & Sibanda, 2007) defined by:

$$C_t = max\,(0,\ C_{t-1} + (Z_t - k));\ C_0 = 0 \quad (4)$$

$$Z_t = ((\bar{X}_t - T_L)/\sigma_{\bar{X}}) \quad (5)$$

$$\sigma_{\bar{X}} = \sigma/\sqrt{n} \quad (6)$$

$$\Delta = \delta\,\sigma_{\bar{X}} \quad (7)$$

$$k = \delta/2 \quad (8)$$

$$T_L = (T_L)_{Standard} - \Delta_S \quad (9)$$

$$\Delta_S = \delta_1\,\sigma \quad (10)$$

where δ_1 is constant.

For this charts, $\bar{X}_t$ is the sample mean at t, T_L is the maximum admissible vibration, σ the process standard deviation, n the sample dimension, Z_t is the reduced form of $\bar{X}_t$, k the reference value and Δ_s the safety factor." (Barbosa, 2012) (Lampreia et al, 2018a)

For the "Modified CUSUM charts" it was considered two limits, one is an Alert Level (AL), and the second is the real Upper Control Level (UCL). The AL and UCL calculations are based on Gan (1991) abacus. It was considered a significance level $\alpha = 1\%$ (ARL = 100) to define the AL and $\alpha = 0.2\%$ (ARL = 500) to define UCL (Lampreia et al, 2016b).

2.3 Phase II – Re-Modified CUSUM chart

Because of the obtained results using the given data, in the presence of high vibration values, considering a condition based maintenance implemented on the organization under study, it was decided to made a re-modification of the Modified CUSUM control chart so the results of the chart reflect the result of a high but maintained vibration, and doesn´t exponential the results. For that, it was applied a logarithmical base (e) and sum 5 units, Equation 8, considering and respecting the original chart limits.

$$C_t = max\,(0, \ln(C_{t-1} + (Z_t - k)) + 5);\ C_0 = 0 \quad (11)$$

For the Re-Modified CUSUM Charts it was considered the same two limits of the Modified CUSUM Control Charts.

3 METHODOLOGY

3.1 Phase I - method

a. Define the parameters to control.
b. Collect data to define the functioning parameters of the equipment.
c. Analyze the collected data, studying the continuity and independence.
d. If the data is independent apply the charts X and MR, and if the charts are under control define functioning parameters, mean and standard deviation.

3.2 Phase II - method

a. Apply the Re-modified CUSUM control charts for online condition monitoring.
b. Rules for intervention, Figure 1:
  ✓ If 10 sequential observations between the AL and the UCL or/with less than 4 sequential above the UCL proceed to a more frequently observation.
  ✓ If 4 observations above the UCL proceed to an intervention of maintenance.

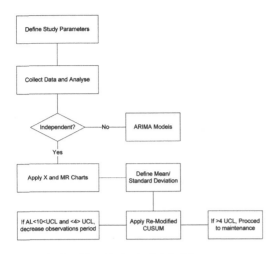

Figure 1. Condition Monitoring Methodology.

4 CASE STUDY

The electro pump under condition monitoring is part of the air-condition (AC) ship system. In the ship there is four refrigerated pump, two for the forward AC and two for the backward. For this system a preventive maintenance plan is defined. Usually the anomalies are early detected with vibration measures. The study will be about an electro pump with a detected anomaly.

It was defined two points of measure of the electro pump, point A and point B, Figure 2. Because of the interesting results, with a registered anomaly, for data treatment the axial and vertical observations of the two selected points was chosen, and decline the horizontal data. In the article the point with better results is the A-V.

After test the data independence on Statistica software applying the autocorrelation function, it was concluding that the data was independent, so the collected data is directly used on the control charts.

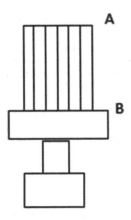

Figure 2. Electro-pump points of measure.

Originally, and because there is lack of data registration, data was simulated on Matlab, for phase I based on data without an anomaly in the pump and in phase II considering an anomalous state and based on simulation on real data.

The normality of data was checked with Kolmogorov-Smirnov test (for $\alpha = 5\%$); and for A-V: d = 0,04584. Since $d < D_{Critico}$ the data was considered normal.

$$D_{Critical} = \frac{0,886}{\sqrt{N}} = \frac{0,886}{\sqrt{200}} = 0,0626$$

Phase I

On phase I the parameters was defined, in Figure 2 and Figure 3 represent respectively the Control charts for individual observation and the moving Range Control Chart using the Statistica software. When all data was between the control limits the functioning parameters for the vibration were defined.

The definition of the parameters was made for the four observation axis considered for the study, where was obtained the mean and standard deviation for each one, Table 2.

When the parameters were defined, it was passed to phase II.

Phase II

Analyzing the obtained data, the highest measures of the four selected points for study was for point A-V and for point B-A.

The graphical results are presented for A-A and A-V.

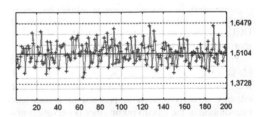

Figure 3. Control chart for individual observation point A-V.

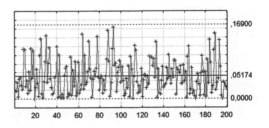

Figure 4. Control chart for Moving Range observation point A-V.

Table 2. Variables - Parameters.

Point/Obs	μ	σ
A-A	1,0833	0,04591
A-V	1,5104	0,04585
B-A	1,1397	0,05216
B-V	1,5320	0,05025

The limits of the Charts for phase II are on Table 3:

Table 3. Variables - Parameters.

	ARL	
	60	370
	LSC (α=0,2%) h	LA (α=1%) h1
$K=\delta/2$	0,25 — 8,5	5,51
	0,5 — 5,1	3,5
	0,75 — 3,5	2,5

In phase II it was used the re-modified *CUSUM* control chart because the modified CUSUM control chart wasn't adequate, because the values were already too high for the chart design, all the data was above the UCL, notice that the UCL it is 8.5 and the first result it is above forty, Figure 5.

On Figure 6 and 7 the observations correspond to vibration measure on point A of the electro pump.

For Figure 6, only the UCL is represent, but the results were all between the Alert Level and the UCL, so the electro pump monitoring should be more frequently since observation nr 10.

For Figure 7, considering a CUSUM Modified (Δ=0,5σ) it also represents the UCL, but the results were all above UCL, so accordingly the defined methodology there is a need to proceed to maintenance intervention of the electro pump since observation nr 4.

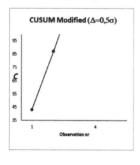

Figure 5. Modified CUSUM Control Chart for A-V observation point.

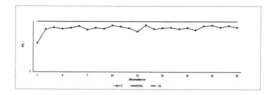

Figure 6. Re-Modified CUSUM Control Chart for A-V observation point.

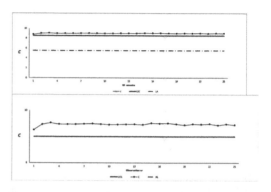

Figure 7. Re-Modified CUSUM Control Chart for A-A observation point.

Because of time limit reasons, it was not possible to simulated other data and test this re-modified charts on other equipment'. Work will be done to obtain more real data from the condition monitoring realized by the ships to try to take more real evidences of these results.

5 CONCLUSIONS

The performance of cooling electro pump is important for ship operation and systems functioning.

In a same equipment, various maintenance systems can be integrated considering its various components.

Using vibration measure the condition of the electro pumps may be defined.

The collected vibration can be treated with statistical techniques, with a re-modification on the Modified *CUSUM* control Charts.

It was considered two phases of the control charts application (phase I and phase II), on phase I historical data was used, and for phase II it should proceed to an online monitoring.

It charts may be applied in order to obtain early damage tendencies. But in this specifically article for control charts it is recommended complemented tests and simulation in others equipment's.

REFERENCES

Barbosa, P. I. 2012. *Monitorização do Estado de Condição de Equipamentos*, Monte da Caparica: FCT-UNL.

Dias, J. M., Requeijo, J. R. e Pereira, Z. L. 2009. "Monitorização do estado de condição dos sistemas reparáveis" (Monitoring the condition state of repairable systems) in: *Riscos: Riscos Industriais e Emergentes;* C. Guedes Soares, C. Jacinto, A. P. Teixeira, P. Antão (Eds), Edições Salamandra, Lisboa, Vol.1, pp. 501–512.

Gan, F. F. 1991, "An Optimal Design of CUSUM Quality Control Charts", *Journal of Quality Technology*, QICID: 11304; Vol. 23, pp. 279–286.

Lampreia, S., Vairinhos, V., Lobo, V. Parreira, R. & Requeijo, J. 2016a. Control Charts Limits Flexibility Based on the Equipment Conditions. Maritime Technology and Engineering 3, ISBN 978-1-138-03000-8, Editors C. Guedes Soares & T.A. Santos, p. 847–852. Taylor & Francis Group, London.

Lampreia, S., Vairinhos, V., Lobo, V. Parreira, R. & Requeijo, J. 2016b. Opportunistic Maintenance Based on CUSUM Control Charts. Maritime Technology and Engineering 3, ISBN 978-1-138-03000-8, Editors C. Guedes Soares & T.A. Santos, p. 853–857, Taylor and Francis Group, London.

Lampreia S., Dias J. Requeijo J., Vairinhos V. M. e Barbosa, P. 2018a. Condition Monitoring Based on Modified Cusum and Ewma Control Charts. Journal of Quality in Maintenance Engineering, Vol. 24 Issue 1, pp. 119–132, Emerald Publishing Limited.

Lampreia, S., Vairinhos, V., Lobo, & Requeijo, J. 2018b. Ships on Condition Data Driven Maintenance Management, Progress in Maritime Technology and Engineering, ISBN 978-1-138-58539-3, Editors C. Guedes Soares & T. A. Santos, p. 475–480. Taylor and Francis Group, London.

Pereira, Z. L. e Requeijo, J. G. 2012. *Qualidade: Planeamento e Controlo Estatístico de Processos (Quality: Statistical Process Control and Planning)*, Co-edition of FCT/UNL Foundation and Editora Prefácio, Lisboa.

Perry, M. B., & Pignatiello, J. J. 2011. "Estimating the time of step change with Poisson *CUSUM* and *EWMA* control charts", *International Journal of Production Research*, Vol. 49-10, pp. 2857–2871.

Sibanda, T., & Sibanda, N. 2007. "The *CUSUM* Chart Method as a tool for continuous monitoring of clinical outcomes using routinely collected data", *Bmc Medical Research Methodology*.

A review of the use of Biodiesel as a green fuel for diesel engines

M. Tadros
Centre for Marine Technology and Ocean Engineering (CENTEC), Instituto Superior Técnico, Universidade de Lisboa, Portugal.
Naval Architecture and Marine Engineering Department, Faculty of Engineering, Alexandria University, Alexandria, Egypt

M. Ventura & C. Guedes Soares
Centre for Marine Technology and Ocean Engineering (CENTEC), Instituto Superior Técnico, Universidade de Lisboa, Portugal

ABSTRACT: Stringent regulations are applied by the international regulators to significantly reduce the exhaust emissions from internal combustion engines. Several solutions are proposed, while the use of biofuels in diesel engines attracts the attention of researchers and automotive companies as an alternative source of energy to cut the amount of exhaust emissions produced. In this review paper, an overview is presented on the use of biofuels in diesel engine applications. This review covers the history and the methods of biofuel production, the performance and the exhaust emissions of diesel engines fueled with biofuels and the main parameters that affect the behavior of the combustion process using biofuels. This paper also describes the numerical models and software developed to easily compute the engine performance for different types of biofuels. Finally, some issues and challenges are presented to improve the biofuel system performance and the required safety aspects.

1 INTRODUCTION

According to the statistics of the International Maritime Organization (IMO), around 90% of world trade is transported by the international shipping industry and some negative environmental impacts are recognized. Therefore, increasing the efforts in the maritime industry to prevent or reduce emissions of greenhouse gases (GHG) as well as nitrogen oxides (NO_x), sulphur oxides (SO_x) and particulate matter (PM) is becoming an essential issue towards climate change mitigation (United Nations, 2019).

IMO, through the six annexes of the International Convention for the Prevention of Pollution from Ships (MARPOL 73/78), has established several guidelines to prevent marine pollution from ships. Also, several indicators and concepts are proposed as controllers to minimize the exhaust emissions from the maritime activities especially in Emission Control Areas (ECAs) as shown in Figure 1, such as the Energy Efficiency Design Index (EEDI), the Energy Efficiency Operational Indicator (EEOI), the Ship Energy Efficiency Management Plan (SEEMP) and the Environmental Ship Index (ESI).

Lloyd's Register (2012) presented several solutions to improve the energy efficiency of existing ships by combining the use of new technologies and renewable energies to compensate for the shortage and the rising cost of fossil fuels (Maghanaki et al., 2013). From the perspective of ship design, increasing the ship deadweight of a ship via reductions in lightweight (Jafaryeganeh et al., 2019), optimizing the hull form to reduce the aerodynamic resistance and to select an efficient propulsive system (Tadros et al., 2018a, Tadros et al., 2020d, Tadros et al., 2021) and using the renewable resources such as wind and solar power are the main solutions considered.

From the viewpoint of operation, the speed of several types of ships is reduced and optimized along the ship trip to control the behavior of the shipmaster (Vettor and Guedes Soares, 2016), to reduce the generated power and thus the fuel consumption and the exhaust emissions (MAN Diesel & Turbo, 2017b, Vettor et al., 2016, Vettor et al., 2018).

From the perspective of technology, the engine manufacturer is responsible to improve the overall performance of the engine by optimizing the different parts of the engine using different types of fuel (Tadros et al., 2016, Tadros et al., 2019, Tadros et al., 2020b). Based on the new technologies, all new marine engines either two-stroke or four-stroke are built according to the international regulations (MAN Diesel & Turbo, 2017a, Tadros et al., 2020c), while different retrofit procedures are applied for the existing ships to reduce their level of exhaust emissions (MAN Diesel & Turbo, 2016).

DOI: 10.1201/9781003216599-51

Figure 1. Emission Control Areas (ECAs) around the world.

Biofuels, such as biodiesel, are becoming an alternative fuel for marine diesel engines to reduce the large amount of emissions as well as to compensate for the rising cost and the shortage of fossil fuels.

Biofuel has been recognized and used by many countries around the world including the European Union (EU), the United States, Brazil and Asia (The Statistics Portal, 2017) either as pure biodiesel (B100) or blended with petroleum diesel (Bxx), where xx represents the percentage of biodiesel, for instance, B10 contains 10% of biodiesel and 90% of diesel oil.

According to ETIP (2019), different types of biofuels are under investigation and are expected to be widely used in the near future, as the raw material can vary from location to location (Avinash et al., 2014). Most of the previous studies have concluded an improvement in the amount of exhaust emissions for the same engine performance (Dwivedi et al., 2011, Xue et al., 2011).

The aim of this paper is to present useful information about the use of biodiesel engine as a main source of power for both automotive and marine applications and to share this information to allow considering biodiesel as an alternative fuel to the fossil and petroleum fuels. Moreover, a review is presented on the simulation software and techniques used, to calibrate, validate and predict the engine performance computed from the experimental tests in different previous studies.

The rest of this paper is organized as follows: 2 presents an overview of the production process of biodiesel fuel. The performance of biodiesel engines is presented in section 3, while section 4 shows the reduction and the increment in the amount of exhaust emissions in biodiesel engine in comparison to the diesel engine. 5 introduces the various parameters that affect the combustion process. An overview of the different numerical software and techniques is shown in sections 6 and 7 to easily compute and optimize the performance of several biodiesel engines. Section 8 presents briefly some of the main issues and challenges that must be considered in further research and finally, some conclusions are presented in section 9.

2 PRODUCTION OF BIODIESEL

In 1893, Rudolf Diesel used peanut oil as a fuel to operate his engine and anticipated that the use of vegetable oils will be as important as petroleum and the coal-tar products to operate the engines (Bart et al., 2010). Chavanne (1938) was granted a patent for his work in transesterification of vegetable oils which becomes the basis for the production of modern biodiesel. This chemical operation was applied to palm oil ethyl esters to operate a commercial bus in Belgium between Brussels and Louvain.

Recently, biofuel can be produced from vegetable oils or animal fats by mixing between this feedstock and alcohol, either methanol or ethanol. Since the 1900s, over 30 types of oils have been considered as a fuel to operate diesel engines (Haldar et al., 2009). Currently ethanol and biodiesel are the two main biofuels produced. In marine applications, the use of higher proportions of ethanol in marine fuel is not compatible with many fuel systems and can cause engine failure and potential safety risks because, as a powerful solvent, it can react with fuel tanks and filters in addition to its higher attraction and absorption to the condensation (BELL, 2019). Biodiesel or Fatty Acid Methyl Esters (FAME) are produced through a chemical process called transesterification, whereby the glycerin is separated from the fat or vegetable oil. The process leaves behind two products: methyl esters, which is the chemical name for biodiesel, and glycerin, which is used in a variety of products (ETIP, 2019). It is an economical and highly efficient process through low pressure and temperature (Mahmudul et al., 2017) in comparison with the other processes such as micro-emulsion (Singh and Singh, 2010), pyrolysis (Balat and Demirbas, 2009) and dilution (Singh and Singh, 2010).

FAME has many advantages such as it is a renewable resource, versatile, easy to use, non-toxic and biodegradable, has similar physical properties to the conventional diesel (Mohd Noor et al., 2018). Otherwise, it is limited due to higher density and viscosity which can make injection problems, a lower calorific value which can increase the brake specific fuel consumption (BSFC), the formation of higher NO_x causing acid rain, variation in the quality of the fuel and the high cost. Table 1 shows the difference between the properties of diesel and biodiesel fuel.

Most of the engine makers such as Wärtsilä, Caterpillar and MAN claimed that their marine engines can be fueled with biodiesel and the trans esterified biofuels must comply with the EN14214 standard. However, the use of such fuels would require some changes to the engines and the material of the on-board storage to ensure the safety of operations.

Moreover, there is not any international standard for the specifications of the marine biodiesel fuel

Table 1. Properties of diesel and biodiesel fuel (Wei et al., 2014).

Property	Diesel	Biodiesel
Oxygen content (wt%)	0	10.32
Carbon content (wt%)	86	77.0
Hydrogen content (wt%)	14	12.18
Specific gravity at 15 °C	852	896
Gross heating value (MJ/kg)	45.76	40
Flash point (°C)	67	105
Viscosity at 40 °C (cSt)	1.57	2.99
Stoichiometric air/fuel ratio	14.60	12.33
Cetane number	49	53

compared to the fuels used in automotive engine applications (Mohd Noor et al., 2018).

3 PERFORMANCE OF BIODIESEL ENGINE

The performance of any engine is defined mainly by the brake power delivered, brake specific fuel consumption and the exhaust temperature of the gas. In this section, a review of the previous research works of these three items in biodiesel engines is presented.

3.1 Brake power

Several published papers claim a slight reduction in the power delivered up to 10%, depending on the raw material used, the percentage of biodiesel blends, the oxygen content in biodiesel and the lower heating value than in diesel oil (Piloto-Rodríguez et al., 2017).

Ali et al. (2016) reported a reduction in brake power by 2.6% when increasing biodiesel ratios up to 30%. Mata et al. (2010) confirmed that the brake power produced using biofuel is lower than using diesel oil. Murillo et al. (2007) conducted experimental studies on the marine engine and found a reduction in brake power especially when using B100. Clume et al. (2019) conducted a research study on diesel engines installed onboard military ships and reported a reduction in brake power with less than 1.5% than in diesel oil for various blends of soybean biodiesel blends. While Roskilly et al. (2008) reported a 1% difference on brake power comparing to diesel oil. This power reduction is due to the lower heat release rate (HRR) during the combustion process of biodiesel, due to the different physical properties of biodiesel fuels such as kinematic viscosity, heating value, cetane number and surface tension (Roskilly et al., 2008, Gokalp et al., 2011).

3.2 Brake specific fuel consumption (BSFC)

Several studies show the effect of marine biodiesel on BSFC. They concluded that the value of BSFC increases when using biodiesel fuel compared with diesel oil based on the fuel properties as mentioned before. Murillo et al. (2007) reported an increase in BSFC up to 11.4% in comparison to the diesel oil to achieve the same output power. Ali et al. (2016) stated that BSFC can increase by 3% when increasing the biodiesel ratios up to 30%. Clume et al. (2019) reported a 5.6% increase in BSFC while Roskilly et al. (2008) achieved a higher BSFC of up to 20.9%. Silitonga et al. (2013) performed experimental tests using Ceiba pentandra and a 23% increase in BSFC is achieved than using diesel oil.

3.3 Exhaust gas temperature (EGT)

The main findings of the previous research work are that the EGT in biodiesel engines can be sometimes increased up to 11.5% when compared to the use of fossil fuel and sometimes show a reduction depending on the type of engine and operating conditions (Mohd Noor et al., 2018). Some factors that affect the EGT are identified by Pullen and Saeed (2014). The advanced injection timing leads to an increase in both combustion pressure and temperature. A higher cetane number improves the combustion process and shortens the ignition delay. This factor increases the EGT. The heating value and the amount of air-fuel ratio (AFR) have a direct effect on the combustion process and on the exhaust temperature. The blend ratio plays an important role in the behavior of the combustion process as mentioned in (Geng et al., 2017, Puškár et al., 2018). Once the percentage of biodiesel blend increases, the generated heat during the combustion decelerated and the combustion temperature decrease.

4 EXHAUST EMISSIONS OF BIODIESEL ENGINE

The amount of different exhaust emissions are reduced such as carbon monoxide (CO), hydrocarbon (HC), sulphur dioxide (SO_2) and PM in addition to the carbon dioxide (CO_2) which are partially absorbed by the photosynthesis of plants (Clume et al., 2019). This reduction in emissions is noticed due to the amount of oxygen in the fuel which can cause complete combustion and an emission reduction (Agarwal and Das, 2001).

Murillo et al. (2007) reported a reduction in CO emissions up to 12% when using the range of B3 to B10 while an increase in NO_x emissions is achieved. An et al. (2012) and Roskilly et al. (2008) reported similar results where the CO emissions increase at a high blend ratio and lower engine speed and vice versa.

Many published papers reported a reduction in HC due to the light hydrocarbon's fractions which can easily evaporate. A range from 15% to 30% of HC reduction in comparison with diesel oil is reported by Monirul et al. (2016) and Juoperi and Ollus (2008).

Biodiesel fuel is considered as a zero-sulphur product, as it is produced from plants, which are free from any sulphur elements. Using biodiesel, a significant reduction in SO_x emissions is achieved and can easily verify international regulations (Prucole et al., 2014).

Since PM depends on the amount of sulphur and ash in the fuel, biodiesel is considered a clean fuel from these elements. Therefore, a significant reduction in the experimental tests is reported in comparison to fossil fuel (Su et al., 2013).

The engines fueled with biodiesel show a significant reduction in CO_2 emissions due to a lower ratio of carbon-hydrogen in the fuel as reported in (Sahoo et al., 2007, Adaileh and AlQdah, 2012, Gabiña et al., 2016). However, Roskilly et al. (2008) noticed an increase in CO_2 emissions due to the increase in fuel density. In addition, a higher amount of NO_x emissions is noticed by about 10% more than the amount of NO_x emissions produced from petroleum fuels as reported in the previous works. The higher temperature during the combustion and the existence of oxygen in the fuel are the two reasons suggested for this increment. Juoperi and Ollus (2008) concluded higher NO_x emissions using palm oil biodiesel fuel. Gabiña et al. (2016) concluded the same results using waste oil obtained lubrication systems. Using different ratios of biodiesel blends, Puškár et al. (2018) concluded a higher amount of NO_x emissions, especially at the high engine speeds and loads.

This increment in NO_x emissions requires some techniques to treat it. Very few studies applied the water injection technique in the intake manifold to reduce the level of NO_x emissions from biodiesel engine by 50% (Tesfa et al., 2012, Prabhu and Venkata Ramanan, 2018). It is noticed a little variation in the thermodynamic properties during the process of combustion. By using after treatment systems, Mizushima et al. (2010) attached a selective catalytic reduction (SCR) coupled with diesel oxide catalyst (DOC) to the engine to achieve more reduction in NO_x emissions. While Solaimuthu et al. (2015) combined SCR and exhaust gas recirculation (EGR) and a good percentage of reduction in NO_x emissions is achieved.

5 COMBUSTION PROCESS OF BIODIESEL ENGINE

As in any diesel engines, the thermo-fluid processes and the chemical reactions during the combustion process must be studied (Tadros et al., 2020e, Tadros et al., 2020a). Using biodiesel fuel with different blends, the engine performance is still under investigation and attracts attention from the researchers, to predict the behavior of burning mass fraction (Wiebe function), the combustion duration, the heat release rate, the ignition delay and in-cylinder pressure for optimum engine performance.

5.1 Wiebe function

Various Wiebe functions are used to describe the behavior of the burning mass fraction during the combustion process of biodiesel engines. Patil (2013) considered the single Wiebe function to simulate the combustion process using different types of diesel and biodiesel blends. Tarabet et al. (2014) used a double Wiebe function to predict a biodiesel engine performance. The heat release rate based on this Wiebe function is fitted well with the experimental data for various operating conditions. Also, Clume et al. (2019) used the same type of Wiebe function and a good agreement is achieved when comparing the simulated in-cylinder pressure diagram with the experimental one. Awad et al. (2013) used a multi-Wiebe function to simulate the performance of the biodiesel engine and a good agreement is achieved between the simulated results and experimental data. It is concluded that combustion behavior is better detected when using more than a single Wiebe function.

5.2 Combustion duration

The combustion duration is the period of the combustion of fuel from 10% to 90%. It is an important factor, which requires more attention in order to control the heat release rate and the in-cylinder pressure. Bittle et al. (2010) observed that the combustion duration using biodiesel fuel is shorter than using petroleum fuels. It is a result of the faster burning rate during the diffusion phase and can be a result of the higher formation of NO_x emissions as mentioned by (Bai-gang et al., 2014). Tse (2016) supported the same conclusion that all the fuels containing diesel and biodiesel blends have a shorter combustion duration than pure diesel oil. From the above references, it is important to study the chemical composition of the fuel to optimize the combustion process in general, and the combustion duration in particular.

5.3 Heat release rate (HRR)

The different physical properties of biodiesel fuels other than the pure diesel oil lead to a significant reduction in HRR especially by increasing the biodiesel blend in the fuel. Several research work observed a reduction in the HRR than in diesel oil (Monirul et al., 2016, Puškár et al., 2018, Gabiña et al., 2016, Shahabuddin et al., 2013) which ends up in a decrease of the engine brake power.

5.4 Ignition delay

The ignition delay plays an important role in the behavior of the combustion process. It depends on the in-cylinder pressure and temperature and on the fuel cetane number. Based on the higher cetane number of biodiesel fuel, which can reach 65 in some types of fuel, the ignition delay becomes shorter than in diesel oil by around 2 degrees crank angle than using the diesel oil (Shahabuddin et al., 2013, How et al., 2014, Geng et al., 2017, Puškár et al., 2018), which leads to a shorter combustion duration, an increase in in-cylinder maximum pressure (Sumito et al., 2014) and thus exhaust gas temperature up to 12%. To compute numerically the ignition delay, Patil (2013) used the equation suggested by Hardenberg and Hase (Heywood, 1988) to compute the delay in the ignition for different types of fuels. Also, Clume et al. (2019) used the same reference to find the correlation of the ignition delay parameters.

5.5 In-cylinder pressure

The in-cylinder pressure diagram is affected by several parameters. Some studies revealed that the maximum pressure inside the cylinder is higher in FAME than in diesel oil due to the higher amount of oxygen in biodiesel than in diesel fuel (Sumito et al., 2014, Puškár et al., 2018). Other published works show a reduction in the maximum pressure inside the cylinder (How et al., 2014, Geng et al., 2017). The effects of the different parameters such as the percentage of biodiesel blends in the fuel, the cetane number, the value of ignition delay, the heating value and the percentage of sulphur must be taken into consideration during the experimental tests or numerical simulation to predict the influence of each parameter on the thermodynamic properties during engine combustion.

6 PERFORMANCE OF BIODIESEL ENGINE USING ENGINE SIMULATION SOFTWARE

The different simulation software that is used to simulate the diesel engine performance, is extended to predict the behavior of the same type of engine fueled by biodiesel fuel. Ngayihi Abbe et al. (2015) developed a 0D model by considering the effect of fuel spray characteristics on the kinetic of combustion to simulate the in-cylinder pressure and temperature diagram and to compute the formation of NO_x emissions. The calculated results from the numerical model show a good agreement with the collected data from the experimental tests. Clume et al. (2019) developed a 1D model to predict the performance of marine engines fueled with diesel oil and biodiesel blends. A double Wiebe function is used to model the combustion process and the ignition delay is computed for the different types of fuel.

Ng et al. (2017) used AVL BOOST commercial software to simulate the performance of a light-duty diesel engine fueled with biofuel and the results fit well with experimental results. McCrady et al. (2008) used GT-Power to simulate diesel engine fueled with soybean and rapeseed biodiesel. They concluded higher exhaust emissions than using diesel oil. Vajda et al. (2015) used AVL Fire to study the influence of physical and chemical properties of various biofuels on spray characteristics. Asadi et al. (2019) investigated the biodiesel premixing effect on engine performance using the computational fluid dynamics (CFD) model.

7 PERFORMANCE OF BIODIESEL ENGINE USING MACHINE LEARNING

As for conventional diesel engines, various optimization and machine learning techniques have been developed during the last century to solve mathematical programming models or to predict the performance of the engine, due to a large number of parameters that need to be controlled (Galindo et al., 2005, Mohd Noor et al., 2015, Chakraborty et al., 2018, Tadros et al., 2018b, Yu and Zhao, 2019, Tadros et al., 2020f). In biofuel engines, Canakci et al. (2006) used an artificial neural network (ANN) to predict in general the performance and exhaust emissions of biodiesel engines for different blends. Tarabet et al. (2014) extended the previous work by applying the same method to predict the behavior of a double Wiebe function to control the heat release rate and it shows a good agreement with experimental data. Ali et al. (2015) used response surface methodology (RSM) to optimize the amount of additive fuel of diethyl ether to B30 blended palm biodiesel-diesel fuel to reduce the amount of exhaust emissions. Wong et al. (2015) used a kernel-based extreme learning machine and cuckoo search to determine the optimal biodiesel ratio for different engine speeds and loads. Shirneshan et al. (2016) determined the optimum condition of biodiesel percentage in fuel mixture to optimize the engine performance and emission characteristics using the Artificial Bees Colony (ABC) algorithm. Silitonga et al. (2018) used a kernel-based extreme learning machine (K-ELM) to predict the values of the parameters of both the engine performance and exhaust emissions and the values obtained show a good agreement with the experimental results.

8 ISSUES AND CHALLENGES

Biodiesel also presents several issues and challenges, as follows:

1. The higher production cost due to the high prices of feedstock as reported in (Atabani et al., 2012) requires an alternative way to reduce the overall cost of fuel production as well as the procedures applied by the government to stimulate this industry.
2. Special protection is needed to reduce fuel oxidation stability, especially in the marine industry. Therefore, a special caring and attention of the tank's materials must be given to limit this phenomenon.

3. The computation of the amount of required power and the CO_2 emissions from the production process of biodiesel fuel must be considered in addition to the CO_2 emissions produced during the engine combustion.
4. The effect of water injection on the biodiesel engine performance as one of the main solutions to reduce the formation of NO_x emissions.
5. The availability of the feedstock for each country and the looking for new alternative sources of biofuels to reduce the overall cost of production while not affecting the human's food source.
6. The safety aspects of the whole system especially on the marine industry to avoid any risks and to achieve the system perfection.
7. The existence of biodiesel standards for both automotive and marine applications as a result of the appearance of several types of raw materials.
8. The development of a generic model to compute easily the parameters of the combustion process for different types of biodiesel fuel.

9 CONCLUSIONS

This paper presents a general review of several aspects of the use of biofuels in diesel engines as an alternative to the fossil fuels. In general, the biodiesel will present a great conversion in the field of energy in the next few years due to its distinction in the reduction of exhaust emissions.

In this paper, the methods of biodiesel production are described. The engine performance, the exhaust emissions and the parameters that affect the combustion process are presented in detail. The authors focus on the benefit of using numerical simulation and machine learning techniques to easily estimate and optimize engine performance. Briefly, several issues and challenges are presented to be considered in future research.

ACKNOWLEDGEMENTS

This work was performed within the scope of the Strategic Research Plan of the Centre for Marine Technology and Ocean Engineering (CENTEC), which is financed by the Portuguese Foundation for Science and Technology (Fundação para a Ciência e Tecnologia - FCT) under contract UIDB/UIDP/00134/2020.

REFERENCES

Adaileh, W. M. & AlQdah, K. S., 2012. Performance of Diesel Engine Fuelled by a Biodiesel Extracted From A Waste Cocking Oil. *Energy Procedia*, 18, 1317–1334.

Agarwal, A. K. & Das, L. M., 2001. Biodiesel Development and Characterization for Use as a Fuel in Compression Ignition Engines *J. Eng. Gas Turbines Power*, 123, 440–447.

Ali, O. M., Mamat, R., Abdullah, N. R. & Abdullah, A. A., 2016. Analysis of blended fuel properties and engine performance with palm biodiesel–diesel blended fuel. *Renewable Energy*, 86, 59–67.

Ali, O. M., Mamat, R., Najafi, G., Yusaf, T. & Safieddin Ardebili, S. M., 2015. Optimization of Biodiesel-Diesel Blended Fuel Properties and Engine Performance with Ether Additive Using Statistical Analysis and Response Surface Methods. *Energies*, 8, 14136–14150.

An, H., Yang, W. M., Chou, S. K. & Chua, K. J., 2012. Combustion and emissions characteristics of diesel engine fueled by biodiesel at partial load conditions. *Applied Energy*, 99, 363–371.

Asadi, A., Zhang, Y., Mohammadi, H., Khorand, H., Rui, Z., Doranehgard, M. H. & Bozorg, M. V., 2019. Combustion and emission characteristics of biomass derived biofuel, premixed in a diesel engine: A CFD study. *Renewable Energy*, 138, 79–89.

Atabani, A. E., Silitonga, A. S., Badruddin, I. A., Mahlia, T. M. I., Masjuki, H. H. & Mekhilef, S., 2012. A comprehensive review on biodiesel as an alternative energy resource and its characteristics. *Renewable and Sustainable Energy Reviews*, 16, 2070–2093.

Avinash, A., Subramaniam, D. & Murugesan, A., 2014. Bio-diesel—A global scenario. *Renewable and Sustainable Energy Reviews*, 29, 517–527.

Awad, S., Varuvel, E. G., Loubar, K. & Tazerout, M., 2013. Single zone combustion modeling of biodiesel from wastes in diesel engine. *Fuel*, 106, 558–568.

Bai-gang, S., Hua-yu, T. & Fu-shui, L., 2014. The distinctive characteristics of combustion duration in hydrogen internal combustion engine. *International Journal of Hydrogen Energy*, 39, 14472–14478.

Balat, M. & Demirbas, M. F., 2009. Bio-oil from Pyrolysis of Black Alder Wood. *Energy Sources, Part A: Recovery, Utilization, and Environmental Effects*, 31, 1719–1727.

Bart, J. C. J., Palmeri, N. & Cavallaro, S. 2010. Vegetable oil formulations for utilisation as biofuels. *Bioenergy Research: Advances and Applications*. Oxford, UK: Elsevier B.V., pp. 114–129.

BELL. 2019. *The Damaging Effects of Ethanol in Your Boats Fuel* [Online]. Available: https://www.bellperformance.com/blog/the-damaging-effects-of-ethanol-in-your-boats-fuel [Accessed 1 November 2019].

Bittle, J. A., Knight, B. M. & Jacobs, T. J., 2010. Interesting Behavior of Biodiesel Ignition Delay and Combustion Duration. *Energy Fuels*, 24, 4166–4177.

Canakci, M., Erdil, A. & Arcaklioğlu, E., 2006. Performance and exhaust emissions of a biodiesel engine. *Applied Energy*, 83, 594–605.

Chakraborty, A., Roy, S. & Banerjee, R., 2018. Characterization of performance-emission indices of a diesel engine using ANFIS operating in dual-fuel mode with LPG. *Heat and Mass Transfer*, 54, 2725–2742.

Chavanne, G., 1938. Procédé de Transformation d'Huiles Végétales en Vue de Leur Utilisation comme Carburants (Procedure for the transformation of vegetable oils for their uses as fuels), Belgian Patent 422,877. *Chem. Abstr*, 32, 43132.

Clume, S. F., Belchior, C. R. P., Gutiérrez, R. H. R., Monteiro, U. A. & Vaz, L. A., 2019. Methodology for the validation of fuel consumption in diesel engines installed on board military ships, using diesel oil and biodiesel blends. *Journal of the*

Brazilian Society of Mechanical Sciences and Engineering, 41, 516.

Dwivedi, G., Jain, S. & Sharma, M. P., 2011. Impact analysis of biodiesel on engine performance—A review. *Renewable and Sustainable Energy Reviews*, 15, 4633–4641.

ETIP. 2019. *Biodiesel (FAME) production and use in Europe* [Online]. Available: http://www.etipbioenergy.eu/value-chains/products-end-use/products/fame-biodiesel [Accessed 10 November 2019].

Gabiña, G., Martin, L., Basurko, O. C., Clemente, M., Aldekoa, S. & Uriondo, Z., 2016. Waste oil-based alternative fuels for marine diesel engines. *Fuel Processing Technology*, 153, 28–36.

Galindo, J., Luján, J. M., Serrano, J. R. & Hernández, L., 2005. Combustion simulation of turbocharger HSDI Diesel engines during transient operation using neural networks. *Applied Thermal Engineering*, 25, 877–898.

Geng, P., Mao, H., Zhang, Y., Wei, L., You, K., Ju, J. & Chen, T., 2017. Combustion characteristics and NOx emissions of a waste cooking oil biodiesel blend in a marine auxiliary diesel engine. *Applied Thermal Engineering*, 115, 947–954.

Gokalp, B., Buyukkaya, E. & Soyhan, H. S., 2011. Performance and emissions of a diesel tractor engine fueled with marine diesel and soybean methyl ester. *Biomass and Bioenergy*, 35, 3575–3583.

Haldar, S. K., Ghosh, B. B. & Nag, A., 2009. Utilization of unattended Putranjiva roxburghii non-edible oil as fuel in diesel engine. *Renewable Energy*, 34, 343–347.

Heywood, J. B. 1988. *Internal combustion engine fundamentals*, New York, McGraw-Hill.

How, H. G., Masjuki, H. H., Kalam, M. A. & Teoh, Y. H., 2014. An investigation of the engine performance, emissions and combustion characteristics of coconut biodiesel in a high-pressure common-rail diesel engine. *Energy*, 69, 749–759.

Jafaryeganeh, H., Ventura, M. & Guedes Soares, C., 2019. Multi-Objective Optimization of Internal Compartment Layout of Oil Tankers. *Journal of Ship Production and Design*.

Juoperi, K. & Ollus, R., 2008. Alternative fuels for medium-speed diesel engines. *WÄRTSILÄ Tech J* 1, 24–31.

Lloyd's Register 2012. Implementing the Energy Efficiency Design Index. London.

Maghanaki, M. M., Ghobadian, B., Najafi, G. & Galogah, R. J., 2013. Potential of biogas production in Iran. *Renewable and Sustainable Energy Reviews*, 28, 702–714.

Mahmudul, H. M., Hagos, F. Y., Mamat, R., Adam, A. A., Ishak, W. F. W. & Alenezi, R., 2017. Production, characterization and performance of biodiesel as an alternative fuel in diesel engines – A review. *Renewable and Sustainable Energy Reviews*, 72, 497–509.

MAN Diesel & Turbo 2016. Exhaust Gas Emission Control Today and Tomorrow. Augsburg.

MAN Diesel & Turbo 2017a. 32/44CR Project Guide – Marine Four-stroke diesel engines compliant with IMO Tier II. Augsburg.

MAN Diesel & Turbo 2017b. Low Container Ship - Speed Facilitated by Versatile ME/ME-C Engines. Augsburg.

Mata, T. M., Martins, A. A. & Caetano, N. S., 2010. Microalgae for biodiesel production and other applications: A review. *Renewable and Sustainable Energy Reviews*, 14, 217–232.

McCrady, J. P., Hansen, A. C. & Lee, C.-F. F. 2008. Combustion and Emissions Modeling of Biodiesel Using GT-Power. *2008 Providence*. Rhode Island.

Mizushima, N., Murata, Y., Suzuki, H., Ishii, H., Goto, Y. & Kawano, D., 2010. Effect of Biodiesel on NOx Reduction Performance of Urea-SCR System. *SAE Int. J. Fuels Lubr.*, 3, 1012–1020.

Mohd Noor, C. W., Mamat, R., Najafi, G., Wan Nik, W. B. & Fadhil, M., 2015. Application of artificial neural network for prediction of marine diesel engine performance. *IOP Conference Series: Materials Science and Engineering*, 100, 012023.

Mohd Noor, C. W., Noor, M. M. & Mamat, R., 2018. Biodiesel as alternative fuel for marine diesel engine applications: A review. *Renewable and Sustainable Energy Reviews*, 94, 127–142.

Monirul, I. M., Masjuki, H. H., Kalam, M. A., Mosarof, M. H., Zulkifli, N. W. M., Teoh, Y. H. & How, H. G., 2016. Assessment of performance, emission and combustion characteristics of palm, jatropha and Calophyllum inophyllum biodiesel blends. *Fuel*, 181, 985–995.

Murillo, S., Míguez, J. L., Porteiro, J., Granada, E. & Morán, J. C., 2007. Performance and exhaust emissions in the use of biodiesel in outboard diesel engines. *Fuel*, 86, 1765–1771.

Ng, J., Wong, K. Y., Chong, C. T. & Rajoo, S. Integrated 1D-chemical kinetics model of a diesel and biodiesel fuelled light-duty diesel engine. 2017 3rd International Conference on Power Generation Systems and Renewable Energy Technologies (PGSRET), 4-6 April 2017 2017. pp. 89–94.

Ngayihi Abbe, C. V., Nzengwa, R., Danwe, R., Ayissi, Z. M. & Obonou, M., 2015. A study on the 0D phenomenological model for diesel engine simulation: Application to combustion of Neem methyl ester biodiesel. *Energy Conversion and Management*, 89, 568–576.

Patil, S., 2013. Thermodynamic Modelling for Performance Analysis of Compression Ignition Engine Fuelled With Biodiesel and its Blends With Diesel. *International Journal of Recent Technology and Engineering (IJRTE)*, 1, 134–138.

Piloto-Rodríguez, R., Sánchez-Borroto, Y., Melo-Espinosa, E. A. & Verhelst, S., 2017. Assessment of diesel engine performance when fueled with biodiesel from algae and microalgae: An overview. *Renewable and Sustainable Energy Reviews*, 69, 833–842.

Prabhu, A. & Venkata Ramanan, M., 2018. A comprehensive review of water injection and emulsion technology for biodiesel-fuelled CI engine. *International Journal of Ambient Energy*.

Prucole, E. d. S., Pinto, R. R. d. C. & Valle, M. L. M., 2014. Use of biodiesel in marine fuel formulation: A study of combustion quality. *Fuel Processing Technology*, 122, 91–97.

Pullen, J. & Saeed, K., 2014. Factors affecting biodiesel engine performance and exhaust emissions – Part I: Review. *Energy*, 72, 1–16.

Puškár, M., Kopas, M., Puškár, D., Lumnitzer, J. & Faltinová, E., 2018. Method for reduction of the NOX emissions in marine auxiliary diesel engine using the fuel mixtures containing biodiesel using HCCI combustion. *Marine Pollution Bulletin*, 127, 752–760.

Roskilly, A. P., Nanda, S. K., Wang, Y. D. & Chirkowski, J., 2008. The performance and the gaseous emissions of two small marine craft diesel engines fuelled with biodiesel. *Applied Thermal Engineering*, 28, 872–880.

Sahoo, P. K., Das, L. M., Babu, M. K. G. & Naik, S. N., 2007. Biodiesel development from high acid value polanga seed oil and performance evaluation in a CI engine. *Fuel*, 86, 448–454.

Shahabuddin, M., Liaquat, A. M., Masjuki, H. H., Kalam, M. A. & Mofijur, M., 2013. Ignition delay, combustion and emission characteristics of diesel engine fueled with biodiesel. *Renewable and Sustainable Energy Reviews*, 21, 623–632.

Shirneshan, A., Samani, B. H. & Ghobadian, B., 2016. Optimization of biodiesel percentage in fuel mixture and engine operating conditions for diesel engine performance and emission characteristics by Artificial Bees Colony Algorithm. *Fuel*, 184, 518–526.

Silitonga, A. S., Masjuki, H. H., Mahlia, T. M. I., Ong, H. C. & Chong, W. T., 2013. Experimental study on performance and exhaust emissions of a diesel engine fuelled with Ceiba pentandra biodiesel blends. *Energy Conversion and Management*, 76, 828–836.

Silitonga, A. S., Masjuki, H. H., Ong, H. C., Sebayang, A. H., Dharma, S., Kusumo, F., Siswantoro, J., Milano, J., Daud, K., Mahlia, T. M. I., Chen, W.-H. & Sugiyanto, B., 2018. Evaluation of the engine performance and exhaust emissions of biodiesel-bioethanol-diesel blends using kernel-based extreme learning machine. *Energy*, 159, 1075–1087.

Singh, S. P. & Singh, D., 2010. Biodiesel production through the use of different sources and characterization of oils and their esters as the substitute of diesel: A review. *Renewable and Sustainable Energy Reviews*, 14, 200–216.

Solaimuthu, C., Ganesan, V., Senthilkumar, D. & Ramasamy, K. K., 2015. Emission reductions studies of a biodiesel engine using EGR and SCR for agriculture operations in developing countries. *Applied Energy*, 138, 91–98.

Su, J., Zhu, H. & Bohac, S. V., 2013. Particulate matter emission comparison from conventional and premixed low temperature combustion with diesel, biodiesel and biodiesel–ethanol fuels. *Fuel*, 113, 221–227.

Sumito, N., Takeyuki, K. & Tetsugo, F. Combustion of biofuel in marine diesel engine and its improvement by hybrid injection system. Proceedings of the 9th international conference marine technology, 2014. pp. 1–7.

Tadros, M., Ventura, M. & Guedes Soares, C. 2016. Assessment of the performance and the exhaust emissions of a marine diesel engine for different start angles of combustion. *In:* Guedes Soares, C. & Santos, T. A. (eds.) *Maritime Technology and Engineering 3*. London: Taylor & Francis Group, pp. 769–775.

Tadros, M., Ventura, M. & Guedes Soares, C. 2018a. Optimization scheme for the selection of the propeller in ship concept design. *In:* Guedes Soares, C. & Santos, T. A. (eds.) *Progress in Maritime Technology and Engineering*. London: Taylor & Francis Group, pp. 233–239.

Tadros, M., Ventura, M. & Guedes Soares, C. 2018b. Surrogate models of the performance and exhaust emissions of marine diesel engines for ship conceptual design. *In:* Guedes Soares, C. & Teixeira, A. P. (eds.) *Maritime Transportation and Harvesting of Sea Resources*. London: Taylor & Francis Group, pp. 105–112.

Tadros, M., Ventura, M. & Guedes Soares, C., 2019. Optimization procedure to minimize fuel consumption of a four-stroke marine turbocharged diesel engine. *Energy*, 168, 897–908.

Tadros, M., Ventura, M. & Guedes Soares, C., 2020a. Data Driven In-Cylinder Pressure Diagram Based Optimization Procedure. *Journal of Marine Science and Engineering*, 8, 294.

Tadros, M., Ventura, M. & Guedes Soares, C., 2020b. A nonlinear optimization tool to simulate a marine propulsion system for ship conceptual design. *Ocean Engineering*, 210, 1–15.

Tadros, M., Ventura, M. & Guedes Soares, C., 2020c. Optimization of the performance of marine diesel engines to minimize the formation of SOx emissions. *Journal of Marine Science and Application*, 19, 473–484.

Tadros, M., Ventura, M. & Guedes Soares, C. 2020d. Optimum design of a container ship's propeller from Wageningen B-series at the minimum BSFC. *In:* Georgiev, P. & Guedes Soares, C. (eds.) *Sustainable Development and Innovations in Marine Technologies*. London: Taylor & Francis Group, pp. 269–274.

Tadros, M., Ventura, M. & Guedes Soares, C. 2020e. Simulation of the performance of marine genset based on double-Wiebe function. *In:* Georgiev, P. & Guedes Soares, C. (eds.) *Sustainable Development and Innovations in Marine Technologies*. London: Taylor & Francis Group, pp. 292–299.

Tadros, M., Ventura, M., Guedes Soares, C. & Lampreia, S. 2020f. Predicting the performance of a sequentially turbocharged marine diesel engine using ANFIS. *In:* Georgiev, P. & Guedes Soares, C. (eds.) *Sustainable Development and Innovations in Marine Technologies*. London: Taylor & Francis Group, pp. 300–305.

Tadros, M., Vettor, R., Ventura, M. & Guedes Soares, C., 2021. Coupled Engine-Propeller Selection Procedure to Minimize Fuel Consumption at a Specified Speed. *Journal of Marine Science and Engineering*, 9, 59.

Tarabet, L., Lounici, M., Loubar, K. & Tazerout, M., 2014. Dual Wiebe Function Prediction of Eucalyptus Biodiesel/Diesel Fuel Blends Combustion in Diesel Engine Applying Artificial Neural Network. 2014-01-2555.

Tesfa, B., Mishra, R., Gu, F. & Ball, A. D., 2012. Water injection effects on the performance and emission characteristics of a CI engine operating with biodiesel. *Renewable Energy*, 37, 333–344.

The Statistics Portal 2017. Leading biodiesel producers worldwide in 2018. Hamburg.

Tse, B. H. 2016. Combustion and Emissions of a Diesel Engine Fueled with Diesel-Biodiesel-Ethanol Blends and Supplemented with Intake CO2 Charge Dilution. *In:* Kyprianidis, K. & Skvaril, J. (eds.) *Developments in Combustion Technology*. IntechOpen, pp.

United Nations. 2019. *Mitigation* [Online]. Available: https://www.unenvironment.org/explore-topics/climate-change/what-we-do/mitigation [Accessed 15 November 2019].

Vajda, B., Lešnik, L., Bombek, G., Biluš, I., Žunič, Z., Škerget, L., Hočevar, M., Širok, B. & Kegl, B., 2015. The numerical simulation of biofuels spray. *Fuel*, 144, 71–79.

Vettor, R. & Guedes Soares, C., 2016. Development of a ship weather routing system. *Ocean Engineering*, 123, 1–14.

Vettor, R., Tadros, M., Ventura, M. & Guedes Soares, C. 2016. Route planning of a fishing vessel in coastal waters with fuel consumption restraint. *In:* Guedes Soares, C. & Santos, T. A. (eds.) *Maritime Technology and Engineering 3*. London: Taylor & Francis Group, pp. 167–173.

Vettor, R., Tadros, M., Ventura, M. & Guedes Soares, C. 2018. Influence of main engine control strategies on fuel consumption and emissions. *In:* Guedes Soares, C. & Santos, T. A. (eds.) *Progress in Maritime Technology and Engineering*. London: Taylor & Francis Group, pp. 157–163.

Wei, L., Cheung, C. S. & Huang, Z., 2014. Effect of n-pentanol addition on the combustion, performance and emission characteristics of a direct-injection diesel engine. *Energy*, 70, 172–180.

Wong, P. K., Wong, K. I., Vong, C. M. & Cheung, C. S., 2015. Modeling and optimization of biodiesel engine performance using kernel-based extreme learning machine and cuckoo search. *Renewable Energy*, 74, 640–647.

Xue, J., Grift, T. E. & Hansen, A. C., 2011. Effect of biodiesel on engine performances and emissions. *Renewable and Sustainable Energy Reviews*, 15, 1098–1116.

Yu, W. & Zhao, F., 2019. Predictive study of ultra-low emissions from dual-fuel engine using artificial neural networks combined with genetic algorithm. *International Journal of Green Energy*, 16, 938–946.

Sensitivity analysis of the steam Rankine cycle in marine applications

M. Tadros
Centre for Marine Technology and Ocean Engineering (CENTEC), Instituto Superior Técnico, Universidade de Lisboa, Portugal.
Naval Architecture and Marine Engineering Department, Faculty of Engineering, Alexandria University, Alexandria, Egypt

M. Ventura & C. Guedes Soares
Centre for Marine Technology and Ocean Engineering (CENTEC), Instituto Superior Técnico, Universidade de Lisboa, Lisbon, Portugal

ABSTRACT: Increasing the efficiency of the ship marine systems using multi-source energies is becoming essential to reduce the amount of fuel consumption and exhaust emissions. In this paper, a sensitivity analysis is performed to study the influence of various parameters of a steam Rankine cycle on its performance. The steam Rankine cycle is modeled in Aspen Plus, a commercial software used to simulate the performance of different types of power systems. The pump, boiler, turbine and condenser are the main parts of the Rankine cycle considered in this study. The exhaust gas of two four-stroke marine diesel engines is the main source of heat for the boiler. The performance of the system is evaluated based on the variation of the condenser pressure, feed pump outlet pressure, the mass flow rate of the working fluid and the outlet gas temperature to the ambient. This study opens the doors to optimize the performance of different marine waste heat recovery systems.

1 INTRODUCTION

The reduction of the amount of fuel consumed from marine engines and the amount of exhaust emissions is becoming mandatory to increase the energy efficiency of ships and to verify the limits of nitrogen oxides (NO_x) and sulphur oxides (SO_x) applied by the International Maritime Organization (IMO) as shown in Figures 1 and 2 respectively.

Different suggestions and guidelines are presented by Lloyd's Register (2012) to improve the marine system performance. Previous publications focus on optimizing the performance of the different parts of the marine propulsion system to study its influence on the ship performance (Vettor et al., 2016, Vettor et al., 2018, Zaccone et al., 2018, Tadros et al., 2020a).

Various tools are developed to simulate the dynamic performance of different types of marine engines either it is spark ignition or compression ignition, supported by experimental data (Benvenuto and Campora, 2002, Benvenuto et al., 2013, Altosole et al., 2017, Stoumpos et al., 2018). A sensitivity analysis is performed for the optimization purposes to study the influence of injection timing on engine performance, the amount of fuel consumed and exhaust emissions (Raeie et al., 2014, Tadros et al., 2016). Then, optimization tools are developed as in (Zhao and Xu, 2013, Tadros et al., 2019) to minimize the fuel consumption of a various types of engines by finding the optimal values of the parameters of the turbocharger, intake valves and injection system and by controlling the parameters of the combustion process (Tadros et al., 2020c).

The use of machine learning techniques also helps to evaluate and optimize the performance of the marine propulsion system (Yu and Zhao, 2019, Marques et al., 2019, Tadros et al., 2020d).

Optimization procedures are extended to optimize the propeller performance either it is fixed pitch propeller (FPP) by increasing the propeller efficiency (Gaafary et al., 2011, Tadros et al., 2018a) and by selecting the propeller at the engine operating point with minimum fuel consumption (Tadros et al., 2020b, Tadros et al., 2021) or controllable pitch propeller (CPP) as presented in (Martelli et al., 2014).

Due to the higher amount of losses to the environment that exceeds 50% of the fuel energy supplied to the engine as shown in Figure 3, the waste heat recovery (WHR) systems take place as another type of power source to convert the heat losses and the exhaust gas to a mechanical or electrical source of power without utilizing more fuel.

The Rankine cycle including Steam, Organic and supercritical, Kalina cycle, exhaust gas turbine system and thermoelectric generation systems are the different types of WHR systems available and are presented in the literature review prepared by Singh and Pedersen (2016). One or more of these technologies can be used depending on the amount of power needed and the

DOI: 10.1201/9781003216599-52

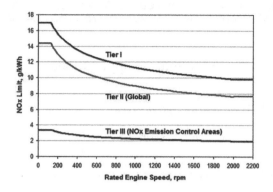

Figure 1. Maximum allowable NO$_x$ emissions for marine engines.

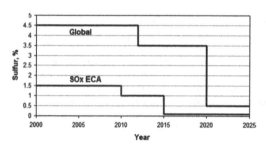

Figure 2. Maximum allowable SO$_x$ emissions for marine engines.

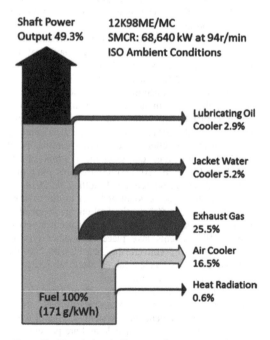

Figure 3. Heat balance diagram of Man marine engine (MAN Diesel & Turbo, 2014).

size of the main prime movers. MAN Diesel & Turbo (2014) recommended the use of power turbine and generator (PTG) or organic Rankine cycle (ORC) when the main power is less than 15,000 kW, if the main power is up to 25,000 kW, the PTG or steam turbine and generator (STG) can be considered. While in case of main power greater than 25,000, a combined ST and PT can be installed where more energy is produced. The quality of the WHR systems is mainly depending on the exhaust temperature from engines which are categorized as low, medium and high levels of utility as shown in Table 1. The first two categories are the main level used in marine applications.

In marine applications, few studies are performed in comparison with the industrial field. Larsen et al. (2014) presented a comparative study between the performance of the steam Rankine cycle (SRC), organic Rankine cycle (ORC) and Kalina cycle (KC). Theotokatos and Livanos (2013) performed a comparison to predict the improvement in system performance when coupling the single pressure WHRS to the two-stroke and four-stroke engines. An increase in the efficiency for both systems is predicted by up to 1.3% when using the two-stroke engine and up to 3% in the case of a four-stroke engine. Benvenuto et al. (2016) optimized the performance of a dual pressure SRC as a WHR system by presenting four different layouts coupled to a two-stroke engine. Lion et al. (2019) presented a techno-economic study of different configurations of Rankine cycle for marine system powered by two-stroke engines. Altosole et al. (2020) optimized the WHR system to improve the recovered heat from a dual fuel engine.

To study the uncertainty in the output of a WHR system, a sensitivity analysis must be performed by changing the value of the several parameters that affect the SRC performance. In a previous study, Liu et al. (2014) presented a sensitivity analysis of the performance of ORC for a binary-cycle geothermal power plant for the various working fluids, efficiencies of pump and turbine and the temperatures of a pinch, superheat and evaporating.

In this paper, a sensitivity analysis is performed at the rated engine speed, to extend the previous publications by studying the variation of the output power of a SRC coupled to two four-stroke marine diesel engines as suggested by MAN Diesel & Turbo (2014), by changing the value of the condenser pressure, feed pump outlet pressure, the mass flow rate of the working fluid and the outlet gas temperature to the ambient. The input data are collected from the numerical models developed by Tadros et al. (2019) and Tadros et al. (2018b) that are suggested to optimize the performance of a complete marine system in further research.

Table 1. Temperature range for each level of quality of heat energy (BCS, 2008).

Quality	Temperature range (C)
Low	Less than 232
Medium	232 - 649
High	Higher than 649

The numerical model of the WHR system is built in Aspen Plus, as a commercial software used to simulate the performance of different types of power systems (Aspentech, 2019). This software is widely used in the simulation of previous researches related to thermodynamic and chemical processes (Stamatis and Andritsos, 2015, Rajabloo, 2017, Ur-Rehman et al., 2018).

The rest of this paper is organized as follows: Section 2 provides a general presentation of the marine diesel engine considered in this study, as well as the exhaust temperature and the mass flow rate as inputs to the boiler. Then, an overview of the numerical model and the simulation software used to perform the computation. Section 3 shows the influence of the selected parameters on the SRC performance. Then, some conclusions are drawn and presented in Section 4.

Table 2. Characteristics of engine performance.

Parameter	Unit	Value
Bore	mm	320
Stroke	mm	440
No. of cylinders	-	18
Displacement	liter	640
Number of valves per cylinder	-	4
Compression ratio	-	17.3:1
bmep	bar	23.06
Piston speed	m/s	11
Engine speed	rpm	750
BSFC	g/kW.h	179
Power-to-weight ratio	kW/kg	0.095
Exhaust flow rate	Kg/kW.h	6.95
Exhaust temperature	C	339

2 NUMERICAL MODEL OF WASTE HEAT RECOVERY SYSTEM

Based on the recommendation suggested by MAN Diesel & Turbo (2014), two identical marine diesel engines MAN 18V32-44CR (MAN Diesel & Turbo, 2016) are used in this study as an input to simulate the performance of a SRC. The exhaust flow rate and the exhaust temperature are used as inputs to the boiler in the WHR system.

The SRC is built in Aspen Plus as shown in Figure 5 by taking into account the four main components of the system as follows:

1. Pump
2. Boiler
3. Turbine
4. Condenser

The water is selected as the main working fluid inside the cycle and the properties of the fluid are computed based on the ASME 1967 steam table correlations (Spencer and Meyer, 1968). Then, the four main components are defined and connected using several material streams.

The pump is modelled based on the pressure ratio and pump efficiency (80%), where the power of the pump, W_{pump}, is computed using the following equation:

$$W_{pump} = h_{2s} - h_1 \qquad (1)$$

where, h_{2s} is the isentropic efficiency and h_1 is the enthalpy at the condenser pressure.

The Boiler is modelled as counter current and the minimum temperature approach is assumed to be 1 degree where the outlet pressure and temperature are computed using the equation of energy balance as follows:

$$Q_{exh} = m_{wf} cp_{exh}(h_3 - h_{2s}) \qquad (2)$$

where, Q_{exh} is the amount of heat added from the engine exhaust gas, m_{wf} is the mass flow rate of the working fluid and h_3 is the enthalpy at the boiler outlet.

The turbine is modelled isentropic in which the discharge pressure is equal to the condenser pressure, and the efficiency is assumed 70%. The work of the turbine, $W_{turbine}$, is computed using equation (3).

$$W_{turbine} = h_3 - h_{4s} \qquad (3)$$

where, $h4s$ is the isentropic enthalpy at the turbine outlet.

As shown in Figure 4, the cycle consists of four processes. In the first one, the water is pumped to increase its pressure. Then, the high-pressure water enters the boiler to be heated by the exhaust gas coming from the combustion of the engine. After that, the vapour produced by the boiler is expanded

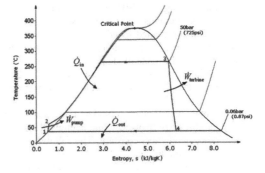

Figure 4. Steam Rankine cycle diagram (Meee, 2020).

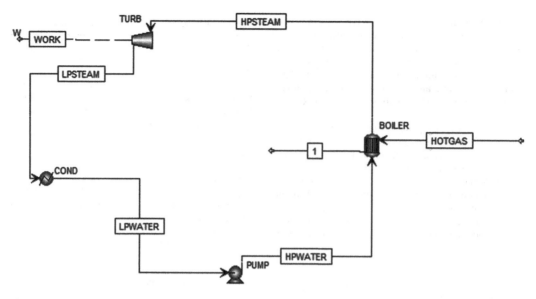

Figure 5. Layout of the numerical model establish in Aspen Plus.

through the turbine generating electricity. Finally, the vapour is condensed at constant pressure and becomes a saturated liquid.

By simulating the numerical model, the thermodynamic properties and the mechanical results are computed along the cycle, while the cycle efficiency, η_{cycle}, is computed using the following equations:

$$W_{net} = W_{turbine} - W_{pump} \quad (4)$$

$$\eta_{cycle} = \frac{W_{net}}{Q_{exh}} \times 100 \quad (5)$$

where, W_{net} is the summation of the power produced from the turbine.

3 RESULTS AND DISCUSSION

After establishing the SRC in Aspen Plus as discussed in the previous section, a sensitivity analysis is performed at the rated speed of the engine to study the influence of the parameters of the different components of the cycle on its performance.

The value of the condenser pressure, feed pump outlet pressure, the mass flow rate of the working fluid and the outlet gas temperature to the ambient are the main parameters considered in this study. Every parameter is changed while keeping the value of the other parameters constant. The following subsections show the influence of the mentioned parameters on the performance of the cycle as follows:

3.1 Condenser pressure

The condenser pressure has a great effect on cycle performance. By reducing the pressure of condenser, more expansion is achieved through the turbine which increases the work done by the turbine, while the inlet steam temperature is also reduced based on the reduction in inlet temperature. Figure 6 shows the influence of the condenser pressure on the power produced by the turbine. A 19% power reduction is achieved due to the increase in condenser pressure and thus the cycle efficiency. While a 27% increase in inlet temperature before the turbine is noticed. This parameter has also influence on the pinch point as shown in Figure 7. A reduction is achieved in the pinch point when the condenser pressure is increased and vice versa due to the variation in

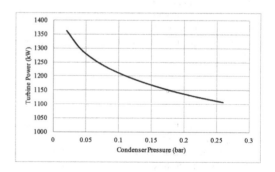

Figure 6. Influence of condenser pressure on power turbine.

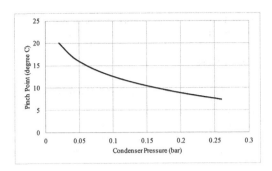

Figure 7. Influence of condenser pressure on pinch point.

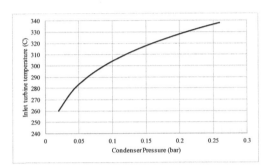

Figure 8. Influence of condenser pressure on inlet turbine temperature.

the overall performance of the Rankine cycle. By reducing the condenser pressure, the inlet steam temperature is also reduced and the quality of steam after the expansion process is also less than 88% as shown in Figure 9, which requires special attention for turbine life and avoids erosion in the turbine blades. Therefore, the condenser pressure must be optimized according to the required loads, the size of the heat exchanger and the system performance.

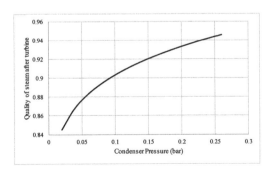

Figure 9. Influence of condenser pressure on quality of steam after expansion.

3.2 Feed pump outlet pressure

The feed pump outlet pressure is the second parameter considered in this study.

The simulation using Aspen Plus is performed by keeping the value of the other parameters constant. Based on the cumulative computation as described before and as shown in Figure 10, the influence of the feed pump outlet pressure has a great effect on the cycle performance. It helps to increase the isentropic enthalpy before the working fluid enters the boiler which increases the steam temperature before the turbine as shown in Figure 12 and more power is

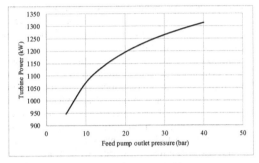

Figure 10. Influence of feed pump outlet pressure on power turbine.

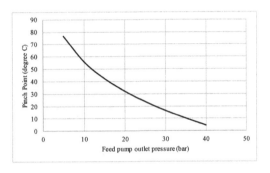

Figure 11. Influence of feed pump outlet pressure on pinch point.

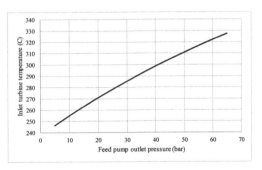

Figure 12. Influence of feed pump outlet pressure on inlet turbine temperature.

produced. By increasing the outlet pressure 8 times, around a 37% increase in the turbine power is achieved and accompanied by a reduction in pinch point as shown in Figure 11. Also, the quality of the steam after expansion is reduced by increasing the feed pump water pressure as presented in Figure 13. Therefore, a special attention is required for the values less than 88%. Therefore, a techno-economic study must be performed to evaluate the system according to the load demand required for the ship.

3.3 Mass flow rate of working fluid

In this section, the performance of the cycle is evaluated by keeping constant the condenser pressure, the feed pump outlet pressure and the outlet gas temperature, while changing the amount of mass flow rate of the working fluid.

Based on the energy balance of the boiler, a lower mass flow rate leads to a higher value of enthalpy and thus a higher inlet temperature to the turbine, w-here more power is produced and vice versa. As shown in Figure 14, the power turbine is reduced for the high amount of mass flow rate and vice versa. The inlet steam turbine temperature is also reduced by increasing the mass flow rate, while it keeps constant after a certain level of mass flow rate as shown in Figure 16. While the power is reduced, the value of the pinch point shows an increment and vice versa as in Figure 15. The quality of the steam after the expansion is significantly reduced at the high level of mass flow rate as shown in Figure 17, which makes the performance of the cycle unfeasible.

3.4 Outlet gas temperature to the ambient

The outlet gas temperature of the heat source depends on the geometry and the exchange rate of the boiler. Therefore, this section presents a sensitivity analysis of the variation of the outlet gas temperature.

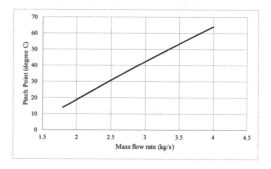

Figure 15. Influence of mass flow rate on pinch point.

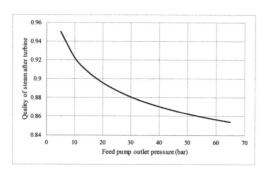

Figure 13. Influence of feed pump outlet pressure on quality of steam after expansion.

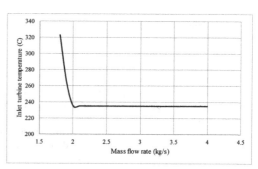

Figure 16. Influence of mass flow rate on inlet turbine temperature.

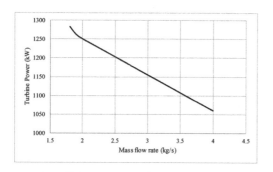

Figure 14. Influence of mass flow rate on power turbine.

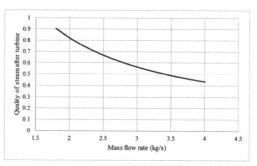

Figure 17. Influence of mass flow rate on quality of steam after expansion.

As shown in Figure 18, the lower the outlet temperature leads to a higher power production due to the higher inlet turbine temperature as shown in Figure 20 which depends on the higher exchange rate vice versa. It is also affected by the pinch point, once the pinch point decreases as in Figure 19, the outlet temperature is also decreased. As mentioned before, this parameter is accompanied by a higher inlet turbine temperature. However, after a certain limit, the inlet turbine temperature becomes the same.

Finally, based on the cumulative simulation, the quality of the steam after the turbine shows a significant reduction by increasing the outlet

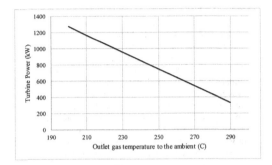

Figure 18. Influence of outlet gas temperature on power turbine.

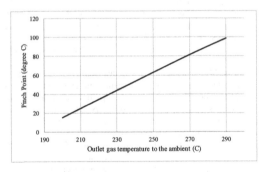

Figure 19. Influence of outlet gas temperature on pinch point.

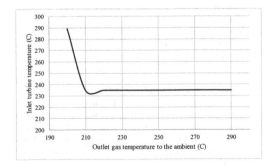

Figure 20. Influence of outlet gas temperature on inlet turbine temperature.

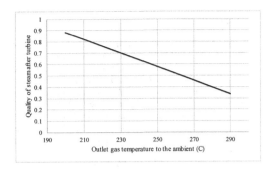

Figure 21. Influence of outlet gas temperature on quality of steam after expansion.

temperature and thus requires careful attention to save the turbine from failure as in Figure 21.

4 CONCLUSIONS

To achieve a great reduction in the amount of fuel consumption and exhaust emissions from ships, waste heat recovery systems are one of the effective solutions to increase ship energy efficiency. Different types of working fluid are used in the Rankine cycle, while this study focuses on the steam Rankine cycle as it is widely used in marine applications due to high power produced.

In this paper, a sensitivity analysis is performed to study the influence of the condenser pressure, feed pump outlet pressure, the mass flow rate of the working fluid and the outlet gas temperature to the ambient on the cycle performance for the same source of heating. The cycle performance is presented by the power produced, the pinch point, the inlet turbine temperature and the quality of the steam after expansion. The calculated results of the numerical model are computed using Aspen Plus.

It has been concluded that the lower the condenser pressure, the higher the feed pump outlet pressure, the higher the mass flow rate of the working fluid and the lower the temperature of the heat source gas to the ambient leads to higher power production. While it is required to perform a techno-economical study-based optimization procedure depending on the ship loads and to verify all the constraints of the system for safety aspects.

ACKNOWLEDGEMENTS

This work was performed within the scope of the Strategic Research Plan of the Centre for Marine Technology and Ocean Engineering (CENTEC), which is financed by the Portuguese Foundation for Science and Technology (Fundação para a Ciência e Tecnologia - FCT) under contract UIDB/UIDP/00134/2020.

REFERENCES

Altosole, M., Benvenuto, G., Campora, U., Laviola, M. & Zaccone, R., 2017. Simulation and performance comparison between diesel and natural gas engines for marine applications. *Proceedings of the Institution of Mechanical Engineers, Part M: Journal of Engineering for the Maritime Environment*, 231, 690–704.

Altosole, M., Benvenuto, G., Zaccone, R. & Campora, U., 2020. Comparison of Saturated and Superheated Steam Plants for Waste-Heat Recovery of Dual-Fuel Marine Engines. *Energies*, 13, 985.

Aspentech. 2019. *The Chemical Industry's Leading Process Simulation Software* [Online]. Available: https://www.aspentech.com/en/products/engineering/aspen-plus [Accessed 10 October 2019].

BCS, L. 2008. Waste heat recovery: technology and opportunities in US industry. Department of Energy (US).

Benvenuto, G. & Campora, U., 2002. Dynamic simulation of a high-performance sequentially turbocharged marine diesel engine. *International Journal of Engine Research*, 3, 115–125.

Benvenuto, G., Laviola, M. & Campora, U. 2013. Simulation model of a methane-fuelled four stroke marine engine for studies on low emission propulsion systems. *In*: Guedes Soares, C. & Peña, F. L. (eds.) *Developments in Maritime Transportation and Exploitation of Sea Resources*. London: Taylor & Francis Group, pp. 591–597.

Benvenuto, G., Trucco, A. & Campora, U., 2016. Optimization of waste heat recovery from the exhaust gas of marine diesel engines. *Proceedings of the Institution of Mechanical Engineers, Part M: Journal of Engineering for the Maritime Environment*, 230, 83–94.

Gaafary, M. M., El-Kilani, H. S. & Moustafa, M. M., 2011. Optimum design of B-series marine propellers. *Alexandria Engineering Journal*, 50, 13–18.

Larsen, U., Sigthorsson, O. & Haglind, F., 2014. A comparison of advanced heat recovery power cycles in a combined cycle for large ships. *Energy*, 74, 260–268.

Lion, S., Taccani, R., Vlaskos, I., Scrocco, P., Vouvakos, X. & Kaiktsis, L., 2019. Thermodynamic analysis of waste heat recovery using Organic Rankine Cycle (ORC) for a two-stroke low speed marine Diesel engine in IMO Tier II and Tier III operation. *Energy*, 183, 48–60.

Liu, X., Wang, X. & Zhang, C., 2014. Sensitivity analysis of system parameters on the performance of the Organic Rankine Cycle system for binary-cycle geothermal power plants. *Applied Thermal Engineering*, 71, 175–183.

Lloyd's Register 2012. Implementing the Energy Efficiency Design Index. London.

MAN Diesel & Turbo 2014. Waste Heat Recovery System (WHRS) for Reduction of Fuel Consumption, Emissions and EEDI. Augsburg.

MAN Diesel & Turbo. 2016. *MAN 32/44CR Engineered to Set Benchmarks* [Online]. Augsburg: MAN Diesel & Turbo. Available: http://marine.man.eu/four-stroke/engines/32-44cr/profile [Accessed 18 January 2017]

Marques, C. H., Caprace, J.-D., Belchior, C. R. P. & Martini, A., 2019. An Approach for Predicting the Specific Fuel Consumption of Dual-Fuel Two-Stroke Marine Engines. *Journal of Marine Science and Engineering*, 7, 20.

Martelli, M., Figari, M., Altosole, M. & Vignolo, S., 2014. Controllable pitch propeller actuating mechanism, modelling and simulation. *Proceedings of the Institution of Mechanical Engineers, Part M: Journal of Engineering for the Maritime Environment*, 228, 29–43.

Meee. 2020. *Rankine cycle* [Online]. Available: https://www.meee-services.com/how-can-we-increase-the-efficiency-of-the-boiler-in-rankine-cycle/rankine-cycle/ [Accessed 01 February 2020].

Raeie, N., Emami, S. & Karimi Sadaghiyani, O., 2014. Effects of injection timing, before and after top dead center on the propulsion and power in a diesel engine. *Propulsion and Power Research*, 3, 59–67.

Rajabloo, T., 2017. Thermodynamic study of ORC at different working and peripheral conditions. *Energy Procedia*, 129, 90–96.

Singh, D. V. & Pedersen, E., 2016. A review of waste heat recovery technologies for maritime applications. *Energy Conversion and Management*, 111, 315–328.

Spencer, R. C. & Meyer, C. A., 1968. The 1967 ASME Steam Tables. *Naval engineers journal*.

Stamatis, A. & Andritsos, N. Modeling of Electricity Generation Using Medium-Temperature Geothermal Resources in Greece Proceedings World Geothermal Congress 2015, 19–25 April 2015 Melbourne, Australia. pp. 1–9.

Stoumpos, S., Theotokatos, G., Boulougouris, E., Vassalos, D., Lazakis, I. & Livanos, G., 2018. Marine dual fuel engine modelling and parametric investigation of engine settings effect on performance-emissions trade-offs. *Ocean Engineering*, 157, 376–386.

Tadros, M., Ventura, M. & Guedes Soares, C. 2016. Assessment of the performance and the exhaust emissions of a marine diesel engine for different start angles of combustion. *In*: Guedes Soares, C. & Santos, T. A. (eds.) *Maritime Technology and Engineering 3*. London: Taylor & Francis Group, pp. 769-775.

Tadros, M., Ventura, M. & Guedes Soares, C. 2018a. Optimization scheme for the selection of the propeller in ship concept design. *In*: Guedes Soares, C. & Santos, T. A. (eds.) *Progress in Maritime Technology and Engineering*. London: Taylor & Francis Group, pp. 233–239.

Tadros, M., Ventura, M. & Guedes Soares, C. 2018b. Surrogate models of the performance and exhaust emissions of marine diesel engines for ship conceptual design. *In*: Guedes Soares, C. & Teixeira, A. P. (eds.) *Maritime Transportation and Harvesting of Sea Resources*. London: Taylor & Francis Group, pp. 105–112.

Tadros, M., Ventura, M. & Guedes Soares, C., 2019. Optimization procedure to minimize fuel consumption of a four-stroke marine turbocharged diesel engine. *Energy*, 168, 897–908.

Tadros, M., Ventura, M. & Guedes Soares, C., 2020a. A nonlinear optimization tool to simulate a marine propulsion system for ship conceptual design. *Ocean Engineering*, 210, 1–15.

Tadros, M., Ventura, M. & Guedes Soares, C. 2020b. Optimum design of a container ship's propeller from Wageningen B-series at the minimum BSFC. *In*: Georgiev, P. & Guedes Soares, C. (eds.) *Sustainable Development and Innovations in Marine Technologies*. London: Taylor & Francis Group, pp. 269–274.

Tadros, M., Ventura, M. & Guedes Soares, C. 2020c. Simulation of the performance of marine genset based on double-Wiebe function. *In*: Georgiev, P. & Guedes Soares, C. (eds.) *Sustainable Development and Innovations in Marine Technologies*. London: Taylor & Francis Group, pp. 292–299.

Tadros, M., Ventura, M., Guedes Soares, C. & Lampreia, S. 2020d. Predicting the performance of a sequentially turbocharged marine diesel engine using ANFIS. *In*: Georgiev, P. & Guedes Soares, C. (eds.) *Sustainable Development and Innovations in Marine Technologies*. London: Taylor & Francis Group, pp. 300–305.

Tadros, M., Vettor, R., Ventura, M. & Guedes Soares, C., 2021. Coupled Engine-Propeller Selection Procedure to Minimize Fuel Consumption at a Specified Speed. *Journal of Marine Science and Engineering*, 9, 59.

Theotokatos, G. & Livanos, G., 2013. Techno-economical analysis of single pressure exhaust gas waste heat recovery systems in marine propulsion plants. *Proceedings of the Institution of Mechanical Engineers, Part M: Journal of Engineering for the Maritime Environment*, 227, 83–97.

Ur-Rehman, M., Khurram, M. S., Rafiq, S., Memon, S. A., Ghauri, M., Jamil, F., Jaffery, M. H. & Doggar, M. G., 2018. Modeling of organic Rankine cycle for suitable working fluid in HYSYS for power generation in Pakistan. *Bulgarian Chemical Communications*, 50, 254–264.

Vettor, R., Tadros, M., Ventura, M. & Guedes Soares, C. 2016. Route planning of a fishing vessel in coastal waters with fuel consumption restraint. *In*: Guedes Soares, C. & Santos, T. A. (eds.) *Maritime Technology and Engineering 3*. London: Taylor & Francis Group, pp. 167-173.

Vettor, R., Tadros, M., Ventura, M. & Guedes Soares, C. 2018. Influence of main engine control strategies on fuel consumption and emissions. *In*: Guedes Soares, C. & Santos, T. A. (eds.) *Progress in Maritime Technology and Engineering*. London: Taylor & Francis Group, pp. 157–163.

Yu, W. & Zhao, F., 2019. Predictive study of ultra-low emissions from dual-fuel engine using artificial neural networks combined with genetic algorithm. *International Journal of Green Energy*, 16, 938–946.

Zaccone, R., Ottaviani, E., Figari, M. & Altosole, M., 2018. Ship voyage optimization for safe and energy-efficient navigation: A dynamic programming approach. *Ocean Engineering*, 153, 215–224.

Zhao, J. & Xu, M., 2013. Fuel economy optimization of an Atkinson cycle engine using genetic algorithm. *Applied Energy*, 105, 335–348.

CO₂ treatment in an autonomous underwater vehicle powered by a direct methanol fuel cell

Antonio Villalba-Herreros, Rafael d'Amore-Domenech, Ricardo Abad & Teresa J. Leo
Departamento de Arquitectura, Construcción y Sistemas Oceánicos y Navales, ETSI Navales, Universidad Politécnica de Madrid, Madrid, Spain

E. Navarro
Departamento de Mecánica de Fluidos y Propulsión Aeroespacial, ETSI Aeronáutica y del Espacio, Universidad Politécnica de Madrid, Madrid, Spain

ABSTRACT: Autonomous Underwater Vehicles are valuable tools in many fields. New sensors and computational sciences have endowed them with capabilities that allow carrying out highly complex missions. These capabilities must be supported by a power plant able to keep the vehicle running for an appropriate time span. Currently, this time is limited to values under 60 hours, considered not enough for new missions. All but one vehicle in the market are powered by batteries, but currently they cannot offer longer navigation times. To solve this, fuel cells constitute an alternative thanks to their higher energy content than batteries. Direct Methanol Fuel Cells present a series of advantages against other fuel cell type as the use of liquid fuel, low temperature operation and quick response. However, they produce CO_2. This work compares three COO2 treatment methods to rank them under a specific set of criteria to help to decide the best alternative.

1 INTRODUCTION

The increase of autonomy of Autonomous Underwater Vehicles (AUVs) is a critical matter for their development. Is this sense, fuel cells represent an alternative to current power plants based on batteries due to their higher energy density and specific energy (Villalba-Herreros et al. 2017)

Among the different types of fuel cells, Direct Methanol Fuel Cells (DMFCs) offer power ranges from several watts to 2 kW, operation at low working temperatures around 358 K (85° C), quick starting and response to load variations, silent operation and use methanol as fuel that is a liquid under ambient conditions of pressure and temperature simplifying fuel management (Dicks and Rand 2018). These characteristics make this type of fuel cells a good candidate to power AUVs. However, DMFCs produce CO_2 as reaction product that must be treated.

This work compares different CO_2 treatment methods in order to select the most suitable option for its application on-board AUVs powered by a power plant based on a DMFC. To do so, one Multiple-criteria Decision-making method (MCDM) is applied attending to relevant characteristics of the different CO_2 treatment alternatives. Although CO_2 must be separated from the aqueous flow from the anode where it is produced, no separation processes are studied here as they would be common to any CO_2 treatment method.

The structure of this work is as follows. Section 2 shows the CO_2 treatment systems studied. Section 3 describes the MCDM used and how it is applied here. The results of this study are presented in Section 4. Finally, the conclusions are collected in Section 5.

2 CO₂ TREATMENT METHODS

Depending on the AUV characteristics and operative conditions, one CO_2 treatment method can be more attractive than others. Its selection will depend on the evaluation of a set of characteristics or criteria. For this work, these criteria are the energy, mass and volume demanded by the system as well as its stealth potential and need for reconditioning between dives. The calculations have been carried out for a 1000 W DMFC stack working at 333 K and 100 kPa during a running time (t) equal to 120 h. This DMFC was designed with Aero-Marine DMFC Designer® (Santiago et al. 2019) encompassing the reduction of fuel consumption, that is, the CO_2 production rate. Under these conditions the mass of CO_2 produced (mCO_2) is equal to 95.64 kg, this is a production rate (CO_2) equal to 0.221 gCO₂/s. Furthermore, the evaluation was carried out at three navigation depths, surface layer (50 m), interior layer

DOI: 10.1201/9781003216599-53

(300 m) and bottom layer (6000 m), in accordance with the classification provided by Alam et al. (Alam et al. 2014).

The value of t is 2 times longer than that of the AUV HUGIN 4500, which offers the longest autonomy commercially available, 60 hours, and an average power equal to 1000 W (Kongsberg 2017).

Next, the three treatment methods studied are described. Table 2 collects the values of energy, mass and volume demanded by each one and a relative comparison on the characteristics of stealth and reconditioning. These two last characteristics have been ranked in such a way that the method with the maximum score, 3, is the best one being 1 the lowest rank.

2.1 Direct disposal (DD)

Direct disposal, see Figure 1, consists on the CO_2 ejection out of the AUV. To do so, the pressure of the CO_2 stream must be raised from the working pressure of the fuel cell, around 100 kPa, to a pressure, at least, equal to the external hydrostatic pressure (p_{ext}) that depends on the navigation depth. The weight loss due to the ejection of CO_2 must be compensated with sea water to keep a neutral buoyancy.

It is difficult to model the energy spent in an actual compressor accurately. However, a simple energy estimation of the compression process can be done under two different idealizations: the isothermal and the isentropic processes. Both represent the lower and upper limits, respectively, of the required power for compression inside an reciprocating compressor. If simplifications are taken further, the CO_2 can be considered a perfect gas, leading to a small error. In this work, and for comparative purposes, the isothermal model is considered. Equations 1 to 2 allow to calculate the power demand ($\dot{W}_{isothermal}$) and the energy required ($W_{isothermal}$):

$$\dot{W}_{isothermal} = \dot{m}_{CO_2} \cdot R_{CO_2} \cdot T_1 \cdot \ln\frac{p_2}{p_1} \quad (1)$$

$$W_{isothermal} = \dot{W}_{isothermal} \cdot t \quad (2)$$

where CO_2 is the CO_2 production rate, 0.221×10^{-3} kg_{CO2}/s; R_{CO2} means the Gas Constant for CO_2, 188.92 $\frac{J}{kg \cdot K}$; T_1 stands for the gas temperature at the initial state, 333 K; p_2 represents the pressure of the final state that depends on the navigation depth; p_1 is the pressure of the initial state, 100 kPa; and, t stands for the time span considered, 120 h.

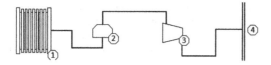

Figure 1. DD method sketch. 1 Fuel cell stacl. 2 CO_2 separator. 3 Compressor. 4 AUV outside.

The estimation of the mass and volume of the compressor can be done by using an extrapolation factor to extrapolate parameters from a known device. Such extrapolation factors depend on other factors that make the problem inherently complex. However, if some parameters affecting the final mass and volume of the compressor are fixed, the problem is simplified. In this work, the piston diameter, crankshaft radius, nominal rpm and input voltage of the electric motor are considered fixed. Also, it must be taken into account that the mass and volume present different extrapolation relations depending on the component of the compressor, the compressor itself or the electric motor. Following the thin-walled pressure vessel stress calculation, it can be established a linear correlation between the compressor components and the outlet pressure (p_{out}) (Beer et al. 2002).mechanics. In contrast, the electric motor presents a linear correlation with the internal wire section, which depends linearly with the rated current. As the voltage is fixed, the current is directly related with the electric power input ($\dot{W}_{in}$). Therefore, the resulting extrapolation equations to estimate the volume (V_{comp}) and mass (m_{comp}) of the compressor and the volume (V_{em}) and mass (m_{em}) of the electric motor are the following:

$$V_{comp} = V_{comp-ref} \cdot \frac{p_{out}}{p_{out-ref}} \quad (3)$$

$$m_{comp} = m_{comp-ref} \cdot \frac{p_{out}}{p_{out-ref}} \quad (4)$$

$$V_{em} = V_{em-ref} \cdot \frac{\dot{W}_{in}}{\dot{W}_{in-ref}} \quad (5)$$

$$m_{em} = m_{em-ref} \cdot \frac{\dot{W}_{in}}{\dot{W}_{in-ref}} \quad (6)$$

where the parameters with the appendix "-ref" make reference to the data from the reference compressor.

In this work, the compressor model 88P from Viair® was used as reference compressor (Viair 2019). This is a compact device equipped with a 12V direct current motor suitable for its installation on-board an AUV and provides a flow at the maximum outlet pressure higher than the CO_2 production rate considered in this study. The relevant data of this compressor are summarized in Table 1.

Regarding the stealth characteristics of this method. It must be noticed that not only the compressor, but also the gas stream delivered out-board of the AUV are noise sources that will disturb the environment. Besides, the CO_2 bubbles will create a visual trail that allows the easy location and monitoring of the AUV.

Finally, this method can be considered free of reconditioning between dives.

Table 1. Relevant data of the reference compressor. Adapted from Viair 2019.

Maximum outlet pressure, $p_{out-ref}$ (kPa)	827
Compressor mass, $m_{comp-ref}$ (kg)	0.612
Compressor volume, $V_{comp-ref}$ (L)	2.2
Maximum electric power, W_{in-ref} (W)	240
Electric motor mass, m_{em-ref} (kg)	1.430
Electric motor volume, V_{em-ref} (L)	5.2

2.2 Storage as pressurized gas (SPG)

This method consists on the compression of CO_2 up to a design storage pressure (p_{stor}) and its storage in a pressurized tank, see Figure 2. In this work, p_{stor} is set to 20 MPa. This is an usual value for Compressed Natural Gas (GNC) cylinders used in the automobile industry that leads to real and abundant data on the cylinders. Besides, this pressure avoids an excessive waste of energy during compression, reducing the size of the compressor. In order to reduce the mass of the system, Type 4 tanks were considered as they can save around 60% of the tank mass compared to Type 1 tanks with the same external dimensions (Faber Cylinders 2019).

Regarding the compressor, as p_{stor} and $\dot{m}CO_2$ are fixed, 20 MPa and 0.797 kg/h respectively, the compressor size, mass and volume are also fixed. In this case, to calculate the energy consumption, it must be taken into account that the power demand varies in accordance with the filling rate of the storage tank. The calculation of the compressor mass and volume were carried out following the same principles than in Section 2.1

In the case of the storage tank, data from 4 manufacturers of GNC cylinders have been analyzed to establish a relationship between the tank net capacity and its weight. In the range up to 100 L, acceptable linear correlations between the mass of the empty tank and its gross volume to its net capacity are observed, see Figure 3. This maximum capacity is enough for the purpose of this work as the density of CO_2 at 20 MPa and 278 K is equal to 1001.3 kg/m³, this translates into a running time of the reference fuel cell equal to 125.6 h, a longer time than the objective time span t, equal to 120 h. To calculate the net volume ($V_{net-stor-tnk}$), mass ($m_{stor-tnk}$) and gross volume ($V_{stor-tnk}$) of the storage tank, equations 7 to 9 apply:

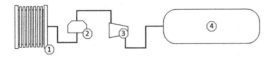

Figure 2. SPG method sketch. 1 Fuel cell stack. 2 CO_2 separator. 3 Compressor. 4 Storage tank.

$$V_{net-stor-tnk} = m_{CO_2} \cdot \rho_{CO_2} \quad (7)$$

$$m_{stor-tnk} = a \cdot V_{stor-tnk} \quad (8)$$

$$V_{stor-tnk} = b \cdot V_{stor-tnk} \quad (9)$$

where m_{CO2} is the ammount of CO_2 to process, 95.64 kg; ρ_{CO_2} is the density of CO_2 at 20 MPa and 278 K, 1001.3 kg/m³; a is the correlation factor between the tank empty weight and its net volume, 831 kg/m³; and, b is the correlation factor between the tank gross volume and its net volume, 0.9696 m³/m³.

SPG method presents better stealth characteristics than DD as no bubbles are expelled out of the AUV. The only source of noise is the compressor, whose noise level is equal to the noise level of the compressor in the DD method when the external pressure is equal to 20 MPa, i.e., when the AUV is navigating at 1989 m under the surface is salt water with a density equal to 1025 kg/m³.

Finally, the reconditioning of the system between dives is limited to emptying the CO_2 storage tank.

2.3 Storage embedded in an adsorbent material (SA)

This method captures the produced CO_2 through physical adsorption. This mechanism, unlike absorption or chemical adsorption, links the molecules to be captured to the adsorbent through weak attractive forces as Van der Waals forces. The inventory of CO_2 adsorbents is extensive, it includes from active carbon to zeolites and metal-organic frameworks. This work considers Zeolite 13X due to its good CO_2 sequestration characteristics and stability (Cavenatiet al. 2004, Bao et al. 2011, Kumar et al. 2015, Majchrzak and Nowak 2017). The capture capacity depends on the temperature and pressure of the process and it is described by the isobaric adsorption curves of the material. This work considers a pressure equal to 100

Table 2. Values of energy, volume and mass of the different CO2 capture methods studied along with the scores regarding stealth and reconditioning. DD, direct disposal, the following number indicates the navigation depth in meters. SPG, storage as pressurized gas. SA, storage embedded in an adsorbent material.

Method	Energy (kJ)	Volume (L)	Mass (kg)	Stealth	Reconditioning
DD 50 m	9715	2	0.6	1	3
DD 300 m	20496	9	2.6	1	3
DD 6000 m	38521	163	45.2	1	3
SPG	26591	148	94.6	2	2
SA	0	1198	824.5	3	1

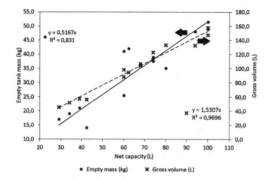

Figure 3. Net capacity to empty tank mass (right) and Net capacity to tank gross volume (left). (Toyota 2017, Faber Cylinders 2019, NGV Technology 2019, Luxfer Gas Cylinders 2019).

kPa in the zeolite tank and a temperature equal to 318 K (45°C). Under these conditions, the CO_2 capture capacity of Zeolite 13X, c_{Z13X}, is equal to 2.90 $mol_{CO2}/kg_{zeolite}$ (0.116 $kg_{CO2}/kg_{zeolite}$) (Bao et al.2011). Figure 4 shows a sketch of this method indicatingits main components.

This method runs with no energy consumption. Adsorption occurs without external intervention, only the pressure drop in the CO_2 circuit must be compensated to keep the gas flowing. Considering a conducting pipe with an internal diameter of 3 mm, the Darcy-Weisbach s formulation is applicable to the CO_2 stream under study (Match number under 0.3 and $5000 \leq Re \leq 10^8$) (White 2010). This formulation predicts a pressure drop equal to 4 kPa/m that can be compensated raising the working pressure of the fuel cell or though a partial vacuum in the zeolite container.

The mass (m_{AD}) and volume (vol_{AD}) of the system are directly proportional to the mass of CO_2 to be treated and can be calculated in accordance with equations 10 and 11.

$$m_{AD} = c_{Z13X} \cdot m_{CO_2} \qquad (10)$$

$$vol_{AD} = \rho_{Z13X} \cdot m_{AD} \qquad (11)$$

mCO_2 stands for the CO_2 mass to capture, i.e. 95.64 kg and ρ_{Z13X} is the density of Zeolite 13X that is equal to 689 kg/m^3 (Lee et al. 2002).

Neither mass nor volume of a container tank are considered. As Zeolite 13X is in solid state and this method works near ambient pressure a structural tank integrated in the AUV body is the best solution.

Regarding the radiated noise, due to the absence of moving parts, this method can be considered completely quiet for this study.

In the case of reconditioning between dives, it is necessary to regenerate the zeolite to remove the captured CO_2. This can be made through pressure and/or temperature swing followed by a N_2 purge to sweep the remaining impurities in the zeolite. The regeneration process allows to reuse the zeolite but it implies a waste of energy on-board the mother vessel.

3 MULTI-CRITERIA DECISION-MAKING METHOD

This work makes use of the Analytical Hierarchy Process (AHP) developed by Thomas Saaty in 1977 Saaty1977 to decide which method of the described in 2 is the most interesting for the objective application. This method has been applied satisfactorily to many areas since its publication and has a series of advantages as its easy usability, scalability and not need of intensive data (Velasquez and Haster 2013). In this work, the selection process was carried out taking into account the following criteria:

- "*Energy*" is the characteristic with the highest priority in accordance with the primary objective of this work, to enlarge the autonomy of AUVs.
- "*Stealth*" is considered a priority over "*Volume*" and "*Mass*" as this is a critical characteristic in many missions, not only to avoid detection but also to enhance sensors measurements and not to disturb the wildlife around the AUV.
- "*Reconditioning*" is the characteristic with the lowest priority as it has not impact in the autonomy of the vehicle.

This is reflected in the criteria paired comparison matrix shown in Table 3. This matrix has a consistency ratio (CR) equal to 0.0825 and results in the normalized weights applicable to the criteria in the selection process showed in Table 4.

Finally, Tables 5 to 7 show the paired comparison matrices among the three methods studied in this work. As it can be observed, none of the CO2 treatment methods has priority over the others. This work has not a preference for none of the methods studied

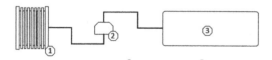

Figure 4. SA method sketch. 1 Fuel cell stack. 2 CO_2 separator. 3 Zeolite tank.

Table 3. Criteria paired comparison matrix.

	Energy	Volume	Mass	Stealth	Reconditioning
Energy	1	4	6	2	6
Volume	1/4	1	1	1/2	6
Mass	1/6	1	1	1/4	6
Stealth	1/2	2	4	1	6
Reconditioning	1/6	1/6	1/6	1/6	1

Table 4. Normalized weights vector.

Priority	Characteristic	Weight
1	Energy	45.02 %
2	Stealth	26.68 %
3	Volume	13.28 %
4	Mass	11.34 %
5	Reconditioning	3.68 %
	Sum	100 %

Table 5. Paired comparison matrices between CO_2 methods with a navigation depth equal to 50 m.

Energy	DD 50 m	SPG	SA
DD 50 m	1	5	1/4
SPG	1/5	1	1/9
SA	4	9	1
Volume	DD 50 m	SPG	SA
DD 50 m	1	2	9
SPG	1/2	1	7
SA	1/9	1/7	1
Mass	DD 50 m	SPG	SA
DD 50 m	1	2	9
SPG	1/2	1	7
SA	1/9	1/7	1
Stealth	DD 50 m	SPG	SA
DD 50 m	1	1	1/9
SPG	1	1	1/9
SA	9	9	1
Reconditioning	DD 50 m	SPG	SA
DD 50 m	1	4	9
SPG	1/4	1	5
SA	1/9	1/5	1

Table 6. Paired comparison matrices between CO2 methods with a navigation depth equal to 300 m.

Energy	DD 300 m	SPG	SA
DD 300 m	1	2	1/7
SPG	1/2	1	1/9
SA	7	9	1
Volume	DD 300 m	SPG	SA
DD 300 m	1	3	9
SPG	1/3	1	7
SA	1/9	1/7	1
Mass	DD 300 m	SPG	SA
DD 300 m	1	2	9
SPG	1/2	1	7
SA	1/9	1/7	1
Stealth	DD 300 m	SPG	SA
DD 300 m	1	1	1/9
SPG	1	1	1/9
SA	1/9	1/9	1
Reconditioning	DD 300 m	SPG	SA
DD 300 m	1	4	9
SPG	1/4	1	5
SA	1/9	1/5	1

Table 7. Paired comparison matrices between CO2 methods with a navigation depth equal to 6000 m.

Energy	DD 6000 m	SPG	SA
DD 6000 m	1	1/3	1/9
SPG	3	1	1/7
SA	9	7	1
Volume	DD 6000 m	SPG	SA
DD 6000 m	1	1	8
SPG	1	1	9
SA	1/8	1/9	1
Mass	DD 6000 m	SPG	SA
DD 6000 m	1	2	9
SPG	1/2	1	8
SA	1/9	1/8	1
Stealth	DD 6000 m	SPG	SA
DD 6000 m	1	1/5	1/9
SPG	5	1	1/4
SA	9	4	1
Reconditioning	DD 6000 m	SPG	SA
DD 6000 m	1	4	9
SPG	1/4	1	5
SA	1/9	1/5	1

and this is reflected in this way. It studies which method covers the best the requirements proposed. This comparison table is applicable to the three studied depths.

4 RESULTS AND DISCUSSION

Tables 8, 9 and 10 show the resulting raking of the three studied CO_2 treatment methods for each considered navigation depth.

The result shows that the storage of CO_2 using an adsorbent agent (SA) is the best choice in all the cases under study. The higher weight of the energy and stealth criteria make this method more advantageous besides its bigger volume and mass. But this is weight distribution is justified by the need of limited energy

Table 8. Resulting ranking of the studied CO2 treatment methods with a navigation depth equal to 50 m.

DD 50 m	2nd
SPG	3nd
SA	1st

Table 9. Resulting ranking of the studied CO2 treatment methods with a navigation depth equal to 300 m.

DD 300 m	3rd
SPG	2nd
SA	1st

Table 10. Resulting ranking of the studied CO2 treatment methods with a navigation depth equal to 6000 m.

DD 6000 m	3rd
SPG	2nd
SA	1st

consumption and high level of stealth. For shallow waters, the ejection of CO_2 would be the best choice due to its reduced size and limited energy consumption, but it must be taken into account that the stealth level is poor leading to a non-acceptable solution. For intermediate navigation depths, although SA is the best choice the compression and storage of CO_2 on-board can be attractive if the size of the system is critical along with a limited energy consumption.

These results are aligned with the priorities described in Section 3. The absence of energy expenditure has a big impact over the final decision and it is accompanied by a quiet operation that beats the good behavior in mass and volume of the other methods.

5 CONCLUSIONS

This work studies the CO2 treatment method that best fits a set of desired requirements for its application on-board an AUV powered by a Direct Methanol Fuel Cell (DMFC) based power plant. With the focus put in an operation with a energy cost as low as possible as well as quiet, the most suitable capture method is the storage of CO2 by means of an adsorbent material, Zeolite 13 X in this case. This method has been revealed more advantageous than the storage on-board as compressed gas or the ejection outside the AUV at any navigation depth. This result contributes to the development of innovative power plants for AUVs that provide them with longer autonomy.

ACKNOWLEDGMENTS

The authors gratefully acknowledge Universidad Politécnica de Madrid, Spain, the partial funding of this work through the foundation SOERMAR and the Spanish Ministry of Science, Innovation and Universities and European Regional Development Fund through Research Project ENE2017-86711-C3-2-R and also ENE2017-90932-REDT.

REFERENCES

Alam, K., T. Ray, & S. G. Anavatti (2014, sep). A brief taxonomy of autonomous underwater vehicle design literature. *Ocean Engineering 88*, 627–630.

Bao, Z., L. Yu, Q. Ren, X. Lu, & S. Deng (2011). Adsorption of CO2 and CH4 on a magnesium-based metal organic framework. *Journal of Colloid and Interface Science 353*(2), 549–556.

Beer, F. P., E. R. Johnston, & J. T. DeWolf (2002). *Mechanics of Materials*. McGraw-Hill.

Cavenati, S., C. A. Grande, & A. E. Rodrigues (2004). Adsorption Equilibrium of Methane, Carbon Dioxide, and Nitrogen on Zeolite 13X at High Pressures. *Journal of Chemical and Engineering Data 49*(4), 1095–1101.

Dicks, A. L. & D. A. J. Rand (2018). *Fuel Cell Systems Explained*. WILEY.

Faber Cylinders (2019). Cylinders for compressed natural gas (CNG). http://www.faber-italy.com/eng-product-cng.asp. [Last access: 27/12/2019].

Kongsberg (2017). Autonomous Underwater Vehicle: The HUGIN Family.

Kumar, A., D. G. Madden, M. Lusi, K.-J. Chen, E. A. Daniels, T. Curtin, J. J. Perry, & M. J. Zaworotko (2015, nov). Direct Air Capture of CO 2 by Physisorbent Materials. *Angewandte Chemie International Edition 54*(48), 14372–14377.

Lee, J.-S., J.-H. Kim, J.-T. Kim, J.-K. Suh, J.-M. Lee, & C.-H. Lee (2002, sep). Adsorption Equilibria of CO 2 on Zeolite 13X and Zeolite X/Activated Carbon Composite. *Journal of Chemical & Engineering Data 47*(5), 1237–1242.

Luxfer Gas Cylinders (2019). G-STOR™ H2 Hydrogen storage cylinders. https://www.luxfercylinders.com/products/g-stor-h2#metric. [Last access: 27/12/2019].

Majchrzak, A. & W. Nowak (2017). Separation characteristics as a selection criteria of CO2 adsorbents. *Journal of CO2 Utilization 17*, 69–79.

NGV Technology (2019). NGV Technology TYPE 4 CNG - 250 Bar Working Pressure. http://ngvtechnology.com/type-4.html. [Last access: 27/12/2019].

Saaty, T. L. (1977, jun). A scaling method for priorities in hierarchical structures. *Journal of Mathematical Psychology 15*(3), 234–281.

Santiago, Ó., M. Aranda-Rosales, E. Navarro, M. A. Raso, & T. J. Leo (2019, apr). Automated design of direct methanol fuel cell stacks: A quick optimization. *International Journal of Hydrogen Energy 44*(21), 10933–10950.

Toyota (2017). 2017 Mirai Product Information.

Velasquez, M. & P. T. Haster (2013, nov). A comparative analysis of multi-criteria decision-making methods. *International Journal of Operations Research 10*(2), 56–66.

Viair (2019). 88P Compressor. https://www.viaircorp.com/portables/88p. [Last access: 31/12/2019].

Villalba-Herreros, A., J. Arévalo-Fuentes, G. Bloemen, R. Abad, & T. J. Leo (2017). Fuel cells applied to autonomous underwater vehicles. Endurance expansion opportunity. In C. Guedes and A. P. Teixeira (Eds.), *IMAN 2017*, Volume 2, pp. 871–879. CRC Press/Balkema.

White, F. M. (2010). *Fluid Mechanics* (7 ed.). New York.

Renewable energy

Wave energy assessment in the São Roque do Pico island for OWC installation

G. Anastas
Portuguese Foundation for Science and Technology, Lisbon, Portugal

J.A. Santos
ISEL – Instituto Superior de Engenharia de Lisboa, Instituto Politécnico de Lisboa, Portugal
Centre for Marine Technology and Ocean Engineering (CENTEC), Instituto Superior Técnico, Universidade de Lisboa, Lisbon, Portugal

L.V. Pinheiro & C.J.E.M. Fortes
National Laboratory of Civil Engineering, Lisbon, Portugal

ABSTRACT: This paper aims to determine the wave energy exploitable for two potential sites, located above the breakwaters of both São Roque do Pico and Madalena city harbors. For that purpose, the third-generation wave model SWAN is used to estimate the sea-wave conditions over the last 40 years. Boundary conditions of the sea states and wind fields are provided by the climate reanalysis datasets (ERA5). Using those results as inputs to the SWAN model, the sea-states were propagated shoreward, in order to estimate and analyze the wave climate conditions in the region of interest. By combining the average energy flux per unit-length of wave front and the probability of occurrence of each sea state, the average exploitable annual energy per unit length of wave crest can be computed. The variability of this energy flux is described, since it is of fundamental importance for the efficiency of the Wave Energy Converters (WEC).

1 INTRODUCTION

In the last decades, the increase in the need for renewable energy sources has led to a steep increase in the research and development of the Wave Energy Converters (WEC) with the aim of satisfying the growing demand for clean and renewable energies.

Its predictability, seasonal stability, low visual impact, and the overall high energy carried by ocean waves (Clément et al. 2002) make the possibilities for this energy exploitation exceeding the expectation in wind or solar energy for electrical production. Wave energy is not only more predictable than wind or solar energy, but it has also a higher energetic density allowing extraction of more energy in smaller areas. In island environments, the importance of implementing such energy extraction systems is enhanced by the fact that they can contribute to the energetic autonomy of the local communities. For the exploitation of this wave energy resource, various technological solutions exist. In this study we are considering the introduction of an Oscillating Water Column (OWC) within the trunk of a breakwater. The design and construction of the structure are the most critical issues (not considering the air turbine technology), in matter of efficiency, environmental impact and financial viability for the OWC technology, which uses waves to compress and expand air so as to rotate an air turbine, which in turn produces electricity.

Most WEC have been conceived as offshore devices, where the highest wave energy densities are found. The installation of WEC in the nearshore has often been dismissed due to the lower gross energy densities without further consideration of the differences between the characteristics of offshore and nearshore wave energy resources. However, a simple scaling of the wave climate inadequately describes the nearshore wave climate. A better representation is required to correctly assess the nearshore wave energy resource potential. With the integration of the plant structure into a breakwater comes several advantages like the fact that constructional costs are shared, that the access for construction, operation and maintenance are simplified, and that it doesn't produce extra environmental impact. Although, since these fixtures aren't omni-directional and installed in fixed positions, it can be easily understood that the amount of energy exploitable is influenced by its own orientation and the relative incident wave directions (Folley & Whittaker 2009). As a consequence, wave directions are also to be considered through wave energy estimated flux, in order to obtain

DOI: 10.1201/9781003216599-54

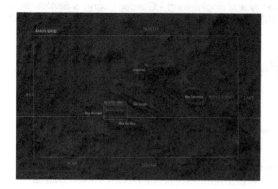

Figure 1. Azores Central group islands: nested computational grids (main, nested, nested1), buoy positions (Graciosa, Vitoria, Faial) and SWAN wave climate inputs positions (north, east, south, west).

a proper assessment. This approach was applied by Electric Power Research Institute Group to determine the available and recoverable wave energy resource on the United States coastline (Electric Power Research Institute 2011). To reach the objective of this paper, an assessment of the wave climate is lead, at both chosen spots, São Roque do Pico and Madalena ports, through a numerical model whose performance is assessed by comparing its results with on-site measurements. Although some other works were performed for the Azores Islands (Azevedo & Gonçalo 2005, Matos 2015, Rusu 2014, Rusu & Guedes Soares 2012), the present work considers a much longer period and introduces the concept of exploitable energy for this specific WEC technology.

Azores is a group of nine islands located in the North Atlantic Ocean about 1200 km west of Portugal. The islands form the largest group of peaks of the Mid-Atlantic Ridge. These nine islands are divided in three groups: the eastern group (Santa Maria and São Miguel), the Central group (Terceira, Graciosa, São Jorge, Pico and Faial) and the western group (Flores and Corvo).

The Central group, which will be the focus of this study, is presented in Figure 1.

2 EXPLOITABLE WAVE ENERGY ASSESSMENT

2.1 Methodology

The wave power density P is the rate at which the wave energy per unit length of wave crest is transmitted along the water column in the direction of wave propagation. Considering the deep-water approximation:

$$P = \frac{\rho g^2}{64\pi} T e H s^2 \quad (1)$$

Where ρ is the seawater density, g the acceleration of gravity, Hs the significant wave height and Te the wave energy period. The significant wave height and the wave energy period are computed from the spectral moments:

$$Hs = 4\sqrt{m_0} \text{ and } Te = \frac{m_{-1}}{m_0} \quad (2)$$

Where the nth order spectral moment is defined as:

$$m_n = \int_{-\infty}^{+\infty} f^n S(f) df \quad (3)$$

As the water depths at both point of interest is about 10m, in order to fit within the deep-water approximation (h > L/2), we are assuming that the wavelength (L) of the incoming waves do not exceed 20m.

Sea waves are often characterized in terms of significant wave height Hs and either peak period (Tp) or mean period (Tz). Considering that the specified period output of the SWAN model is Tp, it can be assumed that:

$$Te = \alpha Tp \quad (4)$$

The coefficient α depends on the shape of the wave spectrum. Since the JONSWAP spectrum with a peak enhancement factor of γ =3.3 has been chosen for the SWAN simulation, α=0.90 and Te=0.9Tp. This necessary assumption introduces some uncertainty into the power estimation. However, for P is proportional to TeHs², errors in period are less crucial than errors in significant wave height.

The wave energy flux along a linear feature depends on the wave power density and on the angle between the wave direction and the orientation of the line crossed by the waves (Electric Power Research Institute 2011). The wave energy flux across a linear feature is then given by:

$$P_\varphi = P\cos(\varphi) \quad (5)$$

In which P is the incoming wave power density given by eq. (1) and φ is the angle between the wave direction and the perpendicular to the breakwater as described in Figure 2.

It is also necessary to consider the effect of the resource variability on performance. Non-linearities in a device's hydrodynamics and the geometry constraints of the electro-mechanical plant do induce a power level threshold above which the incoming energy is unexploitable and it would be appropriate to disregard such sea-states (Cahill & Lewis 2011). This

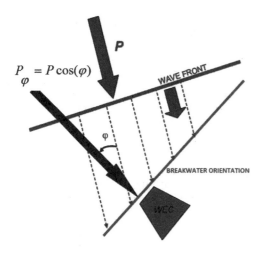

Figure 2. Wave energy flux across a line parallel to the breakwater orientation.

threshold obviously depends on the device technology/design, so there is no definitive value of it. Considering the range of the overall average of the wind energy converter capacity factors (between 25% and 50%) it appears that a reasonable value for it may be four times the average incident wave power (Folley & Whittaker 2009). This new representation of the wave energy resource is called the exploitable wave energy resource since it is more closely related to the amount of wave energy that is exploitable by WEC.

Even if it is assumed that this concept provides a more rigorous estimation of the recoverable energy flux for wave energy converters, the threshold value must be refined by carrying out large scale tests on the final selected device.

3 MODELING THE NEARSHORE CLIMATE

3.1 Paradigm definition:

A third-generation spectral wave model is used to propagate the wave climate from offshore to nearshore. These models are the current state-of-the-art for wave climate. The freely available version of SWAN is used in this paper analysis. Third-generation spectral wave models are based on solving the spectral action balance equation, which determines the evolution of the action density in space and time. The action density is defined as energy density divided by wave frequency and it is used because, unlike energy density, it is conserved in the presence of currents; the energy density is specified using the linear two-dimensional wave spectrum, with the wave energy distributed over frequency and propagation direction.

Three nested computational domains, embracing the Central group of Azores archipelago, were defined. Similar computational schemes were applied with good results in Madeira Archipelago (Rusu et al. 2008), and also on the Portuguese Continental coast (Rusu et al 2008). Some details about the computational domains used for the SWAN simulations are presented in Table 1 and Figure 1. The implementation of the SWAN model was made for 36 directions and 28 frequencies logarithmically spaced from 0.04 Hz to 0.6 Hz with a JONSWAP spectrum, the simulations were being performed in the stationary mode.

A 40-year hindcast was considered, from 01/01/1979 to 31/07/2019, in order to obtain a set of offshore wave data at the four cardinal points at the borders of the main grid every 6 hours (see Figure 1). These data were extracted from the fifth generation ECMWF atmospheric reanalysis of the global climate, **ERA5,** and its reliability are evaluated in the next paragraph. The reanalyzed wind field, also provided by ERA5 dataset, is forced as inputs for all computational grids. It is defined in order to fit the main grid with a 0.25°/0.25° resolution every 6-h covering the whole test period. Due to their weak impact on the sea waves of this region, currents effects were not taken into account, which implies that refraction is only due to water depth spatial variations (Rusu & Guedes Soares 2012) The default bottom friction coefficient proposed by the JONSWAP group ($0.067 m^2 s^{-3}$, Hasselmann et al., 1973) is used. This bottom friction coefficient has been found to be suitable for fully developed wave conditions in shallow water (Bouws & Komen 1983), although clearly variations will undoubtedly occur with different seabed conditions. The physical processes activated in the simulations of the SWAN modeling system are presented in Table 2. They have been fixed balancing the relevance of each factor in the studied problem against its tendency to increase the calculation time.

3.2 Input dataset assessment

Since these islands are in the middle of the Atlantic Ocean, they are exposed to various wave systems. The archipelago is subjected to both direct approach of the swell coming from distant storms as well as the sea waves generated by local winds that create a local wave system. When the swell system crosses the archipelago the wave directions are significantly modified, and this induces the occurrence of various

Table 1. SWAN computational grid dimension and resolutions.

Grids	Dimension		Resolutions	
	Lx (km)	Ly (km)	Δx (km)	Δy (km)
Main	265	149	1.2	1.2
Nested	106.8	54.6	0.6	0.6
Nested1	30	18	0.1	0.1

Table 2. SWAN activated physical processes (x). Tide – tide forcing, Quad – quadruplet nonlinear interactions, Tri – triad nonlinear interactions, Diff – diffraction, Fri – bottom friction.

Physical Processes	Tide	Quad	Tri	Diff	Fri
Grids					
Main	x	o	o	x	o
Nested	x	x	x	x	x
Nested1	x	x	x	x	x

wave systems with different directions in the coastal environment of the archipelago. In this region, in-situ measurements were performed. The most recent measurements became available with the implementation of the project CLIMAAT (Azevedo & Gonçalo, 2005). From the wave buoys deployed within the region defined by the main computational grid, three were selected (Faial/Pico, Praia da Vitoria, Graciosa) to assess the performance of the ERA5 dataset in terms of significant wave height (Hs), peak period (Tp) and Mean Direction (Dir), at the location of each one of them for the period between 04/2013 and 06/2019.

So as to quantify the accuracy of this wave model, which is to be used as input for the SWAN simulations, the following statistical parameters were considered: the normalized Bias (NBias), index of the average component of the error; a value closer to zero identifies a better simulation; values are over-predicted if Bias < 0 and under-predicted if Bias > 0; the normalized root mean square error (NRMSE); the scatter index (SI) which gives the percentage of the expected error for the parameter; the linear correlation coefficient (r) which should be as close as possible to 1 and N – Number of values in the sample. The results presented in Table 3 & 4 show that in all cases Hs is being overestimated (NBias between -0.20 and -0.26) and Tp is being underestimated by the model (NBias around 0.17). After a specific process to avoid the 360° modulus issues, direction results give the lower scatter indexes and seem to be more correlated with the buoy data. The Hs correlation indicator is quite stable over the three considered locations; however, a serious variability for both Tp and Dir correlation indicator can be seen in Table 4 & 5.

Table 3. Hs - ERA5 model against wave buoys between 04/01/2013 and 01/07/2019.

Buoy	NBias	NRMSE	SI	r	N
FAIAL	-0.25	0.35	0.28	0.85	7062
GRACIOSA	-0.26	0.37	0.29	0.84	5061
VITORIA	-0.20	0.31	0.27	0.86	2800

Table 4. Tp - ERA5 model against wave buoys between 04/01/2013 and 01/07/2019.

Buoy	NBias	NRMSE	SI	r	N
FAIAL	0.17	0.22	0.14	0.68	7062
GRACIOSA	0.18	0.21	0.12	0.77	5061
VITORIA	0.17	0.22	0.14	0.66	2800

Table 5. Dir - ERA5 model against wave buoys between 04/01/2013 and 01/07/2019.

Buoy	NBias	NRMSE	SI	r	N
FAIAL	0.10	0.20	0.18	0.87	7062
GRACIOSA	0.12	0.17	0.15	0.94	5061
VITORIA	0.02	0.34	0.34	0.69	2800

Considering each trio (Hs,Tp,Dir), the Vitoria Buoy point is giving the worst results in terms of period and direction, which could be due to the obstacle (Graciosa and Terceira Island) crossed by the majority of the incident wave coming from the N-W quarter, producing diffraction in the wave propagation, exacerbating the modeling difficulties. At the Graciosa buoy location, the ERA5 results are quite similar to the values obtained from the corresponding measurements. In fact, it is fully exposed to the majority of incoming waves with a relative constant bathymetry. The Faial buoy peak period correlation low value (0.68) may be justified by its position, lodged in a water channel created by both Pico and Faial Island that makes sea-wave predictions very difficult. Thus, it can already be foreseen the impact that it will have on the SWAN simulation accuracy at the Madalena location. Taking these conclusions into account, the SWAN simulation is performed with the data provided by the ERA5 reanalysis dataset.

3.3 *Nearshore wave climate modeling result*

3.3.1 *Result assessment*

As attested by Figure 2, the only buoy that remains within the finer grid (nested 1) is the Faial buoy.

In order to evaluate the results of the SWAN simulation, a statistical comparison is performed for the same period as in 3.2 and using the same indicators. These values are reported in Table 6.

It is important to notice that the scatter indexes (see Table 6), are similar to the values found through the ERA5 reanalysis model assessment (3.2), as a consequence, it can be concluded that the SWAN model set-up doesn't introduce any extra error

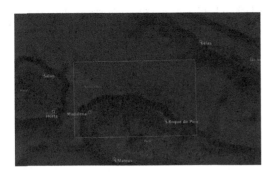

Figure 2. Azores Central group islands: nested computational grids (nested1), Faial buoy position.

Table 6. SWAN model results against Faial wave buoy between 04/01/2013 and 01/07/2019.

Parameters	NBias	NRMSE	SI	r	N
Hs	-0.19	0.29	0.27	0.86	7062
Tp	0.22	0.28	0.17	0.61	7062
Dir	0.092	0.061	0.13	0.86	7062

comparing to the ERA5 model. Moreover, it is necessary to notice that Hs is slightly less overestimated (NBias ERA5: -0.25/NBias SWAN: -0.19) while Tp is more underestimated (NBias ERA5: 0.17/NBias SWAN: 0.22). Those erroneous estimations could, in a way, compensate each other in the calculation the wave power density since it is proportionate to $TeHs^2$, as explained in 2.1.

3.3.2 Point of interest wave climate

Since the aim of this paper is to assess the wave power density in the region of the São Roque and Madalena docks, two target points were selected (Figure 3).

The elected spot for São Roque do Pico (P1: 28.32W 38.53N) is about 30m far from the dock line right above the breakwater where the water depth is about 10m. It happened to be impossible to find a point as close to the Madalena breakwater due to the resolution of the SWAN computational grid. The closest site which allows modeling calculation is about 300m far from the dock line (P2: 28.53W 38.54N), where the water depth is about 15m. However, since the bathymetric lines are parallel, the wave energy is only affected by refraction. Thus, the energy assessment at this point is considered as a viable approximation of the energy available above the breakwater position.

3.3.3 Points of interest wave climate

First of all, it is to be explained that, following the methodology described in 2.1, a few filters were applied to the set of data extracted from the SWAN model results at both points. After computing the exploitable power from equation (5) for each time (every 6h) over the 40 years, the negative values were dismissed with their corresponding set of sea states, which represented 3 values for P1 and 2 for P2. Then, the mean incident wave power was calculated for each point and used to determine the threshold (P1: 24.1 kW/m; P2: 48.6 kW/m) above which all values are excluded (P1: 3030 values; P2: 2025 values). After applying these filters, from the 57828 initial values it remains 54790 for P1 and 55796 for P2.

These filtered climate data series, coming from both points, are employed in order to generate wave roses (Figure 4.1 & 4.2) and scatter diagrams of the Hs-Te joint distributions (Table 7.1 & 7.2). Such a diagram presents the probabilities of occurrences of different sea states expressed in percentages from the total number of occurrences and the color of each bin indicates the percentage according to a color-map, the same for all diagrams. It is structured into bins of 2s×0.25m (ΔTe×ΔHs) (Rusu 2014, Silva et al. 2013).

In P1, the incident waves predominantly come from the North-West direction, between 300° and 360° (75%). The rest is contained in the North-East quarter. The maximum values reached by Hs and Te are respectively, 3.38m and 20.4s. Besides, most seawaves have Hs, between 0.25 and 2m, and Te between 2 and 12s. A peak of occurrences (10.4%) is to be noticed in the Te[2-4]/Hs[0.25-0.5] bin. In P2, the waves are also in a narrow direction sector, between 280° and 340° (90%), which corresponds to the North-West direction. Hs and Te get to the

Figure 3. Target points: São Roque do Pico docks (left) and Madalena (right).

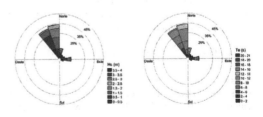

Figure 4.1. Wave roses for the 40-year study at P1 (Sao Roque). Hs (left side) and Te (right side) are represented. The interval of each sector is 20°.

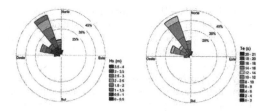

Figure 4.2. Wave roses for the 40-year study at P2 (Madalena). Hs (left side) and Te (right side) are represented. The interval of each sector is 20°.

Table 7.1. P1 - occurrence probability diagram for each sea state over the 40 years of study.

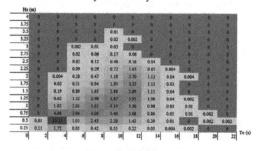

Table 7.2. P2 - occurrence probability diagram for each sea state over the 40-year of study.

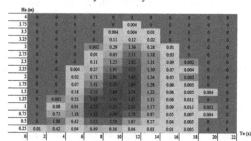

maximum values of, in that order, 3.60m and 18.5s. Furthermore, most sea-waves have Hs between 0.25 and 2,5m, and Te between 6 to 12s. In P2, the wave distribution is significantly narrower in terms of energy period comparing to the P1 distribution.

3.3.4 *Points of interest exploitable wave power density*

To have an idea of the overall exploitable power densities at both points, an average of its values was calculated (P1: 4.2kW/m; P2: 10,4kW/m). However, to truly describe the energy resource, the mean recoverable energy flux was computed for each bin of the Hs-Te scatter diagram, with the following resolution: 2s×0.25m (ΔTe×ΔHs). The outcomes are

Table 8.1. P1 - mean exploitable energy flux per wave front length in kW/m for each sea state over the 40-year of study.

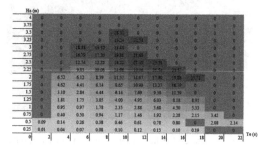

Table 8.2. P2 - mean exploitable energy flux per wave front length in kW/m for each sea state over the 40-year of study.

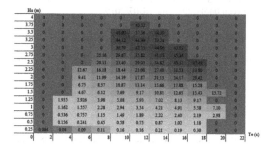

presented in Table 8.1 & 8.2. It reveals that the maximum mean power density in Sao Roque is 23.72kW/m and 48.03kW/m in Madalena do Pico.

By multiplying the mean annual number of hours (8766h) with the average exploitable energy flux per wave front length (Table 8.1 & 8.2) and the occurrence probabilities (Table 7.1 & 7.2) of each bin (Te-Hs), the average annual exploitable energy per unit wave crest length for each sea state is obtained (Table 9.1 & 9.2). The result demonstrates an evident difference between the two locations in terms of total exploitable energy. The total average annual exploitable energy at the São Roque do Pico point is 3724MWm^{-1}year^{-1}, while it is 9150MWm^{-1}year^{-1} at the Madalena point.

The largest contribution for the total annual mean recoverable energy comes from sea states with both high occurrences and high wave power density (red bins), corresponding to sea states with significant wave heights between 1 and 2.25m and energy periods between 8 and 12s for São Roque. This energy represents about 54% of the total amount, and only 25% of the sea state occurrences.

For Madalena, the largest contribution comes from sea states with Hs between 1.25 and 3m and Te between 8 and 14s. This energy represents about 80% of the total amount, and only 40% of the occurrences. This result is linked with the observation raised before, that the occurrence distribution at P2 was narrower in

Table 9.1. P1 - combined occurrences and energy diagram multiplied by 8766h. Each bin indicates the value of the mean exploitable energy flux per wave front length (MWm-1year-1).

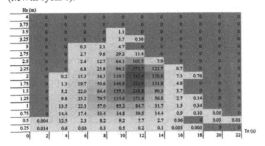

Table 9.2. P2 - combined occurrences and energy diagram multiplied by 8766h. Each bin indicates the value of the mean exploitable energy flux per wave front length (MWm-1year-1).

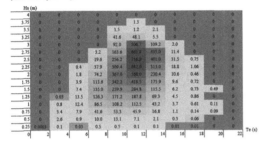

terms of energy period than in P1, which induces that more energy is most likely contained in a smaller range.

These results suggest that WEC developers should design their devices in order to operate efficiently over sea conditions that provide the largest contributions to the total annual of wave energy, instead of aiming only the more commonly sea states that in general offer a small contribution to the overall energy exploitable. From this point of view, the Madalena do Pico spot (P2) seems to be more advantageous with regard to the high overall potential energy to recover and to the low complexity in the design, since the range of energy periods that contribute the most to the more powerful states is narrow.

4 CONCLUSIONS

A third-generation spectral wave model, together with hindcast data from the Era5 reanalysis dataset, has been set-up to investigate, over two prior selected locations, the energetic potential of each one of them.

Because of the large temporal scale of the study (40 years), it should be born in mind that, some choices in term of modeling were made by balancing the calculation time against the impact of each factor on the accuracy of the study. Examples of this are the choice of the activated parameters in each grid, the computational grid resolutions, the stationary mode, and the forced input data at 4 cardinal points instead of spectral inputs at the border. Each one of those simplifications introduces a substantial error; nevertheless, the amount of information produced by such a study gives an accurate overview of the general tendencies.

The concept of exploitable wave energy resource was considered in this study since it provides a more appropriate representation in the context of a unidirectional wave energy converter.

Considering the wave climate, it was demonstrated that the incoming wave directions are concentrated in the wind rose North-West quarter at both points. The Madalena do Pico location (P2) is clearly the best one, since its dock is facing this direction, whereas São Roque do Pico's dock is facing the North-East direction. The occurrence distribution of each sea state (Hs-Te) together with the power distribution, reveals that, for P1, on one hand, the great concentration of occurrences (10%) in the bin Te[2/4]- Hs[0.25/0.5], doesn't comply with the power distribution pattern at this location. This means that this concentration of occurrences barely impacts the total amount of exploitable energy. On the other hand, the energy period deviation of the highest values of occurrences in P2 was smaller than in P1. This fact represents another advantage if it fits the distribution of the highest power value, because in this case, the design of an effective converter, regarding its own eigen-periods, would be eased by the thinner range of wave energy period to be able to convert. In fact, in P2, if the Te-Hs range of highest occurrences is considered, it corresponds to the median power level range. But still, by comparing, either the combined occurrences, and power diagrams values, either the overall exploitable annual energy at both locations, it is clearly demonstrated that the Madalena location (P2) seems to be provided with the greatest energetic potential.

ACKNOWLEDGEMENTS

This work has been performed within the projects OWC-HARBOUR - Harbour protection with dual chamber oscillating water column devices (PTDC/EME-REN/30866/2017) and To-SEAlert – Wave overtopping and flooding in coastal and port areas: Tools for an early warning, emergency planning and risk management system, Ref. PTDC/EAM-OCE/31207/2017, funded by the Portuguese Foundation for Science and Technology.

REFERENCES

Azevedo, E.B. & Gonçalo, V. 2005. The CLIMAAT project and its contribution for monitoring and characterization of the wave conditions in the Archipelago of Azores. In: Proc. 4as Jornadas de Engenharia Costeira e Portuária; p. 20e1. Angra do Heroísmo, Portugal [in Portuguese].

Bouws, E. & Komen, G.J. 1983. On the balance between growth and dissipation in an extreme depth-limited wind-sea in the southern North Sea. Journal of Physical Oceanography; 13:1653–8.

Cahill, B, & Lewis, A.W. 2011 Wave energy resource characterization of the Atlantic marine energy test site. In: Proceedings of the 9th European Wave and Tidal Energy Conference, Southampton, UK.

Clément, A. et al. 2002. Wave energy in Europe: current status and perspectives. Renew Sustain Energy Rev;6: 405e31.

Electric Power Research Institute. 2011. Mapping and assessment of the United States ocean wave energy resource. Technical report.

Folley, M. & Whittaker, T.J.T. 2009. Analysis of the nearshore wave energy resource. Renew Energy;34: 1709e15.

Matos, A. & Madeira, F. 2015 Wave energy at Azores islands. SCACR2015 – International Short Course/Conference on Applied Coastal Research, 28th September – 1st October 2015 – Florence, Italy. 243–254pp. ISBN 78-88-97181-52–1.

Rusu, E. 2014. Evaluation of the Wave Energy Conversion Efficiency in Various Coastal Environments, Energies, 7, 4002–4018; doi:10.3390/en7064002

Rusu, L. & Guedes Soares, C. 2012. Wave energy assessments in the Azores islands, Renewable Energy.

Rusu, E., Pilar, P & Guedes Soares, C 2008. Evaluation of the wave conditions in Madeira Archipelago with spectral models. Ocean Engineering; 35:1357e71.

Rusu, E., Pilar, P & Guedes Soares, C 2008. Hindcast of the wave conditions along the west Iberian coast. Coastal Engineering;55: 906e19.

Silva, D., Rusu, E. & Guedes Soares, C. 2013. Evaluation of various technologies for wave energy conversion in the Portuguese nearshore. 6(3):1344–1364.

A BEM for the performance of surge-type wave energy devices in variable bathymetry

K. Belibassakis & A. Magkouris
School of Naval Architecture & Marine Engineering, National Technical University of Athens, Greece

ABSTRACT: Wave-structure interaction is an important topic concerning the modelling and performance optimization of Wave Energy Converters (WECs) operating in nearshore and coastal areas. In this work a BEM is developed and applied to the investigation of variable bathymetry (bottom slope and curvature) effects on the performance of surge-type wave energy converters excited by harmonic monochromatic waves in the two-dimensional space. Numerical results are presented illustrating the effect that the modification of the wave field has on the devices and the effects of depth variation in conjunction with other parameters like inertia and power-take-off, on their performance.

1 INTRODUCTION

Ocean waves provide a sustainable and widely available source of energy, which could be used to increase the fraction of green energy in the global energy grid. In particular, as concerns wave energy, many devices and concepts have been proposed and thoroughly investigated. However, most of the devices operate in nearshore and coastal regions and variable bathymetry could have significant effects on their performance. Oscillating Wave Surge Converters (OWSCs) exploit the horizontal motion of water molecules during wave propagation to generate renewable electricity (Whittaker & Folley, 2011). A typical OWSC consists of a frame on which a shaft is mounted and a flap which performs angular oscillations with the aforementioned shaft being the center of rotation. The frame is fastened at the seabed (or rests on an auxiliary structure at a lower depth) and is fitted with a hydraulic generator. Fluid is compressed into the hydraulic generator due to the angular oscillation and the pressure is then transferred, by means of an appropriate pipeline system, to a hydroelectric power station to generate electricity.

2 OWSC MATHEMATICAL MODEL

Considering that the flap performs harmonic angular oscillations of maximum width θ_0 with frequency ω, the angle of oscillation at any time will be given by:

$$\theta(t) = \text{Re}\{\theta_0 \exp(-i\omega t)\}. \tag{1}$$

In order to ensure that the system will perform harmonic oscillations, a torsional spring at the hinge point is considered, which restores the flap after its deviation from the vertical position during each period, due to the incident waves. Moreover, the hydraulic generator, which compresses fluid and supplies the hydroelectric power station, uses part of the oscillation's energy and therefore acts as a damper in the contemplated torsional oscillator. For simplicity, power extracted by the system (PTO) is considered to be converted into electricity at the hydroelectric power station without any further losses, e.g. due to transmission through the pipeline system and mechanical losses.

The equation of motion of the angular oscillator is:

$$J_p\ddot{\theta} + B_p\dot{\theta} + C_p\theta = M(t), \tag{2}$$

where J_p is the moment of inertia of the flap with respect to the axis of rotation, B_p is the damping coefficient associated with the PTO, C_p is the spring constant of the installed torsional spring and $M(t)$ is the time dependent torque that the flap receives from the waves. Assuming small angles of deviation from the vertical position (θ_0), the horizontal velocity of any point on the flap will be equal to:

$$u(z) \approx L(z)\dot{\theta} = f(z), \text{ where } L(z) = z + d, \tag{3}$$

indicates the lever arm of a given point on the flap, located at depth z, with respect to the center of rotation and d is the hinge point's depth. Given the assumption of small angles of deviation from the vertical position ($\tan(\theta_0) \approx \theta_0$), the horizontal amplitude of the flap motion at the free surface level is

$$S = 2d\tan(\theta_0) \approx 2d\theta_0. \quad (4)$$

Assuming for simplicity the two-dimensional problem concerning normally incident waves in constant depth, the model of an OWSC is shown in Figure 1. Given that the OWSC's motion is generated by incident waves, a fraction of the in- coming wave (I) received by the device is expected to be reflected (R).

The boundary condition on the flap's surface specifies that the horizontal flap velocity $f(z)$ is equal to the fluid's horizontal velocity for $z \in (-d, 0)$, and in terms of the complex potential φ it is expressed as follows:

$$\left.\frac{d\varphi}{dx}\right|_{x=0} = f(z), \; -d<z<0, \; \left.\frac{d\varphi}{dx}\right|_{x=0} = 0, \; -h<z<-d. \quad (5)$$

The above boundary condition must be satisfied by the wave potential, along with the surface and bottom BCs, which respectively are:

$$\frac{\partial \varphi}{\partial z} - \frac{\omega^2}{g}\varphi = 0, \; z=0, \; \text{and} \; \frac{\partial \varphi}{\partial z} = 0, \; z=-h. \quad (6)$$

The general expression of the complex potential describing the wave field in the semi-infinite constant depth strip is as follows:

$$q^{-1}\varphi(x,z) = [\exp(ik_0x) + R\exp(-ik_0x)]Z_0(z) + \sum_{n=1}^{\infty}[A_n\exp(-k_nx)Z_n(z)]. \quad (7)$$

where $q = -igH/2\omega$ and H is the incident wave height. The first term corresponds to the left-propagating mode, R represents the complex amplitude of the reflected component, and $A_n, n \geq 1$ represent the corresponding amplitudes of the evanescent modes. Moreover, $Z_n(z) = \cos(k_n(z+h))/\cos(k_nh)$ represents the vertical structure of each mode, while $k_0 = i|k_0|$ and k_n are obtained as the roots of the dispersion relation:

$$\omega^2 = -kg\tan(kh). \quad (8)$$

The free surface's elevation is given by:

$$\eta(x) = \frac{i\omega}{g}\varphi(x, 0) \quad (9)$$

And by using the above representation can be expressed as:

$$\eta(x) = \frac{H}{2}\left[A_0^+\exp(ik_0x) + A_0^-\exp(-ik_0x) + \sum_{n=1}^{\infty}A_n\exp(-k_0x)\right] \quad (10)$$

The x-derivative of the wave potential provides the horizontal component of the fluid's particles' velocity in the flow field. The latter evaluated at the position of the flap $x=0$ reads as follows:

$$\left.\frac{\partial\varphi}{\partial x}\right|_{(x=0)} = q\left\{ik_0(R-1)Z_0(z) - \sum_{n=1}^{\infty}[k_nA_nZ_n(z)]\right\}. \quad (11)$$

By expressing the function $f(z)$ of the horizontal velocity of the flap in terms of the vertical eigenfunctions and using it in the boundary condition Eq. (5), we obtain the following relations for the coefficients R and A_n:

$$R = 1 - \frac{i\omega O_0\theta_0}{qik_0\cosh(k_0h)\|Z_0\|^2}, \quad (12)$$

$$A_n = \frac{i\omega O_n\theta_0}{qk_n\cos(k_nh)\|Z_0\|^2}, \quad (13)$$

where

$$\begin{cases} O_0 = \int_{-d}^{0}(z+d)\cosh[k_0(z+h)]dz \\ O_n = \int_{-d}^{0}(z+d)\cos[k_n(z+h)]dz \end{cases} \quad (14)$$

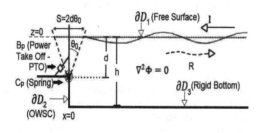

Figure 1. OWSC operating in a constant depth semi-infinite fluid channel.

The equation of motion of the angular oscillator (Eq. 2) is expressed in the frequency domain as:

$$a(\omega)\theta_0 = -\omega^2 J_P \theta_0 - i\omega B_P \theta_0 + C_P \theta_0 = M_0, \quad (15)$$

where M_0 is the moment applied to the flap as result of the fluid's pressure. The latter is expressed in terms of the complex wave potential by integrating the pressure forces ($P = -i\omega\rho\varphi$) multiplied by the lever arm, across the flap's length:

$$M_0 = -i\omega\rho \int_{-d}^{0} \varphi(z+d)dz, \quad (16)$$

and becomes:

$$M_0 = -i\omega\rho q\, m, \quad m = [1+R(\theta_0)]\int_{-d}^{0} Z_0(z+d)dz + \sum_{n=1}^{\infty} A_n(\theta_0)\int_{-d}^{0} Z_0(z+d)dz \quad (17)$$

Substituting the coefficients R and A_n, in accordance with the Eqs.(12) and (13), we finally get:

$$m = \left[2 - \frac{i\omega O_0 \theta_0}{qik_0 \cosh(k_0 h)\|Z_0\|^2}\right]\frac{O_0}{\cosh(k_0 h)} + \sum_{n=1}^{\infty}\frac{i\omega O_n^2 \theta_0}{qk_n[\cos(k_n h)]^2 \|Z_n\|^2} \quad (18)$$

By using the above in Eq. (15) and solving for θ_0, we obtain:

$$\theta_0 = \frac{2i\omega q}{\Pi}\frac{O_0}{\cosh(k_0 h)}, \quad (19)$$

where:

$$\Pi = \frac{a(\omega)}{\rho} - \omega^2 \Lambda,$$

$$\Lambda = \frac{O_0^2}{ik_0\|Z_0\|^2 \cosh(k_0 h)} - \sum_{n=1}^{\infty}\frac{O_n^2}{k_n\|Z_n\|^2 \cos(k_n h)}. \quad (20)$$

Eventually, by substitution of the complex amplitude (θ_0) in the expressions that provide the coefficients R and A_n, the complex wave potential can be obtained.

The performance of the device is estimated as the fraction of the power input that is converted into beneficial output power. The average wave power (P_{in}) associated with the incident wave is given by:

$$P_{in} = \frac{1}{8}\rho g H^2 c_g, \quad (21)$$

where c_g is the group velocity.

$$c_g = \frac{1}{2}\frac{\omega}{k_0}\left(1 + \frac{2k_0 h}{\sinh(2k_0 h)}\right). \quad (22)$$

The average output power converted by the device is calculated through the damping coefficient (hydraulic generator) as:

$$P_{out} = \frac{1}{2}\omega^2 B_P |\theta_0|^2 \quad (23)$$

Subsequently, the performance index (η_{OWSC}) of the device can be estimated by the quotient of the two above. Furthermore, for a given incident wave height H, the reflected wave height will be equal to $|R|H$ and thus,

$$\eta_{OWSC} = \frac{\overline{P}_{out}}{\overline{P}_{in}} = 1 - |R|^2. \quad (24)$$

In order to present numerical results, the following dimensionless parameters are introduced concerning the PTO model:

$$\hat{J}_P = \frac{J_P}{\rho_m d^4}, \hat{B}_P = \frac{B_P}{\rho_m \sqrt{g}d^{7/2}}, \hat{C}_P = \frac{C_P}{\rho_m g d^3}, \quad (25)$$

where ρ_m represents the density of the flap's material. It is noted that, since a two-dimensional analogue of the flap type surge converter is being considered, all the terms of the differential equation of motion of the angular oscillator refer to their respective units per unit length in the transverse direction.

As an example, by setting the non-dimensional PTO parameters equal to $\hat{J}_P = 1, \hat{B}_P = 1.5, \hat{C}_P = 1.5$ and by assuming an OWSC with density $\rho_m/\rho=3$, operating in water depth equal to h=10m, while the device's hinge point is located at the seabed (d=-h), Figures 2 and 3, illustrate the results of the system. More specifically, Figure 2 illustrates the real and the imaginary part of the complex amplitude θ_0, as well as its absolute value, as a function of the non-dimensional frequency, while Figure 3 shows the performance of the device as well as the reflection coefficient R as a function of the same parameter.

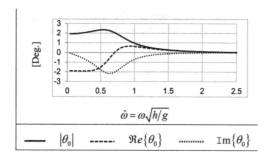

Figure 2. Oscillation Angle Chart as a function of the non-dimensional frequency ($\tilde{J}_p = 1, \tilde{B}_p = 1.5$, h=10m, d/h=1).

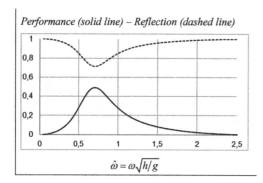

Figure 3. OWSC's Performance and Reflection coefficient as a function of the non-dimensional frequency ($\tilde{J}_p = 1, \hat{B} = 1.5, \hat{C}_p = 1.5$, h=10m, d/h=1).

3 OWSC IN VARIABLE BATHYMETRY

In order to study variable bathymetry effects on the performance of the OWSC a low-order the Boundary Element Method (BEM) is developed. The method is first validated by comparison between the numerical and the analytical results in constant water depth and subsequently the numerical model is used in order to study the operation of OWSCs in variable bathymetry regions. The present panel method is based on simple source-sink distributions. The boundary is approximated by linear elements/panels.

The fundamental solution of the Laplace Equation in the two-dimensional space (Katz & Plotkin, 2001) is:

$$G(\mathbf{x}|\mathbf{x}_0) = \frac{1}{2\pi} ln\|\mathbf{x} - \mathbf{x}_0\|, \quad (26)$$

where $\mathbf{x}(x,z)$ is a general field point in the domain while $\mathbf{x}_0(x,z)$ indicates the point where the singularity is located. The wave potential is represented by

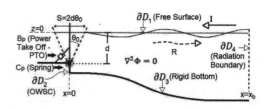

Figure 4. Division of the boundary ∂D into four sections.

$$\Phi(\mathbf{x}) = \int_{\partial D} \sigma(\mathbf{x}_0) G(\mathbf{x}|\mathbf{x}_0) dS(\mathbf{x}_0), \quad (27)$$

where ∂D denotes the boundary of the domain decomposed into four sections as presented in Figure 4.

Hence, the solution of potential flow problems is obtained by discretizing the source function which is assumed to be piecewise constant on each element, and enforcing the boundary conditions on various parts of the boundary on the control points (defined as the center of each element) from which the singularities' strengths σ_j are determined.

The BEM can be applied to domains surrounded by borders that form a closed geometrical shape. As a result, the method cannot be applied to infinite or semi-infinite domains. Overcoming this limitation requires closing the boundary geometry at a finite position of the horizontal axis (x_b) and thus creating a virtual border. It is then required to apply an appropriate radiation boundary condition to the aforementioned border, compatible with the behavior of the solution in the semi-infinite strip at large distances from the OWSC. Considering the finite domain illustrated in Figure 4, the domain's border (∂D) can be divided into four discrete sections so that: $\partial D = \partial D_1 \cup \partial D_2 \cup \partial D_3 \cup \partial D_4$.

Assuming that at the horizontal position $x=x_b$ the evanescent modes are died-out, the complex wave potential can be expressed by means of the propagating modes only, as:

$$\varphi(x,z) = [R \exp(ik_0 x_b) + \exp(-ik_0 x_b)] Z_0^{(R)}(z), \quad (28)$$

where k_0 is the wavenumber corresponding to the given frequency and the water depth at ∂D_4 (radiation boundary) and $Z_0^{(R)}(z) = Z_0(z; x = x_b)$ is the corresponding eigenfunction. (For simplicity in the presentation the factor q is omitted). Furthermore, provided that the bathymetry is uniform around and beyond the horizontal position $x=x_b$, the horizontal wave velocity is calculated by the partial x-derivative of the complex wave potential as:

$$\left.\frac{\partial \varphi}{dx}\right|_{xb} = [ik_0 R \exp(ik_0 x_b) - ik_0 \exp(-ik_0 x_b)] Z_0^{(R)}(z). \tag{29}$$

By projecting the two members of Eq. (28) onto the subspace spanned by the eigenmodes $\{Z_n(z; x = xb)\}$ we obtain:

$$\left\langle \varphi(x_b, z), Z_0^{(R)} \right\rangle = (R \exp(ik_0 x_b) + \exp(-ik_0 x_b)) \left\| Z_0^{(R)} \right\|^2. \tag{30}$$

Eq. (30) can be solved for R, providing an expression of the reflection coefficient as a function of the complex wave potential at $x=x_b$:

$$R = \frac{\left\langle \varphi(x_b, z), Z_0^{(R)} \right\rangle}{\left\| Z_0^{(R)} \right\|^2 \exp(ik_0 x_b)} - \exp(-2ik_0 x_b). \tag{31}$$

Substitution of the reflection coefficient in Eq. (29) results in the following radiation condition on ∂D_4:

$$\left.\frac{\partial \varphi}{\partial x}\right|_{x_b} - ik_0 \frac{\left\langle \varphi(x_b, z), Z_0^{(R)} \right\rangle}{\left\| Z_0^{(R)} \right\|^2} Z_0^{(R)}(z) = -2ik_0 \exp(-ik_0 x_b) Z_0^{(R)}(z) \tag{32}$$

The BCs that apply on the other three sections of ∂D remain the same as described before. In particular, the bottom boundary condition states that the normal velocity vanishes on the sloping seabed ∂D_3.

3.1 Mesh generation

The boundary is discretized by a polygonal line by distributing nodes across its length. In order to define the x-coordinates of the free surface nodes, an initial number of nodes per wavelength (N_1) is defined. Subsequently, by selecting the number of wavelengths (K) that correspond to the domain's length, the total number of nodes to be distributed on the free surface is obtained. Next, the free surface nodes are defined by using a cosine spacing to allow the nodes to be more densely arranged approaching the corners of the domain. The node spacing on the vertical boundaries (OWSC and radiation boundary) approximately matches the finer spacing on the horizontal boundaries near the corners. The bottom boundary is discretized accordingly, with the z-coordinates set equal to $(-h)$ for constant depth or equal to $h=h(x)$ in the case

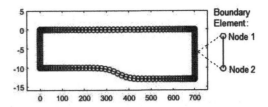

Figure 5. Generated mesh of a non-uniform bathymetry domain's boundary with a total of 164 boundary elements.

of general bathymetry. The number of elements (M_i) at each part of the boundary equals the number of nodes reduced by one ($M_i = N_i - 1$). The result of the aforementioned procedure is illustrated in Figure 5.

3.2 Discrete BEM model

By assuming unit source-sink singularity strengths on each element the induced potential and velocity from each element to each point is analytically calculated (see Katz & Plotkin, 2001). Using the latter quantities φ_{kj}, $\mathbf{U}_{kj}$, $k, j = 1, .., M$ on the collocation points defined as the centers of the elements, where M is the total number of boundary elements, and substituting in the boundary conditions, the matrix coefficient A_{jk} of the system is defined as explained in more detail in the sequel. By denoting with σ_j the strength of the source/sink distributed across the k-element's length and by b_k the boundary data that applies on the k-element, the linear system is:

$$\sum_{j=1}^{M} A_{kj} \sigma_j = b_k \, j, k = 1, 2, ..., M, \tag{33}$$

where $M=M_1+M_2+M_3+M_4$ and b_k are the boundary data. Apart from the discrete source singularities' strengths $\{\sigma_j, j = 1, M\}$, additional unknown parameters are the complex amplitude θ_0 of the OWSC's angular motion as well as the reflection coefficient R. Given that the reflection coefficient has been expressed as a function of the complex wave potential (Eq.31), the extra unknown is only the complex oscillation amplitude θ_0. The additional equation required to complete the linear system is obtained from the equation of motion of the angular oscillator, expressed in the frequency domain (Eq.15)

In order to construct the BEM model, it is necessary to express the boundary conditions in their discrete form. If we denote by $\mathbf{n}_k$ is the unit normal vector on the k- boundary element (directed outwards), the boundary condition on the radiation boundary (Eq. 32) is expressed as:

$$\sum_{j=1}^{M}\sigma_j(\mathbf{n}_k\mathbf{U}_{kj})-ik_0\left\{\int_{-h^{(4)}}^{0}\sum_{j=1}^{M}\sigma_j\varphi_{aj}Z_0^{(R)}(z_a)\right\}Z_0^{(R)}(z_k)=b_k, \quad (34)$$

where $b_k = -2ik_0 \exp(-ik_0 x_b) Z_0^{(R)}(z_k)$ (Eq.32) and z_k denotes the collocation point located at the center of the k-element. The auxiliary index (a) spans the interval of integers that correspond to the elements distributed across ∂D_4. Therefore, if δz_4 is the common length of the boundary elements on the radiation boundary, the integral of the above equation can be replaced by the relation arising from applying a numerical integration rule. Thus, by applying the trapezoidal rule, we get:

$$\sum_{j=1}^{M}\left\{(\mathbf{n}_k\mathbf{U}_{kj})-ik_0\left[\sum_{a=M_A+1}^{M}\sigma_j\varphi_{aj}\delta z_4 Z_0(z_a)\right]Z_0(z_k)\right\}=b_k,$$
$$k \in [1+M_A, M], \quad M_A = M_1 + M_2 + M_3. \quad (35)$$

As earlier mentioned, the boundary condition on the boundary of the OWSC is:

$$\left.\frac{\partial\varphi}{\partial x}\right|_{(x=0)} = f(z) = \begin{cases} -i\omega\theta_0(z+d) & z \in (-d, 0) \\ 0 & z \in (-h, -d) \end{cases} \quad (36)$$

Recalling that the general expression of the complex wave potential involves the q-parameter (see Eq.10), in the present numerical model (for incident wave with unit amplitude), the condition applied to ∂D_2 is:

$$\begin{cases} \left.\frac{\partial\varphi}{\partial x}\right|_{(x=0)} - \frac{i\omega\theta_0(z+d)}{q} = 0, & z \in (-d, 0) \\ \left.\frac{\partial\varphi}{\partial x}\right|_{(x=0)} = 0, & z \in (-h, -d) \end{cases} \quad (37)$$

Eq. (37) is expressed in discretized form as follows:

$$\sum_{j=1}^{M}\sigma_j(\mathbf{n}_k\mathbf{U}_{kj}) + H(z_k+d)\frac{i\omega(z_k+d)}{q}\theta_0 = 0,$$
$$k \in [M_1+1, M_1+M_2]. \quad (38)$$

where H denotes the Heaviside step function. The discretized boundary condition on the free surface and the impermeable bottom (see Eq.6) are respectively expressed as follows:

$$\sum_{j=1}^{M}\sigma_j\left(\mathbf{n}_k\mathbf{U}_{kj} - \frac{\omega^2}{g}\varphi_{kj}\right) = 0, \quad k \in [1, M_1], \quad (39)$$

$$\sum_{j=1}^{M}\sigma_j(\mathbf{n}_k\mathbf{U}_{kj}) = 0, \quad k \in \left[1+M_1+M_2, \sum_{i=1}^{3}M_i\right]. \quad (40)$$

Concerning the additional equation closing the discrete system with respect to the additional unknown θ_0, the dynamic equation governing the angular harmonic oscillator modeling the OWSC, expressed in the frequency domain, is considered

$$\alpha(\omega)\theta_0 = M_0 = -i\omega\rho\int_{-d}^{0}(z+d)\varphi(x=x_a, z)dz, \quad (41)$$

and thus,

$$\alpha(\omega)\theta_0 + i\omega\rho\int_{-d}^{0}(z+d)\,\varphi(x=x_a, z)dz = 0, \quad (42)$$

where $\alpha(\omega)$ is defined by Eq.(15). Considering as before the effect of the q-parameter we have:

$$\frac{\alpha(\omega)}{\rho q}\theta_0 + i\omega\int_{-d}^{0}\varphi(z+d)dz = 0. \quad (43)$$

By converting the above equation in its discrete form, assuming that δz_2 is the common length of the boundary elements on ∂D_2, we obtain:

$$i\omega\sum_{j=1}^{M}\left\{\sum_{a=1+M_1}^{M_1+M_2}H(z_a+d)\varphi_{aj}\delta z_2(z_a+d)\right\}\sigma_j + \frac{\alpha(\omega)}{\rho q}\theta_0 = 0. \quad (44)$$

After solving the linear system and obtaining the strengths of the sources' distribution as well as the complex oscillation amplitude, the reflection coefficient can be calculated from Eq. (31),

$$R = \frac{\sum_{a=M_A+1}^{M}\left(\sum_{j=1}^{M}\sigma_j\varphi_{aj}\delta z_4 Z_0(z_a)\right)}{\|Z_0\|^2 \exp(ik_0 x_b)} - \exp(-2ik_0 x_b). \quad (45)$$

3.3 Validation of the BEM model

Applying the present BEM to constant depth regions allows us to validate the numerical method using the analytical solution described in Sec.2. As an example, we consider an OWSC, operating in constant depth equal to 10m, with the hinge point located one meter above the seabed ($d=9$m). Figure 6 shows the complex amplitude of the device's oscillation as a function of the non-dimensional frequency of the incident wave, as calculated both by the analytical and the numerical methods. Figure 7 illustrates a comparison between the analytical and the numerical approach, regarding the performance of the device as well as the reflection coefficient. The differences between the two solutions are negligible. The results were extracted by setting the length of the understudy domain equal to three times the incident wave's wavelength and by distributing 50 nodes per wavelength across each horizontal boundary.

3.4 Performance of OWSC in variable bathymetry

The numerical approach can be generalized in order to study the device's operation in areas of non-uniform bathymetry, characterized by depth function $h(x)$. In the following examples, the domain's length is set equal to 700m. The number of wavelengths in the domain is a function of the frequency (and the water depth), and is recalculated for each frequency. In order to derive good quality convergent results, the nodes per wavelength, distributed across the free surface and the bottom boundaries, are set to a minimum of 50. In addition, a minimum of 1000 nodes is selected for discretizing the parts ∂D_1 and ∂D_3 of the boundary.

As a first example, a smooth upslope is considered, characterized by a depth profile, defined by:

$$z = h(x) = \frac{1}{2}(10 + 15) - \frac{1}{2}(10 - 15)\tanh[0.02(x - x_m)], \quad (46)$$

where x_m denotes the middle x-coordinate of the domain. The depth of this environment ranges from 10m at the side where the OWSC is located to 15m at the deeper side at $x=700$m. After this point the depth is considered to be constant and equal to 15m, as presented in Figure 8. Figure 9 shows the complex amplitude (θ_0) of the device's oscillation as a function of the incident wave's non-dimensional frequency, as calculated by the present BEM. The water depth at the device's boundary is used for non-dimensionalization.

For comparison, the corresponding results obtained in the case of the same OWSC operating in constant depth equal to 10m, are plotted in the same figure. It can be observed that, in this case, variation of bathymetry results in small changes in the device's performance, especially for lower frequencies. However, it is expected that more significant effects could appear in

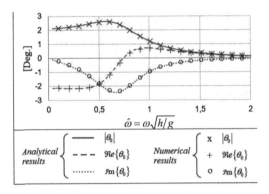

Figure 6. Oscillation Angle Chart as a function of the non-dimensional frequency. Comparison between analytical and numerical results. ($\hat{J}_p = 1, \hat{B}_p = 1.5, \hat{C}_p = 1.5$, h=10m, d/h=0.9).

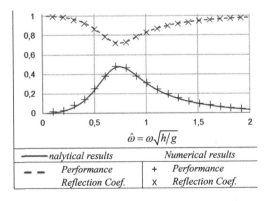

Figure 7. Performance and reflection as a function of the non-dimensional frequency. Comparison between analytical and numerical results. ($\hat{J}_p = 1, \hat{B}_p = 1.5, \hat{C}_p = 1.5$, h=10m, d/h=0.9).

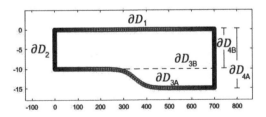

Figure 8. Non-uniform bathymetry domain with smoothly changing depth.

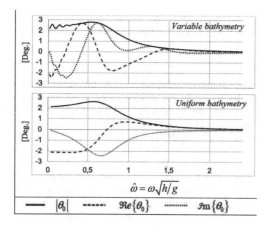

Figure 9. Oscillation Angle Charts as a function of the frequency. ($\hat{J}_p = 1, \hat{B}_p = 1.5, \hat{C}_p = 1.5$, Upper graph: h=h(x), lower graph: h=10m, d=9m).

the case of bottom ripples or other bottom irregularities in the upwave region of the device, as shown below.

The performance of the OWSC is presented in Figure 10. The reflection coefficient is omitted in these diagrams, since it can easily be calculated from the square root of the percentage that is complementary to the device's performance. Near the resonant point of the considered configuration and set-up, a performance index of 45-50% is observed. According to the results shown in these figures, the maximum angle achieved during the oscillation remains virtually unaffected by changes in bathymetry, with some instability occurring in the low frequencies range, due to strong interaction of the incident waves with the seabed. The observed oscillations in the numerical results are due to variations of the phase of various quantities excited by depth irregularities.

In order to examine more realistic bathymetric profiles, another example is considered where the bathymetry of the domain is defined so that it contains bottom corrugations in addition to shoaling effects. In this case the bottom profile is as follows:

$$z = -\frac{1}{2}(10+30) + \frac{1}{2}(10-30)tanh[0.02(x-\bar{x})] + 1.5sin[0.1(x-\bar{x})]exp\left[-0.0003(x-\bar{x})^2\right] \quad (47)$$

Same as before a 700m long region is considered, modeling the upslope environment as illustrated in Figure 11.

Numerical results concerning the response of the OWSC and the corresponding performance index are presented in Figures 12 and 13. Results are derived by determining the number of wavelengths in the domain and the number of nodes per wavelength as described in the previous example.

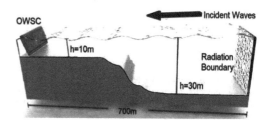

Figure 11. Non-uniform bathymetry modelling an upslope environment with bottom corrugations.

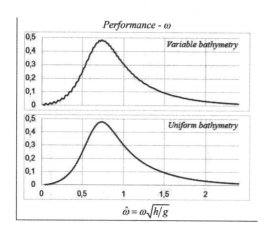

Figure 10. Performance as a function of the frequency. Comparison between analytical and numerical results. $\hat{J}_p = 1, \hat{B}_p = 1.5, \hat{C}_p = 1.5$, Upper graph: h=h(x), lower graph: h=10m, d=9m).

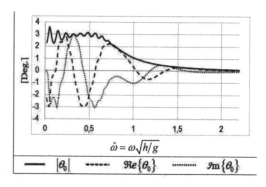

Figure 12. Oscillation Angle Chart as a function of non-dimensional frequency ($\hat{J}_p = 1, \hat{B}_p = 1.5, \hat{C}_p = 1.5$, h=h(x), d/h=0.9.

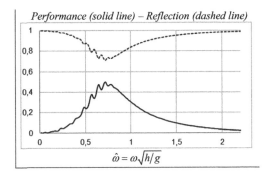

Figure 13. OWSC's Performance and reflection coefficient as a function of the non-dimensional frequency. ($\hat{J}_p = 1, \hat{B}_p = 1.5, \hat{C}_p = 1.5$, h=h(x), d/h=0.9).

4 CONCLUSIONS

Wave-power generation is not currently a widely employed commercial technology, although there have been numerous attempts to use it. It is estimated that the total global wave power resource is 2.11 TW (Gunn & Williams 2012), which - despite not being fully exploitable - could match a significant fraction of the global energy demand.

Most of the devices designed to extract wave energy operate in nearshore and coastal regions. Hence, variations of the seabed's profile could have significant effects on their performance. Extending previous analysis concerning the performance of point-absorber WECs in variable bathymetry regions (Belibassakis et al 2018, Bonovas et al 2019), in this work a BEM is developed and applied to the investigation of bottom slope and curvature effects on the performance of surge-type wave energy converters (OSWCs) excited by harmonic monochromatic waves. Numerical results are presented illustrating the modification of the wave field and the effects of depth variation in conjunction with other parameters like inertia and power-take-off, on their performance.

For simplicity the study is restricted in two dimensions, however the present method is extetable to realistic 3D configurations, where, as stated by Renzi et al (2014), a 3D OWSC's energy capturing factor can be larger than the theoretical 2D limit. This is mainly due to the presence of antisymmetric transverse waves along the flap which can amplify the exciting torque acting on the converter, and will be examined in future work. Moreover, future work will be directed to the extension of the present model to study responses and performance in more realistic irregular wave conditions.

REFERENCES

Belibassakis, K., Bonovas, M., & Rusu, E. 2018. A Novel Method for Estimating Wave Energy Converter Performance in Variable Bathymetry Regions and Applications. *Energies 2018*, 10.3390/en11082092.

Bonovas, M, Belibassakis, K. & Rusu, E. 2019. Multi-DOF WEC Performance in Variable Bathymetry Regions Using a Hybrid 3D BEM and Optimization. *Energies 2019*, 10.3390/en12112108.

Coddington, E. A., Levinson, N. 1972. *Theory of Ordinary Differential Equations*. New Delhi: McGraw Hill Publishing Co. Ltd.

Gunn, K., Williams, C. 2012. Quantifying the Potential Global Market for Wave Power. Proc. *4th Intern. Conference on Ocean Engineering, ICOE 2012* Dublin.

Katz, J., Plotkin, A. 2001. *Low-Speed Aerodynamics*. Cambridge University Press.

Renzi, E., Doherty, K., & Henry, A. 2014. How does Oyster work? The simple interpretation of Oyster mathematics. *European J. Mechanics - B/Fluids* 47: 124–131.

Whittaker, T., Folley, M. 2011. Nearshore oscillating wave surge converters and the development of Oyster. *Proc. Royal Society*. 10.1098/rsta.2011.0152.

Evaluating trends and variability in Portuguese coastal wave energy potential using a 22 years high resolution hindcast

M. Bernardino, D. Silva & C. Guedes Soares
Centre for Marine Technology and Ocean Engineering (CENTEC), Instituto Superior Técnico, Universidade de Lisboa, Lisbon, Portugal

ABSTRACT: The aim of this paper is to evaluate possible changes in available wave energy potential in the coast of the Iberian Peninsula using a 22 years high resolution wave hindcast that represents the historical marine climate in this region. The SWAN model used the wave spectral information data from ERA-Interim together with wind data from an EURO-CORDEX WRF simulation, to produce a high-resolution wave data for the region. For 8 locations in the Portuguese coast, the wave power potential was assessed studying mean and variability at different time scales. Variability was evaluated using the coefficient of variation, seasonal variability index and monthly variability index as well as mean annual variability and inter annual variability. Trends in mean annual wave power were also investigated. The total annual energy available and the exploitable energy for the different locations is presented and a comparison between the western and the southern coasts is performed.

1 INTRODUCTION

The energy from wind waves is a predictable and abundant renewable resource that has been gaining strength among the scientific community. Renewable energies are a clean and sustainable way to produce electricity with a response to the decrease of greenhouse gas effect emission caused by, among others, fuel oils.

According to various studies (Gunn & Stock-Williams 2012, Cornett 2008, Barstow 1998, Clément et al. 2002, Guedes Soares et al. 2012), the highest values of wave energy can be found in the range of 40°-60° latitude (north and south) and due to the west-to-east winds over the North Atlantic Ocean, powerful waves are created in direction of western coasts of Europe. Globally, this resource was quantified by Gunn & Stock-Williams (2012) in about 2TW.

The earlier estimates of wave energy relied on the available methods and data to characterize the wave climate, the direct (in situ) and remote measurements. This approach is realistic and accurate but it has the disadvantage of not having a cover evenly distributed data around the world and has a low frequency of measurements.

Numerical models are widely accepted as efficient tools to the assessment of wave energy accurately and can be used to hindcast, nowcast and forecast (Angelis-Dimakis et al., 2011).

There are third generation spectral wave models that are more efficient in deep waters, such as WAM (Wave model) (WAMDI group, 1988) and WWIII (WAVEWATCHIII) (Tolman, 1991), and others in shallow and intermediate waters, such as SWAN (Simulating WAves Nearshore) (Booij et al., 1999).

The modelling process has some uncertainties associated, some of which related to the seasonal and inter annual atmospheric variability (Mackay et al. 2010a, b). To smooth the variability and improve the estimates, long time series are needed.

Portugal has been a target in renewable energy studies due to its privileged location in the west coast of Europe, approximately at 37°N-42°N and 9.5°W- 7.5°W, and the long fetch near to its coast.

Some studies for wave energy assessment in Portugal continental coast was performed, namely Rusu & Guedes Soares (2009), Silva et al (2015), Silva et al (2012), Silva et al (2018), which identified the north of the country as having the highest wave power resource with a decrease towards the south. The archipelagos of Madeira (Rusu et al, 2008; Rusu & Guedes Soares 2012a) and Azores (Rusu & Guedes Soares 2012b) were also a target for wave energy studies.

The wave's energy is extracted through Wave Energy Converters (WEC). These devices can be installed offshore, nearshore and shoreline (Guedes Soares et al 2012 & Silva et al 2013), and so, it is important to study the wave energy in various locations from offshore to the coastline.

This study presents the energy resource assessment for 8 locations of the Portuguese continental coast, based on 22-years hindcast with SWAN model, with wave spectral information data from ERA-Interim and wind data from EURO-CORDEX.

DOI: 10.1201/9781003216599-56

2 DATA AND METHODS

The evaluation of the wave conditions in the Portuguese coast was made using the SWAN model (acronym from Simulating WAves Nearshore) (Booij et al. 1999). This is one of the state-of-the-art wave models based on the spectrum concept, which solves the spectral wave action balance equation:

$$\frac{\partial N}{\partial t} + \nabla_x \cdot xN + \frac{\partial}{\partial k} kN + \frac{\partial}{\partial \theta} \dot{\theta} N = \frac{S_{tot}}{\sigma} \quad (1)$$

where: N is the action density spectrum (defined as the ratio between the energy density and the relative frequency σ), t is the time, and k is the wave number. The total source (S_{tot}) is expressed in terms of energy density and has various source terms related to the most important physical processes that affect the wave propagation from deep to shallow water.

To force the SWAN model, wave spectral data from ERA- Interim reanalysis was used as boundary conditions.

This reanalysis data is produced by the European Center for Median range Weather Forecast (ECMWF) based on a 2006 release of the Integrated Forecast System. The spatial resolution of the data set is approximately 80 km (T255 spectral) on 60 vertical levels from the surface up to 0.1 hPa. The data assimilation is based on a 12-hourly four-dimensional variational analysis (4D-Var) with adaptive estimation of biases in satellite radiance data. The wave model incorporated into the IFS is based on the Wave Modeling Project (WAM) approach (Komen et al. 1994), and the version used in ERA-Interim includes several enhancements, both in physics and numerics, over the version that was used in the previous reanalysis ERA-40. Also, the wave model used in Era-Interim includes shallow-water physics (Janssen et al, 2005 and Janssen 2008). The updated version of WAM includes a revised formulation of ocean wave dissipation, which has reduced the root-mean-square error in the wave period against the buoy data and shows that the error in the estimate of the wave period is much smaller than that in ERA-40 (Bidlot et al., 2007). A full description of ERA-Interim can be found in Dee et al. (2011).

The SWAN model also requires high resolution wind data as a forcing field. Ten meters wind components were obtained from an EURO-CORDEX simulation forced with ERA-Interim.

Within the EURO-CORDEX framework, an international climate downscaling initiative that aims to provide high-resolution climate scenarios for Europe (Kotlarski et al., 2014) at 50 km (EUR-44) and 12.5 km (EUR-11) resolution (Jacob et al., 2014), the Weather Research and Forecasting (WRF) model has been used to produce high resolution atmospheric data for the European region, that is available on-line. Wind data used in this work was extracted from the European domain for our region of interest, the Iberian coast. Before the SWAN model was run for the complete period, different parameterizations were tested running the model for one year and comparing with observations. In the final implementation SWAN was run in third-generation mode for wind input, quadruplet interactions and whitecapping using the WESTHuysen generation option. Regarding propagation, the BSBT scheme was used in the computations.

The model simulations carried out in the 22-year period (1990-2011) are focused in evaluating the wave power in the Iberian coast. To do this analysis, the energy transport components (denoted also as wave power and expressed in W/m, i.e., energy transport per unit length of wave front) are computed in SWAN with the relationships:

$$E_{TR\lambda} = \rho g \iint c_\lambda E(\sigma, \theta) d\sigma \, d\theta$$
$$E_{TR\phi} = \rho g \iint c_\phi E(\sigma, \theta) d\sigma \, d\theta, \quad (2)$$

where in our case (spherical coordinates are considered) λ represents the longitude and φ the latitude. $E(\sigma, \theta)$ is the wave energy spectrum and c_λ, c_φ are the propagation velocities of the wave energy in the geographical space.

The total wave power magnitude will be then obtained with the relation:

$$E_{TR} = \sqrt{E_{TR\lambda}^2 + E_{TR\phi}^2} \quad (3)$$

while the non-dimensional normalized wave power is computed as:

$$E_{TRn} = \frac{E_{TR}}{E_{TR\max}}. \quad (4)$$

Although wave energy fields were produced at this stage, we will only analyze eight locations, seven in the western coast and one in the south of the study area. The location of the eight points can be seen in Figure 1.

3 RESULTS

3.1 *Wave climate*

In order to analyze the wave climate in the Iberian Peninsula, the spatial distributions of the wave characteristics are considered. Wave data with a temporal resolution of 3 h resulted from 22-year simulations

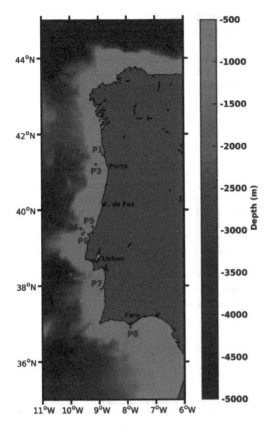

Figure 1. Geographical location of the eight point chosen for analyses P1-Aguçadoura, P2-Leixões Ocean, P3-Leixões, P4-Nazare Ocean, P5-Nazare, P6-Peniche, P7-Sines, P8-Faro.

with the SWAN model (for the time interval 1990-2011) were averaged and the resulted spatial distributions of the average Hs is presented in Figure 2 as well as the 99th percentile.

In Figure 3, the same statistics are showed for mean wave period.

It can be observed that far from the coast, the average value for Hs is higher than 2.5 m, decreasing up to 2 meters in the western coast. In the south the mean wave value for the significant wave height is lower reaching one meter near the coast. The same pattern, but higher values can be seen for the 99th percentile.

Regarding the mean wave period (Figure 3), mean values are around 6 s, but shorter periods can be found in the southern coast, that sometimes is sheltered from swell conditions. The 99th percentile corresponds to periods around 10 s, and is present in all Portuguese coast.

3.2 *Wave energy potential*

The wave energy was obtained directly from the SWAN simulation. Data was extracted for 8 locations

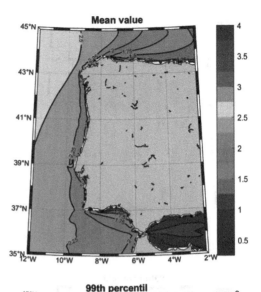

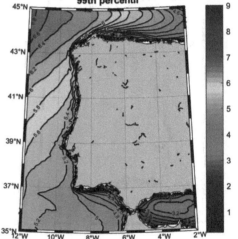

Figure 2. Mean value and 99th percentile of significant wave height of total sea.

in the Portuguese coast, seven in the west coast and one in Faro that is in the southern coast. For both Leixões and Nazaré, two locations at approximately the same latitude but at different depths, one near the coast and another offshore, were selected. The mean values of the wave energy at each location are shown in Table 2 and it can be observed that in the highest values of energy occurs in Leixões. The opposite occurs in Faro which presents less energy. The western coast shows values of mean wave power more than the double of the southern coast. For the Leixões and Nazaré, where the energy assessment was made near and further away from the coast, the wave energy is higher in offshore.

In order to evaluate the variability in the wave power, different indices were used. The coefficient of variation (COV), that quantifies the temporal

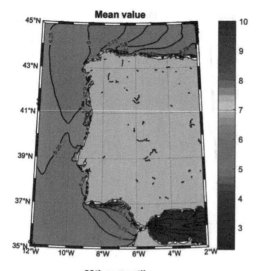

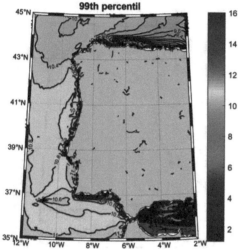

Figure 3. Mean value and 99th percentile of mean wave period.

Peniche and Aguçadoura, the ones with higher variability (1.27) are Faro, Sines, Leixões Ocean and Leixões.

The seasonal variability index (SV) measures the seasonal variability of the wave power, and is calculated as follows (Cornett, 2008):

$$SV = \frac{P_{S1} - P_{S2}}{P_{year}} \qquad (6)$$

where P_{S1} is the mean wave power for the most energetic season (Winter-December to February), P_{S4} is the mean wave power for the least energetic season (Summer-June to August) and P_{year} is the total mean wave power. Table 1 shows that seasonal variability index is rather similar among the different location with values ranging from 1.34 in Peniche and 1.51 in Faro.

The monthly variability index (MV) measures the monthly variability of wave power and is defined as (Cornett, 2008):

$$MV = \frac{P_{M1} - P_{M12}}{P_{year}} \qquad (7)$$

Table 1. Coordinates and depth of the 8 locations.

		Longitude	Latitude	Depth (m)
P1	Aguçadoura	-8.85	41.46	34.64
P2	Leixões Oc	-9.56	41.16	1935.58
P3	Leixões	-9.09	41.20	106.71
P4	Nazare Oc	-9.64	39.52	1624.84
P5	Nazare	-9.21	39.56	109.53
P6	Peniche	-9.31	39.39	362.80
P7	Sines	-8.93	37.92	80.92
P8	Faro	-7.90	36.90	113.99

variability at all time scales and it is the ratio of the standard deviation of the wave power time series by the mean wave power, was computed as the next equation (Cornett, 2008) and the results are also displayed in Table 2.

$$COV(P) = \frac{\sigma(P(t))}{\mu(P(t))} = \frac{\sqrt{\overline{(P - \overline{P})^2}}}{\overline{P}} \qquad (5)$$

It can be seen that this coefficient does not change much amount the different locations and there is no significant difference between the western and southern coast. The locations with less variability (1.18) are

Table 2. Statistical analysis of the wave power, MEAN-mean value obtained for the total 22 periods, COV- Coefficient of variation, MV- Monthly variability index, SV- Seasonal variability index, MAV- Mean annual variability, IAV- Inter annual variability.

	MEAN	COV	MV	SV	MAV	IAV
Aguçadoura	25.40	1.18	1.69	1.45	1.16	0.11
Faro	9.56	1.27	1.63	1.51	1.21	0.18
Leixões	26.59	1.27	1.68	1.43	1.25	0.11
Leixões Oc	28.23	1.27	1.68	1.43	1.25	0.11
Nazare	24.57	1.26	1.64	1.39	1.24	0.11
Nazare Oc	26.47	1.24	1.62	1.39	1.21	0.10
Peniche	23.66	1.18	1.55	1.34	1.16	0.10
Sines	24.95	1.27	1.70	1.46	1.25	0.11

where PM1 is the mean wave power for the most energetic month (January) and PM12 is the mean wave power for the least energetic month (July). MV takes values slightly higher than SV but also among the different locations there is not much variability.

Other indexes used for evaluation variability are the mean annual variability (MAV) and inter-annual variability (IAV). The first index is the average of the annual standard deviation normalized by the annual average; it measures the spread of data, indicating also the seasonal extremes. The variability from year to year along the entire period is indicated by IAV index defined as the standard deviation of the annual means normalized by the overall mean. The relationships for both indexes are (Stopa et al., 2013):

$$\text{MAV} = \overline{\left(\frac{\sigma_k}{\overline{x_k}}\right)} \qquad (8)$$

$$\text{IAV} = \frac{\sigma_{\overline{x_k}}}{\overline{x}} \qquad (9)$$

where the indices k refers to the year.

The MAV ranges from 1.16 in Peniche and Aguçadora to 1.25 in Leixões, Leixões Ocean and Sines. In the IAV, the interannual variability, the differences between the western and southern coasts are marked, with Faro showing a value of 0.18 and all the location in the western coast, values between 0.10 and 0.11.

Another way to evaluate differences between the distributions of the wave power in the different locations is through a whisker diagram. In these diagrams the mean, median, 25th and 75th percentiles are represented as well as the 9th and 91st percentiles and the outliers.

In Figure 4 the whisker diagrams for the wave power in the 8 locations are presented. It can be observed that the distribution obtained for Faro is different than the ones obtained for the other seven locations, both in mean values as in variability. In all the cases, however, the mean and the median are very close, and the distributions show higher variability in the higher values.

In Figure 5, the annual cycle of the wave power of the 8 locations is presented. It can be seen that the month with higher wave power are as expected the winter months, from November to February, reaching values above 40 kW/m in most locations. During the summer the mean monthly wave power is around 10 kW/m. The wave power in Faro, although havening also a marked seasonal, reaches much lower values, below 20 kW/m during the winter and less than 5 kW/m during the summer.

In order to evaluate the existence of trends the mean annual wave power was computed for each location and plotted in Figure 6. It can be observed that the seven locations in the western coast have the same annual evolution and that the absolute values are similar to what was observed in Figure 5. The annual time series plotted for Faro is different than the other ones, both in magnitude (lower mean annual wave power) and in temporal evolution. For the set of location in the west coast, the mean annual values were computed and a trend line adjusted. The same procedure was made for the only location in the southern coast. In both cases there is no significant

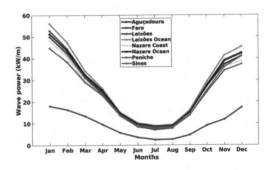

Figure 5. Annual cycle of the wave power in the 8 locations.

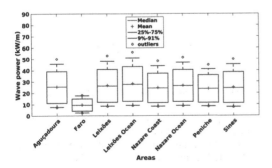

Figure 4. Whisker diagram for the wave power in the different locations. From left to right, Aguçadora, Faro, Leixões, Leixões Ocean, Nazaré, Nazaré Ocean, Peniche and Sines.

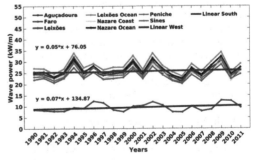

Figure 6. Time series of mean annual wave power.

trend and the adjusted regression line in each case shows slop coefficients of 0.05 and 0.07 respectively.

3.3 Wave energy availability

Wave energy converters are very sensitive to wave forces on the device: large amplitude waves can cause damage to the converter and small amplitude waves will not cause the movement of the mobile part of the device thus no power will be produced. When Hs is greater than 7 m, energy is considered to be non-extractable, while when Hs is smaller than 1 m, energy is considered to be too small to have a meaningful power output from the device (Janjić, et al., 2017).

Considering the Hs time series for the twenty-two years period for the 8 locations, the percentage of time that the time series are above 7m is low but nevertheless, there are events almost every year. Also, there are many situation, especially during summer when Hs is less than 1m and that can be used for device maintenance (Gallagher et al., 2013). We are aware that these values may differ from device to device, but considering this theoretical maxi/min values may give some useful information about possible sites for WEC installation.

Taking into account only the percentage of time when the Hs is between 1m and 7 m, ie, the percentage of time that energy is available for extraction, the frequency of occurrence of year when energy is considered extractable was computed for each location following the methodology describe in (Janjić, et al., 2017) and is shown in Figure 7.

It can be seen that in most locations every year has a percentage of extractable time over 80%, some years reaching even 100%. Offshore location shows better results than the corresponding coastal locations. Faro and Aguçadora are the locations with worst behavior. Faro with extractable time between 68% and 82%, mainly due to low Hs values and Aguçadora with extractable times 82% and 96% due to Hs values higher than 7m.

3.4 Wave energy converters performance

An evaluation of the electric energy that can be extracted from waves was done for five of the locations used in this study (Figure 1). The points, which are P1, P4, P5, P7 and P8, were chosen strategically in order to cover different zones of the study area (north, center and south). To do this evaluation, the WECs (Wave Energy Converters) Pelamis, Wave Dragon and Aqua Buoy were selected to test their performance on each of location. The main characteristics of these WECs are presented in Table 3.

Each WEC has a power matrix associated that indicates the electric power (kW) that can be extracted for a given sea state, defined in terms of significant wave height (Hs) and period peak (Tp) or energy (Te).

The electric power produced by each WEC system is calculated associating the sea states

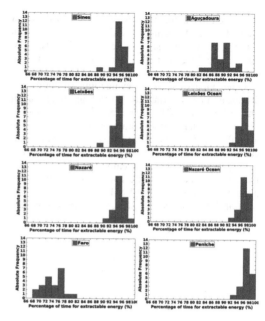

Figure 7. Frequency of occurrence histogram for the percentage of time when wave power is considered extractable. From left to right, top to bottom, Sines, Aguçadora, Leixões, Leixões Ocen, Nazaré, Nazaré Ocen, Faro and Peniche.

Table 3. Main characteristics of the WECs (Rusu & Onea 2015).

WEC device	Principle	Rated capacity (Kw)	Deep (m)
Pelamis	Attenuator	750	>50
Wave Dragon	Terminator	5900	>25
Aqua Buoy	Point absorber	250	>50

(Hs × Tp or Hs × Te) bivariate distribution and the power matrix of the WEC, as follow (Silva et al. 2013):

$$P_E = \frac{1}{100} \cdot \sum_{i=1}^{N_T} \sum_{j=1}^{N_H} a_{ij} \cdot P_{ij} \quad (10)$$

where a_{ij} corresponds to the energy percentage of the sea state bin defined by the column j and the line i and P_{ij} to the electric power at the same bin provided by the power matrix of the WEC.

The bivariate distribution of each point were calculated using bins of 0.5m × 0.5s (ΔHs × ΔTe) to be associated with Pelamis, of 0.5m × 0.5s (ΔHs × ΔTp) to be associated with Wave Dragon and 0.5m × 1s (ΔHs × ΔTp) to be associated with the Aqua Buoy.

Table 4. Electric power produced by each WEC in each point.

	Pelamis (kW/m)	Wave Dragon (kW/m)	Aqua Buoy (kW/m)
P1	66.67	1229.79	27.96
P4	97.06	1609.59	38.78
P5	80.08	1409.37	32.01
P7	75.78	1368.88	30.98
P8	47.84	918.86	16.67

As Tp was available in the model output data but Te was needed to compute the bivariate distribution, a conversion was made using the equation:

$$Te = 0.9 \times Tp \qquad (11)$$

Table 4 presents the electric power produced by each WEC in each location.

Comparing the performance of each WEC, we can see that Wave Dragon can deliver more electric energy than the other devices, following by the Pelamis and finally the Aqua Buoy. The location P4 (1624.8 m depth), that corresponds to deep water ocean, reveals to have more potential for energy extraction than other locations, and this is coherent, as it is in deep water and waves can travel with small loss of energy, that can later be convert into electric power. Nevertheless, it may be too depth to WEC installation. The opposite occurs at location P8 (113.9 m depth), in the southern coast of Portugal. This point is protected by the continent, so when the waves reach it they are less energetic.

Regarding the other locations at western coast, nearshore, the WECs can extract more energy from P5 (109.5 m depth), followed by P7 (80.9 m depth) and P1 (34.6 m depth). Although P1 has a total mean energy higher than the other locations, which is expected since it is the most northerly point. Due to the mostly northwest winds, is in the north that we can find more wave energy (Silva et al 2018) but also the sea states where each WEC can extract more energy occurred less frequently than in the other location situated southern.

4 DISCUSSION AND CONCLUSIONS

A hindcast study based on high resolution results provided by a SWAN modelling system forced with ECMWF Era-Interim spectral data and EURO-CORDEX high resolution wind was made for a 22-year period (1990-2011). In this way a dataset of the sea state conditions in the Iberian coast is produced and used for wave climate analyses and for wave energy resource assessment in 8 locations in the Portuguese coast.

Analysing the wave energy that was extracted directly from the SWAN simulation, it can be concluded that Leixões is the location were more energy is available and that Faro is the one less energetic. In the western coast the mean wave power are more than the double of the southern coast.

For Leixões and Nazaré, where the energy assessment was made in two different locations each, one near the coast and another further away, it can be concluded that it is in offshore ones that the wave power is higher. Regarding the seasonal cycle of the wave power, the winter months, from November to February, show as expected the higher values while in Summer, wave power reaches only about 25% of the winter season. Faro, although havening also a marked seasonal, shows wave power that reaches much lower values than other locations. Mean annual values were computed for different cases, but no significant trend in mean annual wave power was found.

Variability of the wave power was studied at different time scales and no significant difference was found, between the eight locations, for most indices. For seasonal variability and inter annual variability, however, Faro shows higher values than the locations in the western coast.

The energy extractable time, ie, periods with Hs between 1m and 7m was evaluated and for most locations every year has a percentage of extractable time over 80% and some years reaching even 100%. Offshore location shows better results than the corresponding coastal locations. Faro and Aguçadora are the locations with worst behavior.

The electric energy that can be extracted from waves was evaluated for five of the eight location using three different WEC's. From the five locations is Nazaré Ocean that shows better results. Comparing the performance of each WEC, we can see that Wave Dragon produces more electric energy than the other devices, following by the Pelamis and finally the Aqua Buoy.

ACKNOWLEDGEMENTS

This work has been performed within the project CLIMENA- CLimate change Impacts on the Marine Environment of the North Atlantic, funded by the Portuguese Foundation for Science and Technology (Fundação Portuguesa para a Ciência e a Tecnologia) under contract PTDC/EAM_OCE/28561/2017. The work also contributes to the Strategic Research Plan of the Centre for Marine Technology and Ocean Engineering, also financed by Portuguese Foundation for Science and Technology under contract UIDB/UIDP/00134/2020.

REFERENCES

Angelis-Dimakis, A., Biberacher, M., Dominguez, J., Fiorese, G., Gadocha, S., Gnansounou, E., Guariso, G.,

Kartalidis, A., Panichelli, L., Pinedo, I., Robba, M., 2011. Methods and tools to evaluate the availability of renewable energy sources. Renew.Sustain.EnergyRev.15, 1182–1200.

Barstow, S.; Haug, O. & Krogstad, H. Satellite altimeter data in wave energy studies, In: Proc. Waves'97, ASCE, 2, 1998, pp. 339–354.

Bidlot, J., Janseen, P.A.E.M., Abdalla, S., 2007. A revised formulation of ocean wave dissipation and its model impact. ECMWF Tech. Memo. 509, 27 pp.

Booij, N., Ris, R.C. & Holthuijsen L.H., 1999. A third generation wave model for coastal regions. Part 1: model description and validation, J. Geophys. Res. 104 7649–7666.

Clément, A.; McCullen, P.; Falcão, A.; Fiorentino, A.; Gardner, F.; K. Hammarlund, 2002. Wave energy in Europe: current status and perspectives, Renew. Sustain. Energy Rev. 6, 405–431.

Cornett, A.M. 2008. A global wave energy resource assessment, In: International Offshore and Polar Engineering Conference, Vancouver, Canada, Volume: ISOPE-2008-TPC-579.

Dee, D.P., Uppala, S.M., Simmons, A.J., Berrisford, P., Poli, P., Kobayashi, S., Andrae, U., Balmaseda, M.A., Balsamo, G., Bauer, P., Bechtold, P., Beljaars, A.C.M., Van de Berg, L., Bidlot, J., Bormann, N., Delsol, C., Dragani, R., Fuentes, M., Geer, A. J., Haimberger, L., Healy, S.B., Hersbach, H., Hólm, E.V., Isaksen, L., Kållberg, P., Köhler, M., Matricardi, M., McNally, A. P., Monge-Sanz, B. M., Morcrette, J.-J., Park, B.-K., Peubey, C., Rosnay, P., Tavolato, C., Thépaut J.-N. and F. Vitart, 2011. The ERA-Interim reanalysis: Configuration and performance of the data assimilation system. Quart. J. R. Meteorol. Soc., 137, 553–597.

Gallagher, S., Tiron, R. & Dias, F. 2013. A Detailed Investigation of the Nearshore Wave Climate and the Nearshore Wave Energy Resource on the West Coast of Ireland, in ASME 2013 32nd International Conference on Ocean, Offshore and Arctic Engineering. American Society of Mechanical Engineers, 2013, pp. V008T09A046–V008T09A046.

Guedes Soares, C.; Bhattacharjee, J.; Tello M, Pietra L., 2012. Review and classification of wave energy converters. In: Guedes Soares C, Garbatov Y, Sutulo S, Santos TA, editors. Maritime engineering and technology. London, UK: Taylor & Francis Group;. p. 585–594.

Gunn, K. & Stock-Williams, C., 2012. Quantifying the global wave power resource, Renew. Energy 44 296–304.

Janssen, P.A.E.M., 2008. Progress in ocean wave forecasting. J. Comput. Phys., 227, 3572–3594.

Jacob, D.; Petersen, J.; Eggert, B.; Alias, A.; Christensen, O.B.; Bouwer, L.M.; Braun, A.; Colette, A.; Déqué, M.; Georgievski, G.; Georgopoulou, E.; Gobiet, A.; Menut, L.; Nikulin, G.; Haensler, A.; Hempelmann, N.; Jones, C.; Keuler, K.; Kovats, R.; Kröner, N.; Kotlarski, S.; Kriegsmann, A.; Martin, E.; van Meijgaard, E.; Moseley, C.; Pfeifer, S.; Preuschmann, S.; Radermacher, C.; Radtke, K.; Rechid, D.; Rounsevell, M.; Samuelsson, P.; Somot, S.; Soussana, J.-F.; Teichmann, C.; Valentini, R.; Vautard, R.; Weber, B.; Yiuou, P., (2014). EURO-CORDEX: new high-resolution climate change projections for European impact research. Regional environmental change, 14(2),563–578.

Janjić, J., Gallagher, S., & Dias, F., 2017. Wave Energy Extraction in the Northeast Atlantic: Future Wave Climate Availability. In European Wave and Tidal Energy Conference (EWTEC) 2017, Cork, Ireland.

Janssen, P.A.E.M., Bidlot, J., Abdalla, S., Hersbach, H., 2005. Progress in ocean wave forecasting at ECMWF. Thech. Memo. 478, ECMWF: Reading, UK.

Komen, G.J., Cavaleri, L., Donelan, M., Hasselman, K., Hasselmann, S., Janssen, P.A.E.M., 1994. Dynamics and Modeling of Ocean Waves. Cambridge University Press (532 pp.).

Kotlarski, S., Keuler, K., Christensen, O. B., Colette, A., Déqué, M., Gobiet, A., Goergen, K., Jacob, D., Lüthi, D., van Meij- gaard, E., Nikulin, G., Schär, C., Teichmann, C., Vautard, R., Warrach-Sagi, K., and Wulfmeyer, V., 2014 Regional climate modeling on European scales: a joint standard evaluation of the EURO- CORDEX RCM ensemble, Geosci. Model Dev., 7, 1297–1333, doi:10.5194/gmd-7-1297-2014.

Mackay, E. B. L.; Bahaj, A. S. and Challenor, P. G. 2010b, Uncertainty in wave energy resource assessment. Part2: Variability and predictability". Renewable Energy, 2; 35: 1809–1819

Mackay, E. B. L.; Bahaj, A. S. and Challenor, P. G., 2010a, Uncertainty in wave energy resource assessment. Part1: Historic data. Renewable Energy; 35: 1792–1808;

Rusu, E. and Guedes Soares, C., 2009. Numerical modelling to estimate the spatial distribution of the wave energy in the Portuguese nearshore, Renew. Energy, 34, 2009, 1501–1516.

Rusu, E. and Guedes Soares, C., 2012a. Wave energy pattern around the Madeira Islands. Energy 2012; 45:771–785;

Rusu, E.; Pilar, P., and Guedes Soares, C. 2008; Evaluation of the Wave Conditions in Madeira Archipelago With Spectral Models. Ocean Engineering. 35 (13):1357–1371.

Rusu, L. & Onea, F., 2015. Assessment of the performances of various wave energy converters along the European continental coasts. Energy 2015 82: 889–904;

Rusu, L. and Guedes Soares, C., 2012b. Wave energy assess-ments in the Azores Islands". Renewable Energy; 45: 183–196;

Rusu, L., Bernardino, M., & Guedes Soares, C., 2008. Influence of the wind fields on the accuracy of numerical wave modelling in offshore locations. Proceedings of the 27th International Conference on Offshore Mechanics and Arctic Engineering - OMAE2008, ASME, Paper OMAE2008-57861, June 15-20, Estoril, Portugal, Vol. 4, 637–644.

Silva, D.; Bento, A.R.; Martinho, P. & Guedes Soares, C., 2015. High resolution local wave energy modelling for the Iberian Peninsula, Energy 91, 1099–1112, 94:857-858.

Silva, D.; Martinho, P. & Guedes Soares, C. 2012. Modelling wave energy for the Portuguese coast, in: C. Guedes Soares, Y. Garbatov, S. Sutulo, T.A. Santos (Eds.), Maritime Engineering and Technology 2012, Taylor & Francis Group, London, UK, 2012, pp. 647–653.

Silva, D., Martinho, P. Soares, CG., 2018. Wave energy distribution along the Portuguese continental coast based on a thirty-three years hindcast, Renewable Energy, Vol. 127, pp. 1067–1075.

Silva, D.; Rusu, E. and Guedes Soares, C. 2013, Evaluation of Various Technologies for Wave Energy Extraction in the Portuguese Nearshore. Energies; 6: 1344–1364;

Stopa, J. E., Cheung, K. F., Tolman, H. L., and Chawla, A. 2013. Patterns and cycles in the climate forecast system reanalysis wind and wave data. Ocean Modelling, 70: 207–220.

Tolman, H., 1991. A third-generation model for wind waves on slowly varying, unsteady, and inhomogeneous depths and currents, J. Phys. Oceanogr. 21, 782–797.

WAMDI Group, 1988. The WAM model-a third generation ocean wave prediction model, J. Phys. Oceanogr. 18, 1755–1810.

Pre-planning for Black Sea offshore wind farms: A wind speed dataset for three Romanian coastal locations

M. Burloiu & E. Rusu
Faculty of Engineering, Department of Mechanical Engineering, "Dunarea de Jos" University of Galati, Romania

ABSTRACT: This study considers the possibility of wind farms implementation along the Black Sea coast. Currently in Romania the renewable energy represents about 20% of the total energy production, of which wind power is only one quarter. Considering the EU legislation concerning renewable energy, both the initial Renewable Energy Directive (2009) and the recast (2018), it is assumed a share of 34 % of renewable energy sources in gross final energy consumption to be achieved by 2030. Given the environmental legislation requirements and the national geographic characteristics, a study aimed to establish the groundwork and to assess the possibilities for the offshore extraction of the wind power on the coast of the Black Sea, is more than relevant and opportune. Towards this goal, the present study explores wind speed measurements of three potential hotspots in the Romanian coastal environment of the Black Sea. This is based on archived information provided by GFS, NCEP, US NATIONAL SERVICE, which were visually processed into a preliminary dataset.

1 INTRODUCTION

The Energy Union strategy, published in 2015, aims at building an energy union that gives EU consumers – household and business – secure, sustainable, competitive and affordable energy. The energy union builds five dimensions: (1) security, solidarity and trust, (2) a fully integrated internal energy market, (3) energy efficiency, (4) climate action, decarbonizing the economy, (5) research, innovation and competitiveness (Makris et al, 2016).

To meet the EU's energy and climate targets for 2030, Romania elaborated a 10-year integrated national energy and climate plan (NECP) for the period from 2021 to 2030.

By analyzing this document corroborated with its Commission Recommendation (18.6.2019) ("Significantly raise the level of ambition for 2030 to a renewable share of at least 34 % as Romania's contribution to the Union's 2030 target for renewable energy") as well as with other relevant papers (i.e. National Strategy for Sustainable Development of Romania, Programme of the Romanian Presidency of the Council of the European Union 2019, Environmental Report for the Romanian Energy Strategy 2019-2030, with perspectives for 2050 – KVB Consulting & Engineers), the most obvious and relevant conclusion for the opportunity of our study arise: energy efficiency and renewable clean energy are hugely important concepts at global level, for a modern and prosperous climate-neutral economy, which need to be implemented by real and effective measures in order to meet the constantly growing energy demand.

Against the backdrop suggested by these policies, the present study explores three Romanian coastal locations of the Black Sea in terms of wind speed and direction, thus presenting a data set that is useful in further identifying a best case scenario for the first development of offshore wind farms in the region (according to WindEurope-Annual-Statistics-2018, in Romania 10% of the average annual electricity demand is covered by wind power provided only from onshore farms).

While this is but a granular research, measurements are consistent within minor limits with more comprehensive datasets used recently by previous researchers (Onea & Rusu, 2014, 2019), thus integrating a new resource in the information ecosystem available for future studies.

2 METHODS AND DATA

Our research methodology is based on comparison and interpretation of visual processing maps and diagrams of the numerical collected data, statistics and parameters.

We have used archived information measurements of the wind recorded on a daily basis for the time interval of January to December 2018, with a 24-hour temporal resolution, via GFS, NCEP, US NATIONAL SERVICE. Since the GFS grid has a resolution of 1°, intermediate points are interpolated using bilinear interpolation; the whole

DOI: 10.1201/9781003216599-57

processing software is available using earth.null-school.net (on GitHub). For the diagrams integration we used Microsoft Excel software.

The chosen locations that were explored using maps provided by the NaturalEarth project (supported by NACIS - North American Cartographic Information Society) are on the coastal area of Sulina (45.15N, 29.70E), Constanta (44.19N, 28.95E) and Mangalia (43.81N, 28.82E) at 00:00 (midnight time). Also, two height measurements scenarios were considered: at 0m (surface of water) and 1000hPA/110m above the waterline.

While no comprehensive bathymetry data collection was available for this study, in these areas the depth of the continental shelf of the Black Sea does not exceed 60m, within coastal widths between 5 and 50km. This value is relevant for both the costs and the time of implementation of a future project.

At this point of the research we use established values for the extreme waves on the Romanian coastal area of the Black Sea, as reported in several studies, available and considered for the purpose of this study (Rusu et al, 2006, 2014a and Rusu 2010, 2018, 2019), as a basic assumption of future structural requirements for the offshore wind farms.

Other considerations for the purpose of our study:

Location: The wind climate in Romania is influenced by 3 major air masses: polar, marine tropical and continental. Due to this mix, Romania is having a good potential in terms of renewable energy from the wind. This potential is available for the duration of the entire year.

Wind Characteristics - Speed: The wind is a vital resource also for offshore wind power projects because it determines how much energy can be produced at a location.

The following tables (from Table 1 to Table 6) present the registered monthly wind speed for the 3 chosen locations, during 2018, on water surface level. The daily speeds recorded were introduced in Excel spreadsheets and the monthly values calculated as arithmetic average.

In Figures 1-12 the monthly mean wind velocities are presented. From the information presented in these figures, we come to the conclusion that for the coastal area of Constanta the values are the highest and the mean velocity of the wind speed for 2018 is 5.61 m/s at sea level.

In the Figure 13 we present the mean values of wind speed, per month for the duration of 2018 (data provided by GFS, NCEP, US NATIONAL SERVICE), at 0m level.

Figures 14 – 25 present the wind speed measured at 110 m above sea level for the months from January to December.

The maximum value registered in 2018 is 20.28 m/s. In Figure 26 the final comparison between 0m (surface) and 110m height, in Constanta, is shown.

The red line is for the first set of data, the ones measured at the surface of the water, and the orange

Table 1. January mean wind velocities.

	JAN	FEB	MAR	APR	MAY	JUN
1	5.56	5.56	6.11	10.28	3.33	4.72
2	5.00	7.5	6.39	6.39	2.50	6.11
3	4.17	11.11	3.89	6.11	2.50	4.17
4	4.44	7.5	3.89	6.94	0.83	6.11
5	5.83	4.17	8.06	6.94	1.11	2.78
6	8.06	5.00	4.44	5.56	1.39	4.72
7	4.72	6.67	5.56	6.11	5.56	2.22
8	1.39	5.83	3.06	6.94	9.17	4.72
9	5.28	1.11	4.17	6.39	2.78	5.56
10	8.06	9.72	4.17	0.83	5.83	5.28
11	8.89	11.67	2.22	5.00	5.28	3.33
12	10.28	3.89	10.00	3.06	6.67	3.06
13	12.50	6.39	7.22	2.50	6.11	6.39
14	7.50	6.94	2.50	3.89	3.33	4.17
15	5.00	6.11	5.28	2.5	6.11	2.78
16	6.94	2.22	9.72	5.00	7.78	4.44
17	12.22	3.33	6.11	3.89	3.06	5.56
18	16.94	4.72	10.28	2.22	3.06	1.94
19	3.06	9.17	5.56	5.28	5.00	5.83
20	6.11	7.78	7.78	6.11	1.67	4.44
21	10.00	7.50	8.61	7.22	3.06	2.50
22	12.78	8.89	9.72	7.22	4.72	1.39
23	8.89	4.44	8.06	6.67	3.33	4.44
24	4.44	10.83	4.72	5.56	1.11	5.00
25	4.17	9.72	5.00	2.50	3.61	1.94
26	3.33	16.94	4.17	1.94	5.28	5.28
27	3.61	7.22	3.61	4.17	7.78	8.06
28	6.94	12.78	3.89	4.17	6.94	2.78
29	5.28		2.78	3.06	6.67	5.56
30	5.83		3.89	3.89	6.39	6.11
31	4.44		8.33		3.06	

Table 2. Constanta daily wind speed in m/s (from July to December).

	JUL	AUG	SEP	OCT	NOV	DEC
1	8.61	3.89	3.33	7.78	4.44	3.89
2	5.83	7.22	1.94	3.61	5.00	2.78
3	4.17	4.72	3.33	6.39	3.89	1.94
4	1.11	5.00	4.72	9.17	3.33	5.83
5	5.00	3.33	1.94	6.11	6.67	13.61
6	3.06	2.22	6.39	4.17	5.83	8.33
7	3.06	3.33	9.72	6.39	3.89	5.83
8	2.22	3.06	5.28	3.06	4.72	6.11
9	3.06	4.17	6.39	3.06	2.78	1.94
10	3.89	6.11	7.22	6.94	1.39	6.94
11	2.78	6.39	5.56	8.06	3.61	6.11
12	4.44	3.89	7.78	8.06	7.78	5.83
13	3.89	1.94	4.44	9.17	5.00	6.11
14	6.11	1.39	6.67	9.72	4.72	6.94
15	4.72	2.50	5.28	7.78	10.83	10.28
16	5.00	5.00	4.17	6.39	11.11	9.17
17	4.72	4.17	8.61	4.44	8.89	8.89
18	5.28	5.00	4.17	4.72	7.22	12.50
19	5.56	4.17	2.50	1.67	11.11	9.72
20	4.44	5.00	2.78	1.94	5.28	2.78
21	4.44	5.56	3.61	6.67	11.11	4.72
22	2.78	1.94	0.83	8.06	6.94	7.78
23	5.56	3.61	6.11	5.00	4.72	3.06
24	2.78	5.83	4.44	7.78	4.72	13.89
25	5.28	2.78	13.61	13.65	7.78	10.28
26	6.39	1.94	11.11	8.33	3.89	8.33
27	4.44	2.22	7.78	6.94	11.11	5.28
28	2.50	6.39	3.06	8.33	15.00	3.61
29	2.50	5.28	4.17	7.50	11.94	8.06
30	1.67	10.00	11.94	5.56	8.06	1.39
31	1.67	5.56		3.33		4.17

540

Table 3. Mangalia daily wind speed in m/s (from January to June).

	JAN	FEB	MAR	APR	MAY	JUN
1	4.72	6.67	6.11	10.00	3.33	4.17
2	4.17	8.06	7.78	5.56	2.50	5.83
3	3.33	12.50	3.33	5.28	2.50	3.61
4	4.17	5.56	3.89	6.11	1.11	5.56
5	5.28	3.61	7.22	6.11	1.11	3.06
6	7.50	4.44	4.44	5.00	1.94	4.44
7	4.17	5.56	4.17	6.67	3.89	0.56
8	1.39	5.00	2.78	6.94	8.61	4.44
9	5.56	1.11	4.17	6.11	2.78	4.72
10	6.94	10.00	4.72	0.56	4.44	5.00
11	8.33	11.39	2.22	4.72	5.28	0.56
12	10.00	3.33	9.44	3.06	6.39	2.22
13	11.94	6.67	7.22	2.50	4.72	5.28
14	7.22	3.06	1.39	3.89	5.56	3.61
15	3.61	5.83	4.72	2.78	5.28	2.22
16	6.67	2.78	8.89	4.72	7.22	3.06
17	11.94	2.50	8.06	3.61	3.06	4.17
18	15.28	4.17	9.72	2.50	2.78	1.39
19	2.78	8.89	5.56	5.00	4.17	1.39
20	5.83	7.22	6.11	4.17	1.94	5.56
21	9.44	6.94	8.06	6.67	2.50	4.44
22	12.22	8.61	9.72	6.67	4.44	1.94
23	8.33	4.17	8.06	6.11	3.33	3.33
24	5.28	10.00	4.44	4.72	1.94	4.72
25	3.89	9.44	5.00	2.22	3.89	0.83
26	3.06	16.67	5.00	1.11	5.28	5.28
27	2.78	6.39	3.61	3.61	6.94	6.39
28	5.83	11.67	2.78	3.89	6.39	1.94
29	4.44		3.61	3.06	6.11	4.44
30	5.28		2.50	3.89	6.67	5.28
31	3.89		7.50		3.61	

Table 4. Mangalia daily wind speed in m/s (from July to December).

	JUL	AUG	SEP	OCT	NOV	DEC
1	7.50	2.78	3.06	7.78	3.89	3.06
2	5.56	6.39	1.67	3.89	4.44	2.22
3	3.89	5.00	3.61	5.28	3.89	1.94
4	1.94	5.00	3.33	6.94	2.78	6.11
5	4.44	3.06	1.39	3.89	6.11	12.78
6	3.06	0.83	6.11	4.17	5.28	8.06
7	1.67	2.50	9.17	5.83	3.33	5.28
8	1.11	2.50	4.17	2.78	4.17	6.11
9	2.22	4.17	5.00	3.33	2.78	0.83
10	3.06	5.83	6.39	6.11	0.83	7.50
11	3.33	5.83	5.28	7.50	3.06	5.83
12	3.89	3.61	7.50	7.50	7.22	4.72
13	4.17	0.83	4.44	8.33	5.00	4.72
14	5.00	1.94	6.67	8.61	4.44	7.22
15	4.17	3.06	4.72	6.67	10.00	7.78
16	3.61	4.72	3.33	5.28	10.28	8.89
17	4.17	3.89	6.11	3.61	8.61	7.78
18	5.00	4.44	3.61	3.61	7.50	11.94
19	6.39	3.89	3.06	1.11	10.00	9.72
20	4.72	5.00	3.06	1.67	5.28	2.22
21	3.89	5.00	3.61	5.56	10.83	3.61
22	2.78	1.67	0.83	6.94	6.94	6.90
23	4.44	3.33	5.00	4.44	4.17	4.15
24	2.50	5.28	3.89	6.39	3.89	12.22
25	5.28	3.06	13.33	13.33	6.94	8.89
26	6.11	1.39	10.28	7.78	4.44	7.50
27	4.17	1.94	7.50	6.11	10.56	5.28
28	2.78	5.83	1.11	8.33	14.72	3.33
29	2.50	5.00	3.06	7.22	11.11	7.78
30	0.83	8.89	9.72	5.28	8.06	1.11
31	1.67	4.17		2.50		3.61

line is for the second set of data, for a height of approx. 110m above the waterline. The velocities at 110 m above waterline are higher, reaching a mean speed of 6.995 m/s, during 2018.

Wind Direction: Wind direction is also important to consider because it has implications for energy production and the optimal plant layout.

In Tables 7 and 8 the values of the wind directions (in degrees) are presented for the year 2018.

From Table 9 it can observed that the predominant wind direction is from N and N-E for approx. 45% of the duration of the entire year.

Bathymetry: For all the 3 spots (Constanta, Mangalia, Sulina) the depth does not exceed 60m.

As we know there are 3 different types of platforms/mooring systems for shallow waters:

- Monopile: The structure is basically a thick steel cylinder buried down to a depth of 30m in order to support the tower of the turbine.
- Gravity: for this kind of structure the preparation of the terrain is needed before the installation and the structure is actually a concrete or steel platform.
- Jacket: for a depth over 30m. The structure is a steel frame fixed on the seabed in 3 or 4 places.

All these technology systems are well-known and in use around the world. Romania, for the last 50 years, gained a good reputation in shipbuilding and has the capacity of constructing different types of structures. Actually Constanta hosts the biggest shipyard in our country; of course there are also other shipyards (DAMEN, VARD) able to design, build and provide maintenance services for such structures.

Logistics: Constanta as a port can provide facilities for the receipt, storage, assembly, and load-out of components during installation. As a port it can also serve as the O&M base from which the operator coordinates maintenance and repair operations.

Constanta as a shipyard can provide technical support for maintenance and repair operations.

MetOcean Conditions: Favorable - According to the study mentioned in Ref. [3], the maximum values of the significant wave height and wave power are in Constanta H_{smax}=5.3m and P_{wmax}=71 kW/m.

3 DISCUSSIONS AND CONCLUSIONS

Driven by both scientific interest and strategic reasons (EU/national energy policies etc.) research and planning converging to development of future offshore wind farms on the Romanian Black Sea

Table 5. Sulina daily wind speed in m/s (from January to June).

	JAN	FEB	MAR	APR	MAY	JUN
1	4.72	3.89	0.83	9.17	1.39	3.33
2	7.22	5.00	3.06	5.56	1.67	3.61
3	2.50	7.78	4.72	3.33	1.67	3.33
4	2.22	5.28	4.44	5.83	0.56	4.44
5	4.17	2.22	5.83	5.83	1.11	2.78
6	6.11	3.61	3.65	5.00	1.11	4.17
7	2.78	7.22	5.83	4.17	5.56	5.00
8	1.39	4.44	3.06	5.00	6.94	2.50
9	2.50	1.94	4.17	5.28	2.50	4.17
10	6.60	6.11	2.78	0.28	5.28	2.50
11	5.28	8.06	3.33	3.61	3.89	1.67
12	8.33	3.06	8.89	2.22	3.89	2.78
13	9.44	3.61	5.83	1.94	5.56	5.00
14	5.56	7.78	5.00	1.39	1.39	3.33
15	2.50	3.89	3.89	1.11	4.44	0.83
16	4.72	2.22	8.61	4,17	5.83	2.78
17	8.61	2.78	3.89	2.89	1.94	3.89
18	13.06	2.22	8.06	2.22	2.78	3.61
19	3.06	6.11	5.28	4.72	5.83	3.61
20	5.00	6.39	5.28	6.11	1.67	3.61
21	7.50	5.83	5.56	5.28	3.61	3.06
22	10.28	6.39	5.83	6.39	1.94	1.39
23	7.22	2.50	6.39	2.50	1.94	3.61
24	3.06	8.89	3.61	4.44	2.22	6.39
25	3.10	6.94	3.06	2.50	3.06	3.12
26	3.61	12.50	2.78	3.33	4.72	2.78
27	3.33	4.72	2.78	3.89	6.11	6.94
28	5.00	11.11	1.15	3.89	3.61	3.66
29	4.72		1.39	2.50	4.17	2.78
30	5.28		1.11	1.67	5.00	4.44
31	3.33		6.67		2.22	

Table 6. Sulina daily wind speed in m/s (from July to December).

	JUL	AUG	SEP	OCT	NOV	DEC
1	7.22	4.44	3.89	4.72	5.00	2.50
2	3.06	5.56	3.61	1.94	4.17	1.94
3	3.33	3.61	3.33	5.28	2.78	2.50
4	1.67	3.61	4.17	7.22	2.78	1.11
5	3.33	3.61	1.67	4.44	5.56	10.00
6	3.06	2.50	3.06	2.50	5.00	6.39
7	3.89	2.78	5.28	4.44	3.61	0.28
8	1.94	3.89	5.28	0.83	3.33	5.00
9	1.11	2.78	5.28	2.78	1.67	2.78
10	2.22	3.89	5.83	6.39	3.33	3.33
11	3.06	2.78	6.94	5.28	5.56	5.56
12	3.89	2.22	5.56	5.56	5.83	5.56
13	3.33	3.06	1.94	7.22	3.33	4.72
14	4.72	2.50	3.61	6.94	3.33	3.06
15	2.50	0.56	4.17	5.28	7.78	9.44
16	3.61	3.89	1.11	4.17	8.33	7.78
17	2.50	3.33	5.56	4.17	5.83	6.94
18	5.56	3.06	1.94	4.44	4.40	8.61
19	2.22	3.06	1.11	2.22	9.72	7.22
20	2.78	2.22	0.56	2.50	3.89	1.39
21	3.89	2.78	1.94	4.44	7.78	2.50
22	3.89	2.78	0.56	6.39	5.28	5.28
23	5.00	3.06	4.44	3.61	3.61	3.33
24	1.39	3.89	2.78	7.78	3.33	11.29
25	3.33	1.94	9.44	9.72	5.00	8.06
26	3.61	1.11	8.06	6.11	3.06	5.83
27	2.22	0.83	5.00	5.28	7.22	3.89
28	2.78	3.33	2.78	6.67	11.39	3.89
29	0.83	3.06	3.61	6.94	8.33	6.11
30	1.94	7.50	9.44	6.11	6.39	1.94
31	2.22	5.28		3.33		2.78

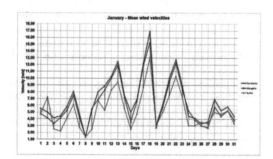

Figure 1. January mean wind velocities.

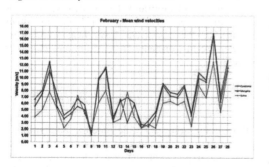

Figure 2. February mean wind velocities.

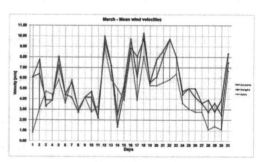

Figure 3. March mean wind velocities.

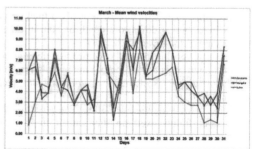

Figure 4. April mean wind velocities.

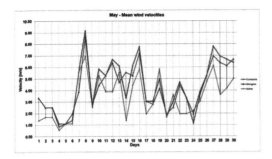

Figure 5. May mean wind velocities.

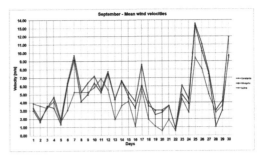

Figure 9. September mean wind velocities.

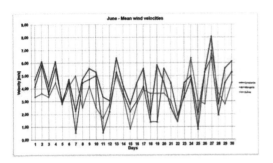

Figure 6. June mean wind velocities.

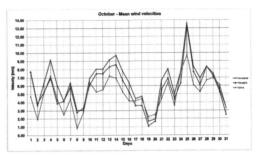

Figure 10. October mean wind velocities.

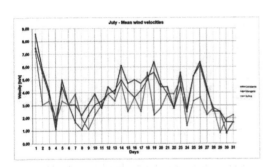

Figure 7. July mean wind velocities.

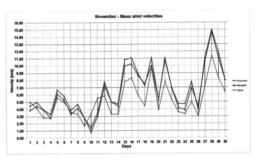

Figure 11. November mean wind velocities.

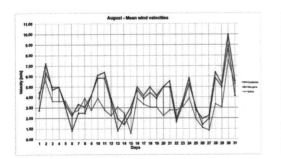

Figure 8. August mean wind velocities.

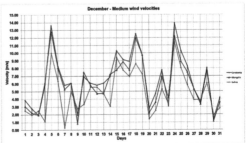

Figure 12. December mean wind velocities.

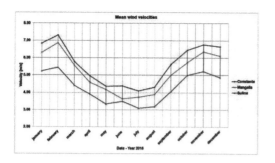

Figure 13. Mean wind velocities for 2018.

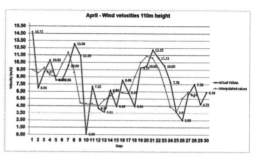

Figure 17. Wind velocities at 110m height in April.

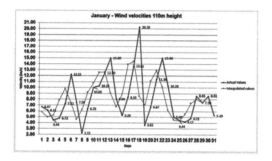

Figure 14. Wind velocities at 110m height in January.

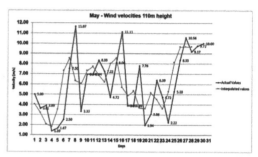

Figure 18. Wind velocities at 110m height in May.

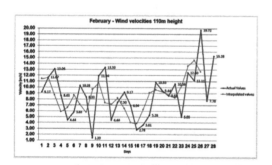

Figure 15. Wind velocities at 110m height in February.

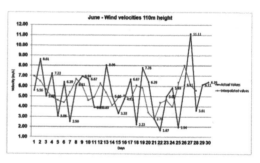

Figure 19. Wind velocities at 110m height in June.

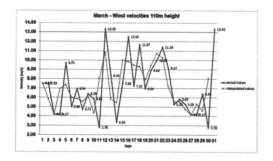

Figure 16. Wind velocities at 110m height in March.

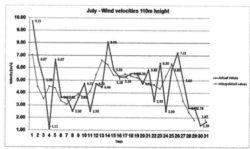

Figure 20. Wind velocities at 110m height in July.

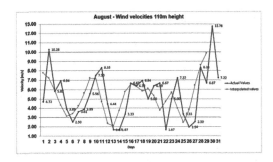

Figure 21. Wind velocities at 110m height in August.

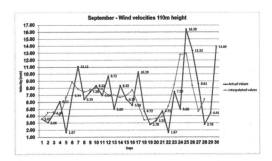

Figure 22. Wind velocities at 110m height in September.

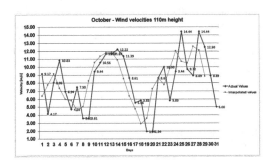

Figure 23. Wind velocities at 110m height in October.

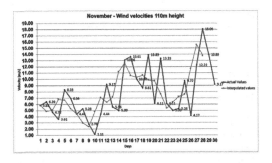

Figure 24. Wind velocities at 110m height in November.

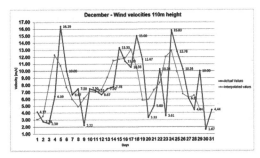

Figure 25. Wind velocities at 110m height in December.

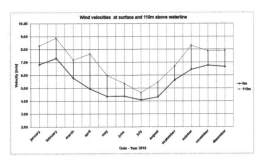

Figure 26. Comparison diagram between 0m and 110m height wind speeds in Constanta.

coastal region will continue to be a matter of interest in the immediate future, our study confirms other findings indicating that this trend is based on actual and consistent wind speed data.

According to various studies, as for example Rusu et al (2009 and 2014b), Ivan et al, 2012, Ganea et al (2017, 2019) and Romania will maintain this naturally stable potential in terms of renewable energy.

It is a privilege to add to the core information available on this subject our limited in scope but supporting contribution, a wind speed dataset for three Romanian coastal locations.

The dataset we used indicates that all the monthly mean values of wind velocities stay over the 3m/s mark.

We also need to understand that all the data gathered (wind speed) was taken once per day and it's not an interval of time. As we know wind speeds are very volatile and unsteady and that's why the results can't tell exactly a percentage of time where the system is working. But analyzing the tables of wind speeds and all the data gathered and keeping in mind the fact that according to various studies (Bak et al. 2013, Jonkman et al. 2009) wind turbines have a cut-in and a cut-off speed (4-25m/s) we came to the conclusion that in

545

Table 7. Constanta daily wind direction (degrees), January - June.

	JAN	FEB	MAR	APR	MAY	JUN
1	155	215	190	53	120	260
2	245	210	205	235	150	75
3	230	215	5	310	115	175
4	295	10	330	195	160	205
5	210	170	110	175	55	190
6	190	155	225	145	55	245
7	295	140	290	45	345	25
8	140	250	30	45	340	95
9	95	305	280	50	345	165
10	110	55	220	175	20	115
11	80	335	150	180	20	45
12	60	325	145	155	50	185
13	45	150	215	90	240	195
14	10	120	300	140	195	165
15	30	345	180	125	145	105
16	210	350	190	155	145	245
17	175	35	185	120	0	30
18	325	115	355	115	285	35
19	225	50	70	355	210	20
20	350	80	280	340	15	35
21	95	55	10	355	300	355
22	0	45	75	235	65	15
23	5	40	355	210	65	240
24	5	10	25	180	85	330
25	75	35	135	185	50	195
26	55	50	235	180	25	40
27	60	15	255	185	45	40
28	255	325	340	55	35	85
29	265		340	135	30	220
30	20		205	105	50	255
31	150		185		20	

Table 8. Constanta daily wind direction (July – December).

	JUL	AUG	SEP	OCT	NOV	DEC
1	340	30	320	45	90	260
2	185	35	10	55	70	265
3	235	355	40	230	60	160
4	135	25	40	335	60	345
5	155	340	215	40	55	355
6	140	205	340	115	55	350
7	220	250	325	120	50	220
8	225	25	5	115	35	220
9	30	40	0	0	40	215
10	35	55	330	35	20	10
11	265	60	335	35	130	340
12	305	50	335	35	65	270
13	265	255	85	50	60	270
14	350	130	35	55	5	75
15	295	90	305	55	15	110
16	310	25	325	45	5	85
17	300	40	15	20	20	40
18	265	20	85	40	60	10
19	280	15	95	25	305	360
20	305	60	100	270	60	215
21	310	55	155	350	50	265
22	265	325	110	10	10	255
23	220	50	215	15	25	290
24	340	50	140	235	195	325
25	20	35	0	345	185	330
26	355	205	355	265	275	290
27	310	135	15	200	30	285
28	285	40	250	200	20	305
29	240	360	15	195	25	340
30	225	360	15	180	335	335
31	10	355		110		65

the best spot chosen for implementation the system will function 20% % of the full year. Yet, since we used 24h as time resolution, we can expect a percentage change when using a narrower interval measurement. In the following table all 3 locations were analyzed and having in consideration the 4-25m/s interval for energy production we see that in Constanta the percentage where the wind is blowing with less than 4m/s is the lowest. There are no values bigger than 25m/s.

In Table 10 the percentages when the turbines are not working (when the wind is blowing with less than 4m/s) are presented for all the cases analyzed.

At a later stage, some possible technological solutions are to be formulated together with estimations of prices for their implementation. In addition, a scenario including calculations of the energy output for a specific period of time will be presented.

Table 9. Percentage of the wind speeds for each predominant direction.

Coordinate	%	Coordinate	%
N	20.27	N	24.11
S	9.32	S	9.86
E	7.67	E	11.23
W	8.22	W	9.32

Table 10. The percentage on each location for the wind velocities below 4m/s.

Location	Percentage
Constanta	30,41%
Constanta 110	20,27%
Sulina	55,62%
Mangalia	38,08%

ACKNOWLEDGMENTS

This work is supported by the project "Excellence, performance and competitiveness in the Research, Development and Innovation activities at "Dunarea de Jos" University of Galati", acronym "EXPERT", financed by the Romanian Ministry of Research and Innovation in the framework of Programme 1—Development of the national research and development system, Subprogramme 1.2—Institutional Performance —Projects for financing excellence in Research, Development and Innovation, Contract no. 14PFE/17.10.2018.

REFERENCES

Bak, C., Frederik, Z., Robert, B., Taeseong, K., Anders, Y., Lars, C.H., Anand, N. & Morten H., 2013, Description of the DTU 10 MW Reference Wind Turbine Institute: DTU Wind Energy.

Ganea, D., Amorțilă, V., Mereuță, E., Rusu, E., 2017, A Joint Evaluation of the Wind and Wave Energy Resources Close to the Greek Islands, *Sustainability Journal*, Special Issue Wind Energy, Load and Price Forecasting towards Sustainability, 2017, 9(6).

Ganea, D, Mereuta, E., Rusu, E., - An Evaluation of the Wind and Wave Dynamics along the European Coasts. *Journal of Marine Science and Engineering* 2019, 7(2), 43.

Makris, C., Galiatsatou, P., Tolika, K., et al., 2016, Climate change effects on the marine characteristics of the Aegean and Ionian Seas, Ocean Dynamics, *Ocean Dynamics* (2016) 66:1603–163.

Onea, F. & Rusu, L., 2019. A Study on the Wind Energy Potential in the Romanian Coastal Environment. *Journal of Marine Science and Engineering*, 7(5): 142.

Onea, F. & Rusu E., 2014. Evaluation of the wind energy in the north-west of the Black Sea, *International Journal of Green Energy* 2014, 14p.

Ivan, A., Gasparotti, C. & Rusu, E. 2012. Influence of the interactions between waves and currents on the navigation at the entrance of the Danube Delta, *Journal of Environmental Protection and Ecology*, Vol. 13 (3A), pp 1673–1682.

Jonkman, J., Butterfield, S., Musial, WW. & Scott, G. 2009. Definition of a 5 MW reference wind turbine for offshore system development, National Renewable Energy Laboratory, U.S.A.

Rusu, E, 2010: Modeling of wave-current interactions at the Danube's mouths. *Journal of Marine Science and Technology*, Vol. 15, Issue 2, pp 143–159.

Rusu E. Study of the Wave Energy Propagation Patterns in the Western Black Sea – *Applied Sciences* 2018, 8(6), 993.

Rusu, E., 2019. A 30-year projection of the future wind energy resources in the coastal environment of the Black Sea. *Renewable energy* 139: 228–234.

Rusu, E. and Macuta, S., 2009: Numerical Modelling of Longshore Currents in Marine Environment. *Environmental Engineering and Management Journal*, January/February 2009, Vol.8, No.1, pp 147–151.

Rusu E., Rusu L., C. Guedes Soares. Prediction of extreme wave conditions in the Black Sea with numerical models - 9th International Workshop on Wave Hindcasting and Forecasting 2006/9.

Rusu, L., Bernardino, M. & Guedes Soares, C. Wind and wave modelling in the Black Sea – Journal of operation oceanography 2014a, Vol 7(1), pp. 5–20.

Rusu, L., Butunoiu, D., Rusu, E, 2014b. Analysis of the extreme storm events in the Black Sea considering the results of a ten-year wave hindcast, *Journal of Environmental Protection and Ecology*, Vol. 15 (2), pp. 445–454.

Derivation of environmental contour by Direct Monte Carlo techniques

G. Clarindo & C. Guedes Soares
Centre for Marine Technology and Ocean Engineering (CENTEC), Instituto Superior Técnico, Universidade de Lisboa, Lisbon, Portugal

ABSTRACT: This paper presents the main steps of environmental contours derivation and the computing steps with a direct and alternative technique. The environmental contours are a widely applied method in engineering and especially in ocean engineering to estimate the extreme conditions and structural system response. A wide variety of environmental contour construction methods have already been proposed for marine structures. In general, they can help to predict the extreme and critical met-ocean combinations at some location allowing the engineers to reach the best structural reliability recommendations. This work derives the extreme environmental contours based on Direct Monte Carlo simulations of fitted joint environmental variables, thus concluding the main steps in the process of environmental contours derivation. The Direct Monte Carlo is tested in a robust and consistent dataset. Some preliminary comparisons with IFORM are made and the Direct Monte Carlo presents a good approximation.

1 INTRODUCTION

This paper presents the derivation of environmental contour lines based on Direct Monte Carlo (DMC) techniques as an alternative procedure to analyses the datasets given in the BenchMark (BM) proposed by Haselsteiner et al. (2019). The BM is focused on open comparison in which researchers are invited to develop and present their own contour derivation approaches based on common datasets that will be available to all. Two exercises are planned: one focuses on applying environmental contour methods derivation to a wide range of datasets (hindcast and observational) and the other focuses on uncertainty characterization. This paper will treat just the exercise one. The key goals of this effort are: i) to work towards the development of more robust statistical models and contour construction methods, ii) to support ongoing work to improve technical specifications and standards.

The environmental contour method has been applied for several structural assessments such as: the analysis of ships (Baarholm & Moan 2001), offshore oil and gas structures (Fontaine et al. 2013, Grime & Langley 2008), offshore wind turbines (Agarwal & Manuel 2009, Karmakar et al. 2016) and wave energy converters (WECs) (Muliawan et al. 2013, Canning et al. 2017). Haver (1985) suggested to consider joint distributions of environmental variables, the so-called design curve, later, Winterstein et al. (1993) formally introduced the notion of environmental contours, based entirely on structural reliability principles. While there are a great variety of methods to derive an environmental contour in the academic literature (Winterstein et al. 1993, Moan et al. 2005, Leira 2008) the BM practitioners might follow some guidance provided in standards such as DNV-GL (2017) as well as NORSOK (2017). Most of these standards recommend use of the IFORM for that task.

In this paper, however, the method suggested by Huseby et al. (2013) to generate environmental contours is followed. In short, this approach is able to establish the environmental contours directly in the original space, and thus eliminate the need for any transformations, as would have to be done by the IFORM approach. The IFORM approach for construct the environmental contour is based in transforming the environmental variables to standard normal space using, for example, Rosenblatt transformation and then identifying a circle in the transformed space with radius equal to the reliability index (β_r).

Nevertheless, Huseby et al. (2013), suggested an alternative approach to compute the environmental contour directly in the original space. This methodology operates Monte Carlo directly in the real space using simulations of a fitted joint conditioned environmental model. Then the different parts of the environmental contours would then correspond to tangents in the original space. Some examples of applications of Monte Carlo simulations in structural reliability analysis are presented by Naess et al. (2009), Jensen et al. (2011), Gaspar et al. (2012), and Gaspar & Guedes Soares (2013). This alternative method presents a good approximation with the IFORM method, as well as some advantages, that can facilitate the practical application for engineering. Taking into account all the previously mentioned, it is the approach adopted in the present study and explained in the next section. The performance of Direct Monte Carlo approach will then

DOI: 10.1201/9781003216599-58

be demonstrated in a consistent dataset provided by BM organizers and the resulting environmental contours preliminarily compared with contours obtained by the IFORM approach.

This study is organized as follows: Section 2 introduces the methodology and the steps employed to derive EC as well the key information of datasets provided. Section 3 presents the theory of direct Monte Carlo techniques used as well as the joint environmental model of sea states (heights and periods) and wind-wave states (near-surface wind velocity and significant wave height) adopted. The results and some discussions of the EC derived by DMC at specific locations of the contour line are presented in Section 4. Finally, conclusions are made in Section 5.

2 METHODOLOGY

This section describes the methodology adopted in the derivation of environmental contours.

Basically, the definition for derivation of environmental contour consists in three main steps such as: (i) establishing a statistical model that characterizes the environment based on a sample of environmental states ("statistical modelling"), (ii) computing the environmental contour based on that statistical model ("contour construction") and (iii) selecting discrete points along the contour for subsequent use in the design process ("design condition selection"), the description and the final result of the process can be seen in Figure 1 and Figure 2.

This paper will follow the suggestion from BM to step (i) using the same statistical baseline, however in step (ii) the environmental contours will be constructed using a Direct Monte Carlo (DMC) technique as an alternative one than that suggested in the BM exercise to accomplish this step.

2.1 Data

The dataset provided by the organizers of the BM consists in different sources of data such as mainly observational data (in-situ buoys and wind masts) and hindcast. Figure 3 shows a map of locations for these datasets.

After consideration of these options, the mixtures of datasets specified in Table 1 were selected. Thus, six cases will be considered: three real measured datasets (A, B, and C) and three hindcast datasets (D, E, and F).

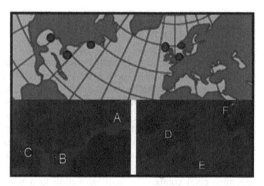

Figure 3. Location of dataset used to derive the EC.

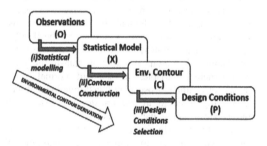

Figure 1. Description of the environmental contour method showing the three distinct steps: statistical modelling, contour construction and design condition selection. Regarding that the environmental derivation is combination of steps (i) and (ii).

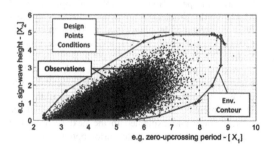

Figure 2. Contour derivation proceeding by Direct Monte Carlo directly in the real environmental space.

Table 1. Data scheme provided to compute the environmental contour derivation.

Datasets	Data Source	Time series	Return period of EC
A	NDBC 44007	10 years	1-yr Hs-Tz
	moored buoy	82,805 data	20-yr Hs-Tz
	(off Maine coast)		
B	NDBC 41009	10 years	1-yr Hs-Tz
	moored buoy	83,917 data	20-yr Hs-Tz
	(off Florida coast)		

(*Continued*)

Table 1. (Cont.)

Datasets	Data Source	Time series	Return period of EC
C	NDBC 42001	10 years	1-yr Hs-Tz
	moored buoy	81,749 data	20-yr Hs-Tz
	(Gulf of Mexico)		
D	coastDat-2	25 years	1-yr Hs-U10
	hindcast	219,145 data	50-yr Hs-Tz
	(off German coast)		
E	coastDat-2	25 years	1-yr Hs-U10
	hindcast	219,145 data	50-yr Hs-Tz
	(off UK coast)		
F	coastDat-2	25 years	1-yr Hs-U10
	hindcast	219,145 data	50-yr Hs-Tz
	(off Norwegian coast)		

3 ENVIRONMENTAL CONTOURS DERIVATION BASED ON DIRECT MONTE CARLO SIMULATIONS

In simulation methods, such as DMC, random samples are generated based on sampling density function and the structural system is evaluated for each sample in order to check if the limit state function (boundary between safe and unsafe regions) is violated or not, thus characterizing a structural system failure. The contours construction step will be computed directly by Monte Carlo Simulations (Huseby et al. 2013). This approach does not involve any transformation of the environmental variables allowing constructing the contour lines directly into a normal-real space. In order to demonstrate the applicability of this alternative method to derive environmental contours lines, the following sections briefly discuss the distribution adopted in the conditional modelling scheme to complete the first step.

3.1 Statistical modelling

To accomplish the step (i) and model statistically the observations, a conditional modelling scheme is adopted and the joint distribution of met-ocean variables is obtained by the Conditional Modelling Approach (CMA). The CMA uses concept of conditional distributions (Guedes Soares et al. 1988, Bitner-Gregersen & Haver 1991), however, because of the practical difficulty of obtaining conditional distributions when the dependency embraces several random variables, this model is usually used to represent the joint distribution of two (maximum three) environmental parameters. Typically, the CMA starts with a long-term distribution of significant wave heights (Ferreira & Guedes Soares 2000; Guedes Soares & Scotto 2011) and with conditional distributions of the other variable. Ferreira & Guedes Soares (2002), Repko et al. (2004) Jonathan et al. (2010), and Dong et al. (2013) used different approaches to model the bivariate distribution of wave height and period. Of course, a full structural wave load not only depends on the wave conditions but have to take into account some meteorological conditions as intensity and directions of the predominant winds (Dong et al. 2015). Due to the numerous combinations of met-ocean variables influence the response of a structure and carry out several loads, a practicable joint environmental model has to be utilized.

As mentioned in the previous section, the case study considers significant height (H_s) and zero up-crossing periods (T_z) of the waves recorded in dataset A, B and C and significant wave high and wind near surface velocity (U_{10}) in D, E and F. The followed statistical baseline in step (i) is showed in Table 2 and these model structures is recommended in DNV-GL (2017) and also suggested in the BM.

The model structure consists of a marginal PDF for H_s and a conditional PDF for co-variables such as T_z and U_{10} (see Equation 1a and 1b). The marginal distribution of H_s is assumed to follow a 3-parameters Weibull distribution to the whole dataset, while a conditional lognormal distribution is used for T_z in A, B and C. For the rest of the dataset a change in the conditional system is applied. The U_{10} distribution is now conditioned by Weibull 2-parameters and the statistical dependence is based on scale and shape parameters, whereas the lognormal has conditioned by the mean and variance of distributions (see Equation 3a-b and 5a-b).

$$f_{H_s,T_z}(h,t) = f_{H_s}(h) f_{T_z|H_s}(t|h) \quad (1a)$$

$$f_{H_s,U_{10}}(h,u) = f_{H_s}(h) f_{U_{10}|H_s}(u|h) \quad (1b)$$

3.1.1 Weibull distribution

The use of the Weibull distribution widely adopted due to its versatility. Depending on the values of the parameters, the Weibull distribution can be used to a variety of forms. Note that in the H_s distribution

Table 2. Baseline statistical model structure recommended in DNV-GL (2017) based on Equations 3a-b and 5a-b for six datasets considered.

H_s (m) Marginal Weibull 3-P	α	β	γ
A	0.944	1.480	0.098
B	1.140	1.600	0.188
C	1.160	1.560	0.056
D	1.580	1.410	0.102
E	1.860	1.490	0.122
F	2.570	1.550	0.225

T_z (s) Conditional Lognormal

		i=1	i=2	i=3
A	a_i	1.470	0.214	0.641
	b_i	0.000	0.308	-0.250
B	a_i	1.410	0.234	0.581
	b_i	0.000	0.241	-0.200
C	a_i	1.240	0.300	0.600
	b_i	0.000	0.155	-0.161

U_{10} (m/s) Conditional Weibull 2-P

		i=1	i=2	i=3
D	c_i	0.000	7.580	0.520
	d_i	0.000	3.890	0.497
E	c_i	0.000	7.400	0.525
	d_i	0.000	3.890	0.398
F	c_i	0.000	5.77	0.525
	d_i	1.970	0.279	1.270

the most general form of distribution will be assumed (3-parameters form, Equation 2a) and the appropriate modifications to obtain the other forms such as the 2-parameters (Equation 2b) form is obtained by setting γ=0.

$$f_x(x) = \frac{\beta}{\alpha}\left(\frac{x-\gamma}{\alpha}\right)^{\beta-1} e^{-\left(\frac{x-\gamma}{\alpha}\right)^\beta} \quad (2a)$$

$$f_x(x) = \frac{\beta}{\alpha}\left(\frac{x}{\alpha}\right)^{\beta-1} e^{-\left(\frac{x}{\alpha}\right)^\beta} \quad (2b)$$

were γ, α and β are parameters of location, scale and shape of the probability function, respectively.

As commented previously the conditional structure for wind-wave datasets is based on 3-parameters Weibull for H_s and modified form 2-parameters Weibull for U_{10} dependence. The scale and shape dependence is modelled by the following functions:

$$\alpha(H_s) = E[U_{10}|H_s] = c_1 + c_2 H_s^{c_3} \quad (3a)$$

$$\beta(H_s) = E[U_{10}|H_s] = d_1 + d_2 H_s^{d_3} \quad (3b)$$

3.1.2 *Lognormal distribution*

The lognormal distribution is considered essential to model statistically the environmental observations because it is not able to model negative values. This is important in probabilistic design role since an engineering phenomenon with negative values is sometimes physically impossible. A random variable x has a lognormal probability distribution when ln(x) is normal. In this case, the PDF are defined by:

$$f_x(x) = \frac{1}{\sqrt{2\pi}\sigma x} \exp\left(\frac{\ln(x)-\mu}{2\sigma^2}\right)^2 ; x > 0 \quad (4)$$

where μ and σ are the mean and standard deviation values. The CMA uses the lognormal distribution to model the T_z conditioned by H_s as showed in the follow Equations:

$$\mu(H_s) = E[\ln T_z|H_s] = a_1 + a_2 H_s^{a_3} \quad (5a)$$

$$\sigma(H_s) = Sd[\ln T_z|H_s] = b_1 + b_2 e^{b_3 H_s} \quad (5b)$$

The applied statistical model structures are currently recommended by certifying organization DNV-GL in their recommended practice DNV-GL (2017).

3.2 *Contour construction*

The step (ii) in the contour derivation process consists in constructs the EC lines based on that statistical model. This step can be computed with a variety of different method as well. Probably the most popular approach to construct EC is based on definition proposed by Winterstein et al. (1993) also called IFORM. However, different definitions for construction of EC such as the definition proposed by Huseby et al. (2013) adopted in this work. This alternative approach to derive the EC does not need to perform any transformations and can be constructed directly on the H_s-T_z and H_s-U_{10} real physical space. The procedures of construction of the EC based on direct Monte Carlo simulations are summarized by following main steps:

1. Generate a proper sample of the joint environmental distribution using Monte Carlo simulations. The numbers of random suitable samples simulated by Monte Carlo are the same number of each dataset evaluated (see Table 1).

Assume an angle (Θ) situated between π and $-\pi$, and for each sample generated in (1) estimate its projection that takes the form of a straight line:

$$X_i(\theta) = T_i \cos(\theta) + H_i \sin(\theta) \quad (6a)$$

$$X_i(\theta) = U_i \cos(\theta) + H_i \sin(\theta) \quad (6b)$$

3. Sort these projections in ascending order, $X_{(1)} \leq X_{(2)} \ldots \leq X_{(n)}$; Then let $(T_{(n)}, H_{(n)}$ and $U_{(n)}, H_{(n)})$ denote the corresponding samples. Estimate the number of samples that will be kept within the desired probability of failure (P_f) in a half space so-called $\Pi(\Theta)^+$, such that it only contains k numbers of samples.

$$P_f = \frac{n-k}{n} \Rightarrow k = n(1 - P_f) \quad (7)$$

5. Assume another angle and repeat the steps excluding step (1). Regarding, t and u represent the T_z and U_{10} projections, practically computed with the same formulation, h are H_s projections respectively.

$$t = \frac{\sin(\theta + \Delta\theta)C(\theta) - \sin(\theta)C(\theta + \Delta\theta)}{\sin(\theta + \Delta\theta)\cos(\theta) - \sin(\theta)\cos(\theta + \Delta\theta)}$$

$$u = \frac{\sin(\theta + \Delta\theta)C(\theta) - \sin(\theta)C(\theta + \Delta\theta)}{\sin(\theta + \Delta\theta)\cos(\theta) - \sin(\theta)\cos(\theta + \Delta\theta)}$$

$$h = \frac{-\cos(\theta + \Delta\theta)C(\theta) + \cos(\theta)C(\theta + \Delta\theta)}{\sin(\theta + \Delta\theta)\cos(\theta) - \sin(\theta)\cos(\theta + \Delta\theta)}$$

where $C(\Theta)$ denotes the value of the projection onto the Θ-line corresponding to the desired failure probability and $\Delta\Theta$ refers to the angular interval between two tangents.

Huseby et al. (2013) indicated that the environmental contour obtained by this approach presents a good approximation to that obtained from the IFORM. Moreover, its advantage is the direct implementation as well is more flexible in that it does not require a joint parametric model for the environmental parameters. This makes it easier to include effects such as those related with long-term trends and future projections of the wave climate into the estimations.

4 RESULTS AND DISCUSSION

The approach used to derive the EC presented above has been employed to obtain the contour lines for six different datasets and two different main targets years of return period. The datasets A, B and C being computed for 1- and 20-years H_s-T_z return period assuming the joint environmental model defined by Equations 1a and 5a-b. For the remaining datasets D, E and F being computed for 1- and 50- years H_s-U_{10} return period following the Equations 1b and 3a-b. The fitted 3-p Weibull distributions of H_s are showed in Table 2 as well the conditional lognormal for T_z and 2-p Weibull for U_{10} dependent of H_s. Figure 4 illustrate the goodness of fit for representative sea states in dataset A and wind-wave states exemplified by dataset F. Regarding for sea states the lognormal dependence is based on mean and standard deviation parameters while the conditional dependence for wind-waves states were based on scale and shape Weibull 2-parameters.

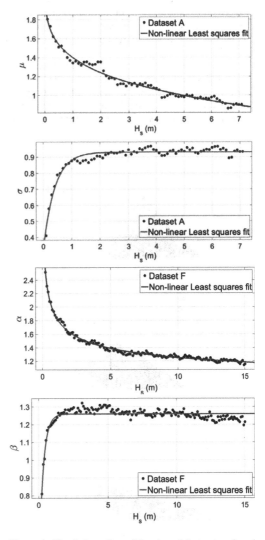

Figure 4. The fitting of conditional model structure based on a lognormal distribution to model dataset A (H_s-T_z). Similarly, a 2-p Weibull distribution used for model the dependent variables for datasets F (H_s-U_{10}).

It is important to note that the fitted dependence functions often had a first coefficient with value zero, in other words, 8 of 12 dependence functions. For lognormal σ-dependence distributions in datasets A, B and C present $b_1 = 0$. For the remaining datasets D, E and F also present zeros values in α-dependence functions of the 2-parameters Weibull distribution being $c_1=0$.

The marginal H_s distribution was performed using the maximum likelihood estimations while the dependence functions fitting (T_z and U_{10}) was performed using non-linear least squares. Then the EC was constructed by DMC based on these fitted models and this procedure led to BM exercise one.

The computed 1-and 20-yrs sea states contours showed in Figure 5 can capture multiple data exceedance. It can also be noticed that the amount of data exceeds the contours lines in multiple regions except the 20-yrs contour based on dataset A which concentrates the exceedance in regions of medium wave periods.

Similarly, based on DMC the 1- and 50-yrs wind-wave EC are computed and as seen in the Figure 6, all contours are exceeded at many different regions. In other words, for example, the 50-yrs wind-wave contours based on Dataset F is exceeded in regions

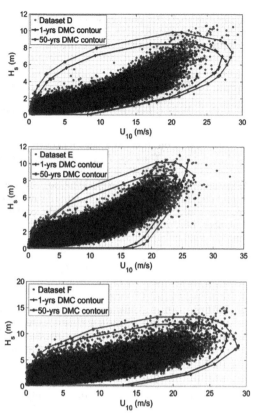

Figure 6. Wave-wind contours derived by Direct Monte Carlo simulations.

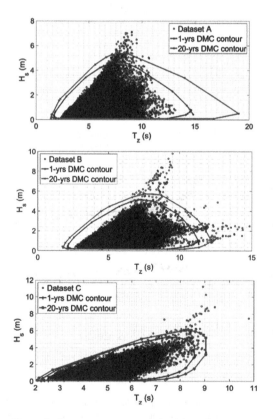

Figure 5. Sea states contours derived by Direct Monte Carlo simulations.

of medium H_s and high U_{10}, regions of high H_s and high U_{10} and finally, regions of low H_s and low U_{10}. It is extremely crucial that the method of EC constructions can be able to assess these regions in which are target regions in the design phase's process. However, the points outside of contours can be different among the methods due to various definitions for exceedance and so, the expected points outside will be different. The definition for exceeding the contour in DMC is based on straight tangent lines for two-dimensional problems which act as limits of failure regions directly in the original environmental space.

For open comparison the EC is computed by IFORM methods based on the same baseline probability model. The IFORM is considered a standard design practice for a wide range of marine engineering applications where the extreme environmental combinations are regions of interest. The DMC-based EC display similar shapes as the IFORM-based EC. In order to compare, a representative dataset for sea and wind-wave states are selected. The Figure 7 (top panel) shows the dataset B to represent H_s-T_z contours and dataset E (bottom panel) to represent H_s-U_{10} wave-wind contours as well the scatter plot jointly. Usually,

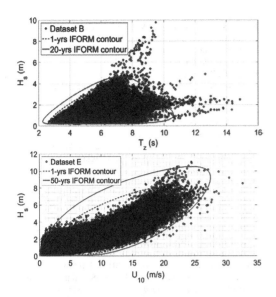

Figure 7. Sea states contours (top panel) and wave-wind contours based on IFORM approach.

using IFORM the contour is defined in the standard normal space (U_j) and then transforms the points to the original variable space (X_j), normally via Rosenblatt transformation, however this procedure introduces errors in the probability of failure, generally underestimated the values in some cases. Contours based on IFORM are extensively used and been published e.g. by Saranyasoontorn & Manuel (2005), Leira (2008), Li et al. (2015), Myers et al. (2015), Valamanesh et al. (2015) and Eckert-Gallup et al. (2016).

The contours lines computed in Figure 7 by IFORM can be directly compared with these contours lines computed by DMC in Figure 5 and 6 at middle panels. While DMC overcomes the problem caused by the Rosenblatt transformation it requires simulations of several environmental states which is computational time expensive than the simple IFORM estimations. It should be noted, that for numerous environmental models the errors due to the Rosenblatt transformation are apparently small for large return-periods where the probability of failure (P_f) itself is very small, and nonetheless, it is a serious consequence of this kind of transformations into normal space. The main motivation behind the DMC approach presented in this work is to be able to derive EC directly in the original space, and thus eliminate the need for any transformation. However, comparisons in the Pf estimations are not the main goal of this study.

The EC based on IFORM estimations compared with the EC derived by the DCM present a very similar behavior, but not identical. In some extreme region of DMC contour, the lines start to display some loops or irregularities. The main justification for this is that for tangent lines corresponding to some angles, the neighboring tangent lines at either side will meet before crossing the line itself. The principal reason why this will happen could be that there are not enough samples to give smooth contour lines, and all the cases it may easily be resolved by increasing the number of simulations, concerning the number of samples is the same to the original dataset time series (see third column on Table 1). The authors of this approach explain that is possible to construct joint environmental distributions where these irregularities are features of the true environmental contours and not just a question of sample size (e.g. for distributions truncated in the tail of the distribution). In such cases, the irregularities correctly define the true boundaries of the failure regions and care should be taken so that the structural failure regions are completely outside at least one tangent line defined by the EC and their respective irregularities. Besides that, it is also noted that for most practical applications and several environmental distributions, this problem is assumed to be negligible and for the joint environmental distribution applied in this studies cases, the irregularities seem to disappear when increasing the number of samples as done by Huseby et al. (2013) in other cases to avoid irregularities.

It is easily to see that constructing the EC based on DMC leads to crude contour lines but some cases not displaying irregularities along the contour lines such as datasets A, C, D and F. Alternatively increasing the number of angles, the DMC requires large number of simulations, making the process time expensive. On the other hand, increasing the angular resolution give a finer contour but display loops and irregularities. The optimal choices are based on the same number of samples of each original dataset and looks like a reasonable compromise.

5 CONCLUSIONS

The analysis of environmental variables and their extreme behaviors conditions are presented by derivation of their respective EC lines based on different period of return. In these cases, the extreme problem to be solved presents a bi-variate and random nature, which makes it of a special complexity. The computed EC are presented as results of exercise one of BM announced at OMAE 2019 conference that consist in estimate extreme environmental conditions applying a statistical baseline and methodology recommended by technical specifications and standards as a part of design marine structural process. Nevertheless, the main goal of BM is an open comparison and researchers are invited to develop and present their own contour derivation approaches based on common datasets for all participants.

Taking into account the description of the EC method suggested by the organizers the same three distinct steps are adopted: statistical modelling, contour construction and design condition selection. Regarding the BM exercise one focuses on contour derivation, which includes statistical modelling and contour construction. To achieve the BM objectives the same statistical set is employed to jointly model the environment based on a sample of environmental observations states. However, for contour construction step we used an alternative approach than these recommended by BM organizers in order to compare if the different methods present a reasonable result that can be directly compared.

The alternative approach, based on the Direct Monte Carlo gives similar results compared to the traditional IFORM-based approach to derive the EC lines. Likewise, due to a wide variety of approaches to construct EC, it can be expected that the shapes of each contour based-approach are different but similar as showed in the results. Moreover, the performance seems reasonable and should be satisfactory in most practical applications.

ACKNOWLEDGEMENTS

This work contributes to the project "Extreme wind and wave modeling and statistics in the Atlantic Ocean" (EXWAV) financed by the Portuguese Foundation for Science and Technology (Fundação para a Ciência e Tecnologia-FCT) under contract PTDC/EAM-OCE/31325/2017 RD0504, This work contributes to the Strategic Research Plan of the Centre for Marine Technology and Ocean Engineering (CENTEC), which is financed by the Portuguese Foundation for Science and Technology (Fundação para a Ciência e Tecnologia) under contract UIDB/UIDP/00134/2020.

REFERENCES

Agarwal, P. & Manuel, L. 2009. Simulation of offshore wind turbine response for long-term extreme load prediction. *Engineering structures.* 31(10): 2236–2246.

Baarholm, G.S. & Moan, T. 2001. Application of contour line method to estimate extreme ship hull loads considering operational restrictions. *Journal of ship research.* 45(3): 228–240.

Bitner-Gregersen, E.M. & Haver S. 1991. Joint environmental model for reliability calculations. *In: Proceedings of the First International Offshore and Polar Engineering conference. Edited by: S. Jin Chung. The International Society of Offshore and Polar Engineering (ISOPE-031):* August 11-16, Edinburgh, United Kingdom

Canning, J., Nguyen, P., Manuel, L. & Coe, R.G. 2017. On the long-term reliability analysis of a point absorber wave energy converter. *In Proceedings of the 36th International Conference on Ocean, Offshore and Arctic Engineering* (OMAE), American Society of Mechanical Engineers (ASME). June 25-30,Trondheim, Norway

DNV-GL. 2017. Recommended practice DNVGL-RPC205: Environmental conditions and environmental loads. *Tech report.*

Dong, S., Wang, N., Liu, W. & Guedes Soares, C. 2013. Bivariate Maximum Entropy Distribution of Significant Wave Height and Peak Period. *Ocean Engineering.* (59): 86–99.

Dong, S., Tao, S., Li, X. & Guedes Soares, C. 2015. Trivariate Maximum Entropy Distribution of Significant Wave Height, Wind Speed and Relative Direction. *Renewable Energy.* (78): 538–549.

Eckert-Gallup, A.C., Sallaberry, C.J., Dallman, A.R. & Neary V.S. 2016. Application of principal component analysis (PCA) and improved joint probability distributions to the inverse first-order reliability method (I-FORM) for predicting extreme sea states. *Ocean Engineering.* (112): 307–319.

Ferreira, J. A. and Guedes Soares, C. 2000. Modelling Distributions of Significant Wave Height. *Coastal Engineering.* 40 (4)361–374.

Ferreira, J.A. & Guedes-Soares, C. 2002. Modelling bivariate distributions of significant wave height and mean wave period. *Applied Ocean Research.* 21(1): 31–45.

Fontaine, E., Orsero, P., Ledoux, A., Nerzic, R., Prevosto, M. & Quiniou, V. 2013. Reliability analysis and response based design of a moored FPSO in West Africa. *Structural Safety.* (41): 82–96.

Gaspar, B. & Guedes Soares, C. 2013. Hull Girder Reliability using a Monte Carlo Based Simulation Method. *Probabilistic Engineering Mechanics.* (31): 65–75.

Gaspar, B., Naess, A., Leira, B. J. & Guedes Soares, C. 2012. System reliability analysis of a stiffened panel under combined uniaxial compression and lateral pressure loads. *Structural Safety.* (39): 30–43.

Grime, A. J. & Langley, R. 2008. Lifetime reliability based design of an offshore vessel mooring. *Applied Ocean Research*, 30(3): 221–234.

Guedes Soares, C., Lopes, L. C. & Costa, M. 1988. Wave climate modelling for engineering purposes. Schreffler, B. A. & Zienkiewicz O. C., (Eds.). *Computer Modelling in Ocean Engineering.* Rotterdam: A.A. Balkema Publishers: 69–175.

Guedes Soares, C. & Scotto, M. G. 2011. Long Term and Extreme Value Models of Wave Data. Guedes Soares, C. Garbatov Y. Fonseca N. & Teixeira A. P., (Eds.). *Marine Technology and Engineering.* London, UK Taylor & Francis Group; pp. 97–108.

Haselsteiner, A. F., Coe, R. G., Manuel, L., Nguyen, P. T., Martin, N., & Eckert-Gallup A. 2019. A benchmark exercise on estimating extreme environmental conditions: methodology & baseline results. *In proceedings of the ASME – 38th International Conference on Ocean, Offshore and Artic engineering (OMAE) –* June 9-14 – Glasgow, Scotland – UK.

Haver, S. 1985. Wave climate off northern Norway. *Applied Ocean Research*, 7(2): 85–92.

Huseby, A. B., Vanem, E. & Natvig, B. 2013. A new approach to environmental contours for ocean engineering applications based on direct Monte Carlo simulations. *Ocean Engineering.* (60): 124–135.

Jensen, J., Olsen S., & Mansour A. 2011. Extreme wave and wind response predictions. *Ocean Engineering.* (38): 2244–2253.

Jonathan P., Flynn J. & Ewans, K. C. 2010. Joint modelling of wave spectral parameters for extreme sea states. *Ocean Engineering.* (37): 1070–1080.

Karmakar, D., Bagbanci, H., & Guedes Soares, C. 2016. Long-term extreme load prediction of spar and semisubmersible floating wind turbines using the environmental contour method. *Journal of Offshore Mechanics and Arctic Engineering.* 138 (2):021601: 9.

Leira, B.J. 2008. A comparison of stochastic process models for definition of design contours. *Structural Safety.* 30(6): 493–505.

Li, L., Gao, Z. & Moan, T. 2015. Joint distribution of environmental condition at five European offshore sites for design of combined wind and wave energy devices. *Journal of Offshore Mechanics and Arctic Engineering:* 137(3):031901: 16.

Moan, T., Gao, Z. & Ayala-Uraga, E. 2005. Uncertainty of wave induced response of marine structures due to long-term variation of extra-tropical wave conditions. *Marine Structures:* 18(4): 359–382.

Muliawan, M. J., Gao, Z., & Moan, T. 2013. Application of the contour line method for estimating extreme responses in the mooring lines of a two-body floating wave energy converter. *Journal of Offshore Mechanics and Arctic Engineering*, 135(3):429–439

Myers, A.T., Arwade, S.R., Valamanesh, V., Hallowell, S.T. & Carswell, W. 2015.Strength, stiffness, resonance and the design of offshore wind turbine monopoles. *Engineering Structures*. (100): 332–341

Næss, A., Leira, B. & Batsevych, O. 2009. System reliability analysis by enhanced Monte Carlo simulation. *Structural Safety*, 31(5): 349–355.

NORSOK. 2007. NORSOK standard N-003: Actions and action effects. *Tech. rep.*

Repko, A., Van Gelder P., Voortman H. & Vrijling, J. 2004. Bivariate description of offshore wave conditions with physics-based extreme value statistics. *Applied Ocean Research*, 26 (3-4):162–170.

Saranyasoontorn, K. & Manuel, L. 2005. On assessing the accuracy of offshore wind turbine reliability-based design loadsfrom the environmental contour method. *Int. J. Offshore Polar Eng.* 15 (2):132–140.

Valamanesh, V., Myers, A.T. & Arwade, S.R. 2015. Multivariate analysis of extreme metocean conditions for offshore wind turbines. *Structural Safety*. (55): 60–69.

Winterstein, S. R., Ude, T. C., Cornell, C. A., Bjerager, P. & Haver, S. 1993. Environmental parameters for extreme response: Inverse FORM with omission factors. *In Proceedings of the 6th International Conference on Structural Safety & Reliability (ICOSSAR)*. August 9-13, Innsbruck, Austria: 551–557.

A review of mechanical analysis of submarine power cables

Pan Fang, Xiaoli Jiang & Hans Hopman
Department of Maritime and Transport Technology, Delft University of Technology, Delft, The Netherlands

Yong Bai
College of Civil Engineering and Architecture, Zhejiang University, Hangzhou, Zhejiang, PR China

ABSTRACT: Submarine power cables play a vital role in transporting electricity between energy-producing devices and consumers. As these devices head to deeper and more distant sea areas with stronger wind and tidal energy, power cables connecting with them would suffer harsher ocean environments, which could corner the cables into failure situations. Mechanical stresses and strains inside power cables are one of the major reasons that influence the overall life and ultimate failures of the structures. Thus the mechanical analysis of them becomes crucial and valuable. Study of mechanical responses of the power cable is complex because inside it there are many layers, which contain various material properties, geometries and surface topographies and, therefore, make the analysis challenging. This paper reviews the history and the recent advances on mechanical studies of power cables and highlights the gaps in existing methods, aiming to facilitate the current mechanical design and cross-section optimization.

1 INTRODUCTION

The past several decades have witnessed the fast development of the offshore energy-producing systems like floating offshore wind farms and wave energy converter (WEC) system etc. An indispensable object appeared in these systems is submarine power cables, as shown in Figure 1. The "lifeline" can transport electric current produced by the floating structures.

Power cables have a long history over 100 years, yet only work on land or overhead at first. Later they dived into the ocean and their structure forms have always been evolving with the ever-changing requirements of the industry. The classification of submarine power cables is various based on different standards. For example, they can be categorised into alternative current (AC) or direct current (DC) type based on the electric current passing through the conductor. They can also be divided into one core or three cores, as shown in Pic. 2, according to the numbers of the conductors used in the middle. The industry on some level classifies them into export, inter-array or inter-platform cable based on the location they are at. Since the study approach of the mechanical analysis about them does not differ very much, we would only introduce the study about the representative submarine power cable here, and the study method is suitable for the other types. For a detailed introduction to the classification please refer to (Worzyk, 2009) & (Ng & Ran, 2016) & (Srinil, 2016). At present, a typical submarine power cable mainly consists of conductor cores, insulation, metallic sheath, armour and serving, see Figure 2. The electricity-relevant parts, the conductor cores, serve as the current-carrying part while the insulation, instead, prevents the current penetrating into the outer layers and generating short circuit phenomenon. The mechanic-relevant parts, metallic sheath, armour as well as serving, function as a protection against the external loading, aging, chemical effects, water ingression etc.

The deeper, harsher and more complicated ocean environment exposes submarine power cables in a more vulnerable situation during operation. The past engineering projects have seen that they ran into trouble over and over again, which caused huge financial losses. Deltares (2018) reported that around 80% of insurance claims within the offshore wind industry are related to cable failures, and Newsletters (2016) stated that 77% of the total global cost of offshore wind farm losses are relevant to subsea cable failures. An appropriate mechanical design of the cable would contribute a lot to the subsea cable industry, from the aspects of both security and economy for the following reasons:

a. A detailed understanding of the mechanical responses inside a cable would help to design and manufacture a reliable yet cost-effective product (Marta et al., 2015).
b. Fatigue life is emphasised as a critical engineering challenge (Trust, 2018); (Yang et al., 2018, Trust, 2018); (Thies et al., 2012), which is affected by the stresses inside the cables.
c. The electrical failure of the insulation layer is discovered highly relevant to the stress of the

Figure 1. Submarine power cables (Rentschler et al., 2019).

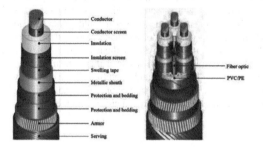

Figure 2. Layer configuration of a typical submarine power cable (Fugløy, 2017).

insulation layer (Du et al., 2017); (Danikas et al., 2019); (Ildstad & Hagen, 1992).

Since the submarine power cable is a type of complex structure containing many layers and some layers are influenced by not only the mechanic but also the electric and temperature etc., the study of it becomes quite troublesome. Besides, the unwillingness to share knowledge or specific results of it because of commercial secrets makes the research much more challenging. Nowadays, a comprehensive overview of mechanical analysis of submarine power cables regarding both its single component and the whole cross section is lacking. For that reason, it is necessary to make an overview to highlight current research gaps and pave the way for future development. This paper teases out the state-of-the-art development of cable mechanical analysis, including the global and local analysis, and elucidating the pros and cons of different study methods. The review is organised as: following the introduction, Section 2 introduces the physical properties of each main single component of the submarine power cables while Section 3 elaborates the mechanical analysis of these layers except the outermost serving due to its simplicity. Section 4 focuses on the global analysis and local cross section analysis. Section 5 concludes the work.

2 CABLE CONFIGURATION

This part clarifies the physical properties of the main layers inside a cable from inside to outside: the conductor, insulation, metallic sheath, wire and serving. The important screen/tape between each main layer will be mentioned as well.

2.1 Conductor

Theoretically, traditional metals like zinc, nickel, iron, aluminium, copper, lead, silver and gold can be used as conducting media. Some researchers are also trying to explore new-style material such as superconducting conductors (Devred et al., 2012); (Devred et al., 2014); (Bajas et al., 2010). However, the selection of conductor material should also satisfy diverse requirements except its conductivity, for example, the cost and availability. Today, aluminium and copper materials are the majority in different types of commercial submarine cables, especially the copper material. Even though when it comes to the current-carrying capability, copper is more expensive than aluminium. Nevertheless, copper allows a smaller cross section and hence requires less material for the outer layers (Worzyk, 2009).

When deciding the shape of a conductor, one has to obtain the optimum shape both in terms of electrical and mechanical characteristics. To be specific, the shape depends on different factors like the amount of voltage, cross-sectional area, water tightness, hole required, etc. Currently, many shapes of conductors are available with the most common ones presented in Figure 3. Among these shapes, the

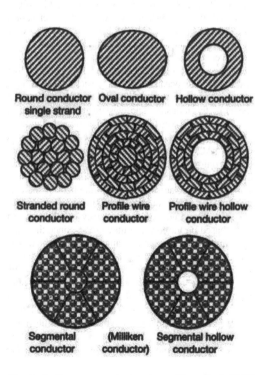

Figure 3. Common conductor shape (Ganguli & Kohli, 2016).

stranded round conductor, shown in Figure 1 and Figure 2, is the majority and frequently appears in the recent publications (Nasution et al., 2013); (Nasution et al., 2014b); (Nasution et al., 2014a); (Bajas et al., 2010). This type of conductor is compressed by the action of dies or roller sets layer by layer and the compressing inducing the deformation of each single conductor wire, which makes the mechanical properties more complex. A more detailed explanation about the design of each type of conductor and its manufacturing process can be found in (Worzyk, 2009); (Ganguli & Kohli, 2016).

2.2 Dielectric system

The dielectric system contains the conductor screen, insulation and insulation screen. The insulation is the most important layer of these three, providing a barrier for potential differences to prevent electrical leakage in the cable. The frequently-used materials for insulation and their specialities are shown in Figure 4. Moreover, recently more researchers are investigating the new XLPE material with better characteristics(Andritsch et al., 2017); (Pleşa et al., 2019); (Li & Du, 2018). However, the commercial process still needs a long time. Nowadays, cross-linked polyethene (XLPE) is the most dominant material for the insulation in submarine power cables. XLPE consists of cross-linked long molecular chains of LDPE forming a three dimensional network. The cross-linking is irreversible and melting is prevented when the XLPE insulation is exposed to high temperatures (Worzyk, 2009).

Due to the rough conductor surface, local electrical stresses will develop between the conductor and insulation, resulting in dielectric strength losses. To prevent local stresses on the insulation, except making the insulation surface cleaner and smoother, a semi-conductive XLPE conductor screen (see Figure 2) is added as a layer between the conductor and insulation. The conductor screen will remove these local stresses through its extremely smooth surface. Also, a semi-conductive XLPE insulation screen is added as a layer between the insulation and swelling tape to protect the insulation for outer layers and to preserve its stable dielectric surface. The three layers of the dielectric system are manufactured simultaneously by triple-extrusion resulting in a high-quality insulation system. The manufacturing details of the insulation layer please refer to (Ganguli & Kohli, 2016).

2.3 Metallic sheath

A water-blocking sheath is added to the submarine cable to prevent water ingression into the dielectric system and conductor. Besides, it also provides protection against Teredo which descends from the aggressive "shipworms" (Worzyk, 2009). Materials like copper, lead, aluminium, stainless steel sheath, polymeric can be used for this purpose in various shapes. Normally, power cables would have a smooth tubular sheath, whereas in some situations a corrugated sheath, see Figure 5, is preferred for HV dynamic power cables (Andresen et al., 1958); (Nelson & Daly, 1975).

In Figure 2, it can be seen that the swelling tape is placed between the insulation screen and metallic sheath. Swelling tapes may be added to the submarine power cable when moisture diffuses into the cable because of longitudinal welding seams. Also, a swelling agent in powder and yarns can be applied to suck moisture in the cable. Swelling agents can also be inserted between the conductor layers to provide longitudinal water tightness.

2.4 Armour

The Armor is the most prominent element in submarine cables, for it provides mechanical protection against external loadings and takes care of the tension stability. The armour consists of metal wires, commonly steel, and are wrapped around the cable with the lay length and lay angle as variables. The lay length is the distance covered by the wire after one complete revolution around the cable with a certain layer angle, see Figure 6. The lay length

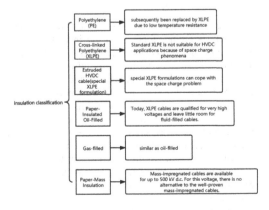

Figure 4. Frequently-used insulation materials.

Figure 5. The configuration of metallic corrugated tubular sheathing (MCTS) (Fugløy, 2017).

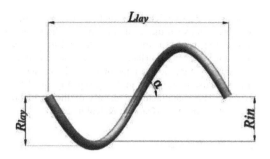

Figure 6. Definition of the basic parameters of the wire. (Kuznecovs et al., 2019).

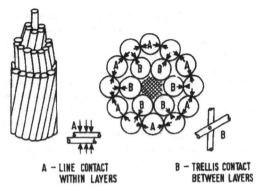

Figure 7. Two contact forms in the conductor (Hobbs & Raoof, 1994).

and layer number of the armour depend on the required tensional stability, bending stiffness and torsional stability.

We can also observe from Figure 2 that bedding is applied underneath the armour layer. The bedding could protect the underlying surface from the undue located press from the armour wires. Besides, it is worth mentioning here that hot bitumen is flushed on the armour layer on some occasions to protect it from corrosion during manufacturing. This temperature-influenced material can change the mechanical behaviour of the armour layer to a large extent during extreme environment situations(Mullins et al., 2015); (Komperød et al., 2019).

2.5 Serving

The last layer of the submarine power cable is the outer serving. This layer protects the armour from scratches, external stresses and corrosion during loading, laying and burying of the submarine power cable. Commonly a polymer material is used as outer serving.

3 ANALYSIS OF SINGLE COMPONENT

3.1 Conductor

Both conductor and armour belong to helical structures and hence share similar mechanical properties. The helical structure theory could date back to (Costello and Phillips, 1974). Based on the theory, Raoof M. did a series of research (Raoof and Hobbs, 1988); (Raoof, 1990); (Raoof, 1991); (Raoof and Huang, 1993); (Hobbs and Raoof, 1994) about helical strands in structural wire ropes mainly via analytical method, with the object to obtain the mechanical stresses and predict the fatigue life of wire ropes under different external cyclic load conditions. Fretting fatigue is investigated in their analytical model which takes fully into account the effect of inline and trellis contact stresses, as shown in Figure 7.

In the experiment and numerical aspects, Nasution et al. (2012b); Nasution et al. (2012a); Nasution et al. (2013); Nasution et al. (2014b); Nasution et al. (2014a) did a series of elaborate studies about bare copper power conductors of two different sizes concerning the individual copper wires and the full cross-section conductor via experimental and numerical method, trying to employ the properties of individual wires to predict the fatigue life of a whole conductor. Individual wires under tension-tension load, as well as full cross-section conductors under tension-tension and tension-bending loads, are investigated. The FEM considers not only the point (trellis) contact between adjacent layers and the inline contact within each layer and between center wire and inner layer, but also the surface irregularities resulting from the manufacturing process. Besides, Buitrago et al. (2013); Karlsen (2010) did experiments in a similar way. The former found that the fatigue failure of the conductor plays a dominate role in the fatigue performance of the cable, and the latter simulated the strain range fatigue mechanism in a specified dynamic power cable by dynamic testing in tension and bending, concluding that the effect of plastic straining of copper conductors should not be disregarded.

3.2 Dielectric system

Although the dielectric system contains three layers, the analysis mainly focuses on the insulation layer. The study of the insulation layer is a complicated and immature job as its failure is influenced by not only mechanical but also electrical and thermal factors. Normally, the final failure is induced by water trees and electrical trees, shown in Figure 8.

Water trees are tree-like defects developing in the insulation layer in the presence of water. The defects usually originate from voids or contaminants. They are usually invisible to the naked eye in the dry condition. Special dying techniques are available, which can make them noticeable. The electrical tree, instead, is readily visible to the naked eyes and formed in the absence of water in dry conditions,

Figure 8. Water tree and electrical tree [38][39].

although they are similarly caused by voids, impurities and defects in the insulation. In certain situations, water trees may initiate electrical trees, eventually cause insulation breakdown (Wang et al., 2012).

While it is possible to identify the conditions which may cause the formation of water trees, the exact mechanism and the chemical processes involved in their development is not yet fully understood. Several scholars Du et al.(2017); Ildstad and Hagen(1992); David et al.(1996); Danikas et al.(2019) identified that mechanical stresses would have effects on the propagation of the electrical tree and water tree by experiment approach. A common conclusion is that tensile stress inside the insulation would accelerate the tree growth while the compress stress would retard the tree growth. An excellent compilation of the literature concerning the influences on mechanical stresses on electrical trees can be found in (Danikas et al., 2019), where the author also pointed out that one of the promising research topics would be studying the combined influences by electrical, mechanical and thermal on insulating materials.

Yet the coupling analysis may only be analysed by numerical method (Kim et al., 2007); (Danikas et al., 2019) due to its complication. According to our review, there is no any researcher studying the insulation failure by combining the three factors. Only until 1994, Haydock et al.(1994) claimed that in his research, it is probably the first time that the FE method is applied to electric field modelling within cables for conditions. Then several scholars Kim et al. (2007); Onchantuek et al. (2009); Talaat (2011); Wang et al. (2012) used this method to study the factors influencing the electrical strength. In conclusion, the multi-physical analysis of insulation failure is still at a very immature stage and needs research in the future.

3.3 Metallic sheath

The metallic sheath used to be a tube-like structure showing simple mechanical properties and hence there is no special study targeting it. Even though currently metallic corrugated tubular sheathing (MCTS) appears and gradually replaces the traditional sheath in dynamic power cables, the research on MCTS is still scarce. There are two papers (Andresen et al., 1958); (Nelson & Daly, 1975) referring to the manufacturing of MCTS cables. One master thesis (Fugløy, 2017) presents experiment work and numerical approach regarding the MCTS analysis.

3.4 Armour

As the introduction in the conductor, the original theory used in the helical structure is similar to the conductor. After 1975, the study experiences two phases. At the first phase, only axisymmetric loading is considered in which Knapp (1975); Knapp (1979); Knapp (1981) did some pioneering work without considering any contacts inside the armour layer. According to (Knapp & Chiu, 1988), two wire contact modes can be identified: cross-wire contact and parallel contact mode, which are the same concept as the two contact forms in section 3.1, though over there trellis contact and inline contact are used. In their papers (Knapp & Chiu, 1988); (Witz & Tan, 1992a); (Bai et al., 2015), only cross-wire contact is developed in their analytical model. Later, Custódio & Vaz (2002); Saevik & Bruaseth (2005) added the parallel contact, which is proved to be influential to the mechanical properties of the armour layer.

At the second phase, a more complicated loading form, bending, is considered. Both Skeie et al. (2012); Sævik (2011) gave an analytical model by assuming that the friction induced by the stick-slip only exist in the bending model. (Mahmood & Al-Kofahi) then develop a dedicated computer program named Helica based on the theory (Skeie et al., 2012). (Chen et al., 2013) also gave a similar theoretical derivation, further considering the radius reduction effects of the helical components. It is observed that the radius reduction and friction has a great effect on the axial and bending stiffness, respectively. Based on Fourier series, Komperød (2017a) presented a numerical solution of an analytical model. The calculated local bending curvatures are compared with several published analytical approximation (Skeie et al., 2012); (Kebadze, 2000), and the results are quite satisfactory. Then Komperød (2017b) applied the numerical techniques on obtaining the stresses in helical cable elements subject to bending and twisting loads. The excellent convergence of this numerical method makes the calculation of stress and strain inside helical elements quite helpful, and the numerical calculations disclose behaviours the analytical approximations fail to capture. Very recently, Dong et al.(2019) proposed a general model which can predict torsion and curvature increments of tensile armours, firstly considering the effects of the twisting rotation of tendon cross-section.

Apart from the above topic, there are some other studies (Olsen et al., 2014); (Komperød et al., 2015); (Komperød, 2015); (Komperød, 2016); (Mullins et al., 2015); (Komperød et al., 2019) on the mechanical properties of bitumen-coated armour after 2014, focusing on the bitumen influences on the mechanical behaviour of armour.

4 CABLE ANALYSIS

In order to obtain the mechanical stresses of submarine power cables performing in the real ocean environment and further optimize the cable, local analysis must be operated after the global responses are gathered by imputing the environment loads and structure parameters in the global analysis, the process is shown in Figure 9. Therefore, this part will be divided into two sub-sessions: global analysis and local analysis. The global analysis would be restricted in the situation of normal operation.

4.1 Global analysis

The mechanical load on the dynamic cable depends on several parameters which include the ocean environment, the structure of the platform and the cable's configuration. Different hanging configurations exist when it comes down to dynamic cables hanging from the floating installation to the sea bed. In Figure 10, an overview of standard flexible risers for floating offshore structures is shown. In practical engineering (Yang et al., 2018); (Robertson et al., 2014); (Jonkman et al., 2009), it is observed that free hanging catenary and lazy wave where the cable is supported with buoyancy floats are frequently used as the cable configurations. The former is easy to manipulate and time-saving while the advantages of the latter are the reduction in maximum tension force, minimisation of dynamic cable response and fewer fatigue cycles. Research has shown that the fatigue life of a Lazy Wave configuration is much higher than a Free Hanging configuration (Thies et al., 2012).

Normally, the mechanical responses of cables are accessed by the numerical method and experimental method. In numerical analysis, the responses of cable to translation, force, curvature etc. are studied by modelling it as a one-dimensional string using global properties such as weight, diameter, axial, bending and torsional stiffness. The axial, bending and torsional stiffness could be calculated based on the reduction formula from (Chen et al., 2013); (Dong et al., 2019). During simulation, one of the points we should pay attention to is the coupling influences between the cable and the floating structure. Yang et al. (2016) assessed the differences between de-coupled and coupled approaches. De-coupled means only the influence of the floating structure on the cable is considered, and it turns out that the model preparation is easier via this approach. Coupled means the mutual influences between both structures are considered, and this approach could give an accurate result. Although de-couple approach appears in the publication (Leroy et al., 2017), Most scholars Marta et al. (2015); Kuznecovs et al. (2019); Young et al.(2018) used coupled approaches to do the analysis.

As for the experiment, Martinelli et al. (2010) used a tank equipped with a wave generator to carry experiments concerning the dynamic movements of cables with catenary-shaped and lazy wave layout, then a simple FEM is applied to compare with the test results. It is suggested that the lazy wave shape performs better in offshore WEC applications. Thies et al. (2012) presented a combined approach. Firstly, a tank experiment is carried to obtain top-end motion response of the floating wave energy converter. Then the data is inputted into a numerical cable model to assess mechanical loading and fatigue cycles. They also found that the lazy wave shape is deemed more suitable in mechanic-wise.

Via global analysis, the mechanical responses of the whole cable can be obtained, in which the most dangerous locations often appear in the upper section near to the floater hang-off point (HOP) where maximum bending is most common. In some instances, however, fatigue also befalls at the touchdown point (TDP) near the seabed (Eriksson, 2011), see Figure 11. Therefore, these two sections deserve more attention during the global analysis.

4.2 Local analysis

The cross section of a power cable is rather complicated. It is impractical if all the layers are accurately considered in the analysis. Therefore, there must be some simplification about the cross section before the local analysis. According to almost all of the known publications (Custódio & Vaz, 2002); (Skeie et al.,

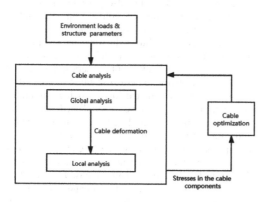

Figure 9. The process of cable analysis.

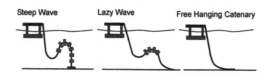

Figure 10. Standard flexible riser configurations for floating offshore structures (Clausen and D'Souza, 2001).

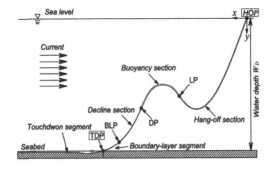

Figure 11. Lazy-wave configuration and its dangerous sections (Ruan et al., 2014).

2012); (Sævik, 2011); (Witz and Tan, 1992b), the geometry of the armour is represented accurately, however, the other layers are simplified to some extent as a cylinder or core.

Some scholars have proved the reliability of this simplification via experiment method. Dhaigude et al. (2018); Ekeberg & Dhaigude (2016) did a series of experiment to obtain the stresses inside umbilical, comparing them with the corresponding stresses calculated by HELICA, a software based on the theory by (Skeie et al., 2012), in which the cross section of the cable and umbilical is simplified in the style stated above. Sævik & Ekeberg (2002) also devised some umbilical tests to obtain the axial strain, axial load, torsion angle, torsion moment, bending moment and curvature, then validate the theoretical model of this paper. The validation results turned out to be quite well.

The numerical method, on the other hand, has the advantage of comparative reliability and lower costs compared to sample testing, it hence becomes an attractive alternative for obtaining the expected results. Tjahjanto et al. (2017) built a linear elastic FEM model including the friction and slip between each layer, then an analytical analysis is also studied focusing on the helical component based on (Skeie et al., 2012); (Sævik, 2011). At last, the stresses of copper conductor of these two methods are compared, and they agree with each other quite well. Leroy et al. (2017) also built a 3D FE model by using ABAQUS, except the armour layer, the other layers are simplified to some extent and bound together. Silva et al. (2012) conducted the numerical analysis by building a 2D model based on the Principle of Virtual Displacements in UFlex2D.

5 CONCLUSIONS AND DISCUSSION

As submarine power cables head toward deeper ocean fields, many mechanic-related challenges occur in practical engineering. Mechanical study of submarine power cables is a complicated task but of great importance to the ocean energy industry. The main purpose of this review is to provide engineers and researchers in this field relevant references required for their work and highlight the barriers in the obtain of mechanical responses. These barriers can be drawn as:

a. The armour layer is a key component affecting the mechanical properties of the whole cable, however, the mechanical analysis of it is a complex issue as it contains many contact strips in which friction, gaps and slip make the results not easy-attainable. Currently, the studies about it make a lot of simplification and mostly are restricted in the linear elastic stage.
b. In the local analysis, the cross section of a power cable needs to be simplified due to the complexity of it. However, the rationality of the simplification of the cross section should be further checked by more experiments and simulations.
c. Many publications have shown that cable failures are normally indicated by the breakdown of the insulation layer, which is highly related to the mechanical stresses inside the insulation layer. The analysis of the coupling effects between different physical fields is quite difficult and still in its infant stage, which requires further study in the future.

For the increasing water depth and higher voltage faced by the submarine power cable operators, an accurate and reliable prediction of the mechanical responses would provide a well-determined cross section for their products, which benefits the cost decrease and cable security. For the future fatigue analysis and multi-physical analysis, such a review would provide a stable guideline as well.

ACKNOWLEDGEMENTS

This work was supported by the China Scholarship Council [grant number 201906320047].

REFERENCES

Andresen, K., Dias, F. & Kenney, N. 1958. Corrugated metallic cable sheath. *Transactions of the American Institute of Electrical Engineers. Part III: Power Apparatus and Systems*, 77, 169–177.

Andritsch, T., Vaughan, A. & Stevens, G. C. 2017. Novel insulation materials for high voltage cable systems. *IEEE Electrical Insulation Magazine*, 33, 27–33.

Bai, Y., Lu, Y. & Cheng, P. 2015. Theoretical and finite-element study of mechanical behaviour of central, large-diameter umbilical cables under tension and torsion. *Ships and Offshore Structures*, 10, 393–403.

Bajas, H., Durville, D., Ciazynski, D. & Devred, A. 2010. Numerical simulation of the mechanical behavior of ITER cable-in-conduit conductors. *IEEE Transactions on Applied Superconductivity*, 20, 1467–1470.

Buitrago, J., Swearingen, S. F., Ahmad, S. & Popelar, C. F. Fatigue, creep and electrical performance of subsea power cable. ASME 2013 32nd International Conference on Ocean, Offshore and Arctic Engineering, 2013. American Society of Mechanical Engineers Digital Collection.

Chen, X., Fu, S., Song, L., Zhong, Q. & Huang, X. 2013. Stress analysis model for un-bonded umbilical cables. *Ocean Systems Engineering*, 3, 97–122.

Clausen, T. & D'souza, R. 2001. Dynamic risers key component for deepwater drilling, floating production. *Offshore*, 61, 89–90.

Costello, G. A. & Phillips, J. W. 1974. A more exact theory for twisted wire cables. *Journal of the Engineering Mechanics Division*, 100, 1096–1099.

Custódio, A. & Vaz, M. 2002. A nonlinear formulation for the axisymmetric response of umbilical cables and flexible pipes. *Applied Ocean Research*, 24, 21–29.

Danikas, M., Papadopoulos, D. & Morsalin, S. 2019. Propagation of Electrical Trees under the Influence of Mechanical Stresses: A Short Review. *Eng. Technol. Appl. Sci. Res*, 9, 3750–3756.

David, E., Parpal, J.-L. & Crine, J.-P. Aging Of XlpE cable insulation under combined electrical and mechanical stresses. Conference Record of the 1996 IEEE International Symposium on Electrical Insulation, 1996. IEEE, 716–719.

Deltares. 2018. *Joint Industry Project Cables Lifetime Monitoring* [Online]. Available: https://www.deltares.nl/app/uploads/2018/04/PB_Joint-Industry-Project-Cables-Life-Time-Monitoring_v2.pdf [Accessed].

Devred, A., Backbier, I., Bessette, D., Bevillard, G., Gardner, M., Jewell, M., Mitchell, N., Pong, I. & Vostner, A. 2012. Status of ITER conductor development and production. *IEEE Transactions on Applied Superconductivity*, 22, 4804909–4804909.

Devred, A., Backbier, I., Bessette, D., Bevillard, G., Gardner, M., Jong, C., Lillaz, F., Mitchell, N., Romano, G. & Vostner, A. 2014. Challenges and status of ITER conductor production. *Superconductor Science and Technology*, 27, 044001.

Dhaigude, M. M., Ekeberg, K. I. & SødahL, N. 2018. Validation of Umbilical Fatigue Analysis by Full-Scale Testing. *International Journal of Offshore and Polar Engineering*, 28, 96–104.

Dong, L., Qu, Z., Zhang, Q., Huang, Y. & Liu, G. 2019. A general model to predict torsion and curvature increments of tensile armors in unbonded flexible pipes. *Marine Structures*, 67, 102632.

Du, B., Su, J., Li, J. & Han, T. 2017. Effects Of Mechanical stress on treeing growth characteristics in HTV silicone rubber. *IEEE Transactions on Dielectrics and Electrical Insulation*, 24, 1547–1556.

Ekeberg, K. I. & Dhaigude, M. M. Validation of the loxodromic bending assumption using high-quality stress measurements. The 26th International Ocean and Polar Engineering Conference, 2016. International Society of Offshore and Polar Engineers.

Eriksson, E., Jeroense, M., Larsson-Hoffstein, M., Sonesson, C., Farnes, K.A., Råd, R. O., Et Al. 2011. *Submarine link - Submarine HVAC cable to the floating oil and gas plat- form at Gjøa*. Available at: https://library.e.abb.com/public/bbcc7542b39ba68bc125796e00527f76/48-53%204m156_ENG_72dpi.pdf *[Accessed* 2 Oct. 2018*]*. [Online]. Available: https://library.e.abb.com/public/bbcc7542b39ba68bc125796e00527f76/48-53%204m156_ENG_72dpi.pdf [Accessed].

Fugløy, B. 2017. *Fatigue Properties of Corrugated Sheathing for Subsea Power Cables*. NTNU.

Ganguli, S. K. & Kohli, V. 2016. *Power cable technology*, CRC Press.

Haydock, L., Allcock, R. P. & Hampton, R. N. 1994. Application of a finite element technique to model an electrical power cable. *IEEE transactions on magnetics*, 30, 3741–3744.

Hobbs, R. & Raoof, M. 1994. Mechanism of fretting fatigue in steel cables. *International journal of fatigue*, 16, 273–280.

Ildstad, E. & Hagen, S. Electrical treeing and breakdown of mechanically strained XLPE cable insulation. Conference Record of the 1992 IEEE International Symposium on Electrical Insulation, 1992. IEEE, 135–139.

Jonkman, J., Butterfield, S., Musial, W. & Scott, G. 2009. Definition of a 5-MW reference wind turbine for offshore system development. National Renewable Energy Lab. (NREL), Golden, CO (United States).

Karlsen, S. Fatigue of copper conductors for dynamic subsea power cables. ASME 2010 29th International Conference on Ocean, Offshore and Arctic Engineering, 2010. American Society of Mechanical Engineers Digital Collection, 275–281.

Kebadze, E. 2000. *Theoretical modelling of unbonded flexible pipe cross-sections*. South Bank University.

Kim, C., Jang, J., Huang, X., Jiang, P. & Kim, H. 2007. Finite element analysis of electric field distribution in water treed XLPE cable insulation (1): The influence of geometrical configuration of water electrode for accelerated water treeing test. *Polymer testing*, 26, 482–488.

Knapp, R. Nonlinear analysis of a helically armored cable with nonuniform mechanical properties in tension and torsion. OCEAN 75 Conference, 1975. IEEE, 155–164.

Knapp, R. 1979. Derivation of a new stiffness matrix for helically armoured cables considering tension and torsion. *International Journal for Numerical Methods in Engineering*, 14, 515–529.

Knapp, R. 1981. Torque and stress balanced design of helically armored cables.

Knapp, R. & Chiu, E. 1988. Tension fatigue model for helically armored cables.

Komperød, M. The Kelvin-Voigt model's suitability to explain the viscoelastic properties of anticorrosion bitumen at large shear strain in subsea cables and umbilicals. Proceedings of the 56th Conference on Simulation and Modelling (SIMS 56), October, 7-9, 2015, Linköping University, Sweden, 2015. Linköping University Electronic Press, 319–330.

Komperød, M. Analytical Calculation of Capacity for Bitumen-Coated Armor Wires in Subsea Cables and Umbilicals. The 26th International Ocean and Polar Engineering Conference, 2016. International Society of Offshore and Polar Engineers.

Komperød, M. Calculating arc length and curvature of helical elements in bent cables and umbilicals using fourier series. ASME 2017 36th International Conference on Ocean, Offshore and Arctic Engineering, 2017a. American Society of Mechanical Engineers Digital Collection.

Komperød, M. Numerical Calculation of Stresses in Helical Cable Elements subject to Cable Bending and Twisting. Proceedings of the 58th Conference on Simulation and Modelling (SIMS 58) Reykjavik, Iceland, September 25th–27th, 2017, 2017b. Linköping University Electronic Press, 374–384.

Komperød, M., Konradsen, B. & Aspli, B. Small-Scale Testing and Mathematical Modeling of Cable Elements' Shear Forces Due to Dry Friction and Bitumen. The 29th

International Ocean and Polar Engineering Conference, 2019. International Society of Offshore and Polar Engineers.

Komperød, M., Konradsen, B. & Slora, R. Viscoelastic large strain model of bitumen used for corrosion protection in subsea cables and umbilicals. ASME 2015 34th International Conference on Ocean, Offshore and Arctic Engineering, 2015. American Society of Mechanical Engineers Digital Collection.

Kuznecovs, A., Ringsberg, J. W., Yang, S.-H., Johnson, E. & Anderson, A. 2019. A methodology for design and fatigue analysis of power cables for wave energy converters. *International Journal of Fatigue*, 122, 61–71.

Leroy, J.-M., Poirette, Y., Brusselle Dupend, N. & Caleyron, F. Assessing mechanical stresses in dynamic power cables for floating offshore wind farms. ASME 2017 36th International Conference on Ocean, Offshore and Arctic Engineering, 2017. American Society of Mechanical Engineers Digital Collection.

Li, Z. & Du, B. 2018. Polymeric insulation for high-voltage dc extruded cables: challenges and development directions. *IEEE Electrical Insulation Magazine*, 34, 30–43.

Mahmood, S. & Al-Kofahi, M. Sesame: Present Status.

Marta, M., Mueller-Schuetze, S., Ottersberg, H., Isus, D., Johanning, L. & Thies, P. R. 2015. Development of dynamic submarine MV power cable design solutions for floating offshore renewable energy applications.

Martinelli, L., Lamberti, A., Ruol, P., Ricci, P., Kirrane, P., Fenton, C. & Johanning, L. Power Umbilical for Ocean Renewable Energy Systems-Feasibility and Dynamic Response Analysis. Proc. Int Conf Ocean Energy, 2010.

Mullins, J., Morin, D., Tyrberg, A., Sonesson, C. & Ekh, J. Bitumen shear mechanics in a dynamic subsea electrical cable. ASME 2015 34th International Conference on Ocean, Offshore and Arctic Engineering, 2015. American Society of Mechanical Engineers Digital Collection.

Nasution, F. P., Sævik, S. & BergE, S. 2014a. Experimental and finite element analysis of fatigue strength for 300 mm2 copper power conductor. *Marine Structures*, 39, 225–254.

Nasution, F. P., Sævik, S. & Gjøsteen, J. K. 2012a. Fatigue analysis of copper conductor for offshore wind turbines by experimental and FE method. *Energy Procedia*, 24, 271–280.

Nasution, F. P., Sævik, S. & Gjøsteen, J. K. Study of Fatigue Strength of Copper Conductor Considering Irregularities Surfaces by Experimental Testings and FE-Analysis. ASME 2012 31st International Conference on Ocean, Offshore and Arctic Engineering, 2012b. American Society of Mechanical Engineers Digital Collection, 269–275.

Nasution, F. P., Sævik, S. & Gjøsteen, J. K. 2014b. Finite element analysis of the fatigue strength of copper power conductors exposed to tension and bending loads. *International Journal of Fatigue*, 59, 114–128.

Nasution, F. P., Sævik, S., Gjøsteen, J. K. & Berge, S. 2013. Experimental and finite element analysis of fatigue performance of copper power conductors. *International journal of fatigue*, 47, 244–258.

Nelson, R. A. & Daly, J. M. 1975. Corrugated Metallic Sheathed Cable–Design and Applications. *IEEE Transactions on Industry Applications*, 196–203.

Newsletters, R. 2016. *Cable incidents are largest cause of losses in offshore wind industry* [Online]. Available: https://www.rivieramm.com/opinion/opinion/cable-inci dents-are-largest-cause-of-losses-in-offshore-wind-indus try-31958 [Accessed].

Ng, C. & Ran, L. 2016. *Offshore wind farms: technologies, design and operation*, Woodhead Publishing.

Olsen, E., Hansen-Zahl, K. A. & KarlseN, S. Viscoelastic behaviour of bitumen in dynamic control umbilicals. ASME 2014 33rd International Conference on Ocean, Offshore and Arctic Engineering, 2014. American Society of Mechanical Engineers Digital Collection.

Onchantuek, W., Marungsri, B., Oonsivilai, A. & Thanatchai, K. 2009. Comparison of electric field and potential distributions on silicone rubber polymer insulators under clean and various contamination conditions using finite element method. *Weseas Transactions on Power Systems*, 4, 67–83.

Pleşa, I., Noţingher, P., Stancu, C., Wiesbrock, F. & Schlögl, S. 2019. Polyethylene nanocomposites for power cable insulations. *Polymers*, 11, 24.

Raoof, M. 1990. Axial Fatigue of multilayered strands. *Journal of Engineering Mechanics*, 116, 2083–2099.

Raoof, M. 1991. Axial Fatigue Life Prediction Of Structural Cables From First Principles. *Proceedings Of The Institution Of Civil Engineers*, 91, 19–38.

Raoof, M. & HOBBS, R. E. 1988. Analysis Of Multilayered Structural Strands. *Journal Of Engineering Mechanics*, 114, 1166–1182.

Raoof, M. & Huang, Y. P. 1993. Cyclic Bending Characteristics Of Sheathed Spiral Strands In Deep Water Applications. *International Journal Of Offshore And Polar Engineering*, 3.

Rentschler, M. U., Adam, F. & Chainho, P. 2019. Design Optimization Of Dynamic Inter-Array Cable Systems For Floating Offshore Wind Turbines. *Renewable And Sustainable Energy Reviews*, 111, 622–635.

Robertson, A., Jonkman, J., Masciola, M., Song, H., Goupee, A., Coulling, A. & Luan, C. 2014. Definition Of The Semisubmersible Floating System For Phase II Of OC4. National Renewable Energy Lab. (NREL), Golden, CO (United States).

Ruan, W., Bai, Y. & Cheng, P. 2014. Static Analysis Of Deepwater Lazy-Wave Umbilical On Elastic Seabed. *Ocean Engineering*, 91, 73–83.

Sævik, S. 2011. Theoretical And Experimental Studies Of Stresses In Flexible Pipes. *Computers & Structures*, 89, 2273–2291.

Saevik, S. & Bruaseth, S. 2005. Theoretical And Experimental Studies Of The Axisymmetric Behaviour Of Complex Umbilical Cross-Sections. *Applied Ocean Research*, 27, 97–106.

Sævik, S. & Ekeberg, K. I. Non-Linear Stress Analysis Of Complex Umbilical Cross-Sections. ASME 2002 21st International Conference On Offshore Mechanics And Arctic Engineering, 2002. American Society Of Mechanical Engineers Digital Collection, 211–217.

Silva, D., Balena, R. & Lisbôa, R. Methodology For Thermoplastic Umbilical Cross Section Analysis. ASME 2012 31st International Conference On Ocean, Offshore And Arctic Engineering, 2012. American Society Of Mechanical Engineers Digital Collection, 407–411.

Skeie, G., Sødahl, N. & Steinkjer, O. 2012. Efficient Fatigue Analysis Of Helix Elements In Umbilicals And Flexible Risers: Theory And Applications. *Journal Of Applied Mathematics*, 2012.

Srinil, N. 2016. Cabling To Connect Offshore Wind Turbines To Onshore Facilities. *Offshore Wind Farms*. Elsevier.

Talaat, M. 2011. Electric Field Simulation Along Silicone Rubber Insulators Surface. *Polymer*, 1, 5.

Thies, P. R., Johanning, L. & Smith, G. H. 2012. Assessing Mechanical Loading Regimes And Fatigue Life Of Marine Power Cables In Marine Energy Applications. *Proceedings Of The Institution Of Mechanical Engineers, Part O: Journal Of Risk And Reliability*, 226, 18–32.

Tjahjanto, D. D., Tyrberg, A. & Mullins, J. Bending Mechanics Of Cable Cores And Fillers In A Dynamic Submarine Cable. ASME 2017 36th International Conference On Ocean, Offshore And Arctic Engineering, 2017. American Society Of Mechanical Engineers Digital Collection.

Trust, C. 2018. *Floating Wind Joint Industry Project Phase I Summary Report* [Online]. Available: https://www.Carbontrust.Com/Media/675868/Flw-Jip-Summaryreport-Phase1.Pdf [Accessed].

Wang, J.-F., Wu, J., Li, Y.-X. & Zheng, X.-Q. Simulation Of Electric Field Distributions In Water Treed XLPE Using Finite Element Method. 2012 Spring Congress On Engineering And Technology, 2012. IEEE, 1–4.

Witz, J. & Tan, Z. 1992a. On The Axial-Torsional Structural Behaviour Of Flexible Pipes, Umbilicals And Marine Cables. *Marine Structures*, 5, 205–227.

Witz, J. & Tan, Z. 1992b. On the flexural structural behaviour of flexible pipes, umbilicals and marine cables. *Marine structures*, 5, 229–249.

Worzyk, T. 2009. *Submarine power cables: design, installation, repair, environmental aspects*, Springer Science & Business Media.

Yang, S.-H., Ringsberg, J. W. & Johnson, E. 2018. Parametric study of the dynamic motions and mechanical characteristics of power cables for wave energy converters. *Journal of Marine Science and Technology*, 23, 10–29.

Yang, S.-H., Ringsberg, J. W., Johnson, E., Hu, Z. & Palm, J. 2016. A comparison of coupled and de-coupled simulation procedures for the fatigue analysis of wave energy converter mooring lines. *Ocean Engineering*, 117, 332–345.

Young, D., Ng, C., Oterkus, S., Li, Q. & Johanning, L. Predicting failure of dynamic cables for floating offshore wind.

Young, D., Ng, C., Oterkus, S., Li, Q. & Johanning, L. Assessing the mechanical stresses of dynamic cables for floating offshore wind applications. Journal of Physics: Conference Series, 2018. IOP Publishing, 012016.

Assessment of the wave conditions in the Azores coastal area

M. Gonçalves & C. Guedes Soares
Centre for Marine Technology and Ocean Engineering (CENTEC), Instituto Superior Técnico, Universidade de Lisboa, Lisbon, Portugal

ABSTRACT: This work provides information on the wave resource and sea state conditions along the Azores Islands. Using spectral boundary conditions from WW3, the SWAN model is used to study the wave evolution in the Azores coastal area (35°N-41°N, 36°W-24°W). The wind input fields used are from ERA5 data base, with time steps of 6 hours, over a grid of 0.25°x0.25° resolution, for a 5-year period between 2012 and 2016. A statistical analysis of the results is performed for the complete period; the numerical results have been compared and validated with buoy measurements from five wave buoys demonstrating that, in general, simulations are well reproduced by SWAN model. The geographical distribution of the wave resource is evaluated, and monthly means, inter-annual and seasonal variability are assessed.

1 INTRODUCTION

The assessment and prediction of the wave conditions is very important for different activities related with marine environment: shipping, fisheries, offshore operations, coastal protection. Wave models have the capability to produce the more realistic assessments of wave conditions in coastal areas in which developments of wave energy parks are being considered.

The third-generation models are the state-of-the-art tools for modeling wave generation and transformation in the offshore and nearshore areas. They solve the spectral action balance equation. WAM (WAMDI Group, 1998) and WAVEWATCH III (Tolman, 1991) are highly used for offshore wave generation while SWAN (Booij et al. 1999) is more appropriate for nearshore wave transformation.

Different types of evaluations have been implemented in different regions. Within the HIPOCAS project "Hindcast of Dynamic Processes of the Ocean and Coastal Areas of Europe" (Guedes Soares, 2008), a 44-years hindcast database of wind and wave was produced along the European waters (Guedes Soares et al. 2002).

In the last years many studies regarding the accuracy of SWAN have been made for the Iberian coast, focusing on the Portuguese coast and the Portuguese harbors (Guedes Soares et al., 2004; Gonçalves et al., 2015; Rusu el al., 2008b, 2011; Rusu & Guedes Soares, 2013) and also for the Madeira islands (Rusu, et al, 2008a) and the Azores islands (Rusu & Guedes Soares, 2012a, 2012b).

As a follow-up study, in the MAREN project (Marine Renewable Energy, Energy Extraction and Hydro-environmental Sustainability, which is partially funded by the Atlantic Area Program 2008-1/007), aiming to characterize the wave energy in different areas in the Atlantic coast of Europe, several hindcast have been made, for example Guedes Soares et al., (2014a) and Guedes Soares et al, (2014b), Silva et al., (2015, 2018), Bento et al. (2018); Gonçalves et al, (2018 and 2020), among others. Results demonstrate good correlations among the predicted wave conditions and the wave measurements.

The ARCWIND project (Adaptation and implementation of floating wind energy conversion technology for the Atlantic region) aims to assess the wind energy potential in the Atlantic Area choosing the best locations for wind energy farms. This project supports to the transition from fixed to floating wind platform systems in more exposed sites in the Atlantic Area. A detailed characterization of the wave conditions in the areas of interest is very important to assess the performance of the floating wind platforms.

The methodology proposed herewith is based on the state of-the-art spectral phase averaging wave model SWAN. The aim of this work is to deliver reliable information on the sea-states conditions, capable of helping on the selection of the best locations for siting floating offshore wind farms.

The Azores Archipelago is volcanic origin located in the North Atlantic Ocean. The archipelago is formed by nine islands, distributed along a 600km, from Santa Maria to Corvo. From the geographical point of view the islands are exposed to the North Atlantic frequent wave systems. The islands are directly subjected to both swell, from distant storms, and sea waves, generated by local wind, creating a local wave system (Rusu & Guedes Soares, 2012b). Being this region characterized by an important maritime

DOI: 10.1201/9781003216599-60

activity, it is very important to have a good assessment of the wave conditions.

In this context, a 5-years hindcast study is presented, focusing on the assessment of the wave conditions and providing information on the areas where consideration is being given to the development of wind farms.

2 MODELS

To assess the wave conditions, two state of the art spectral models were implemented in order to describe the generation and propagation of the waves from deep-water to the coastal environment.

WAVEWATCH III (WWIII) is a full-spectral third generation wind-wave model that resolves an advection type energy balance equation:

$$\frac{DN}{Dt} = \frac{S}{\sigma} \qquad (1)$$

where N is the action density spectrum and S characterizes the source terms.

The right-hand side of equation expresses the kinematics of the model, while the left side-hand describes the physical processes that generate, dissipate and distribute the wave energy. These terms consider the nonlinear effects such as wind-wave interactions, quadruplet wave-wave interactions, and dissipation through whitecapping and bottom friction.

SWAN is a third-generation wave model that solves the action balance equation with parameterization of nonlinear processes. This is appropriate for shallow water processes by including other source terms for triad wave-wave interactions and depth-induced wave breaking as well as the JONSWAP parameterization for dissipation due to bottom friction Hasselmann et al (1973). The model also includes some diffraction effects Holthuijsen et al (2003).

Both models resolve the spectral energy balance equation given by:

$$\frac{\partial N}{\partial t} + \nabla_x \cdot \dot{x}N + \frac{\partial}{\partial k}kN + \frac{\partial}{\partial \theta}\dot{\theta}N = \frac{S}{\sigma} \qquad (2)$$

with k as the wave number vector and σ the relative frequency.

3 HINDCAST SYSTEM

3.1 System set-up

Spectral boundary conditions from WW3, provided by Ifremer IOWAGA (Integrated Ocean WAves for Geophysical and other Applications) project (Ardhuin & Accensi, 2013), with time resolution of 3h, are used to force the SWAN model, to study the evolution of the waves in the area of the Azores Islands.

The bathymetry is provides from GEBCO (General Bathymetric Chart of the Ocean) and the wind input is from ERA-5 data base, produced by the European Center for Medium-range Weather Forecast (ECMWF), with a time resolution of 6 hours, provided over a spatial grid of 0.25°x0.25° resolution.

3.2 Validation of the system

The hindcast system is validated with buoy measurements from five wave buoys for Azores, from CLIMAAT project (Azevedo & Gonçalo, 2005, Barrera et al. 2008), provided by the Azores University (UAC - Universidade dos Açores - Portugal) under the framework of the ECOMARPORT project. Their location can be seen in Table 1 and Figure 1.

The dominant incoming sectors of these energetic sea-states are presented in Figure 2 and it is clear that the largest wave power values correspond to the NNW for buoys B2, B3 and B4, and WSW for buoys B1 and B3, though some other directions can be encountered with less percentage.

A statistical evaluation is performed computing The Bias, Root Mean Square Error (RMSE), Scatter Index (SI) and Pearson's Correlation Coefficient (r), expressed by the following relationships:

$$Bias = \frac{\sum_{i=1}^{n}(X_i - Y_i)}{n} \qquad (3)$$

$$RMSE = \sqrt{\frac{\sum_{i=1}^{n}(X_i - Y_i)^2}{n}} \qquad (4)$$

$$SI = \frac{RMSE}{\tilde{X}} \qquad (5)$$

Table 1. Locations of Azores Buoys.

Buoy	Latitude	Longitude	Depth (m)
Lages (B1)	39° 22.11'N	31° 09.80'W	80m
Graciosa (B2)	39° 05.21'N	27° 57.73'W	97m
Faial/Pico (B3)	38° 35.26'N	28° 32.26'W	110m
Praia Vitoria (B4)	38° 45.05'N	27° 00.62'W	100m
Ponta Delgada (B5)	37° 43.53'N	25° 43.28'W	90m

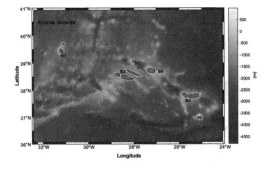

Figure 1. Hindcast system domain and buoy location.

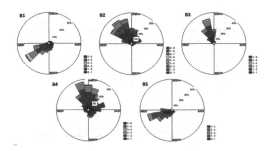

Figure 2. - Directional distribution of the significant wave height.

$$r = \frac{\sum\limits_{i=1}^{n}(X_i - \tilde{X})(Y_i - \tilde{Y})}{\left(\sum\limits_{i=1}^{n}(X_i - \tilde{X})^2 \sum\limits_{i=1}^{n}(Y_i - \tilde{Y})^2\right)^{1/2}} \quad (6)$$

where X_i and Y_i are the measured and simulated values, respectively.

Table 2 summarizes the significant wave height (Hs) results for the Azores area, for the entire period. The statistical results show that the model tends to overestimate buoys B1, B2 and B4 and underestimates buoys B3 and B5. Still, a good correlation between measurements and simulations is obtained, with correlation values above 80%.

Figure 3 shows the QQ-plots for the five buoys. The data from observations and measurements are sorted, showing that the two datasets

Table 2. Statistical results for Hs for Azores Islands.

Buoy	BIAS	RMSE	SI	r	# points
B1	-0.08	0.39	0.24	0.90	5879
B2	-0.23	0.61	0.34	0.81	7235
B3	0.29	0.53	0.31	0.89	9566
B4	-0.08	0.44	0.31	0.85	2662
B5	0.04	0.39	0.29	0.87	6753

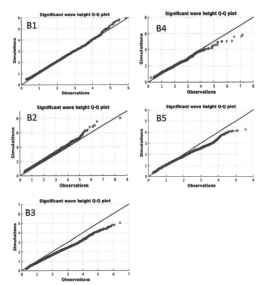

Figure 3. Q-Q plots for the significant wave height for all buoys.

follow a similar statistic up to 4-5m for buoys B1, B2, B4. The poorest results are obtained for buoys B3 and B5.

4 CHARACTERIZATION OF THE WAVE RESOURCE

4.1 *Significant wave height spatial distribution*

A good estimation of the wave conditions is an extremely necessary tool to the assessment of the wave energy, as this is an abundant and clean renewable resource, that is being widely exploited all over the world. A climate analysis is performed in order to evaluate the wave resource available in the coastal area of Azores.

Focused on the assessment of wind energy potential in the Atlantic area, within the ARC-WIND project, 10 areas were selected as possible areas for adaptation and implementation of floating wind energy conversion technology for the Azores region (Diaz & Guedes Soares, 2019). These areas are distributed along the three groups: The Occidental group (Flores and Corvo), the Central group (Terceira, Graciosa, São Jorge, Pico and Faial) and the Oriental group (Santa Maria and São Miguel).

The annual mean and standard deviation are presented in Figure 4 and Figure 5, showing annual average distributions of 2.5m and a standard deviation with a variability of 1m.

As can be seen the Oriental area of Azores is the area with less variability, while the Occidental area the one with more variability, as this is more exposed to the Atlantic storms.

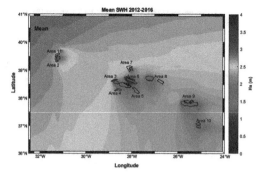

Figure 4. Annual average distribution of the significant wave height (2012-2016).

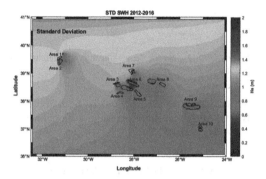

Figure 5. Standard deviation distribution of the significant wave height (2012-2016).

As mentioned in Ponce de Leon & Guedes Soares (2005) and in Rusu et al, (2012), under certain conditions, the Azores Islands may contribute to the dissipation of the spectral wave energy. It is visible a strong sheltering effect to the South/Southeast of the islands, particularly when wave direction is from North/Northwest.

The 95th percentile is evaluated for the tree areas. Figure 6 show that 95th percentile varies between 5-5.5m for the occidental area. In Figure 7 the values vary between 4.5-.5m in the areas that are more exposed to north Atlantic wave conditions (incoming waves are commonly from northwest). In Figure 8 the results show that the 90th percentile varies between 3.5-4.5m

The seasonal distributions of the significant wave height are represented in Figure 9. The winter months (December, January and February) are the most energetic ones, with mean values of 3.5m, against 2.50m during the spring/autumn months and less then 2m in the summer.

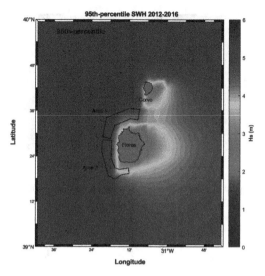

Figure 6. 95th percentile of the significant wave height for the occidental group (2012-2016).

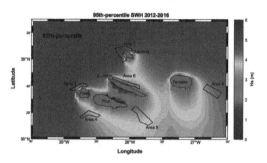

Figure 7. 95th percentile of the significant wave height for the central group (2012-2016).

4.2 *Temporal and seasonal variability*

The variability of the wave resource on a daily, weekly, monthly and seasonal periods is an essential element that will influence the sustainability of any forthcoming energy extraction project. Within the ARCWIND project for instance, it is relevant to understand what the most suitable areas for the implementation of floating wind energy conversion technology are.

To studying the variability of the significant wave height resource in the study area, some coefficients are calculated: the seasonal variability index (SV) and the monthly variability index (MV). They quantify the variability of the wave resource and are given by:

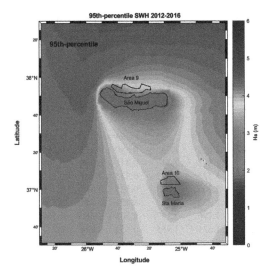

Figure 8. 95th percentile of the significant wave height for the oriental group (2012-2016).

Figure 9. Seasonal distribution of the significant wave height resource (2012-2016).

$$SV = \frac{P_{S1} - P_{S2}}{P_{year}} \qquad (7)$$

$$MV = \frac{P_{M1} - P_{M2}}{P_{year}} \qquad (8)$$

where P_{S1} is the mean significant wave height of the most energetic season (winter), P_{S2} is the least energetic season (summer) and P_{year} is the yearly mean, for the seasonal variability index. And for the monthly variability index, P_{M1} is the mean significant wave height of the most energetic month (January), P_{M2} is the least energetic month (August).

The distribution of wave resource variability can be seen in Figure 10. Small values of SV and MV are

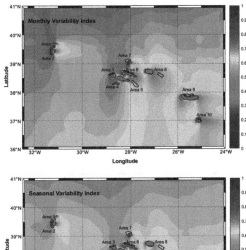

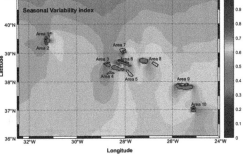

Figure 10. Significant wave height temporal variability indexes: Seasonal variability index (SV), monthly variability index (MV).

indicators of low variability. As can be seen values of SV an MV vary between 0.6 and 0.7.

The coefficient of variation (COV) and the Annual Variability index (AV) are also calculated. The first determines the amount of variability in relation to the mean and is obtained dividing the standard deviation (σ) by the mean (μ). The second quantifies the annual variability of the wave resource. They are given by:

$$COV = \frac{\sigma}{\mu} \qquad (9)$$

$$AV = \frac{P_{A1} - P_{A2}}{P_{year}} \qquad (10)$$

where P_{A1} is the mean significant wave height of the most energetic year, P_{A2} is the least energetic year and P_{year} is the yearly mean.

Figure 11 presents the annual variability and the coefficient of variation of the significant wave height. As can be seen the annual variability is generally low, with values less than 0.1. Low values of the Coefficient of Variation are desirable since it would mean that each year has the similar amount of Hs.

To have a better perspective of the sea states conditions 10 points were selected one in each area. The selected points are found between 80 and

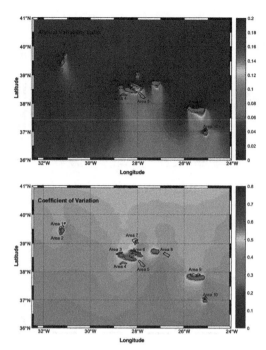

Figure 11. Annual Variability Index (on top) and Coefficient of Variation (on the bottom).

1200 m water depth and their locations are described in Table 3.

The significant wave height is estimated for each point, the total period and winter period is evaluated, and the variability of the significant wave height is presented for each of the selected point. The results are presented in Table 4. The results show that the total mean significant wave height vary between 1.52m and 2.3m and in the wintertime values range between 1.82m and 3.21m for P6 and P2, respectively. The distribution of the coefficient of variability varies between 0.44 for P5 and 0.55 for P2.

Table 3. Locations of the 10 points selected.

Point	Latitude	Longitude	Depth (m)
P1	39.57° N	31.20° W	-175
P2	39.40° N	31.30° W	-80
P3	38.65° N	28.80° W	-695
P4	38.32° N	28.60° W	-755
P5	38.30° N	27.80° W	-460
P6	38.70° N	28.00° W	-790
P7	39.00° N	28.10° W	-186
P8	38.60° N	26.70° W	-540
P9	37.90° N	25.50° W	-1200
P10	37.10° N	25.08° W	-600

Table 4. Significant wave height variability of the selected points.

	Total	Winter				
Point	Hs (m)	Hs (m)	COV	AV	MV	SV
P1	2.150	2.832	0.507	0.014	0.708	0.666
P2	2.309	3.209	0.549	-0.006	0.821	0.737
P3	2.023	2.590	0.524	-0.014	0.660	0.645
P4	2.057	2.788	0.480	0.075	0.705	0.673
P5	1.888	2.415	0.440	0.088	0.565	0.585
P6	1.521	1.822	0.535	-0.002	0.522	0.561
P7	2.205	3.033	0.525	0.017	0.785	0.739
P8	2.223	2.788	0.454	0.041	0.556	0.603
P9	1.796	2.197	0.505	-0.017	0.560	0.594
P10	1.631	1.965	0.452	0.024	0.547	0.521

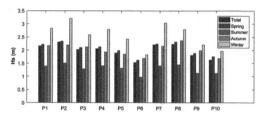

Figure 12. – Mean seasonal significant wave height at the selected points, for the 5-year period.

Finally, Figure 12 shows the mean seasonal significant wave height at the selected points. The results demonstrate that, generally, all points have mean values around 2m all year. Points P6, P9 and P10 are the last energetic points contrasting with P1, P2 and P7, which are the most energetic ones, as they are more exposed to the Atlantic storms.

5 CONCLUSIONS

Given the increasing necessity for clean renewable energies, a good characterization of the wave resources is essential. This study aims to provide a general description of the resources available by characterizing the wave climate around the Azores Islands.

The validation of the hindcast system is presented, showing a good correlation between measurements and simulations.

The geographical distributions of the significant wave height show the high values in the north coast of the Occidental Group of islands (Corvo and Flores islands) in contrast with the low values of the Oriental Group of islands (Santa Maria and São Miguel). The seasonal distribution of the Significant wave height shows available resource ranges between less then 2m in the summer up to 3.5m in the winter.

The seasonal and temporal variability indexes of the significant wave height show the low variability in the eastern coast of the islands, against the high values in the north coasts, as they are more exposed to the direct swell from the North Atlantic Ocean. Also, as pointed out before, low levels of variability are desirable, as this indicates that the amount of wave resource would remain the same each year.

Ten points were selected demonstrating the variability inside their respective areas. P1, P2 and P7, which are the most energetic ones, as they are more exposed to the Atlantic storms.

Although the results obtain in the present work can be considered acceptable, an extended hindcast should offer a better perception of the available resource. Moreover, even though GEBCO data is good for the offshore region, it is not so accurate near the coast suggesting that better bathymetry close to the coastal should increase the results locally.

ACKNOWLEDGEMENTS

This work was conducted within the ARCWIND project–Adaptation and implementation of floating wind energy conversion technology for the Atlantic region (EAPA 344/2016), which is co-financed by the European Regional Development Fund through the Interreg Atlantic Area Programme. The authors are grateful to E.B. Azevedo and F. V. Reis for having made available the wave buoy data collected since 2005 by the project CLIMAAT (MAC/2.3/A3) and now obtained and processed under the framework of the ECOMARPORT project (MAC/1.1B/081). This work was performed within the scope of the Strategic Research Plan of the Centre for Marine Technology and Ocean Engineering (CENTEC), which is financed by the Portuguese Foundation for Science and Technology (Fundação para a Ciência e Tecnologia - FCT) under contract UIDB/UIDP/00134/2020.

REFERENCES

Ardhuin, F., Accensi, M. 2013. IOWAGA - WWIII - HINDCAST - North East Atlantic grid – CFSR. https://sextant.ifremer.fr/record/f7458830-9357-4b81-8181-5492544d0a97/

Azevedo, E. B & Gonçalo, V. 2005. - O Projecto CLIMAAT e o seu Contributo para a Monotorização e Caracterização da Agitação Marítima no Arquipélago dos Açores - 4ªs Jornadas Portuguesas de Engenharia Costeira e Portuária, Angra do Heroísmo, 20 e 21 de Outubro de 2005.

Barrerra, C., Rueda, M. J., Llin ás, O., Azevedo, E. B., & Gelado, M. D. (2008). Real-time monitoring network in the Macaronesian region as a contribution to the Coastal Ocean Observations Panel (COOP). Journal of Operational Oceanography, 1(1), 59–69.

Bento, A. R., Martinho, P. & Guedes Soares 2018. Wave energy assessment for Northern Spain from a 33-year hindcast. Renewable Energy, 127, 457–322–333.

Booij N., Ris R.C. & Holthuijsen L.H. 1999. A third-generation wave model for coastal regions, 1, Model description and validation. Journal of Geophysical Research. 104: 7649–7666.

Gonçalves, M., Rusu, E., & Guedes Soares, C., 2015, Evaluation of Two Spectral Wave Models in Coastal Areas, Journal of Coastal Research, Volume 31, Issue 2: 326–339

Gonçalves, M.; Martinho, P. & Guedes Soares, C. 2018. A 33-year hindcast on wave energy assessment in the western French coast. Energy. 165, 790–801.

Gonçalves, M.; Martinho, P. & Guedes Soares, C. 2020. Wave energy assessment based on a 33-year hindcast for the Canary Islands Renewable Energy 152 (2020) 259–269.

Guedes Soares, C. 2008. Hindcast of Dynamic Processes of the Ocean and Coastal Areas of Europe. Coastal Engineering, 55(11): 825–826.

Guedes Soares, C., Rusu, L. & Pilar, P, 2004, "Wave Hindcast along the Portuguese Continental Coast", Maritime Activi-ties and Engineering (in Portuguese), Guedes Soares, C. and Gonçalves de Brito, V. (Eds.), Edições Salamandra, Lda., 2004, Lisbon, pp. 73–82.

Guedes Soares, C.; Weisse, R.; Alvarez, E., and Carretero, J. C. 2002. A 40 Years Hindcast of Wind, Sea Level and Waves in European Waters. Proc. of the 21st Int. Conf. on Offshore Mechanics and Arctic Engineering (OMAE 2002); Oslo, Norway. ASME paper OMAE2002–28604 .

Guedes Soares, C., Bento, A.R., Gonçalves, M., Silva, D. & Martinho, P. 2014a "Assessment of mean wave energy potential for the Atlantic European coast using numerical models". Developments in Maritime Transportation and Exploitation of Sea Resources. Guedes Soares, C. & Lopez Pena F., (Eds.). Francis & Taylor Group London, UK; 2014; pp. 1003–1012.

Guedes Soares, C., Bento, A.R., Gonçalves, M., Silva, D. & Martinho, P. 2014b. Numerical evaluation of the wave energy resource along the Atlantic European coast. Computers & Geosciences 71: 37–49

Hasselmann K, Barnett TP, Bouws E, Carlson H, Cartwright DE, Enke K, et al. 1973. Measurements of wind-wave growth and swell decay during the Joint North Sea Wave Project (JONSWAP). Deutsche Hydrographische Zeitscheift;. p. 95. A8(12).

Holthuijsen LH, Herman A. & Booij N. 2003 Phase-coupled refraction and diffraction for spectral wave models. Coast Eng, 49(4):291–305

Diaz, H., Guedes Soares, C. 2019. An integrated GIS approach for site selection of floating offshore wind farms in the Atlantic Continental European coastline. Submitted to publication

Rusu, E. Pilar, P., & Guedes Soares C., 2008a. Evaluation of the wave conditions in Madeira Archipelago with spectral models. Ocean Engineering, 35(13), 1357–1371.

Rusu, E., Gonçalves, M. & Guedes Soares, C. 2011, Evaluation of the Wave Transformation in an Open Bay with Two Spectral Models, Ocean Engineering, Vol. 38(16), pp. 1763–1781

Rusu, L., Pilar, P., & Guedes Soares, C., 2008b. Hindcast of the wave conditions along the west Iberian coast. Coastal Eng. 55(11), 906–919.

Rusu, L. & Guedes Soares, C., 2012a. Wave energy assessments in the Azores islands. Renewable Energy, 45(9), 183–196.

Rusu, L., Pilar, P. & Guedes Soares, C. 2012b, "Modelling the Wave Conditions in the Archipelago of Azores", Maritime Engineering and Technology, Guedes Soares, et al. (Eds), Taylor & Francis Group, London, UK, pp. 533–538

Rusu, L. & Guedes Soares, C. 2013. Evaluation of a high-resolution wave forecasting system for the approaches to ports. Ocean Engineering, 58: 224–238.

Ponce de León S., Guedes Soares, C. 2005. On the sheltering effect of islands in ocean wave modelling. Journal of Geophysical Research, 110 (2005), p. C09020

Silva, D.; Bento, A. R.; Martinho, P., and Guedes Soares, C. 2015. High resolution local wave energy modelling for the Iberian Peninsula. Energy. 91 1099–1112 and 94: 857–858.

Silva, D., Martinho, P. & Guedes Soares, C. 2018. Wave energy distribution along the Portuguese continental coast based on a thirty-three years hindcast. Renewable Energy. 127, 1064–1075.

Tolman H. 1991. A third-generation model for wind waves on slowly varying, unsteady, and inhomogeneous depths and currents. Journal of Physical Oceanography; 21 (6):782e97.

WAMDI Group: Hasselmann, S., Hasselmann, K., Bauer, E., Janssen, P.A.E.M., Komen, G. J., Bertotti, L., Lionello, P., Guillaume, A., Cardone, V.C., Greenwood, J. A., Reistad, M., Zambresky, L., and Ewing, J. A., 1988. The WAM Model - A Third Generation Ocean Wave Prediction Model, J. Phys. Ocean., vol. 18, 177 p.

Hydrodynamic performance of semi-submersible FOWT combined with point-absorber WECs

T.S. Hallak
Centre for Marine Technology and Ocean Engineering (CENTEC), Instituto Superior Técnico, Universidade de Lisboa, Lisbon, Portugal

D. Karmakar
Department of Applied Mechanics and Hydraulics, National Institute of Technology Karnataka, Surathkal, Mangalore, India

C. Guedes Soares
Centre for Marine Technology and Ocean Engineering (CENTEC), Instituto Superior Técnico, Universidade de Lisboa, Lisbon, Portugal

ABSTRACT: The numerical investigation is carried out for a hybrid platform for wind and wave energy conversion in the offshore. The analyses are for the DeepCWind semi-submersible as main hull of the Floating Offshore Wind Turbine having 20.0 meters draft, whereas the Wave Energy Converters are conical point-absorbers of diameter within 5.0 – 10.0 meters. The investigation is focused towards the linear hydrodynamic interaction of the wind platform and wave energy devices; the turbine is considered to be non-operative. The wave diffraction/radiation approach is considered for the evaluation of single- and multi-body hydrodynamic coefficients. The numerical investigation is performed to determine devices' Response Amplitude Operators and response spectra. Performance parameters are also evaluated, such as wave converters' capture width, absorbed power and array's q-factor. The study presents a preliminary investigation on the hydrodynamic performance of the hybrid platform, it currently oversimplifies the mechanical coupling created by the Power Take-Offs and connection constraints.

1 INTRODUCTION

The Kyoto Protocol and the Paris Agreement are committed to reduce Earth's greenhouse gas emission. The commitment to reduce the climate change effects and global warming has led to the use of more renewable sources of energy. In the offshore region, the research and development is devoted to the use of offshore renewable energies (wind, waves, tidal).

The most mature sector of those is the wind technology, whereas fixed structures for offshore wind energy already constitute considerable installed power capacity in Denmark, Germany and UK. The recent trend is towards bigger turbines in order to increase efficiency (Leimeister et al. 2016), and the deployment of floating, instead of fixed structures (Xiaojing et al. 2012). Hywind Scotland and WindFloat Portugal are the projects that achieved the milestone of providing several MW of floating offshore wind, in the years of 2017 and 2019, respectively.

With respect to Wave Energy Converters (WECs), some prototypes had already been deployed such as wave flaps (e.g. WaveRoller), overtopping devices (e.g. WaveDragon), attenuators (Pelamis), etc. However, the associated Levelized Cost of Energy (LCoE) is too high and their normal operation is affected by the lack of personnel able to perform the rather expensive maintenance (Rinaldi et al. 2016). In the theoretical domain, the technology for WECs, especially WEC-arrays or active controlled WECs, still present modelling gaps, whereas the response of such devices is highly non-linear in nature.

Recently, some researchers have investigated the use of hybrid wind-wave platforms (Gaspar et al. 2019, Karmakar & Guedes Soares, 2015, Kamarlouei et al. 2019a, Li et al. 2018 & Hallak et al. 2018). Due to the technology gap, WECs are employed to Floating Offshore Wind Turbine (FOWT) structures modifying the main hull. This approach leads to the global decrease on capital and operational expenditures, space saving and reduction of the environmental impact (Karmakar & Guedes Soares 2015). Moreover, point-absorber WECs are identified to be capable of providing extra stability to FOWT structure and reducing the accelerations at the nacelle, and the dimensions of the central hull (Gaspar et al. 2019 & Kamarlouei et al. 2019b).

Such hybrid systems are very complex in nature as they possess many degrees-of-freedom (dof), non-linear geometric constraints, non-linear damping and relevant higher-order effects, which is not fully-encompassed by any available software. Thus, the present study will focus mainly on the linear hydrodynamic interaction between the devices. The mechanical coupling will be considered in a rather simplified manner.

2 METHODOLOGY

In the present study, conical point-absorber WECs are employed around the DeepCWind semi-submersible FOWT at 20.0m draft. The diameter of the WECs is varied within the values 5.0, 7.5 and 10.0m, where the draft equals the radius, and 9 WECs are employed in total considering 3 around each column in concentric configuration (see Figure 1).

The study is focused towards the analysis of linear hydrodynamic interaction of the semi-submersible FOWT and the WECs. The linear diffraction/radiation code Wadam, by DNV-GL's SESAM/HydroD® is used to determine the single- and multi-body hydrodynamic coefficients. Figure 1 presents the multi-body configuration in the case of WECs having 5.0m diameter including FOWT hull's mesh. In a post-processing phase, Response Amplitude Operators (RAOs) are evaluated, also after adding to the linear system a constriction modulus (in order to constrain modes when desired); and a Power Take-Off (PTO) modulus (which accounts for the PTO forces).

Figure 1. DeepCWind semi-submersible FOWT with 5.0m diameter WECs.

The study takes into account two PTO parameters, namely a supplementary mass and a linear damping for each WEC, as in Sinha et al. (2016a,b). The post-processor looks for the best PTO values between an initial set of possible values. This is done for 1) best energy conversion, and 2) best FOWT's pitch dynamics.

The post-processor evaluates performance parameters such as WECs' capture width, absorbed power and WEC array's q-factor; it also outputs the response spectra of the devices for any defined sea state. In this study, the comparison of results for different diameters is performed in order to understand the variations in the hydrodynamic interaction as WEC's dimension reach values closer to FOWT's dimensions.

3 NUMERICAL MODELLING

3.1 *Multi-degrees-of-freedom approach*

In the case of rigid body dynamics, the 6 dof is considered in the hydrodynamic analysis of the wave-structure interaction, but the hybrid systems possess $6N - M$ dof, where N is the number of bodies, and M the number of constraints. The arm connection and hinge constraints are non-linear in nature, suggested by the fact that the distance between the hinge and WEC's pivot is constant. This is given by

$$\sum_{i=1}^{3} \left(x_i^{WEC} - x_i^{Hinge} \right)^2 = L_{arm}^2 := cte. \quad (1)$$

In case the arms are perfectly rigid, horizontal, and rotating on a single direction at the hinge point (where the axis lay on the horizontal plane), a linear set of constraints may be used as first approximation, which is given by

$$\begin{cases} x_1^{WEC} - x_1^{Hinge} := cte. \\ x_2^{WEC} - x_2^{Hinge} := cte. \\ x_6^{WEC} - x_6^{Hinge} := cte. \end{cases} \quad (2)$$

Thus, WECs and platform share all the horizontal motions (surge, sway and yaw) which holds true only in a global reference frame. It is important to note that, for instance, WEC's yaw in the global reference leads to surge and sway motion in WEC's local reference frame. It is not problematic though, if the hydrodynamic coefficients are evaluated based on the global reference frame. For the numerical application of these constraints, it is decided to keep the dimension of the linear system and input unrealistic stiffness values on the constrained modes (e.g. FOWT surge to WECs surge).

Table 1. Assigned critical damping.

Device	Heave	Roll	Pitch
FOWT	4.5%	2.0%	2.0%
WECs	25%	5.0%	5.0%

3.2 Non-linear damping

The present study considers only linear dynamics. Thus, the non-linear (viscous) damping is accounted simply by assigning the damping ratios for both FOWT and WECs, as detailed in Table 1. FOWT's values are based on the OC4 benchmark studies. The added damping matrix evaluated is frequency independent, in opposition to the added mass and potential damping matrices.

3.3 PTO damping and supplementary mass

In order to account for PTO dynamics in the linear system, a variable supplementary mass is added at WECs' heaving modes. Likewise, a variable PTO linear damping is added, acting at the relative heave between WECs and FOWT. The PTO damping is ultimately responsible for wave energy absorption, so these variables should to be optimized. The values of supplementary mass and PTO damping are considered the same for all 9 WECs and only the best values within a set of tested values is considered in the final analysis.

After varying supplementary mass' (A_{sup}) between 0 and 1.0 WEC's displacement; and PTO damping (B_{PTO}) between 0 and 50% of single-WEC's critical damping, the selection is performed considering 1) the maximization of WEC's absorbed power, and 2) the minimization of FOWT's pitch response energy. The tested values are the twenty equal divisions of the limiting ranges of A_{sup} and B_{PTO}.

That said, WEC's absorbed power is evaluated as

$$f_1(A_{sup}; B_{PTO}) = \sum_{i=1}^{9} \int B_{PTO} (\omega \cdot x_3^{WEC_i}(\omega))^2 d\omega \quad (3)$$

and FOWT's pitch response energy

$$f_2(A_{sup}; B_{PTO}) = \int \frac{\omega^2}{g} x_5^{FOWT}(\omega) \cdot d\omega \quad (4)$$

where $g = 9.81 m/s^2$ is the acceleration due to gravity. Instead of a particular sea state, the functions are evaluated considering unit amplitude waves and the set of frequencies: $\omega_i = [0.15, 0.20, 0.25, \ldots, 1.65]$.

3.4 Performance parameters

First, the study evaluates WEC-array's q-factor, which is a measure of how the array is helping (or worsening) wave absorption. The q-factor equals the ratio between the total absorbed power in multi-body case per single-body cases summed up together (Fitzgerald 2006), and does not depend on the linear PTO damping because in the linear case the absorbed energy is proportional to that value, in opposition to non-linear damping. The results are obtained for 6 dof absorption (unrealistic) and only heave absorption (realistic) in order to elucidate how the wave energy absorption is dependent upon the modes of motion.

Further, the study evaluates the capture width of the WECs considering unitary waves at each frequency and the formulation presented by Gomes (2015).

Finally, for any given sea state, the response spectra of the FOWT and WECs may be obtained, as well as the total wave absorbed power. This calculation may highlight the sea conditions for significant wave energy absorption. At this point, results will be shown for a common sea state.

4 RESULTS AND DISCUSSION

4.1 RAOs for FOWT and WECs

Figures 2 to 6 present the RAOs for FOWT and WECs in different conditions. In all plots, the single-body results are shown for comparison.

Figure 2 shows FOWT's heave RAOs in constrained and unconstrained conditions considering only hydrodynamic coupling (i.e. neglecting PTO forces). Very little deviation in FOWT's heave response is noted when considering or neglecting

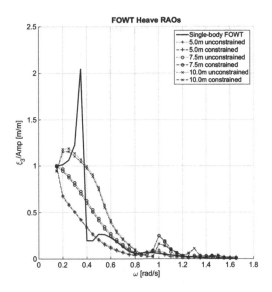

Figure 2. Constrained and unconstrained FOWT's heave RAOs.

such constraints. In the other hand, the effects of WEC's diameter is noted: the higher WECs' diameter, the stronger the interaction and therefore the stronger is FOWT's heave response. However, the peak of the RAO is decreased when considering WECs' coupling effects, and the resonance seem to be mitigated.

Figure 3 presents FOWT's pitch RAOs in constrained and unconstrained conditions considering only hydrodynamic coupling. When comparing with FOWT's heave response, the pitch response is dependent on the constrained/unconstrained conditions and is not really affected by WECs' diameter. This may happen because the WECs are far apart from FOWT's

Centre of Gravity (CoG). Another hypothesis is that coupling effects between surge and pitch are playing an important role, as they may do for semi-submersible FOWTs (Simos et al. 2018), and in the current analysis surge response proved to be highly affected by the motion constraints (see Figure 4).

Figure 4 presents surge RAOs for FOWT and WECs in both constrained and unconstrained conditions, considering only hydrodynamic coupling. The constrained WECs' surge RAOs are usually below the unconstrained ones, whereas WECs surge amplitude lies between 0.5 and 2.0 times the amplitude of the wave. Regarding the platform, the unconstrained FOWT's surge RAO is virtually zero, meaning that unconstrained FOWT does not surge. That happens probably because there is a balance between the different surging coupling forces, whereas the WECs may surge considerably in the same scenario. On the other hand, the constrained FOWT's surge motion is compliant with the WECs' surge, thus, for that case, FOWT and WECs share the same curve in the plot.

Figures 5 and 6 show averaged WECs' heave RAOs for 10.0m WECs, respectively for unconstrained and constrained conditions. Here, the results with optimal PTO are plotted because the PTO parameters are identified as relevant in modifying WEC's response, but not FOWT's. The hydrodynamic coupling is observed to be much stronger than the mechanical coupling. The same trend was observed for 5.0m and 7.5m diameter WECs.

4.2 Performance parameters

Figures 7 to 9 present WEC-array's q-factors for constrained and unconstrained conditions, separately for

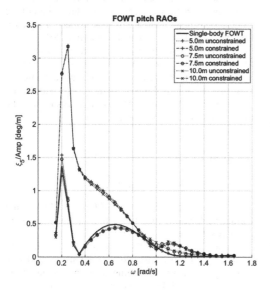

Figure 3. Constrained and unconstrained FOWT's pitch RAOs.

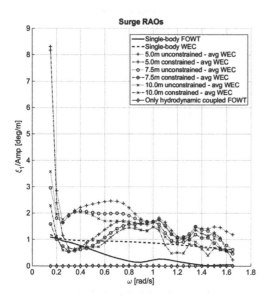

Figure 4. Constrained and unconstrained surge RAOs.

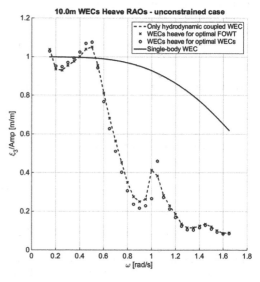

Figure 5. Unconstrained WECs' heave RAOs – 10.0m WECs.

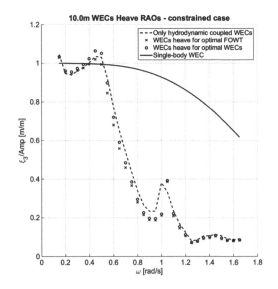

Figure 6. Constrained WECs' heave RAOs – 10.0m WECs.

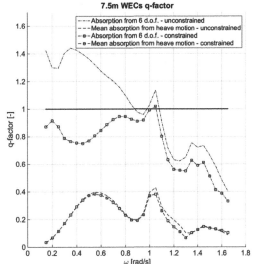

Figure 8. Constrained and unconstrained 7.5 m q-factor.

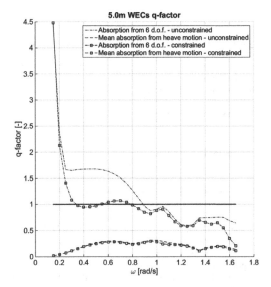

Figure 7. Constrained and unconstrained 5.0m q-factor.

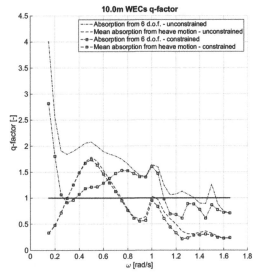

Figure 9. Constrained and unconstrained 10.0m q-factor.

different WECs' diameters. The difference between 6 dof's absorption and 1 dof (only heave) is quite clear. The study shows that the chosen array adds constructive motion interaction between the WEC's but not exactly at the absorption mode (heave), whereas the q-factor is normally below 1.0 for the single mode evaluation. However, for 10.0m WECs within the wave frequency range 0.4 – 0.7 rad/s, there is indeed a strong interaction that intensifies heave motion, which could be well exploited, after all this frequency range corresponds to normal sea conditions in several locations (wave period between 9.0 and 15.0 seconds).

Thus, the hydrodynamic array interaction suggests that the 10.0m diameter WECs are the best option between the diameters considered.

Moreover, very high 6 dof q-factors are noted in the low-frequency range of Figures 7 and 9, which are related to the strong surge motions of the WECs. This is irrelevant for wave energy absorption and the chosen devices (heaving point-absorbers), however, it suggests that surging flaps could be a good option of WECs at the low frequency range for a hybrid concept.

Figures 10 to 12 show the averaged capture width of the WEC devices for the optimal cases. The figures

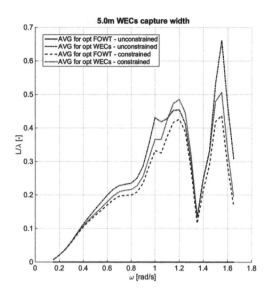

Figure 10. Constrained and unconstrained 5.0m capture width.

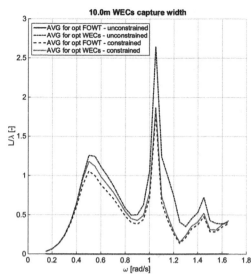

Figure 12. Constrained and unconstrained 10.0m capture width.

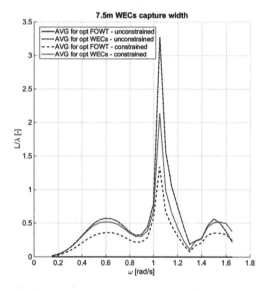

Figure 11. Constrained and unconstrained 7.5m capture width.

Table 2. Optimized PTO parameters for best wave energy conversion.

Optimization scenario 1	Diameter	A_{sup}/M_{wec} [%]	B_{pto}/B_{crit} [%]
Unconstrained	5.0m	100	50
	7.5m	100	50
	10.0m	100	50
Constrained	5.0m	100	50
	7.5m	100	50
	10.0m	100	50

Table 3. Optimized PTO parameters for best FOWT's pitch dynamic response.

Optimization scenario 2	Diameter	A_{sup}/M_{wec} [%]	B_{pto}/B_{crit} [%]
Unconstrained	5.0m	0	0
	7.5m	100	0
	10.0m	0	0
Constrained	5.0m	0	50
	7.5m	0	35
	10.0m	0	50

are presented separately for all diameters in order to compare wave energy absorption as a function of WECs' dimensions. The values of optimized supplementary mass and PTO damping are presented in Tables 2 and 3, respectively for best wave energy conversion and best FOWT's pitch dynamics.

It is interesting to check that 7.5m diameter WECs seem to absorb more energy than 10.0m WECs in the optimal absorption condition. However, the capture width is evaluated considering unit amplitude waves only. Again, usual sea states are characterized by having most of its wave energy between 9.0 and 15 seconds, which is exactly the heap between 0.4 and 0.7 rad/s observed in Figure 12, but not in Figure 11. Thus, the 10.0m diameter WECs actually perform better in such sea states. The capture width heap at this frequency range is related to the constructive heave interactions between WECs (as in Figure 9).

Table 2 shows that the optimal PTO parameters for wave energy conversion are found in the maximum limit of the tested values. Thus, in order to have more wave energy conversion, it is advantageous to increase WEC-PTO's inertia, and employ high damping, such that WECs' heave close to 75% critical damping in the resonance (whereas 25% arise from hydrodynamic damping and 50% from the PTO).

Table 3 shows that the optimal PTO damping for a smoother unconstrained FOWT's pitch response is always zero. Thus, the zero-valued solid line is observed in Figures 10 to 12. In the constrained condition, no supplementary mass should be added, but some damping is advantageous to FOWTs pitch dynamics.

4.3 Response spectra

Figures 13 and 14 present the heave response spectra of both FOWT and WECs (averaged), respectively for the constrained and unconstrained conditions.

Then, Figure 15 presents FOWT's pitch response spectra. All the three plots correspond to the 10.0m diameter WECs' results. The curves were generated for a common sea state, characterized by Pierson-Moskovitz sea spectrum with peak period $T_P = 13.5s$ and significant wave height $H_S = 2.0m$. In Figures 13 and 14, the wave spectrum is plotted, so the curves that nearly match the black solid line correspond to bodies that are riding the wave, which clearly holds true for the coupled WECs, especially near the peak period.

Figure 15 shows that hydrodynamic coupling alone is responsible for an amplification of FOWT's pitch response in the constrained scenario, but the

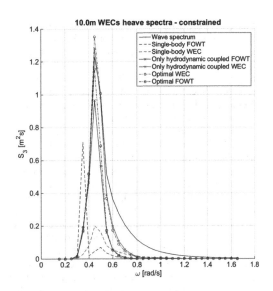

Figure 14. Heave response spectra for constrained condition.

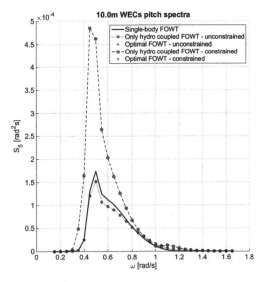

Figure 15. FOWT pitch response spectra for several conditions.

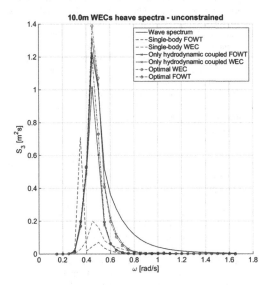

Figure 13. Heave response spectra for unconstrained condition.

opposite happens in the unconstrained scenario. The constriction between horizontal motions seem to generate such amplification, probably due to surge-to-pitch coupling effects, which needs to be well explored.

The effects of wave direction and the consideration of short-crested sea states have not been included in the analyses so far. In the one hand, wave direction affects the hydrodynamic interaction of devices and may lead to higher or lower q-factors, for instance, which could be exploited in order to find the best positioning of the hybrid platform. In the other hand, FOWT's response should also be affected by that and so the trade-offs would need to be balanced. The inclusions of wave direction in the analysis is seen as one of the next steps within the research lines and, as an operative turbine is included in the model, the effects of wind-wave misalignment shall also be analyzed.

For the same sea state considered, i.e. $T_P = 13.5s$ and $H_S = 2.0m$, the total wave absorbed power was evaluated, which was done by summing up the 9 PTOs' averaged absorbed power. It equals 31.9, 92.5 and 199.4 kW for the unconstrained cases of 5.0, 7.5 and 10.0m diameter WECs, respectively. For the constrained cases, the values are about 6 to 8% lower. These values lie within a reasonable and expected range for the kind of WECs employed and, if scaled in terms of size/displacement, the reached values get quite close to the WaveStar prototype. Still, it shows the discrepancy between the possible amounts of energy to be captured between wind and wave energy devices, whereas the single turbine of the platform would have a power capacity of 5.0 MW.

5 CONCLUSIONS

The present study investigates the linear hydrodynamic interaction between DeepCWind semi-submersible FOWT with conical point-absorber WECs of different diameters attached to its columns in concentric configuration by arm-hinge connection. The effects of PTO and mechanical coupling (arms and hinges) are added to the model in a simplified manner.

The main conclusions obtained from the Results section is that multi-body linear hydrodynamic effects alone are responsible for considerable dynamic interaction, especially for the WECs' and FOWT's heave response – usually in the form of motion amplification next to a common sea state peak period (0.5 rad/s). At this point, the 10.0m diameter heaving WECs proved to be the most efficient ones, reaching values of absorbed power close to the WaveStar prototype (scaled). In the other hand, mechanical coupling seems to amplify FOWT's pitch response and thus it deserves more attention, after all the pitching motion might be critical for the wind turbine. Thus, a more realistic PTO model and a constriction modulus should be adopted following the research lines. Indeed, the PTO coupling may be better explored by, e.g. considering different parameters for different WECs, extending the limiting tested values, and devising an exact (or at least linearized from the exact) formulation for the PTO action and reaction forces, which is dependent upon the arm/hinge connection model.

Last but not least, in the present study the turbine was non-operative. Within the research lines, one of the next key steps is to analyze the dynamics of the hybrid system with an operative wind turbine, whereas there are also coupling effects between the aerodynamic and the hydrodynamic models.

ACKNOWLEDGMENTS

The authors acknowledge FCT and DST for India-Portugal Bilateral Scientific Technological Cooperation Project grant no. DST/INT/Portugal/P-13/2017.

REFERENCES

Fitzgerald C. J. (2006). Optimal configurations of arrays of wave-power devices. *Thesis submitted for the Degree of M.Sc.* National University of Ireland, Cork. Department of Applied Mathematics, University College Cork, Ireland. November, 2006.

Gaspar J. F., Hallak T. S. & Guedes Soares C. (2019). Semi-submersible platform concept for a concentric array of Wave Energy Converters. *Advances in Renewable Energies Offshore*, C. Guedes Soares, Ed. London, UK. Taylor & Francis Group, 2016, pp. 307–314.

Gomes R. P. F., Lopes M. F. P., Henriques J. C. C., Gato L. M. C., Falcão A. F. O. (2015). The dynamics and power extraction of bottom-hinged plate wave energy converters in regular and irregular waves. *Ocean Engineering 96*, 2015, pp. 86–99.

Hallak T. S., Gaspar J. F., Kamarlouei M., Calvário M., Thiebaut F. & Guedes Soares C. (2018). Numerical and experimental analysis of a hybrid wind-wave offshore floating platform's hull. *Proceedings of the ASME2018 37th International Conference in Ocean, Offshore and Arctic Engineering*, OMAE2018–78744.

Kamarlouei M., Gaspar J. F., Calvário M., Hallak T. S., Guedes Soares C., Mendes M. J. G. C. & Thiebaut F. (2019a). Prototyping and wave tank testing of a floating platform with point-absorbers. *Advances in Renewable Energies Offshore*, C. Guedes Soares, Ed. London, UK. Taylor & Francis Group, 2019, pp. 421–428.

Kamarlouei M., Gaspar J. F., Calvário M., Hallak T. S., Mendes M. J. G. C., Thiebaut F. & Guedes Soares C. (2019b). On the experimental study of a concentric wave energy array adapted to an offshore floating platform. *Proceedings of the 13th European Wave and Tidal Energy Conference* (EWTEC2019).

Karmakar D. & Guedes Soares C. (2015). Review of the present concepts of multi-use offshore platforms. *Renewable Energies Offshore*, C. Guedes Soares, Ed. London, UK. Taylor & Francis Group, 2016, pp. 867–875.

Leimeister M., Bachynski E. E., Muskulus M. & Thomas P. (2016). Rational upscaling of a semi-submersible floating platform supporting a wind turbine. *Energy Procedia 94*, pp. 434–442.

Li L., Gao Y., Yuan Z., Day S. & Hu Z. (2018). Dynamic Response and power production of a floating integrated wind, wave and tidal energy system. *Renewable Energy 116*, 2018, pp. 412–422.

Rinaldi G., Thies P. R., Walker R. & Johanning L. (2016). On the analysis of a wave energy farm with focus on maintenance operations. *Journal of Marine Sciences Engineering 4*,51.

Simos A. N., do Carmo L. H. S. & Camargo E. C. (2018). On the use of white-noise approximation for modelling the slow-drifts of an FOWT: An example using FAST. *ASME 37th OMAE International Conference on Ocean Offshore and Arctic Engineering*, OMAE2018–77222.

Sinha A., Karmakar D. & Guedes Soares C. (2016a). Performance of optimally tuned arrays of heaving point-absorbers. *Renewable Energy 92*, 2016, pp. 517–531.

Sinha A., Karmakar D. & Guedes Soares C. (2016b). Hydrodynamic performance of concentric arrays of point-absorbers. *The International Journal of Ocean and Climate Systems, 7(3)*, pp. 88–94.

Xiaojing S., Huang D. & Wu G. (2012). The current state of offshore wind energy technology development. *Energy 41*, pp. 298–312.

Numerical and experimental analyses of a conical point-absorber moving around a hinge

T.S. Hallak, J.F. Gaspar, M. Kamarlouei & C. Guedes Soares
Centre for Marine Technology and Ocean Engineering (CENTEC), Instituto Superior Técnico, Universidade de Lisboa, Lisbon, Portugal

ABSTRACT: This paper presents numerical and experimental analyses regarding a conical point-absorber wave energy converter set free to move around a hinge and connected to it through a rigid arm. The tests performed with scale model in wave basin were free decay, regular and irregular wave tests. A numerical model was developed in order to obtain the Response Amplitude Operators and the response spectra of the wave energy converter. A numerical-experimental comparison is performed and the influence of rotational dampers on the motions of the wave energy converter is investigated. Performance parameters such as capture width and absorbed power are also evaluated. For the analyses, the 6 degrees-of-freedom hydrodynamic coefficients of the floating body are converted to a single generalized degree-of-freedom, namely the rotation around the hinge, and the derivation of this transformation is presented in this paper, as it will be an important formulation following research.

1 INTRODUCTION

In several parts of the globe, and especially within the European Union (EU), the concern of governments and organizations on the behalf of the environment had definitely increased in the last decades. For instance, the strategic plan for energy generation and distribution within the EU is clearly devoted towards a higher power capacity relying on green energy resources (European Commission, 2019). Moreover, the United Nations (UN) is devoted to achieve this globally by the next decades while sustainably using the various sea resources, as stated in the General Assembly Resolution (2015). In the Ocean Engineering field, that may be translated to a general trend for Research & Development (R&D) on Offshore Renewable Energies (ORE), such as wind, waves and tidal.

In the case of wave energy, the ocean provides vast amounts of it, normally depending on location and season. Extracting this energy is technically and economically challenging because of the slow, multidirectional and irregular motions of the particles and bodies (Hansen et al. 2013). Technology for such energy conversion devices, namely the Wave Energy Converters (WECs), is in general located at Technology Readiness Level (TRL) 7, whereas no device delivers energy out of the prototype sphere, but some does, or did, as real scale prototypes (e.g. WaveDragon, WaveRoller and Wavestar, to cite a few in various configurations). Other concepts are located at inferior TRL, e.g. the floating Oscillating Water Columns (floating OWCs), which are at most TRL 6. For the specific case of heaving point-absorbers, as the one considered in this paper, TRL is also 7, whereas projects such as Wavestar (Denmark), and Usina de Ondas (Brazil) operated at this level.

Unfortunately, the associated Levelized Cost of Energy (LCoE) for such devices is too high (Castro-Santos et al. 2018); and their normal operation is affected by the lack of personnel able to perform the rather expensive maintenance (Xiaojing et al. 2012; Santos et al. 2018). However, combining wave energy and wind energy may offer better prospects (Castro-Santos et al. 2016).

In the theoretical sphere, the technology for WECs, especially WEC-arrays or controlled WECs, still present modelling gaps, whereas the response of such devices is highly non-linear in nature. The present point absorber concept is usually seen in the WEC-arrays similar to Wavestar. The present work has its origins in the development of an hydraulic power take off system to operate with the point absorber (Gaspar et al. 2016). For the installation of the point absorber, studies have been done on the optimization of the floater shape and array layouts (Sinha et al. 2016) while they have a good potential to be adapted to other offshore renewable energy platforms (Hallak et al. 2018, Gaspar et al. 2019, Kamarlouei et al. 2020).

In the present study, the experimental results from a test campaign accomplished with scale model conical point-absorber will be shown. Then, results will be compared with frequency domain numerical model results. The aim of the study is to develop and calibrate the WEC model to investigate, e.g. the

DOI: 10.1201/9781003216599-62

employment of several WECs in a WEC-array; or the coupling between WECs and other energy device, such as, for instance, a Floating Offshore Wind Turbine (FOWT) in order to compose a hybrid wind-wave platform. Some results with hypothetical parameters will also be shown in order to elucidate the dependency of the results on such parameters.

2 METHODOLOGY

The scale model WEC (1:27 scale) in view is a conical point-absorber of diameter 18.5cm (5.0m diameter in real scale), with 90° of opening angle (therefore the draft equals the radius). The WEC is connected to a hinge by a means of a rigid arm of length 45.5cm, and initial angle from the horizontal plane of 20° (see Figure 1). Both arm and hinge were, at all times, dry. The initial draft of the body was 7.0cm, and the initial distance between waterline and deck, 5.0cm.

Water depth at the wave basin was 1.1m. In most of the wave cases, there was considerable interaction between bottom and water waves (shallow water condition).

The WEC works as a "heaving" point-absorber device, even though the actual mode from which energy is obtained is the rotation around the hinge (uniaxial). Moreover, the pivot connecting the WEC with the arm is rigid, thus, the system consists on a single-degree-of-freedom mechanical system.

That said, the study is focused towards the linear hydrodynamic interaction between waves (regular and irregular) and the device. Thus, in the one hand, linear diffraction/radiation code Wadam, by DNV-GL's SESAM/HydroD® was used when obtaining the hydrodynamic coefficients. In the other hand, a post-processor was coded in Matlab®, which evaluates the Response Amplitude Operators (RAOs) of the device, and accounts for the hinged-arm constraints, transforming the usual 6 degrees-of-freedom (dof) coefficients to a single-mode coefficient (see Section 3 for the derivation of the transform).

Because the mechanical system may be employed to another structure (e.g. a fixed one as part of a WEC-array; or to another floating ORE structure, in order to constitute a hybrid energy system), this single mode may be seen as a generalized mode of motion.

The experimental tests performed were free decay, regular and irregular wave tests. All tests were repeated considering a rotational damper at the hinge with nominal value $B_{PTO} = 0.50$ Nms (1381 kNms in real scale), which has been calibrated before the tests.

In the one hand, time-series of free decay tests were not reproduced numerically, however, the results obtained from these tests are very important in order to check the eigen period and the damping characteristics of the system. Indeed, the empirical value of critical damping was used for the calibration of the numerical damping matrix. In the other hand, response to regular waves may be compared based on the RAOs; and response to irregular waves may be compared based on the response spectra, which the developed post-processor generates for any a-priori given a sea state.

Table 1 summarizes the wave data generated throughout the tests. The wave parameters of conditions RW 12 and IW 6 are close to the physical limits of the basin, especially in terms of wave period/peak period. It was not possible, even though it was desired, to increase such values.

Then, the numerical simulations were repeated with a hypothetical rotational damping parameter $B_{PTO} = 6.0$ Nms, and the same irregular wave conditions of Table 1. This was done in order to show that the same system could extract much more wave energy, because the damper used in the experiments was considerably weak. However, as explained in the results section, the "actual" damping value was higher than the nominal

Table 1. Regular and irregular wave data – Mode scale.

Regular wave condition	Wave period [s]	Wave height [cm]
RW 1	0.5	2.0
RW 2	0.8	2.0
RW 3	1.1	2.0
RW 4	1.4	2.0
RW 5	1.7	2.0
RW 6	2.0	2.0
RW 7	2.3	2.0
RW 8	2.6	2.0
RW 9	2.9	2.0
RW 10	3.2	2.0
RW 11	3.5	2.0
RW 12	3.8	2.0

Irregular wave condition	Peak period [s]	Sig. wave height [cm]	γ-parameter [-]
IW 1	1.27	6.25	1
IW 2	1.39	7.39	1
IW 3	1.49	8.44	1
IW 4	1.60	9.65	1
IW 5	1.70	10.8	1
IW 6 (storm)	1.70	14.0	3.3

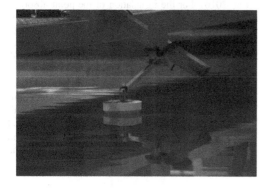

Figure 1. Dry hinged-arm connection and WEC in view.

value of the item, most likely due to manufacturing/ testing issues, for it is very hard to control the damping moment of the device.

Lastly, in the results section (Section 4), some results will also be shown in real scale in order to elucidate the magnitude of the values in a real scenario.

3 SINGLE-MODE MODELLING

3.1 *Multi-degrees-of-freedom to single-degree-of-freedom approach*

In opposition to the 6 dof rigid-body dynamics, the mechanical system possesses a single-dof, namely the rotation around the hinge, which may be described by the trajectory of angle ψ (see Figure 2). Attention must be paid, for ψ is not the angle between arm and horizontal plane, the moment lever is actually the line connecting the hinge and WEC's Centre of Gravity (CoG).

Thus, for the problem in hand, a total of 5 constraints are present, and they are all located at the hinge point. For the numerical application of these constraints, sometimes it is possible to consider models that fully accounts for the dynamics and thus evaluate not only the response of the modes of motion, but also the constraining forces.

Because the system is symmetric and only head waves were considered (i.e. propagation line coincided with arm direction), the formulation derived here is 2-dimensional, and it requires only 2 vertical motion constraints. Likewise, it may offer only the vertical reaction forces at the hinge point. It is still perfectly correct within a linear dynamics framework.

3.2 *Derivation of the single-mode formulation*

In the frequency domain, the hydrodynamics problem of wave diffraction/radiation on a free floating rigid body may be written in the algebraic form as:

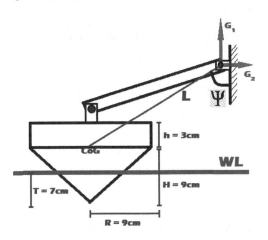

Figure 2. Schematic drawing of the WEC and arm-connection with dimensions specified.

$$[M + M_A(\omega)]\{\ddot{x}(t)\} + [B_{add} + B(\omega)]\{\dot{x}(t)\} + [C_{hyd}]\{x(t)\} = \{f(\omega;t)\} \quad (1)$$

where M is body inertia matrix; $M_A(\omega)$ is the frequency dependent hydrodynamic added mass; $B(\omega)$ is the frequency dependent hydrodynamic damping; B_{add} is the frequency independent additional damping matrix; C_{hyd} is the hydrostatic restoring matrix; x represents body motion; and $f(\omega)$ the wave excitation force.

The reference frame is chosen to be centered at the CoG. This is not simply a reference for the motions, also the hydrodynamic coefficients must be evaluated at this reference in order to have a coherent set of equations.

Now, because at a particular wave frequency ω the excitation force components have the complex form:

$$f_j(\omega;t) = F_j(\omega) \cdot e^{i(\omega t + \mathcal{X}_j)} = \\ F_j(\omega)\cos(\omega t + \mathcal{X}_j) + i \cdot F_j(\omega)\sin(\omega t + \mathcal{X}_j) \quad (2)$$

the solution to this linear system is known to be:

$$x_j(t) = X_j \cdot e^{i(\omega t + \varphi_j)} = X_j\cos(\omega t + \varphi_j) \\ + i \cdot X_j \sin(\omega t + \varphi_j) \quad (3)$$

where $\mathcal{X}_j$ and φ_j are, respectively, the phases between excitation force at mode j and wave crest; and motion of mode j and wave crest. Thus,

$$(-\omega^2[M + M_A(\omega)] + i \cdot \omega[B_{add} + B(\omega)] \\ + [C_{hyd}]) \{X \cdot e^{i(\omega t + \varphi_j)}\} = \{F(\omega) \cdot e^{i(\omega t + \mathcal{X}_j)}\} \quad (4)$$

This is a valid formulation for unconstrained 2- and 3-dimensional problems. If linear constraints are present, it is then required to add the constraining forces into the formulation. For the 2-dimensional problem in hand, the constraints may indeed be linearized if the angle displacement $\Delta\psi = \psi(t) - \psi_0$ is always small:

$$\begin{cases} x_1 = \Delta\psi \cdot L \cos\psi_0 \\ x_2 = \Delta\psi \cdot L \sin\psi_0 \\ x_3 = \Delta\psi \end{cases} \quad (5)$$

where L is the distance between the hinge and CoG. The constraining forces read:

$$\begin{cases} f_1 = F_1(\omega) \cdot e^{i(\omega t + \chi_1)} + G_1 \\ f_3 = F_3(\omega) \cdot e^{i(\omega t + \chi_3)} + G_3 \\ f_5 = F_5(\omega) \cdot e^{i(\omega t + \chi_5)} + G_5 \end{cases} \quad (6)$$

where suffixes 1, 3 and 5 correspond, respectively, to the modes of surge, heave and pitch. Clearly, the hinge offers no resistance to the rotational mode, however, there is a constraining force acting at the pitch mode (G_5) because the reference point is WEC's CoG, and not the hinge point.

The pitch moment due to the constraining forces read:

$$G_5 = G_1 \cdot L \cos \psi_0 - G_3 \cdot L \sin \psi_0 \quad (7)$$

Thus, the variables of the 3 × 3 linear system are not anymore the 3 modes of motion, but ψ, G_1 and G_2.

Due to linearity, it is straightforward to substitute Eq.s (5), (6) and (7) into the linear system (1), isolate G_1 and G_3 in the first two rows and then substitute them back in the third row. In the end, a form for ψ motion is achieved:

$$[M_\psi + M_{A_\psi}(\omega)]\{\ddot{\psi}(t)\} + [B_{add_\psi} + B_\psi(\omega)]\{\dot{\psi}(t)\} + [C_\psi]\{\psi(t)\} = \{f_\psi(\omega;t)\} \quad (8)$$

where:

$$f_\psi(\omega;t) = F_5(\omega) \cdot e^{i(\omega t + \chi_5)} - L \cos \psi_0 F_1(\omega) \cdot e^{i(\omega t + \chi_1)} + L \sin \psi_0 F_3(\omega) \cdot e^{i(\omega t + \chi_3)} \quad (9)$$

$$M_\psi = M_{WEC} R_{gyr}^2 + M_{WEC} L^2 \quad (10)$$

$$M_{A_\psi}(\omega) = -M_{A_{11}} L^2 \cos^2 \psi_0 - M_{A_{13}} L^2 \cos \psi_0 \sin \psi_0 - M_{A_{15}} L \cos \psi_0 + M_{A_{31}} L^2 \cos \psi_0 \sin \psi_0 + M_{A_{33}} L^2 \sin^2 \psi_0 + M_{A_{35}} L \sin \psi_0 + M_{A_{51}} L \cos \psi_0 + M_{A_{53}} L \sin \psi_0 + M_{A_{55}} \quad (11)$$

and $B_\psi(\omega)$, B_{add_ψ} and C_ψ have equivalent forms of Eq. (11), being only required to change $M_{A_{ij}}$ by, respectively, B_{ij}, $B_{add_{ij}}$ and C_{ij}.

In the previous equations, M_{WEC} is WEC's displacement; and R_{gyr} is WEC's pitch radius of gyration (CoG based).

Attention must be paid to the mass model, whereas Eq. (10) is clearly a form of writing the parallel axes theorem. Equation 10 shows that body inertia is being transformed from a CoG- to a hinge-centered value, which is true only under the condition that the weight of the arm may be neglected. Reasonably enough, the arm is always dry, so it is actually straightforward to add an inertial term relative to arm's weight as well, all other things being equal. Also very important, the signs that appear in Eq.s 9 and 11 depend on the signs of Eq. 7, which would change if, for instance, the arm was the mirrored picture of Figure 2. The dynamics of the mirrored system is not expected to be similar to the system analyzed in the present study.

With the formulation devised in this sub-section, it is possible to use CoG-centered hydrodynamic coefficients in order to obtain the solution on the generalized mode ψ. It is also easy, for instance, to obtain the heaving trajectory of the WEC in a local reference frame, simply by using Eq. (5) and transform the results back to the usual modes.

3.3 Non-linear damping

The present study considers only linear dynamics. Thus, non-linear damping is accounted for in a linearized way. This is done by assigning critical damping values for the WEC when running it on the software. The values are detailed in Table 2. The added damping matrix evaluated by the software is a constant matrix, i.e. it does not depend on frequency as the radiation damping and the added mass do; it is still contemplated within the formulation of last subsection.

After solving the linear system, it is possible to estimate the critical damping at variable ψ. The final value will be presented at Section 4.

3.4 PTO damping and capture width

The capture width is one of the most relevant performance parameters of WECs and equals the ratio between absorbed power and wave power density. Because planar waves are supposed, the capture width may achieve values higher than 1, meaning that the WEC absorbs more energy than what is contained in a wavelength of sea (in the direction orthogonal to the wave propagation).

The formulation used when evaluating the capture width L_w is the same as presented by Gomes et al. (2015). The capture width is defined as:

$$L_w(\omega) = P(\omega)/P_w(\omega) \quad (12)$$

Table 2. Assigned critical damping.

Device	Heave	Roll	Pitch
WECs	25%	5%	5%

where the time-averaged absorbed power through the PTO is:

$$P(\omega) = 0.5 \cdot B_{PTO}(\omega|\psi|)^2 \quad (13)$$

and the time-averaged wave energy flux is:

$$P_w(\omega) = \frac{\rho g \omega A_w^2}{4k}\left(1 + \frac{2kh}{\sinh(2kh)}\right) \quad (14)$$

where ρ is water density; g is the acceleration due to gravity; k is the wave-number and h is the local water depth.

3.5 Response to regular and irregular waves

Whilst the response to regular waves is obtained by solving the linear system at variable ψ, it is quite straightforward to transform the results back to the heave mode of the WEC. In the results section, both will be presented.

For irregular waves scenarios, a sea spectrum may be inputted in the code, then, the code generates the response spectra of the system at each sea condition. The code may also output the total wave absorbed power for the given sea state.

4 RESULTS

4.1 Numerical and experimental results

Figure 3 shows the heave RAO of the WEC according to the experiments and the simulations. The experimental values were calculated as the averaged half-difference between maxima and minima after stationary regime was achieved. The results compare well in order of magnitude and trend, but three things deserve attention. First, the experimental values are lower than the numerical, even for high periods when the WEC is practically riding the wave, as it could be observed during the test campaign. This is mostly due to non-linearities and shall be explored in the future.

Second, numerical curves are smooth, while the experimental curves present deviations, this is a likely a consequence of non-ideal conditions at the basin and model. Third, the numerical PTO damping seems to be ineffective, in opposition to the experimental, which reduces response by about 10%. This most likely happens because the damper had a strength much higher than the nominal value, or due to other frictions involved when adding the physical element onto the model.

The natural period of the system was estimated at the basin: $T_n = 0.40$s, while the numerically evaluated on is $T_n = 0.45$s, showing a small deviation. The critical damping ratio at variable ψ was also

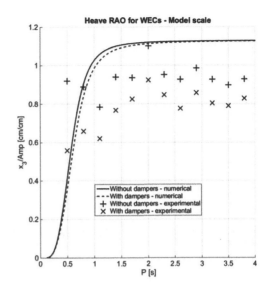

Figure 3. WEC's heave RAO in different damping scenarios.

estimated (numerically): $\zeta_c = 43\%$, which is considerably higher than the one arising only from heave (25%).

Figures 4 – 6 present the heave response spectra in model scale for different damping scenarios.

In Figure 6, the curves represent both damped and no damping conditions, after all the differences found were virtually zero. The trends are very well catch, also as functions of frequency, however, the numerical values are higher than the experimental ones. Again, this must be happening because the "actual" damping is much higher than the nominal value. Also clear from the plots, the difference on the significant amplitude of motion increases as the significant wave height increases, which, again, shall happen due to the non-linearities.

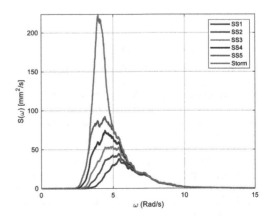

Figure 4. Experimental heave response spectra (no damping).

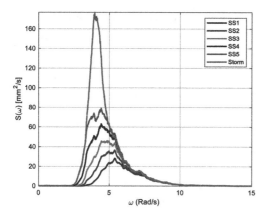

Figure 5. Experimental heave response spectra (with damping).

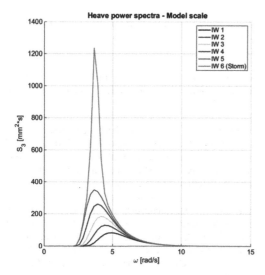

Figure 6. Numerical heave response spectra.

4.2 *Performance in real scale*

Figure 7 presents real scale WEC's RAO at the generalized mode of motion. For long waves and unit amplitude, the angle amplitude at the hinge is 4.9°. It is important to keep this angle small in order to comply with, e.g. maximum stroke requirements.

Then, Figure 8 presents the capture width of the device, which has a peak at $\omega = 1.75$ rad/s. As we shall see in the next sub-section, the small capture width leads to small wave energy absorption, but could be increased if a different B_{PTO} value was chosen (see Table 3).

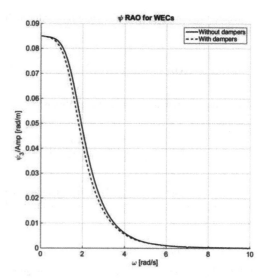

Figure 7. RAO for generalized mode of motion and B_{PTO} = 0.50 Nms.

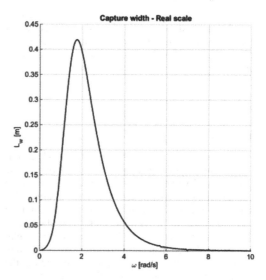

Figure 8. WEC's capture width for B_{PTO} = 0.50 Nms.

Figures 9 and 10 present, respectively, the numerical wave spectra and heave response spectra at real scale. Clearly, for the chosen scenarios, the WEC is mostly riding the wave. Again, the curves for damped and no damping condition practically match at Figure 10.

4.3 *Hypothetical real scale scenario*

Figures 11, 12 and 13 present, respectively, the RAO at generalized coordinate, the capture

Table 3. Absorbed power – Real scale.

B_{PTO}	Wave condition	Absorbed power [kW]
0.50 Nms	IW 1	1.6
	IW 2	2.1
	IW 3	2.6
	IW 4	3.1
	IW 5	3.6
6.0 Nms	IW 1	7.7
	IW 2	10.9
	IW 3	14.2
	IW 4	18.2
	IW 5	22.3

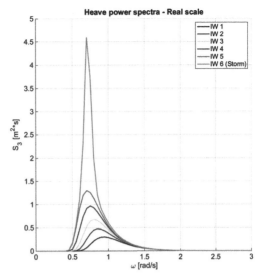

Figure 10. Numerical heave response spectra for B_{PTO} = 0.50 Nms.

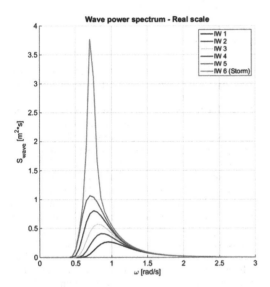

Figure 9. Numerical wave spectra.

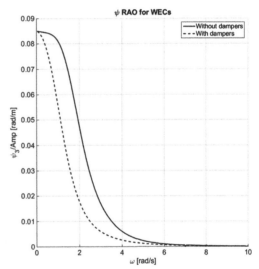

Figure 11. RAO for generalized mode of motion and B_{PTO} = 6.0 Nms.

width, and the heave response spectra for B_{PTO} = 6.0 Nms, all in real scale. Clearly, with the hypothetical damping value, difference is made on the RAO, and especially in the energy performance. This exact B_{PTO} value was verified to be close to the optimal one for energy conversion in a purely numerical analysis, and all other things being equal during the run.

Table 3 presents the values of absorbed power at the PTO (using Eq. 13) for the different damping and wave conditions (IW 6 value is non-representative because the WEC is not operating at storm condition). It is important to note from the table that the results for B_{PTO} = 6.0 Nms reach the order of magnitude of the nominal values for the WaveStar case (Hansen, 2013), i.e. 50.0 kW capacity for 5.28 diameter hemispheric WEC., so in this scenario the WEC is operating as expected.

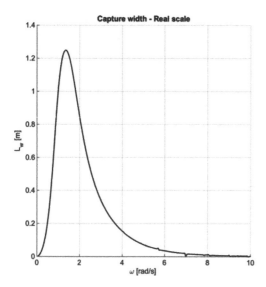

Figure 12. WEC's capture width for B_{PTO} = 6.0 Nms.

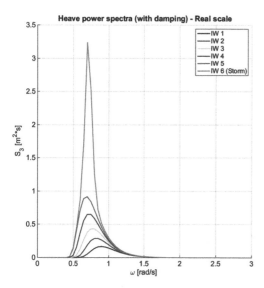

Figure 13. Numerical heave response spectra for B_{PTO} = 6.0 Nms.

5 CONCLUSIONS

The present study investigates the dynamics and performance of a conical point-absorber WEC by comparing experimental with numerical results, also simulating some hypothetical conditions numerically. The numerical model was calibrated, and so the hydrodynamic results compare well.

The system works as a heaving point-absorber, even though the actual mode where energy is being captured is the rotation around the hinge. The experimental damper proved to modify slightly the dynamics, however the nominal value of B_{PTO} is not close to the same numerical prediction if the effects were to be similar. It happens that other frictions might be involved, or that the actual damping during operation was far from the nominal value. Still, the numerical results show that, if considerable amounts of wave energy is to be captured, about twelve times the nominal B_{PTO} should be chosen. Then, the system would capture energy at the same order of magnitude of the WaveStar case, if scaled.

The results presented here are promising, and will be extended within the same research lines, e.g. by coding a non-linear time-domain simulator for the same system. After all, the results show that non-linearities already play an important role on the dynamics of the single-WEC, and will surely get more complex as WEC-arrays or hybrid systems are considered for investigation.

ACKNOWLEDGMENTS

This work was performed within the project "Generic hydraulic power take-off system for wave energy converters" funded by FCT under contract PTDC/EMS-SIS-1145/2014 and the project "Experimental simulation of oil-hydraulic Power Take-Off systems for Wave Energy Converters", funded by FCT under contract PTDC/EME-REN/29044/2017. The testing has received support from MaRINET 2, a Marine Renewable Infrastructure Network for Enhancing Technologies 2 under H2020-EU.1.4.1.2 "Integrating and opening existing national and regional research infrastructures of European Interest", project ID 731084. This work contributes to the Strategic Research Plan of the Centre for Marine Technology and Ocean Engineering (CENTEC), which is financed by the Portuguese Foundation for Science and Technology (Fundação para a Ciência e Tecnologia - FCT) under contract UIDB/UIDP/00134/2020.

REFERENCES

Castro-Santos, L.; Martins, E., and Guedes Soares, C. (2016); Cost assessment methodology for combined wind and wave floating offshore renewable energy systems. *Renewable Energy*. 97:866–880.

Castro-Santos, L.; Silva, D.; Bento, A. R.; Salvacao, N., and Guedes Soares, C. (2018). Economic feasibility of wave energy farms in Portugal. *Energies*. 11 (11):3149.

European Commission (2019). Horizon 2020 – *Work Programme 2018-2020: Secure, clean and efficient energy*. Available from https://ec.europa.eu/research/participants/data/ref/h2020/wp/2018-2020/main/h2020-wp1820-energy_en.pdf.

General Assembly Resolution A/[RES/70/1], *Transforming our world: the 2030 Agenda for Sustainable Development* (25th September 2015). Available from https://www.un.org/ga/search/view_doc.asp?symbol=A/RES/70/1&Lang=E.

Gomes R. P. F., Lopes M. F. P., Henriques J. C. C., Gato L. M. C., Falcão A. F. O. (2015). The dynamics and power extraction of bottom-hinged plate wave energy converters in regular and irregular waves. *Ocean Engineering* 96, pp. 86–99.

Gaspar, J. F., Hallak, T.S., Guedes Soares, C. (2019). Semi-submersible platform concept for a concentric array of wave energy converters. In Guedes Soares C. (ed.), *Advances in Renewable Energies Offshore*, Taylor & Francis Group: 307–314, London, UK.

Gaspar, J. F.; Calvario, M.; Kamarlouei, M., and Guedes Soares, C. (2016) Power take-off concept for wave energy converters based on oil-hydraulic transformer units. *Renewable Energy*. 86:1232–1246.

Hallak, T. S.; Gaspar, J. F.; Kamarlouei, M.; Calvario, M.; Mendes, M. J. G. C.; Thiebaut, F., and Guedes Soares, C. (2018). Numerical and Experimental analysis of a hybrid wind-wave offshore floating platform's hull. *Proceedings of the 37th International Conference on Ocean, Offshore and Arctic Engineering (OMAE 2018);* Vol 11A, ASME paper UNSP V11AT12A047.

Hansen R. H. (2013). Design and control of the power take-off system for a wave energy converter with multiple absorbers. PhD diss., Faculty of Engineering & Science, Aalborg University, Denmark. October, 2013.

Hansen R. H., Kramer M & Vidal E. (2013). Discrete displacement hydraulic power take-off system for the wavestar wave energy converter. *Energies 6* (2013), pp. 4001–4044.

Kamarlouei, M., Gaspar, J. F., Calvário, M., Hallak, T. S., Mendes, M. J. G. C., Thiebaut, F., Guedes Soares, C., (2020). Experimental analysis of wave energy converters concentrically attached on a floating offshore platform. *Renewable Energy, 152*: pp. 1171–1185.

Santos, F. P.; Teixeira, A. P., and Guedes Soares, C. (2018). Maintenance planning of an offshore wind turbine using stochastic petri nets with predicates. *Journal of Offshore Mechanics and Arctic Engineering.* 140(2):021904.

Sinha, A., Karmakar, D., & Guedes Soares, C. (2016). Performance of optimally tuned arrays of heaving point absorbers. *Renewable Energy, 92*, 517–531.

Xiaojing S., Huang D. & Wu G. (2012). The current state of offshore wind energy technology development. *Energy 41*, pp. 298–312.

Experimental analysis of wind thrust effects on the performance of a wave energy converter array adapted to a floating offshore platform

M. Kamarlouei, J.F. Gaspar, T.S. Hallak, M. Calvário & C. Guedes Soares
Centre for Marine Technology and Ocean Engineering (CENTEC), Instituto Superior Técnico, Universidade de Lisboa, Lisbon, Portugal

F. Thiebaut
LiR – National Ocean Test Facility, MaREI center, UCC, Cork, Ireland

ABSTRACT: The objective of this paper is to present the experimental methodologies and challenges of testing a wave energy converter array, concentrically attached to a semisubmersible platform, and in presence of wind thrust forces and moments. The tower of a wind turbine has been placed in the center of the platform and connected to a mass-pulley system through a light weight cable to simulate the wind thrust forces acting on the tower. The testing campaign has been performed with and without wind thrust simulation in different operational sea states, different sets of wave energy converter arrays. The main challenges that were found were related to the parameters included in the wind thrust simulation such as scaling factors, allocation of masses for different sea states, and measuring tension in the cable. The results show that the wind thrust force affects more the platform with less number of wave energy converters in the array.

1 INTRODUCTION

Offshore floating multi-use platform (MUP) concepts, designed to support wave energy converters (WECs) and wind turbines, have been developed to maximize the synergies between resources. The main objective of MUP is to reduce the levelized cost of energy (LCOE) (Castro-Santos et al. 2016, Castro-Santos et al. 2017) and to improve the quality of the power delivered to the grid. The most know MUPs are proposed based on semisubmersible (Sarmiento et al. 2019, Legaz et al. 2018, Hansen et. al. 2015, Perez et al. 2015, Karimirad 2014) and spar type (Muliawan et al. 2013, Ren et al. 2015) floating platform structures.

On the other hand, the investigation on the MUPs is relatively recent (Karmakar & Guedes Soares 2016, Li et al. 2018, Hallak et. al. 2018). Indeed, only a few research institutes have so far performed experiments with models of hybrid concepts. The only hybrid platform that was tested in offshore environment (1:2 scale) was the P37, by Floating Power Plant (Floating Power Plant, 2019). Thus, regarding platform's stability, dynamics, and the energy absorption from WECs, conclusions are generally extracted from simplified numerical methods, estimates and approximations. However, the modelling and numerical simulation of these concepts is naturally very complex: it should account for high non-linearities, second-order effects, and many degrees-of-freedom (DOFs) involved. This is not fully encompassed by any available software, and therefore most analyses come oversimplified.

This paper presents the preliminary experimental study of a hybrid wind and wave offshore platform. The main focus is given to the wind thrust force effects on the performance of the combined floating offshore platform. Thus, the dynamic behaviour of the platform is studied in the operational mode for both wind and wave converters. The heave and pitch motions of the platform are being studied as the critical DOFs in the irregular waves.

In Section 2 the methodology of the experiments is presented and in Section 3 the case study including its main parameters, sea states and test scenarios are discussed. In Section 4, the results are presented and in Section 5, the conclusions of the paper are explained.

2 METHODOLOGY

There are various standard methods for the simulation of the wind thrust in the study of floating offshore platforms. These methods are categorized as uncoupled hydrodynamic tests and coupled aero-hydrodynamic tests.

The first method simulates the thrust forces using the mass-pulley system without the rotor at preliminary stage of the tests. The main goal of these tests

DOI: 10.1201/9781003216599-63

are typically comparing different platform structures in respect of response to the waves and validation of numerical model (ITTC, 2017). In the case of MUPs, the mass-pulley system can be used to study the capability of the WEC array in tackling with the pitching moments caused by the wind turbine in operational mode.

The second method considers the simulation of the rotor either by simplified (without considering an accurate representation of the rotor aerodynamics) (Cermelli et al. 2009) or physical modelling (Shin et al. 2013). According to the major goal of this paper, the methodologies for mass-pulley system are explained further in this section.

2.1 Mass-pulley system

The mass-pulley system is a cost effective and simple approach to simulate the wind thrust forces acting on the wind turbine in floating offshore platforms, mostly at early stage testing (lower TRL). In this method, the wind turbine and the tower are simulated with equivalent masses installed in specific height, to consider the center of the gravity of the system. Then, the point representing the center of the turbine hub is exposed to constant pulling forces applied through the mass-pulley system. However, the thrust force is considered as constant over each test, and so, does not reflect the time varying nature of the wind resource.

The pulley system is generally composed of one or two frictionless pulleys fixed to the bridge or wall of the basin. These pulleys should have the minimum mass and inertia in order to reduce any load damping. A non-elastic rope is attached to the wind turbine nacelle and is extended horizontally (it is supposed to be perpendicular to the gravity vector, $\vec{g}$) back and passed through the pulley system to suspend vertically with a hanging mass. The wire must be chosen to have a sufficiently low density as to avoid any slack and thus variances in the modelled thrust force. The pulley diameter is also an important factor to consider. Bigger pulley diameters should be selected, especially when using small masses.

The force applied on the wind turbine nacelle is calculated as (Matha et al. 2015):

$$F_p = \left(m(g + a.e_2) + \frac{I_{zz}a.e_2}{R_p^2} \right) e_2 \quad (1)$$

where m is the pulling mass, a is the acceleration vector at the turbine nacelle, I_{zz} is the rotational inertia of the wheel, R_p is the wheel radius and e_2 is the normalized vector in the pulling wire's direction.

The pulling mass is selected to provide the Froude-scaled mean thrust force at the chosen wind conditions and is determined by considering the F_p as equal to the turbine thrust force.

2.1.1 Wind thrust force

One of the main parameters in the mass-pulley system is to calculate the proper mass related to the trust force of the turbine in each sea state. Thus, the thrust force should be estimated for the operational sea states (average wind speed between the cut-in and cut-off speeds).

Figure 1 shows a MUP including the wind turbine in the middle and array of point absorbers in operational mode. The thrust force shown in this figure, can be determined using different methods that are briefly presented in this section.

The simplest aerodynamic model of a wind turbine used for determining the thrust force is the actuator disk model. In this model, the rotor is considered as a circular disk that extracts power from the wind. Thus, the thrust force is calculated as:

$$F_T = \frac{1}{2} C_T \rho A_R U_\infty^2 \quad (2)$$

where U_∞ is the wind speed, A_R is the rotor projected area, ρ is the air density, and C_T is the thrust coefficient. C_T can be defined by the ratio of trust force to dynamic force as shown in:

$$C_T = \frac{F_T}{\frac{1}{2}\rho A_R U_\infty^2} \quad (3)$$

However, as demonstrated by (Frohboese et al. 2010), a conservative and relatively accurate approximation for most offshore wind turbines in the specific wind speed range, may be used as:

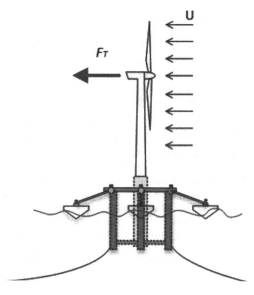

Figure 1. Schematics of wind thrust force acting on a floating wind turbine attached to a multi-purpose platform.

$$C_T = \frac{3.5 \times (2\bar{U} - 3.5)}{\bar{U}^2} \approx \frac{7}{\bar{U}} \quad (4)$$

where $\bar{U}$ is the wind average speed estimated based on the wave spectrum as shown in Figure 2. It should be indicated that the minimum nominal wind speed in the experiments is considered as 7.72 m/s. Thus, the thrust coefficient will always remain below 1.

The average wind speed in each sea state can be estimated using Pierson Moskowitz (PM) spectrum, also used for the simulation of sea states in this paper. Figure 2 shows the relation between the significant wave height and average wind speed in PM spectrum.

The second method for the calculation of the thrust force is the general momentum theory which is an advanced model of previous method considering the angular momentum of the rotor motion (Manwell & McGowan 2009) The third method is the blade element theory which considers the rotor geometry and behaviour of blades due to their motion through the air (e. g. blade airfoil section, chord and twist) (Rijs & Smulders 1990). Finally, the forth method is a combination of the first two methods (based on general momentum theory) and the third one (based on blade element theory), so called Blade Element-Momentum (BEM) theory.

2.2 Platform dynamics

To calculate the platform dynamics, the relative motion of the platform in respect to a fixed global reference frame is captured. The transformation matrix is used to calculate the angular motions. The response spectrum is generated for each sea state and used for calculating the variances of the displacement, velocity and acceleration through the following equations, respectively.

$$m_0 = \int_0^\omega S(\omega)d\omega \quad (5)$$

$$m_2 = \int_0^\omega \omega^2 S(\omega)d\omega \quad (6)$$

$$m_4 = \int_0^\omega \omega^4 S(\omega)d\omega \quad (7)$$

where $S(\omega)$ is the response spectrum and ω is the wave frequency in rad/s. To assess the significant amplitude of motions (Hs_i i = heave, pitch, surge) in different scenarios, two different methods are used. In the first method, the significant amplitude is defined as the average of one-third of highest amplitudes of motion. The amplitude of each single response is measured and then sorted from the highest to lowest and the average of one-third of highest values are calculated as Hs_i. In the second method, the Hs_i is calculated by $2\sqrt{m_0}$, thus the values should match if the simulated sea is well represented by a zero-mean Gaussian process with narrow-banded spectrum.

2.3 Scaling

Reynolds scaling is the standard for testing aerodynamic models. The lift and drag coefficients of a wind turbine blade are very sensitive to the Reynolds number. In this study, the wind thrust is simulated using mass-pulley system which is not subjected to viscosity effects and Reynolds scaling is not used. Moreover, this study requires the use of Froude scaling laws. The Froude law that is broadly used in the study of offshore devices is presented in Table 1 for a 1:27 model scale.

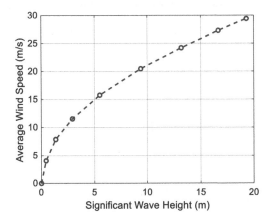

Figure 2. The average wind speed in different wave heights in Pierson Moskowitz spectrum.

Table 1. Froude scaling used for the model test.

Model scale λ = FS/M = 27

Variable	Dim.	Units	Scale ratio	
Length	L	M	λ	2.70E+01
Mass	M	Kg	λ^3	1.97E+04
Angle	None	Rad	1	1.00E+00
Acc.	L/T^2	m/s^2	1	1.00E+00
Angular Acc.	1/T^2	1/s^2	λ^{-1}	3.70E-02
Angular Vel.	1/T	1/s	$\sqrt{\lambda}^{-1}$	1.92E-01
Force	M.L/T^2	Kg.m/s^2	λ^3	1.97E+04
Wave Height	L	M	λ	2.70E+01
Wave Period	T	S	$\sqrt{\lambda}$	5.20E+00
Vel.	L/T	m/s	$\sqrt{\lambda}$	5.20E+00
Moment of Inertia	M.L^2	Kg.m^2	λ^5	1.43E+07

3 CASE STUDY

A floating offshore MUP containing WEC array and wind turbine is used as the case study. Table 2 presents the main characteristics of the platform geometry.

The modification of water line and center of gravity (COG) of the model is carried out by adding 37.5 kg of lead blocks in the extreme bottom of the radial columns and considering ballast tanks in vertical columns.

The experiments are performed in the medium size ocean basin of the Lir NOTF facility. The basin is 25 m × 17 m and 1 m deep with a moveable floor, which increases the depth up to 2.5 m (Figure 3).

The dotted lines around the basin represent the wave paddles and thick lines in the bottom and right side of Figure 3 show the wave absorbing shores to ensure minimum reflected waves. The catenary mooring system with three lines is applied for the soft station keeping, and avoiding excessive surge, sway, and yaw motions. The length of the mooring line in the upwind side is 5.0 m and the two in the downwind side are 2.9 m. The mooring system is made of steel chains, without springs and dampers, with specific weight of 0.0713 kg/m. Also, three wave gauges are installed in parallel with the model to measure incident waves in three critical points, buoys in the bow side, central column, and buoys in the aft of the platform. Four Qualisys cameras are used for capturing the motions of the platform. Thus, six camera tags are used on the platform, four of them to identify the rigid body on the deck of the platform, one on central column for the better definition of COG, and the last one on the top of the wind tower to identify its bending during tests.

3.1 WEC arrays

Two different WEC array layouts are studied, named as 6-WEC and 3-WEC (Figure 4). Point absorber WECs with cone-cylinder shape floaters (with mean absorbed power of 50 kW) have been adapted in both array layouts (Sinha et al. 2015). Floaters are connected to the floating platform using rigid arms that are hinged to the deck. To simulate the damping of the power take-off (PTO) system in the WEC, bidirectional rotational dampers are applied in the hinged joint of the WEC to the platform.

3.2 Wind turbine

The wind turbine model is deployed using a vertical column as the tower and lead elements to simulate the mass of nacelle, blades, and mast, set up on the 2.0 m height tower with a total weight of 1.8 kg. Both tower height and tower mass are simulating a 750 kW wind turbine which is the maximum addressable capacity for the modelled floating platform and represents the extreme moments on this model. Figure 5 shows the general configuration of the floating platform with wind turbine in the middle and mass-pulley system connected to the top of the wind mast.

Figure 6 shows the deployed mass pulley system in the experiments.

Table 2. MUP geometrical properties in full scale.

Property	Value	Unit
Diameter of central column	4.32	m
Diameter of lateral columns	2.97	m
Diameter of radial columns	1.35	m
Height	29.70	m
Draft	25.65	m
Displacement	1380	m^3
Mass	1374	ton
Center of Gravity	9.20	m
Center of Buoyancy	13.00	m
Roll radius of Gyration	17.23	m
Pitch radius of Gyration	17.20	m
Yaw radius of Gyration	9.77	m
Height of Tower	54	m
Weight of Tower	15.75	ton
Weight of Turbine	35.43	ton

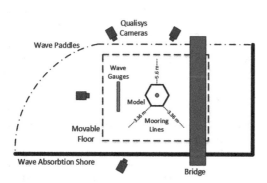

Figure 3. Model installation diagram in the ocean basin.

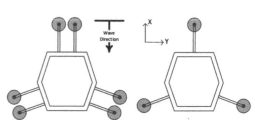

Figure 4. The two WEC array layouts used in this paper.

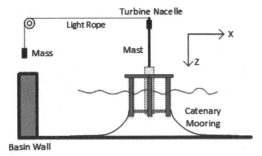

Figure 5. The diagram of the wind turbine model including the mass-pully system.

Figure 6. The main components used in mass-pulley system.

The red circle in the top right side of the Figure 6, shows the load cell used for measuring the wind thrust forces applied to the wind turbine nacelle.

Table 3 indicates the sea states (SS) that are being tested including the corresponding wind speeds and mass-pulley system characteristics in real scale. In the model test using the mass-pully system, equivalent masses are applied to simulate the forces in the last column of Table 3. These masses vary from 0.29 kg to 0.42 kg respectively from sea state 1 to 5.

Two test scenarios are considered, platform with 3-WECs and 6-WECs. Each scenario is tested in with and without thrust force acting on the wind turbine. The results can provide a comparison between the two scenarios focusing on operational conditions in which WECs are extracting power from the wave (one bidirectional damper is installed on each WEC). Also, the heaving performance of WECs can be compared in with and without wind turbine conditions.

4 RESULTS

The results of the irregular wave tests of the two scenarios are presented in this section. Figure 7 (a-c) show the irregular wave generated in the basin, heave and pitch responses of the platform in 3-WEC scenario, respectively. The irregular wave tests are done for 240 seconds (equivalent to 20 minutes in full scale) while for a better presentation, the test period between 150 s to 250 s are presented.

Figure 7 (a and b) present the results in without wind thrust situation and one damper per WEC.

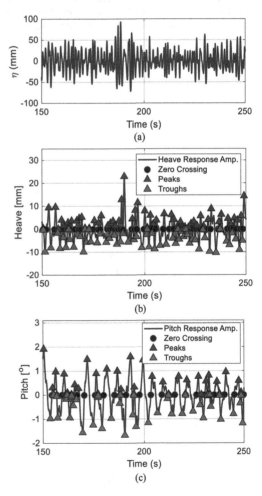

Figure 7. The irregular wave amplitudes in sea state 5 of the model scale platform in 3-WEC scenario with one damper per WEC and without wind thrust. (a) heave response, (b) pitch response amplitudes.

Table 3. Wave & wind conditions & thrust forces.

SS	Hs (m)	Tp (s)	Wind Speed (m/s)	C_T	F (kN)
1	1.69	6.60	7.74	0.93	55.90
2	2.00	7.22	9.20	0.83	62.79
3	2.28	7.74	10.55	0.76	68.89
4	2.61	8.31	11.80	0.69	75.58
5	2.92	8.83	13.00	0.64	81.48

The black markers in these figures show the zero up-crossing waves, the red triangle markers show the peak of the wave and the green triangle markers show the troughs. This data is used for the calculation of the significant response amplitudes as well as the response spectra of the motion. As seen in Figure 7, the pitch amplitudes are relatively smaller than the allowable criteria (± 5 degrees) which shows an acceptable pitching stability of the platform. Also, the heave amplitude in prototype scale reaches up to 0.62 m in prototype scale in sea state 5.

Figure 8 (a and b) show the heave response spectra of the platform (model scale) in 3-WEC array scenario with one damper per WEC, respectively in with and without wind thrust forces.

As seen in Figure 8, adding wind thrust to the platform increases the amount of the energy received by the platform in heave DOF.

Table 4 illustrates the variance of the velocity (VoV) and acceleration (VoA) including the significant response amplitudes (A_s) of the heave motion in 3-WEC and 6-WEC scenarios in different sea states and without wind thrust condition.

In Table 4, it might be noticed that the heave significant amplitude is calculated using two methods presented in the methodology section (the second method is presented in parenthesis). Moreover, it is seen that the platform with 6-WEC array has relatively higher heave amplitudes compared with 3-WEC layout (using both methods). Thus in without wind thrust condition, the array with the 3-WEC layout suggests a better heaving performance for the platform. This observation can be related to the higher damping moment of the PTO (more WECs) in the 6-WEC scenario. The heave motion of the platform in presence of the wind thrust is presented in Table 5.

In the contrary of the without wind thrust, the results in with thrust condition indicate that the platform with 3-WEC array heaves more than the platform with 6-WEC array. Moreover, adding the wind thrust force to the platform increases the heave amplitude of the platform in both scenarios (except in 6-WEC scenario, in the last two sea states, using

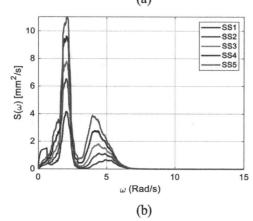

Figure 8. The heave response spectra of the model scale platform in 3-WEC scenario. (a) without wind thrust and (b) with wind thrust conditions.

Table 4. The variance of the velocity and acceleration, including the significant amplitude of the heave motion in different sea states, in without wind thrust condition.

WECs	SS	VoV (mm^2/s^4)	VoA (mm^2/s^6)	As (m)
3	1	7.99	2.32	0.11 (0.09)
	2	12.80	3.35	0.14 (0.11)
	3	17.63	4.16	0.18 (0.13)
	4	22.58	4.84	0.22 (0.15)
	5	29.10	5.83	0.24 (0.17)
6	1	8.45	1.54	0.12 (0.09)
	2	13.80	2.50	0.16 (0.12)
	3	19.10	3.14	0.19 (0.14)
	4	25.63	3.89	0.23 (0.16)
	5	32.76	4.86	0.25 (0.18)

Table 5. The variance of the velocity and acceleration, including the significant amplitude of the heave motion in different sea states, in with wind thrust condition.

WECs	SS	VoV (mm^2/s^4)	VoA (mm^2/s^6)	As (mm)
3	1	14.33	5.72	0.14 (0.12)
	2	21.34	4.85	0.24 (0.15)
	3	28.31	5.21	0.25 (0.17)
	4	38.55	6.53	0.28 (0.20)
	5	48.62	7.95	0.31 (0.22)
6	1	10.94	1.72	0.16 (0.11)
	2	16.52	2.87	0.18 (0.13)
	3	21.74	4.23	0.21 (0.14)
	4	29.52	6.13	0.22 (0.17)
	5	38.19	8.25	0.25 (0.19)

method 1). It is seen that the platform with 6-WEC array has a more stable response to the wind thrust forces (8% average increase in A_s) compared with the one with 3-WEC array (39% average increase in A_s). It is also observed that the variances of the velocity and acceleration of the heave has increased by adding wind thrust.

Table 6 presents the results of the platform's pitch motion in both scenarios in without wind thrust condition.

As seen in Table 6, the amplitudes of the pitch motion in both scenarios are small. Moreover, the platform with 6-WEC pitches less but has a faster (higher acceleration) response to the wave in pitch DOF. The pitch response spectra of the platform (model scale) in 3-WEC scenario is shown in Figure 9.

Similar to the results of the heave motion in Figure 8, in 3-WEC scenario, adding the wind thrust force has increased the absorption of energy by the platform in the pitch DOF. Table 7 shows the results of the pitch motion of the platform in presence of the wind thrust force.

The comparison between Table 6 and 7 shows that in case of the pitch motion, the 6-WEC scenario has a similar trend with the 3-WEC one. In both scenarios, in the first two sea states the pitch amplitude decreased by adding the wind thrust and starting from the third sea state the pitching amplitude increased. Also, the platform either with or without wind thrust force pitches less in 6-WEC scenario compared to the 3-WEC one.

Figure 10 (a and b) show the heave significant amplitudes of one WEC in the front side (a) and another in the back side (b) of the platform with 6-WEC array.

Figure 10 illustrates that in the low sea states the wind thrust can slightly reduce the energy absorption

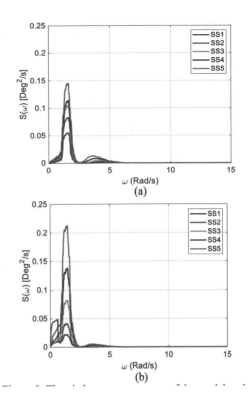

Figure 9. The pitch response spectra of the model scale platform in 3-WEC scenario. (a) without wind thrust and (b) with wind thrust conditions.

Table 7. The variance of the velocity (VoV) and acceleration (VoA), including the significant amplitude of the pitch motion in different sea states, in with wind thrust condition.

	SS	VOV (deg^2/s^4)	VoA (deg^2/s^6)	A_S (°)
3-WEC	1	0.003	0.004	0.34 (0.44)
	2	0.004	0.004	0.44 (0.40)
	3	0.005	0.003	0.65 (0.54)
	4	0.007	0.004	0.89 (0.69)
	5	0.011	0.004	1.19 (0.86)
6-WEC	1	0.004	0.010	0.26 (0.27)
	2	0.006	0.011	0.42 (0.38)
	3	0.008	0.013	0.62 (0.55)
	4	0.010	0.013	0.84 (0.66)
	5	0.014	0.014	1.08 (0.81)

by WECs (between 4 - 5 %) while in sea states higher that 3, it can increase the energy absorption. Indeed, the PTO damping ratio was equal in all sea states and the recorded growths are quite small (below 3 %).

Table 6. The variance of the velocity (VoV) and acceleration (VoA), including the significant amplitude of the pitch motion in different sea states, in without wind thrust condition.

WECs	SS	VOV (deg^2/s^4)	VoA (deg^2/s^6)	A_S (°)
3	1	0.004	0.002	0.36 (0.41)
	2	0.005	0.002	0.45 (0.51)
	3	0.006	0.003	0.57 (0.58)
	4	0.008	0.003	0.68 (0.63)
	5	0.010	0.003	0.91 (0.73)
6	1	0.008	0.012	0.31 (0.50)
	2	0.010	0.013	0.43 (0.61)
	3	0.011	0.012	0.51 (0.67)
	4	0.011	0.011	0.54 (0.69)
	5	0.013	0.012	0.63 (0.74)

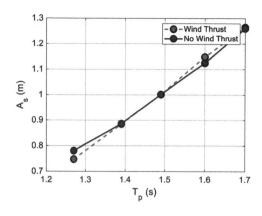

(a)

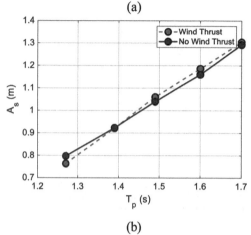

(b)

Figure 10. The heave response amplitude of the WEC in the fore side (a) and aft side (b) of the platform in 6-WEC scenario.

5 CONCLUSIONS

In this experimental study the dynamic performance of a floating offshore MUP containing a wind turbine in the center and two different array layouts is investigated in with and without wind thrust conditions. Dynamic behaviour of the platform in each array layout is studied and the results of the two array layouts are compared.

The results show that wind thrust forces affect the platform with 3-WEC array more than the 6-WEC one. In addition, the 6-WEC array shows a better performance in both heave and pitch DOFs in presence of wind turbine while it can provide higher righting moment against the pitching moment produced by wind turbine. Moreover, the wind thrust force had no significant effect on the dynamic performance of each WEC in high sea states.

As the continuation of this work, the effects of using a damping-stiffness PTO on the WECs and their contribution to the dynamics of the platform will be studied and compared with the presented results.

ACKNOWLEDGMENTS

This work was performed within the project "Generic hydraulic power take-off system for wave energy converters" funded by FCT under contract PTDC/EMS-SIS-1145/2014 and the project "Experimental simulation of oil-hydraulic Power Take-Off systems for Wave Energy Converters", funded by FCT under contract PTDC/EME-REN/29044/2017. The testing has received support from MaRINET 2, a Marine Renewable Infrastructure Network for Enhancing Technologies 2 under H2020-EU.1.4.1.2 "Integrating and opening existing national and regional research infrastructures of European Interest", project ID 731084. This work contributes to the Strategic Research Plan of the Centre for Marine Technology and Ocean Engineering (CENTEC), which is financed by the Portuguese Foundation for Science and Technology (Fundação para a Ciência e Tecnologia - FCT) under contract UIDB/UIDP/00134/2020.

REFERENCES

Castro-Santos, L., Martins, E. & Guedes Soares, C. 2016. Methodology to calculate the costs of a floating offshore renewable energy farm. *Energies* 9(5): 324–350.

Castro-Santos, L., Martins, E. & Guedes Soares, C. 2017. Economic comparison of technological alternatives to harness offshore wind and wave energies. *Energy* 140: 1121–1130.

Cermelli, C., Roddier, D. & Aubault, A. (2009, May). Wind Float: a floating foundation for offshore wind turbines – part II: hydrodynamics analysis. In *ASME 2009 28th International Conference on Ocean, Offshore and Arctic Engineering*. 135–143.

Floating Power Plant. 2019. Available online: http://www.floatingpowerplant.com/(accessed on 25th December 2019).

Frohboese, P., Schmuck, C., & Hassan, G. G. 2010. Thrust coefficients used for estimation of wake effects for fatigue load calculation. In *European Wind Energy Conference*. 1–10.

Hallak, T. S., Gaspar, J. F., Kamarlouei, M., Calvário, M, Mendes, M. J. G. C., Thiebaut, F., & Guedes Soares C. 2018. Numerical and Experimental Analysis of a Hybrid Wind-Wave Offshore Floating Platform's Hull. In *ASME 37th OMAE International Conference on Ocean, Offshore and Arctic Engineering, OMAE2018-78744*.

Hanssen, J.E., Margheritini, L., O'Sullivan, K., Mayorga, P., Martinez, I., Arriaga, A., Agos, I., Steynor, J., Ingram, D., Hezari, R. & Todalshaug, J.H. 2015. Design and performance validation of a hybrid offshore renewable energy platform. In *2015 Tenth International Conference on Ecological Vehicles and Renewable Energies (EVER)* 1–8.

ITTC – Specialist Committee on Testing of Marine Renewable Devices, 2017. Available online: https://www.ittc.info/media/8127/75-02-07-038.pdf (accessed on 25th December 2019).

Karimirad, M. 2014. *Offshore Energy Structures: For Wind Power, Wave Energy and Hybrid Marine Platforms*. Springer International Publishing. DOI 10.1007/978-3-319-12175-8.

Karmakar, D., & Guedes Soares C. 2016. Review of the Present Concepts of Multi-Use Offshore Platforms. In

Guedes Soares C. (ed.), *Advances in Renewable Energies Offshore, Taylor & Francis Group*: 867–875, London, UK.

Legaz, M. J., Coronil, D., Mayorga, P., & Fernández, J. 2018. Study of a hybrid renewable energy platform: W2Power. *Proceedings of the ASME 2018 37th International Conference on Ocean, Offshore and Arctic Engineering OMAE 2018*, Madrid, Spain.

Li, L., Gao, Y., Yuan, Z., Day, S., & Hu, Z. 2018. Dynamic Response and Power Production of a Floating Integrated Wind, Wave and Tidal Energy System. *Renewable Energy* 116: 412–422.

Manwell, J. F., & McGowan, J. G. 2009. *Wind energy explained: theory design and Application*, John Wiley & Sons Ltd.

Matha, D., Sandner, F., Molins, C., Campos, A., & Cheng, P. W. 2015. Efficient preliminary floating offshore wind turbine design and testing methodologies and application to a concrete spar design. *Philosophical Transactions of the Royal Society A: Mathematical, Physical and Engineering Sciences*, 373(2035): 20140350.

Muliawan, M. J., Karimirad, M., & Moan, T. 2013. Dynamic response and power performance of a combined Spar-type floating wind turbine and coaxial floating wave energy converter. *Renewable Energy*, 50: 47–57.

Pérez, C. C., Greaves, D., & Iglesias, G. 2015. A review of combined wave and offshore wind energy. *Renewable and Sustainable Energy Reviews*, 42: 141–153.

Ren, N., Gao, Z., Moan, T., & Wan, L. 2015. Long-term performance estimation of the Spar-Torus-Combination (STC) system with different survival modes. *Ocean Engineering*, 108: 716–728.

Rijs, R. P. P., & Smulders, P. T. 1990. Blade element theory for performance analysis of slow running wind turbines, *Wind Engineering*, 14(2).

Sarmiento, J., Iturrioz, A., Ayllón, V., Guanche, R., & Losada, I.J. 2019. Experimental modelling of a multi-use floating platform for wave and wind energy harvesting. *Ocean Engineering*. 173: 761–773.

Shin, H., Kim, B., Dam, P. T., & Jung, K. 2013. Motion of OC4 5MW Semi-submersible Offshore Wind Turbine in irregular waves. In *Proceedings, 32nd International Conference on Ocean Offshore & Arctic Eng., OMAE2013*: 10463 Nantes, France.

Sinha, A., Karmakar, D., & Guedes Soares, C. 2015. Effect of floater shapes on the power take-off of wave energy converters. In Guedes Soares C. (ed.), *Advances in Renewable Energies Offshore, Taylor & Francis Group*: 375–382.

Experimental and numerical analysis of a spar platform subjected to regular waves

K. Raed & C. Guedes Soares
Centre for Marine Technology and Ocean Engineering (CENTEC), Instituto Superior Técnico, Universidade de Lisboa, Lisbon, Portugal

K. Murali
Department of Ocean Engineering, Indian Institute of Technology (IIT) Madras, India

ABSTRACT: The aim of this study is to investigate the hydrodynamic behavior of a spar-type platform subjected to regular waves through experimental and numerical analyses. In this work, the attention is directed only to the surge, heave, and pitch responses. The experiments were carried out for 1:60 model scale spar-platform with 0.25 m diameter and 1.22 m draft moored with four wired steel cables forming a slack mooring system. The viscous damping matrix is extracted from the pitch and heave free decay tests. This matrix is implemented in the numerical analysis and their influence on the global motions is studied. In addition, a tuned quadratic damping is examined as well. The numerical model of the system is developed using a 3D panel method software based on the potential-flow theory. A nonlinear time domain analysis is conducted, and the cables dynamic effect is explored. From the results, it is observed that the numerical model captures well the resonance responses as well as the combination resonances using the quadratic damping values.

1 INTRODUCTION

Spar type floating platforms are widely used in oil and gas and renewable energy fields due to its capabilities and dynamics behavior in deep water. Haslum and Faltinsen (1999) has observed a higher pitch motion combined with extreme heave amplitudes, which is so-called Mathieu instability. A new hull shapes were proposed with improved heave and pitch motions characteristics to avoid this phenomena. Jain and Agarwal (2003) investigated the hydrodynamic response of the classic spar platform moored with catenary cables considering the response dependent stiffness matrix. This matrix consists of the restoring hydrostatic force, the cables' stiffness, the nonlinear horizontal springs, and the nonlinear vertical springs. Koo et al. (2004) evaluated the damping and coupled effects of the hull, mooring and riser on the principle instability. It has been explored that the damping plays an important role in suppressing the instability. Neves et al. (2008) studied the spar instability in regular wave through experiments and numerical analysis. However, they focused on the uncertainties in the design parameters; e.g. the metacentric height, draft/diameter ratio, associated damping, and mooring system. Yong-Pyo et al. (2005) carried out experiments in regular waves for a spar-type platform and found that combination resonance occurs when the wave frequency is close to the heave natural frequency and double the pitch natural frequency. Zhao et al. (2010) studied the spar's behavior in a long periodic regular wave when the wave frequency approaches the sum of heave and pitch natural frequencies. In this particular case, spar's exhibit complicated dynamic behavior and the available damping will play an important role in suppressing such kind of instability. Choi et al. (2016) observed in his study a combination resonance in the sum and the difference of the wave frequency (ω) and the pitch natural frequency as well as at double the pitch natural frequency ($2\omega_{5n}$).

One of the greatest advantages of adopting the spar as a foundation for the wind turbines is its low water plane area that leads to a small heave and pitch response. Nevertheless, in some circumstances the spar type foundation is vulnerable to a high heave response due to its small water plane area (A_{wp}) compared to the displaced volume. Jonkman (2010) reported the specification of the floating system needed by the Offshore Code Comparison Collaboration (OC3) participants to build an aero-hydro-servo-elastic models. In phase IV for OC3 project, the spar-buoy concept called "Hywind", designed to support a 5-MW wind turbine, developed by Statoil in Norway has been chosen for the modeling activities. Nallayarasu and Saravanapriya (2013a, 2013b) investigated the spar supporting the wind turbine numerically and experimentally in regular and random waves in different loading conditions.

DOI: 10.1201/9781003216599-64

Slack, taut 30°, and taut 45° were tested and the Response Amplitude Operators were compared. They observed that while the turbine is rotating the heave, pitch and surge motions are affected. Hegseth and Bachynski (2019) have developed a linear frequency domain for the spar floating wind turbine and the results has been compared to a nonlinear time domain model. A good agreement has been achieved; however, the results were sensitive to the first bending mode. Jeon et al. (2013) explored the optimum cable length and connection position of mooring cables for a spar floating offshore wind turbine in irregular waves. A nonlinear analysis for the stiffness of a slack and taut mooring systems has been presented by Al-Solihat and Nahon (2016). Xu et al. (2019) presented a comprehensive review of the mooring cables adopted for the wave energy converters which could be also useful in case of spar platforms.

Adding heave plate(s) is an efficient way to reduce the heave response of the spar platform as it helps to increase the added mass and damping which consequently alters the heave natural period and prevent Mathieu instability. One of the pioneering studies in this field was the work done by Thiagarajan and Troesch (1998). They examined the effect of appendages in form of disk to a tension leg platform (TLP) as well as the effect of a uniform small current on the hydrodynamic heave damping. In addition, a scale law has been proposed to extrapolate the heave damping to the full scale. Lake et al. (1999) verified this scaling methodology through experiments with a smaller model with two different configurations of the attached disk. Rho et al. (2002) conducted model test for a classical spar platform with and without damping plates and the results have been compared to numerical ones obtained from potential flow-based code. Likewise, previous studies, it has been observed that the spar with damping plate resulted in a much lower heave motion at resonance compared to the one without damping plate. Tao and Cai (2004) considered the vortex shedding flow around an oscillating vertical cylinder with an attached disk at its keel adopting the finite difference method to solve the incompressible Navier-Stokes equations. It has been observed that the aspect ratio of the disk (t/D) and the disk to spar diameter ratio (D_d/D_s) has a significant influence on the vortex shedding modes and the hydrodynamics damping and added mass. He et al. (2008) conducted experiments to investigate the effect of the thin heave plates on a spar and a TLP. It has been reported that the damping coefficients behaves differently in three Keulegan-Carpenter (KC) regimes. In more recent studies, Sudhakar and Nallayarasu (2013) conducted experiments to investigate the effect of a single and a double heave plates on the hydrodynamic response of a spar in regular waves. The results were compared to those obtained by numerical simulation using ANSYS AQWA. A range of heave plate diameter to spar diameter ratio (D_d/D_s) varying between 1 and 1.5 were examined. Moreover, the effect of varying the spacing between the plates in case of double heave plates with identical diameters were also studied. The viscous damping for the heave and pitch motion was extracted from the free decay tests using the decrement method. Then, these values manually introduced to the software as the software only considers the radiation damping. Regarding the single heave plate, the heave damping ratio has been increased 50% and 100% in case of D_d/D_s is 1.2 and 1.5, respectively. Nallayarasu and Mathai (2016) studied the dynamic behavior of a spar with four heave plate configurations in the near-resonant region of loading. The spar with the heave pate approaching the sea water level experienced the less response. Subbulakshmi and Sundaravadivelu (2016) studied the effect of the heave plate on the heave damping of a spar platform for offshore wind turbine using Computational Fluid Dynamics (CFD) simulations validated through experiments. They tested a spar with single and double heave plates and studied the effect of many parameters, e.g. scaling ratio, diameter ratio, heave plate position to draft ratio and they observed some cases where the heave response was reduced. Lavrov and Guedes Soares (2016) studied the laminar flow around a heaving axisymmetric cylinders with heaving plates using Navier-Stokes equations. They examined cylinders with one disk, with two discs and with pentagonal plate.

In this study, a spar platform subjected to regular waves is tested with a Froude scaling 1:60. Herein, a spar with a scarce loading condition is tested as their pitch and heave natural frequencies fall into the excited waves range. The experiments were carried out in the Department of Ocean Engineering, IIT Madras. Free decay tests were conducted to estimate the heave and pitch natural frequencies of the spar. Then, the spar model was moored by four slack cables to maintain its horizontal position. Three waves heights are considered in this work with a range of varying frequencies, the surge, heave, and pitch motions were measured. A frequency and time domain analyses are conducted using the potential flow-based software ANSYS AQWA and the model was validated by comparing the results to those obtained from the experiments.

2 VISCOUS DAMPING

The potential flow theory assumes that the flow is inviscid and therefore, the drag effect is not considered. Due to the crucial importance of this term, especially for the cylindrical members, this force could be added by the inclusion of viscous damping coefficients. The free decay tests are often used to estimate those coefficients. Malta et al. (2010) gave insights about the linear and nonlinear damping determination from experimental tests. The nonlinear equation of motion of any floating system is given by:

$$(M+A)\ddot{y} + \underbrace{(B_{pot} + B_{viscous})\dot{y}}_{\text{Linear term}} + \underbrace{B_2\dot{y}|\dot{y}|}_{\text{Quadratic term}} + Cy = F(t) \quad (1)$$

where M is the body mass, A is the hydrodynamic mass B_{pot} is the potential damping, $B_{viscous}$ is the linear drag term, B_2 is the quadratic drag term, C is the restoring coefficient, y is the response's displacement and $F(t)$ is the wave-induced force. In case of linear analysis, the quadratic term is assumed to be zero. Whereas the nonlinear analysis considers both linear and quadratic terms. From another perspective, some studies only use quadratic damping (QD) by tuning its value and neglect the linear damping term. For instance, Coulling et al. (2013) adopt only the quadratic damping in the validation process of the DeepCwind semi-submersible and those values were used in many studies; e.g. Raed et al. (2020). However, in this study the focus will be direct to the linear and nonlinear analyses only to extract the damping values.

2.1 Linear analysis

The equation of motion for the free decay tests, considering the linear damping only without the presence of external force is given by:

$$(M+A)\ddot{y} + B_1\dot{y} + Cy = 0 \quad (2)$$

where B_1 is the linear damping term, while y is the displacement at any given time $(t_1, t_2, ...t_n)$ and is given by:

$$y(t_1) = ae^{-\zeta\omega_n t_1}\cos(\omega_d t_1 + \varepsilon) \quad (3)$$

and

$$y(t_2) = ae^{-\zeta\omega_n t_2}\cos(\omega_d t_2 + \varepsilon) \quad (4)$$

where a is the amplitude, ζ is the damping ratio, ω_n is the natural frequency in rad/s, t is the time, ε is the phase angle in rad, ω_d is the damped natural frequency in rad/s, and t is the time in seconds. Eq.(4) can be written in the form of:

$$y(t_2) = ae^{-\zeta\omega_n(t_1+T_d)}\cos(\omega_d(t_1+T_d) + \varepsilon) \quad (5)$$

where T_d is the damped period in seconds and t_1 is the time where the first peak occurs. From eq.(3) and eq.(5), the ratio between $y(t_1)$ and $y(t_2)$ is equal to:

$$\frac{y(t_1)}{y(t_2)} = e^{\zeta\omega_n T_d} \quad (6)$$

By taking the natural logarithm of both sides of eq. (6), the logarithmic decrement (δ) is obtained and is given by:

$$\delta = \ln\left(\frac{y(t_1)}{y(t_2)}\right) = \zeta\omega_n T_d \quad (7)$$

The damped period (T_d) is given by

$$T_d = \frac{2\pi}{\omega_d} = \frac{2\pi}{\omega_n\sqrt{1-\zeta^2}} \quad (8)$$

where ζ is the damping ratio and equal to $B/B_{critical}$, ω_n and ω_d is the natural frequency and the damped frequency in rad/s, respectively. From Eqs. (7) and (8), ζ is given by:

$$\zeta = \frac{\delta}{\sqrt{(2\pi)^2 + \delta^2}} \quad (9)$$

3 EXPERIMENTAL SET-UP

The experimental activity was performed to investigate the surge, heave, and pitch responses of a floating spar platform. The experiments were carried out using 1:60 Froude scale model fabricated with acrylic in the wave flume at the Department of Ocean Engineering, Indian Institute of Technology Madras (IITM), Tamil Nadu, India. The wave flume is 90 m length, 4 m wide and 3 m depth and the water level has been kept to 2.5 m during the experiments.

Figure 1 shows the ballast used in the experiments which consists of steel disks attached to the bottom of the spar.

Thereafter, the spar was installed in the wave flume at 24.7 m away from the wave generator as illustrated in Figure 2. The spar platform is moored by four steel wires cables with 3mm diameter and 3 m length, forming a slack mooring system. Each wire had one end fixed to a fairlead point located 0.62 m below sea water level (SWL) and the other end was attached to the tank bottom. The main purpose of this mooring configuration is to prevent the spar platform from drifting. A plan and side views for the arrangement of the spar, the mooring cables and the wave probes installed in the wave flume is shown in Figure 2.

Two wave probes were aligned with the center line of the spar at its both sides, and another two were installed in front of them to measure the 2D

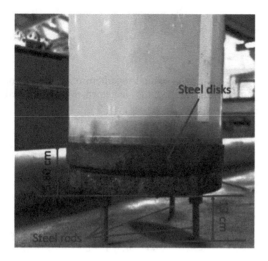

Figure 1. The steel disks (ballast) mounted to the bottom of the spar.

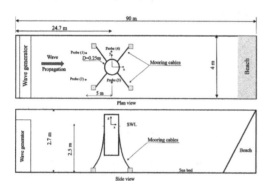

Figure 2. Plan view and side view of the 4 m wave flume and the configuration adopted in the experiments.

propagated waves. Figure 3 shows the spar platform on the wave flume after installation.

Two accelerometers and one inclinometer were mounted on the top of the spar as shown in Figure 4.

Figure 3. The spar platform after the installation in the wave flume.

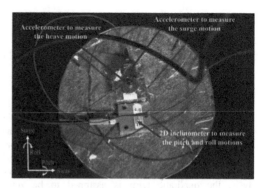

Figure 4. The inclinometer and the two accelerometers used to record the spar responses considered in this study.

These instruments recorded the surge acceleration, heave acceleration, pitch, and roll motions at a sampling rate of 50 Hz. Four resistance-type wave probes are installed to measure the waves generated by the flap-type generator.

4 NUMERICAL MODEL

A numerical model of the spar is developed using the commercial software ANSYS AQWA which is based on potential flow theory. The full characteristics of the spar model are shown in Table 1. A convergence analysis is performed for a mesh size ranging from 1 cm to 4 cm with an interval of 0.5 cm. A maximum element size of 3 cm is adopted as it gives the most accurate displaced volume and metacentric height. The meshed model is shown in Figure 5 which results in 3,224 diffracting elements.

4.1 Mooring specification

The mooring system adopted in the experimental activity is included in the numerical model to

Table 1. Spar platform characteristics used in the experiments.

	Scale model (1/60)
Diameter [m]	0.250
Draft [m]	1.220
Freeboard [m]	0.330
Water depth [m]	2.500
Mass including ballast [kg]	60.14
Center of Mass below SWL [m]	0.953
Center of buoyancy below SWL [m]	0.610
k_{xx}, roll radius of gyration about COG [m]	0.415
k_{uy}, pitch radius of gyration about COG [m]	0.415
k_{zz}, yaw radius of gyration about COG [m]	0.100

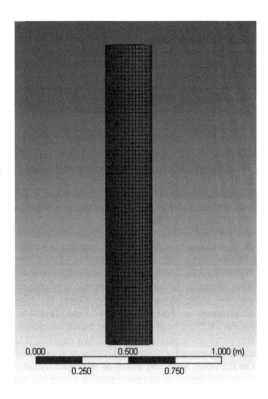

Figure 5. Spar geometry using ANSYS AQWA.

consider the cables damping and their motion on the global responses of the spar. The mooring lines characteristic used in the numerical model are shown in Table 2.

5 RESULTS

In this section, the free decay tests of the spar platform are first presented followed by the experimental and numerical responses in regular and irregular waves, respectively.

Table 2. Mooring characteristics adopted in the experiments.

Number of mooring lines	4
Angle between lines	90°
Radius to the fixed points	1.350 m
Radius to fairleads	0.125 m
Fairleads below SWL	0.640 m
Unstretched line length	2.750 m
Mooring line diameter	3E-03 m
Equivalent mooring line mass density	5E-02 kg/m
Extensional stiffness (*EA*)	3E+06 N
Maximum tension	100 N

5.1 Free decay tests

Heave and pitch free decay tests are carried out to determine the natural periods of the free-floating spar platform. The natural periods of the heave and pitch are estimated to be 2.3 s and 1.9 s, respectively. The viscous damping is explored through linear analysis. Although ANSYS AQWA accounts only for the potential damping, the viscous damping effect is considered by an additional damping matrix; and hence their influence on the global motion is accounted. The linear damping matrix is summarized in Table 3.

The free decay simulation on AQWA is carried out using the exact initial displacement of the measured signal. A comparison between the measured free decay, the numerical simulation of the free decay is shown in Figure 6. A sample of 25 s for the for the heave acceleration and pitch free decay are shown in plot (a) and plot (b), respectively.

The natural period for the 6-degree of freedoms of the spar platform are extracted from ANSYS AQWA for both the free floating and the moored structure. These results are compared to those obtained from the free decay tests and the comparison is presented in Table 4.

5.2 Regular waves tests

The surge, heave, and pitch responses of the spar platform in regular waves are investigated through experiments and numerical simulations. Seven different regular waves propagated in the *x*-direction are tested. A range of wave heights with different wave periods are considered to capture the nonlinearity behavior, if exists. The wave height and period for each test are calibrated using the average peaks and troughs approach. Table 5 presents a comparison between the calibrated and the target wave height and period for

Table 3. Values of the linear damping (B_1) extracted from the free decay tests.

	Heave	Pitch
Linear analysis (B_1)	B_1, N/(m/s)	B_1, N.m/(rad/s)
	8.20	0.90

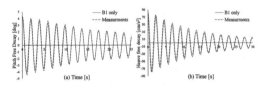

Figure 6. Comparison between numerical and experimental free decay tests for (a) pitch motion and (b) the heave acceleration for the spar platform.

Table 4. Comparison between he experimental and numerical natural periods for the 6-degree of freedom of the spar platform.

	T_n [s] Experiments	T_n [s] AQWA – free floating	T_n [s] AQWA –moored
Surge	-	-	51.32
Sway	-	-	51.32
Heave	2.30	2.29	2.36
Pitch	1.93	2.05	2.06
Roll	1.93	2.05	2.06
Yaw	-	-	15.43

Table 6. Tuned quadratic damping values for the heave, pitch, and roll motions.

	Heave [N/(m/s)^2]	Roll [N.m/(rad/s)^2]	Pitch [N.m/(rad/s)^2]
QD	350.00	2.00	2.00

each test. It is observed that there is an excellent agreement between the calibrated and the target wave periods in all the tests as the deviation do not exceed 0.01 s. On the other hand, the deviation between the calibrated and the target H is more remarkable, where it reaches 8% and 5% in Tests 1 and 21, respectively.

During the experimental activity, it is observed that the responses of the spar is nonlinear for most the sea states considered and the roll motion is small compared to the pitch motion, hence it is neglected. The Fast Fourier Transform (FFT) is applied to the signals and the response amplitude operators (RAOs) corresponds to the wave exciting frequency for the surge acceleration, heave acceleration and pitch motion are estimated. It is observed that Test 10, Test 12, and Test 19 are vulnerable to high response since they are close to the resonance frequency. Hence, quadratic damping is considered to account for the nonlinear drag in case of extreme conditions. Table 6 shows the values of the tuned quadratic damping values used in the numerical model.

Three sets of time domain simulations are carried out using ANSYS AQWA. The influence of the weight drag, and memory effect of the mooring cables on the response are explored by considering the cable dynamics in some sets of simulations.

The first set correspond to the responses obtained by adopting the linear damping matrix considering the mooring cable's drag. The second and third sets comprise of the simulations results from adopting the quadratic damping matrix with and without the cable's drag effect, respectively. Both nonlinear Froude-Krylov force and nonlinear hydrostatic stiffness are considered in the analysis due to their major impact in case of large motion amplitudes, which was the case in some tests. The RAOs obtained from the three sets of simulation are compared to those obtained from the measured data as shown from Figure 7 to Figure 9. In case of the response results from adopting the quadratic damping, it is observed that the cable dynamic slightly affects the heave acceleration in Test 10, Test 12, and Test 19. It results in 7%, 5% and 5% lower heave acceleration compared to response obtained when neglecting the cable dynamics for Tests 10, 12 and 19, respectively. On the other hand, the effect of the cable dynamics in case of the surge and pitch response could be negligible. Taking a deeper look into the RAOs, considering the quadratic damping (QD) together with the

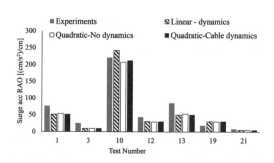

Figure 7. Comparison between the surge RAO obtained from AQWA using linear damping, and quadratic damping, and the experimental data.

Table 5. Target and calibrated values for the regular wave height (H) and period (T) tested.

	Wave Type	H$_{target}$ [cm]	T$_{target}$ [s]	H$_{calibrated}$ [cm]	T$_{calibrated}$ [s]	Error in H (%)
Test01	Regular	3.00	1.64	2.76	1.64	8.00
Test03	Regular	3.00	2.40	3.14	2.39	4.45
Test10	Regular	300	2.00	2.96	2.00	1.30
Test12	Regular	5.00	2.20	5.00	2.20	0.00
Test13	Regular	5.00	1.64	5.20	1.64	3.80
Test19	Regular	6.00	2.20	6.20	2.19	3.20
Test21	Regular	6.00	2.60	5.70	2.62	5.00

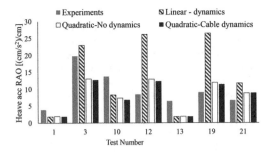

Figure 8. Comparison between the heave RAO obtained from AQWA using linear damping, quadratic damping, and the measured data.

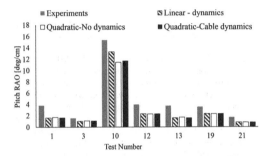

Figure 9. Comparison between the pitch RAO obtained from AQWA using linear damping, quadratic damping, and the experimental data.

cable dynamics results in a quite good agreement between the numerical and experiments in all the tests. It is reported that adopting QD results in 4% lower surge RAO in Test 10 compared to that obtained from the experiments. Moreover, the deviation in the heave response is quite notable as it results in 31% and 21% higher heave RAO in Test 12 and Test 19, respectively. Moreover, it results in 50% lower heave in Test 10 compared to the experiments. In case of pitch motion, considering QD results in 23.9% lower pitch RAO compared to that obtained from thee measured data in Test 10.

On the other hand, adopting the linear damping results in 8% higher surge acceleration in Test 10 compared to that obtained from the experiments, however, the deviation becomes more perceptible in the heave response. As shown in Figure 8, adopting linear damping results in higher heave acceleration in Test 3 (13.7%), Test 12 (67.7%), Test 19 (65.7%), and Test 21 (42.6%) compared to those obtained from the experiments. Whereas it results in 52.5%, 39.5 %, and 71.5% lower heave acceleration in Test 1, Test 10, Test 13, respectively.

A nonlinear behavior for the spar platform is reported as a different RAO values attained in Test 1 and Test 13 even though they have the same wave period. For instance, increasing the wave height (H) from 3 cm to 5 cm results in 11.5%, 12.6% and 34% deviations in the surge acceleration, heave acceleration and pitch RAOs, respectively. Afterwards, comparisons between the numerical simulations considering the QD together with the cable dynamics, and the experimental data are carried out as presented in Figure 10 and Figure 11. Each figure consists of the wave profile (η) and the heave acceleration in the upper plots, whereas the surge acceleration and the pitch motion in the lower plots. Figure 10 presents the comparison between the numerical and experimental responses for Test 12. The wave exciting frequency for Test 12 is very near the heave natural period, hence, it is expected to obtain a high heave response. Adopting quadratic damping results in a good agreement between the numerical and experimental heave response. Although, the same behavior is attained in case of the surge and pitch motion, a deviation is reported in the large peaks.

Regarding Test 10, a quite good match is achieved between the numerical and experimental results in all the responses considered as shown in Figure 11. However, some deviation is notable in case of the nonlinear heave response.

A decomposition for the heave signal for Test 10 is performed by using the fast Fourier transform (FFT) to determine the reason behind the deviation as well as the combination resonances. Figure 12 shows the power spectrum (PSD) of the heave acceleration for

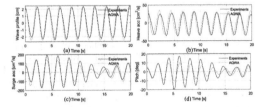

Figure 10. Comparison between the numerical and experimental results for Test 12 (H = 5 cm, T = 2.2 s), (a) wave profile, (b) heave acceleration signal, and (c) surge acceleration signal (d) pitch signal.

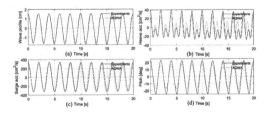

Figure 11. Comparison between the numerical and experimental results for Test 10 (H = 3 cm, T = 2 s), (a) wave profile, (b) heave acceleration signal, and (c) surge acceleration signal (d) pitch signal.

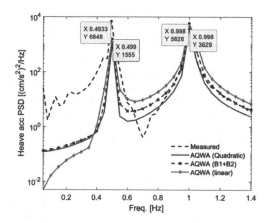

Figure 12. Power spectrum density (PSD) of the heave acceleration signal for Test 10 ($H=4$ cm, $T=2$ s).

Test 10 with a sampling rate 50 Hz. It is observed that the dominant values occur at 0.5 Hz and 1 Hz which represent the excitation frequency (f_{wave}) and the sum of the heave and pitch natural frequencies ($f_{5n}+f_{3n}$), respectively; in this particular case, the $f_{5n}+f_{3n}$ is identical to the double of the pitch natural frequency ($2f_{5n}$). Moreover, the effect of adopting the different damping matrices is examined as shown in the figure. It is observed that the numerical model captures well the higher order motions as shown in the heave acceleration signal.

6 CONCLUSION

The heave, surge and pitch responses of a spar platform were investigated through experiments and numerical simulations. The experiments were carried out using a 1:60 Froude scale model in a wave flume in regular waves with different wave heights and periods. The spar was moored with four wire steel cables forming a slack mooring system. The numerical model was carried out using ANSYS AQWA considering the mooring lines. Two type of analyses were conducted to extract the viscous damping from the free decay tests and their influence on the results were studied. Then, the model was validated, and the results were compared to those obtained from the experiments. Due to the importance of nonlinear drag in the severe sea states, a tuned quadratic damping matrix was adopted in the numerical model. It was found that the system was nonlinear and considering the nonlinear stiffness is of a crucial importance in case of large motion response.

ACKNOWLEDGEMENTS

This work was done under the framework of the joint research project "Large Multipurpose platforms for exploiting Renewable energy in Open Seas" funded by Marie Curie action FP7-PEOPLE-2013-IREAS. The experimental work was carried out in the wave flume of the department of ocean engineering in the Indian institute and Technology, Madras (IITM). The authors would like to express special thanks to Prof. Sundar and Prof. Srineash for providing support during the experimental activity. This work contributes to the Strategic Research Plan of the Centre for Marine Technology and Ocean Engineering (CENTEC), which is financed by the Portuguese Foundation for Science and Technology (Fundação para a Ciência e Tecnologia - FCT) under contract UIDB/UIDP/00134/2020.

REFERENCES

Al-Solihat, M. K. and Nahon, M. 2016. Stiffness of slack and taut moorings. *Ships and Offshore Structures*, 11, 890–904.

Choi, E.-Y., Jeong, W.-B. and Cho, J.-R. 2016. Combination resonances in forced vibration of spar-type floating substructure with nonlinear coupled system in heave and pitch motion. *International Journal of Naval Architecture and Ocean Engineering*, 8, 252–261.

Coulling, A. J., Goupee, A. J., Robertson, A. N., Jonkman, J. M. and Dagher, H. J. 2013. Validation of FAST semi-submersible floating wind turbine numerical model with DeepCwind test data. *Journal of Renewable Energy*, 023116 (5), 1–29.

Haslum, H. A. and Faltinsen, O. M. 1999. Alternative Shape of Spar Platforms for Use in Hostile Areas. *Offshore Technology Conference*. Houston, Texas: Offshore Technology Conference.

He, H., Troesch, A. W. and Perlin, M. Hydrodynamics of Damping Plates at Small KC Numbers. *In*: Kreuzer, E., ed. IUTAM Symposium on Fluid-Structure Interaction in Ocean Engineering, 2008//2008 Dordrecht. Springer Netherlands, 93–104.

Hegseth, J. M. and Bachynski, E. E. 2019. A semi-analytical frequency domain model for eficient design evaluation of spar floating wind turbines. *Marine Structure*, 64, 186–210.

Jain, A. and Agarwal, A. 2003. Dynamic Analysis of Offshore Spar Platforms. *Defence Science Journal*, 53, pp. 211–219.

Jeon, S. H., Cho, Y. U., Seo, M. W., Cho, J. R. and Jeong, W. B. 2013. Dynamic response of floating substructure of spar-type offshore wind turbine with catenary mooring cables. *Ocean Engineering*, 72, 356–364.

Jonkman, J. 2010. Definition of the Floating System for Phase IV of OC3.

Koo, B. J., Kim, M. H. and Randall, R. E. 2004. Mathieu instability of a spar platform with mooring and risers. *Ocean Engineering*, 31, pp. 2175–2208.

Lake, M., He, H., Troesch, A. W., Perlin, M. and Thiagarajan, K. P. 1999. Hydrodynamic Coefficient Estimation for TLP and Spar Structures. *Journal of Offshore Mechanics and Arctic Engineering*, 122, 118–124.

Lavrov, A. and Guedes Soares, C. 2016. Modelling the heave oscillations of vertical cylinders with damping plates. *The International Journal of Maritime Engineering* 158(A3), A187–A197.

Malta, E. B., Goncalves, Rodolfo T., Matsumoto, F. T., Pereira, F. R., Fujarra, A. L. C. and Nishimoto, K. 2010.

Damping Coefficient Analyses for Floating Offshore Structures. *International Conference on Ocean, Offshore and Arctic Engineering*. Shanghai, China.

Nallayarasu, S. and Mathai, T. P. 2016. Effect of Mathieu instability on motion response of Spar hull with heave damping plate. *Ships and Offshore Structures*, 11, 833–846.

Nallayarasu, S. and Saravanapriya, S. 2013a. Experimental and Numerical Investigation of Hydrodynamic Response of Spar with Wind Turbine Under Random Waves. *International Journal of Ocean and Climate Systems*, 4, 261–282.

Nallayarasu, S. and Saravanapriya, S. 2013b. Experimental and Numerical Investigation on Hydrodynamic Response of Spar with Wind Turbine under Regular Waves. *The International Journal of Ocean and Climate Systems*, 4, 239–260.

Neves, M., Sphaier, S., Mattoso, B., Rodríguez, C., Santos, A., Vileti, V. and Torres, F. On the occurrence of mathieu instabilities of vertical cylinders. Proceedings of the ASME 27th International Conference on Offshore Mechanics and Arctic Engineering., June 15–20 2008 Estoril, Portugal. 619–627.

Raed, K., Teixeira, A. P. and Guedes Soares, C. 2020. Uncertainty assessment for the extreme hydrodynamic responses of a wind turbine semi-submersible platform using different environmental contour approaches. *Ocean Engineering*, 195, 106719.

Rho, J. B., Choi, H. S., Lee, W. C., Shin, H. S. and Park, I. K. 2002. Heave And Pitch Motions of a Spar Platform With Damping Plate. *The 12th International Offshore and Polar Engineering Conference*. Kitakyushu, Japan: International Society of Offshore and Polar Engineers.

Subbulakshmi, A. and Sundaravadivelu, R. 2016. Heave damping of spar platform for offshore wind turbine with heave plate. *Ocean Engineering*, 121, 24–36.

Sudhakar, S. and Nallayarasu, S. 2013. Hydrodynamic Response of Spar with Single and Double Heave Plates in Regular Waves. *International Journal of Ocean System Engineering*, 3, 188–208.

Tao, L. and Cai, S. 2004. Heave motion suppression of a Spar with a heave plate. *Ocean Engineering*, 31, 669–692.

Thiagarajan, K. P. and Troesch, A. W. 1998. Effects of appendages and small currents on the hydrodynamic heave damping of TLP columns. *Journal of Offshore Mechanics and Arctic Engineering*, 120, 37–42.

Xu, S., Wang, S. and Guedes Soares, C. 2019. Review of mooring design for floating wave energy converters. *Renewable and Sustainable Energy Reviews*, 111, 595–621.

Yong-Pyo, H., Dong-Yeon, L., Yong-Ho, C., Sam-Kwon, H. and Se-Eun, K. 2005. An Experimental Study On the Extreme Motion Responses of a SPAR Platform In the Heave Resonant Waves. *The Fifteenth International Offshore and Polar Engineering Conference*. Seoul, Korea: International Society of Offshore and Polar Engineers.

Zhao, J., Tang, Y. and Shen, W. 2010. A study on the combination resonance response of a classic spar platform. *Journal of Vibration and Control*, 16(14), 2083–2107.

Experimental and numerical analysis of a spar platform subjected to irregular waves

K. Raed & C. Guedes Soares
Centre for Marine Technology and Ocean Engineering (CENTEC), Instituto Superior Técnico, Universidade de Lisboa, Lisbon, Portugal

K. Murali
Department of Ocean Engineering, Indian Institute of technology (IIT) Madras, Chennai, India

ABSTRACT: This study is a continuation of another one concerned to the spar's behavior in regular waves. Herein, the numerical hydrodynamic analysis of a spar platform subjected to irregular waves is validated through measured data. The experimental activity was conducted in a 4 m wide wave flume for spar with 0.25 m diameter 1.22 m draft moored with four wired steel cables forming a slack system. Two types of analyses are adopted to extract the viscous damping: (1) the linear analysis which results in a linear coefficient, and (2) the nonlinear analysis which results in a combination of linear and quadratic coefficients. Furthermore, a tuned quadratic damping matrix is estimated. Each damping matrix is implemented individually in the numerical simulations and the differences are highlighted through the comparison of response spectrum root mean square. From the results, it is observed that the numerical model captures well the resonance responses as well as the combination resonances using the quadratic damping values.

1 INTRODUCTION

There are many types of floating offshore supports that are used in both oil and gas field, and renewable energy field. Among these types is the spar platform which is commonly used due to its capabilities and dynamics behavior in deep water. Many studies were concerned with the spar behavior in both regular and irregular waves; e.g. Ran et al. (1996) Jain and Agarwal (2003). Regarding its behavior, the studies showed that the low-frequency surge and pitch motions are greater than the wave frequency response. However, the presence of current plays a pivotal role in the reduction of the low-frequency response. Further, it was found that the second-order wave body interaction theory results in a more accurate responses estimation.

Often, the classic spar platform is vulnerable to a high pitch response associated with the extreme heave amplitude. This phenomenon is so-called the Mathieu instability. In an attempt to avoid this phenomena, Haslum and Faltinsen (1999) proposed and examined new hull shapes. One of the most effective way for motion damping of the spar platform is to add heave plates. For instance, Koo et al. (2004) evaluated the damping effect and the coupled effect of the hull, mooring and riser on the instability. They found that the damping is of crucial importance in suppressing the extreme motion (Mathieu instability).

In addition, many studies have been conducted to investigate the effect of heave plates on the spar's response either using potential flow-based codes and software or Computational Fluid Dynamics (CFD) solvers. One of the pioneering studies regarding heave plates was the one done by Thiagarajan and Troesch (1998). Also, Lake et al. (1999) and Rho et al. (2002) studied the effect of heave plates on the spar response. The latter have presented numerical and experimental studies for a classical spar platform with and without the damping plates. However, He et al. (2008) observed in their study that the damping coefficient is strongly influenced by the Keulgan-Carpenter number (KC). Tao and Cai (2004), Sudhakar and Nallayarasu (2013), and Nallayarasu and Mathai (2016) studied different configurations of the heave plates along the spar and the effect of each on the global response. Nallayarasu and Mathai (2016) focused on the effect of those configurations on the near resonance response. In this matter, a number of studies considered the computational fluid dynamics (CFD) as aforementioned. Subbulakshmi and Sundaravadivelu (2016) and Lavrov and Guedes Soares (2016) adopted the CFD to study different configurations of the heave plates with one disk or more. Also, the latter studied the laminar flow around a heaving axisymmetric cylinders with heaving plates.

DOI: 10.1201/9781003216599-65

Many different shapes of the spar platform has been tested and examined, and the responses were investigated. Murray and Yang (2009) studied the response of a spar and a single column floater mounted by an ice breaking cone. Then, Jang and Kim (2019) performed further investigation on the same shape using a nonlinear time-domain simulation program. Another shape called the Belly shape has been initially introduced by Loken et al. (2012). This design has been model tested in a wave and current combination and a good motion has been observed.

Another important thing related to the spar behavior in the combination resonance which occurs at certain frequencies rather than the excitation wave frequency. Yong-Pyo et al. (2005) and Zhao et al. (2010) conducted studies related to the combination resonance, The former carried out experiments in regular waves for a spar-type platform and found that combination resonance occurs when the wave frequency is close to the heave natural frequency and double the pitch natural frequency. The latter studied the spar's behavior in a long periodic regular wave when the wave frequency approaches the sum of heave and pitch natural frequencies. Moreover, Choi et al. (2016) derived the coupled heave/pitch equation of motion to a spar platform in regular waves, and then verified through numerical simulations using ANSYS AQWA. A combination resonance has been observed in the sum and the difference of the wave frequency (ω) and the pitch natural frequency as well as at double the pitch natural frequency ($2\omega_{5n}$).

Recently, the renewable energy gains a lot of attention on most of the works to have increase the clean energy sources. Some studies have tested wind turbine mounted on a spar platform numerically and experimentally. For details about the spar platform wind turbine design and characteristics refer to Jonkman (2010). Nallayarasu and Saravanapriya (2013a, 2013b) investigated the spar supporting the wind turbine numerically and experimentally in regular and random waves in different loading conditions and with different mooring configurations. Hegseth and Bachynski (2019) have developed a linear frequency domain for the spar floating wind turbine and the results has been compared to a nonlinear time domain model. A good agreement has been achieved; however, the results were sensitive to the first bending mode. Jeon et al. (2013) explored the optimum cable length and connection position of mooring cables for a spar floating offshore wind turbine in irregular waves. A nonlinear analysis for the stiffness of a slack and taut mooring systems has been presented by Al-Solihat and Nahon (2016). Xu et al. (2019) presented a comprehensive review of the mooring cables adopted for the wave energy converters which could be also useful in case of spar platforms.

In this work, a spar platform with a scarce loading condition is tested under irregular waves; its pitch and heave natural frequencies fall into the excited wave range. The experiments were carried out in 4 m wide wave flume in the Department of Ocean Engineering, IIT Madras, India. Free decay tests were conducted for the free-floating spar platform. The spar model was moored by four wire cables forming a slack mooring system. Two irregular wave heights are considered with varying frequencies and the surge, heave, and pitch motions were recorded. A frequency and time domain analyses are conducted using the commercial software ANSYS AQWA. Different types of analyses are adopted to extract the viscous damping coefficient. The model was validated by comparing the results to those obtained from the experiments.

2 VISCOUS DAMPING

The potential flow theory assumes that the flow is inviscid, and hence the drag effect is neglected. To overcome this, the viscous damping coefficient corresponds is estimated manually from the free decay tests, and then included through a **[6x6]** damping matrix. The nonlinear equation of motion is expressed as:

$$(M+A)\ddot{y} + \underbrace{(B_{pot} + B_{viscous})\dot{y}}_{\text{Linear term}} + \underbrace{B_2\dot{y}|\dot{y}|}_{\text{Quadratic term}} + Cy = F(t) \quad (1)$$

where M is the body mass, A is the hydrodynamic mass B_{pot} is the potential damping, $B_{viscous}$ is the linear drag term, B_2 is the quadratic drag term, C is the restoring coefficient, y is the displacement and $F(t)$ is the wave-induced force. In the aforementioned equation there are both linear and nonlinear terms. Malta et al. (2010b) presented the methods adopted to determine the linear and nonlinear terms them from the experiments. However, is some particular cases, e.g. Coulling et al. (2013), Raed et al. (2020), only tuned quadratic damping matrix is adopted.

2.1 Linear analysis

The equation of motion for the free decay tests, considering the linear damping only without the presence of external force is given by:

$$(M+A)\ddot{y} + B_1\dot{y} + Cy = 0 \quad (2)$$

where B_1 is the linear damping term, while y is the displacement at any given time ($t_1, t_2, ...t_n$) and is given by:

$$y(t_1) = ae^{-\zeta\omega_n t_1}\cos(\omega_d t_1 + \varepsilon) \quad (3)$$

and

$$y(t_2) = ae^{-\zeta\omega_n t_2}\cos(\omega_d t_2 + \varepsilon) \quad (4)$$

where a is the amplitude, ζ is the damping ratio, ω_n is the natural frequency in rad/s, t is the time, ε is the phase angle in rad, ω_d is the damped natural frequency in rad/s, and t is the time in seconds. Eq.(4) can be written in the form of:

$$y(t_2) = a\,e^{-\zeta\omega_n(t_1+T_d)}\cos(\omega_d(t_1+T_d)+\varepsilon) \quad (5)$$

where T_d is the damped period in seconds and t_1 is the time where the first peak occurs. From eq.(3) and eq.(5), the ratio between $y(t_1)$ and $y(t_2)$ is equal to:

$$\frac{y(t_1)}{y(t_2)} = e^{\zeta\omega_n T_d} \quad (6)$$

By taking the natural logarithm of both sides of eq. (6), the logarithmic decrement (δ) is obtained and is given by:

$$\delta = \ln\left(\frac{y(t_1)}{y(t_2)}\right) = \zeta\omega_n T_d \quad (7)$$

The damped period (T_d) is given by

$$T_d = \frac{2\pi}{\omega_d} = \frac{2\pi}{\omega_n\sqrt{1-\zeta^2}} \quad (8)$$

where ζ is the damping ratio and equal to $B/B_{critical}$, ω_n and ω_d is the natural frequency and the damped frequency in rad/s, respectively. From Eqs. (7) and (8), ζ is given by:

$$\zeta = \frac{\delta}{\sqrt{(2\pi)^2 + \delta^2}} \quad (9)$$

2.2 Nonlinear analysis

According to eq.(1), the quadratic damping term is B_2. This procedure is based on the linearization of the term $\dot{x}|\dot{x}|$ which is given by, Chakrabarti (1994):

$$\dot{y}|\dot{y}| = \frac{8}{3\pi}\omega_n y_k \dot{y} \quad (10)$$

By substituting eq.(10) into eq.(1) considering no external force, it become:

$$(M+A)\ddot{y} + B_1\dot{y} + \frac{8B_2}{3\pi}\omega_n y_k \dot{y} + Cy = 0 \quad (11)$$

Therefore, the total damping ($\grave{B}$) is written as:

$$B' = B_1 + \frac{8B_2}{3\pi}\omega_n y_k \quad (12)$$

And the damping factor (ζ) including the linearized term is given by:

$$\zeta' = \frac{B'}{2(M+A)\omega_n} \quad (13)$$

From the equations, we end-up by the following equation:

$$\frac{1}{2\pi}\ln\frac{y_{k-1}}{y_{k+1}} = \zeta + \frac{4}{3\pi}\cdot\frac{B_2}{M+A}y_k \quad (14)$$

The equation is a straight-line one with the left-hand side represent the Y-axis and the y_K in the right-hand side represent the X-axis. So, by knowing the peak values from the free decay test, the relation is established, and a straight line is fitted using the least squares method. The slope and the intercept of that line represent the linear damping ratio (ζ) and the term $[4B_2/3\pi(M+A)]$, respectively. For more details refer to chapter 10 in Chakrabarti (1994) and Malta et al. (2010a).

3 TEST DESCRIPTION

The surge, heave, and pitch motions for the spar platform are investigated through experimental activity carried out using 1:60 Froude scale model. The tests were executed in a 4 m wide wave flume at the Department of Ocean Engineering, Indian Institute of Technology Madras (IITM), Tamil Nadu, India. During the tests, the water level was 2.5 m and two steel disks were attached to the bottom of the spar to attain the desired loading condition as shown in Figure 1.

Figure 2 shows the plan and side views of the experiment's configuration. The spar is moored by four steel cables; Each cable has one point fixed 0.62 m below sea water level and the other end attached to the tank bottom. Two wave probes were aligned with the center line of the spar at its both sides, and another two at 24.7 m from the wave generator to insure the 2D propagation of the waves generated. The spar was mounted by two accelerometers and one inclinometer as shown in Figure 3. The surge acceleration, heave acceleration, pitch, and roll motions are recorded at 50 Hz sampling rate.

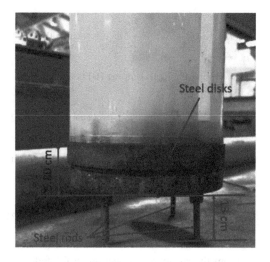

Figure 1. The steel disks (ballast) mounted to the bottom of the spar.

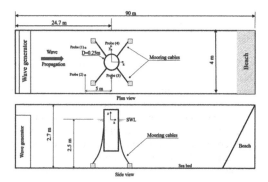

Figure 2. Plan view and side view of the 4 m wave flume and the configuration adopted in the experiments.

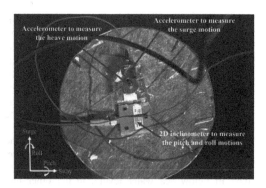

Figure 3. The inclinometer and the two accelerometers used to record the spar responses considered in this study.

4 NUMERICAL MODEL

A numerical model of the spar is developed using the commercial software ANSYS AQWA which is based on potential flow theory. The full characteristics of the spar model are shown in Table 1.

A convergence analysis is performed for a mesh sizes ranging from 1 cm to 4 cm with an interval of 0.5 cm. A maximum element size of 3 cm is adopted as it gives the most accurate displaced volume and metacentric height. The meshed model is shown in Figure 4 which results in 3,224 diffracting elements.

Table 1. Spar platform characteristics used in the experiments.

	Scale model (1/60)
Diameter [m]	0.250
Draft [m]	1.220
Freeboard [m]	0.330
Water depth [m]	2.500
Mass including ballast [kg]	60.14
Center of Mass below SWL [m]	0.953
Center of buoyancy below SWL [m]	0.610
k_{xx}, roll radius of gyration about COG [m]	0.415
k_{uy}, pitch radius of gyration about COG [m]	0.415
k_{zz}, yaw radius of gyration about COG [m]	0.100

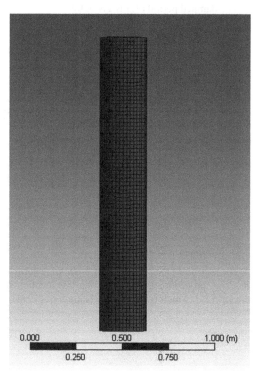

Figure 4. Spar geometry using ANSYS AQWA.

Table 2. Mooring characteristics adopted in the experiments.

Number of mooring lines	4
Angle between lines	90°
Radius to the fixed points from the spar center line	1.350 m
Radius to fairleads from the spar center line	0.125 m
Fairleads below SWL	0.640 m
Unstretched line length	2.750 m
Mooring line diameter	3E-03 m
Equivalent mooring line mass density	5E-02 kg/m
Extensional stiffness (*EA*)	3E+06 N
Maximum tension	100 N

4.1 Mooring specification

The mooring characteristic used in the numerical model are presented in Table 2.

5 RESULTS

In this section, the free decay tests of the spar platform will be discussed presented followed by the experimental and numerical responses in regular and irregular waves, respectively.

5.1 Free decay tests

Heave and pitch free decay tests are conducted to determine the natural periods of the free-floating spar platform. The natural periods of the heave and pitch are 2.3 s and 1.9 s, respectively. The viscous damping is calculated by adopting both linear and nonlinear analyses. The former results in a pure linear damping coefficient (B_1), whereas the latter results in a combination of linear and quadratic coefficients ($B_1 + B_2$). Afterwards, the viscous damping effect is considered in the potential flow-based software through the addition of a damping matrix, hence, its influence on the global motion is accounted. The coefficients matrix obtained from both type of analyses, are summarized in Table 3.

The free decay tests are simulated in AQWA using identical initial displacement as the tests. A comparison between the measured free decay, the numerical simulation of the free decay adopting the pure linear damping coefficient, and the combined damping coefficients is shown in Figure 5. A sample of 25 s for the for the heave acceleration and pitch free decay are shown in plot (a) and plot (b), respectively.

No major deviation is observed in the results as the maximum deviation reported is 4.5%. Additionally, it should be noted that the number of peaks used in the nonlinear analysis is a key factor to achieve accurate coefficient's values. In this study, 22 positive peaks are considered to fit the curve as described in eq. (14).

The natural period for the 6-degree of freedoms of the spar platform are extracted from ANSYS AQWA for both the free floating and moored structure. Then, the results are compared to those obtained from the experiments and the results are presented in Table 4.

5.2 Tuned quadratic damping

From the simultaneous study performed on the same spar subjected to regular waves, it has been observed that this specific loading condition experienced a higher pitch motion. The reason behind that the heave and pitch natural periods fall in the wave period range. Therefore, the nonlinear drag should be considered as it plays a pivotal role in the extreme motions.

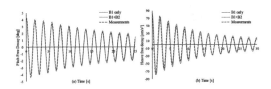

Figure 5. Free decay test for the (a) pitch and (b) heave.

Table 3. Values of the linear and quadratic damping extracted from the free decay tests.

	Heave		Pitch	
Linear analysis (B_1)	B_1, N/(m/s)		B_1, N.m/(rad/s)	
	8.20		0.90	
Nonlinear analysis ($B_1+ B_2$)	B_1, N/(m/s)	B_2, N/(m/s)²	B_1, N.m/(rad/s)	B_2, N.m/(rad/s)²
	6.65	0.1026	0.9495	0.3498

Table 4. Mooring characteristics adopted in the experiments.

	T_n [s] Experiments	T_n [s] AQWA – free floating	T_n [s] AQWA – moored
Surge	-	-	51.32
Sway	-	-	51.32
Heave	2.30	2.29	2.36
Pitch	1.93	2.05	2.06
Roll	1.93	2.05	2.06
Yaw	-	-	15.43

A tuned quadratic damping matrix is set, and the Response Amplitude Operators (RAOs) are compared to those obtained from the regular wave's tests as shown in Figure 6. The values of the tuned quadratic damping used in the numerical model are shown in Table 5.

Herein, the focus will be directed to the RAOs obtained from adopting the quadratic damping values. The memory effect of the mooring cables on the spar's response are explored by investigating it with and without the cable dynamics. Both nonlinear Froude-Krylov force and nonlinear hydrostatic stiffness are considered due to their major impact in case of large motion amplitudes. Briefly speaking, it is noticed that considering the cable dynamics alongside the quadratic damping matrix does not have a great influence on the RAOs. All the results are compared to those obtained from the measured data as shown in Figure 6. In case of the response results from adopting the quadratic damping, it is observed that the cable dynamic slightly affects the heave acceleration in Test 10, Test 12, and Test 19. It results in 7%, 5% and 5% lower heave acceleration compared to response obtained when neglecting the cable dynamics for tests 10, 12 and 19, respectively. On the other hand, the effect of the cable dynamics in case of the surge and pitch response could be negligible. Taking a deeper look into the RAOs, considering the quadratic damping (QD) together with the cable dynamics results in a quite good agreement between the numerical and experiments in all the tests. It is reported that adopting QD results in 4% lower surge RAO in Test 10 compared to that obtained from the experiments. Moreover, the deviation in the heave response is quite notable as it results in 31% and 21% higher heave RAO in Test 12 and Test 19, respectively. Moreover, it results in 50% lower heave in Test 10 compared to the experiments. In case of pitch motion, considering QD results in 23.9% lower pitch RAO compared to that obtained from thee measured data in Test 10.

5.3 Irregular wave test

Four irregular waves are considered in this part of the study with a target significant wave height (H_s) and peak period (T_p) summarized in Table 6. All the irregular waves undergo calibration by analyzing the wave profile. Table 6 shows a comparison between the calibrated and the target values for H_s and T_p. It is observed that that the calibrated H_s always differ from its target value. A deviation of 4.40% is reported in Test 30 between the calibrated and the target H_s. Conversely, the calibrated and target T_p are quite identical in all the tests.

The irregular waves generated in the experimental activity were based on the Joint North Sea Project (JONSWAP) spectrum with peakedness factor equal to 3.3. Figure 7 presents a comparison between the

Table 6. Target and calibrated values for the irregular wave tests.

	H_{s_target} [cm]	T_{p_target} [s]	f_{p_target} [Hz]	$H_{s\_calibrated}$ [cm]	Error in H_s
Test 30	5.00	2.00	0.50	4.78	4.40%
Test 31	5.00	2.30	0.43	4.64	0.40%
Test 32	3.00	1.70	0.59	2.87	4.33%
Test 33	3.00	2.00	0.50	2.91	3.00%

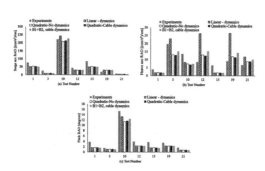

Figure 6. Comparison between the RAOs obtained from AQWA using linear damping and the experimental data for the (a) surge, (b) heave and (c) pitch motion of the spar platform.

Table 5. Tuned quadratic damping values for the heave, pitch, and roll motions.

	Heave [N/(m/s)^2]	Roll [N.m/(rad/s)^2]	Pitch [N.m/(rad/s)^2]
QD	350.00	2.00	2.00

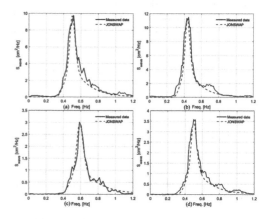

Figure 7. Comparison between the JOSNWAP and the measured wave spectrum for (a) Test 30 (b), Test 31(c) Test 32 and (d) Test 33.

JONSWAP spectrum estimated by using the target values for H_s and T_p, and the measured wave spectrum (S_{wave}). The figure consists of four plots corresponds to the four irregular tests considered.

It is observed that the JONSWAP spectrum excellent agree with the measured wave spectrum for all the tests considered.

Figure 8 to Figure 11 present comparisons between the numerical results using the quadratic

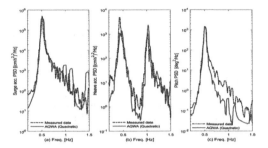

Figure 8. Comparison between the measured data and the numerical simulation for (a) surge acceleration, (b) heave acceleration and (c) pitch for Test 30 (H_s = 5 cm, f_p= 0.5 Hz).

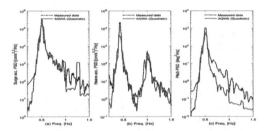

Figure 9. Comparison between the measured data and the numerical simulation for (a) surge acceleration, (b) heave acceleration and (c) pitch for Test 31 (H_s = 5 cm, f_p= 0.43 Hz).

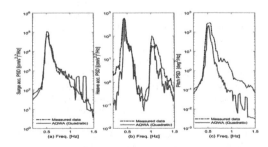

Figure 10. Comparison between the measured data and the numerical simulation for (a) surge acceleration, (b) heave acceleration and (c) pitch for Test 32 (H_s = 3 cm, f_p = 0.59 Hz).

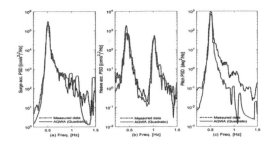

Figure 11. Comparison between the measured data and the numerical simulation for (a) surge acceleration, (b) heave acceleration and (c) pitch for Test 33 (H_s = 3 cm, f_p= 0.5 Hz).

damping matrix and experimental spectra for the four irregular tests. Each figure comprises the surge acceleration, the heave acceleration and the pitch motion spectra result from the numerical simulations and the experiments. The horizontal axis represents the frequency in Hz, whereas the vertical axis represents the power density (PSD) of the response. The numerical spectra agree well with those obtained from the measured data and all the resonances are perfectly captured. Particularly speaking, the numerical heave acceleration in all the tests results in a considerably identical spectrum to the ones obtained from the measured data as shown in plot (b) in all the figures. Also, the numerical surge acceleration and pitch spectra which are presented in plot-(a) and (c), respectively, agree well with the measured data especially for the first-order motions. However, the deviation starts to be notable in the high frequency range (>0.6 Hz) in both response results in all the tests.

Also, it noticed that the heave response's combination resonances that occur at 0.43 Hz and 1 Hz which represent the heave natural frequency ($f3n$) and the sum of the wave-induced frequency and pitch natural frequency ($fwave + f5n$) are captured well by the numerical model.

The root mean square (RMS) of each numerical spectrum are explored and compared to those obtained from the experimental activity. In this part, the results obtained from the linear damping, the combined damping and the quadrating damping are included. Figure 12 shows the results of the RMS for the surge, heave, and pitch motions. Regarding the influence of the damping type, it is observed that identical results in most of the tests are obtained. For instance, adopting the quadratic damping in Test 30 results in 19.8% higher surge RMS, 9.9% lower heave RMS, and 2.2% lower pitch RMS compared to those obtained from the measured data. Regarding Test 31, adopting the quadratic damping results in a quite high deviation between the simulated and the measured heave RMS. The numerical model underpredicts the heave RMS by 44%.

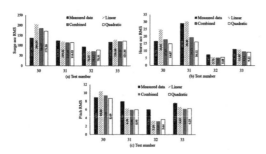

Figure 12. Comparison between the RMS for the (a) surge, (b) heave and (c) pitch results from the measured signal and the numerical simulations adopting pure linear and combined damping.

6 CONCLUSIONS

The heave, surge and pitch responses of a spar platform were investigated through experiments and numerical simulations. The experiments were carried out using a 1:60 Froude scale model in a wave flume in irregular waves with different wave heights and periods. The spar was moored with four wire steel cables forming a slack mooring system. The numerical model was carried out using ANSYS AQWA. Two type of analyses were conducted to extract the viscous damping from the free decay tests and their influence on the results were studied. Then, the model was validated by comparing the results to those obtained from the experiments. Due to the importance of nonlinear drag in case of extreme response, a tuned quadratic damping matrix was adopted in the numerical model.

The numerical simulations using quadratic damping matric agree well with the experimental measurements for all the responses considered. The numerical model captured the first-order resonance as well as the combination resonance. The root mean square (RMS) of the numerical and experimental spectra were compared, and the results agree with each other's. No major difference was reported between the RMS and the skewness results obtained by adopting different types of damping, except for the heave response. Additionally, it was found that deviation is remarkable in the kurtosis results (4th moment).

ACKNOWLEDGEMENTS

This work was done under the framework of the joint research project "Large Multipurpose platforms for exploiting Renewable energy in Open Seas" funded by Marie Curie action FP7-PEOPLE-2013-IREAS. The experimental work was carried out in the wave flume of the department of ocean engineering in the Indian Institute and Technology, Madras. The authors would like to express special thanks to Prof. Sundar and Prof. Srineash for providing support during the experimental activity. This work contributes to the Strategic Research Plan of the Centre for Marine Technology and Ocean Engineering (CENTEC), which is financed by the Portuguese Foundation for Science and Technology (Fundação para a Ciência e Tecnologia - FCT) under contract UIDB/UIDP/00134/2020.

REFERENCES

Al-Solihat, M. K. and Nahon, M. 2016. Stiffness of slack and taut moorings. *Ships and Offshore Structures*, 11, 890–904.

Chakrabarti, K. 1994. Offshore Stucture Modelng. *Advanced Series on Ocean Engineering* World Scientific Publishing Co. Ptc. Ltd.

Choi, E.-Y., Jeong, W.-B. and Cho, J.-R. 2016. Combination resonances in forced vibration of spar-type floating substructure with nonlinear coupled system in heave and pitch motion. *International Journal of Naval Architecture and Ocean Engineering*, 8, 252–261.

Coulling, A. J., Goupee, A. J., Robertson, A. N., Jonkman, J. M. and Dagher, H. J. 2013. Validation of FAST semi-submersible floating wind turbine numerical model with DeepCwind test data. *Journal of Renewable Energy*, 023116 (5), 1–29.

Haslum, H. A. and Faltinsen, O. M. 1999. Alternative Shape of Spar Platforms for Use in Hostile Areas. *Offshore Technology Conference*. Houston, Texas: Offshore Technology Conference.

He, H., Troesch, A. W. and Perlin, M. Hydrodynamics of Damping Plates at Small KC Numbers. *In:* Kreuzer, E., ed. IUTAM Symposium on Fluid-Structure Interaction in Ocean Engineering, 2008//2008 Dordrecht. Springer Netherlands, 93–104.

Hegseth, J. M. and Bachynski, E. E. 2019. A semi-analytical frequency domain model for efcient design evaluation of spar floating wind turbines. *Marine Structure*, 64, 186–210.

Jain, A. and Agarwal, A. 2003. Dynamic Analysis of Offshore Spar Platforms. *Defence Science Journal*, 53, pp. 211–219.

Jang, H. and Kim, M. 2019. Mathieu instability of Arctic Spar by nonlinear time-domain simulations. *Ocean Engineering*, 176, 31–45.

Jeon, S. H., Cho, Y. U., Seo, M. W., Cho, J. R. and Jeong, W. B. 2013. Dynamic response of floating substructure of spar-type offshore wind turbine with catenary mooring cables. *Ocean Engineering*, 72, 356–364.

Jonkman, J. 2010. Definition of the Floating System for Phase IV of OC3.

Koo, B. J., Kim, M. H. and Randall, R. E. 2004. Mathieu instability of a spar platform with mooring and risers. *Ocean Engineering*, 31, pp. 2175–2208.

Lake, M., He, H., Troesch, A. W., Perlin, M. and Thiagarajan, K. P. 1999. Hydrodynamic Coefficient Estimation for TLP and Spar Structures. *Journal of Offshore Mechanics and Arctic Engineering*, 122, 118–124.

Lavrov, A. and Guedes Soares, C. 2016. Modelling the heave oscillations of vertical cylinders with damping plates. *The International Journal of Maritime Engineering* 158(A3), A187–A197.

Loken, R., Laukeland, L. and Hannus, H. 2012. The belly Spar-design and verifcation of an ultra deep water solution. *Offshore Technology Conference*. Houston, Texas, USA: Offshore Technology Conference.

Malta, E., Matsumoto, F., Fujarra, A., Gonçalves, R., Pereira, F. and Nishimoto, K. Damping coefficient analyses for floating offshore structures. 29th International Conference on Ocean, Offshore and Arctic Engineering (OMAE), 2010a Shanghai, China. pp. 1–8.

Malta, E. B., Goncalves, Rodolfo T., Matsumoto, F. T., Pereira, F. R., Fujarra, A. L. C. and Nishimoto, K. 2010b. Damping Coefficient Analyses for Floating Offshore Structures. *International Conference on Ocean, Offshore and Arctic Engineering*. Shanghai, China.

Murray, J. and Yang, C. K. 2009. SS: Spar Technology: A Comparison of the Spar and Single Column Floater in an Arctic Environment. *Offshore Technology Conference*. Houston, Texas: Offshore Technology Conference.

Nallayarasu, S. and Mathai, T. P. 2016. Effect of Mathieu instability on motion response of Spar hull with heave damping plate. *Ships and Offshore Structures*, 11, 833–846.

Nallayarasu, S. and Saravanapriya, S. 2013a. Experimental and Numerical Investigation of Hydrodynamic Response of Spar with Wind Turbine Under Random Waves. *International Journal of Ocean and Climate Systems*, 4, 261–282.

Nallayarasu, S. and Saravanapriya, S. 2013b. Experimental and Numerical Investigation on Hydrodynamic Response of Spar with Wind Turbine under Regular Waves. *The International Journal of Ocean and Climate Systems*, 4, 239–260.

Raed, K., Teixeira, A. P. and Guedes Soares, C. 2020. Uncertainty assessment for the extreme hydrodynamic responses of a wind turbine semi-submersible platform using different environmental contour approaches. *Ocean Engineering*, 195, 106719.

Ran, Z., Kim, M. H., Niedzwecki, J. M. and Johanson, R. P. 1996. Responses of a Spar Platform In Random Waves And Currents (Experiment Vs. Theory). *International Journal of Offshore and Polar Engineering*, 6(1), 1–8.

Rho, J. B., Choi, H. S., Lee, W. C., Shin, H. S. and Park, I. K. 2002. Heave And Pitch Motions of a Spar Platform With Damping Plate. *The 12th International Offshore and Polar Engineering Conference*. Kitakyushu, Japan: International Society of Offshore and Polar Engineers.

Subbulakshmi, A. and Sundaravadivelu, R. 2016. Heave damping of spar platform for offshore wind turbine with heave plate. *Ocean Engineering*, 121, 24–36.

Sudhakar, S. and Nallayarasu, S. 2013. Hydrodynamic Response of Spar with Single and Double Heave Plates in Regular Waves. *International Journal of Ocean System Engineering*, 3, 188–208.

Tao, L. and Cai, S. 2004. Heave motion suppression of a Spar with a heave plate. *Ocean Engineering*, 31, 669–692.

Thiagarajan, K. P. and Troesch, A. W. 1998. Effects of appendages and small currents on the hydrodynamic heave damping of TLP columns. *Journal of Offshore Mechanics and Arctic Engineering*, 120, 37–42.

Xu, S., Wang, S. and Guedes Soares, C. 2019. Review of mooring design for floating wave energy converters. *Renewable and Sustainable Energy Reviews*, 111, 595–621.

Yong-Pyo, H., Dong-Yeon, L., Yong-Ho, C., Sam-Kwon, H. and Se-Eun, K. 2005. An Experimental Study On the Extreme Motion Responses of a SPAR Platform In the Heave Resonant Waves. *The Fifteenth International Offshore and Polar Engineering Conference*. Seoul, Korea: International Society of Offshore and Polar Engineers.

Zhao, J., Tang, Y. and Shen, W. 2010. A study on the combination resonance response of a classic spar platform. *Journal of Vibration and Control*, 16(14), 2083–2107.

Levelized cost of energy of offshore floating wind turbines in different case scenarios of the Madeira Islands

S. Ramos, H. Diaz, D. Silva & C. Guedes Soares
Centre for Marine Technology and Ocean Engineering (CENTEC), Instituto Superior Técnico, Universidade de Lisboa, Lisbon, Portugal

ABSTRACT: One of the main energy-related challenges of Madeira Islands in the scope of EU2020 is the increase of the renewable energy electrical share in the islands up to 50%. The purpose of this paper is to carry a comparative economic assessment of deploying floating wind turbines in three different marine areas of Madeira's coast, and for different energetic case scenarios. The wind farms are designed to produce enough offshore wind renewable energy to achieve the EU2020 objectives, and also in a 100% fossil fuel islands scenario. The evaluation is made through the spatial computation of the Levelized Cost Of Energy and the energy integration costs using the phases of their life cycle and through Geographic Information System methodologies. The results provide information on the available potential of offshore wind energy at or below a given cost in the three different marine areas.

1 INTRODUCTION

In the Madeira Islands, located to the south-west of Portugal, the electrical energy demand has been continuously increasing since 2013 at an annual rate of 0,5% (ERSE, 2018). The increase of energy demand, together with the environmental impacts caused by the predominant use of fossil fuels in the islands (which constituted the 72% of the electric share in 2017), raised severe energy-related challenges in the last decades. Those challenges aimed to inspire the archipelago to fulfil the latest climate and energy targets set up for these islands in the scope of EU2020. The main goals established were the reduction of CO2 emissions in 20% of the emitted in 2005 and to increase the renewable energy share in the islands electrical market up to 50%. (AREAM, 2012).

Islands like the ones of Madeira's archipelago present sustainable-energy growth challenges for different reasons such as remoteness, distance from the big continental energy networks, limited energy resources, strong dependence on hydrocarbon availability and vulnerability to fluctuations on the fuel's price. (AREAM et al., 2012).

Currently, renewable energy represents 28% of the electric market in Madeira Islands, being the most representative the onshore wind and hydropower energies. For both inhabited islands of Madeira, it is crucial to increase the level of energy self-sufficiency to achieve, even late, the objectives set up for EU 2020. This can only be done by deploying new types of renewable energy since the distance and depth to the mainland makes underwater electrical connection economically unviable.

However, available land is scarce in the archipelago, and more than 75% of Madeira's inland territory is under some degree of protection (Benzaken & Renard, 2010).

Nevertheless, being a small island has other advantages, like having vast ocean resources at disposal in comparison with the land regions. Therefore, efforts should be focused on taking advantage of the marine resource and lead the strategies towards different ways of marine energy. These strategies would help to reduce energy dependence and guarantee competitiveness, economic sustainability, employment and quality of life.

Fixed offshore wind energy in North European coastal regions, has been rapidly developed in shallow water during the last years and few wind farms (WFs) are being successfully explored (Diaz & Guedes Soares, 2020).

However, the limited availability of shallow water areas around Madeira raises the necessity for projecting floating wind turbines that could be set up in water depths up to 1000m. A review on the evolution of the offshore wind technology can be found in Guedes Soares et al. (2014).

The floating technology is more unmatured and still needs to overcome critical technological barriers to achieve durability and cost-efficiency. Several floating concepts are under development: semisubmersible (WindFloat and FLOAT-GEN), spar

(Hywind, SWAY) and tension leg platforms (TLWT, TLB). A brief description of them can be found in Bagbanci et al. (2012) and in Mhyr et al. (2014). Comparisons of the motion response between concepts can also be found in Bagbanci et al. (2015) and Vijay et al. (2020).

Included in the scope of the ARCWIND project (ARCWIND, 2017), the purpose of the present paper is to carry a comparative spatial-economic assessment of the deployment of floating wind turbines in three different marine areas of Madeira's coast, and for different energetic case scenarios. The wind farms are designed to produce enough renewable energy to achieve 50% of renewable energy electric share in the region, and also in a hypothetical 100% fossil fuel islands scenario. The current renewable energy deficit is supposed to be fully covered by the contribution of offshore wind energy.

The evaluation is made through the spatial computation, of the Levelized Cost Of Energy (LCOE) using the phases of their life cycle and through Geographic Information System (GIS) methodologies. Integration costs have also been taken into account to calculate the total wind energy cost. The results will provide information on the available potential of offshore wind energy at or below a given cost. Comparing these results to the current electricity cost allows determining if the offshore wind energy potential is economically viable, and which of the three previously selected locations would be more cost-effective. The results constitute a useful tool which helps to support the spatial decision making when projecting the setup of an offshore wind farm (OWF) in the Madeira Islands.

The structure of this paper is organized as follows. Section 2 includes a brief description of the area of interest. Section 3 describes the methodology developed in the study to determine offshore wind cost. Moreover, the section includes an energetic and spatial description of the area and the different case studies. Section 4 provides the main results. Section 5 concludes.

2 AREA OF STUDY

This study is performed in the coastal waters of the Autonomous Region of Madeira, a volcanic archipelago located in the south-west coast of the Portuguese continent. Madeira Islands are constituted by three major islands: Madeira, to the west; Porto Santo in the north-east; and Desert Island to the south. All together form an area of 801 km2, being the island of Madeira the biggest one with a land surface of 741 km2 (Figure 1).

Madeira has an average population density of 317 inhabitants per km2. Almost half of the autonomous region's population concentrates around the capital (Funchal), located in the south coast of Madeira island, where the density reaches around 1500 inhabitants per km2 (PORDATA, 2018).

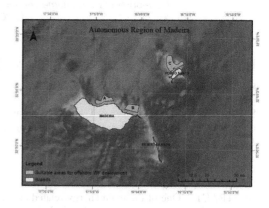

Figure 1. Feasible areas for the deployment of offshore wind farms in Madeira's Archipelago.

About 40% of the territory of Madeira Islands are protected, and all the Desert Islands are natural reserves (Joyce & Woodward, 2015).

The richness on the landscape of the region makes it especially interesting for the tourism, which currently constitutes the most significant engine of the Madeira's economy, even though agriculture, small fishing industries and wine production also make an essential contribution to the regional economy.

Understandably, land availability is an issue on the islands. There is strong territorial pressure on the islands and finding available land for renewable facilities is difficult since they compete with urban, rural, agriculture and tourist developments. Therefore, offshore energy exploration seems to constitute an excellent alternative to boost the renewable energy market share in the islands.

To evaluate the economic viability of floating offshore wind farms development, just previously selected marine areas A, B and C (Figure 1) are considered in this study. These areas were previously determined as the only available ones for the deployment of floating offshore wind farms under the scope of the ARCWIND project. Different technical and spatial exclusion criteria were taken into account for the area selection, such as met-ocean conditions, bathymetry constraints, proximity to facilities, environmental impacts, and other marine uses. Diaz et al. (2019) explain more in-depth the procedure for this site selection.

3 METHODOLOGY

This paper analyses the Life Cycle Cost (LCC) of floating wind farms deployment in three selected areas of Madeira's coastal region. The wind farm will be dimensioned for different energetic case scenarios so that the renewable energy electric share in Madeira reaches the value of 50% and 100% in the islands of Madeira and Porto Santo, both together and independently.

The LCC analysis is later expanded into a spatial-economic Levelized Cost of Energy (LCOE) analysis. The LCOE allows evaluating the LCC results with regards to expected annual energy production in the three different marine areas, underscoring the importance of geospatial site variations on the costs. The LCOE analysis results are the constant unit cost per energy unit of a series of cash flows adding up to the total life cycle cost of the energy generating facility (Bjerkseter & Ågotnes, 2013).

The LCOE can be understood as the minimum unit price for which energy has to be sold to break even on the total investment (Black & Veatch, 2010).

Integration costs are also taken into account and add up to the LCOE to calculate the total wind energy cost and analyse the viability of the offshore wind exploration compared to the current electricity price.

It is important to note that this analysis does not aim to estimate wind electricity costs at any of the locations precisely but to make a comparative techno-economic analysis between the different areas.

3.1 Energy framework analysis in Madeira Islands

Average annual electricity production in the Archipelago of Madeira has been increasing since 2013 at a yearly rate of 0.5% (ERSE, 2018). From the latest available data, it was retrieved an average electric energy production of 867.4 GWh in 2017 (EEM, 2018). The electricity generated is spatially spread through two autonomous electrical grids, one for each Island.

Currently, renewable energy represents a 28.1% of the electric market in the archipelago, while fossil fuels are still the main engine for electricity production. However, renewable energy penetration is not the same in both of the inhabited islands of Madeira. In 2017, the renewable energy in the main Island, called Madeira, constituted a 28.6% of the electric share, almost double than its neighbour island Porto Santo, where the renewables penetration was 15.3%. This difference is mostly due to the poor hydrographic conditions existing in Porto Santo Island, which make impossible the exploration of hydraulic energy. Figure 2 summarizes the energetic production of both islands in the archipelago.

3.2 Spatial characteristics

Each offshore wind site location has a unique set of geospatial variables related to the cost of electric energy delivery. These spatial variables include the quality of the wind resource, turbine accessibility as a result of varying sea states, distance from harbour infrastructures, water depth, substructure suitability and distance to the inland electrical grid. For example, sites that are closer to shore may benefit from lower electric transmission costs, construction costs or operation and maintenance (O&M) costs. However, sites farther from shore may benefit from lower prices as a result of higher energy production (Beiter et al., 2016).

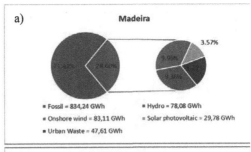

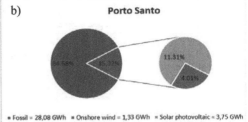

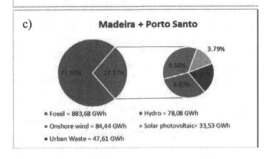

Figure 2. Breakdown of the electric market characteristics in the in both Madeira and Porto Santo (a and b) and the full archipelago as a whole (c) (Source: EEM, 2018).

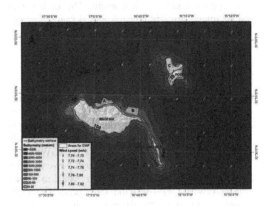

Figure 3. Wind and water depth characteristics in Madeira's region. Wind speed is given at 105m height.

Figures 3 and 4 include maps showing the spatial characteristics of the study area (wind, bathymetry, distance to the port, distance to inland electrical grid), with a spatial resolution of 225 m.

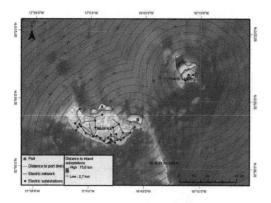

Figure 4. Distance to port and to inland electrical grids of selected offshore regions.

Areas A and B, located to the north of Madeira island's coastal waters, constitute an area of 51,5 and 56,2 km2 respectively. Those areas cover water depths between 50 and 1000m. The third restricted C area, the biggest and shallowest one, extends over an area of 87,8 km2 of Porto Santo's northern coastal waters and covers 20 to 300m water depths.

Using data from the last 40 years (1979-2018) (Dee et al., 2011), an average wind speed of 7.78 m/s was observed over A, B and C areas at 105m high (height of the considered turbine's hub).

The average significant wave height in the archipelago is approximately 1.8m in the summertime and 2.8m in wintertime (Rusu et al, 2008; Rusu & Guedes Soares, 2012). Therefore, the overall met-ocean characteristics in the region have been considered moderate.

Areas B and C are relatively close to inland ports (4km to 16km), while the nearest port from region A is approximately 25 km away. The distance to insular inland grids in areas A and B rages between 3 and 9km, however, in location C this distance goes up to almost 16 km.

3.3 *Case studies*

For the dimensioning and projection of the potential wind farm layout, six energetic case scenarios will be considered. C1) The wind farm needs to supply enough energy to rise the renewable energy electric share up to 50% in Madeira Island (178.61GWh). C2) The wind farm needs to provide enough power to raise the RE electric share to 100% in Madeira Island (595.73 GWh). C3) The wind farm needs to supply enough energy to rise the RE electric share up to 50% in Porto Santo Island (11.50GWh). C4) The wind farm needs to provide enough power to raise the RE electric share to 100% in Porto Santo Island (28.08 GWh). C5) The wind farm needs to supply enough energy to rise the renewable energy electric share up to 50% in both Madeira and P. Santo Islands (190.11GWh); C6) The wind farm needs to supply enough energy to rise the renewable energy electric share up to 100% in both Madeira and P. Santo Islands (623.81GWh).

3.4 *Wind farm layout*

The conceptual offshore wind power design considers turbines of 6.15 MW with a 152 m rotor and a semi-submersible floating platform. The turbine *Senvion 6.2M152* (see Table 1) and the platform *WindFloat* (Banister, 2017) were the technologies chosen for the projection of the wind farms. The turbine's power curve can be found in Figure 5.

Some advantages exist behind the selection of this platform, such as its small environmental impact (is fully removable), it can be located in depths up to 1000m, and it is built entirely onshore, thus is less dependent on the weather conditions (EWEA, 2013).

The turbine model was selected as the best adaptation to the mean wind speed in the chosen geographical area and the maximum availability of spatial-depending cost data, together with the platform, in previous literature (Beiter et al., 2016; Guerrero-Lemus, 2018).

The conceptual wind farms have been laid out with the minimum number of turbines required to achieve the energy targets in each case study.

To simplify the analysis, the turbines are laid out in the most square-shaped grid possible and with an inner distance between each turbine of 1 km radio

Table 1. Characteristics of selected turbine.

Model	Senvion 6.2M152
Rated Power	6150 kW
Rotor dimeter	152m
Cut-in speed	4 m/s
Cut-off speed	30 m/s
Rated wind speed	12 m/s
Hub height	100 m

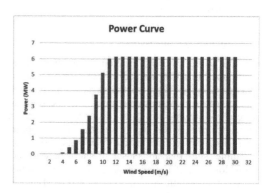

Figure 5. Turbine Senvion 6.2M152 power curve (Source: The WindPower, 2019).

(to minimize energy losses due to wake effects) (Myhr et al., 2014; Principle Power, 2011).

A simple radial inter-array connexion with 33kV cables between turbines is considered.

The distance from the WF to the inland grid for each case scenario determines the type of undersea export system transmission to be used and whether an offshore substation is needed. For distances below 9m from the island grid, no substation is needed, and 33kV cable is considered (i.e. when the WF is to be deployed in C for the supply of the closest Porto Santo island). When distances are higher, up to 100km, a substation and a 115 kV double transmission cable are considered as the most more economical choice (i.e. the WF is located in C for the supply of Madeira island) (Beiter et al., 2016).

Figure 6 shows a schematic general nine turbine layout for the case when an offshore substation is needed.

Throughout the results, the impact on the levelized costs of energy caused by variations on different parameters (farm capacity, water depth, offshore distance to inland ports and grids) will be evaluated.

3.5 LCOE analysis

Different methodologies have been developed to compute LCOE. However, the guidelines and formula followed in this analysis (Eq.1) are inspired in the NREL's method reported in Beiter et al. (2016).

$$LCOE = \frac{(FCR \times CAPEX) + OPEX}{AEP} \quad (1)$$

Where:
FCR = fixed charge rate (%).
AEP = net annual energy production (kWh/yr).
CapEx = capital expenditures (€).
OpEx = annual operational expenditures (€/yr).

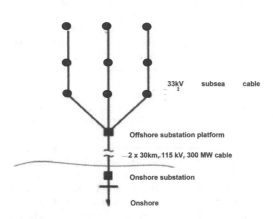

Figure 6. Windfarm generic layout with offshore substation.

3.5.1 Fixed charge rate:

The fixed charge rate represents the total financial cost. This factor is defined as the amount of revenue per euro of investment that must be collected annually to pay to carry charges on the investment as well as taxes. A weighted average cost of capital of 10.5% was applied in this study (Tegen et al., 2011; Beiter et al., 2016).

3.5.2 Net annual energy production:

Represent the potential energy that the conceptual wind farm can produce, considering the gross capacity factor. For each location x,y the AEP is calculated as a function of the characteristic power curve and the mean wind speed at the hub height following Equation 2 (Guerrero-Lemus et al., 2018) and Equation 3 (Hong & Möller., 2011). An energy loss factor (I_{loss}) is applied to account for transmission losses, wake effect losses, downtime losses due to maintenance, technical failure, etc.

Usually, the developers calculate energy losses in the order of magnitude of 10-15% below the theoretical power curves provided for the wind turbines (Wai-Hoo & Sovacool, 2014). A 10% energy loss was assumed; however, the potential offshore wind energy production is so high in comparison to the demand, that this reduction practically does not affect the analysis of results.

$$AEP = 8760h \times I_{loss} \times \sum_{j=V_e}^{V_a} P(v_{hubj}) \quad (2)$$

$$v_{hub} = v_1 \times \frac{\log(Z_{hub}/Z_0)}{\log(Z_1/Z_0)} \quad (3)$$

where:
v_e = cut-in wind speed (m/s)
v_a = cut-off wind speed (m/s)
v_{hub} = mean speed at the hub height (m/s)
I_{loss} = Energy loss facotor
v_1 = mean wind velocity at the lower height (m/s)
Z_0 = ocean surface roughness, a constant sea level roughness of 0.2 mm is assumed (Kalvig et al., 2014).
Z_1 = lower height (m)
Z_{hub} = upper hub height (m)

3.5.3 CAPEX and OPEX:

The CAPEX and OPEX parameters include the expenses associated with each phase of the wind turbine's life-cycle. A breakdown of the main phases can be found at Castro-Santos et al. (2016, 2017, 2020). In this study, these costs were broken into three categories following the method of Beiter et al. (2016): fixed costs, variable costs, and cost multipliers.

Fixed costs are those who do not have a perceptible relationship with the included spatial parameters based on current knowledge and/or market context. Variable costs are expenditures that have apparent relationships with spatial parameters. For example, installation costs are expected to vary with logistical distances (e.g., distance from port to the site), water depth, and met-ocean conditions. Cost multipliers are not explicitly linked to individual spatial factors but tend to vary with total project cost to reflect the complexity of other items. For instance, engineering and management costs incurred from financial close through commercial operations are applied as a percentage of CAPEX. To determine reasonable relationships between project economics with key spatial parameters at the selected locations, such as water depth (WD), distance to ports (Dp), distance to inland electrical grid (Dg), and wind farm capacity (Cwf), a series of parametric equations developed by the NREL in Beiter et al. (2016), Bjerkseter & Ågotnes (2013), and other authors included in Table 2 have been applied.

CAPEX and OPEX where calculated as per Equations 4 and 5, where C_x are the capital costs and O_x operation and maintenance expenditures, in euros. Table 2 gathers the costs considered in the study and shows the parametric equations used to calculate each cost.

$$CAPEX = \sum C_x \; (\text{€}) \quad (4)$$

$$OPEX = \sum O_x \; (\text{€}) \quad (5)$$

3.6 Integration costs

Although the main focus of this study is on offshore wind LCOE assessment, a coarse analysis of the economic viability of the offshore wind exploration is also assessed in a final step. The LCOE alone is not sufficient to determine a site's financial viability. Integration costs need to be considered to account for the adaptation of intermittent renewables into the current electricity market. The variability of renewables, even if correctly forecasted, results in increased regulation and ramping of the conventional system (Schallenberg-Rodríguez & Montesdeoca, 2017; Hirth et al., 2015).

According to Hirth et al. (2015), integration costs can be categorized as follows: balancing costs (caused by the deviation from the day-ahead generation schedules), grid-related costs (caused by grid extensions and reinforcements) and profile costs (related to the impact of the timing of the generation). These costs depend on the power system and increase with the penetration level of intermittent renewables. The calculation of a site-specific integration cost is out of the scope of this article. Nevertheless, integration costs are estimated in 30 €/MWh according to the study made by Hirth et al. (2015), after the review of 100 published studies. This integration cost is added to the average LCOE of each available region to calculate its global energy cost. Finally, a comparative analysis is made between the energy cost and the current electricity price, considered an average of 160 €/MWh (ERSE, 2019). in the islands, provides insights about whether the actual implementation of the proposed projects would be competitive with the current electricity market.

4 RESULTS

4.1 Dimension of the WF for each case scenario

Considering that the wind speed over the three areas is almost invariant, each single wind turbine would be able to produce an average of 21.58 GWh on selected areas. After the energetic analysis, different minimum number of turbines resulted to be needed to supply the different energy targets set up for each case study. For example, 9 turbines would be necessary to provide Madeira island with extra 178,61 GWh to reach a 50% renewable energy market share. In the case we would want to make 100% fossil fuel-free islands (case scenario 6), a wind farm composed of 29 turbines would be required. Table 3 shows the minimum number of turbines needed for each conceptual WF. It also includes the potential total installed capacity in each case scenario.

4.2 Potential LCOE

Figures 7 to 9 show the spatial distribution of the LCOE in the three restricted areas; each figure corresponds to one energetic case study.

Figure 7a and 7b represent the spatial LCOE resulting from the potential deployment of 9 and 28 wind farms, respectively, to supply energy to Madeira Island. Even though region C is characterised by shallower waters than A and B (which means lower mooring and installation costs), the long distances of this region to Madeira's landing electric points, imply higher prices of integration to the grid. The "distance to grid" variable resulted in being more influential than the "water depth" in the overall LCOE values. Therefore, LCOE in region C shows values between 17% and 40% higher than in areas A and B.

In Figures 8a and 8b, the potential LCOE of deploying a single and a double turbine wind farm for the energy supplying of Porto Santo can be observed.

Once again, the impact of the distance to the electrical grid on LCOE values makes the developing of the WF in region C the most cost-effective option, followed by region B, being A the most expensive region in both C3 and C4 case scenarios. Figures 9a and 9b show the potential LCOE of deploying a 9-turbine and a 29-turbine wind farm for the

Table 2. Cost Categories and cost spatial parametric equations.

	Cost (Cx)	Subscost	Category	Model	Units	Source
CapEx	C1: Turbine		Fixed	1,45	€/MW	Beiter el al. (2016)
	C2: Development		Fixed	0,18	€/MW	Beiter el al. (2016)
	C3: Port & Staging		Fixed	0,04	€/MW	Beiter el al. (2016)
	C4: Substructure		Fixed	7500000	€/Turb	Bjerkseter &Ågotnes (2013)
	C5: Mooring	Anchor	Fixed	114000	€/Turb	Bjerkseter &Ågotnes (2013)
		Chain	Spatially Variable	$250 \cdot (-1,5 \cdot WD+410)$	€/Turb	Bjerkseter &Ågotnes (2013)
	C6: Assembly and installation	Substructure	Spatially Variable	$(18408000 - 7875 \cdot WD + 24821 \cdot Dp/100)/1,0887$	€/Turb	Beiter el al. (2016)
		Turbine	Spatially Variable	$(48170500 + 95833 \cdot Dp)/1,0887$	€/Turb	Beiter el al. (2016)
		Port & Staging	Spatially Variable	$(12627913 - 2375 \cdot WD + 22565 \cdot Dp)/1,0887$	€/Turb	Beiter el al. (2016)
	C7: Electric System	Array system	Variable (with WF capacity)	$(1500000/1,0887) \cdot 7,8282 e^{(0,0073 \cdot Cwf)}$	€	Kaiser & Snyder (2010); Beiter el al. (2016)
		Export System	Spatially Variable	If Dg < 9km (No subestation); $(1500000/1,0887) \cdot Dg$	€	Beiter (2016); Bjerkester (2013)
				If 9km <Dg < 50km (Offshore subestation); $(2 \cdot 2000000 \cdot Dg +20000000)/1,0887$	€	Bjerkseter & Agotnes (2013); Beiter el al. (2016)
		Grid connection	Variable (with WF capacity)	$(100000/1,0887) \cdot Cwf$	€	Beiter el al. (2016)
	C8: Engineering & managment		Multiplier	3,5% CAPEX	€	Beiter el al. (2016)
	C9: Insurance		Multiplier	1% CAPEX	€	Beiter el al. (2016)
	C10: Comisioning		Multiplier	1% CAPEX	€	Beiter el al. (2016)
	C11: Installation Contingency		Multiplier	30% InstCAPEX	€	Beiter el al. (2016)
	C12: Procurment contingency		Multiplier	5% NonInstCAPEX	€	Beiter el al. (2016)
	C13: Decomissioning		Multiplier	Null. The decommissioning cost is considered to be balance by the steel scrap sales		Schallenberg-Rodríguez & Montesdeoca (2017)
OpEx	O1: Operations & maintenance		Variable	$y = 152941 \cdot Dp + 6E(+07)$	€/yr	Beiter el al. (2016)

energy supplying of both Madeira and Porto Santo in case scenarios C5 and C6 respectively.

In both cases, region B shows the lower values of LCOE, between 5 and 10% than in neighbour regions A and C. In all scenarios, the LCOE is higher for lower WF installed capacities. This is because, for the WF capacity ranges of this study, the export electric system costs have been considered dependent on the distance but constant with the installed capacity. However, electricity production does increases with the installed capacity. In other words, for same locations, a bigger WF requires the same investment on export cable than a small farm, but produces more electricity, resulting in lower LCOE values.

4.3 *Cost of energy and offshore wind viability*

For each marine region, the mean total electricity cost is included in Table 4. These values result after adding up the integration costs to the mean LCOE values of each area. When comparing these values to the current energy cost of 160 €/MWh in the island, only the offshore wind farm project in case scenario C2, and when deployed in regions A and B, shows more competitive cost values (155 €/MWh).

The remaining case scenarios show total electricity costs markedly higher than the current reference for electricity price in the islands. Especially high prices resulted in case scenarios C4 and C5 (single

Table 3. Wind Farm dimensions per energetic case scenario...

	Mean Net Energy production per turbine (GWh)	Minimum needed WF energy production (GWh)	Minimum number of needed turbines	Potential Installed capacity (MW)
CS1	21.64	178.61	9	55.35
CS2	21.64	595.73	28	172.20
CS3	21.64	11.50	1	6.15
CS4	21.64	28.08	2	12.30
CS5	21.64	190.11	9	55.35
CS6	21.64	623.81	29	178.35

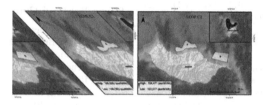

Figure 7. a) Spatial LCOE of deploying 9 turbines to supply energy to Madeira Island (C1) b) Spatial LCOE of deploying 28 turbines to supply energy to Madeira Island (C2).

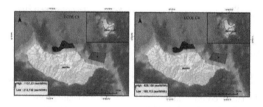

Figure 8. a) Spatial LCOE of deploying a single turbine WF to supply energy to Porto Santo Island (C3). b) Spatial LCOE of 2- turbines WF to supply energy to Porto Santo Island (C4).

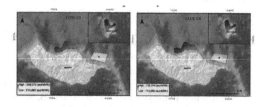

Figure 9. a) Spatial LCOE resulting from deploying 9 turbines to supply energy to Madeira and Porto Santo islands (C5) b) Spatial LCOE of deploying 29 turbines to supply energy to Madeira and Porto Santo islands (C6).

and double wind turbine/wind farm projects to supply energy to Porto Santo Island).

These values call into question the economic viability of setting up such a small size commercial wind farm.

5 DISCUSSION OF RESULTS

The results of this study are conditioned by some limitations that should be mentioned before the conclusions. The methodology used for the spatial-economic assessment in this study is based on existing cost model data and later implemented within the existing GIS data restrictions. No additional structural engineering analysis has been performed. Consequently, the technical simplifications and assumptions considered result in a certain level of incertitude on LCOE results.

However, it is essential to highlight that the main goal of this analysis is to develop a model that exhibit the relative differences in LCOE among potential sites rather than create estimations that accurately describe the absolute LCOE at a specific location.

The relationships among cost, capacity and spatial variables are also subject to a degree of uncertainty. Because no commercial-scale floating offshore wind power project has ever been installed, some costs and scaling assumptions were necessary. In some cases, the cost relationships have been derived from structural parameter studies using first-order design tools that do not fully compile to the rigour of pure engineering methods. The cost multipliers were determined using best-available knowledge, but they are not perfect due to the scarce of real commercial data.

Also, the economic assessment may be subject to uncertainty and fluctuations because of factors such as variability on exchange rates, commodity price, labour rates, supply and demand, etc. The fixed charge rate in this study was considered constant based on literature data. This assumption may not capture the full extent of this variability; different sites may have different risk profiles, which may trigger different return requirements that could have a material impact on LCOE values.

Additionally, the flat rate of 30 €/MWh has been considered for the integration cost, which is a reference value calculated in cases of mid-low levels of penetration of renewable energies on the electric market. Further detailed studies should be deployed to estimate the electricity system cost in scenarios with high penetration of renewable energy.

Considering the aforementioned, the results showed that a 50 MW wind farm would be enough to push the renewable energies up to 50% of the Archipelago's electric share, considering the current electrical requirements in Madeira Islands.

Table 4. LCOE and total cost of different semisubmersible wind farm projects in Madeira Islands.

	Mean wind speed (m/s)	Annual energy production (GWh)						LCOE (€/MWh)						Total cost (€/MWh)					
		C1	C2	C3	C4	C5	C6	C1	C2	C3	C4	C5	C6	C1	C2	C3	C4	C5	C6
A	7.78	194	605	21	43	194	626	153	125	1043	579	235	152	183	155	1073	609	265	182
B	7.81	196	609	21	43	195	630	155	125	741	427	216	145	185	155	771	457	246	175
C	7.77	194	603	21	43	194	625	231	151	291	194	238	152	261	181	321	224	268	182

Approximately 178 MW installed capacity would cover the renewable energies requirements to make the fossil free together with the other renewable energies currently existing.

The resulting LCOE values were found to be inversely proportional to the installed capacity. The reason relies on the fact that some investments, such as the submarine export cables, were considered constant with the wind farm capacity. The LCOE represents the project's total investment per expected annual energy production unit. Therefore, the smaller the wind farm is, the less energy produces, resulting in higher investment per megawatt produced.

6 CONCLUSIONS

From the results of this study, it can be concluded that the distance to the inland grid constitutes the most substantial spatial influence on LCOE values. This parameter showed to have a higher impact on LCOE than the water depth variable, or the distance to ports. Consequently, from the spatial, technical and economic point of view, the most suitable area to deploy an offshore wind farm to supply energy to Madeira Island would be region A, followed closely by region B. For the supply of Porto Santo, region C presented the most economic results. When it comes to the energy supply of both islands simultaneously, region B showed the lowest LCOE values due to its proximity to both islands.

When assessing the total energy cost, case scenario 2 (where 172 MW are installed for the supply of offshore wind to Madeira Island) resulted to be the only case where the final energy prices would be potentially competitive with the current electricity prices, when the turbines are placed on regions A or B.

Finally, some possible future changes in Madeira's electrical infrastructure should be taken into account in future projects which follow the line of this investigation. The electric link between Madeira and Porto Santo islands through a submarine cable connection has been already proposed by the EEM (Empresa de Eletricidade da Madeira), in the scope of the project "Sustainable Porto Santo-Smart Fossil Free Island" (R20, 2016; Gouveia, 2018).

The existence of this electric submarine cable may change the project layout and economic assessment of potential offshore wind farms in the archipelago radically.

ACKNOWLEDGMENTS

This study was completed within the project ARC-WIND - Adaptation and implementation of floating wind energy conversion technology for the Atlantic region, which is co-financed by the European Regional Development Fund through the Interreg Atlantic Area Programme under contract EAPA 344/2016. This work contributes to the Strategic Research Plan of the Centre for Marine Technology and Ocean Engineering (CENTEC), which is financed by the Portuguese Foundation for Science and Technology (Fundação para a Ciência e Tecnologia - FCT) under contract UIDB/UIDP/00134/2020.

REFERENCES

AREAM, DRCIE, & EEM S.A. 2012. Plano de ação para a energia sustentável. *Pact of Islands*: 58. Available at: http://drcie.gov-madeira.pt/drcie/index.php? option=com_content&view=article&id=408&Itemid=842

ARCWIND 2017. Adaptation and Implementation of Floating Wind Energy Conversion Technology for the Atlantic Region. Available at: http://www.arcwind.eu/

Banister, K. 2017. Principle Power, Inc. *WindFloat Pacific Project*. 33. At: https://www.osti.gov/servlets/purl/1339449

Bagbanci, H., Karmakar, D., & Guedes Soares, C. 2012. Review of offshore floating wind turbines concepts. *Maritime Engineering and Technology*, Guedes Soares, C. Garbatov Y. Sutulo S. & Santos T. A., (Eds.). London, UK: Taylor & Francis Group; pp.553–562. https://doi.org/10.1201/b12726-78

Bagbanci, H., Karmakar, D., & Guedes Soares, C. 2015. Comparison of spar and semisubmersible floater concepts of offshore wind turbines using long-term analysis. *Journal of Offshore Mechanics and Arctic Engineering*, 137(6). https://doi.org/10.1115/1.4031312

Beiter, P., Musial, W., Smith, A., Kilcher, L., Damiani, R., Maness, M., Scott, G. 2016. A Spatial-Economic Cost-Reduction Pathway Analysis for U.S. Offshore Wind Energy Development from 2015–2030. *September*. Available at: https://www.nrel.gov/docs/fy16osti/66579.pdf

Benzaken, D. & Renard, Y. 2010: Future directions for biodiversity action in Europe overseas: outcomes of the Review of the Implementation of the Convention on Biological Diversity. IUCN (ed.), *Appendix 8*: 39. ISBN 9782831713762. Available at: https://books.google.es/books?id=gIHG-Jq1TmcC Accessed: 15 November 2019).

Bjerkseter, C. & Ågotnes, A. 2013. Levelised cost of energy for offshore floating wind turbine concepts. *Department of Mathematical Sciences and Technology, University of Life Sciences*: 206.

Black & Veatch. 2010. *Technology Characterization for Renewable Energy Electricity Futures Study: GIS Database of Offshore Wind Resource Competing Uses and Environmentally Sensitive Areas*. Overland Park, KS: Unpublished report

Castro-Santos, L., Martins, E., & Guedes Soares, C. 2016. Methodology to calculate the costs of a floating offshore renewable energy farm. *Energies*, 9(5) pp. 324–350. https://doi.org/10.3390/en9050324

Castro-Santos, L.; Martins, E., & Guedes Soares, C. 2017; Economic comparison of technological alternatives to harness offshore wind and wave energies. *Energy*. 140:1121–1130.

Castro-Santos, L.; Silva, D.; Bento, A. R.; Salvacao, N., 2020. and Guedes Soares, C. Economic feasibility of floating offshore wind farms in Portugal. *Ocean Engineering*. 207: 107393

Dee, D.P., Uppala, S.M., Simmons, A.J., Berrisford, P., Poli, P., Kobayashi, S., Andrae, U., Balmaseda, M.A., Balsamo, G., Bauer, P. 2011. The ERA-Interim reanalysis: configuration and performance of the data assimilation system. *Quart J Meteorol Soc*. 137:553–597

Díaz, H., Fonseca, R. B., & Guedes Soares, C. 2019. Site selection process for floating offshore wind farms in Madeira Islands. In: *Advances in Renewable Energies Offshore*, Guedes Soares, C., (Ed.) Taylor & Francis Group, London, UK, 729–737.

Diaz, H. M. and Guedes Soares, C. 2020. Review of the current status, technology and future trends of offshore wind farms. *Ocean Engineering*. 209: 107381

EEM 2018. Annual Report Relatório e Contas. *Empresa de Eletricidade da madeira*: 7. Available at: https://www.eem.pt/media/353303/relat%C3%B3rio-e-contas-2017.pdf

ERSE 2018. Caracterização Da Procura. Lisboa: Entidade Reguladora Dos Serviços Energéticos (ERSE). Available at: https://www.erse.pt/media/ah5hh1m1/caracteriza%C3%A7%C3%A3o-procura-ee-2018-final-dez17.pdf

ERSE, 2019. Tarifas e Preços para a energia elétrica e outros serviços em 2019. Available at: https://www.erse.pt/atividade/regulacao/tarifas-e-precos-eletricidade/

EWEA 2013. Deep Water - The next step for offshore wind energy. *Brussels: European Wind Energy Association*: 13–26.

Gouveia, L. M. C. 2018. Projeto de Ligação Elétrica Entre a Ilha da Madeira e a Ilha do Porto Santo. *Master thesis*.

University of Madeira. http://hdl.handle.net/10400.13/2239

Guedes Soares, C., Bhattacharjee, J., and Karmakar, D. 2014. Overview and prospects for development of wave and offshore wind energy. *Brodogradnja* 65(2):87–109.

Guerrero-Lemus, R., Nuez, I. de la, & González-Díaz, B. (2018). Rebuttal letter to the article entitled: "Spatial planning to estimate the offshore wind energy potential in coastal regions and islands. Practical case: The Canary Islands." *Energy* 153: 12–16. https://doi.org/10.1016/j.energy.2018.03.091

Hirth, L., Ueckerdt, F., & Edenhofer, O. 2015. Integration costs revisited - An economic framework for wind and solar variability. *Renewable Energy* 74: 925–939. https://doi.org/10.1016/j.renene.2014.08.065

Hong, L., & Möller, B. 2011. Offshore wind energy potential in China: Under technical, spatial and economic constraints. *Energy*, 36(7),4482–4491. https://doi.org/10.1016/j.energy.2011.03.071

Joyce, A. Q. & Woodward, S. L. 2015. Madeira Archipelago. ABC-CLIO (ed.), *Earth's Landscape: An Encyclopedia of the World's Geographic Features 1*: 436. ISBN 1610694465, 9781610694469. Available at: https://books.google.pt/books?id=ErkxBgAAQBAJ

Kaiser, M. J., & Snyder, B. 2010. Offshore wind energy installation and decommissioning cost estimation in the U.S. outer continental shelf. November: 340.

Kalvig, S., Manger, E., Hjertager, B. H., & Jakobsen, J. B. 2014. Wave influenced wind and the effect on offshore wind turbine performance. *Energy Procedia* 53(C): 202–213. https://doi.org/10.1016/j.egypro.2014.07.229

Myhr, A., Bjerkseter, C., Ågotnes, A., & Nygaard, T. A. 2014. Levelised cost of energy for offshore floating wind turbines in a life cycle perspective. *Renewable Energy* 66: 714–728. https://doi.org/10.1016/j.renene.2014.01.017

PORDATA, 2018. Base de dados Portugal Contemporâneo. Available at: https://www.pordata.pt/Municipios/Densidade+populacional-452 (Accessed: 20 September 2019).

Principle Power 2011. WindFloat: Principle renewable energy delivered:1–2.

Gonçalves, R. S., Camacho, R. F., Lousada, S., & Castanho, R. A. 2018. Modeling of maritime agitation for the design of maritime infrastructures: the case study of Madeira archipelago. *Revista Brasileira de Planejamento e Desenvolvimento*, 7(1), 29. https://doi.org/10.3895/rbpd.v7n1.7136

R20-Regions of Climate Action 2016. Sustainable Porto Santo -Smart Fossil Free Island. 1–2. Retrieved from https://regions20.org/wp-content/uploads/2016/10/100-SolutionClimateProject-RE_033.pdf

Rusu, E. and Guedes Soares, C. 2012. Wave Energy Pattern Around the Madeira Islands. *Energy*. 45(1):771–785.

Rusu, E.; Pilar, P., and Guedes Soares, C. 2008. Evaluation of the Wave Conditions in Madeira Archipelago With Spectral Models. *Ocean Engineering*. 35 (13):1357–1371.

Schallenberg-Rodríguez, J., Montesdeoca, N.G. 2017. Spatial planning to estimate the offshore wind energy potential in coastal regions and islands. Practical case: the Canary Islands. *Energy* 143: 91–103. https://doi.org/10.1016/J.ENERGY.2017.10.084.

Tegen, S., Lantz, E., Hand, M., Maples, B., Smith, A., Schwabe, P. 2013. 2011 Cost of Wind Energy Review. *Technical Report*, NREL/TP-5000-56266. *National*

Renewable Energy Laboratory (NREL), Golden, CO (US). Available at: www.nrel.gov/docs/fy13osti/56266.pdf.

The WindPower 2019. Senvion 6.2M152. Available at: https://www.thewindpower.net/turbine_en_955_senvion_6.2m152.php

Vijay, K. G. Karmakar, D. & Guedes Soares, C. 2020. Long term response analysis of TLP-type offshore wind turbine, *ISH Journal of Hydraulic Engineering*. 26:1, 31–43, DOI: 10.1080/09715010.2018.1437790

Wai-Hoo, A. Y., & Sovacool, B. K. 2014. The economics of wind energy. *Sustainability Matters: Asia's Energy Concerns, Green Policies and Environmental Advocacy* 2: 317–340. https://doi.org/10.1142/9789814546829_0026

Dynamic analysis of submerged TLP wind turbine combined with heaving wave energy converter

J.S. Rony & D. Karmakar
Department of Applied Mechanics and Hydraulics, National Institute of Technology Karnataka, Surathkal, Mangalore, India

C. Guedes Soares
Centre for Marine Technology and Ocean Engineering (CENTEC), Instituto Superior Técnico, Universidade de Lisboa, Lisbon, Portugal

ABSTRACT: A submerged tension-leg-platform for offshore wind turbine combined with a heaving type point absorber wave energy converter is analysed considering different configurations of array of wave energy converters. A time domain simulation is performed for the combined platform using fully coupled aero-hydro-servo-elastic simulation. The analysis is performed to study the effect of different combinations of wave energy converters on the responses of the proposed system. The responses considered for the study include the six degrees of motion along with tower base bending moment and shear force of the combined wind and wave energy platform. The study will provide an insight into the dynamic motions of the floating wind and wave concept under operating condition, which will help the designers to develop better design standards.

1 INTRODUCTION

The traditional sources of non-renewable energy are increasingly getting exhausted over the past few decades. The environmentally clean renewable energies like wind, wave, solar and tidal energy have attracted more attention among which the wind energy is gaining more attention due to its conversion rate. As the wind farms located on land are reduced in recent years, so the trend has shifted towards the offshore wind turbines. The capacity of the world's wind power generation has been growing rapidly with an annual increase of 30% over the last decade. France, Canada, United Kingdom, Germany, Spain, China, United States of America and India are the leading countries that produce the most wind energy in the world. Moreover, research institutes like National Renewable Energy Laboratory (NREL) and International Energy Agency (IEA) works on the offshore wind turbine development.

When compared to ocean wind energy, the wave energy is more predictable and has many advantages. Wave energy converter (WEC) devices, captures the power possessed by waves and converts it to electricity. However, ocean wave energy technology is considered as immature compared to other renewable energy technologies. On combining two ocean renewable technologies with considerable synergies, there is a great potential for harnessing combined offshore wind and wave energy. Among the complaint floating platforms, the tension-leg platforms (TLP) provide steady motion due to its high stiffness of their tendon mooring system, which helps in generating good quality of power. The TLPs due to its high stiffness are susceptible to high frequency excitations that can produce resonant heave and pitch motions and cause fatigue damage to tendons. Hence these high frequency excitations should be observed in time domain simulator and the couple dynamic analysis have to be performed to understand its feasibility.

Aerodynamic loads due to turbulent wind imposed on the rotor and tower, second order wave forces acting on the platform, lifting forces due to vortex shredding imposed on the tendons and the viscous drag forces acting on the centre column are the several possible sources of high frequency excitations. Shen et al. (2016) studied the viscosity induced high frequency dynamic responses in both regular and irregular waves. The numerical analysis is performed using FAST for irregular waves. The study showed that for high frequency motion, the damping caused by the radiation of waves is negligible but the viscous damping and aerodynamic damping are critical for determining the pitch resonant amplitude. Ahmad (1996) studied the coupled responses of the TLP platform by sustaining the non-linearities caused by the drag force and by varying the tether tension and by large deformations. The study stated that the heave response and

DOI: 10.1201/9781003216599-67

the tether tension are affected by the coupling between the degrees of freedom. Shen et al. (2016) performed the in-house coupled dynamic analysis for TLP floating type platform. Free decay test was conducted and compared with the results obtained from FAST. The effects of aerodynamic force, viscous drag force and mooring models on the dynamic response of the surge, pitch and tendon tensions in random and regular sea states is studied using time domain statistical analysis and frequency domain spectral analysis. Han et al. (2018) analysed the dynamic responses of the spar platform under different wind and wave conditions using fully coupled FAST code and the results are validated using the model test. The study concluded that the wind and current induces the low-frequency average responses though wave induces the fluctuation range of responses.

In the recent years a significant study on the combined wave and wind energy devices is performed. Stoutenberg et al. (2010) studied the variations in power output for a co-located offshore wind turbines and wave energy converters. The meteorological wind and wave data collected from the National Buoy data center is used to estimate the hourly power output from offshore wind turbines and wave energy converters. Soulard et al. (2013) discussed the technical feasibility for hybrid ocean energy converter considering the total steel mass from the structural calculations and also technical solution for the mooring system is defined. The research involves the study of a 100m diameter circular barge equipped with floating oscillating wave surge converters (OWSCs) and the power performance, mooring line estimations and structural design calculations is conducted. The dynamic response and power performance of a combined spar-type floating wind turbine and coaxial floating wave energy converters was studied by Muliawan et al. (2013). Time domain coupled dynamic analysis is carried out using SIMO/TDHMILL3D to study the motion behaviour of the combined wind-wave concept. Luan et al. (2014) explored the possibility of combining the wind and wave energy on semi-submersible platform and presented the concept of combining 5-MW semi-submersible wind turbine and three rotating flap type WECs. Sensitivity study with reference to the effects of mass of the WECs of the semi-submersible platform is performed and the PTO damping coefficient used in the model were carried out.

The coupled dynamic analysis of floating platform with wave energy converters is performed by Lee et al. (2016) to determine the effects of WECs on the floating platform and one-way coupling considering only the PTO damping of the static WECs. The study concluded that the heave, roll and pitch motion of the platform have significant damping and also the effect of damping influences the mooring line top tensions. Gao et al. (2016) carried out a comparative numerical and experimental study of two combined wind and wave energy concepts considering three combined concepts such as spar torus combination (STC), semi-submersible flap combination (SFC) and an oscillating water column array with a wind turbine. The survival and operational condition of the system are studied and the motions of the platform, platform forces and the power produced are compared. Han et al. (2017) proposed a concept of submerged tension-leg platform (STLP) for the offshore wind turbine. The stability during transportation and installation phase is studied and the dynamic response is performed for the operation phase. The analysis showed that the effect of second order wave loads on the dynamics of STLP is slightly higher in the parked conditions than that on the normal operation condition.

In the present study, the submerged tension-leg platform (STLP) combined with a heaving type point absorber wave energy converter is studied using fully coupled aero-hydro-servo-elastic simulation. The analysis is performed in order to analyse the effect of different number of wave energy converters on the responses of the proposed system as well as to study the responses for different environmental conditions. The response quantities considered for the study include the six degrees of motion of the combined platform. The contour plots for the platform with 4 WEC configuration is plotted as it STLP with 4 WEC showed minimum force and moment at the base of the tower. The study is performed for 8 m/s wind speed for 2.5m, 3.2m and 4.6m wave heights which represents the operating conditions for the turbine. The study will provide an insight into the dynamic motions of the floating wind and wave concept under different operating conditions, which will help the designers to develop better design standards.

2 STLP WITH ARRAY OF HEAVE TYPE POINT ABSORBER

The STLP type wind turbine combined with array of point absorber WEC is modelled and detail coupled dynamic analysis performed aero-servo-hydro-elastic simulation. The detail description of the model and numerical modelling procedure is discussed in the next subsections.

2.1 Description of the model

The submerged tension-leg platform (STLP) for an offshore wind turbine is proposed for moderate water depth of 200m. The submerged tension leg floating platform is self-stable in transportation and installation phase as it has relatively large water plane area. STLP can be wet-towed together with the wind turbine from the shore to the offshore site where it needs to be installed. As the platform is submerged with small water plane area, it has improved hydrodynamic performance. The STLP wind turbine consists of submerged platform, 5 MW NREL wind turbine and four pairs of taunt mooring lines. The submerged platform consists of one column at the centre and four separated cylindrical shaped vertical pontoons connected through

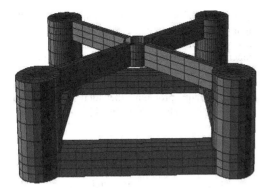

Figure 1. Perspective view of STLP.

Table 2. Dimensions of the cone-cylinder floater.

Base radius of the cone-cylinder floater	5.0 m
Apex angle of the cone portion	90 degrees
Height of cylindrical portion	0.5 m

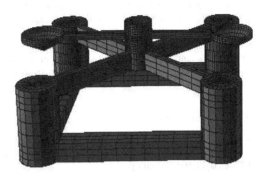

Figure 3. Perspective view of STLP with 2 WECs.

horizontal pontoons as shown in Figure 1. The column and pontoons are connected through cross braces. The dimensions of the submerged platform are listed in Table 1.

The platform is also provided with point absorber type wave energy converters of cone-cylindrical shape (Figure 2), connected with horizontal braces to the top of central column so that the WECs can capture the maximum number of waves coming on to the platform and also provide the sheltering to the platform. The properties of the WEC are listed in Table 2.

The study is conducted for three different configurations such as STLP with no wave energy converters, STLP with two wave energy converters shown in Figure 3 and STLP with four wave energy converters

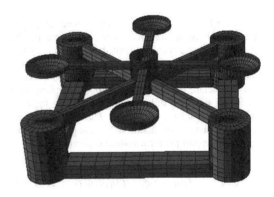

Figure 4. Perspective view of STLP with 4 WECs.

Table 1. Properties of STLP.

Column Diameter	6.5 m
Diameter of vertical pontoon	9.0 m
Height of vertical pontoon	12.0 m
Distance between Vertical pontoons	40.0
Width of vertical pontoon	5.0 m
Height of vertical pontoon	3.0 m
Platform Mass	2.7342×10^6 kg

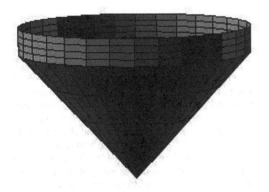

Figure 2. Perspective view of WEC.

as shown in Figure 4. The geometric modelling of the structures below the design water surface, i.e., the wetted surface of the structures is carried out using Rhino3D, which is a rich and versatile computer aided design (CAD) package for parametric design of 3D geometric objects, particularly objects free from curves and surfaces. The model surface is sub divided into patches, and all the patches represent the wetted surface. In order to provide a better continuation, the body surface is discretized by these patches and a set of small elements called panels are defined with these patches. The panel size is modified depending on the accuracy requirements.

The geometric data file (gdf) is obtained from Rhino3D and the coordinates of the submerged portion of the structure are obtained. Hydrodynamic analysis and coupled dynamic analysis for different configurations of the platform is conducted for wind and wave condition. The hydrodynamic analysis is conducted using WAMIT considering only the wave conditions.

The hydrostatics of the floating platform are then obtained from WAMIT is used as an input for FAST where the coupled dynamic analysis is performed. The FAST code which is an aero-servo-hydro-elastic simulation tool considers the real time operation conditions for the wind turbine and the floating platform taking into account the wind, wave, structural load, blade dynamics to determine the responses of the platform.

The study is performed considering the wind speed of 8 m/s and wave height of 2.5m for varying wave period. The two different configurations with two WECs and four WECs are shown in Figure (3-4) having a minimum spacing of 21.5m from the centre of the platform to the WECs.

2.2 Numerical model

The aero-servo-hydro-elastic simulation performed using FAST considers the equations of motion using Kane's dynamics given by

$$F_i + F_i^* = 0, \text{ for } i = 0, 1, 2, 3, \ldots \quad (1)$$

where F_i is the generalized active forces and F_i^* is the generalized inertia forces. The expressions for the support platform included contributions from hydrodynamics, platform mass and inertia, the reaction loads of the mooring system and gravity. It is assumed that the centre of mass of the support platform (not including the wind turbine) is located along the centreline of the undeflected tower. The nonlinear time-domain equations of motion of the coupled wind turbine and support platform system is given by

$$M_{ij}(q, u, t)\ddot{q}_j = f_i(q, \dot{q}, u, t), \quad (2)$$

where M_{ij} is the (i, j) component of the inertia mass matrix, which depends nonlinearly on the set of system DOFs (q), control inputs (u), and time (t). $\ddot{q}_j$ is the second time derivative of DOF j and f_i is the component of the forcing function associated with DOF i. The forcing function f_i depends nonlinearly on the set of system DOFs and their first-time derivatives (q and q respectively), as well as the set of control inputs (u) and time (t), and is positive in the direction of positive motion of DOF. As the hydrodynamic loading is present in the support platform, the hydrodynamic impedance forces including the influence of added mass are important. The total external load on the support platform are given by

$$F_i^{platform} = -A_{ij}\ddot{q}_j + F_i^{hydro} + F_i^{lines}, \quad (3)$$

where A_{ij} is the (i,j) component of the impulsive hydrodynamic-added-mass matrix to be summed with M_{ij}, F_i^{hydro} is the ith component of the applied hydrodynamic load on the support platform associated with everything but A_{ij} and F_i^{lines} is the ith component of the applied load on the support platform from the contribution of all mooring lines.

In the time-domain representation of the frequency-domain problem, the total external load acting on the support platform, $F_i^{platform}$ is replaced with

$$\begin{aligned}F_i^{platform} = &-A_{ij}(\omega)\ddot{q}_j + \text{Re}\{AX_i(\omega,\beta)e^{i\omega t}\} \\ &- [C_{ij}^{Lines} + C_{ij}^{Hydrostatic}]q_j - B_{ij}(\omega)\dot{q}_j,\end{aligned} \quad (4)$$

where A is the amplitude of a regular incident wave of frequency ω and direction β. C_{ij}^{Lines} is the (i,j) component of the linear restoring matrix from all mooring lines, $A_{ij}(\omega)$ and $B_{ij}(\omega)$ are the (i,j) components of the hydrodynamic-added-mass and damping matrices, which are frequency dependent.

The total external load acting on the support platform is obtained by integrating over the length of the cylinder the loads acting on each strip of the cylinder. In the relative form of Morison's representation for the surge and sway modes of motion ($i = 1$ and 2) is replaced with Morison's equation given by

$$\begin{aligned}F_i^{platform}(t,z) = &-C_A\rho\left(\frac{\pi D^2}{4}dz\right)\ddot{q}_1(z) \\ &+ (1+C_A)\rho\left(\frac{\pi D^2}{4}dz\right)a_i(t,0,0,z) \\ &+ \frac{1}{2}C_D\rho D dz[\nu_1(t,0,0,z)-\dot{q}_1(z)]\nu(t,0,0,z)-\dot{q}(z),\end{aligned} \quad (5)$$

where D is the diameter of the cylinder, dz is the length of the differential strip of the cylinder, C_A and C_D are the normalized hydrodynamic-added-mass and viscous-drag coefficients. The above equation is then modified to obtain the other degrees of motion.

3 RESULTS AND DISCUSSION

The coupled dynamic analysis is performed for the three different configurations of the submerged TLP type platform combined with wave energy converters. The responses obtained are plotted against time period to determine the performance of the structure under wind and wave conditions. Table 3 shows values of maximum amplitude of responses and the corresponding wave period for the operation condition of 8 m/s wind speed and 2.5m wave height. The present study considers the submerged tension-leg platform with 0, 2 and 4 wave energy converters connected to the centre column.

Table 3. Maximum amplitude for responses.

Configuration	Surge (m/m)	Sway (m/m)	Heave (m/m)	Roll (deg/m)	Pitch (deg/m)	Yaw (deg/m)
STLP with 0 WEC	1.2	10	0.20	.009	.0115	0.5
STLP with 2 WEC	3.1	16.2	0.40	.005	.0046	4.5
STLP with 4 WEC	6	15.8	0.30	.004	.0082	12.5

From the Table 3 it is evident that the surge, sway and yaw motions are significant for STLP platform as the STLP platform possess restricted motion for heave roll and pitch motions. Figure 5 shows the surge motion versus wave period for different configurations of combined STLP and WEC. The surge motion is observed to increase with the increase in the number of WECs. The surge motion is minimum when STLP is not provided with the WECs and is maximum for four WECs around the centre column showing that the sheltering function of WECs are not efficient for this arrangement of the WECs.

Figure 6 shows the sway motion versus wave period for three different configurations of the STLP platform with WEC. The sway motion is minimum for the configuration with no WECs and for the four number of WECs around the platform, the sway motion is observed to be minimum as compared to the sway motion for the STLP with two WECs. So, the STLP with four WEC configuration is efficient for sheltering the structure against the waves. Comparing both surge and sway motions, the heave motion is very negligible. The heave motion tends to decrease with the increase in the number of WECs around the platform.

In Figure 7 the yaw motion tends to increase with the increase in the wave period. The platform is disturbed with the presence of the WECs around the platform as the motions are increased with the presence of a higher number of WECs around the platform.

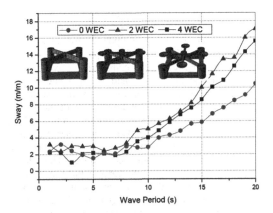

Figure 6. Sway motion versus wave perod for wind velocity 8m/s and wave height 2.5m.

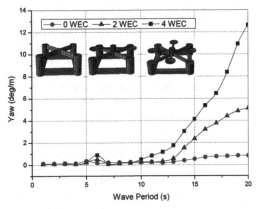

Figure 7. Yaw motion versus wave perod for wind velocity 8m/s and wave height 2.5m.

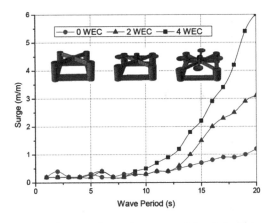

Figure 5. Surge motion versus wave perod for wind velocity 8m/s and wave height 2.5m.

The forces and moments developed on the platform are analysed versus wave period such as fore-aft shear force, side-to-side shear force, and axial force. The forces and moments are developed not only due to the aerodynamic and hydrodynamic load but also due to gravity and inertia loads. Normally, the aerodynamic load will be dominant compared to the tower load when it is in operation, the direct wind loading on the tower is most important for the developed forces and moments.

Table 4. Maximum amplitude for forces and moments.

Configuration	SF$_1$ (kN)	SF$_2$ (kN)	SF$_3$ (kN)	BM$_1$ (kN-m)	BM$_2$ (kN-m)	BM$_3$ (kN-m)
STLP with 0 WEC	20	13.75	9.1	80	520	285
STLP with 2 WEC	16.8	13.5	9.2	550	390	290
STLP with 4 WEC	16	13.7	9	460	380	282

Table 4 shows the values for the tower base shear force and bending moment for operation condition of the wind turbine. In the wind power terminology, fore-aft shear force (SF$_1$) is the force applied at the base of the tower along the x-axis considering x-axis perpendicular to the blade axis, and in the plane passing through the blade and shaft axis in the downwind direction. The maximum value for the fore aft shear force is obtained for the platform with 2 WECs which shows that the addition of WECs increases the forces developed at the platform though the waves get sheltered by increasing the number of WECs. The side-to-side shear force (SF$_2$) is the force applied at the base of the tower along the y-axis considering y-axis perpendicular to the blade axis to give right-hand coordinate system. The side-to-side shear force has negligible relation with the WECs as the result shows almost equal values for the two configurations having WECs.

An axial force (SF$_3$) is defined as the force applied at the base of the tower along z-axis considering z-axis is radially outwards from the hub center along the blade axis. In case of axial force, the magnitude of the force is not having considerable variation for all the three configurations. The maximum axial force is developed for the platform with 2 WECs and the minimum value for the configuration with 4 WECs which depicts the clear understanding of the sheltering effect of the WECs.

In addition, the moments about the x, y and z-axis is determined for different configurations of STLP with WEC. The pitching moment, known as fore-aft moment (BM$_1$) is defined as the moment caused by the fore-aft force about the y-axis. The STLP configuration having four WECs has minimum moment in the y-direction, which confirms the sheltering of the platform from waves by the WECs. The roll moment known as side-to-side moment (BM$_2$) is defined as the moment caused by the side-to-side force about x-axis. The addition of the WECs have increased the moment developed at the tower base in the x-direction. The maximum value of the side-to-side moment is observed for combination of platform with two WECs.

The minimum value for the yaw moments (BM$_3$) are observed for the combination of STLP platform with four WECs. For the better understanding of the distribution of forces and moments, the contours for the same is plotted for the platform with 4 WECs which possess the minimum values for the forces and moments.

The contour plot for the responses are plotted for 2.5m, 3.6m and 4.2m wave height for wave period from 1 to 20s in the case of the wind velocity of 8 m/s, to understand the distribution of responses and moments for the 4 WEC configuration. Figure 8 shows the contour distribution for the fore-aft shear forces developed at the base of the tower under the action of waves and wind. For the fore-aft shear force, 1.723×10^4 N is actively distributed over the time period and wave height and hence suggest the most occurrence of the same. Figure 9 shows the contour plot for distribution of side-to-side shear forces developed at the base of the tower under the action of waves and wind. 1.276×10^4 N is the most developed side-to-side shear force and hence the platform has to be designed to bear this value of shear force.

Figure 10 shows the contour plot for distribution of axial shear forces developed at the base of the tower under the action of waves and wind. Axial shear force of 8910 N is actively distributed over the entire wave period for different wave heights. Hence the structure has to be designed to cater these forces developed on the base of the tower. Figure 11 shows the contour distribution for the side-to-side moment

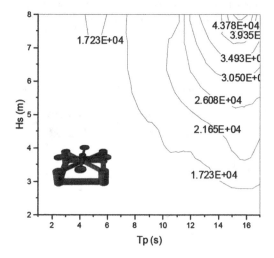

Figure 8. Contour plot for the fore-aft shear force against wave period and significant wave height.

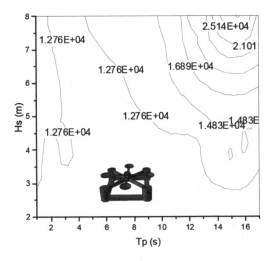

Figure 9. Contour plot for the side-to-side shear force against wave period and significant wave height.

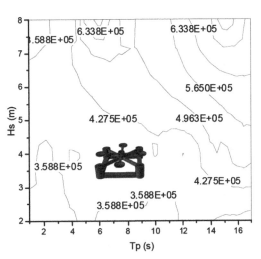

Figure 11. Contour plot for the tower base roll moment against wave period and significant wave height.

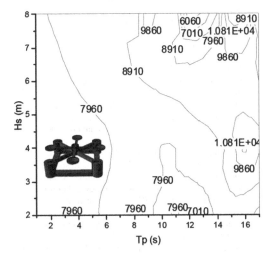

Figure 10. Contour plot for the axial force against wave period and significant wave height.

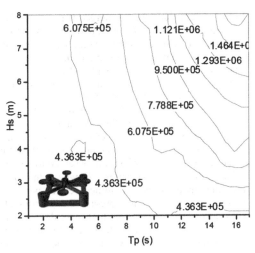

Figure 12. Contour plot for the tower base pitching moment against wave period and significant wave height.

developed due to the fore-aft shear forces at the base of the tower under the action of waves and wind. Maximum value of 6.338×10^5 N-m is observed for wave periods greater than 16s. 3.588×10^5 N-m is actively spread over the wave period for different wave heights.

Figure 12 represents the contour distribution for the fore-aft moment developed due to the side-to-side shear forces at the base of the tower under the action of waves and wind. Maximum value of 9.5×10^5 N-m was observed for wave periods greater than 10s for wave heights more than 4 m. 4.363×10^5 N-m is actively spread over the wave period for different wave heights.

Figure 13 represents the contour distribution for the yaw moments developed due to the axial shear forces at the base of the tower under the action of waves and wind. Maximum value of 2.464×10^5 N-m was observed for wave periods greater than 10s for wave heights more than 4 m. The yaw moment of 2.281×10^5 N-m is actively spread over the wave period for different wave heights and hence the structure has to be designed to resist these forces at the junction of tower and the platform.

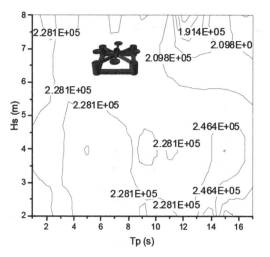

Figure 13. Contour plot for the tower base yaw moment against wave period and significant wave height.

4 CONCLUSIONS

In the present study the submerged tension-leg platform (STLP) with WECs to support 5 MW NREL wind turbine is studied for moderate water depth of 200 m. The study deals with the dynamic response characteristics of the STLP with WECs during the operation phase. The stability of the platform is studied for 8m/s wind speed and 2.5m wave height with four numbers of mooring lines (taut mooring).

Fully coupled dynamic time domain simulations are carried out using the FAST to determine the structural responses of the structure. The motions for surge, sway and yaw motions are observed to be sensitive to the wind-wave actions. However, the surge and yaw motions have minimum effect with the presence of WECs. The fore-aft and side-to-side shear forces and moments are higher for the platform with two WECs compared to four WEC configuration which shows the evidence of the sheltering effect of the WECs against the waves.

The contour distribution for the forces and moments were plotted to understand the distribution of the forces and moments. The maximum forces and moments developed is studied to aid the design of the platform and the most occurred forces and moments for different wave heights and wave period is determined which helps in the design process of the platform.

ACKNOWLEDGEMENTS

The authors acknowledge Science and Engineering Research Board (SERB), Department of Science & Technology (DST), Government of India for supporting financially under the Young Scientist research grant no. CRG/2018/004184 and DST for India-Portugal Bilateral Scientific Technological Cooperation Project grant no. DST/INT/Portugal/P-13/2017.

REFERENCES

Ahmad S, (1996) Stochastic TLP response under long crested random sea. Computers and Structures, 61, 975–993.

Glanville R, Pauling JR, Halkyard J & Lehtinen TJ (1991) Dynamic response of floating substructure of spar type offshore wind turbine with catenary mooring cables. Ocean Engineering, 72, 356–364.

Han Y, Le C, Ding H, Cheng Z & Zhang P (2017) Stability and dynamic response of a submerged tension-leg flatform for offshore wind turbines. Ocean Engineering 129, 68–82.

Han W, Zhi-qiang H, Xiang-yin M (2018) Dynamic Performance Investigation of a spar type floating wind turbine under different sea conditions. Renewable Energy, 32, 256–265.

Jonkman J M (2010) Definition of the Floating System for Phase IV of OC3, National Renewable Energy Laboratory, Golden, CO, USA.

Lee H, Bae Y H, Cho I H, Kim K H, Hong K, (2016) One-way coupled dynamic analysis of floating platform with wave energy converters. Journal of Ocean and Wind Energy, 3(1),53–60.

Luan C, Michailides C, Gao Z, Moan T (2014) Modeling and analysis of a 5 MW semi-submersible wind turbine combined with three flap-type wave energy converters. 33rd International Conference on Ocean, Offshore and Arctic Engineering, 8-13, June, 2014, San Francisco, California, USA, OMAE2014-2421.

López I, Andreu J, Ceballos S, Alegría M I and Kortabarria I (2013) Review of wave energy technologies and the necessary power equipment. Renewable and Sustainable Energy Reviews, 27, 413–434.

Muliawan MJ, Karimirad M, Moan T (2013) Dynamic response and power performance of a combined spar-type floating wave energy converter. Renewable Energy, 50, 47–57

Ramachandran G K V, Robertson A, Jonkman, J M, Masciola M D (2014) Investigation of Response Amplitude Operators for floating offshore wind turbines Report of National Renewable Energy Laboratory.

Shen M, Hu Z, Liu G (2016) Dynamic response and viscous effect analysis of a TLP type floating wind turbine using coupled aero-hydro-mooring dynamic code. Renewable Energy 99, 800–812.

Shen M C, Hu Z Q, Gen T (2016) Coupled hydrodynamics and aerodynamic response analysis of a tension-leg platform floating wind turbine. Journal of Ship Mechanics, 21(3),263–274.

Sinha, A.; Karmakar, D., and Guedes Soares, C. (2015) Numerical modelling of array of heaving point absorbers. In: Guedes Soares, C. (Ed.) Renewable Energies Offshore. London, UK: Taylor & Francis Group; pp. 383–391.

Soulard T, Babarit A, Borgarnio B, Wyns M, Harismendy M, (2013) C-HYP: A combined wave and wind energy platforms with balanced contributions. 32nd International Conference on Ocean, Offshore and Arctic Engineering, 9-14 June, 2013, Nantes, France, OMAE2013-10778.

Stoutenberg D E, Jenkins N, Jacobson Z M, (2010) Power output variations of co-located offshore wind turbines and wave energy converters in California. Renewable Energy, 35, 2781–2791.

Zhang H, Xu D, Zhao H, Xia S, Wu Y (2018) Energy extraction of wave energy converters embedded in a very large floating platform. Energy, 158, 317–329.

An assessment of the wave energy in the European seas based on ERA5 reanalysis dataset

L. Rusu
'Dunarea de Jos' University of Galati, Galati, Romania

ABSTRACT: The objective of this work is to evaluate the wave energy potential in the European seas (Mediterranean Sea, Black Sea and Baltic Sea) using ERA5 dataset. This is the latest ocean wave climate reanalysis data produced by ECMWF (European Centre for Medium-Range Weather Forecasts). The analysis covers a 30-year time period (1989-2018). In each basin, reference points located in the coastal environment were selected for the wave energy assessment. The chosen points correspond to the ERA5 grids. In this way no further data processing was necessary. The characteristics of the main wave parameters over the target areas are provided with 0.5° spatial resolution and 3 hours temporal resolution. The wave power in each reference point was computed based on the significant wave height and wave energy period, values available from ERA5 dataset. The temporal variability of the wave energy over the 30-year is also investigated. The mean wave energy potential and its annual, seasonal and monthly variations are computed and analysed.

1 INTRODUCTION

In the last years, increased interest to find renewable energy resources as a potential alternative to conventional fossil fuel energy is observed. Besides the fact that renewable energy is a clean energy and helps us to reduce the emission of greenhouse gases through the burning of fossil fuels, it also seems to be more and more competitive in terms of the energy price (REN21 2019). In marine environment various renewable energy sources can be exploited (wind, waves, currents, etc.), but the ocean waves represent a remarkable energy resource. Moreover, the wave energy has a low hour-to-hour variability while the seasonal variation brings higher resources in winter time when electrical demand is high.

On the other hand, it works well with the other renewable resources, such as wind and solar (Reikard et al. 2015, Rusu et al. 2018, Azzellino et al. 2019), in order to reduce their variability at different time scales for an easier integration in the power system (Lund 2007). This can be also a solution to increase the energy produced in an exploited area by means of the co-located wind-wave farms (Perez-Collazo et al. 2015, Nilsson et al. 2019).

Even if the ocean wave is a great energy resource, unfortunately it presents a very small portion of the renewable energy market due to various limitations and challenges in harvesting its potential (Mwasilu & Jung 2018). The technology seems to not be currently cost-competitive due in part to the complexity of extracting energy from waves and to the existent variety of the wave conditions (REN21 2019). Therefore, the extraction of the wave power is still in a development stage, with activities developed around the world, but particularly concentrated in Europe and North America.

In order to find the best location for the deployment of the wave farm, evaluation of this resource over a long time period is necessary (Gonçalves et al. 2014, Bernardino et al. 2017, Rusu & Onea 2017) and also an evaluation of the effects on the coastal environment (Bento et al. 2014, Onea & Rusu 2016). From this perspective, the main objective of the present work is directed to the evaluation of the wave energy potential in some European seas, namely Mediterranean, Black and Baltic Seas, using ERA5 dataset (Hersbach et al. 2019).

2 DATA AND METHODOLOGY

2.1 *Target areas*

Figure 1 illustrates the distribution of the reference points chosen to evaluate the wave power in three different European seas, while Table 1 presents the characteristics of these points. The positions of the reference points match the reanalysis grid points. In this way no interpolation was required. From Table 1 can be observed that most of the points are in shallow water, while some points are located in deep water, but near to the coast.

In the Mediterranean Sea (Figure 1c), the largest of the three seas considered, ten reference points denoted from M1 to M10 have been defined and they are

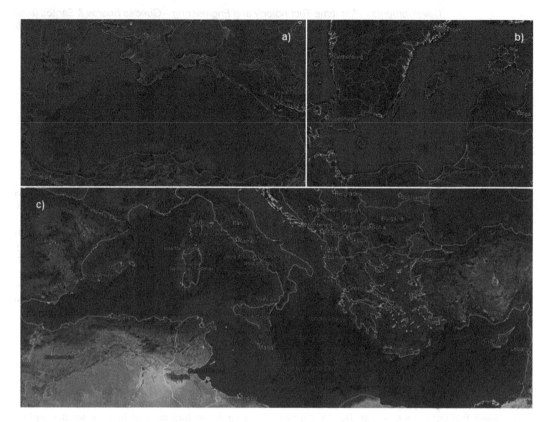

Figure 1. Distribution of the reference points along the European seas. a) Black Sea, b) Baltic Sea and c) Mediterranean Sea. Figures processed from Google Earth (2019).

distributed only along the European coasts. Most of the points in the Mediterranean Sea are located near to the islands. This is because the wave energy extraction can be a viable solution for isolated environments to develop sustainable energy independence and the assessment of the wave power can be very useful (Ganea et al. 2017).

In the Black Sea (Figure 1a) also ten reference points are considered along the entire basin (denoted from BS1 to BS10), while in the Baltic Sea, which is the smallest of the three seas considered, only six reference points were defined. In these two basins the points are chosen in general near to the locations where previous studies show that exists wave energy potential (Rusu 2019a, Soomere & Eelsalu 2014).

2.2 *Reanalysis datasets*

ERA5 dataset is the most up-to-date reanalysis product of the ECMWF (European Centre for Medium-Range Weather Forecasts) that provides global wind and wave information, available from 1979 to present (Hersbach et al. 2019). The wave parameters are provided with a spatial resolution of 0.5°× 0.5° and an hourly temporal resolution.

The wave parameters considered to compute the wave energy in each grid point are H_s (significant height of combined wind waves and swell) and T_{-1} commonly known as the wave energy period T_e. For the present study the wave parameters were chosen with a temporal resolution of 3 hours and the dataset considered covers a 30-year period (1989 – 2018).

3 RESULTS

3.1 *Evaluation of the wave power potential*

Based on the values of the wave parameters in each reference point, the wave power is computed. The wave energy flux per unit of wave-crest length in deep water, also known as the wave power P_w (kW/m) is:

$$P_W = \frac{\rho g^2}{64\pi} T_e H_s^2, \qquad (1)$$

where P_W is the energy flux per meter of wave crest (kW/m), ρ=1025 kg/m^3 is the density of the sea water while g is the gravity acceleration.

Some statistical parameters as mean and maximum values, skewness index (Sk), standard deviation and 50th, 75th, 90th and 95th percentiles are computed

Table 1. Characteristics of the reference points considered.

Points	Longitude (°)	Latitude (°)	Depth (m)	Distance to shore (km)
Mediterranean Sea				
M1	-1.0	37.5	124	7
M2	2.5	41.5	33	5.9
M3	5.0	43.0	191	36
M4	3.5	40.0	152	25
M5	8.0	41.0	1680	16
M6	8.5	42.5	172	14
M7	14.5	36.0	125	7.5
M8	26.5	35.5	944	26
M9	28.0	36.0	459	6
M10	33.0	34.5	949	7.4
Black Sea				
BS1	32.5	45.5	25	5.8
BS2	30.0	45.0	36	26
BS3	29.0	44.5	22	10
BS4	29.0	44.0	48	26.5
BS5	28.0	43.0	20	8.5
BS6	29.0	41.5	100	26.2
BS7	31.5	41.5	1252	14
BS8	35.5	42.0	445	32
BS9	37.5	44.5	1243	19.6
BS10	34.5	44.5	1180	14.1
Baltic Sea				
B1	12.5	54.5	10	3
B2	18.0	55.0	29	18
B3	20.5	55.5	48	36
B4	19.0	57.5	31	11.8
B5	21.0	57.5	45	34
B6	15.0	56.0	26	13.3

Table 2. Wave power characteristics corresponding to the reference points computed for 30-year time interval considered.

Points	Sk	50th (W/m^2)	75th (W/m^2)	90th (W/m^2)	95th (W/m^2)	Max (W/m^2)
Mediterranean Sea						
M1	6.6	0.8	1.9	4.3	6.8	85
M2	9.7	0.5	1.5	3.68	6.2	110
M3	4.5	1.6	5.9	14.3	21.8	216
M4	7.3	1.0	4.0	11.9	22.6	391
M5	5.2	1.8	7.2	21.8	38.2	313
M6	5.5	1.5	6.0	16.7	27.7	377
M7	4.8	1.4	4.2	9.9	16.1	148
M8	4.7	2.5	5.7	11.4	18.1	129
M9	7.3	0.6	1.6	3.9	6.4	89
M10	8.2	0.8	2.0	4.7	8.3	135
Black Sea						
BS1	7.2	0.5	1.6	4.1	6.9	145
BS2	7.1	0.8	2.5	6.4	11.0	163
BS3	6.9	0.5	1.4	3.4	5.7	86
BS4	7.5	0.8	2.4	6.3	11.2	181
BS5	7.5	0.5	1.4	3.8	7.0	119
BS6	7.4	0.8	2.7	7.5	13.8	224
BS7	7.2	0.6	1.9	5.1	8.8	132
BS8	7.3	0.7	1.8	4.6	7.9	124
BS9	8.1	0.6	2.0	5.5	9.5	203
BS10	9.5	0.4	1.3	3.5	6.1	140
Baltic Sea						
B1	5.1	0.4	1.2	3.0	4.5	58
B2	6.4	1.6	5.6	14.7	25.1	389
B3	7.1	1.6	5.2	13.8	23.3	398
B4	4.7	0.7	2.2	5.0	7.8	72
B5	5.7	1.7	5.6	14.3	23.3	296
B6	4.9	0.6	1.8	4.4	7.0	67

with their standard relationships to evaluate the wave power potential in the reference points. The results are presented in Table 2 and Figure 2.

The highest value of the wave power computed for the Mediterranean Sea is found in the point (M5) located near Sardinia Island, where the deep waters can be found near the shore. However, the values in M4 and M6, located in intermediate waters near to the Mallorca and Corsica islands, are very close to those from M5. In the Golf of Lion (on the French coast) is located the reference point M3, where the mean value is comparable with M4, but with a lower variability around the mean as indicated by the skewness index and high values of the percentiles. In this area also, high values of the wind power are encountered (Rusu & Rusu 2019), which suggests that this area is a favorable location for the combined exploitation of the wind and wave energy, as mentioned by Kalogeri et al. (2017).

In the Black Sea basin, the wave power means are lower than in the Mediterranean Sea, with values ranging from 1.4 to 3.2 kW/m. Also, a higher divergence from a normal-symmetric distribution of the wave power potential around the mean value exists, as indicated by skewness index (around 7.5). Three reference points, two located in shallow water (BS2 and BS4) and one in intermediate water (BS6) present higher potential. The first two points are located near Constanta and Sulina ports on the western side of the basin, while the third (BS6) is in the southwestern area of the basin near Bosporus Strait. Some recent studies show that in these locations also the near future projection indicate a slowly increase of the wave power (see for example Rusu 2019b). Some climatic characteristics of the wave power in the Black Sea are presented also by Divinsky & Kosyan (2019).

As regards the Baltic Sea, from Figure 2 (bottom panel) immediately is observed that in three points (B2, B3 and B5) the highest mean and maximum values of the wave power are encountered, namely means around 5.5 kW/m and maximums around 300-390 kW/m. All these three points are located on the

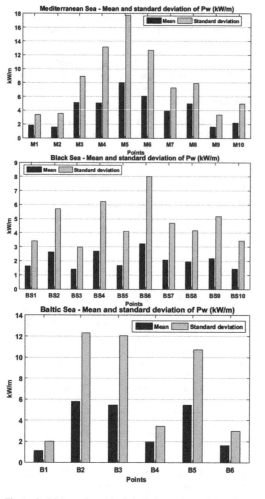

Figure 2. Mean and standard deviation values of the wave power computed in each reference point for the 30-year time interval considered (Mediterranean Sea – top panel, Black Sea – middle panel, Baltic Sea – bottom panel).

means from the quarterly average of the wave power and also monthly variability were assessed and they are illustrated in Figures 3 and 4.

The evaluation of the possible trends in the fluctuation of the annual mean wave power during the 30-year period represents the next step of this local analysis. The annual mean values of the wave power in each reference point were computed and then the slopes of the linear regressions adjusted to these datasets were estimated as shown in Figure 5.

The following seasonal partition was considered to compute the average values: for winter the months December-January-February, for spring the months March-April-May, for summer the months June-July-August while for autumn the months September-October-November. The seasonal variability

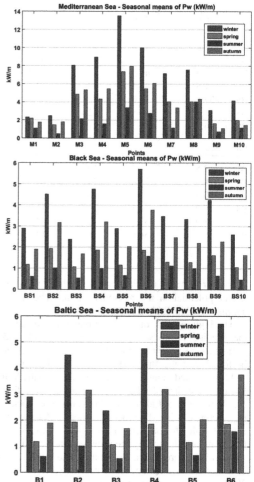

Figure 3. Seasonal means of the wave power in each reference point for the 30-year time interval considered (Mediterranean Sea – top panel, Black Sea – middle panel, Baltic Sea – bottom panel).

eastern part of the basin that seems to present higher values of the wave energy as mentioned also by Stoutenburg et al. (2010). The maximum values in these three points are comparable with values computed in the promising locations from Mediterranean Sea.

3.2 Wave power variability

In the northern hemisphere, where the target areas are located, the wave power is affected by the seasonal variability as is shown in the study of Reguero et al. (2015). Previous studies conducted in the target areas of the present work notice also the presence of the seasonal patterns (see the studies of Soomere & Eelsalu 2014, Besio et al. 2016, Rusu et al. 2018). In order to show how this variability affects the wave power in the reference points the seasonal

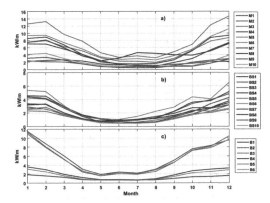

Figure 4. Monthly variations of the wave power in each reference point for the 30-year time interval considered. a) Mediterranean Sea, b) Black Sea, c) Baltic Sea.

in the reference points is clearly shown in Figure 3 and further some observations will be made.

Looking to Figure 3, it is clear that the biggest difference occurs between the winter and summer means. Thus, comparing the values of the mean wave power in the winter season (maximum seasonal values) with those from the summer (minimum seasonal values), in the Mediterranean Sea the means in summer represent between 18-27% of the winter averages, except the points M1 and M10 where the mean wave power value in summer is half that of winter. Between the wave power means computed for spring and autumn seasons there are no significant differences. Usually, the autumn means are slightly higher than the spring means.

In the Black Sea basin, the percentages are slightly higher than those computed in the Mediterranean Sea ranging from 18% to 32%. As regards the Baltic Sea the summer means represent around 22% of those in winter, except in the point B1 where the percentage is 40%.

The monthly variability illustrated in Figure 4 shows that in the points M1, M2, M9 and M10 from the Mediterranean Sea (the most western and eastern positions in the basin) differences between the winter and summer months are smaller as for example compared with M5.

In all the reference points considered in the Black Sea the variability along the year is clear, with higher means in the winter months and their decline in summer months (see also Akpinar et al. 2019). The same pattern is maintained in the points B2, B3 and B5 from the Baltic Sea, while in the other reference points (B1, B4 and B6) there is a reduced variability along the year.

Figure 5 presents the annual means, the five-year running average and the linear trends in a representative point of each basin, namely M3, BS2 and B2. The annual means of the wave power show positive trends in M3 and BS2 with increases

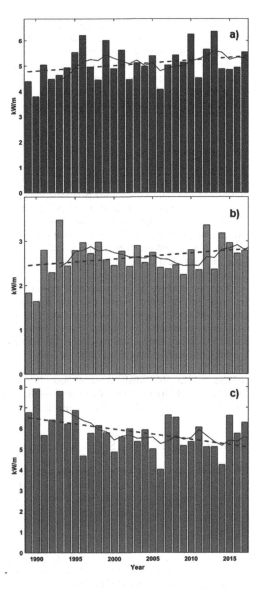

Figure 5. Annual means (bars), five-year running average (solid black line) and linear trend dashed blue line) of the wave power computed in three reference points: a) M3, b) BS2, c) B2.

of about 212 W/m and 134 W/m per decade, respectively, while in B2 is indicated a decrease of about 497 W/s.

In the Mediterranean Sea, positive trends are found in almost all points, except M1 where no trend is visible while a small negative trend (-82 W/m per decade) is encountered in M8 located near Crete Island. All the points from the Black Sea show positive trends of the annual means of the wave power, while those computed for the Baltic Sea points are always negative.

The five-year running average lines for points located in Baltic Sea show a decrease until 2000, followed by light variations until 2018. In the other two basins the variability pattern of the five-year running average lines follows the one encountered in M3 and B2 presented in Figure 5. In these cases, a decrease of the annual means can be observed around the year 2010, followed by a sharp rise.

4 CONCLUDING REMARKS

The evaluation of the wave power potential in three semi-enclosed European seas is performed based on the wave parameters provided by ERA5 in various reference points established in each basin, namely Mediterranean Sea, Black Sea and Baltic Sea. The results cover a 30-year period, from 1989 to 2018, that can provide a comprehensive picture of the climatic trends of the wave power.

Thus, an analysis of the mean wave power values is made for the entire period and also for seasons and months, together with the computation of some statistical parameters. In all the basins a strong seasonal variability is observed in most of the reference points considered. Some exceptions are found in M1 and M10, the westernmost and easternmost points considered in the Mediterranean Sea. Also the monthly variability of the points located on the eastern Baltic Sea coast is lower than in the other points.

ACKNOWLEDGEMENTS

This work was carried out in the framework of the ESA CCI+ Sea State project. The data used in this study is taken from the ECMWF ERA5 reanalysis.

REFERENCES

Akpınar, A., Jafali, H. & Rusu, E., 2019. Temporal Variation of the Wave Energy Flux in Hotspot Areas of the Black Sea. *Sustainability* 11 (3):p.562.
Azzellino, A., Lanfredi, C., Riefolo, L., Contestabile, P. & Vicinanza, D. 2019. Combined exploitation of offshore wind and wave energy in the Italian seas: a spatial planning approach. *Frontiers in Energy Research* 7: 42.
Bento, A.R., Rusu, E., Martinho, P. & Guedes Soares, C. 2014. Assessment of the changes induced by a wave energy farm in the nearshore wave conditions. *Computers & Geosciences*, 71: 50–61.
Bernardino, M., Rusu, L. & Guedes Soares, C. 2017. Evaluation of the wave energy resources in the Cape Verde Islands. *Renewable Energy* 101: 316–326.
Besio, G., Mentaschi, L. and Mazzino, A., 2016. Wave energy resource assessment in the Mediterranean Sea on the basis of a 35-year hindcast. *Energy* 94: 50–63.
Divinsky, B.V. & Kosyan, R.D., 2019. Climatic trends in the fluctuations of wind waves power in the Black Sea. Estuarine, *Coastal and Shelf Science* 235, p.106577.
Ganea, D., Amortila, V., Mereuta, E. & Rusu, E. 2017. A joint evaluation of the wind and wave energy resources close to the Greek Islands. *Sustainability* 9 (6):p.1025.
Gonçalves, M., Martinho, P. & Guedes Soares, C. 2014. Wave energy conditions in the western French coast. *Renewable Energy* 62: 155–163.
Hersbach, H., Bell, B., Berrisford, P., Horányi, A., Sabater, J.M., Nicolas, J., Radu, R., Schepers, D., Simmons, A., Soci, C. & Dee, D. 2019. Global reanalysis: goodbye ERA-Interim, hello ERA5. *ECMWF Newsl.* 159:17–24.
Kalogeri, C., Galanis, G., Spyrou, C., Diamantis, D., Baladima, F., Koukoula, M. & Kallos, G. 2017. Assessing the European offshore wind and wave energy resource for combined exploitation. *Renewable energy* 101: 244–264.
Lund, H. 2007. Renewable energy strategies for sustainable development. *Energy* 32: 912–919
Mwasilu, F. & Jung, J.W. 2018. Potential for power generation from ocean wave renewable energy source: a comprehensive review on state-of-the-art technology and future prospects. *IET Renewable Power Generation* 13(3): 363–375.
Nilsson, E., Rutgersson, A., Dingwell, A., Björkqvist, J.V., Pettersson, H., Axell, L., Nyberg, J. & Strömstedt, E. 2019. Characterization of wave energy potential for the Baltic Sea with focus on the Swedish Exclusive Economic Zone. *Energies* 12 (5):p.793.
Onea, F. & Rusu, E. 2016. The expected efficiency and coastal impact of a hybrid energy farm operating in the Portuguese nearshore. *Energy* 97: 411–423.
Perez-Collazo, C., Greaves, D. & Iglesias, G. 2015. A review of combined wave and offshore wind energy. *Renewable and Sustainable Energy Reviews* 42: 141–153.
REN21 2019. Renewables 2019 global status report, 336 (http://www.ren21.net/gsr-2019/)
Reikard, G., Robertson, B. & Bidlot, J.R. 2015. Combining wave energy with wind and solar: Short-term forecasting. *Renewable Energy* 81: 442–456.
Reguero, B.G., Losada, I.J. and Méndez, F.J., 2015. A global wave power resource and its seasonal, interannual and long-term variability. *Applied Energy* 148: 366–380.
Rusu, L. 2019a. The wave and wind power potential in the western Black Sea. *Renewable energy* 139: 1146–1158.
Rusu, L., 2019b. Evaluation of the near future wave energy resources in the Black Sea under two climate scenarios. *Renewable Energy* 142: 137–146.
Rusu, L. & Onea, F., 2017. The performances of some state of the art wave energy converters in locations with the worldwide highest wave power. *Renewable and Sustainable Energy Reviews* 75: 1348–1362.
Rusu, E. & Rusu, L. 2019. Evaluation of the wind power potential in the European nearshore of the Mediterranean Sea. In *E3S Web of Conferences* Vol. 103, p. 01003, EDP Sciences.
Rusu, L., Ganea, D. & Mereuta, E. 2018. A joint evaluation of wave and wind energy resources in the Black Sea based on 20-year hindcast information. *Energy Exploration & Exploitation* 36(2): 335–351.
Soomere, T. & Eelsalu, M. 2014. On the wave energy potential along the eastern Baltic Sea coast. *Renewable energy* 71: 221–233.
Stoutenburg, E.D., Jenkins, N. & Jacobson, M.Z. 2010. Power output variations of co-located offshore wind turbines and wave energy converters in California. *Renewable Energy* 35(12): 2781–2791.

Comparison of renewables (onshore wind, offshore wind, conventional PV) for Bozcaada Island in Turkey

A.E. Şentürk
Hydraulics Laboratory, Civil Engineering Department, Middle East Technical University, Ankara, Turkey

E. Oğuz
Hydraulics Laboratory, Civil Engineering Department, Middle East Technical University, Ankara, Turkey
Center for Wind Energy Research (METUWIND), Middle East Technical University, Ankara, Turkey

D.D. Çiçek
Hydraulics Laboratory, Civil Engineering Department, Middle East Technical University, Ankara, Turkey

ABSTRACT: Renewable energy sources for the shift from fossil fuel have been considered as a solution to generate energy. In order to determine the optimal alternative for a specific region having more than one renewable energy sources prior to investment, Bozcaada Island is considered in this study. Two different renewable sources, wind and solar sources, are evaluated by life cycle assessment (LCA) methodology. For wind potential, operated onshore wind farm and proposed offshore wind farm are considered. A land based photovoltaic (PV) power plant are proposed to evaluate solar potential. "Cradle to grave" approach is applied for each case. The results of this study indicated that offshore wind farm is more advantageous than onshore wind farm in terms of environmental impacts apart from acidification potential (AP) whereas onshore wind technology is more beneficial than conventional photovoltaic (PV) system in terms of all selected impact categories.

1 INTRODUCTION

Global warming is one of the most alarming problems for the future of the world. A transition from fossil fuel to renewable sources in order to generate clean energy is strongly recommended by many researchers (Da Silva & Branco 2018, Keleş & Bilgen 2012, Larsen, 2014, Özkale et al. 2017) as a solution. However, there is limited research about the selection of the most appropriate renewable sources for a specific region (Oğuz & Şentürk 2019, Piesecka et al. 2019, Schmidt et al. 2017, Franzitta et al. 2016). For this purpose, Bozcaada Island is selected as the pilot area due to its potential for solar and wind energy sources. Three distinct configurations one of which is the actual case, land-based wind farm, and two proposed alternatives of offshore wind farm and conventional open ground photovoltaic power plant, are compared in terms of environmental impacts by means of life cycle assessment (LCA).

Brief descriptions of selected impact categories are summarized in the following. While phases for LCA application of energy generation systems are explained in Section 2.2, system boundaries related for all configurations are drawn in Section 2.3. Following this, source potentials and assumptions related with chosen configurations are mentioned for wind source and solar source in Section 3 and Section 4, respectively. In Section 5, results are compared and comments and future directions take place in Section 6.

1.1 Acidification potential (AP)

Acidification can be defined as the sedimentation of inorganic compounds such as nitrogen oxide (NO) and nitrogen dioxide (NO2) on the surface of the world (Üçtuğ, 2017) which are accepted to be the most significant air pollutants (Cindoruk, 2018). Acidification can alternatively be defined (Taşkın, 2018) as the creation and release of hydrogen ions by specific compounds (Şayan et al. 2010). Due to dissolved inorganic compounds in water, total dissolved inorganic carbon and the alkalinity of water are altered which leads to marine pollution. Atmospheric pollution due to the build-up of inorganic compounds causes acid rains (Kim & Chae, 2016).

1.2 Eutrophication potential (EP)

Eutrophication is a central issue concerning (Doğan-Sağlamtimur & Sağlamtimur, 2018) aquatic ecosystem quality (Frumin & Gildeeva, 2015) which is directly related to the excessive emission of nitrogen and phosphorus (Rabalais et al. 2009). The main symptom is observed that phytoplankton population grows due to extreme loading of nutrients (Yağcı, 2010).

1.3 Cumulative energy demand (CED)

Its description (Merta et al. 2017) is the primary energy requirement per the unit power production and it is calculated with primary energy demand values throughout this study.

1.4 Energy pay-back time (EPBT)

The ratio of total embedded energy to annual energy generation (Gkantou & Baniotopoulos, 2018) is defined as energy pay-back time.

1.5 Global warming potential (GWP)

It is a chosen metric to compare the capacity of heat retention in the atmosphere of each greenhouse gases (relative to CO2). In other words, it is the ratio of the warming caused by a substance which has similar mass to that of carbon dioxide (Demirel, 2014).

2 LIFE CYCLE ASSESSMENT (LCA)

Life cycle assessment is a method for evaluation of environmental impacts of a product, a system or a process (ISO, 2006a, b, Singh et al. 2013).

2.1 Phases for LCA applied energy systems

The methodology of life cycle assessment is applied by dividing the life cycle into four main phases: production, construction, operation and maintenance as well as decommissioning and recycling for energy production systems (Frischknecht et al. 2016).

2.1.1 Production phase
Extraction of raw materials consisting of manufacturing all parts such as transmission lines for the grid connection and infrastructure is included in this phase.

2.1.2 Construction phase
In the second step of LCA, all materials are required to be transported to the operation site. Construction phase also consists of assembly of all materials and testing procedure for the installation.

2.1.3 Operation and maintenance phase
The first stage of this phase is the generation of electricity. It contains periodic maintenance such as the cleaning of panels for PV plants, oil changes for wind plants and defect repairs like broken parts for all types of plants.

2.1.4 Decommissioning and recycling or disposal phase
Marked by the conclusion of electricity generation, the dismantling stage of parts takes place in plants. In this study, only transportation of disassembled parts is included while the recycling procedure is excluded.

2.2 System boundaries

General assumptions concerning all configurations and generalized system boundaries are listed as follows:

- All phases including production, construction, operation and maintenance as well as decommissioning and recycling or disposal are evaluated in a "cradle to grave" approach.
- Life cycle modeling is established with the aid of GaBi.
- Although production processes of primary raw materials such as cast iron and silica are considered in the study, their transportations are excluded from this study.
- During the assessment of the fourth phase, namely the decommissioning and recycling or disposal phase, only the transportation of parts for recycling is considered.
- During the assessment of the fourth phase, circular economy approach is applied for the scrap materials.
- The results are evaluated by means of CML2001-Jan 2016 method due to closeness of the selected region to Europe.
- The functional unit of LCA is selected as the unit power, MWh.
- The results are normalized in order to present them as a single emission type.
- The measure of greenhouse gas emissions is kg CO_2-eq./MWh.
- The measure of acidification potential is kg SO_2-eq./MWh.
- The unit of eutrophication potential is kg PO_4-eq./MWh.
- Energy payback time is measured in years.
- The unit of cumulative energy demand (CED) is MJ/MWh. Primary energy demand (PED) of GaBi database is the same concept of CED used in Ecoinvent database (Swart et al. 2015).
- Google Maps are used for the measurement of transportation distance.

3 WIND POTENTIAL AND ASSESSMENT

As mentioned in the introduction part, Bozcaada Island has wind potential (İncecik & Erdoğmuş, 1995) as a renewable source. Wind potential has been measured with the aid of one 250 kW turbine at the meteo-station (Türksoy, 1995, Dündar & Inan 1995) and its findings are that the average wind speed is 6,4 m/s at 10 m above ground level and the mean energy density is E= 324 W/m² for the island. In another study (Oğulata, 2003), average wind speed is measured as 6,2 m/s at 5 m and 8,4 m/s at 50 m, respectively. Thus, an onshore wind farm was established in 2000 and has been operated since. Offshore wind technology (Argin et al. 2019) can be regarded as an option to evaluate the wind potential of Bozcaada since offshore wind potential is two times higher than onshore wind potential for less than 30 m water depth in Turkey (Gaudiosi, 1994). In this study, the life cycle assessment of offshore wind farm on Bozcaada island is applied for the first time although other renewable systems for the island were considered in the literature (Güzel, 2012, Satir et al. 2018) in terms of environmental and economic characteristics. Hence, offshore wind farm is proposed as an alternative option based on the suggestion (Emeksiz & Demirci, 2019) that Bozcaada with 9,25 m/s mean average wind velocity at 100 m has the highest wind energy potential among all coastal regions in Turkey to evaluate the wind potential of the island and create a comparison to onshore counterparts in this study.

3.1 Other assumptions for wind configurations

In this section, general assumptions concerning the wind potential of the island are listed below:

- Useful life of wind turbines is assumed to be 20 years (Chipindula et al. 2018).
- Linear arrangement is assumed for offshore wind farm because the established counterparts have been arranged linearly.
- Production processes until the production of wind turbines themselves as one of the main parts for the wind farms are included for both the alternatives of onshore and offshore wind turbines. However, transportation of raw materials such as cast iron is excluded.

3.2 Model structures of onshore and offshore wind farms

An onshore wind farm was established and has been operated since 2000. Its installed capacity is 10.2 MW (Sahin, 2008). The farm is located on the west part of the island. The tower height as 44 m for the established farm is taken from the experts who have operated the farm. Underground wiring is 9 km up to the central transformer. The established onshore wind farm consists of 17 wind turbines, whereas 3 wind turbines are considered as the offshore counterparts in order to reach the approximately equal nominal power capacity as in the case of onshore technology. The onshore wind farm was installed with Enercon E-40 (600 kW) turbines (Hepbasli & Ozgener, 2004, TUREB, 2018) and the offshore wind farm is considered to be established with Vestas V-112 3 MW turbines.

In the case of the offshore wind farm, the tower height is accepted as 94 m since wind speed is (Satir et al. 2018) 9.1 m/s at 94 m height around the island. Lateral linear arrangement against the dominant wind direction is assumed for the three turbines. Distances of cabling between the turbines are calculated as 1120 m by means of five rotor diameters (Öksel et al. 2016) to minimize the effects of wake losses. A study suggested that there is no requirement of substation (Huang et al. 2017) for the offshore wind energy plants which has less than 30 MW nominal power. In addition, a substation on the sea is required when the distance of the plant is more than 10 km away from the coastal line even if the nominal power ranges between 30 MW and 120 MW (Huang et al. 2017). In other words, far shore design is needed for the distance that is at least 10 km (Güzel, 2012). Hence, the distance is accepted as 10 km for this study in order to avoid the necessity of the substation (Güzel, 2012, Huang et al. 2017).

High voltage alternating current and high voltage direct current power transmission are two alternative solutions for the transmission loss caused by the transmission cables. High voltage alternating current is the conventional solution for the system that has small or medium capacity (Olguin et al. 2014) and requires less than 100 km transmission line (Kirby et al. 2002). Thus, high voltage alternating current, similar to the other study on Bozcaada island (Köroğlu & Ülgen, 2018), is considered for this study.

3.3 Life cycle inventory (LCI) for onshore and offshore wind farms

In order to establish a wind farm either on land or on the sea, moving parts such as nacelle, rotors and cables, and fixed parts such as tower and base parts are required. However, foundations and roads are needed for onshore as a base, the basement for offshore system depends on water depth and its types can be regarded as monopile (Velarde & Bachynski, 2017), gravity-based or tripod (Kaldellis & Apostolou, 2017) suction caisson, multipod (tripod and jacket) (Oh et al. 2018) and floating (Oguz et al. 2018). For the water depth which is around 30 m in Bozcaada island (Satir et al. 2018) monopile is considered in the same way as in the research of (Oguz & Incecik, 2014).

Basic characteristics of turbines and material weights to manufacture them are listed in Table 1. Enercon E-40 specifications are adopted from the previous studies (Lee et al. 2006, Oğuz & Şentürk, 2019) and the specifications of Vestas V112-3 MW model is found in the study (Tsai, 2013) apart from tower weight and tower height, respectively.

Table 1. Specifications of selected turbine models.

	Onshore	Offshore
	Enercon E-40*	Vestas V-112
Nominal power	0,6 kW	3 MW
Rotor diameter	43.70 m	112.00 m
Tower height	44 m	94 m
Rotor weight	8.27 t	49.18 t
Nacelle weight	19.77 t	92.63 t
Tower weight	29.91 t**	264.38 t ***
Base weight	220.00 t	700.00 t

* It is taken from the website (Enercon E-40/6.44-600,00 kW-Wind Turbine, n.d.)
** By means of linear interpolation, it is calculated for a - 44 m model (Lee, et al., 2006).
*** Tower weight is calculated in accordance with the determined tower height and by means of which is adopted from (Way & Van Zijl, 2015).

During the recalculations of tower weight for both systems, linear interpolation technique is applied for onshore system due to the lack of information related to geometric design or any other researches. However, the tower of offshore system is recalculated with the linear regression method by means of the data found in Way & Van Zijl (2015), which can be seen in Figure 1 as graph.

In the production phase, wind turbines for the onshore wind farm is produced in Germany. Thus, Deutch grid mix, as seen in Table 3, is used. Its nacelle comprises of steel and cast-iron materials. Metal roll forming (Ghenai, 2012) is applied for its production in GaBi. Glass fiber, epoxy resin, and cast iron are the materials utilized to manufacture its hub and blades. The manufacturing process of the tower is similar to the nacelle production. Concrete and steel are utilized as materials in the model of manufacturing foundations and roads. A similar procedure is applied for offshore wind turbine manufacturing. Due to the differences in production line, rotor blades are transported from Italy and nacelles are transported from Denmark in the case of the offshore farm. The location of offshore turbines is arranged laterally across the dominant wind direction. The 33 kV submarine cables (Öksel et al. 2016) are selected for the cables between the turbines of the offshore wind farm. The 132 kV cables (Tsai, 2013) are preferred for the transmission line to the coast. The weight of cables is taken as 29 t/km and 88 t/km for 33 kV submarine cable and 132 kV submarine cable (Birkeland, 2011), respectively. In the case of manufacturing of offshore wind farm parts, European grid mix is utilized to model the energy requirements of the related processes.

Due to the limitation of GaBi, excavator is considered to be assembled the parts together for both configurations. Procedures are similar except the extra motor ship usage for the assembly of offshore system parts throughout construction phase. In addition to this, Greek grid mix is used in the installation of onshore wind farm and offshore counterparts due to the lack of Turkish electricity mix in the software.

The third phase, namely operation and maintenance phase are initiated with the electricity generation from the farms in both cases. Electricity production of onshore wind farm is predicted to be 680 GWh throughout the life of the plant based on the average annual electricity production which is 34 GWh/year obtained from the interview with operating experts. The predicted annual electricity generation is calculated to be 14 GW/h for Vestas V112-3 MW from the research (Güzel, 2012).

The predicted annual energy production of this tower height, which is determined in accordance with the known (Satir et al. 2018) wind speed, 9.1m/s, at 94 m, is applicable as seen in Figure 2 and Table 2.

When the failure of the configurations is considered, spare parts are allocated initially for both systems as seen in Table 3. For the onshore wind farm, 1% of moving parts, namely cables, inverters, nacelle and rotor, is assumed to be broken and replaced. It is added to material flow in GaBi as spare parts. It can be seen in Table 3 that prediction of broken parts throughout useful life is increased to 15 % for generator and gearbox of offshore wind farm technology. Site maintenance is not required for the offshore case. It is also neglected for the

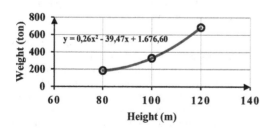

Figure 1. Weight vs height for V112-3MW turbine tower.

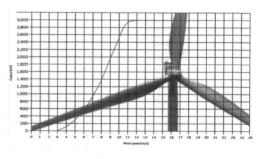

Figure 2. Power curve-Vestas V-112-3 MW-Offshore (Madariaga et al. 2012).

Table 2. Power curve-Vestas V112-3MW-Offshore (Madariaga et al. 2012).

Wind speed (m/s)	Annual Energy Production (MWh)
8.5	13.402
9	14.311
9.5	15.119
10.0	15.826

onshore system no maintenance requirement of access roads which has no traffic jam except maintenance of onshore wind farm.

Maintenance procedure consists of four different types:

- Visual controls are the first type of it. Although there is no material flow (Owens, 2019, Zeinali & Keysan) during the visual controls of both cases. It just should be noted that use of ferry is more necessary when it comes carrying parts of offshore wind farm.
- The requirement to maintain oil and lubricant is regarded as second type of maintenance procedure. The need to supplement oil and lubricant is more frequent for offshore wind farm than onshore wind farm due to the gearbox. According to experts who operates wind farms including Vestas models on the land in Turkey, Vestas V112- 3 MW is assumed to require 15.570 kg lubricant. Experts inform that requirement of oil supplemet depends on the quality and amount of oil. Hence, oil alteration of Vestas models lasts as a whole totally 6-7 years. As a result, oil and lubricant are amended three times completely during the useful life of Vestas models. However, there is no information about the lubricant requirement for Enercon models and turbines due to direct-drive mechanism they have (Owens, 2019, Zeinali & Keysan). The need of lubricants for an onshore wind farm throughout its useful life is assumed with the aid of the report (Razdan & Garrett, 2015) as 3.400 kg.
- The third type of maintenance is counted as mechanical maintenance since mechanic parts in the system should be controlled periodically. According to the research (Chan & Mo, 2017), these parts should be controlled twice a year. During these controls, broken parts should be amended. However, no extra material flow because of the initial allocation of spare parts is considered for both wind farms.
- Electrical maintenance is the last type for both configurations. The notion of its modelling is similar to mechanical ones. It can be seen in Table 3 that transportation distances are assumed as 300 km on the land both the processes of oiling and during the amendment of broken parts for onshore wind farm. In the case of offshore wind farm, 40 km and 200 km on the sea are assumed for repair and oiling procedure, respectively.

Table 3. LCA summary for different wind systems.

Phases	Specifications	Onshore wind farm	Offshore wind farm
	Mechanism	Direct-drive	Gearbox
	Nominal power	10.2 MW	9 MW
Production	Wind turbine	Germany	-
	Rotor blades	-	Italy
	Nacelle	-	Denmark
	Electricity mix	Deutch	European
Construction	Transportation up to/and installation	Extra motor ship usage required for offshore system.	
	Assembly	Excavator is used due to the lack of crane in the software.	
	Electricity grid mix	Greek	
Operation and maintenance	Transportation for periodic or sudden controls	Extra motor ship usage required for offshore system.	
	Amount of oil and lubricant	3400 kg	15570 kg due to gearbox
	Spare parts (allocated initially)	1 % for all moving parts	15 % for generator and gearbox
	Total transportation for the change of broken parts	300 km on the land	40 km on the sea
	Transportation for oiling	300 km on land	200 km on the sea
Decommissioning and disposal or recycling	Decommissioning	Extra motor ship usage required for offshore system	
	Transportation of scrap materials	Same distance is assumed for both systems.	

In the evaluation of decommissioning and disposal or recycling, scrap materials are transported to the same place to be recycled or for disposal as demonstrated in Table 3. Decomposition of offshore wind farm requires the utilization of motor ship although it is not necessary in the case of the onshore wind farm. It is indicated that the main production units such as nacelle and tower are decomposed into their materials as an onset of the fourth phase in order to classify. The ratio of classification into scrap materials and waste for disposal is also demonstrated in Table 4. According to Table 4, offshore wind farm has more variety of decomposed materials due to its more complex structure than onshore system. The end-of life treatment for concrete is landfill based on the suggestions of (Haapala & Prempreeda, 2014) and DTU International Energy Report (Andersen et al. 2014). Due to the difficulty of recycling of composite materials, rotor's end-of life treatment is considered as landfill similar to the International Energy Report of DTU. Open loop strategy, which means that recycled materials are not considered in the production phase, is applied for recycling.

3.4 Life cycle impact assessment (LCIA) for onshore and offshore wind farms

In this section, results based on the phases of each system are tabulated.

The total acidification ratio of the systems is approximately 1,5 for the wind farms. Table 5 shows that production phase causes the highest acidification in the case of the onshore wind farm while the construction phase of the offshore wind farm leads to the highest acidification potential. The reason why the highest acidification appears during the construction phase of the offshore system is excessive requirement of diesel utilized for the assembly and transportation.

Eutrophication potential is higher for the onshore wind farm than the offshore wind farm as indicated in Table 5. The main reason of it can be explained that concrete foundations of onshore system leaves in place.

As seen in Table 6, the offshore wind farm causes less greenhouse gas emissions than the onshore wind farm during the life of each configuration. While the most harmful phase is construction for the offshore wind farm, the production phase is the most harmful phase in the case of the onshore wind farm.

In terms of cumulative energy demand (CED), total energy requirement of the offshore wind farm

Table 4. End-of-life summary for both offshore and onshore wind farms.

	Materials Treated		Ratio		
	Material name	Mass (ton)	Recycling (%)	Landfill (%)	Decomposed Components
Offshore	Steel alloyed	2.343,7	90	10	Nacelle, tower, rotor, cables and monopile
	Aluminum	5,3	95	5	Nacelle and rotor
	Copper	293,8	95	5	Nacelle and cables
	Lead	220,0	90	10	
	Polyethylene	135,2	-	100	Internal and grid connection cables
	Polypropylene	77,1	-	100	
	Polyvinylchloride	5,3	-	100	Miscallenous
	Epoxy	8,2	-	100	
	Glass fiber	23,4	-	100	Rotor
Onshore	Iron	844,1	90	10	Nacelle and tower
	Composite	142,0	-	100	Rotor
	Aluminum	131,9	-	100	Electronic parts
	Concrete	3.740,0	95	5	Foundation

Table 5. Acidification and Eutrophication Potential.

Impact Categories	Acidification Potential (AP) [kg SO$_2$-eq.]		Eutrophication Potential (EP) [kg Phospate-eq.]	
Phases	Onw.	Offw.	Onw.	Offw.
Production	9107.4	492.0	966.3	47.0
Construction	666.5	13417.0	169.1	3248.7
O&M	12.7	1.9	1.3	0.5
DorR	723.1	1211.1	3287.8	250.9
Total	10509.7	15112.0	4424.5	3547.1

Table 6. Global Warming Potential [kg CO2-eq.].

Phases	Onshore W.F.	Offshore W.F
Production	4086925	189495
Construction	277250	4818827
O&M	4.211	295
DorR	2.867.824	1420491
Total	7236210	6429108

Table 7. Energy Demand Ratios Based on Phases [%].

Phases	Onshore W.F.	Offshore W.F
Production	90.236	5.620
Construction	5.570	84.808
O&M	0.262	0.005
DorR	3.931	9.567

and the total energy demand of the onshore wind farm are 81498922.9 MJ and 71374953.9 MJ, respectively. While the construction phase needs 69117297.9 MJ in the case of the offshore wind farm, 64406146.3 MJ is required for the production phase of the onshore wind farm.

It is observed from Table 7 that energy demand for operation of the maintenance phase increases with the number of turbines dramatically independent of the technology utilized gearbox or direct-drive mechanism.

4 SOLAR POTENTIAL AND ASSESSMENT

As mentioned in the introduction part, the solar potential of Bozcaada is one of the important renewable sources for the island (Kalinci, 2015). The island's solar energy potential per day and sunshine duration per day are 308.0 cal/cm^2 and 7,5 hours, respectively (Oğulata, 2003). For this purpose, the proposed land-based photovoltaic power plant is investigated in terms of different perspectives (Kalinci, 2015, Şentürk & Oğuz 2019). Life cycle of proposed land based photovoltaic power plant in Turkey is assessed for the first time in the study (Şentürk & Oğuz, 2019).

4.1 Other assumptions for solar configuration

In this section, necessary terms such as degradation rates, performance ratio are defined firstly. Following this, general assumptions concerning solar source are listed.

Degradation rate

Decrease in the solar panel efficiency due to environmental conditions is degradation. Dusting of solar panels and climatic conditions such as average temperature, humidity, temperature differences and ultraviolet (UV) irradiation are the main factors of the degradation phenomenon (Ascencio-Vasquez et al. 2019). Hence, there is a requirement of test to observe the decline of the efficiency of solar panel for different geographic region like in the study (Ozden et al. 2018) which degradation rate of multi-crystalline solar panel is determined as 0.7 % for Central Anatolia. However, it is dependent on geographical conditions and there is no data for the island. Thus, the overall system degradation ratio is assumed to be 0.6 % based on the research article (Jordan & Kurtz, 2013).

Performance ratio

For the photovoltaic technology, it is the ratio of actual electricity generation to the electricity production expected from the ideal case. Due to the need for actual production data, it depends on geographical conditions similar to degradation rates. However, in Turkey, actual electricity generation data from photovoltaic power plants is limited since the history of on-grid applications, started 2012, is relatively new for the photovoltaic technology (Karadogan et al. 2014). One of its important findings is that the estimation of electricity production of PVGIS database is less deviated from the actual electricity generation in Turkey than Metronom database (Karadogan et al. 2014). Hence, PVGIS database is taken into consideration for this study.

- Production processes until the production of silicon wafer itself are considered in the modeling of the first phase, while transportation of raw materials required to manufacture silica wafers is excluded from the study.
- Multi-crystalline cells are preferred for the plant.
- Useful life of conventional photovoltaic plant is assumed to be 30 years (Ito, 2011).
- Fixed-tilt mounting is assumed.
- Degradation ratio is accepted as 0.6 % as mentioned before.
- Performance ratio is accepted as 0.80 % for the conventional one.
- Useful life of inverters for PV plant is suggested as (Ito, 2011) 15 years. Therefore, change of inverters once throughout its life is applied in the modelling of the plant.

4.2 Model structure of photovoltaic (PV) system

Since solar configuration is hypothetical, nominal power capacity is accepted as 1.2 MW in order to make comparison easy because the established wind farm area of 20560 m^2 is utilized for the application of land-based PV plant. Site clearance is neglected in the selected area since there is no obstacle such as vegetation or slope for the application of land based farm. Optimum design parameters, provided by PVGIS database, which are 32° slope and 3° azimuth angles are accepted for the array of solar panels.

4.3 Life cycle inventory (LCI) for photovoltaic (PV) system

Due to the nominal capacity assumed, the number of total solar modules, each of which consists of 60 cells, are 4615 for the configurations. Mounting components are regarded as fences, support structures and cables for the conventional PV plant. In addition to this, low and medium voltage switchboards and inverters are required.

In the production phase, silicon wafers are produced in Taiwan by means of the Chinese electricity grid mix. They are transported 8689 nautical miles with an ocean-going ship. Open ground mounting structure for the conventional one is composed of aluminum and zinc coated steel.

Construction phase onsets with the transportation of the components. Solar panels are transported from Tekirdağ and transportation distance for three string inverters is totally 459 km (by 451 km truck and 8 km ferry).

During the operation and maintenance phase, spare inverters are changed once due to its limited life expectancy. Tap water is required for the cleaning of solar panels against dusting. 15 solar modules are assumed to be replaced in the conventional PV plant. Transportation for changing broken parts are considered by 371 km truck and by 10 km ferry. Cleaning of solar modules are required the transportation by 80 km truck. Total electricity generation throughout the PV plant is estimated to be 52.31 GWh with the aforementioned degradation rate.

In the last phase of the life cycle assessment, on-site deconstruction is applied to separate the scraps into recycling and disposal. Aluminum and copper, steel scraps coming from inverters, frames and cables are common scrap materials. These scrap materials are transferred by 300 km truck and by 8 km ferry transportation to the recycling area. Solar panels are transferred to Deutsche Solar AG Recycling Plant (Appleyard, 2009) by a cargo plane. Open loop recycling which means that there are no recycled materials turning to the production processes is applied apart from scrap solar panels.

4.4 Life cycle impact assessment (LCIA) for photovoltaic (PV) system

Impact assessment for solar configuration on Bozcaada island is evaluated by the LCA of open ground photovoltaic plant.

As seen in Figure 3, the highest energy which is 91.38 % of total energy demand is required for the production phase of PV plant whereas its operation and maintenance phase needs almost no energy.

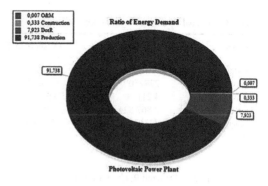

Figure 3. Ratio of energy demand of PV plant.

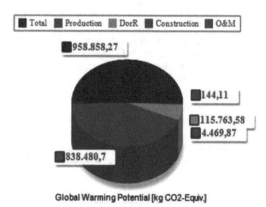

Figure 4. Global Warming Potential (GWP) of PV Plant.

In addition to this, Figure 4 indicates that greenhouse gas emissions during its operation is low for PV technology. The recycling procedure with current technology leads to high emission for photovoltaics although the highest ratio of global warming potential occurs in the production phase. Total GWP for the proposed PV plant throughout its life is 958858,27 kg CO2-eq.

5 RESULTS

The results based on functional unit of each system are tabulated in order to make comparison among all configurations. Selected impact categories for all configurations are tabulated in Table 8.

The offshore wind farm requires less energy to establish than does the onshore wind farm and land-based photovoltaic plant. In other words, it is the most advantageous system in terms of primary energy demand. As a result, its energy pay-back time

Table 8. Selected Impact Categories.

Specifications	Onshore Wind Farm	Offshore Wind Farm	Land-Based PV Plant
AP[kg SO$_2$-eq./MWh.]	0.01545	0.01801	0.09816
EP[kg PO$_4$-eq./MWh.]	0.00651	0.00422	0.00794
GWP[kg CO$_2$-eq./MWh]	10.64	7.65	18.33
CED[MJ/MWh]	104.95	97.02	234.53
EPBT[year]	0.617	0.579	2.06
Total Production-[MWh]	680	840	52.31

is shorter than the other two alternatives related with energy demand.

In terms of environmental characteristics, it can be said that wind source is cleaner than solar source for Bozcaada since wind configurations cause less AP, EP and GWP than the land-based photovoltaic system. Although the offshore wind farm leads to more acidification than the onshore wind farm, it causes less eutrophication and global warming than its onshore counterpart.

6 DISCUSSION

In order to determine environmental characteristics, a road map can be derived with the aid of life cycle assessment of the proposed alternatives prior to investment.

As a suggestion related to the land-based photo-voltaic technology, the new methods should be investigated to diminish the impact of its production phase. The onset of grid-connection of photovoltaics on the world, when has been since the beginning of 1990s (Yudha et al. 2018), is taken into considerations, research on the recycling of solar panels should be accelerated in order to save the world from its contaminative effects.

As a result, offshore wind technology is recommended for the island in terms of environmental specifications by means of life cycle assessment. However, in order to determine the most feasible and sustainable alternatives, firstly, the number of systems examined should be increased. For instance, photovoltaics, floating photovoltaic plant can be considered as another alternative to assess the solar potential of the island or the wave potential of the island (Kalinci, 2015) should be evaluated. Secondly, economic aspects and risks of the options should be investigated with the aid of life cycle methodology to achieve the most feasible option for the island.

ACKNOWLEDGEMENTS

The authors would like to thank Miss. Denizay Önol for her help with the final proofreading.

REFERENCES

Andersen, P., Bonou, A., Beauson, J. & Brøndsted, P., 2014. *Recycling of Wind Turbines*, Lyngby, Denmark, 2014: Technical University of Denmark (DTU).

Appleyard, D., 2009. Light cycle: recycling PV materials. *Renewable Energy World Magazine*, 12(2), pp. 28–36.

Argin, M. et al., 2019. Exploring the offshore wind energy potential of Turkey based on multicriteria site selection. *Energy Strategy Reviews*, Volume 23, pp. 33–46.

Ascencio-Vásquez, J. et al., 2019. Global Climate Data Processing and Mapping of Degradation Mechanisms and Degradation Rates of PV Modules. *Energies*, 12 (24).

Birkeland, C., 2011. *Assessing the Life Cycle Environmental Impacts of Offshore Wind Power Generation and Power Transmission in the North Sea*. s.l.:Norwegian University of Science and Technology Department of Energy and Process Engineering.

Chan, D. & Mo, J., 2017. Life cycle reliability and maintenance analyses of wind turbines. *Energy Procedia*, Volume 110, p. 328–333.

Chipindula, J. et al., 2018. Life Cycle Environmental Impact of Onshore and Offshore Wind Farms in Texas. *Sustainability*, Volume 10, p. 2022.

Cindoruk, S. S., 2018. Havadaki NO ve NO2 Parametrelerinin Marmara Temiz Hava Merkezi Ölçümleri Kapsamında İncelenmesi. *Ömer Halisdemir Üniversitesi Mühendislik Bilimleri Dergisi*, 7(2), pp. 600–611.

CML-Institute of Environmental Sciences,Department of Industrial Ecology, 2016. *CML-IA Characterisation Factors*, Leiden, The Netherlands: Leiden University.

Da Silva, G. D. P. & Branco, D. A. C., 2018. Is floating photovoltaic better than conventional photovoltaic? Assessing environmental impacts. *Impact Assessment and Project Appraisal*, 36(5), pp. 390–400.

Demirel, Y., 2014. Thermoeconomics. In: *Nonequilibrium Thermodynamics-Transport and Rate Processes in Physical, Chemical and Biological Systems*. Lincoln, USA: University of Nebraska, pp. 265–302.

Doğan-Sağlamtimur, N. & Sağlamtimur, B., 2018. Sucul Ortamlarda Ötrofikasyon Durumu ve Senaryoları. *Ömer Halisdemir Üniversitesi Mühendislik Bilimleri Dergisi*, 7(1), pp. 75–82.

Dündar, C. & Inan, D., 1996. Investigation of wind energy application possibilities for a specific island (Bozcaada) in Turkey. *Renewable Energy*, 9(1-4), pp. 822–826.

Emeksiz, C. & Demirci, B., 2019. The determination of offshore wind energy potential of Turkey by usingnovelty hybrid site selection method. *Sustainable Energy Technologies and Assessments*, 36(December), p. 100562.

Enercon E-40/6.44-600,00 kW-Wind Turbine, n.d. [Online] Available at: https://en.wind-turbine-models.com/turbines/68-enercon-e-40-6.44 [Accessed 13 July 2019].

Franzitta, V., Curto, D., Rao, D. & Viola, A., 2016. *Renewable energy sources to fulfill the global energy needs of a country: The case study of Malta in Mediterranean Sea*. Shanghai, China, OCEANS 2016.

Frischknecht, R. et al., 2016. *Methodology Guidelines on Life Cycle Assessment of Photovoltaic Electricity: 3rd Edition*. United States: s.n.

Frumin, G. & Gildeeva, I. M., 2015. Eutrophication of water bodies — A global environmental problem. *Russian Journal of General Chemistry*, 84(13), pp. 2483–2488.

Gaudiosi, G., 1994. Offshore wind energy in the mediterranean countries. *Renewable Energy*, 5(1-4), pp. 675–691.

Ghenai, C., 2012. Life Cycle Analysis of Wind Turbine. In: *Sustainable Development—Energy, Engineering and Technologies—Manufacturing and Environment*. Melbourne, FL, USA: InTech, p. 27.

Gkantou, M. & ve Baniotopoulos, C., 2018. *Life Cycle Analysis of Onshore Wind Turbine Towers*. Catanzaro Lido, Italy, The 2nd International TU1304 WINERCOST.

Güzel, B., 2012. *Açık Deniz Rüzgar Enerjisi, Fizibilite Adımları ile Bozcaada ve Gökçeada Örnek Çalışması*. İstanbul: İstanbul Teknik Üniversitesi Enerji Enstitüsü.

Haapala, K. & Prempreeda, P., 2014. Comparative life cycle assessment of 2.0 MW wind turbines. *Int. J. Sustain. Manuf.*, 3(170–185).

Hepbasli, A. & Ozgener, O., 2004. A review on the development of wind energy in Turkey. *Renewable and Sustainable Energy Reviews*, 8(3), pp. 257–276.

Huang, Y.-F., Gan, X.-J. & Chiueh, P.-T., 2017. Life cycle assessment and net energy analysis of offshore wind power systems. *Renewable Energy*, 102(Part A), pp. 98–106.

Incecik, S. & Erdoğmuş, F., 1995. An investigation of the wind power potential on the western coast of Anatolia. *Renewable Energy*, 6(7), pp. 863–865.

ISO, 2006a. *ISO 14040: EnvironmentalManagement–Life Cycle Assessment–Principles and Framework*, Geneva, Switzerland: International Organization for Standardization.

ISO, 2006b. *ISO 14044:2006: EnvironmentalManagement–Life Cycle Assessment–Requirements and Guidelines*, Geneva, Switzerland: International Organization for Standardization.

Ito, M., 2011. Life Cycle Assessment of PV Systems. In: *Crystalline Silicon - Properties and Uses*. London, UK: s.n.

Jordan, D. C. & Kurtz, S. R., 2013. Photovoltaic Degradation Rates—an Analytical Review. *Progress in Photovoltaics*, 21(1), pp. 12–29.

Kaldellis, J. & Apostolou, D., 2017. Life cycle energy and carbon footprint of offshore wind energy. Comparison with onshore counterpart. *Renewable Energy*, 108 (August), pp. 72–84.

Kalinci, Y., 2015. Alternative energy systems for Bozcaada island. *Renewable and Sustainable Energy Reviews*, 45 (May), pp. 460–480.

Karadogan, O., Kilicarslan, T. & Celiktas, M., 2014. *The Actual Performance Value of Photovoltaic Solar System In Turkey and Compare with Software Result*. İzmir, Turkey, SOLARTR.

Keleş, S. & Bilgen, S., 2012. Renewable energy sources in Turkey for climate change mitigation and energy sustainability. *Renewable and Sustainable Energy Reviews*, 16(7), pp. 5199–5206.

Kim, T. H. & Chae, C. U., 2016. Environmental Impact Analysis of Acidification and Eutrophication Due to Emissions from the Production of Concrete. *Sustainability*, Volume 8, p. 578.

Kirby, N., Xu, L., Luckett, M. & Siepmann, W., 2002. HVDC transmission for large offshore wind farms. *Power Engineer*, 16(3), pp. 135–141.

Köroğlu, M. Ö. & Ülgen, K., 2018. *Denizüstü Rüzgâr Enerji Santralleri: Çanakkale Örneği*. Ankara, s.n.

Larsen, S. V., 2014. Is environmental impact assessment fulfilling its potential? The case of climate change in renewable energy projects. *Impact Assessment and Project Appraisal*, 32(3), pp. 234–240.

Lee, Y., Tzeng, Y. & Su, C., 2006. *Life Cycle Assessment of Wind Power Utilization in Taiwan*. Tsukuba, Japan, The 7th International Conference on Eco Balance.

Madariaga, A. et al., 2012. Current facts about offshore wind farms. *Renewable and Sustainable Energy Reviews*, 16(5), pp. 3105–3116.

Merta, G., Linkeb, B. & Auricha, J., 2017. Analysing the Cumulative Energy Demand of Product-Service Systems for wind turbines. *Procedia CIRP*, Volume 59, pp. 214–219.

Oguz, E. et al., 2018. Experimental and numerical analysis of a TLP floating offshore wind turbine. *Ocean Engineering*, 147(January), pp. 591–605.

Oguz, E. & Incecik, A., 2014. *Feasibility of Installing Offshore Wind Farms in the North Agean Sea, Turkey*. Tokyo Big Sight, Tokyo, Japan, s.n.

Oguz, E. & Şentürk, A. E., 2019. Selection of the Most Sustainable Renewable Energy System for Bozcaada Island: Wind vs. Photovoltaic. *Sustainability*, 11(15), p. 4098.

Oğulata, R. T., 2003. Energy sector and wind energy potential in Turkey. *Renewable and Sustainable Energy Reviews*, 7(6), pp. 469–484.

Oh, K.-Y.et al., 2018. A review of foundations of offshore wind energy convertors: Current status and future perspectives. *Renewable and Sustainable Energy Reviews*, 88(May), pp. 16–36.

Olguin, R. E. T., Garces, A. & Bergna, G., 2014. HVDC Transmission for Offshore Wind Farms. In: *Large Scale Renewable Power Generation*. Singapore: Green Energy and Technology.Springer, pp. 289–310.

Owens, B. N., 2019. Europe Sails Ahead. %1 içinde*The Wind Power Story-A Century of Innovation That Reshaped The Global Energy Landscape*. New Jersey, Canada: WILEY-IEEE Press, p. 245.

Ozden, T., Akinoglu, B. G. & Kurtz, S., 2018. *Performance and Degradation Analyses of two Different PV Modules in Central Anatolia*. Ankara,Turkey, IEEE-Institute of Electrical and Electronics Engineers.

Öksel, C., Koç, A., Koç, Y. & Yağlı, H., 2016. Antakya Körfezi Deniz Üstü Rüzgar Eenerjisi Potansiyel Araştırılması. *SUJEST*, 4 (1),pp. ISSN: 2147-9364 (Elektronik).

Özkale, C., Celik, C., Türkmen, A. C. & Cakmaz, E. S., 2017. Decision analysis application intended for selection of a power plant running on renewable energy sources. *Renewable and Sustainable Energy Reviews*, 1011-1021, p. 70.

Piasecka, I. et al., 2019. Life Cycle Analysis of Ecological Impacts of an Offshore and a Land-Based Wind Power Plant. *Applied Sciences*, 9(2), p. 231.

Rabalais, N. N., Turner, R. E., Díaz, R. J. & Justić, D., 2009. Global change and eutrophication of coastal waters. *ICES Journal of Marine Science*, 66(7), p. 1528–1537.

Razdan, P. & Garrett, P., 2015. *Life Cycle Assessment of Electricity Production from an onshore V110-2.0 MW Wind Plant*, Hedeager 42, Aarhus N, 8200, Denmark: Vestas Wind Systems A/S.

Sahin, A. D., 2008. A Review of Research and Development of Wind Energy in Turkey. *Clean Soil Air Water*, 36(9), pp. 734–742.

Satir, M., Murphy, F. & McDonnell, K., 2018. Feasibility study of an offshore wind farm in the Aegean Sea, Turkey. *Renewable and Sustainable Energy Reviews*, 81 (2), pp. 2552–2562.

Schmidt, K., Alvarez, L., Arevalo, J. & Abbassi, B., 2017. Life Cycle Impact Assessment of Renewable Energy Systems: Wind vs. Photovoltaic Systems. *International Journal of Current Research*, 9(10), pp. 59140–59147.

Singh, A., Olsen, S. I. & Pant, D., 2013. Importance of Life Cycle Assessment of Renewable Energy Sources. In: A. Singh & S. I. Olsen, eds. *Life Cycle Assessment of Renewable Energy Sources. Green Energy and Technology*. London: Springer.

Swart, P., Alvarenga, R. A. & Dewulf, J., 2015. Life Cycle Impact Assessmet. In: M. Z. Hauschild & M. A. Huijbregts, eds. *LCA Compendium-The Complete World of Life Cycle Assessment*. Dordrecht: Springer Science+Business, p. 252.

Şayan, Y., Özen, N., Kırkpınar, F. & Polat, M., 2010. *Organik Hayvansal Üretim ve Çevre*. Kelkit, s.n.

Şentürk, A. E. & Oğuz, E., 2019. *Life cycle assessment of two different renewable energy systems for a selected region: Bozcaada Island*. Varna, Bulgaria, CRC Press.

Taşkın, E., 2018. *Linyit Yakıtlı Pilot Termik Santral İçin Baca Gazı Emisyon Azaltma Seçeneklerinin Yaşam Döngüsü Değerlendirmesi*. Ankara: Hacettepe Üniversitesi, Çevre Mühendisliği Bölümü.

Tsai, L., 2013. *An Integrated Assessment of Offshore Wind Farm Siting: ACase Study in the Great Lakes of Michigan*. Michigan: The University of Michigan.

TUREB, 2018. *Turkish Wind Energy Statistic Report*, Ankara, Turkey: Turkish Wind Energy Association.

Türksoy, F., 1995. Investigation of wind power potential at Bozcaada, Turkey. *Renewable Energy*, 6(8), pp. 917–923.

Üçtuğ, F. G., 2017. Stakeholder Opinion-Based Comparison of Life Cycle Environmental Impacts of Eelectricty Generation in Turkey with Selected European Countries. *Anadolu Üniversitesi Bilim ve Teknoloji Dergisi A- Uygulamalı Bilimler ve Mühendislik*, 18(1), pp. 178–198.

Velarde, J. & Bachynski, E. E., 2017. Design and fatigue analysis of monopile foundations to support the DTU 10 MW offshore wind turbine. *Energy Procedia*, 137(October), pp. 3–13.

Vestas, 18th December 2015. *Life Cycle Assessment of Electricity Production from an onshore V110-2.0 MW Wind Plant*, Hedeager 42, Aarhus N, 8200,Denmark: Vestas Wind Systems A/S.

Way, A. & Van Zijl, G., 2015. A study on the design and material costs of tall wind turbine towers in South Africa. *Journal of the South African Institution of Civil Engineering*, 57(4), pp. 45–54.

Yağcı, M. (., 2010. Göllerde Ötrofikasyon, Kontrolü ve Planktonik Gösterge Türler. *YUNUS Araştırma Bülteni*, 10(1), pp. 11–14.

Yudha, H. M., Dewi, T., Risma, P. & Oktarina, Y., 2018. *Life Cycle Analysis for the Feasibility of Photovoltaic System Application in Indonesia*. s.l., IOP Publishing Ltd, p. 012005.

Zeinali, R. & Keysan, O., 2019. A Rare-Earth Free Magnetically Geared Generator for Direct-Drive Wind Turbines. *Energies*, 12(3), p. 447.

Validation with satellite data of SWAN model for wave conditions at the Madeira archipelago

D. Silva & C. Guedes Soares
Centre for Marine Technology and Ocean Engineering (CENTEC), Instituto Superior Técnico, Universidade de Lisboa, Lisbon, Portugal

ABSTRACT: This work aims to present the sea state conditions around Madeira archipelago, with an emphasis on the three areas selected under the ARCWIND project, with a hindcast system of 5 years (2012-2016). The WAVEWATCH III (WWIII) model was used to provide the boundary conditions for SWAN (Simulating WAves Nearshore), which performs the calculations of the wave spectrum evolution in the nearshore. SWAN also used the bathymetry from GEBCO (General Bathymetric Chart of the Ocean) and wind fields from ERA5, provided by ECMWF (European Center for Medium-Range Weather Forecasts). The validation was done against satellite data using the statistics parameters *Bias*, Root Mean Square Error (*RMSE*), Scatter Index (*SI*) and Pearson's Correlation Coefficient (r). Grid maps with *Hs* averages for the total, summer and winter cases are presented as well the 90th-percentile. For each of the areas, one point was selected and studied in terms of the *Hs* temporal variability (Coefficient of Variation, Seasonal Variability, Monthly Variability, Mean Annual Variability and Inter-Annual Variability), the *Hs/Tp* mean, max, min and the sea sate (*Hs/Tp*) with more occurrences.

1 INTRODUCTION

A reliable wave climate prediction in the areas where sea waters activities occur is an important objective. This knowledge helps not only ensure people safety but also to study the responses of the marine structures to the wave forcing, helping the constructors to design infrastructurs and devices according to the local wave climate.

The sea waves are a phenomenon in nature that is complex to understand. The ones generated by the wind are the most powerful with a high energy concentration, gaining notability in the scientific community in the scope of renewable energies. They appear with the wind blowing, grow amid storms and interactions with other waves and disappear after the wind cease blowing.

The concept of significant wave height was introduced by Sverdrup and Munk (1947). They understood that sea waves are a random process composed by large and small waves. The height of the significant waves, as representative of a particular sea state, is defined by the mean of the heights of the highest one-third waves in a wave group (Goda 2000).

The sea waves were recognized has being irregular and the concept of wave spectrum was introduced as a basic tool to describe it. The wind wave's generation, propagation and transformation in nearshore are explained in detail through the wave spectrum (Goda 2000).

The wave climate characterization using the directional wave spectrum is of great importance to have a reliable knowledge of the sea states conditions in specific sites (Portilla-Yandúm et al. 2019, Lucas et al. 2011, Lucas & Guedes Soares 2015a, b, Lucas et al. 2019).

The third generation spectral wave models are a widely accepted efficient tool to determine the sea states with an accurate description of the spatial variability for a long time period. In terms of efficiency, some models are more applicable in deep waters, such as WAM (Wave model) (WAMDI group 1988) and WWIII (WAVEWATCHIII) (Tolman 1991), and others in more shallow waters, such as SWAN (Simulating WAves Nearshore) (Booij et al. 1999).

The studies using the spectral wave models have some uncertainties associated to the modelling process. Some are related to climate variability in different time scales, like seasonal and interannual as described by Mackay et al. (2010a, b). The climate changes will increase this uncertainty (Caretero et al. 1998, Reeve et al. 2011, Charles et al. 2012). To improve the estimates, long time series to smooth the variability are needed.

Several authors studied the wave climate using a long-term hindcast. Cuttler et al. (2020) studied the western coast of Australia using a 38-years hindcast with SWAN. Lin et al. (2020) used the 44-years (1958-2001) HIPOCAS (Hindcast of Dynamic Processes of the Ocean and Coastal Areas of Europe) hindcast (Guedes Soares et al. 2002, Guedes Soares 2008) to study the Hs/Tz bivariate distribution. The

DOI: 10.1201/9781003216599-70

U.S. West coast was studied by Wu et al (2020) using a long-term hindcast with WWIII and SWAN. The works mentioned above are just some of the studies performed.

For Madeira archipelago, the area of this study, Rusu et al. (2008) made an evaluation of the wave conditions using WAM model for deep water and SWAN for nearshore simulations, with wind fields from the project HIPOCAS (Guedes Soares et al. 2002, Guedes Soares 2008). The authors studied the model results when activating some nearshore physical processes, namely the triad wave-wave interactions and the diffraction. Two cases were considered, a high energetic situation (26/01/2001 12h) and an average energetic situation (14/12/2000 24h). For the first case the incoming wave was from the northwest with Hs > 5 m and Tm of about 11 s, and for the second case the incoming wave was from the same direction (northwest) with Hs of about 2.5 m.

The ARCWIND project (Adaptation and implementation of floating wind energy conversion technology for the Atlantic region) has the goal to contribute for the development of offshore floating wind platform systems in sites more exposed in the Atlantic Area. The project includes the the assessment of wind energy potential to be used in a multicriteria approach to select the best locations for installation of wind farms (Diaz & Guedes Soares 2020). The choice of the locations are also related with the prevailing wave conditions and thus the need of the present study.

This study, which is in the scope of the ARCWIND project, validates the model to be used and at the same time provides an initial description the wave climate in the Madeira archipelago based on a 5-years hindcast (2012-2016) using the models WWIII and SWAN and wind fields from ERA5.

2 METHODOLOGY

2.1 Study region

Madeira archipelago is part of Portugal country and is situated in the north Atlantic about 900 km southwest of Portugal continental coast and 700 km west of the Moroccan coast (Rusu at al. 2008). Its territory is composed by two principal islands, Madeira and Porto Santo, and two groups of uninhabited islands, Desertas and Selvagens (the last one is not included in the area of study used).

The bathymetry of the area varies suddenly from very deep water to shallow water and for this reason very strong gradients in terms of depth are present all over the archipelago.

Figure 1 represents the bathymetry of the area used in the study, which is within the coordinates 18.5°-15.5°W and 31.5°-34°N.

The focus of this study includes the areas selected by Diaz et al (2019) for the development of an offshore floating wind farms in Madeira archipelago. These areas are represented in Figure 2 together with the

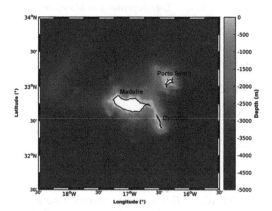

Figure 1. Area bathymetry.

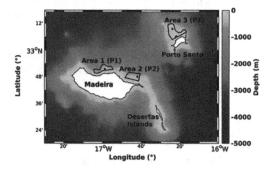

Figure 2. Areas of the ARCWIND project for Madeira archipelago. P1- point of Area 1; P2- point of Area 2 and P3- point of Area 3.

position of the points (black dot) used for a particular assessment of wave conditions in each area.

The geographic coordinates and the depth of the points (P1, P2 and P3) are displayed in Table 1.

2.2 Spectral wave models

WWIII and SWAN are third generation spectral wind-wave models that describe the evolution of wave spectrum by solving the spectral energy balance equation, based on a Eulerian formulation, represented by:

$$\frac{DN}{Dt} = \frac{S}{\sigma} \qquad (1)$$

Table 1. Geographic coordinates and depth for P1, P2 and P3.

	Lat/Lon (°)	Depth (m)
P1	32.86°N/16.98°W	68
P2	32.80°N/16.70°W	242
P3	33.16°N/16.40°W	30

in terms of time, geographical and spectral spaces calculated as:

$$\frac{\partial N}{\partial t} + \nabla_x . \dot{x} N + \frac{\partial}{\partial k} \dot{k} N + \frac{\partial}{\partial \theta} \dot{\theta} N = \frac{S}{\sigma} \quad (2)$$

$$\dot{x} = c_g + U \quad (3)$$

$$\dot{k} = -\frac{\partial \sigma}{\partial d}\frac{\partial d}{\partial s} - k.\frac{\partial U}{\partial s} \quad (4)$$

$$\dot{\theta} = -\frac{1}{k}\left[\frac{\partial \sigma}{\partial d}\frac{\partial d}{\partial m} - k.\frac{\partial U}{\partial m}\right] \quad (5)$$

where N is the wave action density spectrum (N is conserved in presence of currents while energy density E is not, $N=E/\sigma$), c_g is the group velocity of wave energy in x, y spatial space, U is the mean current velocity, d is the water depth, σ is the relative frequency, k is the wave number, s and m are the space coordinates of wave propagation direction θ.

The general sources and sinks used by the models are represented by S defined as:

$$S = S_{in} + S_{dis} + S_{qua} + \underbrace{S_{bf} + S_{br} + S_{tri}}_{\text{Shallow water processes}} + \ldots \quad (6)$$

which account for atmospheric input (wave generation by wind), whitecapping dissipation, non-linear wave-wave interactions (quadruplet) and in case of shallow waters the dissipation by bottom friction, depth induced wave breaking and non-linear wave-wave interactions (triad).

WWIII is used in deep waters, in global scales, while SWAN is in intermediate and shallow waters, in smaller scales.

2.3 Hindcast system

The hindcast system implemented in this study used the two spectral wave models referred above, one to account for wave generation (WWIII) and the other one the nearshore simulations (SWAN) in the area of study.

The WWIII wave spectral outputs with a time resolution of 3 hours, provided by Ifremer IOWAGA (Integrated Ocean WAves for Geophysical and other Applications) project (Ardhuin & Accensi 2013), were used as wave boundary conditions to force SWAN. The other forcings were the wind fields from ERA5 (Hersbach & Dee 2016), provided by ECMWF (European Centre for Medium-Range Weather Forecasts), over a spatial grid of 0.25°x0.25° resolution and a time resolution of 6 hours. The bathymetry was from GEBCO (General Bathymetric Chart of the Ocean) with the original resolution (0.0083°×0.0083°) interpolated for 0.02°×0.02°.

3 VALIDATION OF THE RESULTS

The SWAN model results were validated against the Significant Wave Height (SWH) of satellite altimetry from the project called GlobWave (globwave.ifremer.fr). This project is funded by European Space Science with the goal to collect satellite altimetry data from different missions (ERS-1, ERS-2, ENVISAT, TOPEX/POSEIDON, Jason-1, Jason 2 and GEOSAT FollowON) enabling public access.

To match the points data between the model and the satellite, the Matlab toolbox ALTWAVE (Appendini et al. 2016) was used. This toolbox accepts for validation the data within the temporal limit of 1h30m and spatial limit of 0.25°. The statistics parameters Bias, Root Mean Square Error (RMSE), Scatter Index (SI) and Pearson's Correlation Coefficient (r) were then calculated taking into account all the points included in the match. The formulas are expressed bellow:

$$Bias = \frac{\sum_{i=1}^{n}(X_i - Y_i)}{n} \quad (7)$$

$$RMSE = \sqrt{\frac{\sum_{i=1}^{n}(X_i - Y_i)^2}{n}} \quad (8)$$

$$SI = \frac{RMSE}{\tilde{X}} \quad (9)$$

$$r = \frac{\sum_{i=1}^{n}(X_i - \tilde{X})(Y_i - \tilde{Y})}{\left(\sum_{i=1}^{n}(X_i - \tilde{X})^2 \sum_{i=1}^{n}(Y_i - \tilde{Y})^2\right)^{1/2}} \quad (10)$$

where Xi and Yi are the measured and simulated values, respectively. The results are presented in a scatter diagram for the Hs parameter (Figure 3).

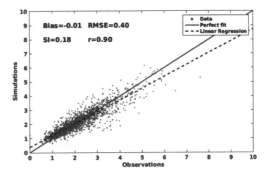

Figure 3. Scatter Index of SWAN model simulations against satellite data.

The results show a good correlation between SWAN model simulations and satellite data. The parameters statistics presented good values, with a value of 0.90 for the correlation coefficient, of 0.18 for *SI*, of 0.40 for *RMSE* and of -0.01 m for *Bias*. The negative Bias shows that the hindcast system tends to overestimate the satellite data.

4 EVALUATION OF WAVE CONDITIONS

A more accurate approach to describe the sea state conditions is to use the spectral wave parameters, as e.g. Lucas et al. (2019), but the focus here is to get the spatial overview of the Significant Wave Height (*Hs*), so the parametric *Hs* parameter was used.

For the *Hs* spatial grid approach, the Madeira archipelago is divided in two zones: Madeira Island, with Area 1 and Area 2, and Porto Santo with Area 3, to facilitate the analysis results.

The spatial distribution of the *Hs* grid points average is presented in terms of Total time (all period), the seasons with the minimums and maximums occurrences for *Hs*, summer (June, July and August) and winter (December, January and February) (Figures 4-9), as well as the 90th percentile (Figures 10, 11). Except for the 90th percentile, the color bar presented in the maps was fixed with the same limits of *Hs* to be visible the differences between the time cases.

The total time maps (Figures 4, 5) show that for the total period of the hindcast (2012-2016), the entire area of Porto Santo presents higher values of *Hs* than Madeira Island. Looking for the particular cases, the *Hs* in Area 3 varies between 2-2.30 m and in Area 1 and Area 2 between 1.70-2 m.

Comparing the summer (Figures 6, 7) and winter (Figures 8, 9) seasons, it is quite clear the differences between the *Hs* values, with winter presenting the highest ones and summer the lowest ones, as expected. The Madeira archipelago region is affected in the winter by the anticyclone of Azores, which is dislocated south from its usual position, and the anticyclone of Morocco, reason why the wave conditions in winter time are more energetic (Rusu at al. 2008).

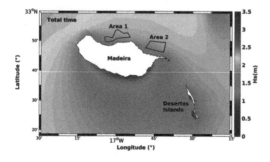

Figure 4. *Hs* average spatial distribution in Madeira Island for Total time.

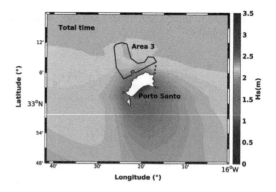

Figure 5. *Hs* average spatial distribution in Porto Santo for Total time.

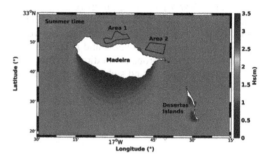

Figure 6. *Hs* average spatial distribution in Madeira Island for summer time.

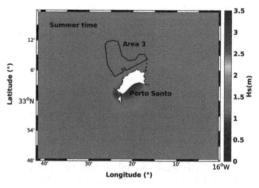

Figure 7. *Hs* average spatial distribution in Porto Santo for summer time.

Furthermore, the patterns of the *Hs* spatial distribution suggested that the incoming waves are mostly from north and west with the islands inducing a shelter effect, being more evident in the winter time case.

The *Hs* 90th percentile (Figures 10, 11) varies between 2.6-3 m within the Areas 1 and 2, and 3.2-3.5 m within Area 3. This means that 89% of

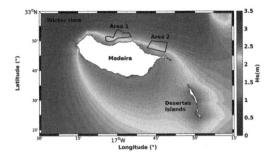

Figure 8. Hs average spatial distribution in Madeira Island for winter time.

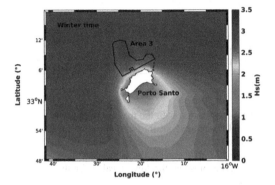

Figure 9. Hs average spatial distribution in Porto Santo for winter time.

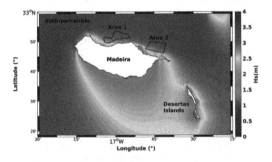

Figure 10. 90th percentile for the *Hs* in Madeira Island.

the time series data in these areas are below these values and 10% are above.

4.1 Hs temporal variability

To quantify the temporal variability of a variable there are some coefficients that can be calculated. In this study they are calculated in relation to *Hs* for the points P1, P2 and P3.

The Coefficient of Variation (*COV*) is a measure of data dispersion around the mean and is represented as next (Cornett 2008):

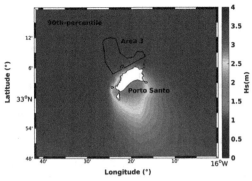

Figure 11. 90th percentile for the *Hs* in Porto Santo.

$$COV(Hs) = \frac{\sigma(Hs(t))}{\mu(Hs(t))} = \frac{\sqrt{\overline{(Hs - \overline{Hs})^2}}}{\overline{Hs}} \quad (11)$$

where σ is the standard deviation and μ is the mean of *Hs* total period. The *Hs* variability decreases as this index becomes smaller.

The Seasonal Variability index (*SV*) measures the seasonal variability of *Hs* and is calculated as follows (Cornett 2008):

$$SV = \frac{Hs_{S1} - Hs_{S4}}{Hs_{year}} \quad (12)$$

where Hs_{S1} is the mean *Hs* for the most severe wave conditions season (winter-December to February), Hs_{S4} is the mean *Hs* for the least severe wave conditions season (summer-June to August) and Hs_{year} is the total mean *Hs*.

The Monthly Variability index (*MV*) measures the monthly variability of *Hs* and is defined as (Cornett 2008):

$$MV = \frac{Hs_{M1} - Hs_{M12}}{Hs_{year}} \quad (13)$$

where Hs_{M1} is the mean *Hs* for the most severe wave conditions month (February) and Hs_{M12} is the mean *Hs* for the least severe wave conditions month (July).

Table 2 shows the min and max results for the seasonal and monthly means. The point P1 presents the lower values for all the cases and P3 the higher values.

The Mean Annual Variability (*MAV*) is the average of the annual standard deviation (σ_k) normalized by the annual average (x_k), for the k year, measuring the *Hs* data dispersion. The formulation to calculate this index is (Stopa et al. 2013):

Table 2. Season and month (min and max) used in SV and MV calculations for P1, P2 and P3 points.

		P1	P2	P3
Seasonal mean (m)	min	summer (1.43)	summer (1.50)	summer (1.64)
	max	winter (2.31)	winter (2.39)	winter (2.76)
Monthly mean (m)	min	July (1.38)	July (1.45)	July (1.58)
	max	February (2.44)	February (2.50)	February (2.84)

$$MAV = \left(\frac{\overline{\sigma_k}}{\overline{x_k}}\right) \quad (14)$$

The Inter-Annual Variability (*IAV*) is defined as the standard deviation of the annual means (σ_{x_k}) normalized by the overall mean (x), for the k year, indicating the variability from year to year of *Hs* along the entire period (Stopa et al. 2013):

$$IAV = \frac{\sigma_{\overline{x_k}}}{\overline{x}} \quad (15)$$

The temporal variability coefficients are presented in Table 3.

The results of Table 3 show that although P3 presents, in general, higher variability than the other points, since it has the highest values (smaller values indicate lower variability), the differences are minimum, with the *SV* presenting the highest difference. For the three points, *Hs* have more variability between the months (*MV*) and less variability between the years (*IAV*).

4.2 Sea states Hs/Tp

The statistics parameters mean, maximum and minimum for the sea states *Hs/Tp* were calculated (Table 4). In addition, the *Tp* associated with the maximum and minimum of *Hs* were found.

In terms of mean, the point P3 has the highest values for *Hs* and *Tp*, followed by P2 and P1. The *Tp*

Table 3. Temporal variability coefficients for P1, P2 and P3.

	P1	P2	P3
COV	0.39	0.39	0.39
MV	0.55	0.53	0.56
SV	0.46	0.45	0.50
MAV	0.39	0.38	0.39
IAV	0.05	0.05	0.05

Table 4. Hs/Tp means, maximums and minimums.

		P1	P2	P3
mean	Hs (m)	1.92	1.98	2.26
	Tp (s)	10.67	10.70	10.89
max	Hs (m)/	7.78/	8.02/	8.04/
	Tp (s) associated	15.25	15.25	15.25
	Tp (s)	20	18.69	20
min	Hs (m)/	0.48/	0.47/	0.67/
	Tp (s) associated	10.26	10.16	6.33
	Tp (s)	4.50	4.51	4.21

Table 5. Hs/Tp that occurred more often.

	P1	P2	P3
Hs (m)	1.5-2	1.5-2	2-2.5
Tp (s)	12-12.5	12-12.5	12-12.5

that is associated with the maximum of *Hs* is the same for all the points, but for the minimum, the P3 has the lowest value. Even though P3 has the highest *Hs* values for all the statistics parameters, in terms of *Tp* this point presents the lowest value for the minimum case.

The sea sates *Hs/Tp* that occurred more often during the 5-year period (2012-2016) are displayed in the Table 5. The number of occurrences was calculated using bins of 0.5s×0.5m ($\Delta Tp \times \Delta Hs$).

The points P1 and P2 have the same pairs of *Hs/Tp*, which are 1.5-2m/12-12.5s, and P3 only differs in the *Hs* parameters with a difference of 0.5 m (2-2.5 m).

5 CONCLUSIONS

This study presents the validation with satellite, of a 5-year (2012-2016) hindcast system with the spectral wave models WWIII and SWAN. Although being a 5-year study, already allows some statistics to characterize the wave climate.

The validation results showed a good correlation between SWAN model simulations and satellite data, with a high correlation coefficient (0.90). The output data of the hindcast system tends to overestimate the satellite data.

The assessment of wave conditions in the areas selected for Madeira Archipelago within the ARC-WIND project was performed. The *Hs* spatial distribution was presented in terms of Total time (all period), summer (June, July and August) and winter (December, January and February) averages, as well as the 90th percentile.

For total time, the area in Porto Santo (Area 3) presents higher values of *Hs* than the areas in

Madeira Island (Area 1 and 2), with 2-2.30 m against 1.70-2 m. The differences between the seasons are clear, with winter presenting the highest values for *Hs* and summer the lowest ones, as expected. The 90th percentile is higher in Area 3, with an *Hs* of 3.2-3.5 versus 2.6-3 m in the other two areas.

The temporal variability for the *Hs*, were studied through the index parameters *COV, MV, SV, MAV* and *IAV*. The point P3 (in Area 3), despite being a minimal difference, presents higher variability than the other points. The *Hs* for all the points have more variability between the months (*MV*), in opposite to the variability between the years (*IAV*).

The mean, maximum and minimum of the wave parameters *Hs/Tp* were calculated. The P3 has the highest *Hs* values for all the statistics parameters, but in the case of *Tp*, this point has the lowest value for the minimum cases.

Finally, the sea sates *Hs/Tp* that occurred more often are 1.5-2m/12-12.5s for P1 and P2, and 2-2.5 m for P3, a difference of 0.5 m.

ACKNOWLEDGEMENTS

This work was conducted within the ARCWIND project–Adaptation and implementation of floating wind energy conversion technology for the Atlantic region (EAPA 344/2016), which is co-financed by the European Regional Development Fund through the Interreg Atlantic Area Programme. This work contributes to the Strategic Research Plan of the Centre for Marine Technology and Ocean Engineering (CENTEC), which is financed by the Portuguese Foundation for Science and Technology (Fundação para a Ciência e Tecnologia) under contract UIDB/UIDP/00134/2020.

REFERENCES

Appendini, C. M. Camacho-Magaña, V. and Breña-Naranjo, J. A. 2016. Altwave: Toolbox for use of satellite L2P altimeter data for wave model validation. *Advances in space Research* 57:1426–1439;

Ardhuin, F., Accensi, M. 2013. IOWAGA - WWIII - HINDCAST - North East Atlantic grid – CFSR.

Booij, N.; Ris, R.C.; Holthuijsen, L. H., 1999. A third generation wave model for coastal regions. Part 1: Model description and validation. *Journal of Geophysical Research* 104: 7649–7666;

Carretero, JC; Gomez, M; Lozano, I; de Elvira, AR; Serrano, O; Iden, K; et al. 1998. Changing waves and storms in the northeast Atlantic. *Bulletin of the American Meteorological Society* 79:741–760;

Charles, E; Idier, D.; Delecluse, P.; Déqué, M.; Le Cozannet G. 2012. Climate change impact on waves in the Bay of Biscay, France. *Ocean Dynamics* 62:831–848;

Cornett, A. M. 2008. A global wave energy resource assessment. *International offshore and Polar Engineering conference*, Vancouver, Canada, Volume: ISOPE-2008-TPC–579;

Cuttler, M. V. W., Hansen, J. E. & Lowe, R. J. 2020. Seasonal and interannual variability of the wave climate at a wave energy hotspot off the southwestern coast of Australia. *Renewable Energy* 146:2337–2350;

Diaz, H. M., Fonseca, R.B. e Guedes Soares, C. 2019. Site selection process for floating offshore wind farms in Madeira Islands. *Advances in Renewable Energies Offshore*, Guedes Soares, C., (Ed.), Taylor & Francis, London, UK, 729–737.

Diaz, H. M. and Guedes Soares, C. 2020. An integrated GIS approach for site selection of floating offshore wind farms in the Atlantic Continental European coastline. Renewable and Sustainable Energy Reviews. 134:110328

Goda, Y. 2000. *Random seas and design of maritime structures*. World Scientific Publishing Advanced series on Ocean Engineering 15;

Guedes Soares, C., 2008. Hindcast of dynamic processes of the ocean and coastal areas of Europe. *Coastal Engineering*, 55(11):825–826.

Guedes Soares, C., Weisse, R., Carretero, J.C., Alvarez, E., 2002. A 40 years hindcast of wind, sea level and waves in European waters. In: *Proceedings of the 21st International Conference on Offshore Mechanics and Arctic Engineering (OMAE'02)*, ASME Paper OMAE2002-SR28604;

Hersbach, H. and Dee, D. 2016. ERA5 reanalysis is in production, *ECMWF Newsletter* 147:7, https://www.ecmwf.int/en/newsletter/147/news/ERA5-reanalysis-production

Lin, Y., Dong, S. & Tao, S. 2020 Modelling long-term joint distribution of significant wave height and mean zero-crossing wave period using a copula mixture. *Ocean Engineering* 197:106856;

Lucas, C., Boukhanovsky, A. & Guedes Soares, C. 2011. Modelling the climatic variability of directional wave spectra. *Ocean Engineering* 38:11–21;

Lucas, C. & Guedes Soares, C. 2015a. On the modelling of swell spectra. *Ocean Engineering* 108:749–759;

Lucas, C. & Guedes Soares, C. 2015b. Bivariate distributions of significant wave height and mean wave period of combined sea states. *Ocean Engineering* 106:341–353;

Lucas, C., Silva, D. and Guedes Soares, C. 2019. Assessment of the wave spectral characteristics in the Portuguese test zone. *Advances in Renewable Energies Offshore*, Guedes Soares, C. (Ed.), Taylor & Francis Group, London, UK, 59–66;

Mackay, E. B. L.; Bahaj, A . S. and Challenor, P. G. 2010a Uncertainty in wave energy resource assessment. Part1: Historic data. *Renewable Energy* 35:1792–1808;

Mackay, E. B. L.; Bahaj, A . S. and Challenor, P. G. 2010b. Uncertainty in wave energy resource assessment. Part2: Variability and predictability. *Renewable Energy* 35:1809–1819.

Portilla-Yandún, J., Barbariol, F., Benetazzo, A. & Cavaleri, L. 2019. On the statistical analysis of ocean wave directional spectra. *Ocean Engineering* 189:106361;

Reeve, DE; Chen, Y; Pan, S; Magar, V; Sim-monds, DJ; et al. 2011. An investigation of the impacts of climate change on wave energy generation: the Wave Hub, Cornwall, UK. Renewable *Energy* 36:2404–2413;

Rusu, E.; Pilar, P.;Guedes Soares, C. 2008 Evaluation of the wave conditions in Madeira Archipelago with spectral models. *Ocean Engineering* 35:1357–1371;

Stopa, .J.E., Filipot, J.F., Li, N., Cheung, K.F. Chen, Y.L. and Vega, L. 2013. Wave energy resources along the Hawaiian Island chain. *Renewable Energy* 55:305–321;

Sverdrup, H. U. & Munk, W. H. 1947. Wind, Sea, and Swell; Theory of Relations for Forecasting, U.S. Navy Hydrographic Office, H. 0. Publ. No. 601.

Tolman, H., 1991. A third-generation model for wind waves on slowly varying, unsteady, and inhomogeneous depths and currents. *Journal of Physical Oceanography* 21:782–797;

WAMDI Group 1988. The WAM model-a third generation ocean wave prediction model. *Journal of Physical Oceanography* 18:1755–1810;

Wu, W., Wang, T., Zhaoqing, Y & Gacía- Medina, G. 2020 Development and validation of a high-resolution regional wave hindcast model for U.S. West Coast wave resource characterization. *Renewable Energy* 152:736–753.

An integrated design approach for a self-float capable tension leg platform for wind energy

E. Uzunoglu & C. Guedes Soares
Centre for Marine Technology and Ocean Engineering (CENTEC), Instituto Superior Técnico, Universidade de Lisboa, Lisbon, Portugal

ABSTRACT: The paper discusses the necessity of developing an integrated concept evaluation and hydrodynamic design system for floaters. The shortcomings of employing spreadsheets or using several specialized software in the design of such structures are explained and an alternative system is presented. The target is to integrate 3D modelling, hydrodynamics, hydrostatics, and mooring analysis. The components of this type of a system are explained here, and their application is discussed using CENTEC-TLP, a free-float capable tension leg platform for wind energy.

1 INTRODUCTION

The surging interest in renewable energy sources has put wind turbines into focus. In this area, onshore applications provide a basis for industrial experience and offshore fixed-bottom solutions have been functional for decades (Diaz & Guedes Soares, 2016). However, moving onto deeper waters contains challenges associated with floaters and their design (Bagbanci et al. 2012; Uzunoglu et al. 2016).

The current progress in offshore wind platforms resembles the progression of the oil and gas industry as it moved offshore. For instance, comparing second and fifth-generation semisubmersibles would give a good understanding of how the hull forms consolidated over time. A similar evolution can be expected from wind energy, but currently, the topic is open to testing novel designs, which can be termed as "concept evaluation".

A few examples of hull geometry variations may be seen by looking at the current forms. The Wind-Float semisubmersible comprises of three cylindrical columns joined with braces (Cermelli *et al.* 2009, Roddier *et al.* 2010) while a braceless V-shaped alternative with prismatic columns is studied in Karimirad & Michailides (2015). Similarly, single column tension leg platforms with pontoons based on the SeaStar design (Kibbee *et al.* 1994) have been studied extensively (Tracy 2007, Bachynski & Moan 2012). As an alternative, the GICON TLP (Adam *et al.* 2013) and the model presented in Yanqing *et al.* (2017) focus on forms four-column designs.

Each of these alternatives starts with a conceptual design and progress onto the next stage as the idea develops. The numerical tools used in the development of these structures are heavily component-focused. An example is the progression in mooring codes from quasi-static to dynamic options (Xu et al, 2019) assuming that the other parts of the design are fully carried out and their data is available. However, parts of systems can only be isolated in this manner at later design stages. For instance, the hull mass and inertia need to be known to calculate the motions of the platform so that the mooring code can provide a dependable set of results. Hence, these studies require a series of constants, assumptions, or external calculations on the remaining components of the system.

This case is less problematic in settled fields where statistics are available (e.g., a bulk carrier or a container ship). Contrarily, in novel research areas, the concept design of a platform likely starts with a "blank-sheet" scenario, where there is nothing known apart from an idea. The general method of dealing with these cases is to employ spreadsheet type solutions to get basic estimates of the mass properties (Park *et al.* 2015); then, various simplifications are introduced get the hydrodynamic coefficients such as making use of tabular data for cylinders as in Clauss *et al.* (1992). An early assessment of the motions can be obtained through closed-form equations.

It should be clear that these methods lack the precision that 3D models can deliver. They are also case-specific, signifying that the solution needs to be revised completely when the structure is changed. On the other hand, 3D models generally require multiple software to deliver a solution (e.g., a model for mass and inertia, a second model for hydrodynamics, and a third model for hydrostatics) for which the software may either be unavailable or simply the process may require too much time commitment to be applicable.

DOI: 10.1201/9781003216599-71

A third alternative is developing an interconnected and modular system that can deal with each one of these components in a shorter time, with an acceptable level of accuracy. This work explains how to apply this type of a solution to the design CENTEC-TLP, a self-float capable tension leg platform for a 10 MW turbine, published in (Uzunoglu & Guedes Soares 2020). It serves to describe the connection between the previous works that give solutions for the 3D modeller (Uzunoglu & Guedes Soares 2018), systemisation (Uzunoglu & Guedes Soares 2019).

2 THE CONCEPT EVALUATION AND THE HYDRODYNAMIC DESIGN PROBLEM

2.1 Overview of the requirements

Consider the following scenario to understand the requirements to evaluate a concept. The design of a wind turbine platform is generally carried out for a given tower and turbine configuration. The remaining components (i.e., the floater and the moorings) need to be developed to host this setup. Given that the performance of the turbine is related to the platform motions, a large part of the design process is obtaining favourable dynamics. Eventually, this is a case of solving the equation of motion, which can be provided in a simplified form as follows:

$$F = M_t \ddot{x} + B_t \dot{x} + C_t x \quad (1)$$

The force (F) can be broken down into its components from wind and waves:

$$F = F_{wind} + F_{waves} \quad (2)$$

For early design stages, the wind force (F_{wind}) can be estimated from the thrust curves of the turbine. In later stages, there needs to be a detailed study including turbulent cases.

The wave forces (F_{wave}), on the other hand, are not straightforward. For small members, the Morison Equation will provide the information. Otherwise, a closed-form equation or a potential flow solution may be required. Hence, the wave forces become the first unknown.

On the right side of the equation of motion, the total mass is subdivided into two components:

$$M_t = M_{ij} + A_{ij} \quad (3)$$

M_{ij} is the 6 by 6 mass matrix. It is necessary to stress that it includes not only the mass but also the inertial values. It can be solved for analytically for basic shapes such as cylinders. However, as geometric complexity increases, simplified solutions such as spreadsheets become insufficient in determining these values. This case leads to significant problems in the design stages. For instance, take a case where a tension leg platform is being optimised for mooring line fatigue (e.g., Lee et al. 2007). When undertaking these studies, not only the mass needs to be updated, but also there needs to be a correct solution for inertia. Mooring line responses of a tension leg platform are highly dependent on rotational motions. If the inertia is incorrect, the rotational motions are incorrect. When the rotational motions are incorrect, the tendon tensions are also incorrect. Therefore, a simple problem in mass matrix estimation can propagate into a series of issues, causing the results to be unreliable.

The hydrodynamic contribution consists of the added mass (A_{ij}) and damping (B_{ij}). The solution for the added masses serves two purposes. They factor in the overall responses of the platform, and they also define the natural frequencies. It is important to note that these values are also frequency dependent. Accordingly, assuming the infinite frequency value to be correct will cause altered eigenvalue estimates. It is possible to use tabularised data such as the ones provided by Clauss et al. (1992); however, their applicability may be low as discussed in Adam et al. (2013). A potential flow solution will also cover this requirement.

The damping coefficient (B_{ij}) can be broken down into the potential (B_p) and viscous (B_v) components.

$$B_t = B_v + B_p \quad (3)$$

For a tension leg platform, the viscous damping will be of interest only in resonant cases (O'Kane et al. 2002). For other platform types, usually, a percentage of the critical damping is considered (Lopez-Pavon & Souto-Iglesias 2015). For suitable structures, potential flow solution can provide the B_p component.

The restoring forces (C_t) are represented as a sum of the mooring line and the hydrostatic stiffness values:

$$C_t = C_h + C_m \quad (3)$$

The hydrostatic component (C_h) is a function of the waterplane area, and it can be calculated analytically for simple shapes such as cylinders and rectangular barges. As the geometric complexity increases, alternative solutions become necessary.

The mooring restoring coefficient (C_m) on the other hand, requires some consideration. In the time domain, there are dynamic options for the responses that involve lumped mass or finite element solutions. In the frequency domain, these dynamic effects on the mooring lines are difficult to account for. Accordingly, a linearized stiffness matrix is needed to represent their role in motion dynamics. This solution depends on the mooring line setup (i.e., taut or catenary) as provided in Al-Solihat & Nahon (2016).

All components described above need to be obtained as correctly as possible to solve Equation (1), in the fastest manner possible.

2.2 Current use of 3D model and spreadsheet-based solutions for early design stages

A precise solution to the problem previously described with the Equation (1), the equation of motion, can be implemented using 3D models. However, since these codes are highly specialized to solve only a part of the problem (e.g., mooring, hydrostatics, hydrodynamics), a series of models and software is required.

Figure 1 gives an example of a 3D modelling based higher precision workflow. The chart is colour coded, with components presented in light grey background for works that need to be carried out by a person, white background for "joint effort" (i.e., a numerical model needs to be prepared by a person, and then the computer solves it), and dark grey background for a computer only solution. When carried out correctly, this approach would provide precision within the limits of the mentioned software.

In the case that all the above-mentioned options are available, there is another fundamental issue that makes 3D solutions difficult to employ in early stages. It is a specialization related problem where each software provides only a partial solution to problem based on the manual input from another code. The result is a significant loss of time and room for possible human error while moving the input data. Consider the chart in Figure 1. WAMIT (Lee & Newman 2005) provides a panel method solution that is often relied on in many applications including NREL's FAST (Jonkman 2007). The mesh for WAMIT can be obtained with Rhino3D and its panelling tools or an alternative (e.g., Multi-Surf). If frequency domain wave responses are needed, the mooring stiffness and mass matrices from the third and fourth software become additional requirements.

As a result, a significant amount of time needs to be committed to making multiple models in multiple software and manually carrying the data between them. Manual operations, once more lead to a loss of time and make room for errors. On the other hand, multiple models in multiple software itself is a source of significantly increased time requirements. Ultimately, since none of this software solves the problem at hand in an integrated manner, they either partially or completely get replaced by manual solutions with lower precision.

In the case of partial replacement, some of the components need to be solved manually (e.g., spreadsheets). Once obtained, the output of this process is to be moved (e.g., copy-pasted) between the relevant software to become the input. As the geometrical complexity increases, the workaround of using spreadsheets also leads to oversimplification, lack of accuracy, and possible errors.

In the case of a full replacement, the precision for most components reduce drastically, especially for complex geometries. Additionally, the spreadsheet applications are non-generic solutions. For instance, the volume formula that applies to a cylinder needs to be updated for a prismatic shape. Therefore, the equations that held true for one structure will need to be revised for the second problem.

In summary, this lack of integration between software causes an issue where the concept design starts with one problem and ends with another while trying to address it. This issue is summarised in the schematics of Figure 2.

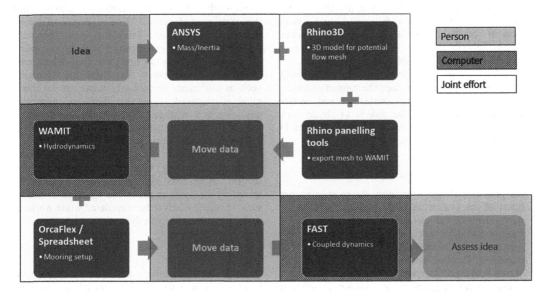

Figure 1. 3D modelling based precision workflow for hydrodynamic design and concept evaluation.

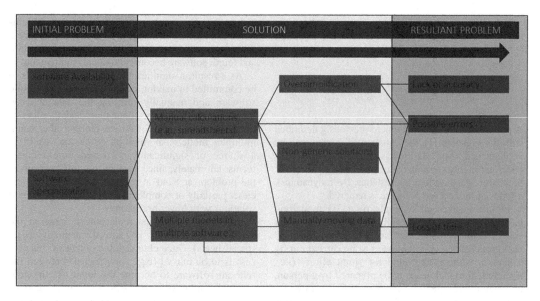

Figure 2. Schematics of early design issues and applied solutions that lead to resultant problems.

3 AN IMPROVED SOLUTION WITH INTEGRATED DESIGN COMPONENTS

For the reasons outlined above, despite the availability of higher precision solutions, spreadsheets are still the most applied option in early design. However, they can be improved upon if several requirements and constraints are observed.

The alternative needs to be a flexible solution (i.e., equally applicable to different geometries) to avoid the shortcomings that spreadsheets present. Interconnection becomes an obligation as each component should interact with the one other without the need for human intervention. Finally, the system should be considered as a framework to be built upon. It should be possible to extend it as better options become available in to replace the current ones, or when additional solutions are required.

Following these constraints, a system can be built to increase the precision, reduce the number of errors, and save time in concept evaluation and hydrodynamic design stages. The task is to obtain each component of the Equation of motion (Equation 1) within this system within the framework.

3.1 Geometric design and mass matrix

The geometric design is arguably the most important aspect of the system setup. It needs to be a multi-purpose solution that can deliver the mass matrix with precision and suit a panel method solution to obtain the hydrodynamic coefficients. The solution to this type of a problem, ParMod, was described in Uzunoglu & Guedes Soares (2018), and it is summarised below.

The primary requirement is a numerical solution for the modelling process (i.e., having the capability of parametrising the shape so that it can be altered by changing a number instead of relying on a graphical user interface that dictates human interaction). If the geometry can be delivered as a set of quadrilateral panels, it can be used by potential flow solvers with the right file formatting.

A quadrilateral is represented by the location of its four vertices in Cartesian coordinates. Hence, 12 data points (x, y, and z location of each vertex) are needed for the geometry itself. Extending the format for quadrilaterals to include the thickness and density of each panel will allow calculating the mass data for shell-type elements.

Similarly, the volume, centre of gravity, and the other related mass data (e.g., centre of buoyancy) can be obtained using the same approach. Accordingly, for a mesh model with known plate thicknesses, there is no need for spreadsheet calculations. In the cases that there are elements such as stiffeners, these components can be modelled if required. However, they are generally unknown at this stage. They can be considered as a part of the hull using an equivalent thickness or increased steel density.

It is important to note that to obtain the mass matrix of a floating wind turbine and use it for motion calculations, the entirety of the geometry, including the sections above the waterline is necessary. This case needs to be considered while working on hydrostatics and hydrodynamics.

3.2 Hydrostatics

There are a few methods to obtain the hydrostatic restoring matrix. Using the mesh model, it is possible to integrate the hydrostatic pressure on each panel

(Schalck & Baatrup 1990). Alternatively, the waterplane area can be used.

It was stated when discussing the mass matrix that it requires the entirety of the structure. However, for use in hydrodynamics, the submerged body needs to be extracted. This requirement can also serve as an intermediate stage to deliver the hydrostatic matrix.

For this purpose, the panels above the waterline are eliminated. The ones intersecting the waterline are interpolated and meshed again. The submerged sections are kept unchanged.

The resulting vertices that intersect the waterplane are used to obtain the waterplane area and the hydrostatic restoring coefficients. Green's theorem serves to consider each section of the enclosed area at the water level as a 2D polygon (e.g., if a structure has four columns, then it requires four polygons) and calculate the associated moments.

3.3 Hydrodynamics

A method for solving hydrodynamic coefficients is to rely on a potential flow solver. When the geometry is prepared as described in the geometric design section, and truncated from the waterline as in the hydrostatics section, it is straightforward to feed it to a potential flow solver. WAMIT, NEMOH (Babarit and Delhommeau 2015), or any other alternative can serve this purpose in the absence of an in-house solution. NEMOH is an open-source alternative, therefore, it can be regarded to have higher availability without the need for licencing. In all cases, the mass matrix and the mooring stiffness are inputs for the correct estimation of hydrodynamic responses,

3.4 Mooring design

For the tension leg platform, the design of the moorings is highly coupled with the dynamics of the platform. It is not possible to alter one without causing significant effects in the other. For this reason, motion dynamics and resonant frequencies should be checked for each considered mooring line configuration and thickness.

In the initial stages, the stiffness can be provided as a linearized matrix. To solve for topics such as fatigue life, a detailed study is required.

3.5 Motion dynamics

Obtaining each of the variables above leads to the solution to the equation of motion. The responses to waves can be obtained from the panel method code, leaving the wind responses as the missing component. At the initial stages, the force can be obtained directly from the turbine thrust values. The platform's static responses to these forces can be estimated using the hydrostatic restoring matrix as in Matha (2010).

3.6 Time-domain evaluation

If a concept can pass a checkpoint in the frequency domain, it can be moved onto the time domain verification stage. At this stage, the motions of the structure should already be approximated and understood, unlike the case of a limited spreadsheet solution. The time requirements for wind turbine simulations in codes such as NREL's FAST are rather high. For this reason, it is best reserved for cases that the idea merits further evaluation.

3.7 Systematisation

Bringing the components of this system eliminates the need for multiple software or spreadsheets. The solution is delivered using a single multi-purpose 3D model, with higher precision, in lesser time compared to using multiple models or spreadsheets. Being a generic solution, it does not need to be altered when the platform changes.

A schematic of the replacement is given in Figure 3. In this scenario, once there is an idea for a concept, a single model (a ParMod model) is made, the rest of the process is taken care of by the computer without human involvement. Only the end-result is evaluated by a person to decide whether the idea is worth investigating further.

4 APPLICATION OF THE DESIGN SYSTEM ON THE CENTEC-TLP

The approach described in the previous sections was used to design the CENTEC-TLP that hosts the DTU 10 MW wind turbine and tower (Bak *et al.* 2013). The platform's details and motion dynamics were published in (Uzunoglu & Guedes Soares 2020). The geometry is given in Figure 4.

The platform is a dual-purpose structure. In transport, it floats on the pontoons to be towed to the installation site by ordinary tugs. The draft is kept low to overcome shore-side depth limits. When installed, it is lowered 20 meters, and the requirement is providing favourable motion dynamics and safety for the turbine. The safety criteria involve checks against mooring line breaking, slack mooring occurrences, and large surge amplitudes.

This type of dual-target design requires a slight alteration to the previously described process. Two alternatives can be selected. Either the motions of the installed platform need to be verified first followed by its free-floating condition, or the free-floating platform needs to be verified first followed by the installed condition. Both methods are acceptable and should yield identical results. The details of the two cases are explained below.

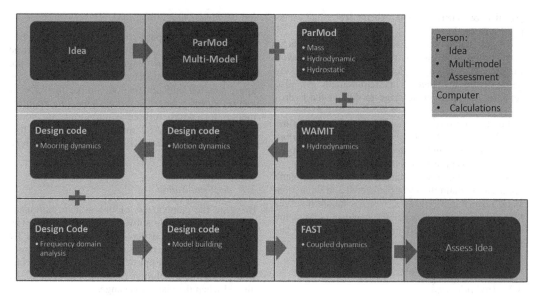

Figure 3. Alternative workflow using a multi-model for hydrodynamic design and concept evaluation.

Figure 4. CENTEC-TLP hull form.

4.1 The free-floating condition

In the free-floating condition, the mooring line stiffness ceases to be a contributor to the restoring matrix. At the same time, the aerodynamic forces are different than what is defined by the turbine thrust. In transport, the turbine is parked, and the blades are feathered to minimize the loading on the shaft. In this condition, the relevant forces are the tower drag and the loads on the parked rotor.

The tower drag can be obtained assuming that it is a cylindrical structure exposed to wind and employing the formulation provided by DNV (Det Norske Veritas (DNV) 2012). The wind forces on the exposed rotor can also be calculated in a similar manner. It is also obtainable through simulating the case with an aerodynamics code such as FAST and then removing the inertial forces from the total force to reduce it to aerodynamic thrust.

For a free-floating condition, there needs to be a balance between buoyancy and mass. If the volume at each draft (e.g., obtained through a calculation exemplified in Uzunoglu & Guedes Soares 2018) and the total mass are known, the structure's floatation draft can be calculated, along with the related hydrostatic properties. Motion dynamics can then be estimated assuming aerodynamic loads as previously described. There is no change in the estimation of hydrodynamic loads and related motions apart from the absence of the mooring restoring contribution. Accordingly, they can be obtained from the panel method code, and the summation of wind and wave motions would provide the general information on the free-floating condition dynamics.

This stage should result in minimal motions for the towing phase, staying under the stability limits of the platform. In this condition, the waterplane area should not be subject to significant changes when the platform moves in waves. Figure 5 shows the platform dynamics under the influence of isolated wave forces. It is seen that the pitching RAO is limited below 0.5 degrees, and the heave is approximately 0.8 meters. In the free-float case, the most relevant wavelengths are between 5 to 15 seconds as most of the smaller waves

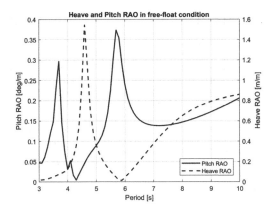

Figure 5. Heave and pitch motions of CENTEC-TLP in free-floating condition.

(up to 3 meters of height) will be located in this region (Silva *et al.* 2015, 2018).

4.2 *The installed condition*

In the installed condition, the mooring restoring forces are reintegrated into the equation of motion, and the aerodynamic loads are added for a running turbine.

For a tension leg platform, there is no balance between weight and buoyancy forces. The mooring pretension is taken as their difference at the design draft.

Regarding the moorings, physical constraints should be considered. These limits include the thicknesses of each line. It is possible to disregard this number mathematically, as a calculated total can be distributed into several mooring lines later. In both cases, the total force is identical. However, in practice, this approach does not bring the desired result when chains or spiral strands are used. For instance, if the total thickness is 1.4 meters (e.g., TLP1 in Bachynski & Moan 2012), 10 mooring lines per fairlead would be required for the structure, given that the largest commercially available mooring line is approximately 15 centimetres as of date. Accordingly, it is important to carry out the design for a set of possible thicknesses and materials. There should be a limit thickness and number of mooring lines that eliminate a platform from the list of candidates.

A sample of the dynamics of the CENTEC-TLP under above-rated conditions (22.5 m/s turbulent wind, 8 m significant wave height at 11.5 second period) is given in Figure 6. For the TLP, having mooring lines breaking or losing tension are failure cases. Under this scenario, the mooring lines do not approach their

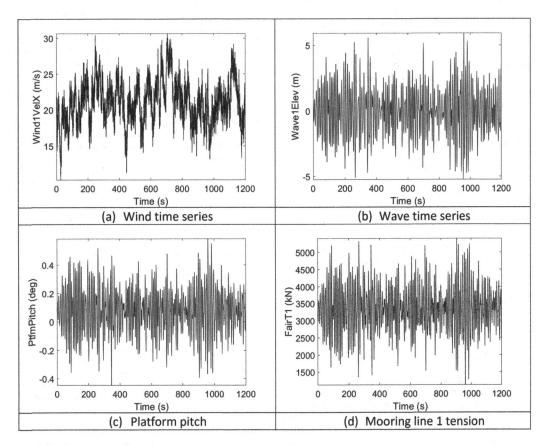

Figure 6. Time series of platform responses in above rated conditions.

breaking strength of 12,500 kN. They also do not come close to becoming slack, keeping minimally 40% of their tension.

The correlation between larger pitching angles and mooring line tension loss becomes apparent when the subfigures Figure 6 (c) and (d) are compared. These figures underline the correct estimation of inertial values so that rotational motions and the related failure states can be obtained with precision.

5 CONCLUSIONS

The paper discussed the necessity of providing an alternative to replace the use of spreadsheets or multiple specialized software in conceptual and hydrodynamic design stages. The shortcomings of the spreadsheet type methods were explained, along with the difficulties in using the 3D geometry at initial design stages.

3D models perform better in the estimation of geometry-based variables such as inertial values and hydrodynamic coefficients. When their use is limited due to the lack of interconnection between various software, they are replaced by simplified methods that allow room for human errors and reduced precision. These problems can be overcome using a multi-purpose 3D model, allowing people to focus on the ideas instead of calculations.

The requirements of a replacement system were defined as being a flexible, interconnected, and expandable. An example of an integrated setup was given using the CENTEC-TLP, a free-float capable tension leg platform for wind energy.

ACKNOWLEDGEMENTS

This work was conducted within the ARCWIND project–Adaptation and implementation of floating wind energy conversion technology for the Atlantic region (EAPA 344/2016), which is co-financed by the European Regional Development Fund through the Interreg Atlantic Area Programme. This work contributes to the Strategic Research Plan of the Centre for Marine Technology and Ocean Engineering (CENTEC), which is financed by the Portuguese Foundation for Science and Technology (Fundação para a Ciência e Tecnologia) under contract UIDB/UIDP/00134/2020.

REFERENCES

Adam, F., Steinke, C., Dahlhaus, F., & Großmann, J., 2013. GICON®-TLP for Wind Turbines – Validation of Calculated Results. *In: The 23th International Offshore and Polar Engineering Conference.* Anchorage, Alaska: International Society of Offshore and Polar Engineers, ISOPE-I-13-093.

Al-Solihat, M.K. & Nahon, M., 2016. Stiffness of slack and taut moorings. *Ships and Offshore Structures*, 11 (8), 890–904.

Babarit, A. & Delhommeau, G., 2015. Theoretical and numerical aspects of the open source BEM solver NEMOH. *In: Proceedings of the 11th European Wave and Tidal Energy Conference (EWTEC2015).* Nantes, France, hal-01198800.

Bagbanci, H.; Karmakar, D., & Guedes Soares, C. 2012. Review of offshore floating wind turbines concepts. Guedes Soares, C. Garbatov Y. Sutulo S. & Santos T. A., (Eds.). *Maritime Engineering and Technology. London*, UK: Taylor & Francis Group; pp. 553–562.

Bachynski, E. & Moan, T., 2012. Design considerations for tension leg platform wind turbines. *Marine Structures*, 29 (1), 89–114.

Bak, C., Zahle, F., Bitsche, R., Taeseong, K., Yde, A., Henriksen, L.C., Natarajan, A., & Hansen, M.H., 2013. *Description of the DTU 10 MW Reference Wind Turbine.* Report-I-0092.

Cermelli, C., Roddier, D., & Aubault, A., 2009. WindFloat: A floating foundation for offshore wind turbines—Part II: hydrodynamics analysis. *In: ASME 2009 28th International Conference on Ocean, Offshore and Arctic Engineering.* American Society of Mechanical Engineers, 135–143.

Clauss, G., Lehmann, E., & Östergaard, C., 1992. *Offshore Structures: Volume I: Conceptual Design and Hydromechanics.* 1st ed. Springer–Verlag.

Det Norske Veritas (DNV), 2012. *DNV-RP-C103, Column-Stabilised Units.* Hovik, Norway.

Diaz, H. M. & Guedes Soares, C. 2020.; Review of the current status, technology and future trends of offshore wind farms. *Ocean Engineering.* 209: 107381

Jonkman, J.M., 2007. *Dynamics modeling and loads analysis of an offshore floating wind turbine.* NREL/TP-500-41958. National Renewable Energy Laboratory (NREL), Golden, CO.

Karimirad, M. & Michailides, C., 2015. V-shaped semisubmersible offshore wind turbine: An alternative concept for offshore wind technology. *Renewable Energy*, 83, 126–143.

Kibbee, S.E., Chianis, J., Davies, K.B., & Sarwono, B.A., 1994. The Seastar Tension-Leg Platform. *In: Offshore Technology Conference.* Texas, USA, 243–256, OTC 7235.

Lee, C.H. & Newman, J.N., 2005. Computation of wave effects using the panel method. *In*: S. Chakrabarti, ed. *Numerical Models in Fluid Structure Interaction.* Southampton, United Kingdom: WIT Press, 211–251.

Lee, J.Y., Koo, B.J., Ltd, S.H.I.C., Clauss, G., and Berlin, T.U., 2007. Automated Design of a Tension Leg Platform with Minimized Tendon Fatigue Damage and its Verification by a Fully Coupled Analysis. *Ship Technology Research*, 54 (1), 11–27.

Lopez-Pavon, C. & Souto-Iglesias, A., 2015. Hydrodynamic coefficients and pressure loads on heave plates for semi-submersible floating offshore wind turbines: A comparative analysis using large scale models. *Renewable Energy*, 81, 864–881.

Matha, D., 2010. Model Development and Loads Analysis of a Wind Turbine on a Floating Offshore Tension Leg Platform. *European Offshore Wind Conference*, (February), 129.

O'Kane, J.J., A.W. Troesch,, & Thiagarajan, K.P., 2002. Hull component interaction and scaling for TLP hydrodynamic coefficients. *Ocean Engineering*, 29 (5), 513–532.

Park, Y., Jang, B.-S., & Kim, J. Du, 2015. Hull-form optimization of semi-submersible FPU considering seakeeping capability and structural weight. *Ocean Engineering*, 104, 714–724.

Roddier, D., Cermelli, C., Aubault, A., & Weinstein, A., 2010. WindFloat: A floating foundation for offshore wind turbines. *Journal of Renewable and Sustainable Energy*, 2 (3), 33104.

Schalck, S. & Baatrup, J., 1990. Hydrostatic stability calculations by pressure integration. *Ocean Engineering*, 17 (1–2), 155–169.

Silva, D., Bento, A.R., Martinho, P., & Guedes Soares, C., 2015. High resolution local wave energy modelling in the Iberian Peninsula. *Energy*, 91, 1099–1112.

Silva, D.; Martinho, P., & Guedes Soares, C. 2018. Wave energy distribution along the Portuguese continental coast based on a thirty three years hindcast. *Renewable Energy*. 127(4):1067–1075.

Tracy, C., 2007. Parametric Design of Floating Wind Turbines. *Master's thesis*. Massachusetts Institute of Technology (MIT), Cambridge, Massachusetts, U.S.

Uzunoglu, E. & Guedes Soares, C., 2018. Parametric Modelling of Marine Structures for Hydrodynamic Calculations. *Ocean Engineering*, 160, 181–196.

Uzunoglu, E. & Guedes Soares, C., 2019. A system for the hydrodynamic design of tension leg platforms of floating wind turbines. *Ocean Engineering*, 171, 78–92.

Uzunoglu, E. & Guedes Soares, C., 2020. Hydrodynamic Design of a Free-float Capable Tension Leg Platform for a 10 MW Wind Turbine. *Ocean Engineering*, 197, 106888, pp. 2–17.

Uzunoglu, E.; Karmakar, D., & Guedes Soares, C. 2016. Floating offshore wind platforms. L. Castro-Santos & V. Diaz-Casas (Eds.). *Floating Offshore Wind Farms*. Springer International Publishing Switzerland; pp. 53–76.

Xu, S.; Wang, S., & Guedes Soares, C. 2019. Review of mooring design for floating wave energy converters. *Renewable and Sustainable Energy Reviews*. 111:595–621.

Yanqing, H., Conghuan, L., Hongyan, D., Zhengshun, C., & Puyang, Z., 2017. Stability and dynamic response analysis of a submerged tension leg platform for offshore wind turbines. *Ocean Engineering*, 129, 68–82.

Fishing and Aquaculture

Validation of tools for the analysis of offshore aquaculture installations

T.A. Bernardo & C. Guedes Soares
Centre for Marine Technology and Ocean Engineering (CENTEC), Instituto Superior Técnico, Universidade de Lisboa, Lisbon, Portugal

ABSTRACT: The work starts by reviewing the current procedures for computing the loads on net structures. It proceeds to a review of the most prominent solutions available in the industry to face the challenge of offshore aquaculture developments, going also through the design considerations for this particular challenge. The feasibility of a commercially available numerical tool, SIMA, is assessed through a thorough validation process, where increasingly complex models are tested and the results compared. Then the mooring system of a real-life farm, located in the Madeira archipelago, is analyzed. The last step of this work is to combine the knowledge obtained throughout the elaboration of this thesis and propose a possible concept to be deployed in an offshore location. A hydrodynamics analysis of the concept is performed using the numerical tool SIMA.

1 INTRODUCTION

Portugal, along with other countries, has seen an increased need of supplying the market of sea products with aquaculture productions. Due to the decline of fisheries stocks and the continuously demand for sea products. This need is well expressed in the "Estratégia Nacional para o Mar 2013-2020" (Portugal, 2013), where it is considered one of the five most important domains to develop. The sea states during winter months of the continental western coast and north coast of the Atlantic islands can be very challenging. Driving a need to develop systems that could endure the harsh conditions (DGRM, 2014).

According to the latest available statistics produced by the Instituto Nacional de Estatística (INE) (INE & DGRM, 2017), referring to the year of 2016, the majority of the national aquaculture production was molluscs and crustaceans (Figure 1).

In their publication "The State of the World Fisheries and Aquaculture" (FAO, 2018), the Food and Agriculture Organization of the United Nations (FAO) states that in 2016 the global fish production surpassed the global fisheries capture. The demand for food and feed is increasing, and the expansion of aquaculture production presents itself as one good solution. However, the growth of land and near coast aquaculture has several setbacks due to environmental, spatial and social restraints. Thus, the expansion of aquaculture to offshore waters is globally understood as a viable solution (Lovatelli et al., 2013).

As DNV-GL mentioned (Flagstad et al., 2018) big expectations are placed on the aquaculture production and this will require an advance in knowledge, in order to fully take advantage of the offshore water's capabilities. The overall impression is well expressed in the report written by CEA, (2018), where it is said that Norway and China are leading the development of the offshore aquaculture production, with big investments being made in the field and a lot of research as well.

2 LITERATURE REVIEW AND BACKGROUND

The above-mentioned need to move further offshore the production of sea products brings with it some challenges. Offshore structures are subjected to larger and harsher loads from the environment than coastal close structures.

These loads are caused by their exposure to waves, wind and current. Therefore, the goal to move aquaculture systems further offshore introduces the need to study and understand how these structures behave under the imposed loads and conditions. In this section a short description of the work and efforts done to model the loads on the main components of a typical aquaculture system is done.

Aquaculture systems are on its essence made by three components. A rigid, or somewhat flexible, construction that provides the structural support of the system and its solidity. A flexible, or in some close cage designs rigid, structure that provides a mean to imprison the fishes commonly through the use of a net or fabric, in a bag like fashion structure, and a mooring system to maintain the farm in a particular location. The loads on the structure and the net are crucial to the design of the mooring system. The forces on the net vary with its shape, which brings the issue of

DOI: 10.1201/9781003216599-72

Figure 1. Portuguese Marine Aquaculture Production in 2016 (INE & DGRM, 2017).

maintaining a minimum volume for the fish welfare (Shainee et al., 2013; Faltinsen, & Shen, 2018, Guo et al 2020).

2.1 Nets

Some work has been developed on permeable structures, with an increase of research in recent years. Kristiansen & Faltinsen, (2012) defended that computational fluid dynamics (CFD) are impractical to assess the hydrodynamic forces, due to the large (in the order of millions) number of twines of a net. The same authors also say that two types of hydrodynamic force models are used: screen models and models based on the Morison equation.

Løland, (1991) proposes a wake model and a method to compute the forces on the net through the use of the drag and lift coefficients and by the division of the net in a set of panels.

$$C_D = C_D(Sn, \theta); C_L = C_L(Sn, \theta) \quad (1)$$

Kristiansen & Faltinsen, (2012), present a screen model, where the forces are dependent of the Reynolds number (Rn).

$$C_D = C_D(Sn, Rn, \theta) C_L = C_L(Sn, Rn, \theta) \quad (2)$$

This is important when validating model tests. This screen approach discretizes the net in a series of surface elements, whose properties reflect the twine and knot geometry of the actual net. In this screen model approach the drag and lift coefficients depend on the solidity ratio (Sn), angle of attack (θ) and the Reynolds number (Rn).

The Morison based approach implies the subdivision of the net in a smaller number of twines, in the form of cylinders, exemplified by Figure 2, in such a way that the projected area is kept the same. A model where the drag and lift coefficients depend on the Reynolds number (Rn) is used by Le Bris & Marichal, (1999) on their work on the behaviour of submerged nets, and by (Moe et al., 2010; Tsukrov et al., 2002).

A super-element model was proposed by Lader et al., (2001), where the net is divided in small patches of four-sided super elements. The forces are computed through the Morison equation and the drag and lift coefficients are dependent on the Solidity ration (Sn) and angle of attack (θ), the Reynolds number (Rn) is not explicitly accounted for. This dependency of Sn and θ is also the base of the work of Aarsnes et al., (1990), later refined in the model of Løland, (1991).

On their paper Le Bris & Marichal, (1999) pointed out that the hydrodynamic interactions between mesh sides are not taking into account. This is also referred by Kristiansen & Faltinsen, (2012) as one of the objections to the Morison based approach. The objections are namely: each twine does not influence the adjacent ones, meaning that "shading effect" and velocity changes due to decrease in projected area for each twine are not accounted for; for inflow angles larger than 45°, the drag force computed is exaggerated.

2.1.1 Empirical Loads on Nets

From the towing tests of Rudi et al., (1988), Aarsnes et al., (1990) derived an empirical formulation for the hydrodynamic forces on stiff net panels under uniform flow. This method, that could be used for a preliminary assessment of loads, is limited for the range of solidity ratios (Sn) and Reynolds number (Rn) of the towing experiments, where the Reynolds number is based on the twine diameter. As a result, the empirical formulas proposed do not account for the drag and lift coefficient Reynolds number's dependency (Lader & Fredheim, 2006).

On their work, Lader & Enerhaug, (2005), compared the hydrodynamic forces computed with the empirical formulas of Aarsnes et al., (1990), eq. (3) and (4). and measurements of a model test.

$$F_D = \frac{1}{2}\rho C_D A U^2$$
$$F_L = \frac{1}{2}\rho C_L A U^2 \quad (3)$$

$$C_D = 0.04 + \left(-0.04 + 0.33S + 6.54S^2 - 4.88S^3\right)\cos\alpha$$
$$C_L = \left(-0.05S + 2.3S^2 - 1.76S^3\right)\sin2\alpha$$
$$(4)$$

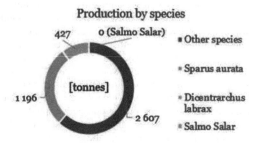

Figure 2. Lift and drag forces on a twine in a uniform current.

According to them, the use of direct formulas for computing the global hydrodynamic forces on net cages overestimates the forces (the lift force is not shown, but a similar phenomenon occurs). Mainly because these empirical formulas do not take into account the net deformation and change of geometry. The presence of the attack angle of the net in the formulas of the drag and lift coefficient implies a high dependency between the drag and lift force on the net and its geometry.

2.2 *Structure*

The majority of the work done in the analysis of fish farm behaviour under loads was performed for floating collar structures. Since those have been the standard in the industry for a long time. As referred by Li et al., (2017) the responses of these structures are usually done by means of a strip theory analysis, and the drag force included via Morison equation. However, it is remarked that 3D frequency-dependent interactions and hydroelasticity effects are not accounted for in a 2D analysis. Since these effects are of major importance, the same authors proposed a beam model to compute the motions of the floating collar Such an approach was also previously done by Li & Faltinsen, (2012).

As seen before, the emerging designs for offshore locations differ from the traditional floating plastic collar and become more similar to floating rigs and vessels. Therefore, the same procedures used for these structures can be applied, with the added complication to include the forces caused by the net cage. As clearly stated by Chakrabarti, (2005) the method to compute loads on floating structures depend on their size relative to the wavelength. For slender structures normally the Morison equation is used to computed wave and current's loads. For larger structures a diffraction and radiation linear analysis is used.

2.3 *Mooring*

Mooring systems are used to maintain the structure in the desired place against waves, current and wind, by reducing its horizontal offset (Xu et al. 2019). Two systems are traditionally used, taut and catenary configurations. The modelling of the mooring lines is mainly dictated by the software tool chosen. Shen et al, (2018) use elastic trusses, with adequate weight and stiffness, to model the mooring lines and the forces are computed by Morison equation. Other approaches adopted, (Bore & Fossan, 2015) used tubular beam elements to model the mooring lines due to limitations of the software employed.

Two approaches are taken regarding mooring analysis: uncoupled and coupled. The uncoupled analysis is recognized to be simpler and faster, and the coupled to be more accurate, although more time consuming.

The uncoupled analysis consists in computing the floating body motions and then, in a second analysis, imposing these motions as conditions at the end of the mooring system. The drawbacks of this analysis are the failure to incorporate the damping effect (on the low frequencies motions of the body) and current loads of the mooring system, and not accounting with the influence of the mooring system in the body wave frequency motion. These drawbacks gain more importance as the depth of the system increases. In a coupled approach, the motions and loads of both the floating body and the mooring system are solved for each time step. Therefore, the interaction between the two is considered. For a coupled analysis regularly a non-linear time domain method is used, aiming for equilibrium at each time step (Jo et al., 2013).

3 VALIDATION

The chosen software for the analysis of a fish farm is SIMA- Simulation Workbench for Marine Applications (SIMA) by DNV-GL. The software is a well-established and trusted commercially available tool.

The validation is done in five stages. One with the analysis of Moe et al., (2010) a second with the numerical analysis of Li e al., (2011), a third with the work of Liu et al (2021), the fourth is reported in Mohapatra et al. (2020), and the last with the results of the numerical software FhSim, provided by SINTEF. Some analysis uses more complex systems than others, the criteria for their choice was mainly due to their strength as good sources of results and the possibility of emulating their models in the SIMA platform.

4 CASE STUDY

On the south side of Madeira island there is an aquaculture farm for the production of gilt-head bream (*Sparus Aurata*) with around 20 cages on a site approximately 0.5 nautical miles from the coast.

The ocean floor geometry of the site was replicated as possible, so the mooring system model is closer to the real one deployed (a cross view is shown on Figure 3. The mooring line's pre-tensions were included, displayed in Figure 4.

An overview of the entire system is given in Figure 5.

A review of the mooring system of the farm was conducted. An analysis of the implemented system was performed, with a 40 year long wave data record, collected in situ and provided by the company.

5 DESIGN

One of the key parameters for the design of an aquaculture system is the fish demands, with each species having its own requirements regarding temperature, oxygen levels, salinity, among others (Shainee et al., 2013). Although the perfect levels of this requirements might not be known for the farmed species,

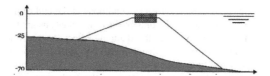

Figure 3. Top and cross section of 3D bottom model.

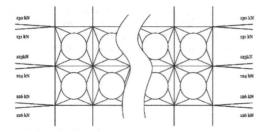

Figure 4. Mooring lines pre-tension force.

Figure 5. 3D model built in SIMA of Madeira's system.

adequate levels have been found through experience and studies (Pillay, 1992).

The concepts and designs developed for offshore locations are building on much experience from the offshore oil and gas industry. Reason why a certain resemblance is visible between rigs and some of the emerging design solutions. Nonetheless, some interesting solutions are being pursued such as vessel shaped farms and close cage systems.

- *Close Cage*

In a closed system, a better control over the fish environment exists, with a better management of the water flow and quality. In addition, an improved handling of the fish waste is possible. Therefore, reducing the environmental pollution. Being a closed structure exposed to sea loads and having a free surface, this system will have sloshing inside. The structure can be flexible or rigid. If flexible, then the deformation due to loads will affect the hydrodynamic behaviour of the structure.

- *Vessel Shape*

The two known designs of a vessel shaped cage differ from each other, but on its essence, they are a vessel shaped floater divided in multiple cages and making use of a single-point mooring (SPM) solution. As well described by Li et al., (2017). This choice of mooring aims to allow the farm to position itself in a favourable position when facing waves and currents.

- **Rig Type**

As mentioned before, one of the strategies to tackle the offshore environment challenges is by seeking knowledge and solutions from the offshore oil and gas industry and adapting it to the aquaculture needs (Bore & Fossan, 2015). These designs are made of a series of joint beams, sometimes forming a truss like structure.

From the literature review it can be said that the rules and standards for offshore aquaculture production systems are still on their beginnings.

A Norwegian technical standard is already in place and used for aquaculture systems, the NS 9415. On 2017 DNV-GL came forward with a document stating the rules for classification of offshore fish farm units (DNVGL-RU-OU-0503).

The desired class notation for offshore fish farming installations is the OI notation. This notation applies for non-self-propelled fish farming installations, deployed at a given location for an extended period, in conformity with all the offshore standards of the classification society.

In the design process the requirements or each stakeholder should be identified. According to Shainee et al., (2013) the requirements for the fish, farmer and society hold the biggest importance in the design of an aquaculture system.

For the fish, the parameters are mainly biological such as: salinity, temperature, pollution, stocking density, among others. The water motion and available cage volume are also important.

For the farmer, the system should provide good accessibility conditions and allowed tasks be performed, such as: feeding, harvesting, treatment. It should also provide good conditions for monitoring, whether through a clear water visibility or through installed monitoring technology, or both.

For the society, the production system should have a low environmental impact, with low pollution, low escapes and a small impact on the ecosystem. It should be a good source of employment, income and provide good quality produce.

Shainee et al., (2013) make a very interesting review and categorization of different concepts. It proposes two categories, based on the ability of the system to endure the external conditions. In each category a subdivision is done, with respect to the strategy employed. The categories are:

- *Designed to withstand and dissipate the loads:*
  - Floating rigid - Gravity net cages

- *Designed to avoid the loads*
  - Submerged - Submersible

6 RESULTS

The results of the validation process, case study and concept proposal provided some insights of the feasibility of the chosen software, SIMA, in the design stage.

6.1 Validation

It was concluded that this software is not the best tool to analyze the behavior of a free hanging net. As can be seen by the results, there are some discrepancies between the experimental net behaviors and the ones predicted by the software. An example of such results is the one from the validation's stage on, shown in Figure 6. One major cause of these might be the way the software represents a net panel, through an equivalent single vertical cable/bar element. This of course does not consider the physical linkage between two twines. Another important point is the influence of each twine in the flow of the others. The wake effect is not properly modelled in the SIMA software, which may lead to higher loads on the net elements located downstream and an overall increase of the cage load (Aksnes, 2106). Although there is the possibility to set the velocity reduction factor for each net element, it remains constant throughout the simulation. When ideally it should be adjusted with the changing position and angle of the elements.

Therefore, for a more detailed analysis of the net geometry a numerical tool with a more complex description of the equivalent net element should be used, but this work is focused mainly on the forces caused by the environment onto the net cage. The suitability of this tool for this purpose was backed up by the results, which lead to state that the global forces on the net cage were being reasonably well computed. Therefore, the results of these validation processes suggest that the chosen software SIMA is a good tool to perform an assessment of the loads on a fish farm system and its mooring systems.

6.2 Case study

The intention was to verify the design of the installed mooring system, making use of the proposed numerical tool and method, by evaluating the mooring system with an Ultimate Limit State (ULS) analysis, through the computation of the utilization factors (u) for each condition, presented in Table 1, as advised by DNV-GL. The utilization factor is a ratio between the load on the cable and its characteristic strength (DNV-GL, 2015).

$$u = \frac{T_{c-mean}\gamma_{mean} + T_{c-dyn}\gamma_{dyn}}{S_C}, u \leq 1 \quad (5)$$

In addition, the long-term probabilities of exceedance of the mooring lines are also computed, as depicted on Figure 7.

Table 1. Mooring lines utilization factors, u<1.

	W. Line 2	W. Line 4	W. Line 6	E. Line 2	E. Line 4	E. Line 6
WC1	0.53	0.63	0.52	0.32	0.31	0.35
WC2	0.52	0.62	0.51	0.33	0.34	0.35
WC3	0.58	0.83	0.60	0.38	0.48	0.42
WC4	0.61	0.87	0.65	0.37	0.48	0.45

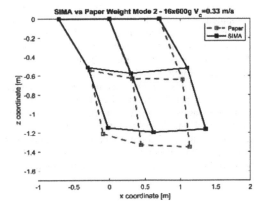

Figure 6. Side view comparison, numerical vs SIMA results.

The results showed that the current mooring system satisfies the class requirements regarding the ULS capacity of the lines. Although it is important to remark that this analysis was done for one single current velocity and direction. A full evaluation of this aquaculture mooring system would require a much more thorough analysis. Thus, such analysis is thought to be out of the

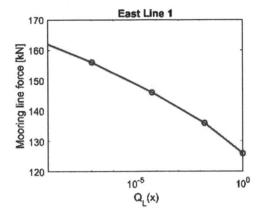

Figure 7. Long term probability of exceedance of mooring line axial force.

scope of this work, which intended, among other things, to demonstrate the feasibility of the numerical tool SIMA in the analysis of this kind of structures.

6.3 Design proposal

The concept proposed in this work is a submersible cage shaped in a hexagonal prism. With an outer rigid structure composed by two circular rings connected by rigid columns members, displayed in Figure 8.

A hydrodynamic analysis of the concept was performed. Firstly, the RAOs (Response Amplitude Operators) of the cage itself (structure plus net) are computed. Thenceforth, the RAOs of the cage plus mooring system are recomputed. In this way a brief comparison is made between the two conditions. The results for heave motion of both conditions are presented in Figure 9 and 10.

Because the structure does not have suspended nets, all net panels are attached to the structure at their boundaries (non-deformable), the current loads on the cage should be significant. To access this, a study of the axial force of the mooring lines was performed for different current velocities (without waves), Figure 12. Moreover, the computation of the

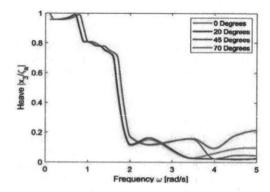

Figure 10. Moored structure RAO for heave motion.

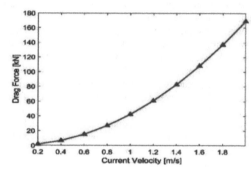

Figure 11. Cage's drag Force due to current, orientation of 0°.

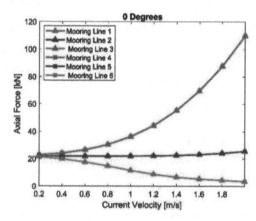

Figure 12. Axial force of mooring lines under different current velocities.

overall current induced drag force on the cage was computed and the results shown on Figure 11.

7 CONCLUSIONS

The purpose of the present work was to lay off the foundational work for further research. This was

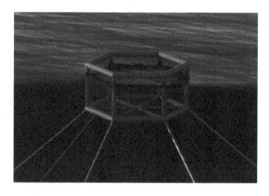

Figure 8. Concept Proposal of a 765 m3 cage.

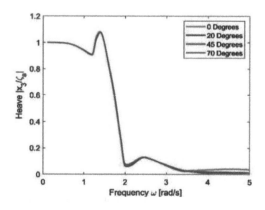

Figure 9. Non-moored structure RAO for heave motion.

done through the formulation of the design criteria, identification of environmental constraints and the proposal of a numerical tool to assist in the study of the main components during the design process. It ended with the analysis of an existing system and the design, plus analysis, of a new system concept.

Using the knowledge gained throughout the elaboration of this work, a rough analysis was done to an existing system. The analysis was simple enough and the tool coped well with the size and complexity of the system, strengthening the point that this tool can be an aid in the design process.

Lastly, making use of the criteria and requirements discussed, a basic design concept was introduced. The main point was to illustrate the role that the different criteria and requirements had in each design decision and how the SIMA tool could be used for an initially assess of the loads and help the mooring design. SIMA proved to be a very useful tool due to its in-built fish net element that simplified the design and analysis. Although, there is a downside. It is a very time-consuming task, due to long computational times and required post treatment.

The most important lesson from this process being the weaker performance of the tool, when compared with other codes, to access the net behavior in a detailed way. Although it performed well in the assessment of the loads onto the nets. These two main observations can be summarized in a recommendation: this tool is not the best for a more academic study of the net behavior, such as the sensitivity to different parameters or predicting the net shape, but it is a good choice for the study of more complete systems, where the focus is in the behavior of the cages and its complementary elements, such as moorings. Ideally this tool should be used in association with experimental trials, in such a manner as to allow a good tuning of the model.

ACKNOWLEDGMENTS

Dr. Carlos Andrade, of the Madeira government, is acknowledged for his help to obtain information about the existing aquaculture farm in Madeira.

REFERENCES

Aarsnes, J.V., H. Rudi, and Geir Løland. 1990. "Current Forces on Cage, Net Deflection." In Engineering for Offshore Fish Farming, Thomas Telford, 137–52.

Aksnes, V. 2106. Modelling of Aquaculture Net Cages in SIMA. Trondheim.

Bore, P. T., & Fossan, P.A. 2015. "Ultimate- and Fatigue Limit State Analysis of a Rigid Offshore Aquaculture Structure.". NTNU.

CEA, California Environmental Associates. 2018. Offshore Finfish Aquaculture - Global Review and U.S. Prospects.

Chakrabarti, Subrata K. 2005. I Offshore Structures Analysis Handbook of Offshore Engineering. Elsevier.

DGRM, Direcção-Geral de Recursos Naturais Segurança e Serviços Marítimos. 2014. Plano Estratégico Para A Aquicultura Portuguesa, 2014–2020.

DNV-GL. 2015. OS-E301: Position Mooring.

DNG-GL. 2017. RU-OU-0503: Rules for Classification Offshore Fish Farming Units and Installations.

FAO, Food and Agriculture Organization of the United Nations. 2018. The State of the World Fisheries and Aquaculture.

Flagstad, Ole Andreas, and Harald Tvedt. 2018. Ocean Space Aquaculture Going Offshore.

INE, Instituto Nacional de Estatísitca, and Direcção-Geral de Recursos Naturais Segurança e Serviços Marítimos DGRM. 2017. Estatísticas Da Pesca 2017.

FAO, Food and Agriculture Organization of the United Nations. 2018. The State of the World Fisheries and Aquaculture.

Guo, Y. C.; Mohapatra, S. C., and Guedes Soares, C. 2020. Review of developments in porous membranes and net-type structures for breakwaters and fish cages. Ocean Engineering. 200: 107027

Jo, C H, Kim,DY & Rho, YH 2013. "A Comparison of Coupled and Uncoupled Dynamic Analysis for the Flexible Riser in Shallow Water." In International Conference on Offshore Mechanics and Arctic Engineering.

Faltinsen, O.M.; & Shen, Y. 2018. Wave and current effects on floating fish farms. J. Mar. Sci. Application. 17, 284–296.

Kristiansen, T., and Faltinsen. OM, 2012. "Modelling of Current Loads on Aquaculture Net Cages." Journal of Fluids and Structures 34: 218–35.

Lader, PF, Arne Fredheim, & Jorgen Krokstad. 2001. "Modelling of 3D Net Structures Exposed to Waves and Current." In Open Ocean Aquaculture Symposium, 1–27.

Lader, PF, & Birger Enerhaug. 2005. "Experimental Investigation of Forces and Geometry of a Net Cage in Uniform Flow." IEEE Journal of Oceanic Engineering 30 (1): 79–84.

Lader, PF, & Arne Fredheim. 2006. "Dynamic Properties of a Flexible Net Sheet in Waves and Current-A Numerical Approach." Aquacultural Engineering 35(3): 228–38.

Le Bris, Fabien, and Dominique Marichal. 1999. "Numerical and Experimental Study of Submerged Supple Nets: Applications to Fish Farms." Journal of Marine Science and Technology (1998): 161–70.

Li, Yu-Cheng et al. 2011. "Numerical Investigation of the Hydrodynamic Behaviors of Multiple Net Cages in Waves." Aquacultural Engineering 48: 6–18.

Li, Peng, and Odd M. Faltinsen. 2012. "Wave-Induced Vertical Response of an Elastic Circular Collar of a Floating Fish Farm." In 10th International Conference on Hydrodynamics.

Li, Lin, Muk Chen Ong, and Zhiyu Jiang. 2017. "A Preliminary Study of a Vessel-Shaped Offshore Fish Farm." In International Conference on Ocean, Offshore and Arctic Engineering, 1–11.

Li, Peng, Odd M. Faltinsen, and Marilena Greco. 2017. "Wave-Induced Accelerations of a Fish-Farm Elastic Floater: Experimental and Numerical Studies." In International Conference on Ocean, Offshore and Arctic Engineering, 1–10.

Liu, ZC.; Mohapatra, S. C., and Guedes Soares, C. 2021. Finite Element Analysis of the Effect of

Currents on the Dynamics of a Moored Flexible Cylindrical Net Cage. Journal of Marine Science and Engineering. 9: 159

Løland, Geir. 1991. "Current Forces on and Flow through Fish Farms." Aquaculture International 89: 149.

Lovatelli, Alessandro, Jose Aguilar-Manjarrez, and Doris Soto. 2013. FAO Technical Workshop Expanding Mariculture Farther Offshore: Technical, Environmental, Spatial and Governance Challenges.

Moe, Heidi, Arne Fredheim, and Odd Sture Hopperstad. 2010. "Structural Analysis of Aquaculture Net Cages in Current." Journal of Fluids and Structures 26(3): 503–16.

Mohapatra, S. C.; Bernardo, T. A., and Guedes Soares, C. 2020. Dynamic wave induced loads on a moored flexible cylindrical net cage with analytical and numerical model simulations. Applied Ocean Research. Revised version submitted.

Pillay, T.V.R. 1992. Aquaculture and the Environment Second Edition. Second. Blackwell Publishing.

Portugal, Goverment of. 2013. Estratégia Nacional Para o MAR 2013-2020.

Rudi, H., Geir Løland, and L. Furunes. 1988. Model Tests with Net Enclosures. Forces on and Flow through Single Nets and Cage Systems.

Shainee, Mohamed, Bernt J. Leira, Harald Ellingsen, and Arne Fredheim. 2013. "An Optimum Design Concept for Offshore Cage Culture." In International Conference on Ocean, Offshore and Arctic Engineering, 85.

Shen, Yugao, Marilena Greco, Odd M. Faltinsen, and Ivar Nygaard. 2018. "Numerical and Experimental Investigations on Mooring Loads of a Marine Fish Farm in Waves and Current." Journal of Fluids and Structures 79: 115–36.

Tsukrov, Igor et al. 2002. "Finite Element Modeling of Net Panels Using a Consistent Net Element." Ocean Engineering 30(2): 251–70.

Xu, S.; Wang, S., and Guedes Soares, C. 2019. Review of mooring design for floating wave energy converters. Renewable and Sustainable Energy Reviews. 111:595–621.

Definition of landing profiles in the Portuguese coastal multi-gear fleet

A. Campos, V. Henriques & P. Fonseca
IPMA, Portuguese Institute for the Sea and Atmosphere, Lisboa, Portugal; and, CCMAR, Centre of Marine Sciences, Universidade do Algarve, Campus de Gambelas, Faro, Portugal

G. Araújo & J. Parente
IPMA, Portuguese Institute for the Sea and Atmosphere, Lisboa, Portugal

ABSTRACT: The coastal fleet (seiners and trawlers excluded) operating in Portuguese continental waters is a multi-gear, multi-species fleet, accounting for a considerable amount of the Portuguese mainland landings. In 2018, they accounted for 45.0% of the total fish landed weight (INE, 2018). This study presents the results obtained from applying non-hierarchical classification techniques to the 2012–2016 daily trips per vessel to define landing profiles (LP), i.e., groups of trips that are relatively homogeneous concerning species composition. A total of 14 different LPs, each defined by the relative importance of target and secondary species, emerged from the analysis. A correspondence between some of these LPs and specific vessels could be established, thus evidencing the existence of well-defined "*métiers*", or groups of vessels displaying a consistent activity over time. A clear correspondence could not be found between the remaining LP and individual vessels, where specific fisheries are not attributable to a group of vessels, the prevailing situation corresponding to vessel engagement in different types of LP targeting different species.

1 INTRODUCTION

The Portuguese coastal multi-gear fishing fleet, including vessels longer than 9 m and shorter than 33 m, operates along the entire continental coast (ICES Division IXa), using a range of different gears, including gillnets and trammel nets, hooks, longlines, traps and pots, to capture a great diversity of benthic, demersal and pelagic species (fish, shellfish, cephalopods and crustaceans). This fleet segment is responsible for an important amount of the Portuguese mainland landings, representing in 2018, 45.0 % of the total fish landed weight corresponding to 58,497 t (INE, 2018).

The existence of species-directed fisheries by groups of vessels using specific gears is recognized within this fleet. However, most vessels hold licenses for more than one gear, being actively involved in capturing different target species at different times, corresponding to different fishing trips, or even during the same fishing trip. In smaller vessels, which account for most of this fleet, the lack of onboard living conditions for observers hinders their monitoring by the National Biological Sampling Plan. Therefore, the number of vessels and trips sampled is low, resulting in a poor knowledge on the fleet dynamics, namely the fishing trips types, fishing gear used and operations.

For these vessels in particular, given the diversity of the gears used, the way they are operated, and the species captured, there is a need to investigate the existence of homogeneous groups in terms of species compositions, based on landings data, as well as their spatial/temporal boundaries. Such groups, usually defined by means of multivariate analysis, have been referred to either as "fishing trip types" (Silva et al., 2002; Jiménez et al., 2004); "fishing tactics" (Maynou et al., 2003) or "landings profiles" (Ulrich and Andersen, 2004; Castro et al., 2007). The relationship between these homogeneous groups and vessel types can lead to the definition of "fleet components" (Silva et al., 2002; Jiménez et al., 2004), or "*métiers*" (Biseau, 1998), i.e., groups of vessels that have the same exploitation pattern over time.

In this study, daily landings data are analyzed to characterize landing profiles (LP, fishing trip types) based on different species composition. Landing profiles were then assigned to vessels in an attempt to identify and characterize individual fleet components (FC) dedicated to particular fisheries. As far as we know, the current analysis represents the first attempt to define fleet components in the multi-gear fisheries off the Portuguese coast. However, a previous study was carried out for the trawl fisheries (Fonseca et al. 2007), where a group of trawlers targeting cephalopods emerged, thus evidencing the previously unsuspected importance of this taxonomic group as a targeted resource for this fleet. The definition of vessel behavior patterns contributed to the design of simpler and more efficient sampling schemes,

DOI: 10.1201/9781003216599-73

allowing more critical examination of by-catch and discards, and a better estimation of species-specific effort and fishery-based abundance indexes, such as catch per unit effort (CPUE).

The objective of this study is to contribute to a better understanding of the multi-gear fleet dynamics in support of effective fisheries management.

2 METHODS

2.1 Data sources

The data used in this analysis comprised the daily landings per vessel for a total of 492 vessels during the period 2012-2016, including date, landing port, species identification and species weight (in kilograms).

Each vessel was associated with the respective technical characteristics and fishing licenses.

Georeferenced data from the Vessel Monitoring System (VMS) were also available for those vessels with the MONICAP system installed (overall length equal or higher than 15 meters). Vessel position is reported every two hours and includes timestamp (date and time), geographical coordinates (latitude and longitude), heading (in degrees) and speed (in knots). All datasets were provided by the Directorate-General for Natural Resources, Safety and Maritime Services (DGRM).

2.2 Data analysis

In order to identify LPs, daily sales were assumed to correspond to daily landings for each vessel and were adopted as a unique descriptor for fishing trips. Due to the large volume of data (254,436 daily trips and a total of 50 species), a non-hierarchical classification technique was applied, CLARA (Clustering LARge Applications) (Kaufman and Rousseeuw, 1990), consisting of a partitioning algorithm that divides the dataset into k clusters, where k needs to be specified a priori. To define the ideal number of clusters, corresponding to landing profiles, k was selected based on a quality index provided by the algorithm, the Overall Average Silhouette Width (OASW), (Struyf et al., 1997). The Average Silhouette Width (ASW) is used to define the importance of each cluster, where values of this parameter varying between 0.51 – 0.71 and above 0.71 define "reasonable" and "strong" quality grouping respectively, while values from 0.26 – 0.50 and below 0.26 define "weak" and "unstructured" group structure, respectively (Struyf et al., 1997). Clustering analysis was run over a dataset with landings in weight expressed as the frequency of the total daily trip landings for a group of 50 species, previously selected based on their highest occurrence and landed weight. The analysis based on landing weight evidences biological aspects of fisheries related to species abundance.

The relationship between landing profiles and the vessels in the study was analysed through correspondence analysis (CA), based on a frequency matrix (492 x 14) of the number fishing trips for each vessel within each cluster, to define vessel groups related to the different LP, corresponding to fleet components dedicated to specific fisheries over time ("*métiers*").

3 RESULTS

3.1 Definition of fishing trip types

The values of OASW index are plotted against k in Figure 1. A total of 14 clusters were identified, corresponding to the highest value of this index, 0.607.

In Table 1, each cluster (LP) is characterized in terms of its three main species, designated by their 3-alpha FAO species codes, as well as its contribution to the total landings in weight and in number of fishing trips.

A total of 8 out of the 14 LP's were classified as "strong", corresponding to higher ASW values above 0.71, where the first species is the primary target, being the second species drastically below its magnitude, contributing in most cases with very low landing percentages. This is the case of LP's 11 to 14, exclusively targeting different species of clams: (the smooth clam, *Callista chione*; the bean clam, *Donax spp*; the surf clam, *Spisula solida*; and the saltwater clam, *Chamelea gallina*); LP 10, targeting the black scabbardfish, with a residual by-catch of deep-sea sharks (the gulper shark, *Centrophorus lusitanicus*, and the tope shark, *Galeorhinus galeus*) and LP 6, where octopus is the only landed species. LP 8 and LP 7 are also strong clusters, with pouting and sea bass as target species, but higher by-catch fractions.

Three LP's were classified as "reasonable": LP 2, where hake is the target species and horse mackerel a less captured species; LP 3 targeting cuttlefish, where octopus and sole are also present; and finally, LP 4 dedicated to monkfish, with hake by-catch. Unlike LP 6, LP 5, also targeting octopus, was classified as "weak"; the presence of by-catch species, among which pouting and hake, in higher percentages, contributes to the definition of a more heterogeneous trip type. Another LP defined as "weak" is LP 9, where soles represent less than half of the percentage

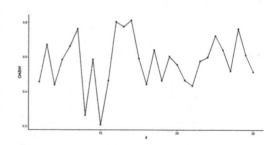

Figure 1. Overall average silhouette coefficient (OASW) against k, with k from 2 to 30.

Table 1. Identification of landing profiles (LP) and, for each LP, average silhouette width (ASW) classification; number of vessels involved; number of fishing trips; target species; and the three main landed species. S – strong; R – reasonable; W – weak; U – unstructured. Each species is designated by the corresponding, 3-alpha FAO species code. HOM: horse mackerel, *Trachurus trachurus*; HKE: hake, *Merluccius merluccius*; CTC: cuttlefish, *Sepia officinalis*; MON: monkfishes, *Lophius spp*; OCC: common octopus, *Octopus vulgaris*; BSS: sea bass, *Dicentrarchus labrax*; BIB: pouting, *Trisopterus luscus*; THS: soles, *Microchirus spp*; BSF: black scabbardfish, *Aphanopus carbo*; KLK: smooth clam, *Callista chione*; DON: bean clam, *Donax spp*; ULO: surf clam, *Spisula solida*; SVE: saltwater clam, *Chamelea gallina*; SWO: swordfish, *Xiphias gladius*; CPL: lowfin gulper shark, *Centrophorus lusitanicus*; EQI: sword razor shell, *Ensis siliqua*; COE: conger, *Conger conger*; SOL: common sole, *Solea solea*; JOD: john dory, *Zeus faber*; SBA: axillary seabream, *Pagellus acarne*; GAG: tope shark, *Galeorhinus galeus*.

LP	Sil. Class.	No. Vessels	No. Trips	1st Spp	%	2nd Spp	%	3rd Spp	%
1	U	419	67,838	HOM	14.5	SWO	11.5	COE	7.8
2	R	256	16,202	HKE	66.0	HOM	12.0	MON	3.3
3	R	195	11,301	CTC	55.5	OCC	8.1	SOL	8.0
4	R	144	5,597	MON	66.8	HKE	6.9	JOD	3.8
5	W	311	33,443	OCC	59.4	BIB	10.4	HKE	4.1
6	S	329	71,753	OCC	97.4	BIB	0.9	COE	0.5
7	S	163	2,166	BSS	73.2	BIB	6.6	SOL	3.5
8	S	207	12,972	BIB	58.7	OCC	17.6	COE	4.1
9	W	96	3,679	THS	45.9	HKE	6.6	SBA	6.3
10	S	22	10,237	BSF	93.0	CPL	5.8	GAG	1.1
11	S	21	3,269	KLK	96.9	EQI	1.9	DON	0.6
12	S	40	4,111	DON	93.6	SVE	3.1	ULO	1.8
13	S	46	7,187	ULO	98.0	SVE	1.3	EQI	0.4
14	S	24	4,681	SVE	87.6	ULO	10.2	DON	2.1

of trips, with hake and axillary seabream as second and third species, respectively. LP 1 was the only cluster classified as "unstructured", with the first three main species accounting only for around 30% of trips.

3.2 Fleet segmentation

The first two dimensions of the correspondence analysis were found to explain only 28.7 % of the total variance within the data (Figure 2). However, a correspondence between several vessels and LP's could be observed, suggesting the existence of two individualized components, i.e. groups of vessels developing the same fishing pattern over the 5-year period under analysis. The first axis differentiates between a small fleet (16 units) associated to LP 10, targeting black scabbard fish, and the remaining vessels. In the second axis, dredge vessels associated to LP's 11 to 14, in a total of 40 units, contrast with the rest of the fleet. The remaining vessels could not be associated to particular LP's in the present analysis.

In Table 2, these groups of vessels, corresponding to fleet components, were characterized in terms of their number of vessels and technical characteristics, including total length, engine power, gross tonnage and year of construction, as well as their activity through their relative contributions to the total number of daily trips in each LP.

The group of 16 vessels forming the first component has an average length of around 17 metres. While it contributes to only 3.76% for the total number of daily trips within the multi-gear fleet, its trips are almost exclusively in LP 10, despite having a small number of trips in LP 1 and LP 2. The second component is older in age, smaller in size (average length around 11 metres) and with the 40 vessels involved mostly dedicated to LP's 11 to 14, contributing with 6.58% for the total number of trips. This second component lands in LP's 11 to 14, having less than 5% of the total number of trips in LP 1 and also in LP 6.

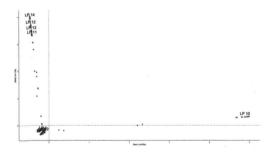

Figure 2. First two dimensions of Correspondence Analysis between vessels (grey dots) and identified LP's (black triangles).

Table 2. Definition of fleet components (FCs). Each component is defined by the average characteristics of vessels in each group and their relative contribution to the total number of daily trips in each LP. Standard deviations are in brackets.

	FC 1	FC 2	Total
No. Vessels	16	40	56
LP's	-	-	-
1	136	292	428
2	13	1	14
3	-	-	0
4	-	-	0
5	-	-	0
6	-	245	245
7	-	-	0
8	-	-	0
9	-	-	0
10	9,410	-	9,410
11	-	2,615	2,615
12	-	3,436	3,436
13	-	5,947	5,947
14	-	4,213	4,213
No. Trips	9,559	16,749	26,308
% Trips	36.3	63.7	100
Length (m)	17.3 (2.7)	11.5 (1.8)	-
GT	46 (36)	10 (4)	-
HP	256 (80)	102 (24)	-
Age	30 (11)	43 (22)	-

4 DISCUSSION AND CONCLUSIONS

The current analysis partly updates previous work carried out by Castro et. al. (2007) in the Iberian Peninsula waters, including the Portuguese continental coast, for the period 2003-2005. The number of LPs defined for the multi-gear fisheries was similar in both studies, with a common number of "strong" LPs, including those targeting the black scabbard fish and the octopus. However, many differences can be noticed when comparing these results with those in the previous study, both in LP structure and importance, namely for the LPs targeting clams, pouting and monkfishes, among others. A new, previously unexisting LP emerged from the present analysis, targeting the sea bass, corresponding to a recent fishery.

A number of LP's classified as "strong" contributed to define several fleet components in the present study. One of such landing profiles (LP 10) represents a well individualized fleet component, constituting a *"métier"*, the deep water longlining black scabbard fishery, involving a relatively small longline fleet targeting the black scabbard with very low landing fraction corresponding to deep-sea sharks. This LP, operating in specific areas of the continental coast, near the canyons off Sesimbra and Peniche. Also well-defined in the analysis is a fleet component targeting bivalves, engaging a total of 40 vessels and four landing profiles (LP 11 to LP 14), targeting four different species, where clams, together with the sword razor shell, are the only landed species.

Both these components correspond to well-known fleets associated to the use of specific gears. However, not all LP's classified as "strong" contributed to define FC's. Despite the existence of strong LP's targeting octopus, pouting and sea bass, a clear correspondence could not be established between these trip types and individualized groups of vessels. In other words, there are landing profiles (fishing trip types) that cannot be attributable to a subset or group of vessels. A common situation in this multi-gear fleet is vessel engagement in different types of fishing trips, targeting different species at different times, or even in the same fishing trip, which is a consequence of the simultaneous use of various fishing gears, or simultaneous exploitation of diverse fishing grounds.

While general patterns of fleet activity could be defined, further analysis must be carried out on a yearly basis, allowing to confirm the persistence of the observed patterns along an extended time period. Refining the analysis for each LP is also important in order to seek for possible effects of seasonality, particularly for those LP classified as "strong", contributing to better characterization of landing profiles and associated fleet.

A further step in the analysis will be to address the fleet's spatial dynamics by using the vessel's position data at the individual fishing trip level based on data from MONICAP. the Portuguese fishing Vessel Monitoring System. The spatial activity of the vessels associated with the different landing profiles will be depicted, at different time scales, allowing to define fishing activity patterns along the entire Portuguese coast. The progress of this study may further contribute to the design of more efficient sampling schemes, allowing a better estimation of species-specific effort and fishery-based abundance indexes thereby contributing to a more effective coastal multi-gear fisheries management.

ACKNOWLEDGEMENTS

This study was carried out at the scope of the project TECPESCA – Project Mar 2020 16-01-04-FMP-0010 – IPMA. The fisheries data was supplied to IPMA by the Portuguese Directorate-General for Natural Resources, Safety and Maritime Services (DGRM).

REFERENCES

Biseau, A. (1998). Definition of a directed fishing effort in a mixed-species trawl fishery, and its impact on stock assessments. *Aquat. Living Resources*, 11(3), 119–136.

Castro, J., Abad, E., Artetxe, I., Cardador, F., Duarte, R., García, D., Hernández, C., Marín, M., Murta, A., Punzón, A., Quincoces, I., Santurtún, M., Silva, C., Silva, L. (2007). Identification and segmentation of mixed-species fisheries operating in the Atlantic Iberian Peninsula waters (IBERMIX). *Final Report to the European Commission, Directorate-General for Fisheries and Maritime Affairs*. Contract Ref.: FISH/2004/03-33.

Fonseca, T., Campos, A., Afonso-Dias, M., Fonseca, P., & Pereira, J. (2008). Trawling for cephalo-pods off the Portuguese coast—fleet dynamics and landings composition. *Fisheries Research*, 92(2-3), 180–188.

INE (2018) - Estatísticas da Pesca 2018. INE - Instituto Nacional de Estatística, Lisboa, Portugal. ISBN: 978-989-25-0489-6.

Jiménez, M. P., Sobrino, I., & Ramos, F. (2004). Objective methods for defining mixed-species trawl fisheries in Spanish waters of the Gulf of Cádiz. *Fisheries Research*, 67(2), 195–206.

Kaufman, L., & Rousseeuw, P. J. (1990). Partitioning around medoids (program pam). Finding groups in data: an introduction to cluster analysis, 344, 68–125.

Maynou, F., Demestre, M., & Sánchez, P. (2003). Analysis of catch per unit effort by multivariate analysis and generalised linear models for deep-water crustacean fisheries off Barcelona (NW Mediterranean). *Fisheries Research*, 65(1-3), 257–269.

Silva, L., Gil, J., & Sobrino, I. (2002). Definition of fleet components in the Spanish artisanal fishery of the Gulf of Cadiz (SW Spain ICES division IXa). *Fisheries Research*, 59(1-2), 117–128.

Struyf, A., Hubert, M., & Rousseeuw, P. (1997). Clustering in an object-oriented environment. *Journal of Statistical Sofware*, 1(4), 1–30.

Ulrich, C., & Andersen, B. S. (2004). Dynamics of fisheries, and the flexibility of vessel activity in Denmark between 1989 and 2001. *ICES Journal of Marine Science*, 61(3), 308–322.

A new approach to sustainable integrated cultures

J.P. Garcês, H. Quental-Ferreira, M. Theriaga, D. Neto & P. Pousão-Ferreira
IPMA - Portuguese Institute for the Ocean and Atmosphere, EPPO - Aquaculture Research Station, Olhão, Portugal

ABSTRACT: Integrated multi-trophic aquaculture (IMTA) is the combined cultivation of organisms that extract organic and inorganic matter from the rearing environment together with those that need food from external origins, creating a balanced production system. It is thus considered as an adequate approach to increase profitability in semi-intensive aquaculture carried out in earth ponds. An open experimental 5-tank circuit has been implemented in laboratory facilities at IPMA-EPPO (Aquaculture research station) over a year (October 2018 to October 2019), with the purpose to develop the combined culture of several species of high economic value: Oysters (*Crassostrea gigas*, and *Crassostrea angulata*), sea-cucumbers (*Holothuria arguinensis*), polychaetes (*Marphysa sp.* and *Diopatra neapolitana*), sea hares (*Aplysia fasciata* and *Aplysia punctata*) and macroalgae (*Ulva sp.*) without food supply, using only the water from the aquaculture ponds. Growth, reproduction and survival were also studied. At the end of the study, this integrated culture system showed a perfect trophic equilibrium in all tanks, demonstrating the possibility to combine the production of these valuable species at very low cost.

1 INTRODUCTION

Facing a growing human demand and needs, the aquaculture role must be re-balanced in terms of its diversity, environmental impacts and dependence on feed ingredients (Troell et al. 2014). It is therefore necessary to change aquaculture system designs to increase production in quantity and quality while preserving the environment, developing new relationships among producers, consumers, and production systems. The fish-farming sector is currently based on two main strategies: the offshore culture, where carrying capacity is not a constraint but requiring larger cages and larger infrastructure investments; or the Recirculating Aquaculture Systems (RAS) or Zero Exchange Systems, to limit interactions with natural ecosystems and better manage waste, requiring technological investments and more energy to operate (Blancheton et al. 2009, Martins et al. 2010). A third, viable and credible alternative to reduce the impact of fish effluents on the environment, is the Integrated Multi-Trophic Aquaculture (IMTA). The growing interest in IMTA led to experimental work carried out in recent years by many countries, among which Canada, Chile, South Africa, Israel and China (Chopin et al. 2008; Barrington et al., 2009) and more recently, the United Kingdom (in particular Scotland), Ireland, Spain, Portugal, France, Turkey, Norway, Japan, Korea, USA and Mexico. It is commonly agreed that one of the most complex stages in these processes is to select efficient species and to find out the right proportion of fish, seaweed, molluscs, crustaceans and other marine invertebrates for each system. The use of different trophic levels enables the creation of a balanced system, allowing improvements both in production and in water quality.

Part of the bottom sediment surface consists of uneaten feed and fecal materials, both of which contain nutrients that represent a potential feed source (Nicholas et al., 2011). Organisms that may feed on this waste include deposit-feeding detritivores, such as sea cucumbers (Ahlgren, 1998), polychaete worms (Nicholas et al. 2011) and Sipuncula (Mark and Monika, 2009). The potential for sea cucumbers (Ahlgren, 1998, Li et al. 2013) and polychaete worms (Bischoff et al. 2009, Honda & Kikuchi, 2002, Nicholas et al. 2011, Palmer, 2010) to ingest and assimilate sediment has been demonstrated in many polyculture systems. As bioturbators, Sipunculans can play a significant role in benthic ecosystems (Graf, 1989, Mark & Monika, 2009) efficiently using the sediment given their presence at high densities (Murina, 1984). The diversification of aquaculture as an alternative to monoculture, is one of the best paths to environmental sustainability, economic viability and social acceptance.

2 METHODS

2.1 *Description of the system*

A system was developed at the Aquaculture Research Station (Estação Piloto de Piscicultura de Olhão, EPPO), of the Portuguese Institute of Sea and Atmosphere (Instituto Português do Mar e Atmosfera, IPMA), south Portugal (37° 02′ N; 07°

DOI: 10.1201/9781003216599-74

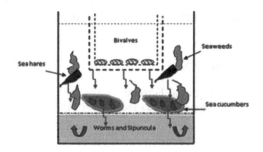

Figure 1. IMTA concept developed at EPPO.

49′W) (Figure 1). The purpose of this system was to create a trophic structure in equilibrium.

Bivalves (oysters) as filtering organisms, and sea hares (*Aplysia*) as herbivorous, are the basis of this entire food chain. Oysters use organic particulate matter in water, as well as phytoplankton, and Aplysia feeds on macroalgae, mainly *Ulva sp.* generated by bloom of nutrients, from the aquaculture tank and excretions inside the study tank. Their feces provide food for sea-cucumbers, Sipunculans, and polychaetes. Sea-cucumber feces are used by polychaetes and polychaetes feces are used by sea cucumbers. The vegetable feces of sea-hares are also used by sea-cucumbers and polychaetes, closing the cycle.

To evaluate the ability of interaction between these species, belonging to different functional groups, five different treatments (Table 1) were compared. The experiments were carried out from October 2018 to October 2019. The combinations in each treatment are shown in Table 1. The species include one filter-feeder (oyster: *Crassostrea gigas*), three deposit feeders (sea-cucumber: *Holothuria arguinensis*, Sipuncula: *Sipunculus nudus*, and two polychaete species: *Marphysa* sp. and *Diopatra neapolitana*) one herbivorous (*Aplysia fasciata*) as well as an unknown number of organic particulate matter, primary producer species (phytoplankton) and macroalgae (*Ulva sp.*) that naturally developed inside the tanks.

2.2 *Tank management*

The tanks (Figures 2-4) were operated in a continuous water renewal, with water pumped from another aquaculture tank.

Figure 2. Rearing tank used, west-east oriented, under shadow protection. EPPO. October 2018.

Figure 3. Pump (A), water inlet tube (B), and entrance tube (C). EPPO. October 2018.

Table 1. Rearing tanks details along with species composition in each tank=treatment.

Tank	size [cm]	Sand layer[cm]	Species
T1	100x120x60	10	- *C. gigas* - *H. arguinensis* - *Marphysa sp.* - *Ulva sp.*
*T2	100x120x60	20	- *C. gigas* - *H. arguinensis* - *S. nudus* - *Ulva sp.*
T3	150x150x30	10	- *C. gigas* - *H. arguinensis* - *D. neopolitana* - *Ulva sp.*
*T4	150x150x50	20	- *C. gigas* - *Aplysia fasciata* - *H. arguinensis* - *S. nudus* - *Ulva sp.*
T5	150x150x50	10	- *H. arguinensis* - *Marphysa sp.* - *Ulva sp.*

* Tank 2 and 4 had a higher sand profile due to the presence of *S. nudus*.

Figure 4. Water inlet (A), water outlet (B), oyster supports (C) and macroalgae (D). EPPO. October 2018.

Each tank was filled with a 10 cm layer of beach sand. The sand was previously screened to remove any associated macrofauna and detritus, sun dried, and rinsed several times alternately. The water circulation is from the bottom to top, through a perforated pipe, placed in the centre, which also ensures the regulation level (Figure 4). This allows a uniform water movement across the substrate preventing the creation of stratified and anoxic zones.

No additional food was provided during the study, except in tank 3 with *Diopatra neapolitana*, a carnivorous worm, which was supplied *ad libitum* 3 times per week a commercial diet. In the remaining tanks, all the food was supplied only by the water from the aquaculture tank and by the waste from the various organism's present. The tanks were regularly monitored to determine mortality. Water parameters (temperature, salinity, dissolved oxygen, pH) were measured.

Species farming

Oysters

The juvenile's oysters were placed inside the tanks in a suspended tray (Figure 4), avoiding close contact with the bottom, to allow a good dispersion of faeces. The oysters were regularly monitored to avoid biofouling and mortality.

Macroalgae

Macroalgae occur naturally in the ponds (Figure 4) being almost impossible to avoid their growth and the most abundant genus was *Ulva*. *Aplysia* populations are important to control macroalgae growth and proliferation. The macroalgae also support an important population of amphipods and other benthic organisms, especially those that grow at the bottom that also serve as food for the polychaetes.

Polychaetes

The polychaetes, collected from the natural environment, were placed inside the tanks T1 and T5 (*Marphysa sp.*) and tank T3 (*Diopatra neapolitana*). During the first 48 h of acclimatisation, the worms could settle (construct and establish burrows). No samples were taken to evaluate polychaete growth to avoid disturbance of sediment surface and/or destroying the galleries. In the tanks (T1) and (T5) the presence of galleries was monitored in the sediment surface. Significantly higher orifice density was observed in tank (T1) under oyster structures. In the tank (T3), *Diopatra* activity inside the tubes was monitored (Figure 5).

In June, periodic samples were taken from the tanks to assess recruitment. A 2 cm diameter core was used, and 6 sampling zones were randomly selected.

Figure 5. *D. neapolitana* tubes in tank 3. EPPO. May 2019.

Sea-cucumbers

With the purpose to clean the surface of the sediment, oyster faeces and organic matter as food, sea-cucumbers (*Holothuria arguinensis*) collected from a natural environment (Alvor ria) were placed in all tanks (Figure 6).

In turn, their faeces would serve as an alternative food for polychaetes and other benthic organisms (Figure 7). Their growth was recorded at the beginning and at the end of the study.

Aplysia fasciata

In order to control the growth of macroalgae, and compare the results with other studies already carried out, whose results are being treated, *Aplysia fasciata* were used but were only placed in tanks with Sipuncula.

Sipunculida farming

The peanut worm *Sipunculus nudus* Linnaeus (Figure 8), which belongs to the phylum *Sipuncula*, has a wide geographical distribution and are very abundant in the South China Sea region, in various

Figure 6. *H. arguinensis* used in the study. EPPO.

Figure 7. *Holothuria arguinensis* feces near a spawning of *Aplysia fasciata*. EPPO.May 2019.

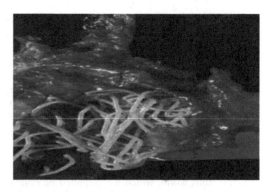

Figure 9. *Aplysia fasciata* spawning. May 2019. EPPO.

Figure 8. *Sipunculus nudus* from Tank 2 (T2). EPPO. May 2019.

biotopes, mainly sandy beaches along the intertidal habitats of the seashore (Adrianov & Maiorova 2010).

The polyculture of *S. nudus* with other animals can improve the economic benefits of the culture system, indicating the potential ecological importance of Sipuncula based on their burrowing behavior (Mark and Monika, 2009 and references there in). This is an omnivorous species, dioecious animals; no sexual dimorphism is shown, and fertilization is external (Adrianov & Maiorova 2010).

In this study, the individuals were introduced in tanks T(2) and T(4).

3 RESULTS AND DISCUSSION

3.1 *Integrated-culture system*

The different multitrophic systems evaluated in the experiment worked quite well both in terms of quality and efficiency of production. No relevant problems of coexistence, predation and competition were revealed between the species for each tank analyzed. *Ulva* sp. developed at high growth rate. Because its high growth rate it was periodically removed to avoid that surface layer was completely covered by the algae, impeding sunlight passage through the tank. No significant differences were noticed in the growth rate of *Ulva* sp. between the tanks, with the conclusion that this species of macroalgae may growth well and with good results (in terms of harvest yield) in a multitrophic system. Oysters supported quite well the adaptation in these systems, with no observed mortality. The sea-cucumbers introduced, with the main objective to reduce the content of organic matter inside the system, were acclimatized. Regarding *A. fasciata*, the growth was very fast especially in the summer months, reaching adult status in about 2 months. Once adults, their postures were practically continuous (Figure 9). Their role was very positive, as they controlled the growth of macroalgae, and their feces served as food for sea cucumbers and Sipunculans.

Interesting results have been obtained regarding polychaetes. Despite the fact that polychaete sampling was not carried out in order to avoid gallery destruction, numerous polychaete fertilized eggs, larvae and juvenile were found, confirming the existence of recruitments for this group Figures 10-11).

In Table 2 the initial and final biomass values of Oysters, *Sipunculida* and Sea-cucumbers introduced

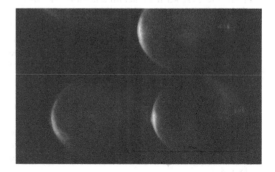

Figure 10. *Marphysa sp.* Larvae. Magnifying glass (x40) EPPO, June 2019.

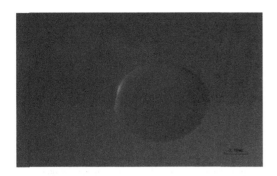

Figure 11. *D. neapolitana* larvae. EPPO. Magnifing glass (x40). June 2019.

Table 2. - Initial (Wi) and final (Wf) weight of oysters, sea cucumbers and Sipunculans used in the IMTA study.

Tanks	Weight (g)	Organisms		
		Oysters	Sea-cucumbers	Sipuncula
T1	Wi	26,5±9,8	321,1±62,2	
	Wf	69,7±14,6	382,6±50	
T2	Wi	29,2±9,9	252±66,8	30,7±7,3
	Wf	74,4±11,7	487,1±38	69,4±6,1
T3	Wi	26±10,2	268,1±68,5	
	Wf	61,2±14,7		
	Wi	28,2±9,9	494,4±45,5	
	Wf	62,3±10,7		
T4	Wi	28,4±12,5	257,6±69,5	29,5±7,2
	Wf	64,5±14,9		
	Wi	29,4±11,7	489,8±35,8	80,10±6,4
	Wf	71,9±13		
T5	Wi		264,7±72,4	
	Wf		503,0±36,4	

in each tank at the beginning and the end of the study are shown.

Although these results cannot be compared with those obtained from other fish culture systems, because the production scale is different, such as ponds, cages, flow-through systems, and recirculating aquaculture systems, shows that this IMTA system is a good alternative to a monoculture production system. For the three groups in Table 2, final biomass attained values between 2 and 3 times their respective values at the beginning of the study at very low cost.

4 CONCLUSIONS

In conclusion, with water from an aquaculture tank, it was possible to produce several organisms of high commercial value of different trophic levels in an environmentally sustainable way, reducing eutrophication and increasing economic diversification. Several studies are already being developed in EPPO on a larger scale in order to control this food chain. The choice of fish species and culture system must take into account both environmental and economic factors, as well as, the interaction between the two.

Prospects for continued fast growth of the global aquaculture industry are indeed bright, but there are many challenges that must be overcome. If these challenges can be met, the aquaculture industry will maintain its fast rate of growth and will continue to be one of the most important sources of protein in the entire world.

ACKNOWLEDGEMENTS

This study was carried out at the scope of the project Diversiaqua II (Mar2020 01/02/16 FMP006).

REFERENCES

Adrianov A.V. & Maiorova A.S., 2010. Reproduction and Development of Common Species of Peanut Worms (Sipuncula) from the Sea of Japan. Russian Journal of Marine Biology, 2010, Vol. 36, No. 1, pp. 1–15.

Ahlgren, M.O., 1998. Consumption and assimilation of salmon net pen fouling debris by the red sea cucumber *Parastichopus californicus*: implications for polyculture. J. World Aquacult. Soc. 29, 133–139.

Bailey-Brock, J.H., 1984. Ecology of the tube-building polychaete *Diopatra leuckarti* Kinberg, 1865 (Onuphidae) in Hawaii: community structure, and sediment stabilizing properties. Zoological Journal of the Linnean Society 80, 191–199.

Barrington, T., Chopin, S., Robinson, M.C., 2009. In book: Integrated Mariculture: a Global review. Chapter: Integrated multi-trophic aquaculture (IMTA) in marine temperate waters. Publisher: FAO. Editors: D. Soto.

Bischoff, A.A., Fink, P., Waller, U., 2009. The fatty acid composition of *Nereis diversicolor* cultured in an integrated recirculated system: possible implications for aquaculture. Aquaculture 296, 271–276.

Blancheton, J.P., Bosc, P., Hussenot, J.M.E., d'Orbcastel, E.R., Romain, D. 2009. The 'new' European fish culture systems: recirculating systems, offshore cages, integrated systems. Cahiers d'Agriculture. 18: 227–234.

Chopin, T., Robinson, S.M.C., Troell, M., Neori, A., Fang, J. 2008. Multitrophic Integration for Sustainable Marine Aquaculture. Encyclopedia of Ecology, 2463–2475.

Graf, G., 1989. Benthic–pelagic coupling in a deep-sea benthic community. Nature 341, 437–439.

Honda, H. & Kikuchi, K., 2002. Nitrogen budget of polychaete *Perinereis nuntia* vallata fed on the feces of Japanese flounder. Fish. Sci. 68, 1304–1308.

Li, J.W., Dong, S.L., Gao, Q.F., Wang, F., Tian, X.L., 2013. Total organic carbon budget of integrated aquaculture system of sea cucumber *Apostichopus japonicus*, jellyfish *Rhopilema esculenta* and Shrimp *Fenneropenaeus chinensis*. Aquac. Res. http://dx.doi.org/10.1111/are.12131.

Mark, A.S. & Monika, K., 2009. A deep burrowing sipunculan of ecological and geochemical importance. Deep-Sea Res. I 56, 2057–2064.

Martins, C.I.M., Eding, E.H., Verdegem, M.C.J., Heinsbroek, L.T.N., Schneider, O., Blancheton, J.P., d'Orbcastel, E.R., Verreth, J.A.J., 2010. New developments in recirculating aquaculture systems in Europe: a perspective on environmental sustainability. Aquacultural Engineering 43: 83–93.

Murina, G.V.V., 1984. Ecology of sipuncula. Mar. Ecol. Prog. Ser. 17, 1–7.

Nicholas, B., Stephen, E., Stefanie, P., 2011. Utilization of waste from a marine recirculating fish culture system as a feed source for the polychaete worm, *Nereis virens*. Aquaculture 322–323, 177–183.

Palmer, P.J., 2010. Polychaete-assisted sand filters. Aquaculture 306, 369–377.

Small, B.C., Hardy, R.W., & Tucker, C.S., 2016. Enhancing fish performance in aquaculture. Animal Frontiers, Volume 6, Issue 4, 42–49.

Troell, M., Naylor, R.L., Metian, M., Beveridge, M., Tyedmers, P.H., Folke, C., Arrow, K.J., Barrett, S., Crépin, A.-S., Ehrlich, P.R., Gren, Å., Kautsky, N., Levin, S.A., Nyborg, K., Österblom, H., Polasky, S., Scheffer, M., Walker, B.H., Xepapadeas, T., de Zeeuw, A. 2014. Does aquaculture add resilience to the global food system? Proceedings of the National Academy of Sciences 111: 13257–13263.

Numerical modelling of full-scale aquaculture cages under uniform flow

Z.C. Liu, Y. Garbatov & C. Guedes Soares
Centre for Marine Technology and Ocean Engineering (CENTEC), Instituto Superior Técnico, Universidade de Lisboa, Lisbon, Portugal

ABSTRACT: A review of some representative aquaculture structural studies is presented, including modelling technology, field tests, and experimental studies. The results show that the volume of the cages reduces rapidly under the effect of current and cages of different dimensions perform differently under a similar fluid field. To study the effect of the dimensions and sinker weight on the effective volume of the cage under the effect of current, numerical models of full-scale aquaculture cages under uniform flow are developed here. It is shown that diameters of the cages have no significant effect on the change in volume but an increase in depth of the cage can lead to reduced normalised volume. Furthermore, a heavier sinker can also help to maintain the volume even under high current. The results of this paper can provide knowledge in the design phase of a fish cage to estimate the cultivation capacity of the cages.

1 INTRODUCTION

Nowadays, aquaculture is becoming a source of fish in the society. Comparing with the production of traditional capture, which does not increase since the 1990s, the creation of aquaculture keeps growing and occupied close to 50% of the total fish production in 2016, as indicated in Figure 1 (FAO, 2018). Besides, due to the pollution and the limited area in the inshore environment, more and more fish farms are moving to offshore regions with higher water quality, rapid transport of waste production and less influence from terrestrial runoff (Holmer et al. 2010; Benetti et al. 2010). However, the harsh environment, including strong current and waves requires more reliable structures for safe and stable operation in the fish farm.

Among different types of fish cages, which are developed for offshore aquaculture, the "gravity" type cage is the most widely used because of its sizeable culturing volume and simple operating process (Lader et al. 2008). A gravity cage usually is composed of a floating collar, net, sinkers and a mooring system. However, due to the large projected area of the gravity cage, the hydrodynamic load on the cage is also significant, which leads to a rapid reduction of the cage volume (Klebert et al. 2015; Moe et al. 2010). Therefore, an accurate method to predict the behaviour of the gravity cage under the offshore environment is essential (Loverich et al. 1997; Endresen et al. 2014).

Past studies of the prediction of the behaviour of a fish cage include both experimental and modelling work. Lader et al. (2008) measured the instantaneous position of several points on the cages at two Atlantic salmon farms in Norway and the Faroe Islands by pressure sensors and estimated the volume using the geometry formed by the measured points. Gansel et al. (2018) towed a full-scale fish cage at different speeds and used a similar method to calculate the volume of the cage as Lader (2008). DeCew et al. (2013) measured the deformation of a small-scale gravity cage by acoustic sensors, which can measure both vertical and horizontal position of the net. However, this method cannot be applied to large offshore cages due to limited measurement distance and locations, and biological interference.

Because it is hard to create a fluid field with large Keulegan-Carpenter numbers (KC) in an experimental area, Fu et al. (2013) did forced oscillation tests to simulate the water particle motions around a hollow cylinder in waves and obtained added mass and drag coefficients in the Morison Equation. Berstad and Tronstad (2005) built a numerical model of a 10 cage fish farm under both current and regular and irregular waves and computed the mooring forces. Bai et al. (2016) used shell elements to simulate the HDPE floating collar and derived the fatigue life by the deterministic method basing on the S-N curve and the Palmgren-Miner rule. Endresen et al. (2013) derived a numerical method to calculate the wake effect on flexible aquaculture nets with porous nature and considered it in their model by FhSim. Lee et al. (2005) used the mass-spring model to build computation model of a fish cage and a pound net.

Li et al. (2013) used "Buoyancy Distribution" method to the partly immersed collar to analyse the dynamic responses of a fish cage in irregular waves. Yao et al. (2016) and Faltinsen & Shen (2018) used Computational Fluid Dynamics methods to predict

DOI: 10.1201/9781003216599-75

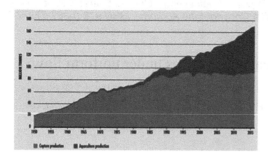

Figure 1. World capture and aquaculture production (FAO, 2018).

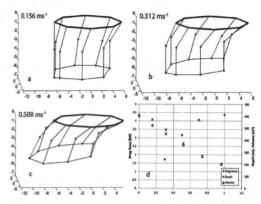

Figure 2. Deformation and volume of the fish cage undercurrent. (a) shape of the cage undercurrent of 0.156m/s, (b) shape of the cage undercurrent of 0.312m/s, (c) shape of the cage undercurrent of 0.509m/s, (d) effect of the current speed on volume and drag force (Gansel et al. 2018).

the current forces on rigid and flexible net cages. Moe et al. (2005) inclined the cross ropes and bottom ropes on the net to decrease the stress concentration during lifting, which reduced the risk of tearing of the net and escape of cultured fish. A more extensive and detailed review of methods used to model aquaculture cages can be found in Guo et al. (2020).

In the present work, the review of some representative cases of research on the behaviour of gravity cage showed that the volume reduction ratio of the cages under the effect of current is one of the major concerns of these designs, and this is further studied in this paper. A numerical model is built and the effect of different structural parameters is considered, which can provide knowledge in the design phase to estimate the cultivation capacity of a fish cage.

2 LITERATURE REVIEW

A review of three cases of research on the behaviour of gravity cage is presented in this section. All three cases include both experimental and numerical work. The normalized volumes of the cages under similar condition are still different due to the different parameters and the results are compared in Section 4. Furthermore, the effect of the diameter, depth and the sinker weight is studied in this work.

2.1 Case 1 Towing tests of a gravity cage in the field

A full-scale circular gravity cage was towed in a fjord environment of southern Norway, where ambient current speed and wave heights were small (Gansel et al. 2018). The cage had a diameter of 12 m and a depth of 6m. The collar was mounted onto the top of a steel frame, and pressure tags were fixed on two horizontal layers of the net. The dynamic pressure and the elongation of the net were neglected, and the tags were assumed to move in one plane, with the current and upwards to the surface. Therefore, the horizontal displacement and depth of tags could be determined.

The volume of the cage was represented by the geometry formed by the tags, and the current speed was assumed to be the same as the towing speed. The deformation and volume of the cage under different rates are shown in Figure 2. The distortion of the net increased with the current rate. The decrease of the volume was close to linear under current speed from 0.15m/s to 0.7m/s, but the volume reduced slower at both low current rate (<0.15m/s) and high current speed (> 0.7m/s).

2.2 Case 2 Numerical and physical model of high solidity net cage

Solidity is defined as the ratio of the projected area to the circumscribed area of the net, which is an essential parameter and determines the projected area. Moe-Føre et al. (2016) built an enhanced numerical model of high solidity (>0.30) net cages and obtained a good agreement with experimental results. Due to the limitation of the water tank, the diameter and height of the model were scaled by a factor from 16 to 29 to represent full-scale cages. The twine width and current speed were not scaled to simulate the fluid field. Mooring lines were not modelled because their effect on loads and shape of the cage was small compared to the large projected area of the net.

Similarly, the horizontal net panels on the bottom were not modelled to increase the calculation efficiency. The net was mounted on a steel ring, which was connected to a force transducer to measure drag and lift forces. The model was placed in uniform flow and the current speed increased from 0.12 m/s to 0.93 m/s.

Three-dimensional truss elements were used to model the net, which had a negligible bending or compressive stiffness. Morison's equation was used to calculate the hydrodynamic loads and the drag coefficient was 1.15. The hydrodynamic loads were

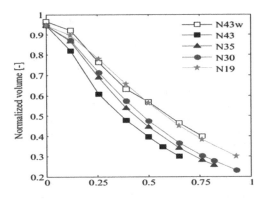

Figure 3. Normalized volume of cages under uniform flow (Moe-Føre et al. 2016).

Table 1. Field test and numerical results (DeCew et al. 2013).

Pinger group	Current speed(m/s)	Field volume(m^3)	Numerical volume(m^3)	% Different
1	0.006	18.15	18.8	-3.58
1	0.138	18.49	18.54	-0.27
1	0.376	20.57	16.36	20.46
1	0.006	18.97	18.09	4.64
2	0.138	18.61	17.8	4.35
2	0.376	20.09	15.66	22.05
2	0.138	18.96	18.24	3.8
3	0.376	13.43	13.94	-3.79
3	0.502	15.82	10.76	31.98

assumed to be vertical to the truss elements, and tangential loads were neglected. The normalised volume of the cages under different current speeds is shown in Figure 3. Increasing current rates would reduce the volume and at a speed of 0.65 m/s, only 30-46 % of the original volume remained. The volume would increase with the decreasing of the net solidity.

2.3 *Case 3 Field tests of cage deformation and volume by acoustic sensors*

Different from the first two cases to use pressure sensors to measure the positions of the net, the motion of the net was monitored by acoustic sensors for 60 days in the project conducted by DeCew et al. (2013). Twelve pingers were fixed on the net, and four hydrophones collected data from pingers. The volume of the cage was represented by a shape formed by 9 pingers, as indicated in Figure 4. However, due to the limited number of pingers, the selection of the pingers did affect the calculated volume. So different groups of pingers were used to calculate the volume, and the result was listed in Table 1. The difference between the field test result and the numerical model was about 20% to 30% when the current speed is 0.376 m/s and 0.502 m/s.

A more accurate approach to the volume assessment, as shown in Figure 5, is to form the circle in each plane firstly and connect the circles to create a volume. Figure 6 compared the result in this model and the numerical model. This method can estimate the volume of the cage better, especially under high current speed. The difference between the 3-layer field result and the numerical result under low rates was due to the failure to consider the hourglass shape caused by Nylon net.

3 NUMERICAL MODEL

From the above studies, it is clear that the volume of a fish cage reduces with the increasing current speed, and it depends highly on the dimensions of the cage and the weight of the sinkers. To quantify the effect,

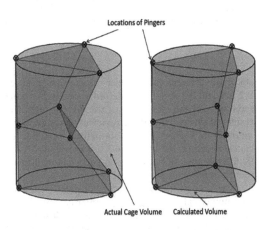

Figure 4. Cage volume calculation.

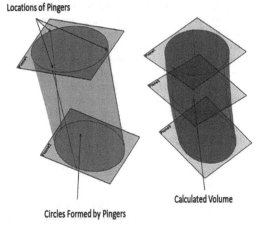

Figure 5. Cage volume from field measurement (DeCew et al. 2013).

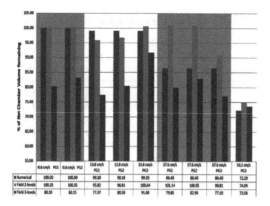

Figure 6. Numerical and new approach volume calculation (DeCew et al. 2013).

Table 2. Parameters of the net structure of a 20mx20m cage.

	Original structure	Adjusted structure
Single twine Diameter(mm)	2	N.A.
Mesh width(mm)	14.926	N.A.
No. of horizontal net lines	N.A.	19
No. of vertical net lines	N.A.	40
Diameter of horizontal net lines (mm)	2	141.053
Diameter of vertical net lines (mm)	2	210.487
Young's modules of horizontal net lines (MPa)	350	4.963
Young's modules of horizontal net lines (MPa)	350	3.326
Density of horizontal net lines (kg/m^3)	1140	16.164
Density of vertical net lines (kg/m^3)	1140	10.832

finite element method was used to build a numerical model.

Similarly, as in Case 2, the top of the cage was fixed, and the cage was placed in a uniform flow. Truss elements were used to model the net with a solidity of 0.25. To study the behaviour of cages in difference sizes, the diameters of the cages are considered as 10m, 20 m and 30 m, and the depths of cages are 0.5, 1 and 1.5 times the diameters. The sinker is a ring structure, which is modelled by beam elements. The density of the bottom ring increased from 2,500 kg/m^3 to 4,000 kg/m^3. The bottom ring with diameters of 10m, 20m and 30m is composed of 80, 160 and 240 beam elements respectively.

Twines with 2 mm-diameter were assumed to form the whole net structure. To increase the calculation efficiency, the thin twines were combined into a structure with horizontal net lines, of 1m each, distributed uniformly along with depth, and vertical net lines of 1.57 m each, distributed evenly along the circle. For instance, the net of a 20 m x 20 m cage can be combined into a structure with 19 horizontal lines and 40 vertical lines. In this way, much fewer truss elements are used to form the structure. To keep the same weight and tensile stiffness as the original structure, density and Young's modulus must be adjusted. Table 2 shows the parameters of the modified net lines of a 20mx20m cage. Furthermore, the value of the buoyancy should be adjusted according to the volume changes of the net. The net is composed of 800 to 21600 truss elements depending on the diameter and depth of the cage.

3.1 *Deformation and volume of cages with different dimensions*

This section presented the distortion and volume of cages with different dimensions. The solidity of the net was fixed as 0.25, and the weight of the bottom ring was 3,000 kg/m^3. Figure 7 is the projected

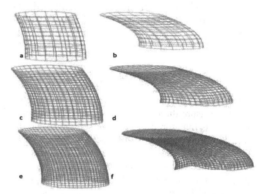

Figure 7. Calculated distortion of cages of different dimensions in various flows. (a) shape of 10 m x 10 m cage undercurrent of 0.2 m/s, (b) shape of 10 m x 10 m cage undercurrent of 0.5m/s, (c) shape of 20 m x 20 m cage undercurrent of 0.2 m/s, (d) shape of 20 m x 20 m cage undercurrent of 0.5 m/s, (e) shape of 30 m x 30 m cage undercurrent of 0.2 m/s, (f) shape of 30 m x 30 m cage undercurrent of 0.5 m/s.

shape of different cages under the current speed of 0.2 m/s and 0.5 m/s. Cages deform more and volume reduces with the increasing of the current rate. The results of this paper and the reviewed cases are summarised in Figure 8 The normalised volumes of cages undercurrent of 0.2 m/s are between 79 and 97.6 while the ones of cages undercurrent of 0.5 m/s reduce to between 40.9 and 82.6.

Even though there is insufficient data to validate the numerical model, the similarity in shapes between Figure 2 and Figure 7, and the close results between the reviewed studies and the numerical

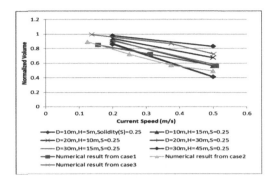

Figure 8. Normalized volume of cages in different dimensions under uniform flow.

model in Figure 8, can indicate that the numerical method is producing shapes that resemble full scale measurements qualitatively.

Figure 9 shows the normalised volumes of the cages with the same depth and different diameters. The normalised volume of the cage with a depth of 10 m and a diameter of 15 m is 0.91 under the effect of current of 0.2 m/s and 0.56 with a current of 0.5 m/s.

While one of the cages with a diameter of 30 m and the same depth is 0.906 with a current of 0.2 m/s and 0.58 under a current of 0.5 m/s. The difference is only 0.5 % and 3.8 %, respectively. Similarly, the normalised volume of all the cages with the same depth and different diameters are close, which means the diameter of a cage has no significant effect on the volume. Because of the horizontal displacement of the net under a current, sufficient distance should be left between cages on a farm. Thus, when the depth of the cages is fixed due to the environment, more full cages can produce more culturing capacity.

On the other hand, Figure 10 shows the normalised volumes of cages with different depths. The normalised volumes of cages with a diameter of 10m decrease from 0.83 to 0.56 when the depths increase from 5m to 15m. The normalised volumes of the cages with a diameter of 30 m decrease from 0.58 to 0.41 when the depths rise from 15m to 45 m, an undercurrent of 0.5 m/s.

Depth has a much more significant effect on the volumes than the diameter, and from all three diagrams in Figure 10, the increase of depth can result in a decrease in normalised volume, especially under

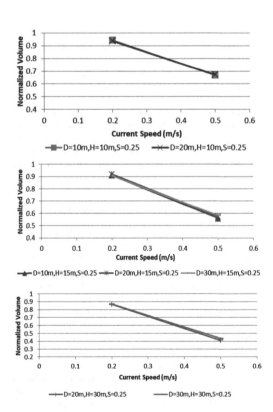

Figure 9. Normalized volumes of cages with same depth and different diameters.

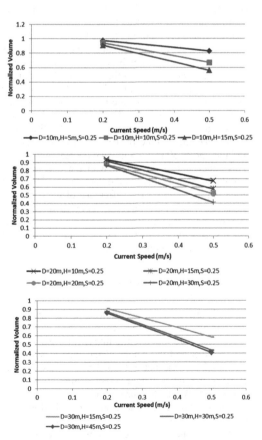

Figure 10. Normalized volumes of cages with same diameters and different depths.

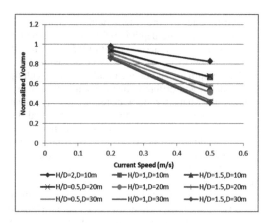

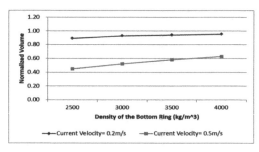

Figure 11. Normalised volume of cages with the same ratio of depth to diameter.

Figure 12. Normalised volume of a 20 m x 20 m cage with a bottom ring of different density.

the large current, which means a cage with more considerable depth deforms more and the volume reduces more under current.

It should be noted that cages are arranged in series in fish farms. Deeper cages require greater separation distance between each other due to more considerable deformation. Therefore, increasing depth is not an efficient method as increasing diameter to expand the culturing capacity.

Figure 11 shows the normalised volume of cages with the same ratio of depth to diameter. The normalised volumes decrease with the increase of the dimensions. Under a current of 0.5 m/s, the normalised volume of 10 m x 10 m cage is 66.8, while, with the same ratio of depth to diameter, the normalised volume of 30 m x 30 m cage is only 43.56. Similarly, the normalised volume of 10mx15m cage is 56.06, and the one of 30 m x 45 m cage decreases to 40.89. This conclusion is consistent with the results above that the width has little but the depth has a significant effect on the volume. The difference of the cage volumes with the same ratio of depth to diameter is mainly due to the difference of the depth. Therefore, when setting up an experiment, the scale factor of the depth is more of a concern than the one of diameter.

3.2 Deformation and volume of cages with different sinker weight

To study the effect of sinker weight, the density of the sinker is increased from 2,500 kg/m^3 to 4,000 kg/m^3. To exclude the impact of other factors, the diameter and the height of the cage is 20m, and the solidity of the net is 0.25. From Figure 12, the effect of the sinker weight is increasing with the current speed. When the current speed is 0.2 m/s, the normalised volume of the cage with a bottom ring density of 2,500 kg/m^3 is 88.89, which is only 6.72 % smaller than the one with a density of 4,000 kg/m^3. However, when the current speed increases to 0.5 m/s, the normalised volume of the cage with a bottom ring density of 2,500 kg/m^3 decreases to 45.03, which is only 71.66 % of the one with a density of 4,000 kg/m^3.

Increasing the bottom weight is an effective method to keep the volume, especially in an environment with high current speed. On the other hand, while increasing the volume and decreasing the deformation of the net, the heaver sinker also results in a larger projected area, which under the same current, can increase the hydrodynamic force, requiring a stronger mooring system.

4 DISCUSSION

Current numerical technology can predict the deformation of the cage under low current speed (≤0.5m/s) accurately, but with the increase of current speed, the error increases and large deviations between the experimental and numerical results occur (Gansel et al. 2018; Moe-Føre et al. 2015). The main reasons for the error include the limitation of experimental technology, the uncertainty of the three-dimensional flow field and the error of the drag coefficient, which are discussed following in this section.

4.1 Limitation of experimental technology

Pressure sensors and acoustic technology are the two primary technical methods to predict the deformation and volume of the cage. When applying the pressure sensors, the dynamic pressure is neglected, and the result is treated as static pressure to calculate the depth. Besides, the net between two pressure sensors is assumed as a straight line with a fixed length to calculate the horizontal displacement. That also neglects curvature of the net.

On the other hand, the signal of acoustic technology is unstable under the water, and it cannot be applied to large offshore cages. Besides, the measurement points of the two methods are finite, and the shape of the cage is assumed as the volume formed by these measurement points. That can also increase the error of experiment results.

4.2 Uncertainty of the three-dimension flow field

Two-dimensional flow is applied in this paper. However, at the field test, the flow field is three-dimensional and not uniform. The major current is measured and used as the current in the model, but the currents in other directions also affect the shape and volume of the cage. That increases the deviation between the experimental and numerical results. Besides, even if a single slender structure does not have a considerable effect on the flow field, the porous net does reduce the current speed inside and after the cage. Moe-Føre et al. (2016) found that the velocity reduced 24 % for the net with a solidity of 0.19 and 61 % for the net with a solidity of 0.43 experimentally. Their results also indicated that the velocity reduction may be independent of the velocity value, but the further experiment is necessary to confirm that. However, in the study of Gansel et al. (2018), two methods were proposed: one method assumed that the velocity reduction was 20% while the other method assumed that the velocity reduction increased from 50 % to 70 % while the current velocity increased from 0.156m/s to 1.056m/s. he found that the modelling results of Method 2 obtained a better agreement with his experimental work.

Endresen et al. (2013) considered both local and global wake effect in their model and even reduced the error partly, but the deviation with the experimental result is still significant under high current. One reason is that the horizontal bars and knots are not considered when computing the wake effect. Besides, the distance between the upstream and downstream lines is changed due to the large displacement of the net, which is also not considered in the model.

Because the current in this paper is smaller than 0.5 m/s, the wake effect is not considered. Furthermore, in a fish farm, fish cages are arranged in series, which makes the fluid flow more complex. The crowd school of fish can also affect the fluid inside the cage (Ortuno et al. 2001). Thus, a full understanding of the three-dimensional fluid flow inside a fish cage and in the whole field of a fish farm is essential for the further improvement of the model.

4.3 Error of drag coefficient

Another factor influence the accuracy of the model is the error of the drag coefficient, which is used to calculate the hydrodynamic load. The hydrodynamic load can be expressed as:

$$f = \frac{1}{2} C_D \rho D u^2 \tag{1}$$

where f is the force per length unit, C_d is the drag coefficient, ρ is the density of fluid and u is the current speed. The drag coefficient is measured in the experiment. For a flexible structure, it is hard to measure the drag force on it directly and calculate the drag coefficient.

The drag coefficient in the numerical model is constant, but because of the large deformation of the net, the velocity in the normal direction of the net decreases and the Reynold number changes. That also leads to a variation of the drag coefficient and an error in the model. Thus, to improve the accuracy of the model, experimental technology to obtain accurate drag coefficient and a model can apply to change drag coefficient need to be developed.

5 CONCLUSIONS

With an increase of the current speed, gravity fish cages deform more, and their volume decreases. The remaining volume is a significant concern for every fish farm because it determines the culturing capacity and is essential for the health of fish inside (Jensen et al. 2010, Fredheim & Langan, 2009 and Harper & Wolf, 2009). Review of three cases is presented including both numerical technology and experiment. Pressure sensors and acoustic technology can be used to measure the volume. However, the number of measurement points is limited and the remaining volume can be only estimated from the geometry formed by the measuring points. On the other hand, current numerical technology can obtain a good agreement with the experiment result under small current speed (≤ 0.5 m/s).

The numerical model, which was built in this study, successfully simulated the deformation of the cages in different dimensions' undercurrent. From the result, the remaining volumes of cages decrease with the increase of the depth and the diameter has little effect on the remained volume. Thus, the ratio to scale the depth and width of a physical model should be studied due to the limitation of the experiment field. Furthermore, a heavier sinker can prevent the deformation of the cage and increase the remaining volume. To increase the accuracy of the numerical model, especially under high current speed, a better understanding of the three-dimension flow field and more accurate coefficients are the further research goal of the study. Furthermore, to modify and improve the numerical model, it will be compared with other theoretical and numerical methodologies (Guo et al. 2020) in the future study.

ACKNOWLEDGEMENTS

This work was performed within the Strategic Research Plan of the Centre for Marine Technology and Ocean Engineering, which is financed by Portuguese Foundation for Science and Technology (Fundação para a Ciência e Tecnologia-FCT) under contract UIDB/UIDP/00134/2020.

REFERENCES

Bai, X., Xu, T., Zhao, Y., Dong, G. & Bi, C., 2016. Fatigue assessment for the floating collar of a fish cage using the deterministic method in waves. *Aquacultural Engineering*, 74, 131–142.

Benetti, DD., Benetti, GI., Rivera, JA., Sardenberg, B., O'Hanlon, B., 2010. Site Selection Criteria for Open Ocean Aquaculture. *Mar Technol Soc J* 44: 22–35.

Berstad, A.J., & Tronstad, H., 2005. Response from current and regular/irregular waves on a typical polyethylene fish farm. In Guedes Soares, C. Garbatov Y. & Fonseca, N. (eds), *Maritime Transportation and Exploitation of Ocean and Coastal Resources*: Taylor & Francis Group, London. 1189–1196.

DeCew, J., Fredriksson, D.W., Lader, P.F., Chambers, M., Howell, W.H., Osienki, M., Celikkol, B., Frank, K., Høy, E., 2013. Field measurements of cage deformation using acoustic sensors. *Aquacultural. Eng.* 57, 114–125.

Endresen, P. C., Fore, M., Fredheim, A., Kristiansen, D. & Enerhaug, B., 2013, Numerical Modelling of Wake Effect on Aquaculture Nets, *Proc. of 32nd International Conference on Ocean, Offshore and Arctic Engineering*, ASME Paper No. OMAE2013-11446.

Endressen, C., Birkevold, J., Feae, M., Fredheim, A., Kristiansen, D., Lader, P., 2014. Simulation and validation of a numerical model of a full aquaculture net-cage system. *Proc. of 33rd International Conference on Ocean, Offshore and Arctic Engineering*, ASME Paper No: OMAE2014-23382, V007T05A006.

Faltinsen, O.M. & Shen, Y., 2018. Wave and current effects on floating fish farms. *Journal of Marine Science and Application*, 17, 284–296.

FAO, 2018. *The State of World Fisheries and Aquaculture*. Fisheries and Aquaculture Department, Food and Agriculture Organization of the United Nations. Publishing Policy and Support Branch, Office of Knowledge Exchange, Research and Extension, Rome, Italy.

Fredheim, A., Langan, R., 2009. Advances in technology for offshore and open ocean finfish aquaculture. *New technologies in aquaculture: improving production efficiency, quality and environmental management*. G. Burnell, Allan, G., Woodhead Publishing in Food Science, Technology and Nutrition. 914–944.

Fu, S., Xu, Y., Hu, K. & Zhang, Y., 2013. Experimental investigation on hydrodynamics of floating cylinder in oscillatory and steady flows by forced oscillation test. *Marine Structures*, 34, 41–55.

Gansel, L., Oppedal, F., Birkevold, J. & Tuene, S., 2018. Drag forces and deformation of aquaculture cages—Full-scale towing tests in the field. *Aquacultural Engineering*, 81, 46–56.

Guo, Y.C., Mohapatra, S.C. & Guedes Soares, C. 2020. Review of developments in porous membranes and net-type structures for breakwaters and fish cages. *Ocean Engineering*, 200, 107027

Harper, C. & Wolf, J., 2009. Morphologic effects of the stress response in fish. Institute for Laboratory Animal Research 50 (4), 387–396.

Holmer, M., 2010. Environmental issues of fish farming in offshore waters: perspectives, concerns and research needs, *Aquac Environ Interact* 1: 57–70.

Jensen, F., Dempster, T., Thorstad, E.B., Uglem, I., Fredheim, A., 2010. Escapes of fishes from Norwegian sea-cage aquaculture: causes, consequences and prevention. *Aquac. Environ. Interact.* 1, 71–83.

Klebert, P., Patursson, Ø., Endresen, P., Rundtop, P., Birkevold, J. & Rasmussen, H., 2015. Three-dimensional deformation of a large circular flexible sea cage in high currents: Field experiment and modelling. *Ocean Engineering*, 104, 511–520.

Lader, P., Dempster, T., Fredheim, A., Jensen. F., 2008.Current induced net deformations in full-scale cages for Atlantic salmon (Salmo salar). *Aquacultural Eng.* 38, 52–65.

Lee, C.W., Kim, H.S., Lee, G.H., Koo, K.Y., Choe, M.Y., Cha, B.J. & Jeong, S.J., 2005. Computation modeling of the moored flexible structures. In Guedes Soares, C. Garbatov Y. & Fonseca, N. (eds), *Maritime Transportation and Exploitation of Ocean and Coastal Resources*: Taylor & Francis Group, London. 1239–1243.

Li, L., Fu, S. & Xu, Y., 2013. Nonlinear hydro elastic analysis of an aquaculture fish cage in irregular waves. *Marine Structures*, 34, 56–73.

Li, L., Fu, S., Xu, Y., Wang, J. & Yang, J., 2013. Dynamic responses of floating fish cage in waves and current. *Ocean Engineering*, 72, 297–303.

Loverich, G F., Gace, L., 1997. The effects of currents and waves on several classes of offshore sea cages. In: Helsley CE, *Open Ocean Aquaculture: Charting the Future of Ocean Farming*. University of Hawaii, Maui, Hawaii, USA 131–144.

Moe-Føre, H., Christian E. P., Gunnar, A. K., Jensen, J., Føre, M., Kristiansen, D., Fredheim, A., Lader, P. & Reite, K., 2015. Structural Analysis of Aquaculture Nets: Comparison and Validation of Different Numerical Modeling Approaches. *Journal of Offshore Mechanics and Arctic Engineering*, 137(4).

Moe-Føre, H., Lader, P., Lien, E. & Hopperstad, O., 2016. Structural response of high solidity net cage models in uniform flow. *Journal of Fluids and Structures*, 65, 180–195.

Moe, H., Fredheim, A. & Heide, M.A., 2005. New net cage designs to prevent tearing during handling. In Guedes Soares, C. Garbatov Y. & Fonseca, N. (eds), *Maritime Transportation and Exploitation of Ocean and Coastal Resources*: Taylor & Francis Group, London. 1265–1272.

Moe, H., Fredheim, A. & Hopperstad, O.S., 2010. Structural analysis of aquaculture net cages in current. *J. Fluids Struct.* 26, 503–516.

Ortuno, J., Esteban, M.A., Meseguer, J., 2001. Effects of short-term crowding stress on the gilthead seabream (Sparus aurata L.) innate immune response. *Fish Shell Immunology* 11 (2), 187–197.

Yao, Y., Chen, Y., Zhou, H. & Yang, H., 2016. Numerical modelling of current loads on a net cage considering fluid-structure interaction. *J Fluids Struct*, 62, 350–366.

The anchovy fishery by the Portuguese coastal seine fleet - landings and fleet characteristics

J. Parente
IPMA, Portuguese Institute for the Sea and Atmosphere, Lisboa, Portugal

V. Henriques & A. Campos
IPMA, Portuguese Institute for the Sea and Atmosphere, Lisboa, Portugal
CCMAR, Centre of Marine Sciences, Universidade do Algarve, Campus de Gambelas, Faro, Portugal

ABSTRACT: The number of Portuguese coastal seiners has been decreasing along the last decades. However, in the same period this fleet has undergone a significant technological modernization, with the improvement of equipments and deck layouts aimed at improving safety, ergonomics, fish conservation and cargo handling on board. Alongside with this improvement the target species for this fleet have also changed as a result of the decline in sardine (*Sardina pilchardus*) stocks since 2008, and currently, landings of Atlantic chub mackerel (*Scomber colias*) and the European anchovy (*Engraulis encrasicolus*) are important to the global yields achieved by this fleet. In this study, we give an account of the changes undergone by the Portuguese seine fleet as well as of the recent economic significance of the European anchovy in the seine fishery. The relative fishing power and the catch per unit of standardized effort are estimated, allowing to compare vessels productivity.

1 INTRODUCTION

The number of coastal seiners operating on the Portuguese coast has been steadily decreasing since the country's entry in 1986 to the European Economic Community (now the EU). From 180 registered units in 2010, only around 135 were active in 2016 when considering the landing records and the deck equipment fitted for seine fishing operations (Parente, 2020).

This fleet has registered a significant technological evolution in the last 20 years, namely through the introduction of equipment and structures aimed at improving safety and ergonomics, as well as improving the conservation of fish on board (isothermal containers with ice) and the handling cargo on board (cranes and gantries). The installation on board of new detection and navigation equipment, such as sonar and network probe, also contributed to this modernization process.

Seine gear dimensions vary depending on vessel size, reaching about 1000 m length onboard larger vessels (Parente, 2003). Fishing trips take place in the vicinity of the landing ports and they last 8 hours on average (from 3 to 15 hours, (Feijó, 2013). Fishing operations can take 1.5 to 2 hours, depending on fishing gears dimensions and the degree of the vessel modernization (Parente, 2000).

Landings of the European sardine (*Sardina pilchardus*), the traditional main target species, significantly decreased since 2008, as a result of decline in the stock status and subsequent restrictions to capture aiming at protecting this resource. In view of this situation, the Portuguese purse seine fleet started to direct its activity towards the capture of other small pelagics, namely the Atlantic chub mackerel (*Scomber colias*) and the European anchovy (*Engraulis encrasicolus*).

Mackerel has replaced sardine as the most captured species since 2012, while anchovy, although may not be regarded as a target species, is often captured when available (apparently strongly conditioned by climatic and oceanographic variations) due to its higher commercial value compared to the other species.

In this study, the importance of anchovy in the activity of the Portuguese coastal seine fleet is briefly analyzed over the recent years, based on landings and their economic value, as well as on the fishing effort and vessels characteristics for the fleet involved in the fishery.

2 METHODS

2.1 *Data sources*

The data analysed comprised: 1) historical landings from 2009 to 2019 for the coastal seine fleet segment, data compiled from the statistical series issued annually by the General Directorate of Natural Resources, Safety and Maritime Services

(DGRM), to the coastal fishing fleet operating in ICES zone IXa; 2) Landings for the vessels that recorded anchovy in 2016 at the scope of their operational activity, including total annual landings, annual landings of sardine, mackerel, European anchovy, horse mackerel and blue jack mackerel (*Trachurus picturatus*), both in weight (Kg) and in value (€); 3) for these vessels, the number of months in operation as well as the number of trips in 2016; and 4) their technical characteristics, including length overall LOA (m); GT gross tonnage (tM); engine power (kW); year of construction; and port of register.

2.2 Data analysis

The relative fishing power FP_{rel} and the catch per unit of standardized effort ($CPUE_{std}$), were estimated for each vessel in the anchovy fleet, with the objective to compare the productivity among the different vessels depending on their characteristic dimensions and their degree of modernization. These parameters were obtained through a factor analysis based on the Principal Component method for factor extraction (Ortega et al., 1992), using the method of the main components for the extraction of the factor weights (Carvalho, 2013). Each vessel was characterized according to five variables: one associated with age (year of construction), three dimensional variables (length overall, gross tonnage and engine power) and, finally, the degree of modernization. This latter index is associated with the number of supplementary equipment fitted, structural or mechanical, in addition to the existing purse seine winch and net hauler, which are considered the minimum equipment essential for the performance of seine fishing operations. The degree of modernization assigned to each vessel varies from 1 (absence of supplementary equipment) to a maximum of 8 (Table 1). For example, a vessel with a triplex and a purse seine winch, fitted with a net bobbin as a supplementary equipment, will be assigned a degree of modernization 2.

The higher the degree of modernization of the vessel, the greater will be, in theory, its efficiency on the performance of fishing operations.

Table 1. List of supplementary equipment in the deck layout of a coastal seiner, each scoring 1 point.

Supplementary equipment	Valuation points
Absence of suppl equipment	1
Supplementary net hauler	1
Board roller	1
Crane (serving the net parking)	1
Deck gantry	1
Net bobin	1
Fish isotermic containers	1
Net stowage (function)	1

Each main component (C_i) is a linear combination of the 5 vessel characteristic parameters (x_j):

$$C_i = \sum_{j=1}^{5} \beta_{i,j}(x_j - \bar{x}_j)/\sigma_j \quad (1)$$

where $\beta_{i,j}$ is the eigenvector of the j coordinate of the main component C_i, representing the contribution of each characteristic x_j (with mean $\bar{x}_j$ and standard deviation σ_j). When considering only the m Ci components that explain most of the total variability and as long as there is a strong correlation between them and the capture per unit of nominal effort ($CPUE_{nom}$), it will be possible to define the CPUE (kg/trip) as follows:

$$CPUE = a_0 + \sum_{i=1}^{m} a_i C_i \quad (2)$$

From equation 2 it is possible to obtain the relative fishing power for each vessel, having as reference the standard vessel for which all the main components are null, i.e, the one with average characteristics. Since the catch per standardized unit effort ($CPUE_{std}$) is equal to a_0, it is possible to calculate the relative fishing power (FP_{rel}) using the following expressions:

$$FP_{rel} = CPUE_{nom}/CPUE_{std} \quad (3)$$

Rearranging with equation 2,

$$FP_{rel} = 1 + \sum_{i=1}^{m} \frac{a_i C_i}{a0} \quad (4)$$

Multiplying FP_{rel} by the nominal fishing effort (FE_{nom}), expressed as the number of trips, it will be possible to estimate the standardized fishing effort FE_{std} for each vessel as:

$$FE_{std} = FP_{rel}.FE_{nom} \quad (5)$$

3 RESULTS

3.1 Historical evolution of the coastal seine fleet landings

Some fluctuations were registered in the annual landings of the coastal seine fleet, especially after 2013 (Figure1), as a result of the sharp decrease in sardine landings and the increase in mackerel landings. The unit sale price of the main landed species shows a significant increase for sardine, especially until

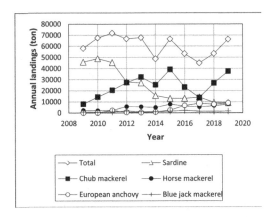

Figure 1. Total annual landings for the main species in the coastal seine fleet, from 2009 to 2019.

2015, stabilizing at around € 2/kg in subsequent years (Figure 2).

The anchovy price is historically higher than that of the sardine, but it has been decreasing since 2013, possibly due to significant increase in landings since that date, stabilizing sales prices in around 1.5 €/kg as of 2017 (Figure 2). A correlation is shown between the average annual sale price of anchovy and the quantity landed annually, from 2009 to 2019 (Figure 3). The

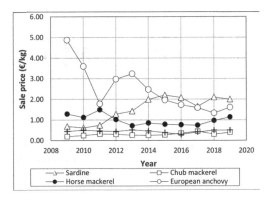

Figure 2. Sale price (€/kg) of the main species landed by the seine fleet in the period from 2009 to 2016.

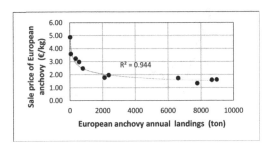

Figure 3. Relationship between the average annual sale price of anchovy and the amount landed (kg), from 2009 to 2019.

selling price stabilizes at 2000 ton, with values between 2 €/kg and 1.5 €/kg, slightly lower than those practiced for sardine.

Figure 4 shows the historical evolution, from 2009 to 2019, of the average annual sales for the seine fleet considering all species, as well as of pelagic species whose landings were more significant during this period. For sardine, the average annual sales decline significantly over the years, being offset by the increase in sales that each vessel made for landings of Atlantic chub mackerel, anchovy, horse mackerel and blue jack mackerel, in addition to other less important species.

The value of the total annual sale has undergone some fluctuations from 2009 to 2019, as a result of fluctuations in market prices for the most important species, corresponding to an annual average of € 306536 per vessel over this period.

3.2 *Characterization of the seine fleet for anchovy*

The coastal seine fleet with registers of anchovy landings in 2016, hereafter identified as 'anchovy fleet', consists of 54 vessels ranging from 9 to 27 meters in length, with an average value of 19.5 m and the median of 21.5 m. Figure 5 shows the relationship between length overall and engine power in this group of vessels, with correlation between these two variables ($R^2 = 0.84$).

Three groups of vessels are defined in this fleet, one more numerous, consisting of larger vessels with lengths between 21 and 27 m; a second group whose lengths vary between 9 and 14 m; and a third group, with only 4 vessels, with intermediate lengths between 17 and 19 m.

The fleet is mostly registered in northern ports (Figure 6), with anchovy being exploited in this region. Most of the fleet, in a total of 41 vessels, develop their activity between 6 to 7 months a year, with no correlation between their size and the number of months of operation.

The total landings for the group of vessels that make up the anchovy fleet varied, in 2016, between

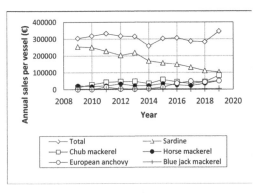

Figure 4. Total annual sales per vessel and for the main species landed, from 2009 to 2019.

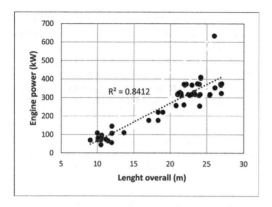

Figure 5. Relationship between overall length (m) and power (kW), for the anchovy fleet, in 2016.

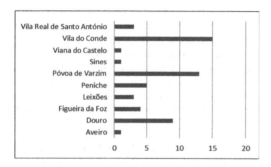

Figure 6. Number of vessels by port of register for the anchovy fleet in 2016.

78 and 720 tons per vessel (Figure7) while the anchovy landings per vessel (by weight) varied between a minimum of 32 and a maximum of 178 tons, with the average value of 104 tons per vessel, representing 73% of the corresponding value for sardines. This demonstrates the importance of anchovy for this group of vessels.

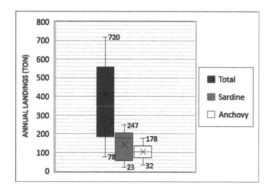

Figure 7. Annual landings (kg) (total, sardine and anchovy) related to coastal seine vessels with anchovy landings in 2016.

As expected, the average percentage of chub mackerel and horse mackerel in landings made in 2016 by the anchovy fleet, was less relevant (30%) in weight compared to that recorded for the universe of vessels that make up the entire coastal seine fleet (48%).

Figures 8, 9 and 10 relate, for each vessel, the percentage of anchovy in the 2016 landings with the vessel length (m), the annual landings (kg) and the number of trips in 2016, allowing to confirm the importance of this species in the structure of landings for this fleet.

Although correlation between the percentage of anchovy in the annual landing of vessels and its length is weak, it is possible to observe that there is a trend for smaller vessels to present a higher percentage of this species in their landings (Figure 8). On the other hand, the percentage of anchovy landed by vessels in this fleet in 2016 is inversely related to the landings volume (Figure 9).

Despite the weak correlation, results in Figure 10 suggest that the percentage of anchovy decreases with the increase in the annual number of trips for each vessel (2016).

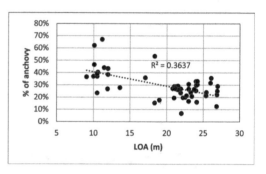

Figure 8. Relationship between the percentage of anchovy (in relation to the annual landing) and length overall (m) (2016).

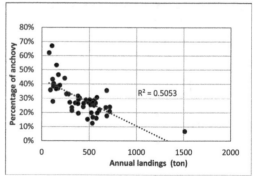

Figure 9. Relationship between the percentage of anchovy (in relation to the annual landings) and the annual landings, for each vessel (2016).

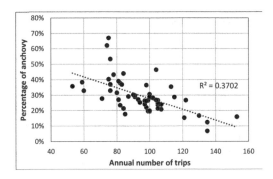

Figure 10. Relationship between the percentage of anchovy (in relation to the annual landing) and the number of trips made annually by each vessel (2016).

3.3 Relative fishing power and standardized CPUE for seine vessels that landed anchovy in 2016

Table 2 shows the values of the correlation coefficients, the mean and the standard deviation, of the parameters selected for the factor analysis, namely the year of construction (YEAR), length overall (LOA), gross tonnage (GT), engine power (kW) and modernization degree (GMOD), for the vessels in the anchovy fleet operating in the north of the Portuguese coast.

Strong correlation was found between all parameters, with the exception of the year of construction.

By applying a factor analysis to the correlation matrix (Table 2), the values of the characteristic parameters of the vessels ("Eingenvalues") are obtained, indicating the percentage of variance associated with each component (Table 3).

Table 3 shows that the percentage of variance for the first component is 71.52% of the total variance, while the first two components account for 94.13%.

The eigenvectors (Table 4) show that all characteristic parameters, except the year of construction, have an individual importance in explaining the first component. A second component is mainly explained by the year of construction.

The values of C1 and C2 were determined for each vessel, based on their characteristic parameters, on the coordinates of the eigenvectors of each main component and also on the values of the mean and standard deviation of each of the parameters. However, when a multiple regression is performed between the CPUE variable (dependent variable) and the two components C1 and C2, for the vessels under study, it was found that only the C1 component is significantly correlated with CPUE (kg/trip) (Table 5), being the only component to be considered in linear regression with the variable CPUE, resulting in the following equation:

$$CPUE_{nom} = 1099.254 - 59.052 \times C_1 \quad (6)$$

Dividing both members of the equation by the $CPUE_0$ of the standard vessel for which all the main components are null ($CPUE_0 = 1099.254$),

Table 2. Matrix of the correlation coefficients, mean and standard deviation of the selected parameters for the factor analysis (continental coast).

	Mean	Std. dev.	YEAR	LOA	GT	kW	GMOD
		Correlations (in bold, significant correlation for p<0.05 N=54					
ANO	1992.94	12..89	1.00	-0.23	-0.04	-0.08	0.25
LOA	19.55	5.80	-0.23	1.00	**0.94**	**0.92**	**0.80**
GT	52.89	30.82	-0.04	**0.94**	1.00	**0.91**	**0.81**
kW	260.48	128.23	-0.08	**0.92**	**0.91**	1.00	**0.76**
GMOD	6.82	1.63	0.25	**0.80**	**0.81**	**0.76**	1.00

Table 3. Extraction of Eigenvalues: (anchovy fleet).

		Eigenvalues		
Value	Eigenvalue	% Variance	Cumulative Eigenvalue	Cumulative %
1	3.576077	71.52155	3.576077	71.5215
2	1.130510	22.61021	4.706588	94.1318
3	0.180495	3.60990	4.887083	97.7417
4	0.084058	1.68117	4.971141	99.4228
5	0.028859	0.57718	5.000000	100.0000

Table 4. Extraction of "Eigenvectors" using the principal components method (anchovy fleet).

Variable	Eigenvectors Extraction: Principal components				
	Factor 1	Factor 2	Factor 3	Factor 4	Factor 5
YEAR	0.047164	**-0.991185**	-0.115877	0.020846	0.038283
LOA	**-0.971635**	0.183625	0.033687	0.036506	0.140501
GT	**-0.970525**	0.011824	-0.098931	0.208197	-0.069337
kW	**-0.951921**	0.060258	-0.234597	-0.185209	-0.029620
GMOD	**-0.884142**	-0.332526	0.317977	-0.068138	-0.044360

Table 5. Summary of the linear regression between the independent variable CPUE and the dependent variables C1 and C2 (anchovy fleet).

Dependent variable: CPUE					
R=.56253132 R²= .31644149 R² adjusted= .28963527 p<0.00006					
N=54	Beta	Std.Err.of Beta	B	Std. Err.of B	Valor-p
Intercept			1099.254	43.44282	**0.000000**
C1	**-0.557535**	0.115772	-59.052	12.26219	**0.000014**
C2	0.074811	0.115772	25.065	38.78846	0.521050

corresponding to the vessel with average characteristics), it is possible to obtain the equation of relative fishing power (FP$_{rel}$) and standardized fishing effort (FE$_{std}$):

$$FP_{rel} = 1 - (59.052/1099.254) \times C_1 \quad (7)$$

$$FE_{std} = FP_{rel} \times FE_{nom} \quad (8)$$

$$FE_{std} = (1 - 0.054 \times C1) \times FE_{nom} \quad (9)$$

Figures 11 and 12 show how the nominal fishing effort FE$_{nom}$ and standard fishing effort vary depending on the length, considering all vessels in the anchovy fleet in 2016, showing a correlation (R^2=0.51) when the dependent variable of FE is standardized. No

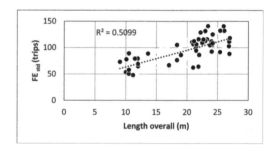

Figure 12. Relationship between standardized fishing effort FE$_{std}$(trips) and length overall (m) for vessels in the anchovy fleet in 2016.

correlation was found, as expected, between nominal fishing effort FE$_{nom}$ and length overall (Figure11).

4 CONCLUSIONS

Landings of anchovy on the Portuguese continental coast, resulting from the activity of the seine fleet, have been registering steady increases, especially since 2015, due, on the one hand, to restrictions on sardine fishing and on the other, to the increase in the quota allocated to Portugal.

The analysis of vessels dimensions and of anchovy landings in 2016 does not allow us to consistently state that there is a well-defined group of vessels that direct their activity to anchovy fishing, to the detriment of other pelagic species. In fact, there is no sub-segment in the seine fleet especially directed at anchovy fishing (i.e. a *métier*), but rather

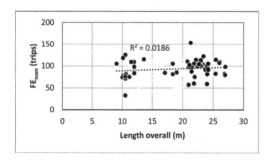

Figure 11. Relationship between nominal fishing effort FE$_{nom}$(trips) and length overall (m) for vessels in the anchovy fleet in 2016.

a significant number of vessels for which this species has progressively gained a prominent place in the landings structure.

It is possible to observe that most of vessels engaged in this fishery are registered and operate in the northern region. Two main vessels groups were defined differing in their lengths, one consisting of larger vessels between 21 and 27 m and a second group whose lengths vary between 9 and 14 m. The percentage of anchovy on landings tends to be higher in smaller vessels.

No correlation was found between nominal fishing effort and vessel length, but a correlation was demonstrated when the fishing effort was standardized, demonstrating the importance of the estimaton of the relative fishing power (FPrel) and standardized fishing effort (FEstd) to compare vessels productivity.

This study only included data from 2016. It will be necessary to investigate how the availability for fishing of other target species, such as sardines and mackerel, and the respective first sale prices will evolve in the future, in order to come to more consistent results on the relative importance and continuity of anchovy landings for this fleet.

ACKNOWLEDGEMENTS

This study was carried out at the scope of the project TECPESCAS – Project Mar 2020 16-01-04-FMP-0010 – IPMA. The fisheries data was supplied to IPMA by the Portuguese Directorate-General for Natural Resources, Safety and Maritime Services (DGRM).

REFERENCES

Carvalho, F., 2013 Factorial Analysis. (in Portuguese). Dissertation for the obtention of MSc. Degree in Mathematics, specialization in Statistics, Optimization and Mathematics. University of Coimbra.

Feijó, D., 2013. Characterization of the seine fishing in the Portuguese coast (in Portuguese). Faculty of Sciences, University of Porto, 93 p. (MSc. thesis). DOI: 10.13140/RG.2.1.3102.4241.

Ortega-Garcia, S., Gómez-Muñoz, V., 1992. Standardization of fishing effort using principal component analysis of vessel characteristics: the Mexican tuna purse-seiners. Sci. Mar. 56(1): 17–20.

Parente, J., 2000. Coastal seine fleet. Analysis of the dimensions and some exploration parameters, from a global and regional perspective (in Portuguese). Relat. Cient. e Téc. Inst. Invest. Pescas Mar, nº62, 48 p.

Parente, J., 2003. Characterization of the coastal seine fleet and prospects for modernization (in Portuguese). Dissertation presented to access the category of Research Assistant,at the Fisheries and Sea Research Institute (IPIMAR), 216 p.

Parente, J., 2020. Coastal seine fleet - historical evolution, analysis of dimensional parameters and identification of vessel types (in Portuguese). Project Sardinha 2020, WP6 - Fishing and production activity. Portuguese Institute of Sea and Atmosphere, 68 p.

Reducing uncertainties in Baltic herring and sprat abundance estimates: Alternative approach to acoustic analyses

E. Sepp, T. Raid, L. Saks, K. Hommik & T. Arula
Estonian Marine Institute, University of Tartu, Tallinn, Estonia

O. Kaljuste
Department of Aquatic Resources, Swedish University of Agricultural Sciences, Öregrund, Sweden

ABSTRACT: Hydroacoustic studies using acoustic measurements combined with biological data obtained from trawl hauls remain a challenging task. The main purpose of the present study is to identify sources of uncertainty and compare the calculation methods for a mixed pelagic fish community of Baltic Sea. Most of the calculation methodologies use conventional statistical borders to split the study area, ignoring the possible natural population distribution areas. We compared the proposed "nearest haul" and the "subdivision average" with the conventional "rectangle average" on the Estonian regular acoustic surveys in the northeast Baltic Sea. The abundance estimates of the target species – European sprat Sprattus sprattus (Linnaeus 1758) and Baltic herring Clupea harengus membras (Linnaeus 1758) – with the "nearest haul" were significantly different from the currently used method, which indicates a strong effect of the allocation method. Our results indicate a need for a large scale comparative study to consider alternative calculation methodologies.

1 INTRODUCTION

Two main commercial pelagic fish species in the Baltic Sea are European sprat Sprattus sprattus (Linnaeus 1758) and Baltic herring Clupea harengus membras (Linnaeus 1758), whose spatiotemporal distribution co-occur in the pre-wintering feeding grounds (Parmanne et al., 1994). Herring and sprat stock assessment in the Baltic Sea is the responsibility of countries sharing their management and is performed under the guidance of the International Council for the Exploration of the Sea (ICES) (ICES, 2017b). Most important fisheries independent input into their stock assessment in the Baltic Sea is data from regular acoustic-trawl surveys (ICES, 2014). Because of extensive coverage, hydroacoustics data combined with trawl hauls has proven to be the most cost-effective survey type to estimate pelagic fish population abundance (Simmonds & MacLennan, 2005).

Acoustic surveys (AS) of fish abundance and distribution, combined with trawl data to receive more accurate estimates of species composition and biological information, have been applied in marine and freshwater ecosystems routinely already for decades (Godø et al., 1998; Orłowski, 1999; Simmonds, 2003; Simmonds & MacLennan 2005 Jurvelius et al., 2005; Rudstam et al., 2009). AS results depend on how to allocate backscattered energy into fish species data (Simmonds & MacLennan, 2005). Analysis of AS echogram together with targeted trawl hauls are used to link echo traces to species (Nakken & Dommasnes, 1975; Simmonds & MacLennan, 2005). In mixed-species fishery, where sprat and herring schools cannot be distinguished by echogram, interpretation of species composition relies on trawl haul data (Orłowski, 1999; Páramo & Roa, 2003; Simmonds & MacLennan, 2008; ICES, 2014). Effectiveness and accuracy of such identification depend on the number and location of trawls (Massé & Retière, 1995). Survey acoustic track and fish trawling plan is ascertained before the survey and modified during the survey (Oeberst, 2011; ICES, 2014). In the Baltic Sea, the AS are conducted every year, i.e. in May (not analysed in this paper) and from September to October, principally by nine countries, each covering their economic zone, and the results obtained are combined in order to achieve numerical abundance estimates that are used as fisheries independent input in the sprat and herring stock assessment models (ICES, 2017a).

The Baltic Sea AS have been conducted according to standardized procedures since 1998 (ICES, 2014). The Baltic Fish Committee of the ICES decided to apply the Manual of International Baltic Acoustic Surveys (IBAS) to the Baltic International Acoustic Surveys (BIAS) in September 1997 (ICES, 2014). This manual states, amongst others, the exact methodology of species identification and allocation of trawl hauls. "Trawl catches within each ICES rectangle are

DOI: 10.1201/9781003216599-77

combined to give an average species composition of the catch. Each catch is given equal weight unless it is decided that a trawl catch is not representative to reflect the fish concentrations. In this case, the particular trawl catch is not used" (ICES, 2014). The Manual for International Pelagic Surveys (IPS) also states that acoustic values should be averaged to ICES statistical squares and later compiled with biological data (ICES, 2015). This gives a good framework in order to avoid differences in calculation methods from different countries. Nevertheless, survey data averaging can reduce the accuracy of results, affecting the credibility of outcome in estimated fish stocks abundance (Simmonds & MacLennan, 2005).

To get representative abundance estimates in the observed ICES rectangle, trawl hauls should reflect the average characteristics of fish aggregations in the given rectangle. This is a complicated task as rough weather conditions, marine traffic or dangerous areas for working at sea may force to modify the initial survey plan. In addition, observed fish concentrations may change the trawling locations, since according to manual, fish samples should be taken from areas with high acoustic values (Simmonds & MacLennan, 2005; Yule et al., 2013). Due to the heterogeneous distribution of fish, peaks of acoustic values can occur in border areas of ICES rectangles where the interpretation of results can produce bias due to the different resolutions of the data. Fish control-haul made in such area contribute into one rectangle (according to the IBAS manual) and therefore does not explain the acoustic values observed in close vicinity at the neighboring ICES rectangle. All the aforementioned factors imply to survey realization being unsuitable for the current methodology of calculations using averaging and therefore may produce biased abundance estimates.

In this study fish species abundance estimates by applying two alternative haul allocation methods: "Nearest haul" and "Subdivision average" are compared with the conventional ICES methodology. The hypothesis is that due to the strong spatial demarcations in calculations, the current methodology used by the ICES Baltic International Fish Survey Working Group (WGBIFS) provides biased abundance estimations of Baltic sprat and herring.

2 MATERIAL AND METHODS

2.1 Study area and data collection

The material was collected during the annual Estonian part of BIAS survey realised on board of the RV "Baltica" in October 2013 – 2016, in the ICES Subdivisions 28, 29 and 32 (Figure 1.). All data were collected in accordance with the Manual of International Baltic Acoustic Surveys (ICES IBAS) for BIAS with coverage of minimum 60 nautical miles and at least two trawling stations for each stratification unit (rectangle of 30' N x 1° E) (ICES, 2014).

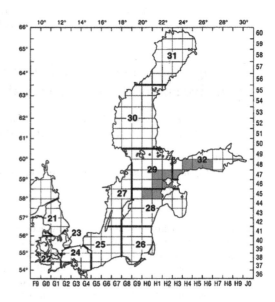

Figure 1. Map with the ICES statistical subdivisions and rectangles in the Baltic Sea. Blue rectangles denote data collection area during the Baltic International Acoustic Survey.

2.2 Acoustic-trawl combination methodologies

All calculations from NASC (m2/nmi2) (nautical area scattering coefficient (Simmonds & MacLennan, 2005)) values to fish abundances were carried out according to the same procedure as described in detail in ICES IBAS manual (ICES, 2014). Acoustic data were collected during day time with the Simrad EK60 echosounder equipped with 38kHz transducer and analyzed with "Echoview v4.3" software. Fish numbers were estimated using the standard target strength-length (TS-L) regressions for clupeids (TS = 20logL-71.2) and gadoids (TS = 20logL-67.5) for Baltic Sea (ICES, 2014). Total fish densities (nr/nmi2) were obtained using the mean cross section of fish (σ) as the weighted mean of all species related cross sections (described in detail in IBAS manual) (ICES, 2014). The same procedure was followed for all methods tested.

2.2.1 Rectangle average method (IBAS)

We used the abundance estimations for total pelagic fish and for sprat and herring separately, calculated according to the ICES IBAS methodology. All acoustic and fish biological samples are first allocated to an ICES statistical rectangle according to their location. Average nautical area scattering coefficient (NASC) is calculated for the whole rectangle and combined with an average trawl result. All trawl haul metrics (σ, length and weight frequency) in one ICES rectangle are averaged with each catch given equal weight. All fish abundance calculations are made based on that allocation and results are obtained with the resolution of ICES rectangle (ICES, 2014).

2.2.2 Nearest haul method

The second allocation method analysed was the nearest haul method (NHM). The allocation process here depends solely on the proximity of sampling units. Firstly, the nearest trawl haul for each acoustic elementary sampling unit (ESDU) (one nautical mile in our case) were calculated irrespective of the echo traces and ICES rectangles, using geographical coordinates (Petitgas et al., 2003; Yule et al., 2009). Then all the fish abundances for each ESDU were calculated separately. Finally, the abundances were allocated to ICES rectangles (average value of ESDU abundance multiplied by ICES rectangle area) for comparison with other tested methods. The purpose of which is to give results that are more accurate when trawl hauls are not perfectly distributed inside the ICES rectangle and specific fish concentrations are found across the borders of rectangles. This method is suggested only if the trawl samples are good representatives of the underlying fish assemblages (Sète, 2005), which in this study is not restrictive, since the IBAS manual states that, if it is decided that the trawl catch is not representative for the fish concentrations sampled, the particular trawl catch is not used (ICES, 2014).

2.2.3 Subdivision- average method

The third method is similar to the current IBAS manual, but instead of averaging trawl catches and NASC values to ICES rectangles prior to combination, we averaged by ICES subdivisions (SDM). With averaging to larger scale, the local differences in fish aggregation properties should not be so effective, but larger number of data points in one unit makes it more suitable for further statistical analysis with lower coefficient of variance (Godø et al., 1998). All trawl results were averaged to the scale of ICES subdivisions (SD) with on the average of 4.5 hauls in SD 28, 6.25 hauls in SD 29 and 8.5 hauls in SD 32 (the Estonian BIAS surveys in 2013-2016). The calculations do not comprise the whole ICES subdivisions, as the Estonian survey covers the ICES subdivisions only partially (Figure 1.).

2.3 Statistical treatments

Since the fish abundance values are strongly influenced by the annual fluctuations of their abundances, relative scale (percentages) for statistical analysis to remove year- effects were used. Percentages were calculated by comparing the new estimates with abundances obtained with the IBAS method, therefore the relative difference quantifies only the effect of the method. In addition, different spatial resolution for comparisons of results was used to keep the highest possible qualities of data.

When comparing results from SDM with IBAS method, all values to ICES subdivisions and results from the NHM method were summarized and compared with the results of the IBAS method on ICES rectangle level. For confidence interval estimates, the average abundances were calculated using NASC of each applied nautical mile in combination with the method specific sigma (σ) and fish species composition percentages. Variation from NASC is therefore constant for all tested methods and differences in confidence intervals are solely from the usage of haul averaging methods.

If the effects of the new methods on results are similar for all species, then the relative changes in fish abundances could be considered as a random sample from some continuous distribution, which is identical for all species. Thus, herring and sprat relative abundances were compared using two-sample Kolmogorov-Smirnov test. Statistically significant differences ($p<0.05$) would therefore mean that the distribution is not identical for all species and the new method has a significant effect on species estimates. Statistical analyses was conducted using R software (R Core Team, 2017).

For evaluating the performance of the proposed methods the comparison of internal consistency of the cohorts was used (as used in ICES 2017b). The abundance numbers of herring and sprat at age were plotted against numbers at age+1 of the same cohort in the following year. Higher value of correlation coefficient within cohorts should indicate a better performance of the method. Numbers-at-age of subdivisions instead of total survey area were used to increase the number of data points.

3 RESULTS

3.1 Fish abundance

There was no consistent pattern in the differences of total fish abundances between the applied IBAS, NHM and SDM methods (Figure 2). None of the methods displayed a tendency to systematically over- or underestimate the total abundances of fish. Mostly, highest values were observed by NHM (7 cases from total 12), although differences in fish abundance estimates were marginal. Generally, in 2013-2016, the highest fish concentrations were found in inspected parts of the ICES SD 32 and the lowest in ICES SD 28.2.

Herring abundance estimates by the NHM method tended to differ from the IBAS and SDM estimates, which were more similar to each other (Figure 3A). Contrary to herring, sprat estimates showed highest abundances by the NHM method compared that to the IBAS or SDM methods (9 out of 12 cases, Figure 3B).

3.2 Comparing results from SDM and NHM methods with IBAS method

Herring and sprat abundance estimates were lower when using the SDM method compared with the IBAS method (Figure 4). The differences in 2016 were close to 50% in ICES SD 28.2 and on average the SDM estimation was 8.8% lower. Sprat and herring relative abundances were not different (Kolmogorov-Smirnov two-sample test D = 0.33, p = 0.54, n = 12).

Sprat abundance estimates according to the NHM method were on average 25% higher and herring

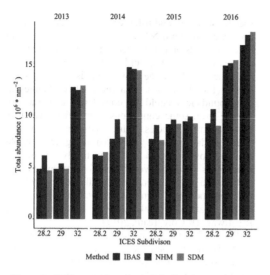

Figure 2. Differences in pelagic fish abundances obtained by the NHM, IBAS and SDM methods in 2013-2016.

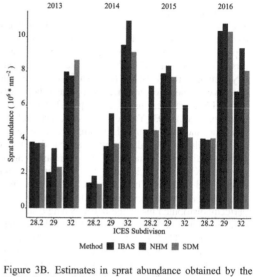

Figure 3B. Estimates in sprat abundance obtained by the NHM, IBAS and SDM methods in 2013-2016.

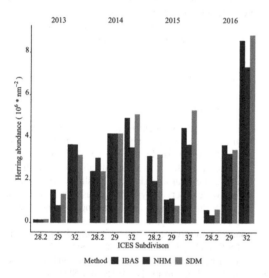

Figure 3A. Estimates in herring abundance obtained by the NHM, IBAS and SDM methods in 2013-2016.

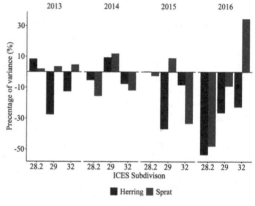

Figure 4. Differences of herring and sprat abundances while SDM method was applied compared to IBAS methodology in 2013-2016 accordingly to the ICES Subdivisions 28, 29 and 32.

estimations 17% lower when compared to the IBAS method, with the exception of the ICES SD 28.2 in 2014. Sprat and herring relative abundances were different in NHM vs. IBAS comparison on statistically significant level (Kolmogorov-Smirnov two-sample test D = 0.38, p = 0.007, n = 40, Figure 5).

3.3 Internal consistency

Analysis resulted with good correlations of ages 1vs2 of both sprat and herring ($r2=0.63$ to $r2=0.89$). Correlations of older age groups were considerably lower. Comparison of methods based on internal consistency did not show a clear pattern. Average correlation coefficients (ages 1 to 5) of methods were $r2=0.26$ to $r2=0.30$ for herring (NEAR method having the highest value) and $r2=0.20$ to $r2=0.30$ for sprat (SD method having the highest value).

4 DISCUSSION

The inconsistency in spatial definition of the local populations and high mobility of pelagic fish has prevented the reasonable stratification of acoustic surveys of pelagic stocks in the Baltic Sea. High-resolution

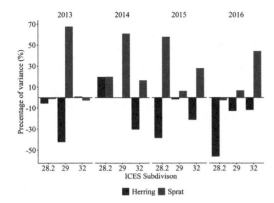

Figure 5. Differences of herring and sprat abundances while NHM method was applied compared to IBAS methodology in 2013-2016 accordingly to the ICES Subdivisions 28, 29 and 32.

abundance estimates are therefore still based on ICES statistical areas instead of natural population borders. Comparison of three different approaches to analysing the acoustic results presented in this study show notable effects of haul allocation methods on the obtained northeast Baltic Sea fish abundance estimates. The species composition obtained by the most straightforward NHM method estimated the sprat share to be significantly higher than that of current methodology (IBAS) used by WGBIFS.

The results of conventional acoustic surveys in the Baltic Sea depend on the number and locations of the trawl hauls and distribution of fish assemblages. The reliance of the accuracy of the fish stocks abundance estimates on trawling locations is expected to be highest in the NHM method and lowest in the SDM approach since the first-mentioned is based on defining the region close to every single haul and the second uses averaging over a large area (ICES Subdivision). Averaging of the trawl results could smooth the possible bias resulting from the incorrect choice of trawling locations (Simmonds & MacLennan, 2005). In the current study, total abundances obtained by all methods did not result in discrepancy. In a similar haul allocation study, comparing four different allocation methods, Petitgas et al. (2003) also found minimal differences in terms of the abundance estimates. The results of this study show that the two methods that used averaging of haul results (IBAS, SDM) did not give statistically different fish species composition results. The significant difference was observed between NHM and IBAS approaches, suggesting that the effect of smoothing induced by averaging in current conditions is producing significantly different results from the most straightforward NHM method in terms of species composition. It is suggested that averaging should be used in cases when individual trawl haul results are not highly representative of the underlying fish assemblages (Sète, 2005).

Many similar fish population assessment studies use some degree of averaging (Petitgas et al., 2003; Sète, 2005) due to the possibility that single hauls may not adequately represent the underlying fish assemblages. According to the IBAS manual, unrepresentative trawl catches are to be excluded from the analysis (ICES, 2014) and therefore all the hauls used are assumed to be representative. Gimona and Fernandes (2003) indicate that the incorrect choice of area for averaging could smooth out important small-scale information. However, these potential losses are not important from the population size estimation process, where sprat and herring are assessed on a very large scale (e.g. Baltic sprat is managed as one unit) (ICES, 2017b), and the higher resolution is needed for more specific studies. Based on the results, the absence of averaging produces significantly different abundance estimates, which are theoretically not biased, but should be further tested on larger datasets. For small-scale distribution studies, the highest possible resolution of results should be preserved, which is only possible with reduced amount of averaging included in the analysis. In the current setup of the Baltic Sea acoustic survey (BIAS), the possible areas used for averaging are purely statistical and do not rely on any habitat or local population distribution areas (ICES, 2014) and therefore, have no ecologically valid origin.

Adding a weighing factor on averaging of trawl-catches results would limit the smoothing effect (Simmonds & MacLennan, 2008). Results of spatial averaging are highly affected by the choice of area averaged on (Woillez et al., 2009). For high accuracy results, this choice should not be made without prior knowledge of any preliminary results, so the choice would be best made, based on characteristics of fish assemblages observed in acoustic or haul data. Therefore, the usage of strict statistical borders together with averaging is not the most suitable solution. Averaging should be based on the similarity of fish assemblages observed. Based on the results of the present study it can be suggested that some characteristics of acoustic signals are more related to the presence of single species community, which should be taken into account before the process of combining the acoustic and haul data. The choice of trawling location also has a strong impact on the outcome since trawl haul should be located as to represent the whole water column being observed by acoustic equipment. This factor is usually dealt with by choosing the trawling depth layer with the strongest acoustic signals recorded by the acoustic equipment or trawling in several layers during one haul.

Use of geostatistical methods could preserve the spatial resolution of results, while taking into account the multiple variables affecting the fish assemblages observed (Petitgas et al. 2017). Several geostatistical approaches have been proposed for combining acoustic and haul data obtained by similar ICES manual for North Sea herring (Maravelias et al., 1996; Gimona &

Fernandes, 2003; Woillez et al., 2009). Their concern is mainly related to the fish length distribution variations and a high number of zero values in datasets, since herring stock in the North Sea is composed of dense schools of single species. The mixed herring-sprat schools observed in the Baltic Sea are scattered in multiple layers with virtually no zero values, but species are indistinguishable on echograms. It is suggested (Woillez et al., 2009; Yule et al., 2013) that the usage of geostatistical approaches and automated procedures (e.g. conditional simulation, classification trees, kriging) should be considered after mapping the possible biases in current standard procedures. Possible biases mapped in our study serve as valuable inputs for future works related to the use of geostatistical methods in the Baltic Sea AS.

The present study suggest that current standard procedures used by WGBIFS for allocating trawl catch-station data to acoustic values in the Baltic Sea pelagic fish surveys should be reviewed in order to enhance the accuracy of the results. Without the knowledge of the actual fish population structure, it is difficult to argue whether smoothing should be included in the calculation process or not. Since theoretically, all used hauls are representative, there is no need to use averaging. Our results, based on only a small area of the Baltic Sea, indicate a strong difference in species composition when using different haul allocation methods. Unfortunately, due to small dataset, we cannot make a conclusion in choosing the best method. Results of the study at hand indicate that analysis combining data across the Baltic Sea need to be conducted to control whether the current findings are applicable. Current study is among the first practices in mapping the possible biases in the process of improving the quality of the Baltic Sea acoustic surveys. Based on these results, a discussion should be started for improving the calculation methodology together with preserving the ability to compare with historical time series data.

ACKNOWLEDGEMENTS

The study was partly supported by the European Maritime and Fisheries Fund (EMFF) through European Data Collection Framework.

REFERENCES

Gimona, A., & Fernandes, P. G. (2003). A conditional simulation of acoustic survey data: advantages and potential pitfalls. Aquatic Living Resources, 16(3), 123–129.

Godø, O. R., Karp, W. A., & Totland, A. (1998). Effects of trawl sampling variability on precision of acoustic abundance estimates of gadoids from the Barents Sea and the Gulf of Alaska. ICES Journal of Marine Science, 55(1), 86–94.

Berdahl, A., Westley, P.A.H., Levin, S.A., Couzin, I.D. & Quinn, T.P. (in press.) A collective navigation hypothesis for homeward migration in anadromous salmonids. Fish and Fisheries.

ICES. (2011). Final Report of the Baltic International Fish Survey Working Group. WGBIFS Report 2011 (No. ICES CM 2017/SSGESST:05) (p. 540). Kaliningrad, Russia.

ICES. (2012). Final Report of the Baltic International Fish Survey Working Group. WGBIFS Report 2012 (No. ICES CM 2012/SSGESST:02) (p. 531). Helsinki, Finland.

ICES. (2014). Manual of International Baltic Acoustic Surveys (IBAS) (Series of ICES Survey Protocols SISP 8 - IBAS) (p. 24). ICES.

ICES. (2015). Manual for International Pelagic Surveys (IPS) (Series of ICES Survey Protocols SISP 9 – IPS) (p. 92).

ICES. (2017a). Final Report of the Baltic International Fish Survey Working Group. WGBIFS Report 2017 (No. ICES CM 2017/SSGIEOM:07) (p. 684). Riga, Latvia.

ICES. (2017b). Report of the Baltic Fisheries Assessment Working Group (WGBFAS): 19-26 April 2017, Copenhagen, Denmark. International Council for the Exploration of the Sea.

Jurvelius, J., Auvinen, H., Kolari, I., & Marjomäki, T. J. (2005). Density and biomass of smelt (Osmerus eperlanus) in five Finnish lakes. Fisheries Research, 73(3), 353–361.

Maravelias, C. D., Reid, D. G., Simmonds, E. J., & Haralabous, J. (1996). Spatial analysis and mapping of acoustic survey data in the presence of high local variability: geostatistical application to North Sea herring (Clupea harengus). Canadian Journal of Fisheries and Aquatic Sciences, 53(7), 1497–1505.

Massé, J., & Retière, N. (1995). Effect of number of transects and identification hauls on acoustic biomass estimates under mixed species conditions. Aquatic Living Resources, 8(2), 195–199.

Nakken, O. & Dommasnes, A. (1975). The application of an echo integration system in investigations on the stock strength of the Barents Sea capelin (Mallotus villosus, Müller) 1971-1974. ICES.

Oeberst, R. (2011). Species composition in scattered layers during acoustic surveys estimated by means of trawling stations. (Working document). Report of the Baltic International Fish Survey Working Group (WGBIFS) ICES CM 2011, 386–395.

Orlowski, A. (1999). Acoustic studies of spatial gradients in the Baltic: Implications for fish distribution. ICES Journal of Marine Science, 56(4), 561–570.

Páramo, J. & Roa, R. (2003). Acoustic-geostatistical assessment and habitat–abundance relations of small pelagic fish from the Colombian Caribbean. Fisheries Research, 60(2), 309–319.

Parmanne, R., Rechlin, O., & Sjöstrand, B. (1994). Status and future of herring and sprat stocks in the Baltic Sea. Dana, 10(1994), 29–59.

Petitgas, P., Massé, J., Beillois, P., Lebarbier, E., & Le Cann, A. (2003). Sampling variance of species identification in fisheries acoustic surveys based on automated procedures associating acoustic images and trawl hauls. ICES Journal of Marine Science: Journal Du Conseil, 60(3), 437–445.

Petitgas, P., Woillez, M., Rivoirard, J., Renard, D., and Bez, N. (2017). Handbook of geostatistics in R for fisheries and marine ecology. ICES Cooperative Research Report No. 338. 177 pp.

R Core Team. (2017). A language and environment for statistical computing. R Foundation for Statistical Computing, Vienna, Austria. Retrieved from http://www.R-project.org/

Rudstam, L. G., Parker-Stetter, S. L., Sullivan, P. J., & Warner, D. M. (2009). Towards a standard operating procedure for fishery acoustic surveys in the Laurentian Great Lakes, North America. ICES Journal of Marine Science, 66(6), 1391–1397.

Sète, F. (2005). Report of the Workshop on Survey Design and Data Analysis (WKSAD).

Simmonds, E. (2003). Weighting of acoustic- and trawl-survey indices for the assessment of North Sea herring. ICES Journal of Marine Science, 60(3), 463–471.

Simmonds, J., & MacLennan, D. N. (2008). Fisheries acoustics: theory and practice. John Wiley & Sons.

Woillez, M., Rivoirard, J., & Fernandes, P. G. (2009). Evaluating the uncertainty of abundance estimates from acoustic surveys using geostatistical simulations. ICES Journal of Marine Science, 66(6), 1377–1383.

Yule, D. L., Stockwell, J. D., Schreiner, D. R., Evrard, L. M., Balge, M., & Hrabik, T. R. (2009). Can pelagic forage fish and spawning cisco (Coregonus artedi) biomass in the western arm of Lake Superior be assessed with a single summer survey? Fisheries Research, 96(1),39–50.

Yule, D. L., Adams, J. V., Warner, D. M., Hrabik, T. R., Kocovsky, P. M., Weidel, B. C., Sullivan, P. J. (2013). Evaluating analytical approaches for estimating pelagic fish biomass using simulated fish communities. Canadian Journal of Fisheries and Aquatic Sciences, 70(12), 1845–1857.

On UAV-assisted data acquisition for underwater IoT in aquaculture surveillance

Qubeijian Wang & Hong-Ning Dai
Faculty of Information Technology, Macau University of Science and Technology, Macau SAR, China

Qiu Wang
School of Computer Science & Technology, China University of Mining and Technology, Xuzhou, Jiangsu, China
Department of Electrical and Computer Engineering University of Saskatchewan, Canada

Mahendra K. Shukla
Department of Electrical and Computer Engineering University of Saskatchewan, Canada

ABSTRACT: Underwater exploration activities have grown significantly due to the proliferation of underwater Internet of Things (UIoT). Recently, UIoT can potentially be used in fishing and aquaculture for environment surveillance such as water quality and temperature monitoring. UIoT nodes are distributed in the aquaculture region to collect sensor data. However, to transmit sensor data from UIoT to remote onshore data processing center requires huge cost of deploying and maintaining communication infrastructures. In this paper, we propose an Unmanned Aerial Vehicles (UAVs)-assisted underwater data acquisition scheme by placing multiple sink nodes on the water surface to serve as intermediate relays between underwater sensors and UAVs. Since the path connectivity from an underwater sensor node to the UAV is crucial to guarantee reliable data acquisition tasks, we establish a theoretical framework to analyze the path connectivity via the intermediate sink node. Extensive simulation results validate the accuracy of the proposed analytical model.

1 INTRODUCTION

With the proliferation of various marine activities, Underwater Internet of Things (UIoT) has attracted much attention since UIoT can be widely deployed in various underwater environments (such as fresh-water and marine ecosystems) (Yildiz et al. 2019). As a promising technic in aquaculture, surveillance provides useful data including temperature, salinity, turbidity, etc. After collecting such data, the corresponding measures will be given, so that to increase the yield of aquaculture. It is worth mentioning that UIoT can potentially be used in aquaculture surveillance (Cai et al. 2019). When UIoT is used in aquaculture surveillance, it typically consists of numerous sensor nodes and sink nodes (mainly used for data gathering). Underwater sensor nodes transmit sensor data to sink nodes which are typically deployed on the water surface. Thereafter, sink nodes transmit the collected data to offshore equipments (like ships and boats). Due to the computing and energy limitations of offshore equipments, computational-intensive data processing tasks have to be conducted at remote data processing centers, which are typically deployed far from UIoT. However, it is not cost-effective to establish and maintain the infrastructure to connect UIoT and onshore data centers especially considering remote ocean aquaculture surveillance tasks.

1.1 Motivation

UAV-assisted data acquisition is a promising technology to establish a communication bridge between onshore data processing centers and UIoT. Figure 1 shows an example of UAV-assisted data acquisition schemes, in which sensor nodes are distributed in the underwater environment and sink nodes (also named buoys) are deployed on the water surface. Electromagnetic (EM) signals have extremely higher attenuation in the underwater environment than in the air. Thus, acoustic signals are typically used to establish communication links in the underwater environment (see red dash lines in Figure 1). These underwater links can typically cover a range from hundred meters to several kilometers (Wang et al. 2017). In the air, EM signals have been typically adopted to establish air links between sinks and UAVs (see blue lines in Figure 1).

There are a few studies on UAV-assisted data acquisition schemes. In particular, Zolich et al. (2016) propose to use a buoy sink to establish a communication bridge between underwater sensors and Unmanned

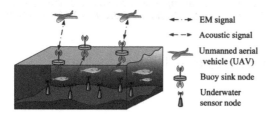

Figure 1. UAV-assisted data acquisition scheme.

Vehicles (UV). In their proposal, the buoy node first receives the data from a sensor node then stores the received data. When a UAV flies over the sea, the buoy node transmits the acquired data to the UAV. Meanwhile, the work of Sollesnes et al. (2018) shows that UAVs can be potentially used to support water-surface data transmission when existed infrastructures cannot be used or cannot cover the sensor nodes. However, most of existing studies either concentrate the hardware design of buoy sinks or the issues of establishing air links between sink nodes and UAVs. Few studies investigate the reliability of the whole transmission path from underwater sensor nodes to UAVs while it is crucial to ensure the path connectivity from data source to data destination since the path connectivity is essentially affected by diverse factors, e.g., underwater links are influenced by wind speed and acoustic signal frequency. Moreover, most of existing studies do not take the distribution of sink nodes into consideration though it plays an important role in guaranteeing the path connectivity.

1.2 Contributions

To fill this gap, this paper aims at investigating the performance of UAV-assisted data acquisition schemes in UIoT. In particular, we consider a similar setting of sink nodes to the prior work (Zolich et al. 2016), in which sink nodes can collect sensor data from underwater sensor nodes through acoustic signals. When the UAV flies over to approach the sink nodes (i.e., buoys), sink nodes transmit the sensor data to the UAV through EM signals. In this design, the UAV can either fly back to transmit the collected data to the onshore data processing center or serve as a relay between sinks and the onshore data processing center (Sollesnes et al. 2018). This paper mainly concentrates on the path connectivity from underwater sensors to UAVs through both underwater acoustic links and air EM links. However, it is non-trivial to establish a theoretical model to analyze the connectivity of UAV-assisted acquisition schemes with consideration of both underwater acoustic links and air EM links together.

To this end, we propose a theoretical model to analyze the path connectivity between underwater sensor nodes and the UAV with consideration of underwater acoustic channel and air EM channel. The major research contributions of this paper can be summarized as follows.

- Firstly, we propose a UAV-assisted data acquisition scheme by placing multiple sinks on the water surface to serve as the relays between UAVs and underwater sensor nodes.
- We then introduce the path connectivity to evaluate the performance of transmission between a sensor node and a UAV. In order to derive the path connectivity, we also analyze the underwater link connectivity and the air link connectivity.
- We conduct extensive simulations to evaluate the connectivity of our proposed model. The simulation results match the analytic results thereby validating the accuracy of our proposed analytical model. Our results also reveal the relationship between the density of sink nodes and the path connectivity with different parameters.

The rest of this paper is organized as follows. Section 2 presents the system model of our proposed data acquisition scheme. Thereafter, we conduct the path connectivity in Section 3. Next, we present the simulation results in Section 4. Finally, the conclusions are drawn in Section 5.

2 SYSTEM MODEL

2.1 Network model

In this paper, we mainly consider a UAV-assisted data acquisition scheme where an underwater sensor node firstly collects the data and then transmits it to a sink node through the underwater acoustic signal. Thereafter, the data received at the sink node is forwarded to the UAV through the air EM signal, as illustrated in Figure 1. Herein, we consider a sink nodes deployment strategy that sink nodes are randomly distributed on the water surface according to Homogeneous Poisson Point Process (HPPP) with density λ.

2.2 Channel model

In this work, we consider two channel models: 1) underwater acoustic communication model; 2) air EM communication model. These two models are introduced as follows.

1) Underwater acoustic communication model: we model the transmission between a sensor node and a sink node as the underwater acoustic communication. Similar to underwater acoustic communication channel model presented by Yildiz et al. (2019), we consider that in the underwater environment, the acoustic signal is assumed to experience the attenuation (path loss). Particularly, the attenuation of acoustic signal denoted by $\eta(r,f)$ is given by $\eta(r,f) = r^k \varphi(f)^r$, where r is the transmission distance, $\varphi(f)$ is an absorption coefficient of acoustic signal frequency f, and k is a spreading factor (ranging from 1 to 2). Moreover, the expression of the attenuation in dB can be given as,

$$10\log\eta(r,f) = k \cdot 10\log r + r \cdot 10\log\varphi(f). \quad (1)$$

If f is larger than a few hundred Hz, the absorption coefficient $10\log\varphi(f)$ in dB/km can be expressed as,

$$10\log\varphi(f) = \frac{0.11f^2}{1+f^2} + \frac{44f^2}{4100+f^2} + 2.75 \times 10^{-4}f^2 + 0.003. \quad (2)$$

Commonly, four kinds of ambient noise models are modeled in underwater acoustic communication channel, i.e., turbulence, shipping activities, waves, and thermal noise. Specifically, the noise of shipping activities varies with the activity factor s. The noise of waves caused by wind is expressed as a function of wind speed w (m/s). Then, these noise components in dB re μPa per Hz is expressed as follows,

$$\begin{aligned}
10\log N_{t(f)} &= 17 - 30\log(f), \\
10\log N_s(f) &= 40 + 20(s - 0.5) + 26\log(f) - 60\log(f + 0.03), \\
10\log N_w(f) &= 50 + 7.5w1/2 + 20\log(f) - 40\log(f + 0.4), \\
10\log N_{th}(f) &= -15 + 20\log(f),
\end{aligned} \quad (3)$$

where $N_t(f)$, $N_s(f)$, $N_w(f)$, and $N_{th}(f)$ are the noise produced by turbulence, shipping activity, wind and thermal noise, respectively. Then, the total noise is expressed as,

$$10\log N(f) = 10\log(N_t(f) + N_s(f) + N_w(f) + N_{th}(f)). \quad (4)$$

2) Air EM communication model: the transmission between a sink node and a UAV is modeled as the air EM communication. In the air environment, the EM channel is assumed to experience path loss and Rayleigh fading (Zhang et al. 2019). In this case, the received power of UAV is proportion to $p_a h z^{-\alpha}$, where p_a is the transmitting power of EM signal, z is the transmission distance between the UAV and the sink node, α is the path loss exponent and h is a random variable following an exponential distribution with mean $1/\mu$.

2.3 *Transducers and antennas*

Since there are two types of signals (i.e., acoustic signal and EM signal) to be transmitted, different devices are used to transmit/receive these signals. In particular, transducers are used to transmit/receive acoustic signals for underwater communications, while antennas are used to transmit/receive EM signals for air communications. We next briefly discuss transducers and antennas, respectively.

Transducers are used for both transmission and reception of an acoustic signal in the underwater environment (Hodges 2011). Usually, a transducer used as a receiver is called a hydrophone. Since the relative positions of the sink nodes are unknown for a sensor node, we choose isotropic hydrophones used at sink nodes to receive acoustic signals from all directions.

Antennas are used for both transmission and reception of EM signal in the air environment. We have two kinds of antennas in this paper, including isotropic antennas deployed at sink nodes and directional antennas mounted at UAVs. Isotropic antennas are usually used for omni-directional data transmission, whereas directional antennas are used for direction-al data transmission. Moreover, we introduce the antenna gain to measure the directivity of an antenna. The antenna gain of an isotropic antenna is denoted by Go. Obviously, Go =1, as an isotropic antenna transmits (or receives) signal uniformly in all directions. However, a directional antenna mainly radiates (or receives) signals toward a specific direction. The realistic antenna model is so complicated that it is not tractable in theoretic analysis (Dai et al. 2013). A simplified directional model named as keyhole model is typically used to substitute the realistic model. A keyhole model (Singh et al. 2015) consists of one main beam with beamwidth θ_m and a joint side/back lobe with beamwidth $2\pi - \theta_m$. The antenna gain G_m of the main lobe in a keyhole model is given as follows (Wang et al. 2017),

$$G_m = \frac{2 - G_s\left(1 + \cos\frac{\theta_m}{2}\right)}{1 - \cos\frac{\theta_m}{2}}, \quad (5)$$

where G_s is the antenna gain of the side/back lobe in a keyhole model. Thus, the gain of keyhole antenna denoted by G is G_m for the main lobe and G_s for the side/back lobe.

3 PATH CONNECTIVITY

The data transmission between a sensor node and a UAV cannot be directly conducted. Actually, the data transmission is processed in two steps (Zolich et al. 2016). As shown in Figure 1, the captured data is firstly transmitted from a sensor node to a sink node. Then, the data is transmitted from a sink node to a UAV. In particular, we define the transmission route starting from an underwater sensor node and destining at a UAV as a transmission path which essentially consists of an underwater link from the sensor node to the sink node and an air link from the sink node to the UAV. We model the reliability of the transmission path between the sensor node and the UAV by path connectivity denoted by $\mathbb{P}_{con}$. The definition of $\mathbb{P}_{con}$ is given as follows,

Definition 1 Path connectivity *is the probability that a sensor node can establish a data transmission path with a UAV via an intermediate sink node. The data transmission path consists of both underwater link and air link.*

In order to investigate the path connectivity, we define *underwater link connectivity* and *air link connectivity*. In particular, we define a performance metric of transmission link between a sensor node and a sink node as underwater link connectivity, denoted by $\mathbb{P}_u$, and define a performance metric of transmission link between a sink node and a UAV by air link connectivity, denoted by $\mathbb{P}_a$. The definitions of Pu and Pa are given as follows, respectively,

Definition 2 Underwater link connectivity *is the probability that a sensor node can directly establish a data transmission link with a sink node.*

Definition 3 Air link connectivity *is the probability that a sink node can directly establish a data transmission link with a UAV.*

3.1 Underwater link connectivity

According to Definition 2, the underwater link connectivity $\mathbb{P}_u$ is given by,

$$P_u = \mathbb{P}[\text{At least 1 sink node appears at detection region}]. \tag{6}$$

The *detection region* is a region in which at lease one sink nodes fall into the detection range of a sensor node. The detection range is the *maximum detection distance* in which the sink node is able to receive signal from a sensor node. The detection region can be essentially represented with a sphere in a 3-D space. Figure 2 presents different views of the detection region of a sensor node, where the front view (i.e., Figure 2(a)) shows the detection region (depicted as the green region) in the water. It is worth mentioning that sink nodes are buoyant on the water surface. Therefore, we need to consider the projection of the 3-D sphere on the water surface, which is depicted as a yellow circle with radius r_s as shown in the top view as shown in Figure 2(b). Moreover, we denote the area of the detection region on the water surface by A. Thus, $\mathbb{P}_u$ highly depends on A.

The radius r_s can be calculated according to the triangle relationship, as shown in Figure 2. The distance

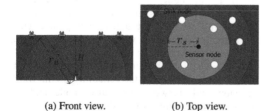

(a) Front view. (b) Top view.

Figure 2. Detection region of a sensor.

H is the deployment depth of a sensor node and the distance r_u is the maximum detection distance, which can be calculated via the analysis of the received signal-to-noise ratio (SNR) at the sink node. The SNR at the sink node can be expressed as $\text{SNR} = p_u/[\eta(r,f)N(f)]$, where p_u represents the transmission power of acoustic signal. The SNR of the sensor node received signal in dB can be given as,

$$\text{SNR}_{\text{dB}} = 10\log p_u - 10\log \eta(r,f) - 10\log N(f). \tag{7}$$

When SNR_{dB} is no less than an SNR threshold T_u, the information can be decoded by the sink node. We assume $\text{SNR}_{\text{dB}} = T_u$. Then, the maximum detection distance of a sensor node denoted by r_u can be obtained by combining Eqs. (1)-(5) and Eq. (7). Furthermore, the radius of the detection region on the water-surface denoted by r_s is $\sqrt{r_u^2 - H^2}$. Therefore, the area of the detection region on the water-surface A is expressed as $A = \pi(r_u^2 - H^2)$.

In this paper, the sink nodes are randomly distributed according to HPPP. Thus, the probability of k sink nodes being located in the detection region is expressed as $\mathbb{P}(x = k) = \left[(\lambda A)^k e^{-\lambda A}\right]/k!$. According to Eq. (6), the underwater link connectivity denoted by $\mathbb{P}_u$ is given by the following equation,

$$\mathbb{P}_u = 1 - e^{-\lambda \pi (r_u^2 - H^2)}. \tag{8}$$

3.2 Air link connectivity

According to Definition 3, the air link connectivity denoted by Pa is given by,

$$\mathbb{P}_a = \mathbb{P}[A\ UAV\ can\ decode\ information\ from\ a\ sink\ node]. \tag{9}$$

A UAV can decode EM signal transmitted by a sink node, if the signal-to-interference-plus-noise ratio (SINR) of the UAV is larger than a SINR threshold T_a. The SINR expression can be as

$$\text{SINR} = \frac{p_a h z^{-\alpha}}{\sigma^2 + I_t} > T_a, \tag{10}$$

where z is the distance between the UAV and the aimed sink node, σ^2 is noise power, and I_t denotes the cumulative interference from other sink nodes. Thus, the air link connectivity $\mathbb{P}_a$ can be mathematically expressed as

$$\mathbb{P}_a = \mathbb{P}[\text{SINR} > T_a]. \tag{11}$$

Then, we obtain Theorem1.
Theorem 1 *The air link connectivity is expressed as,*

$$\mathbb{P}_a = exp(-\mu T z^\alpha \sigma^2 + \pi\lambda(\frac{2bG(z\sqrt{\tan^2\theta+1})^{2-\alpha}}{(\alpha-2)\mu}$$
$$_2F_1\left(1, \frac{\alpha-2}{\alpha}; 2-\frac{2}{\alpha}; -\frac{bG_d(z\sqrt{\tan^2\theta+1})^{-\alpha}}{\mu}\right)$$
$$+ (z\sqrt{\tan^2\theta+1})^2$$
$$_2F_1\left(1, \frac{2}{\alpha}; \frac{\alpha+2}{\alpha}; -\frac{\mu}{\{G_ob(z\sqrt{\tan^2\theta+1})^{-\alpha}\}}\right))),$$
(12)

where $_2F_1(a, b; c; z)$ is a Gaussian hypergeometric function.

Proof: According to Definition3, we have air link connectivity $\mathbb{P}_a$ as follows,

$$\mathbb{P}_a = \mathbb{P}\left[\frac{p_a G_m h z^{-\alpha}}{\sigma^2 + I_t} > T_a\right] \quad (13)$$

Herein, the cumulative interference I_t emitted from sink nodes can be categorized into two scenarios. The first case is interference I_d received by the main lobe of the directional antenna, whereas another case is interference I_o received by the side/back lobe of the directional antenna. Therefore, total interference I_t is equal to the sum of them, i.e., $I_d + I_o$. Thus, Eq. (13) is derived as follows,

$$\mathbb{P}_a = e^{-\mu T_a d^\alpha \sigma^2} \mathcal{L}_{I_d}\left(\frac{b}{p_a}\right) \mathcal{L}_{I_o}\left(\frac{b}{p_a}\right) \quad (14)$$

where $b = \frac{\mu T_a z^\alpha}{G_m}$, $\mathcal{L}_{I_d}\left(\frac{b}{p_a}\right)$ is the Laplace transform of the cumulative interference $I_d = \sum_{x_i \in \Phi \setminus \{SN\}} p_a G_m g_i x_i^{-\alpha}$ from all the other sink nodes (except the target sink node denoted by SN) and $\mathcal{L}_{I_o}\left(\frac{b}{p_a}\right)$ is the Laplace transform of the cumulative interference $\mathcal{L}_{I_o}\left(\frac{b}{p_a}\right) = \sum_{x_i \in \Phi \setminus \{SN\}} p_a G_s g_i x_i^{-\alpha}$ from all the other sink nodes (except the target sink node denoted by SN). We derive these two Laplace transforms as follows, respectively.

First, the Laplace transform $\mathcal{L}_1\left(\frac{b}{p_a}\right)$ is derived as follows,

$$\mathcal{L}_{I_d}\left(\frac{b}{p_a}\right) = E_\Phi\left[\Pi_{x_i \in \Phi \setminus \{SN\}} \frac{\mu}{\mu + bG_m x_i^{-\alpha}}\right]. \quad (15)$$

The probability density function (PDF) of the HPPP states that $E[\Pi_{x \in \Phi} f(x)] = exp(-\lambda \int_V (1-f(x))dx)$ for a function $f(x)$. Then, Eq. (15) can be further derived as follows,

$$\mathcal{L}_{I_d}\left(\frac{b}{p_a}\right) = exp\left(-\pi\lambda \int_0^{(z\tan\theta_m)^2} \frac{bG_m(\sqrt{y^2+t^2})^{-\alpha}}{\mu + bG_m(\sqrt{y^2+t^2})^{-\alpha}} dy^2\right)$$
(16)

Furthermore, replacing variable $(\sqrt{y^2+t^2})^{-\alpha}$ by u where $y = (\sqrt{y^2+t^2})^{-\alpha}$, we then have,

$$\mathcal{L}_{I_d}\left(\frac{b}{p_a}\right) = exp\left(-\pi\lambda \frac{2bG_m(z\sqrt{\tan^2\theta_m+1})^{2-\alpha}}{(\alpha-2)\mu}\right.$$
$$\left. _2F_1\left(1, \frac{\alpha-2}{\alpha}; 2-\frac{2}{\alpha}; -\frac{bG_m(z\sqrt{\tan^2\theta_m+1})^{!-\alpha}}{\mu}\right)\right).$$
(17)

Following the similar derivation procedure as used to derive Laplace transform of $\mathcal{L}_{I_d}\left(\frac{b}{p_a}\right)$ obtained in Eq. (17), the Laplace transform of $\mathcal{L}_{I_o}\left(\frac{b}{p_a}\right)$ can be obtained as,

$$\mathcal{L}_{I_o}\left(\frac{b}{p_a}\right) = exp\left(-\pi\lambda(z\sqrt{\tan^2\theta_m+1})^2\right.$$
$$\left. _2F_1\left(1, \frac{2}{\alpha}; \frac{\alpha+2}{\alpha}; -\frac{\mu}{G_s b(z\sqrt{\tan^2\theta_m+1})^{-\alpha}}\right)\right).$$
(18)

Finally, substituting Eq. (17) and Eq. (18) into Eq. (14), the air link connectivity can be obtained.

3.3 Path connectivity

We next derive the path connectivity between the sensor node and the UAV, which is denoted by $\mathbb{P}_{con}$. According Definition 1, the path connectivity $\mathbb{P}_{con}$ is essentially the product of the underwater link connectivity $\mathbb{P}_u$ and the air link connectivity $\mathbb{P}_a$, which is shown as $\mathbb{P}_{con} = \mathbb{P}_u \mathbb{P}_a$. Thus, the path connectivity is shown as follows,

$$\mathbb{P}_{con} = \left(1 - \exp\left(-\lambda\pi\left(r_u^2 - H^2\right)\right)\right)$$
$$\exp\left(-\mu T d^\alpha \sigma^2 + \pi\lambda \left(\frac{2bG_m\left(z\sqrt{\tan^2\theta + 1}\right)^{2-\alpha}}{(\alpha-2)\mu}\right.\right.$$
$$\left._2F_1\left(1, \frac{\alpha-2}{\alpha}; 2-\frac{2}{\alpha}; -\frac{bG_m\left(z\sqrt{\tan^2\theta+1}\right)^{-\alpha}}{\mu}\right)\right.$$
$$+ \left(z\sqrt{\tan^2\theta+1}\right)^2$$
$$\left.\left._2F_1\left(1, \frac{2}{\alpha}; \frac{\alpha+2}{\alpha}; -\frac{\mu}{G_s b\left(z\sqrt{\tan^2\theta+1}\right)^{-\alpha}}\right)\right)\right) \tag{19}$$

We omit the proof of path connectivity here since the derivation directly follows the similar analysis in Section 3.1 and Section 3.2.

4 SIMULATIONS RESULTS

The underwater and air environment parameters can affect the path connectivity $\mathbb{P}_{con}$. Moreover, wind speed w, signal frequency f, and path loss factor α are main parameters which determine the communications. We investigate the impact of these parameters on $\mathbb{P}_{con}$, respectively.

Wind speed w is an uncontrollable parameter for path connectivity $\mathbb{P}_{con}$, because of varied weather conditions. Figure 3(a) presents the path connectivity $\mathbb{P}_{con}$ versus the wind speed w for the different values of density of sink nodes λ. In particular, the curve is analytical results of $\mathbb{P}_{con}$; while markers are simulation results to verify analytical results. When λ is low, w increases with the decreased value of $\mathbb{P}_{con}$. However, when λ is high, variation of w does not affect $\mathbb{P}_{con}$. This result implies that a relatively high density of sink nodes is necessary to guarantee the path connectivity in heavy wind conditions.

Acoustic signal frequency f is another parameter affecting the path connectivity $\mathbb{P}_{con}$. It is worth mentioning that acoustic signal frequency f determines the maximum transmission distance. When f is larger, the maximum transmission distance is smaller. Thus, the range of frequency is limited by the depth of the sensor node. Figure 3(b) shows the path connectivity $\mathbb{P}_{con}$ versus the acoustic signal frequency f for different values of density λ. We find that f increases with the decreased value of $\mathbb{P}_{con}$ when λ is low. But, when λ is high, variation of f also does not affect Pcon. As a result, a relatively high density of sink nodes is necessary for a high f while a relatively low density of sink nodes is necessary for a low f.

Path loss factor α is a crucial parameter to evaluate the variation of air environment. We present the path connectivity $\mathbb{P}_{con}$ versus the density of sink nodes λ for the different values of path loss factor α as shown in Figure 3(c). We find that α increases with an increased value of $\mathbb{P}_{con}$ when λ is high. But, when λ is low, a variation of α also does not affect $\mathbb{P}_{con}$.

5 CONCLUSION

In this paper, we have proposed a novel UAV-assisted data acquisition scheme in underwater acoustic sensor networks. Moreover, we have comprehensively investigated the effectiveness of our UAV-assisted data acquisition scheme via analyzing underwater link connectivity, air link connectivity and path connectivity. Extensive simulations are conducted to verify the analytical results. The results also reveal the impacts of underwater environment, air environment and antenna beamwidth on the path connectivity of our proposed scheme. These results have provided useful insights on the practical deployment in UAV-assisted data acquisition for UIoT.

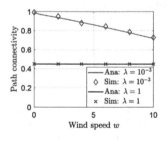
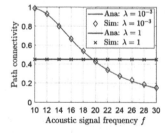
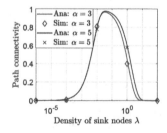

(a) $\mathbb{P}_{con}$ versus wind speed w. (b) $\mathbb{P}_{con}$ versus signal frequency f. (c) $\mathbb{P}_{con}$ with different values of path loss factor α.

Figure 3. Relationship between path connectivity $\mathbb{P}_{con}$ and environment parameters.

ACKNOWLEDGEMENTS

The work described in this paper was partially supported by Macao Science and Technology Development Fund under Grant No. 0026/2018/A1 and Grant No. 0002/2019/APJ.

REFERENCES

Cai, S., Y. Zhu, T. Wang, G. Xu, A. Liu, & X. Liu (2019). Data collection in underwater sensor networks based on mobile edge computing. *IEEE Access* 7, 65357–65367.

Dai, H.-N., K.-W. Ng, & M.-Y. Wu (2013). On busy-tone based MAC protocol for wireless networks with directional antennas. *Wireless personal communications* 73 (3),611–636.

Hodges, R. P. (2011). *Underwater acoustics: Analysis, designand performance of sonar*. John Wiley & Sons.

Singh, S., M. N. Kulkarni, A. Ghosh, & J. G. Andrews (2015). Tractable model for rate in self-backhauled millimeter wave cellular networks. *IEEE Journal on Selected Areas in Communications* 33(10), 2196–2211.

Sollesnes, E., O. M. Brokstad, B. Vågen, A. Carella, A. Alcocer, A. P. Zolich, T. A. Johansen, et al. (2018). Towards autonomous ocean observing systems using miniature underwater gliders with UAV deployment and recovery capabilities. In *2018 IEEE/OES Autonomous Underwater VehicleWorkshop (AUV)*, pp. 1–5. IEEE.

Wang, Q., H.-N. Dai, C. Cheang, & H. Wang (2017). Link connectivity and coverage of underwater cognitive acoustic networks under spectrum constraint. *Sensors* 17(12), 2839.

Wang, Q., H.-N. Dai, Z. Zheng, M. Imran, & A. Vasilakos (2017). On connectivity of wireless sensor networks with directional antennas. *Sensors 17 (1)*,134.

Yildiz, H. U., V. C. Gungor, & B. Tavli (2019, Feb). Packet size optimization for lifetime maximization in underwater acoustic sensor networks. *IEEE Transactions on Industrial Informatics 15*(2), 719–729.

Zhang, C., Z. Wei, Z. Feng, & W. Zhang (2019). Spectrum sharing of drone networks. *Handbook of Cognitive Radio*, 1279–1304.

Zolich, A., J. A. Alfredsen, T. A. Johansen, & K. R. SkØien (2016). A communication bridge between underwater sensors and unmanned vehicles using a surface wireless sensor network-design and validation. In *OCEANS 2016-Shanghai*, pp. 1–9. IEEE.

Coastal structures

Modeling of navigability conditions of rivers in the Amazon and the occurrence of ENSO events

H.M. Borges, L.C.P. Campos Filho, N.M. de Figueiredo, R.S. Saavedra & P.I.D. Lameira
Federal University of Pará, Belém, Brazil

ABSTRACT: The understanding of causes and effects of the oceanic-atmospheric interactions allow us to evaluate the correlation between variables that controls the precipitation regime of our planet with the conditions of navigation of the amazon rivers, being for studies or for forecasts. The present paper seeks to find correlations between water level data of stations on Tapajós Rivers with the variables, here denominated as "extreme data", that are influencing variables of the Enos phenomena such as temperature, pressure and radiation. The used forecast model is a multilayered neural network of the perceptron type with backpropagation algorithm. For the using of the neural network, data referring to Enos phenomena were collected, and as for the output, 30 years of water level historical data were collected so that the training process and validation of the models developed in Python could be made. After the results were obtained, a forecast analysis can be made to understand its behavior, the results and the possible theories that can explain the errors using RSME and R^2.

1 INTRODUCTION

The phenomena ESNO, El niño and La niña are major influencers of the world's climate dynamics. Both represent anomalous variations in the equatorial Pacific ocean surface temperature, the first being characterized by an increase in surface temperature, and the second, viewed as the opposite, characterized by the cooling of the Pacific ocean surface temperature. Enos phenomena alter Walker's cell, which is a circulating cell of the Pacific, originated from the temperature gradient of this ocean. The bottom of the ocean surface has an air flow that goes from east to west for much of the surface tropics, and the top at high latitudes flows and west to east. The air that descends from the east and rises from the west closes with the air flow forming an atmospheric loop (Bjerknes, 1969). The Enos phenomena (Figure 1) alter the structure of Walker's circulation cell, and Walker impacts the rain near the equator on several continents, influencing the evapotranspiration regime and, consequently, the precipitation regime of the Amazon region. Climate anomalies have persistence of several months of cyclic and irregular character, ranging from 2 to 4 years, with an average duration of 18 to 24 months. It is observed that this temperature variation, caused by variables not yet fully detaile d, has different effects in each region of the globe. In Brazil, with its continental dimensions, we can observe different results of this phenomenon when compared north and south of the country. Considering that precipitation is dependent on climate characteristics of the planet, as well as pressure variation, it is possible to evaluate the correlation between precipitation rates of Amazonia and the phenomenon named El ñino - Southern Oscillations (ENSO) which associates temperature of the Pacific Ocean surface with pressure variation in Tahiti and Darwin, Australia and together represent a phenomenon of atmospheric interaction (NOAA, 2019). It is also possible to analyze the variations of the Extreme phenomena themselves based on Pacific decadal and interdecadal, seasonal and multidecadal Atlantic oscillations, and other variables that involve other regions of the globe outside the Pacific. The objective of this work was to develop a neural network model to analyze and validate the relationships between the variational behavior of ENSO events and the fluctuations of water levels of fluviometric stations in the Amazon basin.

2 METHOD

Data for the development of this paper were obtained from the National Oceanic and Atmospheric Administration | U.S. Department of Commerce, (NOAA); in the scientific division department (PSD); and data regarding hydrological variables were obtained from the ANA national water agency website, through the HIDROWEB platform.

The first index evaluated is called Southern Oscillation Index, (SOI). This variable, which is associated with the southern oscillations, was developed from a study based on pressure analysis of various regions of the globe, with the variables of interannual trend

DOI: 10.1201/9781003216599-79

Figure 1. Effects on Sea Surface Temperature by ENSO Phenomena.

relations. An unknown relationship was observed in the early 20th century between pressure variation in the region of Indonesia and South America, and since then theories have been formulated to explain the phenomenon (NOAA). South oscillations, due to their direct relationship with trade winds, are known to have a strong influence on Enos phenomena. The speed of trade winds over the equatorial pacific influences the rising phenomenon that occurs east of the ocean, where deeper waters flow due to the movement of warmer waters. The temperature regime of the oceans influences the pressure variation and this, the characteristics present in the trade winds. The South Oscillation Index is an index defined by the difference between sea level pressure from Tahiti and Darwin in Australia. The data obtained from this index have a good correlation with the Enos data. Long periods of negative index may indicate a warming of Pacific waters, which is indicative of the El ñino phenomenon, and positive values indicate the other phenomenon, La ñina (National Center for Atmospheric Research Staff, 2019).

The second index collected is called the ENO multivariate index (MEI). Enos phenomena occur in different circumstances by different variables. El ñino period are strongly indicated by not only surface water anomalies in the Pacific, but also pressure anomalies in Indonesia and the Central Tropical Pacific, as well as low pressure on the Eastern Tropical Pacific, reduction or reversal of trade winds, weak tropical convection over Indonesia and western pacific, increased convection over pacific center, as well as radiation.

Evaluating all phenomena is not a simple task, and for this reason, MEI is an empirical variable that abstracts all this information to analyze not only the presence of the extreme phenomenon but also its intensity based on these aforementioned sets of variables that define the occurrence in the phenomenon. It is noteworthy that we will not always have an equal relationship between the presence of extreme phenomena and the MEI index. The abstracted data associated with the MEI index are variably related, so all data obtained from the MEI indexes are bimonthly (Klaues & Timlin, 2011; NOAA PSD, 2019). Another data collected corresponds to the Pacific decade oscillation (PDO). The latter is considered another phenomenon and is a great aid in defining the regime of the Enos effects themselves (Diaz. & Markgraf, 2000).

The PDO is determined by fluctuations in the Pacific basin and the climate of North America. As well as the el ñino/south oscillation phenomenon, the PDO is classified as hot or cold by the anomaly of the ocean temperature in the Northeast and the tropical Pacific Ocean. When the interior of the Pacific North is cold, the Pacific Coast is warm, and sea level pressures are below average compared to the Pacific North, we have a positive value of this variable, and in reverse situations negative values. (NOAA PSD, 2019). Another data obtained from the NOAA website was the ocean surface temperatures in different regions of the Pacific. Each region receives an appointment, running east to west on El nino 1 + 2, el nino 3, el nino 3.4, el nino 4, as seen in Figure 2. The climate anomaly El nino and La nina can also be defined by variation. continuous temperature at about 0.5 degrees above or below average for a period of three consecutive months (ZUBAIR, 2007). Although scientists mainly adhere to the el niño 3 + 4 region for the definition of the phenomenon, we cannot ignore the effects that different regions of the Pacific, such as near the coast of Peru, have on the precipitation regime of the Amazon. Other information also collected from NOAA data was the Nino Oceanic Indexes (ION in portuguese). This variable is a measurement standard that characterizes the phenomenon by temperature anomaly in three consecutive months, so the data collected are three-monthly. All data obtained from the NOAA website were referred to in this article as extreme data.

The data collected on the ANA website were specifically the hydrological data that served as the basis for the correlations, namely precipitation data and water depth data. The collected quota stations were a total of seven, all referring to the Tapajós river, namely: Três Marias, Barra de são manoel, fortaleza, jatobá, acará dos tapajós, Buburé and Bela vista.

All methodologies for this work were developed using Python software, under the MIT license so that

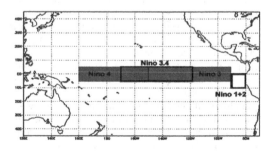

Figure 2. - Subdivision of the Enos regions in the equatorial pacific.

the analysis process of each time series, as well as the tests for selection and validation of neural networks were done automatically. Thus, the script in question can be tested with any other time series as input to the routine, provided that this, until the present moment of the issuance of this article, has the data filled.

2.1 The routine

The perception of the effects generated by extreme data on hydrological variables does not occur immediately, it is known that there is a lag between event and effect, especially of temperature and pressure variables with hydrological data, these delays may be unique for each region. Knowing this, we sought to find the relationships of the data, through a lag between all the obtained variables, to identify which the best preceding months provide me. relationship, a certain water level in a given season. In the routine of the present work two specific models were developed, with different inputs for Perceptron networks. For each station and model, several types of MLP networks were randomly developed with unique characteristics, then the selection of the most suitable neural network for each time series of each station under analysis in this article. For the sake of simplicity, the first model, which relates hydrological data to temperature-only data, will be named MLP_TEMP, and the second, which associates hydrological data to all the variables collected in the above-mentioned NOAA, will be called MLP_MULT. The script operation diagram can be seen in the flowchart of Figure 3.

To use the developed tool, data were obtained from seven stations present in the Tapajós River, with data filled by auto-regression using the tool ANOVA do Excel.

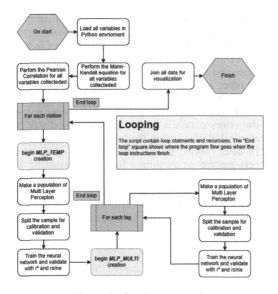

Figure 3. - Python script flowchart executed.

The script in question is responsible for performing all data analysis for the purpose of this work, from capturing the time series, downloaded from the ANA and NOAA website, to the development of artificial neural networks for estimation. The program steps and their operation are best explained by the flow chart shown in Figure 3. all stations and their respective time series are loaded into the script for analysis; as well as variables related to Enos data. Is loaded too inside the routine. The first step for data analysis is the adequacy of these series, due to different formatting both in the date patterns and in the distribution of the series itself, which came into conflict in the script because the NOAA data is in the American standard. The collected data are available in matrix form, and the conversion of each data was performed to unify in a single table all the collected variables. Mann Kendall test was performed to evaluate the trend of time series, which are hydro-meteorological, have a strong tendency to be distorted and rarely follow a normal distribution.

In addition, the Mann Kendall Test has low sensitivity to outlier's and is not affected by the current distribution of the series data (Hamed, 2007), contrasting with other parametric tests present such as linear regression tests, coefficient tests that assume that the data follow a normal distribution.

However, as will be seen in the results section, the trends of the series collected for this work have practically zero trend, which ends up becoming indifferent to possible probability distributions among the different variables obtained. Then, a permutation of all series obtained was performed, including between the hydrological data themselves and the ENSO data. This correlation was important for analyzes that will be explained in the results section.

Pearson's correlation, or product-moment correlation coefficient, is a variable that tells the degree of linear correlation between two distinct variables. According to GARSON (2009), the correlation is defined by a bivariate association of the relationship level between two variables. For Moore (2007), Correlation dictates not only the direction, but also the degree of linear relationship between two quantitative variables. The variables in question may be associated at variance level and this correlation will confirm this. Pearson's correlation gives us a value ranging from 1 to -1, the first being indicative of a high direct linear relationship, and the other value indicating a high reverse linear relationship; And knowing this, the interesting thing is to know if the value is as far as possible from zero, which is indicative of a nonexistent linear relationship between two variables.

There is no exact criterion for defining whether a correlation is considered satisfactory or not, and it is up to the analyst's personal choice. However, according to Dancey & Reidy (2005), a good indication can be given with the following values r = 0.10 to 0.30 (weak); r = 0.40 to 0.6 (moderate); r = 0.70 to 1 (strong).

The script in question, as quoted, created two distinct neural network models. The first model is a model derived from the results obtained using Pearson's correlation. In the second model, an analysis is performed using all the extreme data collected on the NOAA website directly, seeking to find some relationship between these variables and the hydrological data, through manual attempts at each lag. In order for all correlations to be evaluated, for the MLP_TEMP model, the script in question performs a permutation of all variables lagging each month within 60 months, and in addition, a relationship of hydrological data with differentiation was tested. extreme data, also lagging data by up to 60 months; whereas when a differentiation of the extreme data is performed, there is already a lag of one month of this, so it was iterated in the routine 59 months. In this script, visually expressed by the flowchart of Figure 3, it shows that the MLP_TEMP model is selected from successive models created by the script defined as a population, starting from one of the principles of genetic programming.

After the development of each model, one of the steps known as genetic programming is performed, which consists in selecting the neural network that is most adapted to the extreme data. Next, the MLP_MULTI model is created following a similar criterion. However, the process of creating various neural network models is performed for each lag performed in the script, in order to find some relationship between cause and effect latency.

After splitting, the routine checks, for the development of MLP_TEMP, for each variable obtained from the NOAA website, which lag gave me a greater linear correlation of variance, captures all variables and obtains a time series in each lag, to serve as a training input for the neural network that will be created later. After that, the routine creates several neural network models, with different numbers of neurons, and performs training with data that is separated for calibration (about 75% of the entire time series) and then the root mean errors are calculated. square error) and R² using the remainder of the time series, separated for validation.

In the other method used, which created the MLP-MULT model, we captured all the extreme data to be input. Different combinations were searched for the best correlation based on lags that were performed through iterations within the program for up to 5 years. For this second model, the process of creating the MLP neural network was similar; However, Pearson correlation was not used in this analysis in order not to exclude possible variables that have a correlation that the Pearson correlation model could not find. Thus, the routine trained, with a calibration sample and validated, with a validation sample, for each season and each model, the best lag that allows us to characterize hydrological events with extreme events. For both models, either MLP_TEMP or MLP_MULT, part of the sample was separated for calibration and validation with different separation methods, called direct and cross validation.

In the direct validation process, the first values of the series were obtained to perform one operation and the remainder to another, which in this case is validation and calibration. The second selection method randomly obtains a defined amount of n data for calibration and separates the remainder for validation, where n is the number of months in a time series. The difference between both models is that direct validation can get a larger error due to possible outliers being captured for training, so that the network can move away from a more optimal value, as well as in validation where it can be obtained. a higher error value due to the presence of some non-computed anomaly, data padding, or measurement errors.

Studying the best model for each station is not a simple task, considering that an autocorrelation analysis between each time series should be performed and the assessment of better definition of the integration polynomial. However, Python software has a tool called Pyramid for the development of an automatic ARIMA model, also allowing the user to define constraints such as maximum values of the autoregressive, integrating and moving average components, either monthly or seasonal, or desired AIC and BIC values. Although the library used seems to be black box, the code for Pyramid development is open.

2.2 *Calibration and validation measurement*

The root mean square deviation, (RSME), is an error measure used to define the difference between the actual values and the values predicted by a model, in this case, neural networks, with the observed model. The purpose of this error calculation is that this is a precision measure to compare prediction errors of models on the same scale, regardless of the time series size (Abrahart & See, 1998). The RSME calculation aggregates all residues and gives us the standard deviation of these. In other words, we are told how data is concentrated around the best fit line. The determination coefficient r² gives us how much, in percentage, of the errors obtained in the data prediction can be eliminated when using the least squares regression. In other words, it will show us the relationship between the errors from a linear regression of the data to the errors obtained from an average of the data obtained from the actual sample data. In mathematical terms, the above errors can be defined by Equation 1 and Equation 2, respectively.

$$RMSE = \sqrt{\frac{\sum_{t=1}^{n}\left(\frac{Y_t - \hat{Y}_t}{Y_t}\right)^2}{n}} \qquad (1)$$

$$R^2 = 1 - \frac{\sum_{t=1}^{n}(Y_t - \hat{Y}_t)^2}{\sum_{t=1}^{n}(Y_t - \bar{Y})^2} \qquad (2)$$

n is the number of months presents in the time series, Y is the real number, and $\hat{Y}$ is the predicted value.

2.3 Multi layer perceptron network

Due to the range of applications of this tool, Multi Layer Perceptron (MLP) models are used in many areas of scientific knowledge, not just in hydrology; with different methods, ways of learning, and different models. Nevertheless, almost all models follow a single system that is based on a set of inputs associated with a given output. The neural network must have an understanding of how to correlate input data by defining its importance from synaptic weights. The neural network model model used in this work is classified as supervised, where the input data have their correlations defined, from the training, based on the known output samples. Although several models are proven to be useful in hydrology, such as recursive nets, fuzzy nets, kohoven and Adaline; For the present work, a Perceptron supervised neural network with backpropagation algorithm was chosen to define the above correlations. In this model, the weight matrices of the neural networks will be adjusted whenever a large error is detected between the expected value, compared to the value generated by the network based on the inputs in question. Each sample of data obtained, whether by the Hidroweb platform or the NOAA website, are variables that have relationships, and the MLP models that were created to prove this and to predict water level data. Figure 4 shows subroutine showing the steps of creating, training, and returning the neural network to the main routine presented in the flowchart of Figure 3.

The idea behind the backpropagation algorithm is to minimize errors by decreasing the gradient in each neuron present. A neural network follows the following steps to arrive at a result based on the inputs, as shown in flowchart 2. First, we have the input of the data, which is then multiplied by their respective weights and summed into a single output. This output is then domain F (x) of an activation function, which will bring me as result the value of the image, called activation function, which may be the final output of my network, or just one more input for more. a neuron if the network has more intermediate layers, so that the output of the function can be multiplied to other weights to generate another activation function in the succeeding layers. It can be defined mathematically through the expressions expressed in Equation 3 and Equation 4. Flowchart at Figure 4 is a sequence of instructions built into Python's main routine. For this reason, this is named as a subroutine.

$$z_i = \sum w_i.x_{i-1} + b_i \qquad (3)$$

$$y_i = g(z_i) \qquad (4)$$

z the sum of all weights with the predecessor data entries. w is the weight and i represents the current network layer. Since neural network training will take place with periods with water depth present, the script can supervise the neural network by stating whether the result was correct or not, based on the error calculation. In case of an error above 10e-4, the weights of the last layer will be recalculated and so on to the previous layers by changing their respective weights, so a new check is performed.

To minimize errors, the gradient values for each weight are calculated as quoted. Since we are referring to an error function, we can infer that we want the error function to decrease, so we must get the negative gradient variation to find the ideal weights. The mathematical definition can be expressed by Equation 5.

$$W_{n+1} = W_n - N.\frac{\partial E}{\partial W} \qquad (5)$$

W_n is the actual weight, W_{n+1} is the weight of the next iteration. It's important to remember that the correction process also occurs with the neural network bias, following the same methodology of the weights with the gradient.

According to Figueiredo (2016), due to its high learning capacity to obtain experimental knowledge, the technique in question is widely used to solve complex and nonlinear problems, thus being able to make generalizations and inferences, reveal relationships, patterns. and predictions of complex systems. Artificial Neural Networks are extremely versatile in defining relationships between variables whose associations are not, or not well known. It can be deduced from the first understanding that the greater

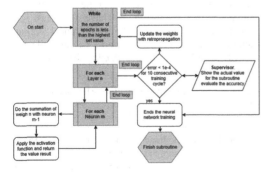

Figure 4. Subroutine with steps of creating, training and returning.

the number of neurons in the middle layer, the more capable of nonlinear associations it will have. However, too complex a neural network, too simple (few neurons), with high or low bias value, may have difficulty in performing simple relational analyzes between the variables defined in the inputs, causing convergence problems and difficulty in reaching the next result. expected, known under the terms "underfitting" and "overfitting" (Aldemario, 2017; Silva, 2017). Taking this into account, different neural network models with different numbers of neurons were tested for the same output variable to achieve the best convergence.

For the present work, all neural networks had the following characteristics in common: all had as output function the linear function (RELU), due to the ease that this gives the neural network its optimization; and how the resolution or weight adjustment model is used for the stochastic gradient technique proposed with Kingma, Diekeric, and Jimmy Ba. (model called ADAM). The optimization ranges are 200 sample elements. The learning rate remains constant throughout the training process, with a value of 0.001. The maximum number of allowed iterations has been set to 2000 iterations, that is, when a network fails to converge with data prepared for validation within 2000 iterations, the created neural network model is discarded. Different numbers of iterations have been tested, namely 200, 500, 1000 and 2000, and the good results obtained have been from just under 500 iterations. The high number of iterations was due to the methodology adopted for the network selection process: several models of neural networks are created, and it is necessary that all of them have their weights as volatile as possible for comparison, leaving the criterion of stop only defined by the values obtained from the gradient, so if the network cannot perform more than 10 consecutive iterations without guaranteeing a large variation in the optimization value (less than 1x10-4 which implies a low gradient), or large variation in the call loss function or cost function, the training process is stopped, the last two previous processes ensure that a network can be discarded which probably reached a very specific local error value, relatively far away if a solution considered optimal. The beta decay of the stochastic gradient model was 0.9. The error function, which is used to define the end of the iterations of each neural network, is defined by the mean square error equation.

3 RESULTS

Assuming that the time series under analysis are serially independent, the man-kendall test was used to check whether the series is biased or not. The Python library that was used to prepare the method performs a hypothesis test and makes two considerations, the first being that the time series has no tendency (null hypothesis), and the second that the time series does have, some tendency (alternative hypothesis). Considering the null hypothesis, we must consider the variable Z, expressed in Equation 6, as a variable that will tell us the degree of tendency of a series. The sign in the expression will occur if the value S defined in Equation 7 is less than or greater than zero for the plus and minus signs respectively. The value of σ^2 can be obtained from Equation 8.

$$Z = \frac{S \pm 1}{\sigma} \quad (6)$$

$$\sum_{k=1}^{n-1} \sum_{j=k+1}^{n} sign(x_j - x_k) \quad (7)$$

$$\sigma^2 = (n(n-1)(2n+5) - \sum_{j=1}^{p} t_j(t_j - 1)(2t_j + 5) \quad (8)$$

The Python function also gives us other values such as p-value, shown in Table 1. The results obtained in some water depth stations can be saw in Table 4.

Based on the data in Table 1, we can highlight the presence of p-value and z-value, as well as a textual column that tells us if the series in question has any tendency and a value called 'h' that represents a boolean variable that tells us if the series has a variation in its intensity. It is worth noting that, of all water level variables, only the Acará do Tapajós and Três Marias station has a greater than normal Z value variation compared to the others, which makes the test determine if the water levels collected at that season have some tendency. Nevertheless, the Z value obtained is not sufficient to consider that the time series in question has some tendency, only that the value has some variation in its distribution, but may have been due to any other unknown factors, and does not represent something of the phenomenon itself.

From the analysis of rainfall in Table 2, we can observe that the Z values presented a zero result that indicates a non-biased cyclical character of the time series. However, when we look at the Enos data from Table 3, we can see that they all have some bias. Temperature data for the coast of Peru (El ñino 1 + 2) and central equatorial Pacific (El ñino 3 sst), as well as the decadal oscillation of the Pacific, have Z values

Table 1. Man Kendall test data for each water level.

Station	Tendency	h	p	z
TRÊS MARIAS	no trend	FALSE	0,247716	1,155915
BSM	no trend	FALSE	0,561667	-0,58037
FORTALEZA	no trend	FALSE	0,991211	-0,01102
ACARÁ DOS TAPAJÓS	no trend	FALSE	0,262079	-1,12149

Table 2. Data from the Man Kendall test for each precipitation.

Station	Tendency	h	p	z
AGR. CAJABI	no trend	FALSE	1	0
BSM	no trend	FALSE	1	0
CUPARI	no trend	FALSE	1	0
JACAREACANGA	no trend	FALSE	1	0
JATOBÁ	no trend	FALSE	1	0
KM 1385 - BR 163	no trend	FALSE	1	0
R. P. MÉDICI	no trend	FALSE	1	0
BACAVAL	no trend	FALSE	1	0
BOCA DO INFERNO	no trend	FALSE	1	0
BRASFOR	no trend	FALSE	1	0
BRASNORTE	no trend	FALSE	1	0
CACHIMBO	no trend	FALSE	1	0
COLIDER	no trend	FALSE	1	0
DECIOLÂNDIA	no trend	FALSE	1	0
FONTANILHAS	no trend	FALSE	1	0
INDECO	no trend	FALSE	1	0
JUARA	no trend	FALSE	1	0
JUÍNA	no trend	FALSE	1	0
JURUENA	no trend	FALSE	1	0
KM 947 BR 163	no trend	FALSE	1	0
KM 1027 BR 163	no trend	FALSE	1	0
KM 1326 BR 163	no trend	FALSE	1	0
NOVA BRASILÂNDIA	no trend	FALSE	1	0
NOVA MARINGÁ	no trend	FALSE	1	0
NOVO TANGARA	no trend	FALSE	1	0
PADRONAL	no trend	FALSE	1	0
VILA ALEGRE	no trend	FALSE	1	0

Table 3. Man Kendall's test data for each extreme data.

Variable	Tendency	h	p	z
EL NINO 3+4	increasing	TRUE	0,003762	2,897452
MEI	increasing	TRUE	0,000000	6,105126
EL NINO 1+2	increasing	TRUE	0,018141	2,362736
INDICE BIVARIAVEL ENO	increasing	TRUE	0,016838	2,390225
NOA 3 SST	increasing	TRUE	0,003472	2,922465
OSCILAÇÃO DECADAL DO PACÍFICO	increasing	TRUE	0,000000	9,257103
INDICE DE OSCILAÇÃO SUL	decreasing	TRUE	0,004650	-2,830340
INDICE OCEÂNINO NINO	decreasing	TRUE	0,000006	-4,534890

indicating a positive trend of the time series in question with emphasis on the Enos multivariate indices (MEI). On the other hand, the southern oscillation indices and the nino oceanic index have a negative tendency, indicating a decrease in the value.

Table 4. Metrics obtained with the best models.

	r2	rmse
TRÊS MARIAS	0,8	104,651
BSM	0,82	83,168
FORTALEZA	0,795	60,97
ACARÁ DOS TAPAJÓS	0,812	75,583
BUBURÉ	0,877	41,448
JATOBA	0,838	80,412

Regarding the use of Pearson correlation, the routine performs a permutation with all variables included in Python, as well as predecessor relationships between the data, as well as the differentiation of the variables. In other words, the Pearson correlation equation is applied for all variables and for all relationships between a given n present with another past given, considering a range of up to 60 months (five years), evaluating both monthly values individually and the variation of these. After all calculations, the routine saves to a spreadsheet in Excel for simpler and more visual analysis.

4 CONCLUSIONS

Analysis of the Man-Kendall Test on a set of correlated time series shows us the importance of this method in verifying the integrity of the time series. According to Yue (2002), this test is commonly used to evaluate the significance of trends in a hydrometeorological time series, because this non-parametric model is used to evaluate non-normally distributed models. It is known that the hydrological cycle, in general, has a seasonal character, without. We also know that the water level data are strongly correlated with the rainfall data as can be observed, and all data collected near the season do have a very weak or nonexistent bias, so considering that the correlation we are analyzing is seasonal and without tendency, we can say that there is an oscillation in the value of water levels that are not under the control of the precipitation regime, which may involve other factors such as changes in soil characteristics, or differential factors whose Pearson method does not can relate; Nevertheless, the neural network has tried to integrate these unknown factors if they are in the domain of the input variables of the neural network, and if not, will be responsible for the errors obtained. There is a strong possibility that the higher variance obtained in the Acará dos Tapajós rain season compared to other seasons is a consequence of factors such as a measurement with errors greater than the other periods collected, added to the regression method used to fill in the data. data that the station needed to pass etc. It is also important to state that a large change in the hydrological cycle intensity of the data obtained at all stations in the last period of the total time series sample is observed. One of the effects of this sudden change can be observed by analyzing the difference in error results obtained by the different validation methods.

In Pearson Correlations, we can see that we obtain a similar relationship between different defasation for each fluviometric station used in this work. In other words, it can be seen that there is an almost fixed relationship between reaction time between phenomena, such as precipitation events and effects on water level variation. Another thing to note is that correlation finds almost no relationship of extreme data to any of the hydrological variables in almost all situations analyzed except temperature data. However, the results obtained show that there is a relationship between extreme data and hydrological data.

Another aspect to discuss is about the "Lurking's" variables. These variables are often not part of the main analysis and they are responsible for delivering the true correlation between the variables 'a' and 'b', for example (Stephanie, 2018). We can assume from the linear correlations that the temperature effects influence the water level data of the Tapajós River. Nevertheless, performing a technical interpretation of this formulation, physically there is no relationship between the influence of the extreme data with the water depth data, however both variables have a relationship in common with a third variable, which is precipitation. Therefore, we know that the effects of temperature, for example, influence the precipitation regime in the Amazon basin, and this factor, added to other factors such as the tide, influence the water level of the river. Despite this possible interpretative problem that may occur, we can perform an evaluation between the extreme data and the water level data without problem, since the precipitation regime can only be seen as an intermediate variable, exposed to the analysis and, considering that it is intermediate relationship will always exist without change during the analysis period, it can be stated that the variable "precipitation" is not a "lurking variable". However, some routine correlations should be carefully evaluated to make sure that the correlation intensity between two variables is not being controlled by a third unknown, uncontrollable variable that may affect the interpretation of the relationship as the influence of Enos phenomena with those of water level occur. Therefore, there can be no concentrated confirmation by merely evaluating the linear methods hitherto cited in this section. The python library that gives us Pearson's correlation does not provide the p-value of the null hypothesis of this correlation, which tells us the approximate likelihood that a system that has no correlation will produce the results at least as extreme as the values computed by the correlation.

REFERENCES

Adhikari S., Liyanaarachchi S., Chandimala J-N, Nawarathna B. K., Bandara R., Yahiya Z. and Zubair L., Rainfall Prediction Based On The Relationship Between Rainfall And El Niño Southern Oscillation (Enso). [S.I] 2010.

Andreoli, R. & Kayano, M. (2007). The Relative Importance Of The Southern Tropical Atlantic And Eastern Pacific In The Variability Of Precipitation In Northeast Brazil. Brazilian Journal Of Meteorology. 22. 10.1590/S0102-77862007000100007.

Araujo, R. G. et al. The Influence Of The El Niño - South Oscillation And Equatorial Atlantic Event On Rainfall Over The North And Northeast Regions Of South America. Acta Amaz. [Online]. 2013, Vol.43, N.4, Pp.469–480. Issn 0044-5967.

Caioni et al. Analysis Of The Rainfall Distribution And Occurrence Of The Climatic Phenomenon In The Municipality Of Alta Floresta. Mt. 2014

Diaz, H. F. & Markgraf, V., El Nino And The Southern Oscillation, Multiscale Variability And Global And Regional Impacts. Cam-Bridge University Press. 2000. P. 3–10,13,474.

Dolling, O. & Varas, E., Artificial Neural Networks For Streamflow Prediction. Journal Of Hydraulic Research - Department Of Hy-Draulics, Universidad Nacional De San Juan, San Juan, Argentina - (09/11/2014)

Elaine R., Knight K. (1996) Artificial Intelligence. Chapter 18 Connectionist Models. Mc Graw Hill 2nd Edition Pp.537–581.

Figueiredo, N. M. Multi-Use Water Management Model: A Case Study For The Tapajós River Basin. Proderna, Postgraduate Program In Natural Resources Engineering In The Amazon.2016 P. 49–97

Holbrook, N. J., Davidson, J., Feng M., Hobday A. J., Lough, J. M., Mcgregor S., Risbey, J.S. 7. El Nino - Southern Oscillattion, Impacts And Adaptation Responses. [S.I] 2012.

Maciel, S. A. Analysis Of The Rain-Flow Relationship In The Hydrographic Basin Of The Paranaí-Ba River, Brazil. Graduate Program In Geography, Ufu. [S.I] 2017.

National Oceanic Atmospheric Administration, Psd. El Nino/Southern Oscilattion (Enso), Available At: <Https://Www.Ncdc.Noaa.Gov/Teleconnections/Enso/>, Accessed On: May. 2019.

Rumelhart, D.E., Mcclelland, J.L., and The Pdp Research Group. (1986). Parallel Recognition In Modem Computers. In Proceeding: Explorations In The Micro-Estructure Of Cognition. Vol 1. Foundations, Mit Press/Bradford Books, Cmbridge Mass.

Wolter, K. & Timlin, M. S., El Nino/Southern Oscilation Behavior Since 1871 As Diagnosed In An Extended Multivariate Enso Index (Mei.Ext). International Journal Of Cli-Matology. 2011

Yue, Sheng et. al. Power Of The Mann - Ken-Dall And Spearman's Rho Tests For Detecting Monotonic Trends In Hydrological Series. Journal Of Hydrology - 2002

Zubair, L., Siriwardhana, M., Chandi-Mala, J. & Yahiya, Z. (2007). Pre-Dictability Of Sri Lankan Rainfall Based On Enso. International Journal Of Climatology.

Optimizing the configuration of flow guide grid to reduce turbulence in a wave flume for coastal hydraulic research

D.M. Fellows
ERASMUS trainee at Bulgarian Ship Hydrodynamics Centre, University of Central Lancashire (UK), Varna, Bulgaria

G. Nikolov & R. Kishev
Bulgarian Ship Hydrodynamics Centre, Varna, Bulgaria

ABSTRACT: A new wave flume for coastal research, marine ecology and marine renewable energy applications is under construction at BSHC. It will be equipped with wave generator as well as with a close-loop current generation system. To enable generation control and realization of a combined wave-current flow, computer modeling and systematic flow simulations have been performed and results validated by tailored experiment. The initial objective of the study was to achieve uniform current flow in the flume and to check the potential range of axial velocity gradient control. Then, the operation of the piston-type wave maker was modeled using dynamic meshing to simulate the oscillating movement of the paddle. Experimental validation of this solution has been done. Basic results of the study are illustrated in several ways in order to trace the influence of flume design parameters on the waves-over-current flow generated in the flume and to enable control on its parameters.

1 INTRODUCTION

1.1 Overview

Once the design of a basin that generates a variable current as well as waves was complete, an investigation begun on how much turbulence would be created due to the flow of current within the basin, how it will affect the surface of the water and what can be done to direct it. This report consists of simulations for the flow of current at three different velocities at three heights with no flow directors in place and then with the same conditions, trials of different setups of flow directors to show how the final design was concluded. To limit the amount of figures, only two velocities and heights will be shown within this report.

1.2 Previous studies

In this area of hydrodynamics there has been many studies focused on modeling tidal waves which can help give a base of understanding on how to mathematically model this study. One study reviled that for shallow flows simulated using a simple horizontal mixing model, the bed friction can be accurately represented via the K-ε model (Stansby, 2013).

Another study found that the most used and most effective material to create a wave breaker is sand, gravel and stone which has been considered in the model (Khalilabadi & Bidokhti, 2011) and simulated as a porous zone of 0.4.

A study that was heavily referred to during the set up and operating conditions of the basin was a report carried out by State Key Laboratory of Ocean Engineering (Shan et al, 2010). This report included a similar size basin to the one that has been designed for BSHC, therefore the operating conditions of having a current inlet velocity between 0.1m/s and 0.4m/s.

2 GEOMETRY AND MESH

2.1 Setup

The geometry and scale was from the drawings in Figure 1, which show the entire structure of the basin. For the purpose of this simulation only a simple outline of the basin was needed but in order to show the behavior of the free surface, another boundary was included to become the air boundary as shown in Figure 2. To get the two surface areas to interact with each other, the surfaces were generated separately then formed as a new part together. To achieve different water heights, the lower boundary area representing water is altered accordingly to the conditions. The total length is 60m with a height of 4.8m from the bottom of the inlet and outlet to the top of air section.

DOI: 10.1201/9781003216599-80

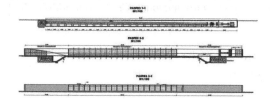

Figure 1. Technical drawing of basin.

Figure 2. Geometry of basin in ANSYS.

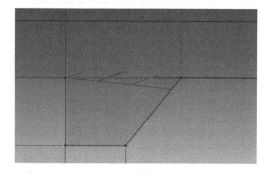

Figure 3. First direction grid design.

2.2 Basin additions

After all conditions where simulated, flow directors were added to the geometry as shown in Figure 3, this also allowed for them to be altered easily to experiment with different setups, along with an addition of a wave breaker later on once the optimum setup of flow directors had been achieved.

Once the geometry was created, the mesh was generated by using mesh mapping and bias techniques to manipulate the mesh into generating a higher concentration of nodes within the water boundary as this is the area of interest which can be seen in Figure 4. This was done so that the node count did not go too high as this would slow down the simulation. To setup the

Figure 4. Mesh quality.

model and to check if it worked correctly a course mesh was used as shown in Table 3. To experiment with configurations a medium mesh was used and for the addition of waves, the fine mesh type was used.

3 BOUNDARY CONDIDTIONS

3.1 *Fluent options*

As this is a 2D CFD model and it is assumed that it is a steady state flow with an incompressible fluid, the calculations to determine the momentum and conservation of mass are governed by the Navier-Stokes equation (Yang, et al, 1998). When setting up the simulation, boundary conditions are selected which are presented in Table 1. These boundary conditions provide a template to follow when carrying out a simulation so that it is an accurate representation as well as providing consistently when influencing factors are changed. Table 2 includes all the geometry parts and what type they are classed as within fluent.

3.2 *Configuration of flow directors*

To start with a configuration of three, straight flow directors at an angle of 30° from the bottom face of the basin but this did not direct the flow along the basin enough and disrupted the water surface too much as

Table 1. Calculation options.

Fluent calculation options	Option selected
Solver	Pressure based, transient time, gravity -9.81
Multiphase	Volume of fluid
Viscous	SST, K-omega
Materials	Air, water, aluminum
Operating conditions	Reference pressure location: y=2.9 Specific operating density
Cell zones	Wave breaker zones: porous zone=0.45
Solution method	SIMPLE, First order Implicit
Solution controls	Default

Table 2. Boundary conditions.

Sections	Type
Inlet	Velocity
Outlet water	Outflow
Outlet air	Symmetry
Walls	Wall
Flow directors	Wall
Interior air	Interior
Interior water	Interior
Wave breakers	Interior
Wave reduces	Walls

Table 3. Mesh statistics.

Mesh type	water height		
	0.5	1	1.5
Course	160x10^3	170x10^3	180x10^3
Medium	240x10^3	240x10^3	260x10^3
Fine	340x10^3	340x10^3	N/A

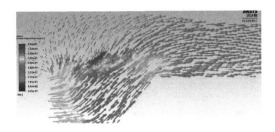

Figure 7. Direction grid configuration.

Figure 5. Straight flow directors at 30°.

Figure 6. Curved direction grid at 30°.

shown in Figure 5. Another configuration that was tried was having the three flow directors slightly curved and staggered by 5° but as seen in Figure 6, there a lot of turbulence caused by the top flow director which also disturbs the surface water too much.

After the previous simulation it was clear that the angle of the flow directors needed to be decreased to direct the flow, the issue with this was that this would also shorten the space for the fluid to flow through, causing a drop in pressure and increase in velocity which would affect the overall velocity of the current within the basin. The best angle to use was found to be 18° but the distance between the bottom flow director and the wall of the basin was too close and velocities where too great. This is why the top too have a slight curve and the 3rd has been kept straight to give the final configuration in Figure 7, to be used for future simulations.

4 RESULTS AND DISCUSSION

4.1 Velocity vectors

Below from Figure 9a-12b are the results from the series of CFD simulations on how the current basin will behave at three different water levels and three different inlet velocities. The figures show the fluid flow velocity magnitudes via vectors and color map, Figure 8 shows the reference points where the result values were taken from. These set of results are to show how the flow of fluid behaves through the direction grid . As shown by the screenshots the turbulence of the flow of fluid increases with velocity and a decrease in height, which can be seen when comparing Figure 9a and Figure 12a. The objective of the task was to direct the flow of fluid and reduce the amount of turbulent flow caused by the inlet, the result of the thought to be optimum combination of flow directors are shown alongside the simulated environment without them in place to compare how the fluid flows and how well the direction grid performs.

Throughout the simulations the performance of the direction grid varies as Figures 9 and 11 which show the flow at a water height of 1m and intake velocities of 0.6m/s and 0.3m/s, indicate that there is a lot more of a split in directions when the fluid flows through the direction grid in comparison to the other results. Suggesting that the combination of the flow directors needs to be adjusted. In most other cases the direction grid worked well, when looking at the first case the flow is directed more into a laminar flow and the velocities in Figure 9a, between the inlet and the midsection have a smaller difference in comparison to the velocity difference in Figure 9b. All velocity comparison figures can be found in Table 4 and Figure 13. As the results show, there is a slight increase caused by the flow directors which is to be expected and the difference will increase with the number of additional flow directors due to Bernoulli's equation (Hall 2015).

Figure 8. Reference points.

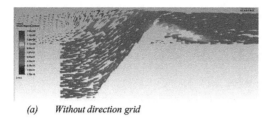 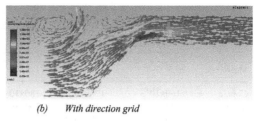

(a)   Without direction grid   (b)   With direction grid

Figure 9. Flow at water depth of 1.0m with 0.6m/s velocity.

(a)   Without direction grid   (b)   With direction grid

Figure 10. Flow at water depth of 0.5m with 0.6m/s velocity.

 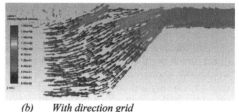

(a)   Without direction grid   (b)   With direction grid

Figure 11. Flow at water depth of 1m with 0.3m/s velocity.

(a)   Without direction grid   (b)   With direction grid

Figure 12. Flow at water depth of 0.5m with 0.3m/s velocity.

The above mentioned concludes that the direction grid design needs to be reviewed to work more effectively and suitable for all water heights. Hence why a new design as shown in Figure 14, was put into place. This new design is the final configuration that the following simulations have been calculated with. The final design has flow directors separated at 0.2m apart from each other, set at 18°, on a gradient of 5°.

4.2 *Fluid behavior*

To analysis the effect of the direction grid configuration over the entire basin, the height of the free surface area along three points, two of which are within the work area and the other is at start of the outlet, to plot the overall behavior of the water within the basin.

Due to the findings in the report by State Key Laboratory of Ocean Engineering (Shan et al, 2010),

Table 4. Velocity vectors results.

Case		Midsection avaerage velocity	
Inlet velocity	water depth	without	with
0.6	1.5	0.39	0.4
	1	0.79	0.746
	0.5	1.72	1.3
0.3	1.5	0.2	0.2
	1	0.4	0.4
	0.5	0.79	0.89
0.1	1.5	0.07	0.068
	1	0.13	0.16
	0.5	0.28	0.35

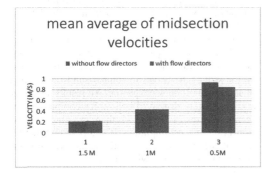

Figure 13. Mean results from velocity vectors.

Figure 14. Final direction grid configuration.

the operating conditions of the basin would never excide a water height of 1.5m, therefore it was regarded as a waste of time to simulate further. As mentioned previously, the finding in the report also stated that the current velocity had operating conditions between 0.1m/s and 0.4m/s. Therefor these will be the conditions simulated along with the wave generation to give an accurate representation of the model.

To show that the overall flow of fluid is being directed in the direction that is required, streamlines can be used to simply and give a visual aid into understanding the overall direction of the fluid flow. Streamlines are a group of curves that follow the tangent line of the velocity vector to indicate the overall direction of that stream of velocity (Wikipedia, 2019). This is calculated by using the divergence cross product rule of the velocity vector, Equation 1a, and the difference in displacement of the massless fluid element, Equation 1b, which results as Equation 1c, this is defined by the following (MIT, 2011);

$$\vec{V} = (x, y, z, t) = v\hat{i} + u\hat{j} + w\hat{k} \quad (1a)$$

$$\vec{ds} = d\hat{i} + dy\hat{j} + dz\hat{k} \quad (1b)$$

$$\therefore$$

$$\vec{ds} \times \vec{v} = 0$$

$$\therefore$$

$$wdy - vdz)\hat{i} + (udz - wdx)\hat{j} + (vdx - udy)\hat{k} \quad (1c)$$

This calculation can then be applied to the generated data from the fluent module to simulate the streamlines through the tank to compare how well the flow directors preform.

The first case is shown in Figure 15, which has the highest water level and velocity of 1m and 0.6m/s.

When making a comparison of the streamlines in Figure 15-18, it is clear that the flow directors are successful in directing the flow of fluid and there is a direct relationship between the current velocity and turbulence generated within the basin as it seems to be that with the increase of velocity in Figure 15 compared to Figure 16, there is a tolerable increase in turbulence.

Figure 15. Streamlines of 1m water depth and 0.6m/s velocity.

Figure 16. Streamlines of 1m water depth and 0.4m/s velocity.

Figure 17. Streamlines of 0.5m water depth and 0.6m/s velocity.

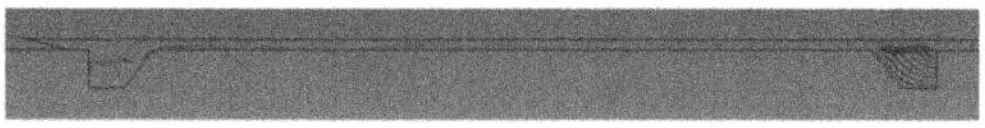

Figure 18. Streamlines of 0.5m water depth and 0.4m/s velocity.

It would also seem that, the water height also has the same relation with turbulence as we can see when comparing Figure 16 and Figure 18.

4.3 *Generating waves*

In order to accurately simulate the behavior of the fluid within the basin within operation, the geometry needs to be altered with the additions of a wave breaker and wave maker. The geometry in Figure 19 shows the updated geometry, as the wave generation system is made with a piston instead of a pivot, a paddle will resemble the piston which is located 2m away from the vertical wall. As mentioned previously, the wave breaker section will become a porous zone within ANSYS *FLUENT.*

Due to mesh mapping, the water level will be indicated via patch. To generate the waves accurately, dynamic mesh is needed in order to move the paddle in a horizontal motion. For the dynamic mesh to work a UDF is needed which is the law of motion that the selected geometry will follow. Equation 2 is the one that is used for the paddle in all cases, only the variables change value to change the speed, start position and velocity of the wave maker, resulting in different types of waves.

$$vel[0] = a * \omega * \sin(\omega * time - p) \qquad (2)$$

Where, vel = the directional vector, a= amplitude, ω = frequency and p = starting position within the period cycle. The dynamic mesh method that was selected was layering as the model is 2D, all cells are bounded to one sided face and are adjacent to each other. The dynamic mesh zones are as followed in Figure 20.

4.4 *Addition of waves results*

In order to create a detailed picture of the current basin in operation there are many aspects to look at; free surface behavior, current velocities, force acting on wave generation paddle and how the behavior of the wave maker has an influence.

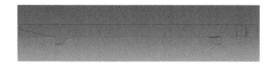

Figure 19. Additions to geometry.

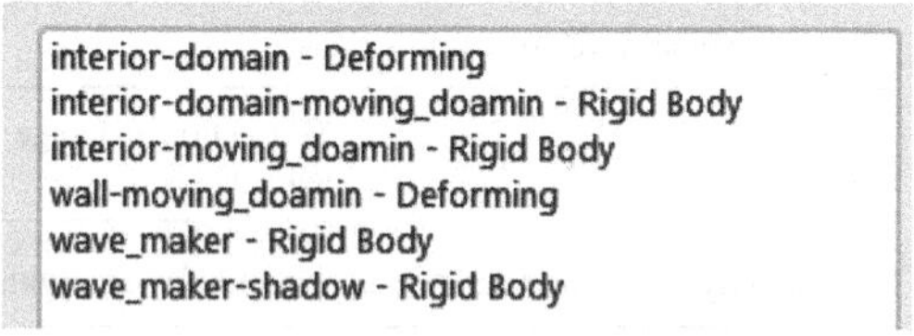

interior-domain - Deforming
interior-domain-moving_doamin - Rigid Body
interior-moving_doamin - Rigid Body
wall-moving_doamin - Deforming
wave_maker - Rigid Body
wave_maker-shadow - Rigid Body

Figure 20. Dynamic mesh meshing zones.

To organize this, the wave maker behavior has been split into cases were a handful of variables can be changed to discover the relationships. Case A has the just under the maximum amplitude the wave maker can operate at 584mm of travel, case B has an amplitude of 254mm and case C has an amplitude of 140mm. All cases have an inlet velocity of 0.4m/s as this is what is stated as a high operating condition and all measurement datum's are taken from the left end wall of the basin.

As shown above, the main cause for an increase of drag is unsurprisingly the increase in the water height, however this variable seems to have more of an effect on the size of the waves in comparison to the change in amplitude of the wave paddle. All results are tabled and graphically displayed bellow for comparison. As seen in Figures 21, 26 and 31, there is a gradual diffusion in the waves amplitude. It's to be noted that the rate at which the waves diffuse at are different between CFD and in towing tanks.

Case A:

Water height (m)
1.1
1.05
1
0.95
0.9
0.85
-10
40
90
140
190
240
Time (sec)
30 meters
15 meters
12 meters

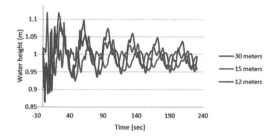

Figure 21. Free surface behavior graph of case A at 1m.

Position (m)
58.05
58
57.95
57.9
57.85
57.8
57.75
0
50
100
150
200
250
Time (sec)

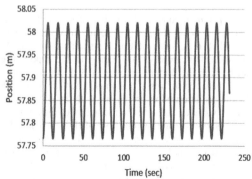

Figure 22. Wave paddle behavior graph of case A at 1m.

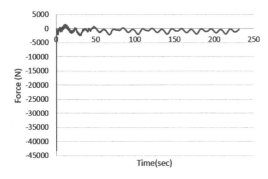

Figure 23. Drag force graph of case A at 1m.

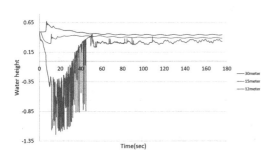

Figure 24. Free surface behavior graph of case A at 0.5m.

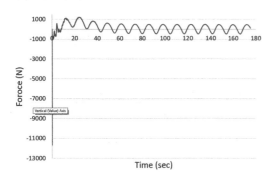

Figure 25. Drag force graph of case A at 0.5m.

Case B:

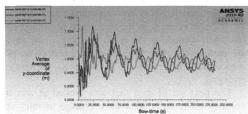

Figure 26. Free surface behavior graph of case B at 1m.

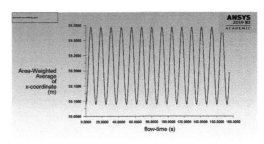

Figure 27. Wave paddle behavior graph of case B at 1m.

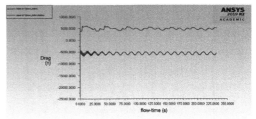

Figure 28. Drag force graph of case A at 1m.

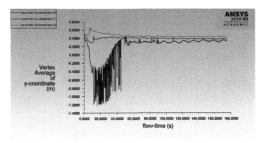

Figure 29. Free surface behavior graph of case B at 0.5m.

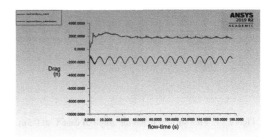

Figure 30. Drag force graph of case B at 0.5m.

Case C:

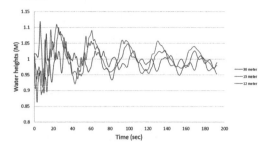

Figure 31. Free surface behavior graph of case C at 1m.

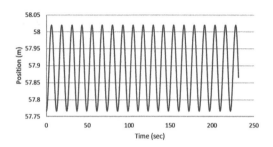

Figure 32. Wave paddle behavior graph of case C at 1m.

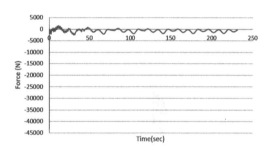

Figure 33. Drag force graph of case C at 1m.

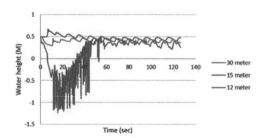

Figure 34. Free surface behavior graph of case C at 0.5m.

As Tables 5, 6 and 7 show, there is not much difference in the maximum velocity and average velocity with a smaller displacement of the wave paddle but a minor difference when the wave paddle is operating at maximum displacement. The same study has been used in the 0.5m water height with the results displayed in Table 8 and 9.

Unfortunately, there was no results recovered for the average velocity in the maximum amplitude case but when comparing the result in Table 7, the values are particularly close to each other, therefore an estimation can be made by looking at the pattern emerging.

The next set of data that was looked at was the velocity differences between a change in inlet velocity and the water level height as shown in Table 10. For this Case C will be used throughout to gives a clear image on how the relationship between the two variables influence the fluids behavior.

Table 5. Wave heights in all cases graphically displayed.

Frequency (Hz)	Amp (mm)	\multicolumn{3}{c	}{0.5}	\multicolumn{3}{c}{1}
		Max	Min	Avg	Max	Min	Avg
0.624	70	0.7	-1.25	0.4	1.2	0.83	0.99
0.51	127	0.7	-1.23	0.4	1.2	0.86	1.1
0.395	294	0.7	-1.2	0.4	1.12	0.8	1.0

Table 6. Maximum velocities in 1m water with 0.4m/s inlet velocity.

		\multicolumn{3}{c}{Position along x-axis}
		47.76	30	15
Frequency (Hz)	Amp (mm)	\multicolumn{3}{c}{Velocities (m/s)}
0.624	70	0.475	0.82	0.8
0.51	127	0.9	0.7	0.91
0.395	294	0.7	0.7	0.6

Table 7. Average velocities in 1m water with 0.4m/s inlet velocity.

		\multicolumn{3}{c}{Position along x-axis}
		47.76	30	15
Frequency (Hz)	Amp (mm)	\multicolumn{3}{c}{Velocities (m/s)}
0.624	70	0.473	0.725	0.79
0.51	127	0.9	0.69	0.87
0.395	294	0.4	0.664	0.6

Table 8. Maximum velocities in 0.5m water with 0.4m/s inlet velocity.

Frequency (Hz)	Amp (mm)	Position along x-axis		
		47.76	30	15
		Velocities (m/s)		
0.624	70	1	1.95	1.85
0.51	127	1.1	1.8	1.95
0.395	294	1.1	1.8	2

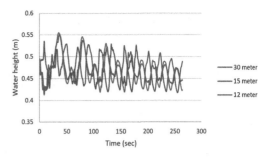

Figure 35. Free surface behavior graph of case C at 0.5m With 0.1m/s velocity.

Table 9. Average velocities in 0.5m water with 0.4m/s inlet velocity.

Frequency (Hz)	Amp (mm)	Position along x-axis		
		47.76	30	15
		Velocities (m/s)		
0.624	70	1	1.7	1.75
0.51	127	1.14	1.8	1.95
0.395	294	-	-	-

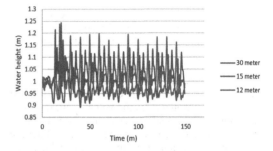

Figure 36. Free surface behavior graph of case C at 1m With 0.1m/s velocity.

Table 10. Velocity differences with change in water height and inlet velocity.

Water height (m)	Inlet velocity (m/s)	Vmax			Vavg		
		15m	30m	47m	15m	30m	47m
1	0.4	0.91	0.7	0.9	0.87	0.69	0.9
0.5		1.85	1.95	1.0	1.4	1.8	0.85
1	0.1	1.1	1.8	1.1	1.8	1.8	1.14
0.5		0.5	0.5	0.575	0.48	0.46	0.59

The results show that either end of the tank has a tolerable amount of difference in velocity, also there seems to be an increase in velocity with a smaller body of fluid in both inlet velocity cases.

Having a low inlet velocity also aligns the flow of water throughout the basin considerably more than with the 0.4m/s velocity as shown in Figure 35 and 36.

In comparison, the average water height starts to stabilize within the larger water depth out of the two a lot sooner, which contradicts the previous results.

This indicates that the inlet velocity is a key influencing factor on the turbulence within the basin.

5 CASE VALIDATION

The case has been validated by using of experimental setup installed in the Seakeeping and Maneuvering basin at BSHC. Table 11 shows the paddle oscillating motion frequency – Fz [Hz], the prescribed value of piston amplitude, predicted values and corresponding measured paddle oscillation amplitude values, the amplitude of the generated waves and the maximum force acting on the piston for the three generated wave series.

The numbers in Table 11 show good convergence for the third (larger) wave. It has to be realized, that the pressure sustained within the hydraulic drive system does not depend on the forces acting on the wave maker flap in its oscillatory motion – whatever waves generated, the pressure will be kept constant, while forces in the piston are proportional to the dynamic water pressure on the flap. This is the reason to have better agreement between calculated and measured piston force values at maximum loading of the system.

Table 11. Predicted and measured wave parameters at wave slope s=1/20.

	Frequency	WG piston amp.	Paddle amplitude Calculated	Measured	Wave amplitude Calculated	Measured	Force Calculated	Measured
	F_z [Hz]	[mm]	[mm]	[mm]	[mm]	[mm]	[kg]	[kg]
1	1,249	14,7	25,00	24,24	25,00	26,00		20 728
2	0,51	111	188,60	198,99	150,00	198,08	12 281	19 978
3	0,422	177,4	301,50	293,64	200,00	248,17	20286	22 692

6 CONCLUSIONS

To conclude, the installation of flow directors appears to be successful in directing the flow of current along the basin, in the desired direction causing a reduction in turbulence. This however has, in operating condition cases, increased the velocity within the working area of the basin by a mean average of 0.05m/s. With the addition of waves this also increases the velocity but only significantly with a small water depth of 0.5m. As the results show, the current velocities are influenced more by the change in water depth and inlet velocity than the change in the amplitude of the wave generation paddle. One of the main areas that is subject for further review is the length of the flow directors as this was an item that was not experimented with a lot and also the difference in changing the distance from the paddle to the end of the basin.

ACKNOWLEDGEMENTS

This research was partially supported by:

- Erasmus+ EC Project
- MASRI – Infrastructure for Sustainable Development of Marine Research including the Participation of Bulgaria in the European Infrastructure Euro-Argo, an object of the National Roadmap for Scientific Infrastructure (2017-2023) of Republic of Bulgaria
- Bulgarian Ministry of Education and Science under the National Research Program "Young Scientists and Postdoctoral Students" approved by DCM # 577/17.08.2018

REFERENCES

Bidokhti, M. K. (2011). Design and Construction of an Optimum Wave Flume. *Journal of Applied Fluid Mechanics, Vol. 5, No. 3, pp. 99-103, 2012.*, 100–102.

Chan kyu Yang, S. W. (1998). Control of Current in Ocean Engineering Basin. *Internatinal Workshop on Modeling of Ocean Enviroments in Wave & Current Basin* (pp. 215–225). Taejon: RealSea '98.

Hall, N. (2015, 05). *Bernoulli's equation*. Retrieved from NASA: https://www.grc.nasa.gov/www/k-12/airplane/bern.html.

MIT. (n.d.). *MIT: Fluids – Lecture 8 Notes*. Retrieved from MIT:http://web.mit.edu/16.unified/www/FALL/fluids/Lectures/f08.pdf

Stansby, P. K. (2013). Coastal hydrodynamics – present and future, Journal. *Journal of Hydraulic Research*, 343.

Streamlines, streaklines, and pathlines. (2019, 09). Retrieved from Wikipeadia: https://en.wikipedia.org/wiki/Streamlines,_streaklines,_and_pathlines.

Tiebing Shan, H. L. (2010). Numerical, experimental and full-scaled investigation on the current generation system of the new deepwater offshore basin. *ASME 2010 29th International Conference on Ocean, Offshore and Arctic Engineering*. Shanghai.

Effect of vertical rigid wall on a moored submerged horizontal flexible porous membrane

Y.C. Guo, S.C. Mohapatra & C. Guedes Soares
Centre for Marine Technology and Ocean Engineering (CENTEC), Instituto Superior Técnico, Universidade de Lisboa, Lisbon, Portugal

ABSTRACT: The effect of vertical rigid wall on a moored finite submerged flexible porous membrane under oblique wave interaction is analysed. The mathematical model is based on the assumption of linearized potential theory and structural response. The analytical solution is obtained using the matched eigenfunction expansion method and the numerical results are computed by solving complex dispersion relation using numerical perturbation scheme. The convergence of the series solution is checked through numerical computation by analysing the values of reflection coefficient and wave forces. Further, the present results are validated against published analytical and experimental data. Several numerical results of reflection coefficient, wave forces, and free surface elevations on different design parameters are analysed to study the effect of rigid wall. It is observed that the wave reflection greatly depends on the width of the membrane and the optimum distance from rigid wall.

1 INTRODUCTION

During the last two decades, there is a significant interest on wave interaction with submerged flexible porous-type structures for wave attenuation in the marine environment to model as an effective breakwater and protecting coastal infrastructures by creating tranquillity zone. The effectiveness of these structures is due to the fact that it does not block the incoming waves and can be properly tuned for attenuating the wave height and on the other hand, they are able to reflect, absorb, dissipate wave energy, cost-effective, and be environmentally friend. In the recent time, there is a more interest in the use of floating/submerged flexible porous membrane-type structures for protection of coastal areas as breakwater and support structure for floating wind turbine platform in close proximity.

An interesting aspect of submerged flexible porous membrane/plate under the action of waves is the presence of vertical wall near the submerged structure due to the significant reduction of wave reflection (Cho & Kim, 2008; Hu & Wang, 2005). Recently, researchers are interested to study the various effects of vertical wall near the submerged flexible porous membrane on different wave phenomena such as wave reflection, transmission, dissipation, and wave forces. The matched eigenfunction expansion method and boundary-element method (BEM) using simple-sources are generally taken to analyse this kind of problem, There has been a little study made by few researchers on the wave interaction with a horizontal submerged flexible porous membrane based on analytical approach.

For instance, Cho & Kim (2008) investigated the interaction of waves with submerged horizontal porous flexible membrane using eigenfunction expansion and BEM under the consideration of fixed edge conditions in two-dimensions. Porous type membrane structure has been used below the floating cylindrical breakwater for better performance as a breakwater system based on a numerical and experimental study.

Ji et al (2015, 2016b) investigated a cylindrical floating breakwater with a mesh cage and balls in two-dimensional wave flume and three-dimensional wave basin respectively. Ji et al (2016a) investigated four types of floating breakwaters: cylindrical floating breakwater, porous floating breakwater, mesh cage floating breakwater type-I and mesh cage floating breakwater type-II. The result shows that the two kinds of mesh cage floating breakwater have a good performance on incident wave transmission.

Further, in order to improve the wave-blocking efficiency, many researchers have analysed the horizontal flexible porous structures as more wave energy can be dissipated by adding a proper porosity to an impermeable flexible structure. Mohapatra & Guedes Soares (2016) analysed the reflection and transmission coefficients to study the effect of submerged flexible membrane on moored finite elastic plate in finite water depth.

Very recently, Guo et al. (2020b) reviewed the various aspect of applications of porous membranes and net-type structures for breakwaters and fish cages. On the other hand, Guo et al. (2020a) studied the wave energy dissipation of a submerged horizontal flexible porous membrane over flat bottom based on complex

DOI: 10.1201/9781003216599-81

dispersions (complex wave numbers) under analytical approach.

Advancing further the work of Guo et al. (2020a), in the present study a mathematical model associated with wave interaction with a moored submerged horizontal flexible porous membrane near a vertical rigid wall is formulated and the analytical solution is presented to analyse the effect of wall on the moored submerged porous membrane. Using the matched eigenfunction expansion method, the analytical solution is obtained and MATLAB code is developed along with numerical perturbation scheme to solve the complex dispersion.

The present results of reflection and vertical force are compared with known published analytical and experimental data. It is observed that the present results are in good agreement with the analytical and experimental data. Further, several numerical results of reflection coefficient, non-dimensional vertical wave force on the membrane and non-dimensional horizontal wave force on rigid wall for different design parameters are analysed to study the effect of vertical rigid wall on submerged flexible porous membrane.

2 MATHEMATICAL FORMULATION

Under the assumption of linearized potential theory, the mathematical formulation of the boundary value problem is considered in three-dimensional Cartesian coordinate system (x, y, z) with x-z being the horizontal plane that coincides with the undisturbed free surface and the y-axis vertical downward positive direction. The horizontal flexible porous membrane of width $2a$ is infinitely long in z-direction and submerged at a depth h in the fluid region with constant water depth H. The rigid wall is placed after the origin O with distance L and thus, the distance between the wall and the membrane is $b=L-a$. Therefore, the fluid domain is divided into four regions: region 1 ($-\infty < x < -a$, $0 < y < H$), region 2 ($-a < x < a$, $0 < y < h$), region 3 ($-a < x < a$, $h < y < H$) and region 4 ($a < x < L$, $0 < y < h$).

A progressive wave with angular frequency ω is obliquely incident on the porous membrane and makes an angle θ with the positive x-axis (see Figure 1). It is assumed that the fluid is inviscid, incompressible and the motion is irrotational, then there exist velocity potentials Φ_j $(x, y, z; t)$ that can be defined as Φ_j $(x, y, z; t) = \mathrm{Re}\{\phi_j(x, y)\exp(ilz-i\omega t)\}$, where $j=1, 2, 3$ and 4 refer to region 1, region 2, region 3 and region 4, respectively, with $l=k_0\sin\theta$ is the wave number in z-direction. Further, the free surface elevation $\eta(x, z; t)$ and the submerged flexible porous membrane deflection ζ $(x, z; t)$ are of the forms $\eta(x, z; t)=\mathrm{Re}\{\eta(x)\exp(ilz-i\omega t)\}$ and $\zeta(x, z; t)=\mathrm{Re}\{\zeta(x)\exp(ilz-i\omega t)\}$, respectively.

The incident wave potential of linear waves propagating to the positive x- and z-directions is given by

$$\phi_I = \frac{igA}{\omega}\frac{\cosh k_0(H-y)}{\cosh k_0 H}e^{i\alpha_0 x}, \quad (1)$$

where $\alpha_0=\sqrt{k_0^2-l^2}$, $i=\sqrt{-1}$, A is the incident wave amplitude, and g is acceleration due to gravity. Further, the wavenumber k_0 satisfies the dispersion relation $\omega^2=gk_0\tanh(k_0H)$.

The spatial velocity potentials in each region satisfy the reduced wave equation as

$$\frac{\partial^2 \phi_j}{\partial x^2} + \frac{\partial^2 \phi_j}{\partial y^2} - l^2\phi_j = 0 \text{ for } j = 1, 2, 3, 4. \quad (2)$$

These velocity potentials also satisfy the free surface and the bottom boundary conditions as

$$\frac{\partial \phi_j}{\partial y} + K\phi_j = 0, y = 0, \ -\infty<x<L, j = 1, 2, 4. \quad (3)$$

$$\frac{\partial \phi_j}{\partial y} = 0, \ y = H, \ -\infty<x<L, j = 1, 3, 4 \quad (4)$$

where $K=\omega^2/g$.

Zero flux across the rigid wall is given by

$$\frac{\partial \phi_j}{\partial x} = 0, \ 0<y<H, \ x = L, j = 4 \quad (5)$$

The kinematic boundary condition on the submerged porous membrane is (Guo et al. 2020a)

$$\frac{\partial \phi_2}{\partial y} = \frac{\partial \phi_3}{\partial y} = -i\omega\zeta + ik_0G(\phi_2 - \phi_3), y = h, |x| \le a. \quad (6)$$

Dynamic boundary condition on the submerged porous flexible membrane:

$$\left(T_f\frac{\partial^3 \phi_3}{\partial y^3} - m_p\frac{\partial \phi_3}{\partial y} + K\phi_3\right) - K\phi_2$$
$$+ ik_0G\left(T_f\frac{\partial^2}{\partial y^2} - m_p\right)(\phi_3 - \phi_2) = 0, \ y = h, |x| \le a, \quad (7)$$

where $T_f=\sigma/\rho g$, $m_p=m_m\omega^2/\rho g$, with σ and m_m are the tension and mass of unit length of the membrane, and $G=G_r+iG_i$ is the complex porous-effect parameter (as in Jensen et al. 2014; Mohapatra et al. 2018).

It is assumed that both ends of the horizontal flexible membrane are anchored by spring moorings

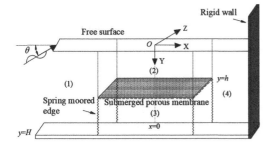

Figure 1. Schematic diagram of a moored submerged flexible membrane near a vertical wall.

with spring stiffness ks_1 and ks_2 at $x=-a$ and $x=a$, respectively. Hence, the edge conditions of the submerged porous membrane are given by

$$\sigma\zeta_x = ks_1\zeta, \quad x = -a, \; y = h, \qquad (8a)$$

$$\sigma\zeta_x = ks_2\zeta, \quad x = a, \; y = h. \qquad (8b)$$

The far field radiated condition is assumed to take of the form

$$\phi = \phi_I(x,y) + R_0\phi_I(-x,y), \quad x \to -\infty, \qquad (9)$$

where R_0 is the reflection wave amplitude.

The continuity of pressure and velocity across the vertical interfaces at $x=\pm a$ are given by

$$\phi_1 = \begin{cases} \phi_2, & x = -a, 0<y<h \\ \phi_3, & x = -a, h<y<H, \end{cases} \qquad (10)$$

$$\phi_4 = \begin{cases} \phi_2, & x = a, 0<y<h \\ \phi_3, & x = a, h<y<H, \end{cases} \qquad (11)$$

and

$$\frac{\partial\phi_1}{\partial x} = \begin{cases} \frac{\partial\phi_2}{\partial x}, & x = -a, 0<y<h \\ \frac{\partial\phi_3}{\partial x}, & x = -a, h<y<H, \end{cases} \qquad (12)$$

$$\frac{\partial\phi_4}{\partial x} = \begin{cases} \frac{\partial\phi_2}{\partial x}, & x = a, 0<y<h \\ \frac{\partial\phi_3}{\partial x}, & x = a, h<y<H. \end{cases} \qquad (13)$$

Next section will discuss the analytical solution procedure for the determination of velocity potentials in each region associated with oblique wave interaction with submerged flexible porous membrane near a rigid wall.

3 SOLUTION

The method of separation of variables has been used to obtain the analytical expressions of the velocity potentials and associated eigenfunctions. Applying the reduced wave equation (2) and the relevant boundary conditions (3-7), velocity potentials for each region are obtained as

$$\phi_1 = I_0 f_0(y)e^{i\alpha_0(x+a)} + \sum_{n=0}^{\infty} R_n f_n(y)e^{-i\alpha_n(x+a)}, \qquad (14)$$

$$\phi_2 = \sum_{n=0}^{\infty}\left\{A_n e^{-i\gamma_n(x+a)} + B_n e^{i\gamma_n(x-a)}\right\}U_n(y), \qquad (15)$$

$$\phi_3 = \sum_{n=0}^{\infty}\left\{A_n e^{-i\gamma_n(x+a)} + B_n e^{i\gamma_n(x-a)}\right\}D_n(y), \qquad (16)$$

$$\phi_4 = \sum_{n=0}^{\infty} C_n \cos\{\alpha_n(x-L)\}f_n(y), \qquad (17)$$

where

$$I_0 = \frac{ig}{\omega}\frac{\sqrt{\varepsilon_0}}{\cosh(k_0 H)}A, \qquad (18)$$

$$\alpha_n = \sqrt{k_n^2 - l^2}, \quad n = 0, 1, 2, \ldots \qquad (19)$$

$$\omega^2 = gk_n \tanh(k_n H), \quad n = 0, 1, 2, \ldots \qquad (20)$$

$$\gamma_n = \sqrt{p_n^2 - l^2}, \quad n = 0, 1, 2, \ldots \qquad (21)$$

with the wave number p_n, $n=0, 1, 2, \ldots$ satisfy the complex dispersion relation (as in Liu et al. 2008):

$$K - p_n \tanh(p_n H) = F_n\{K\tanh(p_n H) - p_n\}, \qquad (22)$$

where

$$S_n = T_f p_n^2 - m_p, \quad n = 0, 1, 2, \ldots, \qquad (23)$$

$$F_n = \frac{S_n p_n L_n^2}{S_n p_n L_n - (1 - L_n^2)(K + ik_0 GS_n)}. \qquad (24)$$

with $L_n=\tanh p_n(H-h)$ with $n=0,1,2,\ldots$. The roots of the dispersion relation (22) are obtained by applying the perturbation scheme as discussed in Mendez & Losada (2004).

The eigenfunctions $U_n(y)$'s and $D_n(y)$'s are given by

$$U_n(y) = \cosh p_n(H-y) - F_n \sinh p_n(H-y), \quad (25)$$

$$D_n(y) = (1-T_n)\cosh p_n(H-y), \quad (26)$$

with

$$T_n = F_n \coth p_n(H-h). \quad (27)$$

The eigenfunctions $f_n(y)$'s are given by

$$f_n(y) = \frac{\cosh k_n(H-y)}{\sqrt{\varepsilon_n}}, \quad n = 0, 1, 2, \ldots \quad (28)$$

with

$$\varepsilon_n = \frac{2k_n H + \sinh(2k_n H)}{4k_n}, \quad n = 0, 1, 2, \ldots \quad (29)$$

The eigenfunctions $f_n(y)$'s are orthogonal and is defined as

$$F_{mn} = \langle f_m(y), f_n(y) \rangle$$
$$= \int_0^H f_m(y) f_n(y) dy = \begin{cases} 0, & m \neq n \\ 1, & m = n \end{cases} \quad (30)$$

Considering the four continuity conditions (10-13) at the fluid-structure interfaces, the mooring edge conditions (8), and the orthogonal relation (30), a linear system of $4(N+1)+2$ algebraic linear equations can be obtained to determine the unknowns A_n, B_n, R_n, C_n, associated with the velocity potentials (14-17) by truncating the infinite series to finite number of term $N+1$ for A_n, B_n and N for R_n, C_n. After obtaining all the unknowns, the reflection coefficient K_r, the free surface elevation η_j in each region, the non-dimensional vertical wave forces K_f on the submerged porous membrane, and the non-dimensional horizontal wave forces K_w on the rigid wall can be computed by using the following-formulae:

$$K_r = |R_0/I_0|, \quad (31)$$

$$\eta_j = \frac{i}{\omega}\frac{\partial \phi_j}{\partial y}, y = 0, j = 1, 2, 4, \quad (32)$$

$$F_v = \rho i \omega \int_{-a}^{a}(\phi_3 - \phi_2)dx, \text{ for } y = h, \quad (33)$$

$$K_f = \frac{F_v}{\rho g A H}, \quad (34)$$

$$F_w = \rho i \omega \int_0^H \phi_4 dy, \; x = L, \quad (35)$$

$$K_w = \frac{F_w}{\rho g A H}. \quad (36)$$

Next section will present and analyse several numerical results of reflection coefficient, wave forces, and free surface elevations to study the effects of non-dimensional distance between membrane and rigid wall, non-dimensional membrane width, spring stiffness, oblique angle and submergence depth. Matlab codes are developed along with complex roots over porous membrane based on a perturbation scheme to compute the numerical results. In the present computations, MATLAB-R2017b, 64-bit (win64) is used to perform calculation and all numerical computations were performed in a desktop machine with Intel ® core i7-4790 CPU with 3.60GHz processor and 32 GB of ram memory. On an average, each case took roughly 5-7 minutes to finish.

4 NUMERICAL RESULTS AND DISCUSSION

In order to check the accuracy of the numerical computation, recently, Guo et al. (2020a) studied the convergence of the similar problem without rigid wall by computing the reflection, transmission, and dissipation coefficients for different number of roots along with mooring stiffness and porous-effect parameter in finite water depth.

In the context of the present work, the convergence of the method is demonstrated in the Table 1 by computing the reflection coefficient and wave forces for different wave periods, taking into account the different number of terms N of the series solution. For computational accuracy, the number of terms N in the series solution is restricted to 30 throughout the computation. In addition, all numerical computations are executed by considering fluid density $\rho = 1025 \text{kgm}^{-3}$ and acceleration due to gravity g = 9.8ms^{-2} unless mentioned otherwise.

Figure 2 shows the comparison of reflection coefficient and non-dimensional vertical wave force on the flexible porous membrane between the present analytical results and data from Wu et al. (1998) for h/H=0.2, λ=4H (λ is the incident

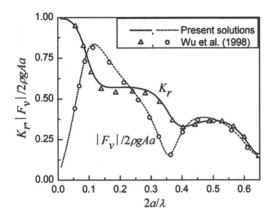

Figure 2. Comparison of reflection coefficients K_r and non-dimensional vertical force on the porous membrane between the present solution and data from Wu et al. (1998).

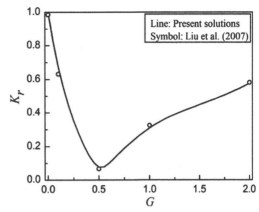

Figure 3. Comparison of reflection coefficients K_r between the present solutions and data from Liu et al. (2007).

Table 1. Convergence of K_r, K_f and K_w with increasing values of N at h/H=0.1, a/H=0.5, b=a, $\sigma/\rho g H^2$=0.1, θ=30°, ks_1=ks_2=10^6 N/m, m_m=0 kg/m^2, and G=0.1+i.

	N	K_r	K_f	K_w
T = 4s	0	0.8725	0.0487	0.2151
	10	0.8706	0.0479	0.2173
	20	0.8710	0.0443	0.2189
	30	0.8711	0.0428	0.2196
	31	0.8711	0.0427	0.2197
	32	0.8711	0.0425	0.2197
T = 10s	0	0.9628	0.4295	0.7836
	10	0.9109	0.7343	0.3911
	20	0.9116	0.7280	0.3969
	30	0.9120	0.7256	0.3992
	31	0.9120	0.7253	0.3995
	32	0.9120	0.7251	0.3997

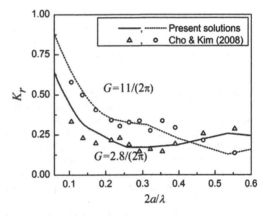

Figure 4. Comparison of reflection coefficients K_r between the present solutions and experimental data from Cho and Kim (2008).

wavelength), b=0, m_m =0 kg/m^2, θ =0.1°, ks_1= ks_2 =10^9 N/m and G=1/2π.

In order to compare with the flexible porous plate, the tension of the present membrane is assumed to be $\sigma/\rho g H^2$ =75. The comparison showed that the present results are in well agreement with Wu et al. (1998). Moreover, it is seen that the flexible porous membrane with infinite tension works like a flexible porous plate.

Figure 3 gives the comparison of reflection coefficient versus porous-effect parameter G between present result and Liu et al. (2007) with k_0H=1.3, h/H=0.2, a/λ=0.15, b=0, $\sigma/\rho g H^2$ =0.7, m_m =0 kg/m^2, θ =0.1° and ks_1= ks_2=10^8 N/m. It is seen that reflection coefficients of the present structure are in good agreement with that of a perforated wall breakwater with a submerged horizontal porous plate.

Figure 4 compares the present results with experimental data from Cho & Kim (2008) for h/H=0.025, a/H=0.5, b=0, $\sigma/\rho g H^2$=0.9, m_m=0 kg/m^2, θ=0.1° and ks_1= ks_2=10^8 N/m. It is observed that the present result is well-agreed with experimental data from published papers.

Figure 5 presents the reflection coefficient K_r as a function of the non-dimensional width of the membrane $2a/\lambda$ for different non-dimensional finite distances between membrane and rigid wall b/λ. It is seen that for $2a/\lambda$<0.5, the reflection coefficient K_r decreases rapidly with increasing $2a/\lambda$ whilst, the non-dimensional width of the membrane $2a/\lambda$ has small effect on K_r for 0.5<$2a/\lambda$<1.5 where less than 20% incident waves are reflected by the porous membrane. Moreover, the effect of $2a/\lambda$ and b/λ on the reflection coefficient K_r are negligible for $2a/\lambda$>1.5 and less than 10% incident waves are reflected. Therefore, the optimal non-dimensional width of the membrane nears $2a/\lambda$=1.5 for better performance on incident wave reflection reduction.

Figure 6 plots the (a) reflection coefficient K_r, (b) non-dimensional horizontal wave force on the rigid wall K_w, and (c) non-dimensional vertical wave force on the flexible porous membrane K_f versus non-

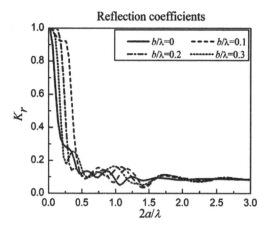

Figure 5. Variations of the reflection coefficient K_r for different b/λ with $T=7$s, $h/H=0.2$, $\sigma/\rho gH^2=0.6$, $m_m=0$ kg/m^2, $\theta=0.1°$, $ks_1=ks_2=10^8$ N/m and $G=0.5$.

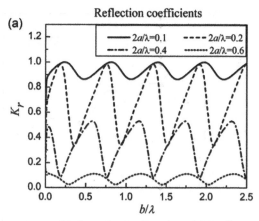
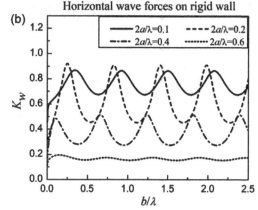
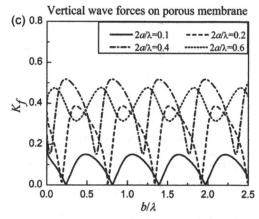

dimensional distance b/λ between the submerged flexible porous membrane and the rigid wall for different non-dimensional width of the porous membrane $2a/\lambda$. It is observed that with increase in the values of $2a/\lambda$, K_r and K_w are decreases periodically whilst the average value of K_f increases. This is due to the fact that as the membrane width increases the porous area of the flexible membrane increases which implies more wave dissipates by the membrane that leads to less reflection and smaller horizontal wave force on the wall. This finding is consistent with results shown in Figure 5. Further, it is seen that the reflection coefficient K_r is periodic in nature for b/λ and minimum reflection occurs at some specific points. This phenomenon of minimum reflection is called wave trapping (as in Chwang and Dong, 1984).

The non-dimensional water free surface elevation amplitude $|\eta|/A$ is help for understanding the phenomena of minimum and maximum reflections. In Figure 7, the effect of non-dimensional b/λ on the non-dimensional free surface elevation amplitude $|\eta|/A$ versus dimensionless x/a with same calculating parameters as in Figure 6 except $2a/\lambda=0.2$ are plotted.

It is observed that the free surface elevation amplitude $|\eta|/A$ in region 1 for $b/\lambda=0.2$ is more than twice of that for $b/\lambda=0.4$, which can be explained by the maximum and minimum reflection coefficient K_r at $b/\lambda=0.2$ and $b/\lambda=0.4$ respectively for $2a/\lambda=0.2$ in Figure 6(a). It is also observed that for $b/\lambda=0.2$, the wave amplitude in the downstream region is larger than that in the upstream and structure covered regions. This is because of the amount of wave energy concentrated in the downstream region is not trapped by the vertical wall and that amount of energy not able to absorbed by the porous membrane.

Figure 8 shows the (a) reflection coefficient K_r, (b) non-dimensional horizontal wave force on

Figure 6. Variations of the (a) reflection coefficient K_r, (b) horizontal wave forces on rigid wall K_w and (c) vertical wave force on the porous membrane K_f, for different a/λ with $T=7$s, $h/H=0.2$, $\sigma/\rho gH^2=0.6$, $m_m=0$ kg/m^2, $\theta=30°$, $ks_1=ks_2=10^8$ N/m and $G=0.5$.

the rigid wall K_w, and (c) non-dimensional vertical wave force on the flexible porous membrane K_f versus non-dimensional distance b/λ for different spring stiffness ks_1, ks_2 with $T=7$s, $h/H=0.2$, $a/\lambda=0.3$, $\sigma/\rho gH^2=0.6$, $m_m=0$ kg/m^2, $\theta=30°$ and

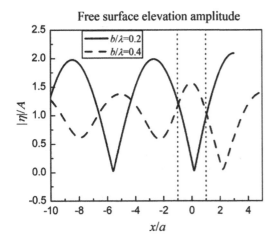

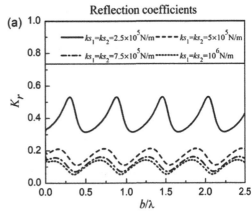

Figure 7. Variations of the free surface elevation $|\eta|/A$ for different b/λ with $T=7s$, $h/H=0.2$, $2a/\lambda=0.2$, $\sigma/\rho g H^2 =0.6$, $m_m=0$ kg/m^2, $\theta=30°$, $ks_1=ks_2=10^8$ N/m and $G=0.5$.

$G=0.5$. It is seen from Figure 8(a) and (b) that with the increase of the spring stiffness ks_1, ks_2, less incident wave will be reflected by the flexible porous membrane and the non-dimensional horizontal wave force acting on the rigid wall K_w decreases. This is due to the fact that spring moorings with higher stiffness restrict the displacement of two ends of the flexible porous membrane better and therefore, less scattered wave produces and reflected by the membrane.

Moreover, as the spring stiffness increases, its effect on K_r and K_w decreases. Figure 8(c) shows that spring moorings with higher value of stiffness has negligible effect on wave force acting on the flexible porous membrane. The observations and reasons are similar as in Guo et al. (2020a).

In Figure 9, effects of oblique angle on the (a) reflection coefficient K_r and (b) non-dimensional horizontal wave forces on the rigid wall K_w versus non-dimensional finite distance b/λ with $T=7s$, $h/H=0.2$, $a/\lambda=0.3$, $\sigma/\rho g H^2=0.6$, $m_m=0$ kg/m^2, $ks_1=ks_2=10^8$ N/m and $G=0.5$. It is observed that the reflection coefficient K_r and dimensionless horizontal wave forces on the rigid wall K_w vary periodically with increasing b/λ at different periodic interval for all incident wave angle θ. Moreover, with the increase of the incident wave angle θ, the average value of reflection coefficients K_r decreases firstly as $\theta <15°$ and then followed by an increasing trend as $\theta >15°$ whilst, the average value of K_w keeps increasing for all θ.

Figure 10 shows the (a) reflection coefficient K_r, (b) non-dimensional horizontal wave forces on the rigid wall K_w, and (c) non-dimensional vertical wave forces on the porous membrane K_f for different submergence depth h/H as a function of non-dimensional

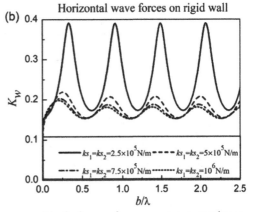

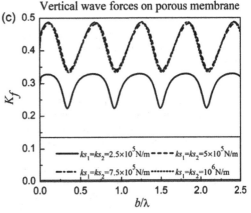

Figure 8. Effect of spring stiffness ks_1, ks_2 on the (a) reflection coefficient K_r, (b) horizontal wave forces on rigid wall K_w, and (c) vertical wave forces on the porous membrane K_f versus b/λ.

finite distance b/λ with $T=7s$, $a/\lambda=0.3$, $\sigma/\rho g H^2 =0.6$, $m_m=0$ kg/m^2, $\theta=30°$, $ks_1=ks_2=10^8$ N/m and $G=0.5$. Similar as in Figure 6 and Figure 9, K_r, K_w and K_f all vary periodically with increasing b/λ for each submergence depth h/H. Further, it is observed that larger submerged depth of the porous membrane leads to more incident wave reflection and larger

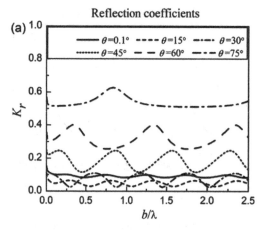
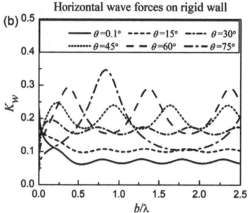
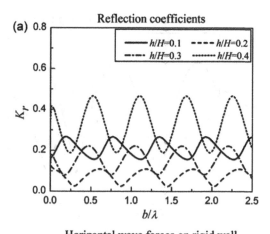
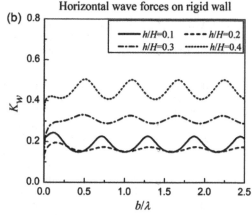
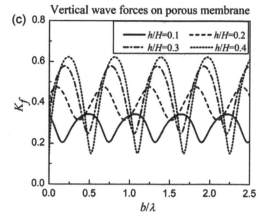

Figure 9. Effect of oblique angle on the (a) reflection coefficient K_r and (b) horizontal wave forces on rigid wall K_w versus angle θ.

wave force on the rigid wall as $h/H \geq 0.2$ whilst the pattern is in contrast for $h/H < 0.2$. Nevertheless, with the increase of h/H, wave forces on the flexible porous membrane increase too. This is due to the fact that as the submerged membrane is away from the free surface, submerged flexible membrane is having less effect in dissipating the wave energy concentrating near the surface and thus the wave reflection by the rigid wall increases and as well wave forces.

Figure 11 shows the reflection coefficient K_r as a function of non-dimensional distance b/λ for different porous-effect parameter G with $T=7s$, $h/H=0.2$, $a/\lambda=0.3$, $\sigma/\rho gH^2=0.6$, $m_m=0$ kg/m^2, $\theta=30°$ and $ks_1 = ks_2 = 10^8$ N/m. It is seen that for a membrane with small value of porosity ($G \leq 1$), with the increase of G, the reflection coefficient K_r decreases too, whilst larger porous-effect parameter G makes the reflection coefficient K_r increases as $G \leq 1$. This is due to the fact that the real part of the porous-effect parameter G relates to the resistance effect of the porous membrane, therefore increasing G leads to more incident wave energy dissipation. Moreover, the

Figure 10. Effect of submergence depth h/H on the (a) reflection coefficient K_r, (b) horizontal wave forces on rigid wall K_w, and (c) vertical wave forces on the porous membrane K_f versus b/λ.

porous-effect parameter G also represents the porosity of the porous membrane. With the increase of G, the membrane becomes transparent gradually and finally disappear as $G \to \infty$, thus more incident wave will be transmitted to the rear of the membrane and then be reflected by the rigid wall.

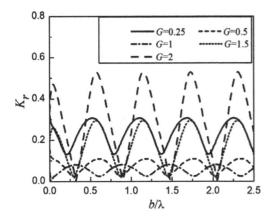

Figure 11. Effect of porous-effect parameter G on the reflection coefficient K_r versus b/λ.

5 CONCLUSIONS

Effect of vertical rigid wall near a moored submerged horizontal flexible porous membrane in finite water depth is analyzed using the matched eigenfunction expansion method. Convergence of the present analytical solution is checked and the accuracy of the code has been validated with analytical results and experimental data available in the literature. In numerical results, effects of the width of the porous membrane, finite distance between porous membrane and rigid wall, porous-effect parameter, the spring stiffness and incident wave angle on the reflection coefficient and wave forces acing on the rigid wall and porous membrane are studied.

It is observed that the incident wave reflection greatly depends on the width of the horizontally submerged flexible porous membrane and the finite distance from it to the rigid wall. A porous membrane with appropriate width could make incident wave reflection less than 20%. Further, the finite distance b/λ has a non-standard sinusoidal effect on the reflection coefficient and wave forces on the flexible porous membrane and the rigid wall. Moreover, optimal values of the porous-effect parameter, incident wave angle and submergence depth of the porous membrane exist for the best performance on trapping of incident waves.

As a future study of the present work, considering the complicated sea bed and including flexible porous vertical wall to design a wave absorber in 3D system. Furthermore, the model could be compared with different relevant methodologies in order to optimize the model characteristics for engineering applications.

ACKNOWLEDGEMENTS

The paper is performed within the project Hydroelastic behaviour of horizontal flexible floating structures for applications to Floating Breakwaters and Wave Energy Converters (HYDROELAST-WEB), which is co-funded by the European Regional Development Fund (Fundo Europeu de Desenvolvimento Regional - FEDER) and by the Portuguese Foundation for Science and Technology (Fundação para a Ciência e a Tecnologia - FCT) under contract 031488_770 (PTDC/ECI-EGC /31488/2017). The work of the first author has been supported in part by the scholarship from China Scholarship Council (CSC) under Grant No. 201707920004. The second author has been contracted as a Researcher by the Portuguese Foundation for Science and Technology (Fundação para a Ciência e Tecnologia-FCT), through Scientific Employment Stimulus, Individual support under the Contract No. CEECIND/04879/2017. This work contributes to the Strategic Research Plan of the Centre for Marine Technology and Ocean Engineering (CENTEC), which is financed by the Portuguese Foundation for Science and Technology (Fundação para a Ciência e Tecnologia - FCT) under contract UIDB/UIDP/00134/2020.

REFERENCES

Cho, I.H. & Kim, M.H. 2008. Wave absorbing system using inclined perforated plates. *Journal of Fluid Mechanics* 608: 1–20.

Chwang, A.T. & Dong, Z.N. 1984. Wave-trapping due to a porous plate. In: *Proceedings of the 15th Symposium on Naval Hydrodynamics*, pp. 407–414.

Guo, Y.C., Mohapatra, S.C. & Guedes Soares, C. 2020a. Wave energy dissipation of a submerged horizontal flexible porous membrane under oblique wave interaction. *Applied Ocean Research* 94: 101948.

Guo, Y.C., Mohapatra, S.C. & Guedes Soares, C. 2020b. Review of developments in porous membranes and net-type structures for breakwaters and fish cages. *Ocean Engineering* doi.org/10.1016/j.oceaneng.2020.107027.

Hu, H.H. & Wang, K.H. 2005. Damping effect on waves propagating past a submerged horizontal plate and a vertical porous wall. *Journal of Engineering Mathematics* 131(4): 427–437.

Jensen, B., Jacobsen, N.G. & Christensen, E.D. 2014. Investigations on the porous media equations and resistance coefficients for coastal structures, *Coastal Engineering* 84: 56–72.

Ji, C.Y., Chen, X., Cui, J., Yuan, Z.M. & Incecik, A. 2015. Experimental study of a new type of floating breakwater. *Ocean Engineering* 105: 295–303.

Ji, C.Y., Chen, X., Cui, J., Gaidai, O. & Incecik, A. 2016a. Experimental study on configuration optimization of floating breakwaters. *Ocean Engineering* 117: 302–310.

Ji, C.Y., Guo, Y.C., Cui, J., Yuan, Z.M. & Ma, X.J. 2016b. 3D experimental study on a cylindrical floating breakwater system. *Ocean Engineering* 125: 38–50.

Liu, Y., Li, Y.C. & Teng, B. 2007. Wave interaction with a perforated wall breakwater with a submerged horizontal porous plate. *Ocean Engineering* 34(17-18): 2364–2373.

Liu, Y., Li, Y.C., Teng, B. & Dong, S. 2008. Wave motion over a submerged breakwater with an upper horizontal porous plate and a lower horizontal solid plate, *Ocean Engineering* 35(16): 1588–1596.

Mendez, F.J. & Losada, I.J. 2004. A perturbation method to solve dispersion equations for water waves over dissipative media, *Coast Engineering* 51: 81–89.

Mohapatra, S.C. & Guedes Soares, C. 2016. Effect of submerged horizontal flexible membrane on moored floating elastic plate. *In*: Guedes Soares and Santos (Eds), *Maritime Technology and Engineering* 3. London: Taylor & Francis Group, pp. 1181–1188, ISBN: 978-1-138-03000-8.

Mohapatra, S. C., Sahoo, T. & Guedes Soares, C. 2018 Surface gravity wave interaction with a submerged horizontal flexible porous plate. *Applied Ocean Research* 78: 61–74.

Wu, J., Wan, Z. & Fang, Y. 1998. Wave reflection by a vertical wall with a horizontal submerged porous plate. *Ocean Engineering* 25(9): 767–779.

The multi-objective optimisation of breakwaters using evolutionary approach

Nikolay O. Nikitin, Iana S. Polonskaia, Anna V. Kalyuzhnaya & Alexander V. Boukhanovsky
ITMO University, Saint Petersburg, Russia

ABSTRACT: In engineering practice, it is often necessary to increase the effectiveness of existing protective constructions for ports and coasts (i. e. breakwaters) by extending their configuration, because existing configurations don't provide the appropriate environmental conditions. That extension task can be considered as an optimisation problem. In the paper, the multi-objective evolutionary approach for the breakwaters optimisation is proposed. Also, a greedy heuristic is implemented and included to algorithm, that allows achieving the appropriate solution faster. The task of the identification of the attached breakwaters optimal variant that provides the safe ship parking and manoeuvring in large Black Sea Port of Sochi has been used as a case study. The results of the experiments demonstrated the possibility to apply the proposed multi-objective evolutionary approach in real-world engineering problems. It allows identifying the Pareto-optimal set of the possible configuration, which can be analysed by decision makers and used for final construction.

1 INTRODUCTION

To identify the optimal breakwater layout for a specific problem, the decision maker (that usually is a strong expert in the field) should propose or choose the configuration which best matches the set of cost and quality criteria (Steuer & Steuer 1986). In most cases, the decision maker tries to find the solution based on previous experience and the subject area knowledge. This problem is often considered as a minimisation of the risks (Sørensen & Burcharth 2004), (Alises et al. 2014) during the coastal structures life cycle.

However, the optimal design problem is difficult for expert analysis, especially in the case of high-dimensional problems, because the expert should take into account all objective functions, problem constraints and check a large number of new construction configurations to find a near-optimal solution. Therefore, the intelligent optimisation methods (e.g. evolutionary algorithms) are widely used for this task (Lagaros et al. 2002)structural. Also, the involvement of the numerical metocean models make it possible to simulate the local environmental conditions for different layouts of the protective constructions and obtain the values of quality metrics for proposed configuration.

The existing approaches to this task and similar structural optimisation problems are considered in Section 2. In Section 3, the formulation of the breakwater optimisation task as a multi-objective optimisation problem is described. It includes several objective functions and constraints. Also, this section includes the description of the SWAN wind-wave model's configuration for the port water area that is used for wave height estimation. Several implemented evolutionary approaches are presented in Section 4. Section 5 includes the description of the experiments' setup and the experimental results for the breakwaters layout optimisation in the Sea Port of Sochi as a case study. Finally, conclusions and future plans are presented in Section 6.

2 RELATED WORK

Each particular optimal design problem has a lot of peculiarities, and it is necessary to take them into account during the algorithm developing process. However, it is useful to create some generalized approach which could be applied for a broad range of breakwaters' optimisation problems and could provide the opportunity to select the optimisation objectives and constraints for different real-world cases. The correct selection of objective function and constraints is the main part of the considered optimisation problem-solving process. There are a lot of objectives and constraints that can be involved. The comprehensive survey of constraints and criteria that can be taken into attention in problems of optimal harbor's design identification and improvement is provided in (Diab et al. 2017).

Usually, authors simplify the analysed problem to find a solution faster, because time and computational resources are strictly limited in many cases. Thus, in (Elchahal et al. 2013), a genetic optimisation approach for the design of small detached

DOI: 10.1201/9781003216599-82

breakwaters with three segments is used. It considers wave disturbance inside the port and ship manoeuvring constraints. In (Diab et al. 2014) the two-segment breakwater was optimised using an evolutionary algorithm in the strictly restricted range of spatial coordinates, directly transformed to a numerical chromosome. A wave disturbance constraint was added to the fitness function. Also, two other constraints related to breakwater geometry characteristics have been taken into account. Decisions with unsatisfactory geometry characteristics (incorrect angle between two segments or undesired location) are discarded during optimisation. In both papers, each segment of the breakwater is presented in the chromosome using the end coordinates.

Besides the spatial coordinates of breakwater's segments, there are other breakwater characteristics that can be optimised. For example, in (Nikoo et al. 2014) and (Somervell et al. 2017), the structural parameters of the double-layered breakwater were optimised using multi-objective genetic algorithms. In the first case, three parameters of a compound breakwater were optimised: porosities of each breakwater wall and the gap between them, in the second case five parameters such as porosities of the upper part of the wall for each breakwater layer, the relative depths of submergence of upper parts of these walls into the water and the relative gap between the vertical walls. Optimisation problem statement combines two conflicting objectives: maximisation of the wave energy dissipation coecient and minimisation of the material volume in the breakwater in the first case. The second case also combined conflicting wave reflection and wave transmission objectives.

It is noticed that a lot of marine optimisation engineering problems can be solved more reliably using multi-objective optimisation approaches. Thus, in (Elkinton et al. 2008), the authors compared five different optimisation approaches, including evolutionary algorithms, to optimise the layout of an offshore windfarm. A fitness function is based on a trade-off between maximum energy production on the farm and minimum cost. A similar problem was solved in (Gonz´alez-Gorbeña et al. 2019) for the array of tidal turbine generators. To reduce the computational cost of simulations, the surrogate model was used during optimisation. The optimisation of fairway design parameters was considered in (Gucma & Zalewski 2019). In (Rustell et al. 2014), a genetic algorithm was used for the selection of optimal structural parameters for the gas terminal layout. The genetic chromosome representation is based on nine different characteristics describing the certain terminal configuration. The fitness function includes three objectives (capital cost, maintenance cost and vessel downtime due to waves) which are simultaneously minimised. The proposed algorithm allows finding a few configurations that are better than the design obtained using the traditional approach and decreases the cost by a factor of 30.

However, the described approaches are tested mostly for specific simplified cases. The proposed algorithms are aimed to resolve low-dimension tasks with a short chromosome, that can describe the real harbour constructions only in a coarse way. For that reason, it is useful to develop the multi-objective approach for the breakwater optimisation and validate it with a real-world test case.

3 PROBLEM STATEMENT

3.1 Breakwater design as optimisation task

The extension of existing breakwaters' configuration can be separated into several aspects: the selection of the attached segments number, the attachment points' location for the new segments, the spatial area for defence and coordinates of control points. These variables can be involved in the optimisation problem, but they can also be defined in the preliminary step by the economic and engineering criteria and then considered as static. The optimal design task for this case is presented in Figure 1.

The problem of breakwater design identification can be formulated as multi-objective function optimisation in the space of structural parameters of breakwaters and written as:

$$\theta_{opt} = \arg\min_\theta F(\theta),$$
$$F(\theta) = \mathcal{G}(H_j(Y(\theta)), C(\theta), N(\theta)), \quad (1)$$

where $\mathcal{G}(\bullet)$ is an operator for multiobjective transformation to a function F for a given structural parameters set θ, H_j is the wave height objective function for certain control points, C is the objective function for construction cost, N is objective function for manoeuvring safety, Y is the environmental characteristics simulation results.

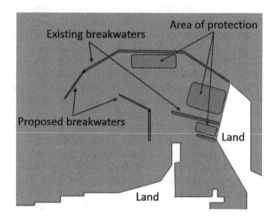

Figure 1. The scheme of harbor with existing breakwaters and the structure of attached breakwaters that should be optimised.

There are additional objectives exists that can be taken into account during optimisation using the proposed approach (the implemented software architecture allow to specify the custom objective functions set). For example, the resonant periods associated with eigenfrequencies in the port area can be calculated to estimate the possibility of harbor seiches' occurrence. However, the experimental studies in this paper are based on the objectives described in subsection 3.3.

3.2 Structural parameterisation

There are various parameterisation approaches that can be used to represent the optimisable structure in the most efficient way (Samareh 2001). The breakwaters' layout can be represented as a grid with binary (solid/wet) values in each cell; as a set of absolute or relative spatial (Cartesian) coordinates; as parameters of approximating function (polynomial or spline). The most widely used approach for breakwater structure representation - Cartesian encoding - has several disadvantages for numerical optimisation. This encoding does not allow to modify the length and direction of the breakwater segment separately (Bendsøe & Kikuchi 1988). So, it is not convenient to "rotate" the part of a breakwater to an optimal angle using crossover or mutation operators of the genetic algorithm.

To resolve this issue, the modified approach based on encoding in relative polar coordinates is proposed. Since the transformation of Cartesian coordinates to polar ones is objective, there is no structural simplification in this step (the relative position of each segment is still represented by two numerical values - angle and direction instead of X and Y values for Cartesian coordinates). However, the evolutionary transformations of a polar chromosome can be implemented in a more effective way. The Cartesian and angular chromosomes are represented in Figure 2.

3.3 Objective functions

The correct selection of the objective functions is an important part of the formalisation of the real-world breakwater design issue to the optimisation problem. As it noted in (Diab et al. 2017), there are a lot of various criteria (environmental, hydro-dynamical, mechanical, economical, manoeuvring, etc.) that should be taken into attention during the decision-making process. However, to construct the objective function, it is necessary to implement the algorithm for their numerical evaluation. To evaluate the metric for the navigational objective, the complex port simulation model (Olba et al. 2018) state or the ship path model (Sutulo et al. 2002) mathematical can be used. Cost objectives can be based on probabilistic economic models (Piccoli 2014).economic. Also, the additional penalty for the complexity of solution (e.g. number of segments with non-zero length) can be involved, but usually, the cost objective takes it into account in a non-direct way)

In a frame of proposed multi-objective evolutionary algorithms, several objectives are used. They are described in Table 1. In addition to the main objectives (cost, navigational, and wave height-based), structural constraints were added. They restrict the generation of unrealistic solutions (self-crossing and land-covering breakwaters) during the evolutionary optimisation because such configurations can cause unstable behaviour of the wind-wave model.

The value of cost objective is directly proportional to summary breakwaters' length:

$$C = \sum_{i=1}^{n} \sqrt{(x_{2,i} - x_{1,i})^2 + (y_{2,i} - y_{1,i})^2} \cdot s, \quad (2)$$

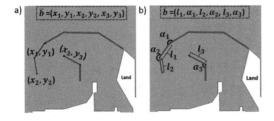

Figure 2. The breakwater parameterisation in different encoding: a) with Cartesian coordinates b) with angular coordinates.

Table 1. The objective functions and constraints considered in breakwater optimisation problems.

ID	Name	Description	Measurement unit
1	Relative cost objective	Total cost of new breakwaters construction	Wave height in each control point
2	Relative navigational objective	The safety of ships' maneuvering scheme represented as minimum length between each point of new breakwaters and central line of fairways	
3 4 5	Relative wave height objective	Wave height in each control point	
6	Structural constraint	Self-intersections are not allowed	Number of selfintersections
7	Navigational constraint	Breakwater shouldn't intersect fairway center line	Number of fairway center line intersections
8	Relative quality objective	Used in single – objective evolutionary algorithm and should consider all necessary objectives	The composition of the rest relative objectives

where n is a number of breakwaters' segments, s is a grid step.

The value of the wave height objective is a vector of significant wave heights h in control points (where m is the number of control points):

$$H = (h_1, h_2, ..., h_m) \qquad (3)$$

The navigational objectives are evaluated by a simple geometrical model described in Figure 3 and written as:

$$N = min(\|p_{i,j}^b - p_k^f\|), \\ i = \overline{1, n_1}, j = \overline{1, n_2}, k = \overline{1, n_3} \qquad (4)$$

where n_1 is a number of breakwaters, n_2 is a number of breakwater points, n_3 - number of fairway points, and p^b and p^f are breakwater and fairway points.

Relative value of each objective type is calculated as:

$$f_i^{rel} = \frac{f_i^{new} - f_i^{old}}{f_i^{old}} \cdot 100\%, i = \overline{1, t} \qquad (5)$$

where t is a number of objectives.

The objective function for the single-objective optimization approach is presented as the following convolution of objectives:

$$f_{single}^{rel} = \frac{100 + mean(f_2^{rel}) + f_3^{rel}}{100 - f_1^{rel}}, \qquad (6)$$

This function combines all objectives to achieve the best relative quality of obtained solutions.

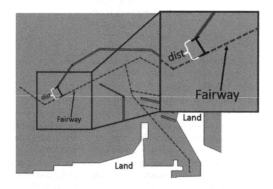

Figure 3. The concept of navigational objective based at minimal fairway distance.

3.4 Wave simulation

The analysis of the effectiveness of a specific breakwater layout requires the corresponding numerical simulation of met-ocean conditions for the proposed harbour design. The numerical models of wind-wave interaction allow calculating the wave characteristics based on depth, wind direction and constructions configuration in the harbour. A common approach is to use the third-generation wind-wave model for this purpose. According to the community experience (Niculescu & Rusu 2018), the spectral wind-wave model SWAN (Booij et al. 1999) third was used to reproduce the integral wave characteristics in the desired area. Numerical simulation was performed on a regular grid with cell size 25x25m. The parameters of extreme storms were used as a boundary conditions for simulation. The spatial structure of breakwaters' configurations was represented using obstacles (the reflection coefficients was set differently for the solid wall and tetrapod breakwaters).

The simulations were run for each breakwaters' conguration generated by the evolutionary algorithm. The estimation of the wave height was carried out in several control points.

The simultaneous reproduction of the reflection and diffraction effects inside harbor by the SWAN model is quite limited (Violante-Carvalho et al. 2009). However, the better simulation of the diffraction effect can be achieved by modification of the model as described in (Kim et al. 2017).

The scheme of interaction between the evolutionary algorithm and the SWAN model in the frame of the described optimisation task is presented in Figure 4.

4 EVOLUTIONARY APPROACHES TO THE BREAKWATER OPTIMISATION

4.1 Multi- and single- objective evolutionary optimisation

Evolutionary algorithms (EA) are population-based methods for global search that especially demonstrate their advantages over classical optimization approaches in multi-objective and multi-dimension optimization problems. In addition, this class of

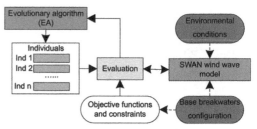

Figure 4. The scheme of interaction between of evolutionary algorithm and wind wave model during optimisation.

algorithms can easily be adapted to the problem at hand. In this study, the multi-objective approach - the Strength Pareto Evolutionary Algorithm (SPEA2) and the single-objective evolutionary approach - Differential evolution (DE) are used for solving the multi-objective breakwaters optimization problem.

The selection of parents is the first stage of evolutionary optimisation, then, the crossover and mutation of selected individuals are performed. The main difference between using multi-objective and single-objective genetic algorithms consists in the parents' selection strategy and the fitness evaluation strategy. Tournament selection is used in single-objective DE and the fitness function is defined as the combination of all optimisation criteria (objectives described in Section 3). The multi-objective approach uses the special type of selection adapted to multi-criteria problems and includes few steps (environmental selection and binary tournament selection).

The crossover operator allows the individuals to interchange the genetic material. Thus the algorithm has an opportunity to combine effective breakwater's segments from different individuals. Figure 5 illustrates the crossover operator which is applied for the breakwater design problem with three attached segments. According to this concept, two selected parents swap genetic information between blocks created by chromosome separation at a randomly generated crossover point. In this implementation (pairwise crossover), the spatial coordinates (Cartesian or angular) belonging to the same breakwater's segment cannot be separated by a crossover point.

Mutation introduces random changes to chromosome genes that allow the algorithm to avoid local minima. The implemented mutation operator for breakwaters' chromosome is demonstrated in Figure 6. First, genes are selected with a certain mutation probability, then the randomly generated values obtained from normal distribution $N(\mu, \sigma^2)$ (μ and σ are set for each variable type) are added to genes that were selected on the previous stage.

4.2 Greedy evolutionary heuristics

The greedy algorithms perform a locally optimal choice at each optimisation stage in order to obtain

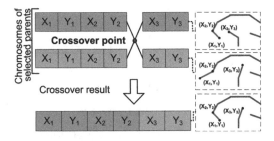

Figure 5. Illustration of the one-point crossover for 3-segment breakwater.

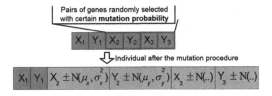

Figure 6. Mutation process representation for N-segment breakwater.

global or local optimum in the end (DeVore & Temlyakov 1996). Greedy heuristics in evolutionary algorithms can be used to intensify the convergence and improve the quality of the obtained solutions (Julstrom 2005). The idea of a greedy evolutionary application for the breakwater optimisation is to separate the complex task of simultaneous optimisation of all breakwaters' segments to several stages of individual optimisations for each segment. The application of this concept for the breakwaters' optimal design task is presented in Figure 7.

The pseudocode of the final implementation of the greedy heuristic in a frame of the SPEA2 evolutionary algorithm is presented in Alg. 1.

Data: populationSize,
archiveSize, crossoverRate, mutationRate
Result: best individual from archive
pop InitPopulation(populationSize)
archive;
while not ConvergenceCriterion() do
for individ in pop do
waveHeightObj, costObj,
navigationalObj
CalculateObj(individ, waveModel)
end
union archive + pop
for individ in union do
individ.fitness
CalculateFitness(individ)
end
archive TakeNonDominated(union, archiveSize)
matingPool
BinaryTournamentSelection(union, populationSize)

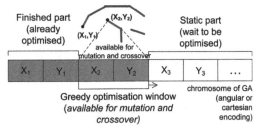

Figure 7. The chromosome modification with greedy approach to evolutionary optimisation.

```
pop
CrossoverAndMutation(matingPool,
greedyMask, crossoverRate,
mutationRate) greedyMask
ShiftRight(greedyMask)
end
```

5 EXPERIMENTAL STUDIES

5.1 Case study

As far as it is necessary to validate the proposed evolutionary approach in the real-world case, the harbour of Sea Port of Sochi was selected as an experimental case study. The port is located in 43.58N, 39.71E (the coast of the Black Sea). The configuration of harbour and breakwaters are presented in Figure 8. As can be seen, there are two existing protection structures: the main breakwater attached to the coast and the additional detached breakwater.

The actual problem for this port is the events of strong pitching of moored ships caused by rare extreme weather conditions (storms). The proposed solution is to build additional breakwaters in addition to the existing one. It raises the task of optimal design identification.

To use this task as a case study, we simplify it to make the experimental results of the algorithms validation more clear and interpretable. There are three static points for breakwaters' attachment. Each additional breakwater consists of two segments.

5.2 Experimental results

The plan of experiments consists of several stages: 1. Experimental validation of SOEA with angular and Cartesian encoding for the attached breakwaters optimisation problem; 2. Experimental validation of MOEA with both encoding for the same problem; 3. Estimation of a greedy heuristic for both algorithms. 4. Analysis of stability for obtained solutions.

During the optimisation, 30 generations with 30 individuals in each generation were examined. The Figure 9 represents the example of Pareto fronts variability (for the multi-objective algorithm) for five independent runs. The values of the cost-based objective function and the averaged wave height objective function in different points were used to obtain 2-dimensional fronts for visualisation. It can be seen that the common pattern is the same, but not all non-dominating solutions are found during each run.

The hypervolume indicator is widely applied in the evaluation of MOEA effectiveness (Chugh et al. 2019) and analysis of convergence. The Figure 10 illustrates the variability of non-dominated hypervolume for five independent optimisation runs. Despite the fact that one of the runs converges not in the best-found value of the hypervolume, other runs achieved convergence in the same range.

The Figure 12 represents the comparison of Pareto fronts for multi-objective and single-objective algorithm. It can be seen, that the multi-objective algorithm with Angular encoding provides a better set of non-dominated solutions. Also, angular encoding allows increasing of effectiveness of all examined algorithms. The impact of the greedy heuristic is not so clear from this figure, but it provides competitive results.

The dependency of the hypervolume value from a number of wave model runs during evolution is presented in Figure 13 for different approaches. It can be noted that the multi-objective algorithm with angular encoding allows finding better solutions in comparison with other algorithms. Also, it's clear that the greedy heuristic included in the algorithm makes it possible to obtain a competitive solution at

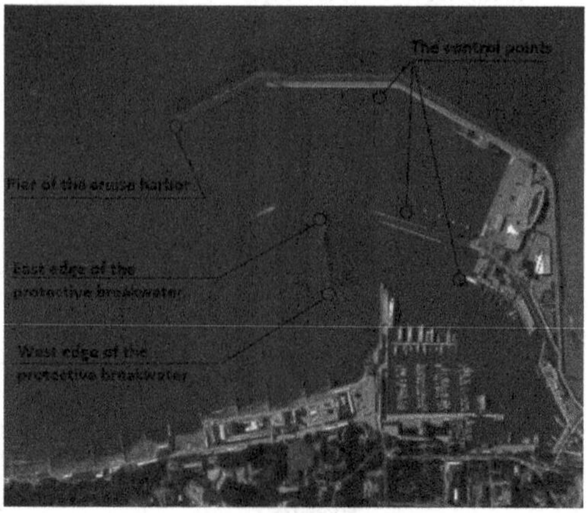

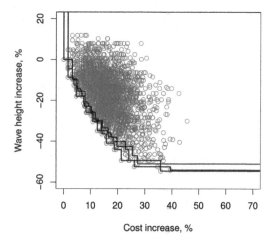

Figure 8. The satellite image of Sea Port of Sochi. The orange points represent locations for new attached breakwaters, the orange lines represents existing constructions.

Figure 9. The example of variability of Pareto fronts (non-dominated points) for five independent optimisation runs. The gray color represents the dominated-points.

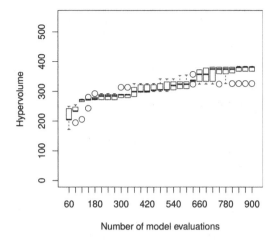

Figure 10. The boxplots of convergence of hypervolume metric in objectives space for five independent optimisation runs.

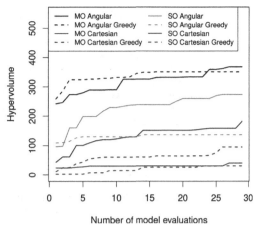

Figure 13. The convergence of the hypervolume metric in the full objectives space for the multi-objective algorithm with angular and Cartesian encoding. The solid lines are the basic algorithm, the dashed lines are the greedy modification.

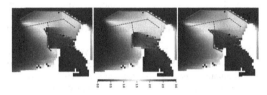

Figure 11. The variants of Pareto-optimal breakwaters' configurations and corresponding significant wave height fields (in meters). The coast is represented as a white mask.

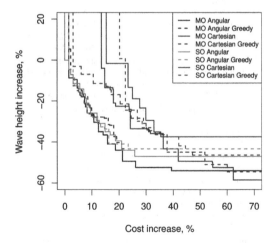

Figure 12. The comparison of Pareto fronts for the multi-objective algorithm with angular and Cartesian encodings. The solid lines are the basic algorithm, the dashed lines are the greedy modification.

early generations for an evolutionary algorithm. Finally, all variants of the single-objective algorithm demonstrate worse performance.

Several examples of simulations' results obtained from the Pareto front are presented in Figure 11. It can be seen that redundant segments are shrunk to zero length even without an additional structural complexity penalty. Since the optimisation approach is a Pareto-based, the breakwaters' configurations with different trade-offs between objective functions (mostly construction cost and wave height decrease) can be found it the final solutions set.

It should be noted that the choice of the most appropriate solution from the Pareto front is a complicated task (Horn 1997). The final decision should be based on an expert's experience, additional numerical and physical simulations and involvement of more detailed objectives.

6 CONCLUSIONS

In this paper, we formulate the task of breakwater layout optimal design identification as a computationally-intensive multi-objective optimisation problem. There are several evolutionary approaches validated using the Sochi port as a case study. The experiments were conducted with two different chromosome encodings (angular and Cartesian), two algorithms (single-objective differential evolution and multi-objective SPEA2). The multi-objective approach with angular chromosome encoding was selected as the most effective. Also, the effectiveness of greedy heuristics was evaluated as a part of the optimisation approach, and the faster convergence of the results set was obtained.

The source code of the implemented algorithms and software system used for experimental studies is available in the public repository (https://github.

com/ITMO-NSS-team/breakwaters-evolutionary-optimisation).

The future extension of this research is planned as a generalisation of optimisation approaches to both attached and detached breakwaters, implementation of more realistic and detailed task cases, the involvement of additional synthetic and real-world test cases into experimental studies, and comparison of obtained configurations with expert solutions.

ACKNOWLEDGEMENTS

This research is financially supported by The Russian Scientific Foundation, Agreement #19-11-00326.

The research is carried out using the equipment of the shared research facilities of HPC computing resources at Lomonosov Moscow State University.

REFERENCES

Alises, A., Molina, R., Gómez, R., Pery, P., & Castillo, C. (2014). Overtopping hazards to port activities: Application of a new methodology to risk management (port risk management tool). *Reliability Engineering & System Safety 123*, 8–20.

Bendsøe, M. P. & Kikuchi, N. (1988). Generating optimal topologies in structural design using a homogenization method. *Computer methods in applied mechanics and engineering 71*(2), 197–224.

Booij, N., Ris, R. C., & Holthuijsen, L. H. (1999). A third-generation wave model for coastal regions: 1. model description and validation. *Journal of geophysical research: Oceans 104*(C4), 7649–7666.

Chugh, T., Kratky, T., Miettinen, K., Jin, Y., & Makonen, P. (2019). Multiobjective shape design in a ventilation system with a preference-driven surrogate-assisted evolutionary algorithm. In *Proceedings of the Genetic and Evolutionary Computation Conference*, pp. 1147–1155.

DeVore, R. A. & Temlyakov, V. N. (1996). Some remarks on greedy algorithms. *Advances in computational Mathematics 5*(1), 173–187.

Diab, H., Lafon, P., & Younes, R. (2014). Optimisation of breakwaters design to protect offshore terminal area. *MSI*, 70–75.

Diab, H., Younes, R., & Lafon, P. (2017). Survey of research on the optimal design of sea harbours. *International Journal of Naval Architecture and Ocean Engineering 9*(4), 460–472.

Elchahal, G., Younes, R., & Lafon, P. (2013). Optimization of coastal structures: Application on detached breakwaters in ports. *Ocean Engineering 63*, 35–43.

Elkinton, C. N., Manwell, J. F., & McGowan, J. G. (2008). Algorithms for offshore wind farm layout optimization. *Wind Engineering 32*(1), 67–84.

González-Gorbeña, E., Pacheco, A., Plomaritis, T. A., Ferreira, Ó., Sequeira, C., & Moura, T. (2019). Surrogate-based optimization of tidal turbine arrays: A case study for the faro-olhão inlet. In *International Conference on Computational Science*, pp. 548–561. Springer.

Gucma, S. & Zalewski, P. (2019). Optimization of fairway design parameters: Systematic approach to manoeuvring safety. *International Journal of Naval Architecture and Ocean Engineering*.

Horn, J. (1997). Multicriterion decision making, handbook of evolutionary computation, volume 1, f1. 9: 1–f1. 9: 15.

Julstrom, B. A. (2005). Greedy, genetic, and greedy genetic algorithms for the quadratic knapsack problem. In *Proceedings of the 7th annual conference on Genetic and evolutionary computation*, pp. 607–614. ACM.

Kim, G. H., Jho, M. H., & Yoon, S. B. (2017). Improving the performance of swan modelling to simulate diffraction of waves behind structures. *Journal of Coastal Research 79*(sp1), 349–353.

Lagaros, N. D., Papadrakakis, M., & Kokossalakis, G. (2002). Structural optimization using evolutionary algorithms. *Computers & structures 80*(7-8), 571–589.

Niculescu, D. M. & Rusu, E. V. (2018). Evaluation of the new coastal protection scheme at mamaia bay in the nearshore of the black sea. *Ocean Systems Engineering-an International Journal 8*(1), 1–20.

Nikoo, M. R., Varjavand, I., Kerachian, R., Pirooz, M. D., & Karimi, A. (2014). Multi-objective optimuma design of double-layer perforated-wall breakwaters: Application of nsga-ii and bargaining models. *Applied Ocean Research 47*, 47–52.

Olba, X. B., Daamen, W., Vellinga, T., & Hoogendoorn, S. P. (2018). State-of-the-art of port simulation models for risk and capacity assessment based on the vessel navigational behaviour through the nautical infrastructure. *Journal of Traffic and Transportation Engineering (English Edition) 5*(5), 335–347.

Piccoli, C. (2014). Economic optimization of breakwaters-case study: Maintenance of port of constantza's northern breakwater.

Rustell, M., Orsini, A., Khu, S.-T., Jin, Y., & Gouldby, B. (2014). Decision support for designing new lng terminals. In *Proceedings of the 33rd PIANC World Congress San Francisco. San Francisco, USA*.

Samareh, J. A. (2001). Survey of shape parameterization techniques for high-fidelity multidisciplinary shape optimization. *AIAA journal 39*(5), 877–884.

Somervell, L. T., Thampi, S. G., & Shashikala, A. (2017). A novel approach for the optimal design of a vertical cellular breakwater based on multi-objective optimization. *Coastal Engineering Journal 59*(04), 1750019.

Sørensen, J. D. & Burcharth, H. F. (2004). Risk-based optimization and reliability levels of coastal structures. In *International Forum on Engineering Decision Making, First Forum December*, pp. 5–9.

Steuer, R. E. & Steuer, R. (1986). *Multiple criteria optimization: theory, computation, and application*, Volume 233. Wiley New York.

Sutulo, S., Moreira, L., & Soares, C. G. (2002). Mathematical models for ship path prediction in manoeuvring simulation systems. *Ocean engineering 29*(1), 1–19.

Violante-Carvalho, N., Paes-Leme, R. B., Accetta, D. A., & Ostritz, F. (2009). Diffraction and reflection of irregular waves in a harbor employing a spectral model. *Anais da Academia Brasileira de Ciências 81*(4), 837–848.

Statistical analysis of the oil production profile of Campos' basin in Brazil

L.M.R. Silva & C. Guedes Soares
Centre for Marine Technology and Ocean Engineering (CENTEC), Instituto Superior Técnico, Universidade de Lisboa, Lisbon, Portugal

ABSTRACT: An analysis is made of a series of key parameters required to characterize the individual reservoir production performance and from them to adopt a development strategy for an oil basin composed of several oilfields. The early reservoir characterization and production profile estimation is of key importance for the decision making process of the most feasible development strategy of an oilfield project. The estimation of the initial hydrocarbon reserves and reservoir production performance allows the design of a range of technical and economic feasible concepts to exploit an oilfield. The use of reservoir analogy is adopted for the estimation of petroleum reserves required for such technical determinations. An improved model of the reservoir production performance can reduce the uncertainty of the new development by narrowing the range of outcomes for the decision maker. A case study is considered to apply the method to characterize the production profile of the Campos basin, located in Brazil.

1 INTRODUCTION

In order to recover the maximum fraction of the hydrocarbon initially in place, a comprehensive reservoir characterization and production plan aims to satisfy, at the same time, among other constraints, the operational, technological, economic and regulatory constraints.

The accuracy of the estimated reservoir performance is dictated by the quality of the reservoir model. Silva et al., (2017) highlighted that the main challenge of the reservoir management is to obtain a good predictive reservoir model. According to Santos et al., (2017) a collection of additional information can be useful to reduce the geological uncertainties associated with the recoverable reserves and flow characteristics.

Pertinent information about the reservoir production can go far beyond the typical reservoir data, as well as, depth, pressure, temperature, porosity, permeability and oil gravity. Descriptive parameters as for example, reservoir drive mechanism, fluid injection, artificial lift methods and drilling schedule are useful to establish a good production scheme.

The early reservoir characterization and production profile estimation is of key importance during the decision making process of the most feasible development strategy of an oilfield project.

Several authors addressed some production profile parameters, to guide the decision making process at the conceptual selection phase (Silva & Guedes Soares 2019; Wang et al. 2019; Iyer et al. 1998).

Silva & Guedes Soares (2019) developed a mathematical model that attempts to integrates the selection of the most feasible floating and subsea system layouts based on the estimated maximum flowrate. Moreover, the mathematical model presented by Wang et al. (2019) receives as input data the estimated production decline curve and water production rate as important parameters that impact on the Net Present Value (NPV) of the oilfield development scenarios. Iyer et al. (1998) formulated a model to plan and schedule the investment of the offshore oilfield facilities based on the field life-cycle production.

Furthermore, the knowledge of some production profile parameters can also be useful to quantify the risk of an oilfield project. Silva & Guedes Soares (2016) and Silva et al. (2019) demonstrated that the risk of subsea pipeline system is directly influenced by the severity criterion, which is a function of the amount of production flowrate transported by each pipeline. Silva et al. (2019) highlighted that the results in terms of the risk levels of each alternative concept of a pipeline system can be useful to rank these scenarios aiming at the reduction of the inherent uncertainty in the development of an oilfield at the design selection phase.

Therefore, the aim of this paper is to study a list of key parameters that are required to establish the oilfield production profile. The paper is structured as follows: section 2 characterizes the oilfield development project phases; section 3 discusses a list of key parameters of production profile; section 4 presents a case study and section 5 highlights the main conclusions.

DOI: 10.1201/9781003216599-83

2 OILFIELD DEVELOPMENT PROJECT

On the system engineering perspective, an oilfield development project is divided into four life cycle phases: pre-acquisition, acquisition, utilization and retirement. In accordance with these phases, the oilfield development project assumes the pre-acquisition phase as the exploration step; the acquisition phase includes the appraisal and development steps; the utilization phase comprises the operational step; and, the retirement phase is seen as the field abandonment step.

As a main goal, the exploration step gather all the necessary data to characterize the reservoir, focusing on the identification of potential hydrocarbon accumulation. The appraisal and development steps attempt to provide a precise picture of the size, shape and predictability of the accumulation and it is responsible for the transformation of the functional baselines, technical requirements and logical descriptions into the physical implementation of the production system.

Based on the expected reservoir production profile, defined in the previews steps, the operational step aims at optimizing the trade-off between increase the project revenue versus the minimization of the capital and operational investments. Moreover, the abandonment of the field is done when the cash flow of the project is lower than the economic limit established by the oil company. Figure 1 and Figure 2 presents a general production profile and the respective project cash flow.

The estimation of the initial hydrocarbon reserves and reservoir dynamic behaviour during the early stage of the field life cycle allows the design of a range of technical and economic feasible concepts to exploit the field. The feasibility studies analyses different subsurface and surface facilities, which support production, storage and transportation, and provide the respective cash flows of each alternative concept.

3 OILFIELD PRODUCTION PROFILE

The production profile represents the behaviour of the reservoir production during the oilfield life cycle. This section discuss the main features that are important to characterize the production profile.

3.1 Type of reservoirs

The classification of the reservoir type is related with the properties of the fluid that occupies the pore space of the reservoir rock. The fluid properties determine the amount of each fluid contained into the reservoir. Mainly, the pore spaces are filled with water and hydrocarbons. In addition, the hydrocarbons can exist in three different forms as well as solid, liquid and gas, ranging from dry natural gas to ultra-heavy oil. Its impact on the unique strategies to effectively develop and produce the reservoir.

The classification of hydrocarbons reservoirs can be based on the phase behaviour of the fluid as a function of pressure, volume and temperature variables during the flow path of the hydrocarbon. The changes in phase behaviour is described, in a general form, using the PVT phase diagram.

The PVT diagram is a graphical model that assumes that the petroleum existing in two phases: liquid and vapour; the reservoir pressure declines at a constant temperature during the flow path of the hydrocarbon inside the reservoir; and, the reservoir pressure and temperature decline when the hydrocarbon flow to the surface separator.

According to Satter & Iqbal (2016) the hydrocarbon reservoirs can be classified as follows:

- Dry gas reservoir: no liquid phase is formed when the pressure drops during the life cycle of the reservoir production.
- Wet gas reservoir: As the production starts, and the hydrocarbons flow to the surface separator, a fewer amount of heavier gas molecules is converted to liquid.
- Gas condensate reservoir: as the pressure declines, a relative abundance of heavier gas molecules is condensate out of the reservoir.
- Volatile oil reservoir: is considered as a saturated oil reservoir where the hydrocarbons are in the liquid phase and the oil is recognized as volatile, which means that the molecules of oil are relatively lighter. As the production starts, a relative abundance of oil is vaporized.
- Black oil reservoir: the saturated oil reservoir is considered less volatile, due to the molecules of

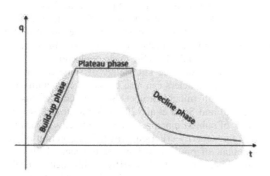

Figure 1. General oilfield production profile.

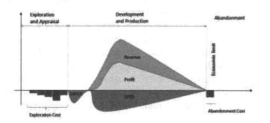

Figure 2. General cash flow of the oilfield project.

oil are relatively heavier. As the production starts, a free-phase gas drops out of the oil.
- Heavy oil reservoir: Due to the high viscosity of the oil molecules, as the production starts, the single liquid phase remains liquid.

3.2 Degrees API gravity scale

The American Petroleum Institute (API) developed a specific gravity scale to measure the rough quality index of the hydrocarbons. The scale range approximately from 70° for condensate to zero degrees of the extra heavy crude oil (crude bitumen). Table 1 presents the full-scale classification.

The degrees API scale represents the relationship between hydrocarbon density and viscosity. The hydrocarbon density is the characteristic that determines the fluid behavoiur during the flow inside the reservoir and pipelines, instead of, the oil viscosity characterizes the fluid internal resistance to flow, which corresponds to the internal notion of thickness.

Besides, the specific gravity is inversely proportional to both parameters (density and viscosity). Consequently, a light oil have high degree API, low viscosity and density, which implies that the oil can easily go through porous media and pipelines. Although, a heavy oil would requires more energy to flow and usually needs unconventional methods of recovery.

The API specific gravity scale allows identifying the type of oil that distinguishes the reservoir types. For instance, the light oil characterizes the volatile oil reservoir type; the medium oil fills the black oil reservoir type; and, the heavy and extra heavy oil constitute the heavy oil reservoir type.

3.3 Reservoir drive mechanisms

As described in the section 3.1, the reservoir pore space can contain hydrocarbons in gas and/or liquid-phases and water, being the oil the highest value commodity of the reservoir.

The fluids at the initial reservoir conditions normally supply the natural energy to produce the reservoirs. The mechanisms of gravity drainage, rock compression and liquid expansion, solution gas, gas cap, water drive and a combination of them, provides the natural lift of the reservoirs.

Table 1. American Petroleum Institute specific gravity scale.

API gravity	Degrees scale
Condensate	50 < °API > 70
Light oil	31 < °API > 45.5
Medium oil	22 < °API > 31
Heavy oil	10 < °API > 22
Extra heavy oil	0 < °API > 10

The mechanism of gravity drainage results in the separation of fluids due to the gravitational forces (the gas is located on the top of the reservoir, the oil underlies the gas and the water underlies the oil) and the drainage rate is dependent upon the viscosity of the oil. In addition, the primary energy source of rock compression and liquid expansion influences the volume and compressibility of each fluid and pore space during the field production.

The mechanism of solution gas drive works with the gas liberation from the crude oil when the production starts and, consequently, the pressure declines. There are no externals fluids (the aquifer is considered small or negligible and there is no free gas presented into the reservoir) to support the pressure resulting in a rapidly pressure drops.

In the gas cap mechanism, the huge amount of free gas cap expands during the reservoir production stimulating the oil to flow and maintaining the reservoir pressure. The degrees of reservoir pressure maintenance depends upon the volume of gas cap compared to the volume of oil. There is no aquifer or the size of the aquifer can be negligible.

The primary energy of the water drive comes from the water moving into the pore space replacing and displacing the oil, volume for volume, to the wellbore. Its results in a very gradual decline pressure providing an efficient drive mechanism. There is no gas cap into the reservoir. In addition, the mechanism of combination drive is commonly available in some degree of oil displacement to produce the wells.

Therefore, the drive mechanisms serve as a performance metric to predict the reservoir oil production and, consequently, the field project economics. However, a complete recoverable amount of hydrocarbon initially in place is not possible due to the complexity of the reservoir rock properties, geometry and fluid flow behaviour under dynamics conditions (Höök et al. 2014). Only a percentage amount of hydrocarbons is recoverable over the field lifetime production.

The recovery factors of the gravity drainage mechanism and the rock and liquid expansion mechanism is considered relatively low when the reservoir produce only by one of them. Moreover, when those mechanisms can be combined with others, it can provide a greater oil displacement.

To take advantage of the solution gas primary recovery, it is necessary to keep the light molecules of gas inside the oil zone during the field production to afford a better displacement of the oil to the wellbore. Although, in practice, the gas rapidly exceed the saturation point and the free gas easily flow through oil increasing the production of the gas-oil ratio. Consequently, the primary recovery factor of the reservoir is considered lower (less than 30%).

The expansion of the free gas cap provides a better oil recovery than the solution gas mechanism (between 25 and 35%). However, when the well completion is near to the gas cap zone, the gas-oil ratio rapidly increases and, sometimes, the well is closed.

The higher efficiency of the water influx (between 30 and 50%) is directly related with the oil flowrate. Whether the production is at a high flowrate, the aquifer cannot do the pressure maintenance of the reservoir. Therefore, it is necessary to find an optimal oil flowrate during the filed lifetime to recovery the maximum amount of oil.

3.4 Artificial lift systems, secondary and tertiary recovery methods

In summary, the section 3.3 describes that the recovery factor of the primary drive mechanisms vary in accordance with the oil displacement efficiency, thus, the pressure maintenance during the lifetime of the reservoir production becomes the main objective of the oil companies to enhance the oil recovery.

Whether the primary energy of the reservoir do not have enough potential to lift the hydrocarbons, the artificial lift systems can supply energy to the wellbore: the secondary recovery methods can add artificial pressure maintenance into the reservoir and, the tertiary recovery methods can vary the fluids properties.

The artificial lift systems works by means of mechanical devices (mainly pumps or gas lift valves), installed inside the wellbore, to increase the flow of liquids. The secondary recovery inject produced water into the aquifer and/or gas into gas cap zone to supply the reservoir pressure; and, the tertiary recovery uses the miscible gas flooding, thermal or chemical injection methods to decreases the oil viscosity.

The reservoir production can requires the artificial lift systems at any time during the filed life cycle, instead of, the secondary and tertiary recoveries are considered as two extra stages of the reservoir production.

3.5 Drilling schedule development plan

As described in the section 2, the production begins when the exploration step identifies the potential of the hydrocarbon accumulation. During the exploration prospect, discovery wells are drilled to establish the reservoir boundaries. Furthermore, to predict the reservoir production, it is necessary to drill the delineation wells. These wells are important to gather and validate the initial geological and fluid information.

Depending on this initial information, the multidisciplinary technical group, responsible for the exploration and production development plan of an oilfield, need to figure out the precise number of production wells to develop an oilfield. However, the degree of geological uncertainty decreases when more information is gathered during the reservoir production life.

Whether the reservoir characterization is properly defined, considering a certain low degree of uncertainty, all the production wells are drilled at the same time during the exploration step and starts the production at the same time reaching the field production plateau (maximum peak of production) in a short time. Meanwhile, when it is difficult to reduce the degree of uncertainty, the field development is divided in modules allowing the oil company to drill only a few amount of production wells to achieve more knowledge about the field and to plan how to develop the next module of the reservoir. This strategy of reservoir development is called as Early Production System.

The main goal of the Early Production System is to gather new information from each production modules/phases allowing the studies of different technical-economic feasibility development concepts until the definitive concept be implemented.

4 CASE STUDY

The case study analyses the production profile of Campos basin located in Brazil. According to EIA (2019), Brazil was considered the ninth-largest oil producer in the world, representing 3% (3.43 million barrels per day) of the total oil produced by the top ten countries. Moreover, Brazil reached the second position of the top five largest offshore oil producer in the world presenting 58% of grew in the offshore production between 2005 and 2015 (EIA 2016). From the total oil produced in Brazil, 84% represents Brazil's offshore oil production (ANP 2019).

Campos's basin is located in the offshore of the southeast portion of Brazil and, nowadays, it is responsible for approximately 40% of the total Brazil's oil production. The Brazilian state-controlled oil company (Petrobras) started the exploration and characterization of the Campos basin in 1968. The Campos's basin development can be discriminated in three major phases of reservoir characterization and management: shallow water fields, deepwater fields and deep to ultra-deepwater fields.

The development of the Campos basin starts from the shallow water fields in 1977 until 1983, exploring and producing fields located at water depths ranging from zero to 300 meters. Petrobras continuously moved the exploration to deepwater (which ranges from 301 to 1000 meters) discovering new fields during more five years, 1984 to 1989. After gathered more knowledge of deepwater exploration and, as a long-term goal of Brazilian government to increase the oil production, since 1990 to nowadays Petrobras still move the exploration from deep to ultra-deepwater.

4.1 Results and discussion

In the present study, the production trends of 36 oilfields located in Campos's basin provide pertinent information to establish a good overview of production profile. From 36 oilfields analysed, 20 of them are still in production, 12 oilfields have the production considered as temporarily stopped and four oilfields registered the production as finished. Therefore, the average time of total production life cycle equals 32 years.

4.1.1 Reservoir type and API gravity scale

The average of the API gravity of the 36 oilfields analysed is 25 degrees, the median is 25 degrees and the mode is 20 degrees. It implies that the most common type of reservoir is the black oil. The only volatile oil reservoir that was identified is the Namorado oilfield, where the average of the API gravity equals 36 degrees. Moreover, heavy oil reservoirs have been discovered more frequently in deep and ultra-deepwater fields.

4.1.2 Primary drive mechanism

The frequency bar chart in Figure 3, presents that the most common mechanisms actuating in Campos basin reservoirs are the water drive (2), solution gas (4) and, the combined mechanism of water drive and solution gas (7).

4.1.3 Artificial lift system, secondary and tertiary recovery methods

Figure 4, shows that the most common secondary recovery method is the water injection. Moreover, the method of gas injection is only applied in combination with the injection of water.

The frequency bar chart in Figure 5 indicates that 81% of the oilfields studied did not use artificial lift system and, the gas lift system is the only method applied in 19% of the reservoirs. Furthermore, in the present case study, no one of the chemical and thermal injection or miscible gas flooding was applied as tertiary recovery methods.

4.1.4 Drilling schedule

Another feature that was analysed in the present case study is the drilling schedule development plan. From the 36 oilfields in the sample, 24 (67%) fields implemented the Early Production System. Analysing the sample that contain the shallow water oilfields, the average time between the first-oil to the beginning of production declines is 6 years and the median is 6 years. Figure 6 shows that the two most common mode classes of the total time of the first-oil to the beginning of production declines, ranges from zero to four and from five to eight.

Furthermore, analysing the sample of the fields located in deep to ultra-deepwater, the average of the

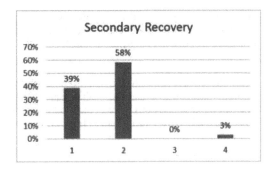

Figure 4. Secondary recovery methods: (1) No one; (2) Water injection; (3) Gas injection; (4) Water and gas injection.

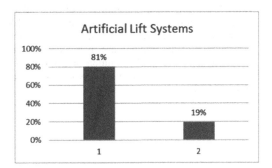

Figure 5. Artificial lift systems: (1) No one; (2) gas-lift system.

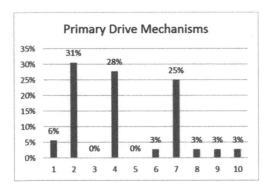

Figure 3. Primary drive mechanisms: (1) Fluid and rock compression; (2) Water drive; (3) Gas cap; (4) Solution gas; (5) Gravity drainage; (6) Water drive and gas cap; (7) Water drive and solution gas; (8) Water drive, gas cap and solution gas; (9) Gas cap and solution gas; (10) Solution gas and rock compression.

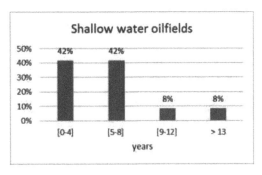

Figure 6. Histogram of the first-oil to production declines of the Early Production Systems adopted by the shallow water oilfields.

total time is 12 years and the median is 11 years. The most common mode class, presented in the histogram of Figure 7, ranges from nine to 12 years.

4.1.5 Recovery factor

From the sample of oilfields, the average of the recovery factor is 25% and the median equals 21%. Thus, in the histogram of Figure 8, the most common mode class of recovery factor ranges from 11 to 20%.

4.2 Final remarks

The recovery factor and the production profile are interlinked with all the key parameters described in the paper. As for example, the recovery factor of Piraúna and Namorado oilfield are the two highest factors included in this sample, which equals 57%. **Table 2** presents the key parameters of both of the oilfields and it is possible to note that even with different oil degrees and reservoir types, the production performance of the oilfields are maintained, during the production life, by the solution of gas (into the reservoir or wellbore) and the influx of water (natural or by injection).

Table 2. The key parameters of the Piraúna and Namorado oilfields.

	Piraúna	Namorado
Oil degrees	25°/medium	36°/light
Reservoir type	Black oil	Volatile oil
Primary mechanism	Water influx	Gas solution
Secondary mechanism	-	Water injection
Artificial lift method	Gas lift system	-
Early production system	2 years	8 years
Recovery factor	57%	57%

An empirical correlation can also be established with the total time of reservoir production life and recovery factor. The correlation presented in Figure 9 is considered weak, because it was established for all the oilfields contained in the sample space.

However, it is possible to separate the sample space into two set of oilfields according to each oilfied location, establishing the set of shallow water oilfields and the set of deep to ultra-deep water oilfields.

In the fields located in shallow water, the correlation is null (Figure 10) because the lower waterdepth provides an easy access to the reservoirs

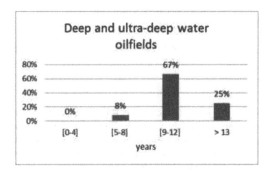

Figure 7. Histogram of the first-oil to production declines of the Early Production Systems adopted by the deep to ultra-deepwater oilfields.

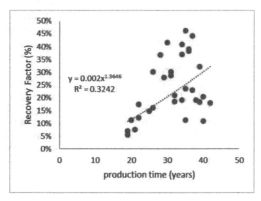

Figure 9. Correlation of the recovery factor and production lifetime of the Campos basin oilfields.

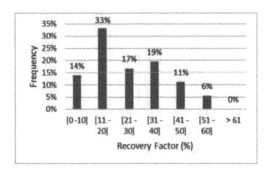

Figure 8. Histogram of the oilfields recovery factors.

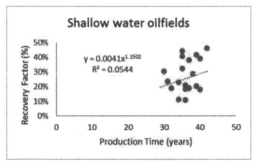

Figure 10. Correlation of the recovery factor and production lifetime of the shallow water oilfields.

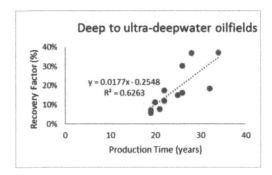

Figure 11. Correlation of the recovery factor and production lifetime of the deep to ultra-deep water oilfields.

allowing to gather more information and to develop an accurate reservoir production profile and model.

Moreover, the correlation of the fields located in deep to ultra-deepwater can be considered strong (Figure 11) because the reservoir model is affected by the lack of reservoir knowledge. Therefore, the longer oilfield production time, the lower uncertainties of the reservoir model, which generates a greater hydrocarbon recovery in deep to ultra-deepwater fields.

5 CONCLUSIONS

Due to the intensive initial investments, the oilfield development plan needs to consider all production features and uncertainties. The statistical analysis of the key production parameters of an oilfield allows establishing empirical correlations among the main production features. The production profile of an oil basin can provide the expectation of the production performance of an oilfield reducing the uncertainty of the new development by narrowing the range of outcomes.

The study of a list of important key parameters to characterize the development scheme of an oil basin is the main goal of present paper. The analogy of main production parameters, as well as, reservoir type, oil gravity, primary drive mechanism, secondary and tertiary methods, artificial lift systems and drilling schedule development plan, serve as useful technical method to establish the production profile of an oil basin, and especially, the oilfields located in Campos's basin, Brazil.

The Campos's basin has been in production during the last 51 years, and has continuously evolved from shallow to deep and ultra-deepwater oilfields development, which allows the identification and characterization of the basin production profile.

In summary, the production profile of Campos's basin was characterized from the sample of 36 oilfields. As main conclusions of the statistical analysis of Campos basin production profile, it is possible to highlight that, the oil gravity reservoir types is found as black and heavy oil reservoirs, being the medium oil (22 < °API > 31) and the heavy oil (10 < °API > 22) the most frequent types of oil found at the reservoirs conditions.

Furthermore, the water influx actuates, as primary drive mechanism, in 62% of the reservoirs and, consequently, the water injection has been widely used (58% of the reservoirs) due to the good oil displacement and gradual pressure decline characteristics.

Moreover, the gas-lift system is the only type of artificial lift system that has been applied (19% of the reservoirs). The Early Production Systems were employed as the drilling development plan in 67% of the oilfields. Thus, the most common mode class of Campos's basin recovery factor ranges from 11 to 20% (the average is 25% and the median equals 21%).

ACKNOWLEDGEMENTS

The first author holds a PhD scholarship financed partially by the University of Lisbon and partially by the Centre for Marine Technology and Ocean Engineering (CENTEC). This work was performed within the scope of the Strategic Research Plan of the Centre for Marine Technology and Ocean Engineering (CENTEC), which is financed by the Portuguese Foundation for Science and Technology (Fundação para a Ciência e Tecnologia - FCT) under contract UIDB/UIDP/00134/2020.

REFERENCES

ANP, 2019. Monthly Report of Oil and Natural Gas Production. (in portuguese) *Agência Nacional de Pertóleo, Gás Natural e Biocombustíveis*.

EIA, 2016. Offshore production nearly 30% of global crude oil output in 2015. *U.S. Energy Information Adminstration*.

EIA, 2019. The 10 largest oil1 producers and share of total world oil production in 2018. *U.S. Energy Information Adminstration*.

Höök, M., Davidsson, S., Johansson, S. & Tang, X., 2014. Decline and depletion rates of oil production: A comprehensive investigation. *Philosophical Transactions of the Royal Society A*, 372.

Iyer, R.R., Grossmann, I. E., Vasantharajan, S., & Cullick, A. S., 1998. Optimal Planning and Scheduling of Offshore Oil Field Infrastructure Investment and Operations. *Industrial and Engineering Chemistry Research*, 37, pp.1380–1397.

Santos, S.M.G., Gaspar, A.T.F.S. & Schiozer, D.J., 2017. Value of information in reservoir development projects: Technical indicators to prioritize uncertainties and information sources. *Journal of Petroleum Science and Engineering*, 157(August), pp.1179–1191.

Satter, A. & Iqbal, G.M., 2016. *Reservoir Engineering: the fundamentals, simulation and management of conventional and unconventional recoveries*, Elsevier Inc.

Silva, L.M.R. & Guedes Soares, C., 2019. An integrated optimization of the floating and subsea layouts. *Ocean Engineering*, 191 (April).

Silva, L.M.R. & Guedes Soares, C., 2016. Study of the risk to export crude oil in pipeline systems. In C. & S. T. A. Guedes Soares, ed. *Maritime Technology and Engineering 3*. London: Taylor & Francis Group, pp. 1013–1018.

Silva, L.M.R., Teixeira, A.P. & Guedes Soares, C., 2019. A methodology to quantify the risk of subsea pipeline systems at the oilfield development selection phase. *Ocean Engineering*, 179 pp.213–225.

Silva, V.L.S., Emerick, A.A., Couto, P., & Alves, J.L.D., 2017. History matching and production optimization under uncertainties – Application of closed-loop reservoir management. *Journal of Petroleum Science and Engineering*, 157, pp.860–874.

Wang, Y., Estefen, S.F., Lourenço, M.I. & Hong, C., 2019. Optimal design and scheduling for offshore oil-field development. *Computers and Chemical Engineering*, 123, pp.300–316.

Waves and currents

Surface circulation in the Eastern Central North Atlantic

J.H. Bettencourt & C. Guedes Soares
Centre for Marine Technology and Ocean Engineering (CENTEC), Instituto Superior Técnico, Universidade de Lisboa, Lisbon, Portugal

ABSTRACT: The surface circulation in the Eastern Central North Atlantic is studied using a high resolution primitive equation regional ocean model simulation. The model is forced by climatological surface momentum, heat and freshwater fluxes and open ocean boundary conditions. Comparisons with drifter-derived velocity estimates show that the model is able to reproduce the main features of the surface circulation in the coastal Portuguese waters and in the Portuguese archipelagos of Azores and Madeira. The Azores Current (AzC) appears as a meandering zonal jet centered around 34° N, flowing eastward. The western Iberian margin is characterized by an seasonal upwelling regime where a cooling of near shore waters occurs between late spring and early autumn. Mesoscale activity is present in the upwelling front as coastal filaments and mesoscale eddies. The northward Portugal Coastal Counter Current is a prominent feature of the coastal circulation.

1 INTRODUCTION

The Eastern Central North Atlantic (ECNA) is the stretch of the eastern north Atlantic basin between the subtropical and subpolar gyres, possibly including their northern and southern borders, respectively. The region also coincides with the Portuguese territorial waters and its Economic Exclusive Zone, whose monitoring and management is a national maritime policy goal. To aid in this goal, the OBSERVA.FISH project (Piecho-Santos et al.,2021) aims to provide datasets from autonomous ocean observing systems, to be used in, among other purposes, support of an ocean forecast system that will be developed based on the simulations presented herein.

Although most of the large scale circulation patterns in the North Atlantic reside outside of the ECNA (Tomczak & Godfrey, 2013), the ECNA has been a region of intense oceanographic research due to the special characteristics of its features such as the Azores current (AzC), a permanent zonal jet subject to an intense meandering regime set by its baroclinicity (Alves & Colin de Verdière, 1999), the Mediterranean Outflow (MO), that carries heat and salt in to the northern basin and partially regulates the weather at those latitudes (Baringer & Price, 1997; Ellett, 1993) or the West Africa and West Iberia upwelling systems (WIbUS), that comprise the northernmost section of the North Atlantic Upwelling Region (Relvas et al., 2007). Earlier modeling studies such as Jia (2000), Johnson & Stevens (2000), Peliz et al. (2007) have focused on these aspects of the circulation in the ECNA.

The eastward flowing AzC is part of the northern branch of the Eastern Subtropical Gyre, that also includes the southward Canary Current and the western North Equatorial Current and is a permanent feature of the region's circulation. Localized between 33°N-36° N, it crosses the Mid-Atlantic Ridge and flows towards the Gulf od Cadiz. The AzC is a deep (up to 1000 m) current 250 km wide. Its average transport is 10-12 Sv (1 Sv = 10^6 m^{3}s^{-1}) and has a convoluted topology due to its meandering jet character. Average speeds are 0.1-0.15 ms^{-1}.

The AzC is associated to a thermohaline front, the Azores Front, that separates the eastern subtropical and subpolar gyres. In the Azores Current and Front system, temperature and salinity jumps of 2°C and 0.3 PSU have been registered. Its convoluted nature has been attributed to quasi-stationary Rossby waves originated in the eastern boundary of the Canary Basin and to baroclinic instabilities of the AzC jet. Meanders form to the north (cyclonic) and to the south (anticyclonic) of the AzC jet core and mesoscale eddies with typical diameter of 200 km have been observed in both flanks of the front.

The WIbUS is a seasonal upwelling system located in the western coast of the Iberian Peninsula. In the summer, the Azores High strengthens and is displaced northward, setting up upwelling favorable (equatorward) winds over the western Iberian coast that force an offshore Ekman transport and subsequent upwelling of subsurface cold, nutrient rich waters. Due to geostrophic adjustment, an equatorward jet is formed at the surface compensated by poleward subsurface flows. Coastal upwelling filaments extending to 200 – 250 km offshore and exporting coastal waters are a common feature of the WIbUS and are formed by either topographic forcing or upwelling front instabilities (Haynes et al., 1993).

In this work we employ a the climatological simulation with the aim of reproducing the equilibrium structure of the region's circulation and the mesoscale variability that is essentially determined by the instabilities of large-scale structures such as currents and fronts.

In section 2 the circulation model and the ECNA configuration are described. Section 3 describes the results and section 4 provides the conclusions.

2 DATA AND METHODS

The model used in this work is the Regional Ocean Modelling System (ROMS, Shchepetkin & McWilliams (2005, 2003)). ROMS is a free-surface terrain-following model which solves the primitive equations using the Boussinesq and hydrostatic approximations. In the primitive equation framework, the prognostic variables are the zonal and meridional velocity components (u,v) and the free surface elevation ζ. The momentum equations in Cartesian coordinates are:

$$\frac{\partial(H_z u)}{\partial t} + \frac{(uH_z u)}{\partial x} + \frac{(vH_z u)}{\partial y} + \frac{(\Omega H_z u)}{\partial s} - fH_z v = -\frac{H_z}{\rho_0}\frac{\partial p}{\partial x} - H_z g\frac{\partial \zeta}{\partial x} - \frac{\partial}{\partial s}\left(\overline{u'w'} - \frac{v}{H_z}\frac{\partial u}{\partial s}\right)$$ (1)

$$\frac{\partial(H_z v)}{\partial t} + \frac{(uH_z v)}{\partial x} + \frac{(vH_z v)}{\partial y} + \frac{(\Omega H_z v)}{\partial s} + fH_z u = -\frac{H_z}{\rho_0}\frac{\partial p}{\partial y} - H_z g\frac{\partial \zeta}{\partial y} - \frac{\partial}{\partial s}\left(\overline{v'w'} - \frac{v}{H_z}\frac{\partial v}{\partial s}\right)$$ (2)

$$0 = -\frac{1}{\rho_0}\frac{\partial p}{\partial s} - \frac{g}{\rho_0}H_z \rho$$ (3)

where (3) is the vertical momentum equation, which in the hydrostatic approximation is a simple relationship between the vertical pressure gradient and the weight of the fluid column. The continuity equation is:

$$\frac{\partial \zeta}{\partial t} + \frac{\partial(H_z u)}{\partial x} + \frac{\partial(H_z v)}{\partial y} + \frac{\partial(H_z \Omega)}{\partial s} = 0$$ (4)

and the scalar transport equation is:

$$\frac{\partial(H_z C)}{\partial t} + \frac{\partial(uH_z C)}{\partial x} + \frac{\partial(vH_z C)}{\partial y} + \frac{\partial(\Omega H_z C)}{\partial s} = -\frac{\partial}{\partial s}\left(\overline{c'w'} - \frac{v}{H_z}\frac{\partial c}{\partial s}\right) + C_{source}$$ (5)

In (1-5) s is a vertical stretched coordinate that varies from $s = -1$ (bottom) to $s = 0$ (surface). The vertical grid stretching parameter is $H_z = \partial z/\partial s$ and Ω is the vertical velocity in the s coordinate. The Coriolis parameter is f, p is the hydrostatic pressure and g is the acceleration of gravity. An overbar denotes averaged quantities, primed (′) variables are departures from the average and v is molecular diffusivity (momentum or scalar). Vertical turbulent momentum and tracer fluxes are:

$$\overline{u'w'} = K_M\frac{\partial u}{\partial z};\ \overline{v'w'} = -K_M\frac{\partial v}{\partial z};\ \overline{c'w'} = -K_H\frac{\partial \rho}{\partial z}$$ (6)

where K_M and K_H are momentum and tracer eddy diffusivities. The equation of state for seawater is given by $\rho = f(C,p)$.

ROMS is highly configurable for realistic applications and has been applied to a wide variety of space and time scales across the globe (Haidvogel et al., 2008).

The model domain (Figure 1) is part of the Eastern Central North Atlantic and covers the western Iberian margin extending to the Azores and Madeira archipelagos (34.4° to 5.7°W and 29° to 46°N). The average horizontal resolution is 4.2 km in the meridional direction and 4.4 km in the zonal direction. The vertical discretization used 20 sigma layers, stretched to increase the resolution near the surface and bottom. The bathymetry is interpolated from ETOPO and smoothed to satisfy a topographic stiffness-ratio of 0.2 (Haidvogel & Beckmann, 1999). The minimum depth used is 10 m.

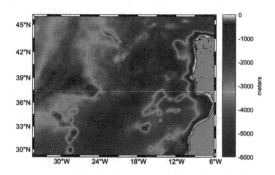

Figure 1. Domain of the ECNA simulation.

The model configuration uses a third-order upstream advection scheme for momentum and tracers, a fourth-order centered scheme for vertical advection of momentum and tracers, and the KPP scheme for vertical mixing (Large et al., 1994). Explicit horizontal momentum and tracer diffusion is set to zero. Bottom drag uses a quadratic law with drag coefficient of 0.003.

The model was run in climatological mode where a yearly cycle was repeated for 20 years. The model was forced by surface monthly climatological momentum, heat, freshwater and shortwave radiation fluxes from the Comprehensive Ocean-Atmosphere Data Set (COADS, Woodruff et al (1987)), that collects global weather observations taken near the ocean's surface since 1854, primarily from merchant ships. At the open boundaries, values of 2D (barotropic) and 3D (baroclinic) velocities, and active tracers (potential temperature and salinity) were nudged to climatological values. The offline nesting procedure employed here used a nudging region of 40 km along the model boundaries. In this layer, the 3-D model variables (temperature, salinity, and currents) were pushed toward their climatological values. The nudging time scale was set to 5 days at the boundaries, decaying linearly to zero inside the nudging layer. At the boundaries, outgoing radiation conditions were used for the baroclinic variables (Marchesiello et al., 2001). Climatological sea surface height and barotropic currents were imposed at the boundaries using Chapman boundary conditions (Chapman, 1985).

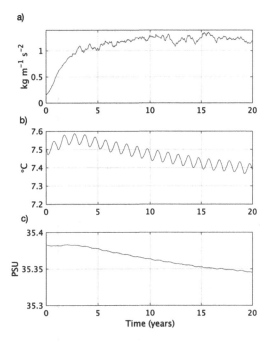

Figure 2. Time series of volume averaged a) kinetic energy; b) potential temperature; c) salinity.

3 RESULTS

3.1 *Equilibrium solution*

The model achieved equilibrium after a spin up period of 4 model years, after which the volume average total kinetic energy $1/V \cdot \int_V 0.5\rho(u^2+v^2)\, dV$ (Figure 2a) reaches a plateau and then fluctuates around 1.2 kg m^{-1} s^{-2} until the end of the simulation. Domain averaged temperature levels (Figure 2b) show a strong seasonal signal, superposed to a declining trend from year 4 onward. Domain averaged salinity (Figure 2c) shows a declining trend without clear seasonality.

The average surface velocity field from the ROMS (Figure 3a) shows the characteristic surface circulation patterns in the region. North of 36°N the circulation is mainly south-eastward due to the southward branches of the Gulf Current that separate approximately at 54°W, leaving the North Atlantic Drift and the southward PC between 18° and 12°W (Reverdin et al., 2003). East of the PC the circulation is influenced by the MO and the WIbUS. The main features of the average coastal circulation in the western Iberian shelf are the Cape São Vicente westward jet that flows along the slope of Gulf of Cadiz and the western Iberia coastal counter-flows. The poleward flow along the Iberian margin matches descriptions of the Portugal Coastal Counter-Current, that is known to bend anticyclonically when passing the north-western corner of the Iberian peninsula (Álvarez-Salgado et al., 2003), and of other coastal poleward counter-flows reported in the literature (Peliz et al., 2005, 2002)

Below 36°N, the AzC appears as the eastward jet between 33° and 36° N, clearly visible in Figure 2a until the Gulf of Cadiz, with maximum velocities of the order of 10 cm s^{-1}. The AzC partially turns south and joins the general westward and southward drift of the West Africa and the subtropical gyre. The eastward jet's location agrees with the well-known AzC location (Alves et al., 2002; Gould, 1985; Klein & Siedler, 1989), and it can be seen reaching the Gulf of Cadiz.

The comparison of the model average surface velocity field with the Surface Velocity Program climatology (Laurindo et al., 2017) shows that the model velocities are generally lower than those of the SVP climatology. However, the position of the main features is well reproduced, especially the position of the AzC and the general south-eastward velocity field in the northern part of the domain. The discrepancies highlight the limitations of the limited area modelling approach and the use of a climatological forcing. The first factor introduces errors at the boundaries e.g, the velocity imposed on the boundary is computed from geostrophy only while the SVP dataset is computed from real drifter velocities. The climatological forcing on the other hand limits the model response only to an annual cycle while the SVP dataset contains also interannual forcing effects.

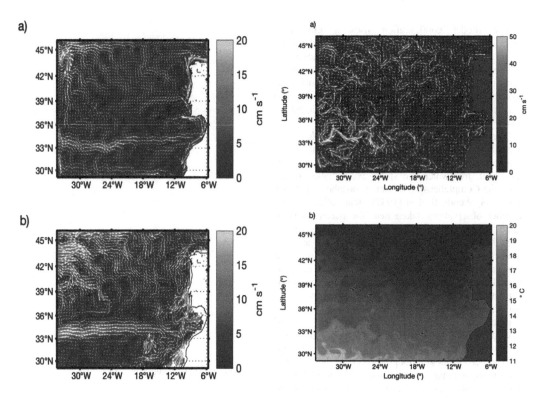

Figure 3. Average surface velocity from a) ROMS model and b) SVP climatology.

Figure 4. Instantaneous maps of a) surface velocity and b) sea surface temperature. Maps are for the 4th of March of S.Y. 18.

3.2 The Azores current

The average surface velocity field (Figure 3a) shows the AzC as a purely zonal eastward jet. The instantaneous AzC, however, is known to have a large degree of meandering with mesoscale vortices shedding northward and southward of the mean current axis. The velocity field for 4 March of simulation year (S.Y.) 18 (Figure 4a) shows the AzC as the predominant circulation feature in the region with instantaneous velocities up to 50 cm/s in the current axis. The axis itself is severely deformed, forming an cyclonic meander centered at approximately 32°W. South of the current axis three closed cyclonic circulations can be observed between the western boundary and 30°W. These cyclones have length scales on the order of 100 – 300 km and are present due to the pinching off of cyclonic vortices formed northward of the jet axis (Alves et al., 2002). In a purely zonal jet, positive (cyclonic) vorticity is found northward of the jet axis and negative (anticyclonic) vorticity is found south of the jet axis. Although the idealization is far from being verified in this simulation, the situation depicted in Figure 4a conforms to this model,. Indeed, just under the meander we can find a weak anticyclonic circulation.

The stirring (Abraham & Bowen, 2002) of the sea surface temperature (SST) field by the mesoscale circulation is visible in the SST map for 4 March S.Y. 18 (Figure 4b), superposed on the gyre scale SST North-South gradient. The association of the AzC with the SST front is clearly observed as the position of the AzC meander coincides with the position of a strong change in SST. In addition, it is observed that the position of the large cyclone south of the current axis matches the position of a pool of cooler water, indication that the cyclonic had its origin north of the current axis and, as it moved south, carried with it the colder waters found north of the jet axis.

3.3 The West Iberia upwelling

The circulation in the WIbUS is highly seasonal and strongly influenced by mesoscale processes (Relvas et al., 2007). A winter surface velocity map for the 13 January of S.Y. 18 (Figure 5a) shows some of the main elements of the winter circulation scheme proposed by Peliz et al. (2005). North of 39° N the coastal circulation is dominated by the poleward flow while the offshore flow is mainly southward. South of 39°N the influence of the Gulf of Cadiz circulation is clearly visible as an inflow to the southern Iberian basin. The summer situation is very different (Figure 5b): the surface poleward flows are absent and the dominant coastal circulation is equatorward, forced by the summer equatorward winds. In addition, an offshore drift is clearly observable due to the generation of

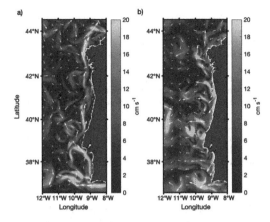
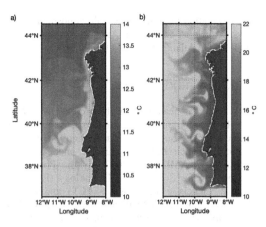

Figure 5. Instantaneous maps of surface velocity for a) 13 January and b) 4 August of S.Y. 18.

Figure 7. Instantaneous maps of sea surface temperature for a) 13 January and b) 4 August of S.Y. 18.

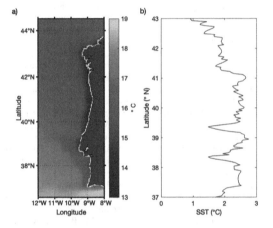

Figure 6. A) Average SST map; b) Upwelling index based on average coast to offshore SST differences. Positive values indicate colder waters at the coast.

filaments and eddies by the upwelling front, that is known to be unstable to short wavelength instabilities (Durski & Allen, 2005).

The average SST field off the western Iberian coast (Figure 6a) shows the signature of the West Iberia upwelling dynamics as a coastal strip of lower than average temperatures associated to successive upwelling cells along the coast. The SST difference between the coast and offshore waters (Figure 6b) shows that this difference is about 2.5°C between 37° and 41° N and then decreases poleward, due to the decrease in offshore SST values (Figure 6a).

Instantaneous SST maps for the same dates as Figure 5 show the difference in SST distributions for winter and summer. In winter (Figure 7a) the western Iberian shelf is under the influence of the Gulf of Cadiz circulation whose inflow to the Iberian basin along the coast and subsequent entrainment in the Iberian Poleward Current brings warm water in to the Iberian shelf and slope (Peliz et al., 2005). In the summer (Figure 7b) the upwelling is noticeable and the whole shelf shows SST colder than the offshore by about 6°C. The mesoscale patterns in the SST distribution indicate the strong mesoscale dynamics of the upwelling front that presents several cold upwelling filaments extending 100 – 200 km offshore.

4 CONCLUSIONS

The Eastern basin of the North Atlantic between the subtropical and subpolar gyres presents a series of characteristics of oceanographic interest. The use of regional simulation models is a powerful tool to study the features that define the circulation in this region. High resolution climatological simulations allow to simulate the equilibrium solution of the circulation and its intrinsic variability, providing necessary data to study the processes that control the circulation in the ECNA.

The AzC is a prominent feature of the circulation in the region. Its average position and its meandering character was unveiled by the simulation, showing that it controls the shape of the Azores Thermal Front and that thermal fluxes across the mean front position must be mediated by the mesoscale cyclones and anticyclones that are pinched off the AzC meanders.

The WIbUS is a seasonal upwelling system that in the winter is dominated by the Gulf of Cadiz circulation and the large scale offshore circulation. In the summer however, the coastal dynamics is strongly influenced by the upwelling front dynamics. The shelf and slope circulation is strongly modulated by mesoscale processes in both seasons.

To complement this type of studies, future work will use interannual forcing to study the response of the circulation to slow, large scale atmospheric processes such as the North Atlantic Oscillation, El Niño or the Atlantic Decadal Oscillation.

ACKNOWLEDGEMENTS

This study has been made in the project OBSERVA.FISH: Autonomous Observing Systems in Fishing Vessels for the Support of Marine Ecosystem Management, which has been funded under contract (PTDC/CTA-AMB/31141/2017) by the Portuguese Foundation for Science and Technology (Fundação para a Ciência e Tecnologia - FCT) and by EU FEDER POR-Lisboa2020 and POR-Algarve2020 programs. This work also contributes to the Strategic Research Plan of the Centre for Marine Technology and Ocean Engineering (CENTEC), which is financed by FCT under the contract UIDB/UIDP/00134/2020.

REFERENCES

Abraham, E.R., Bowen, M.M., 2002. Chaotic Stirring by a Mesoscale Surface-Ocean Flow. *Chaos* 12: 373–381.

Álvarez-Salgado, X.A., Figueiras, F.G., Pérez, F.F., Groom, S., Nogueira, E., Borges, A.V., Chou, L., Castro, C.G., Moncoiffé, G., Ríos, A.F., Miller, A.E.J., Frankignoulle, M., Savidge, G., Wollast, R., 2003. The Portugal coastal counter current off NW Spain: new insights on its biogeochemical variability. *Prog. Oceanogr.* 56: 281–321.

Alves, M., Gaillard, F., Sparrow, M., Knoll, M., Giraud, S., 2002. Circulation patterns and transport of the Azores Front-Current system. *Deep Sea Res. Part II Top. Stud. Oceanogr., Canary Islands, Azores, Gibraltar Observations (Canigo) Volume II: Studies of the Azores and Gibraltar regions* 49: 3983–4002.

Alves, M.L.G.R., Colin de Verdière, A., 1999. Instability Dynamics of a Subtropical Jet and Applications to the Azores Front Current System: Eddy-Driven Mean Flow. *J. Phys. Oceanogr.* 29: 837–864.

Baringer, M.O., Price, J.F., 1997. Mixing and Spreading of the Mediterranean Outflow. *J. Phys. Oceanogr.* 27: 1654–1677.

Chapman, D., 1985. Numerical Treatments of Cross-Shelf Open Boundaries in a Barotropic Coastal Ocean Model. *J Phys Ocean.* 15: 1060–1075.

Durski, S.M., Allen, J.S., 2005. Finite-Amplitude Evolution of Instabilities Associated with the Coastal Upwelling Front. *J. Phys. Oceanogr.* 35: 1606–1628.

Ellett, D.J., 1993. The north-east Atlantic: A fan-assisted storage heater? *Weather* 48: 118–126.

Gould, W.J., 1985. Physical oceanography of the Azores front. *Prog. Oceanogr.* 14: 167–190.

Haidvogel, D.B., Arango, H., Budgell, W.P., Cornuelle, B.D., Curchitser, E., Di Lorenzo, E., Fennel, K., Geyer, W.R., Hermann, A.J., Lanerolle, L., Levin, J., McWilliams, J.C., Miller, A.J., Moore, A.M., Powell, T.M., Shchepetkin, A.F., Sherwood, C.R., Signell, R.P., Warner, J.C., Wilkin, J., 2008. Ocean forecasting in terrain-following coordinates: Formulation and skill assessment of the Regional Ocean Modeling System.
J. Comput. Phys., Predicting weather, climate and extreme events 227: 3595–3624.

Haidvogel, D.B., Beckmann, A., 1999. Numerical Ocean Circulation Modeling, Series on Environmental Science and Management. IMPERIAL COLLEGE PRESS.

Haynes, R., Barton, E.D., Pilling, I., 1993. Development, persistence, and variability of upwelling filaments off the Atlantic coast of the Iberian Peninsula. *J. Geophys. Res. Oceans* 98: 22681–22692.

Jia, Y., 2000. Formation of an Azores Current Due to Mediterranean Overflow in a Modeling Study of the North Atlantic. *J. Phys. Oceanogr.* 30: 2342–2358.

Johnson, J., Stevens, I., 2000. A fine resolution model of the eastern North Atlantic between the Azores, the Canary Islands and the Gibraltar Strait. *Deep Sea Res. Part I Oceanogr. Res. Pap.* 47, 875–899.

Klein, B., Siedler, G., 1989. On the origin of the Azores Current. *J. Geophys. Res. Oceans* 94: 6159–6168.

Large, W.G., McWilliams, J.C., Doney, S.C., 1994. Oceanic Vertical Mixing: A Review and a Model with a Nonlocal Boundary Layer Parameterization. *Rev. Geophys.* 32: 363–403.

Laurindo, L.C., Mariano, A.J., Lumpkin, R., 2017. An improved near-surface velocity climatology for the global ocean from drifter observations. *Deep Sea Res. Part Oceanogr. Res. Pap.* 124: 73–92.

Marchesiello, P., McWilliams, J.C., Shchepetkin, A., 2001. Open Boundary Conditions for Long-Term Integration of Regional Oceanic Models. *Ocean Model.* 3: 1–20.

Peliz, A., Dubert, J., Marchesiello, P., Teles-Machado, A., 2007. Surface circulation in the Gulf of Cadiz: Model and mean flow structure. *J. Geophys. Res. Oceans* 112.

Peliz, Á., Dubert, J., Santos, A.M.P., Oliveira, P.B., Le Cann, B., 2005. Winter upper ocean circulation in the Western Iberian Basin—Fronts, Eddies and Poleward Flows: an overview. *Deep Sea Res. Part I Oceanogr. Res. Pap.* 52: 621–646.

Peliz, Á., Rosa, T.L., Santos, A.M.P., Pissarra, J.L., 2002. Fronts, jets, and counter-flows in the Western Iberian upwelling system. *J. Mar. Syst.* 35: 61–77.

Piecho-Santos, A. M. P., Hinostroza, M., Rosa, T., Guedes Soares, C., 2020. Autonomous Observing Systems in Fishing Vessels, in: Guedes Soares, C. & Santos T. A., (Eds.). *Developments in Maritime Technology and Engineering London, UK: Taylor and Francis.*

Relvas, P., Barton, E.D., Dubert, J., Oliveira, P.B., Peliz, Á., da Silva, J.C.B., Santos, A.M.P., 2007. Physical oceanography of the western Iberia ecosystem: Latest views and challenges. *Prog. Oceanogr.* 74: 149–173.

Reverdin, G., Niiler, P.P., Valdimarsson, H., 2003. North Atlantic Ocean surface currents. *J. Geophys. Res. Oceans* 108: 2–1–2–21.

Shchepetkin, A.F., McWilliams, J.C., 2005. The regional oceanic modeling system (ROMS): a split-explicit, free-surface, topography-following-coordinate oceanic model. *Ocean Model.* 9: 347–404.

Shchepetkin, A.F., McWilliams, J.C., 2003. A method for computing horizontal pressure-gradient force in an oceanic model with a nonaligned vertical coordinate. *J. Geophys. Res. Oceans* 108.

Tomczak, M., Godfrey, J.S., 2013. *Regional Oceanography: An Introduction.* Elsevier.

Woodruff, S.D., Slutz, R.J., Jenne, R.L., Steurer, P.M., 1987. A Comprehensive Ocean-Atmosphere Data Set. *Bull. Am. Meteorol. Soc.* 68: 1239–1250.

Assessment of Hurricane Lorenzo metocean forecast

R.M. Campos, M. Gonçalves & C. Guedes Soares
Centre for Marine Technology and Ocean Engineering (CENTEC), Instituto Superior Técnico, Universidade de Lisboa, Lisbon, Portugal

ABSTRACT: Improving extreme wave predictions in the North Atlantic Ocean is an urgent demand in a scenario of climate change. This paper evaluates the wave forecast of NCEP/NOAA for Hurricane Lorenzo – the easternmost category 5 Atlantic hurricane on record, which occurred in September 2019. The assessment is focused on the Azores archipelago, using wave buoy measurements at Ponta Delgada. The peak of the storm presented Hs of 8 m on October 2nd, which is analyzed in detail. Results show accurate forecasts of Hs for prognostics issued since seven days prior to the event, with small errors around only 0.5 meter for the maximum Hs. A discussion on the time of the peak of the storm, predicted by different forecast cycles, is conducted, where delays and early arrival were reported. It has been found that such discrepancies are mostly related to the storm positioning, pointed as the most critical feature for this event.

1 INTRODUCTION

Extreme wave pose a major threat to ship traffic, coastal activities, and marine operations in general. Accurate predictions of extreme events are crucial to protect life and property. However, the quality of metocean forecasts is usually high for the first forecast days but rapidly deteriorates after the 5-day lead time (Bidlot, 2017; Campos et al., 2019a). In the North Atlantic Ocean, this issue becomes even more important due to severe wind and wave climate associated with tropical cyclones, especially in a scenario of climate change (Solomon, 2007; Bengtsson et al., 2007; Catto et al., 2011). Therefore, detail assessments of forecast products, with emphasis on extreme events, are essential to reduce risks and improve alerts. In this context, our goal is to investigate the performance of the wave forecast for Hurricane Lorenzo, issued by the National Centers for Environmental Prediction (NCEP/NOAA).

Hurricane Lorenzo was the easternmost category 5 Atlantic hurricane on record, occurred in September 2019. The tropical storm was generated close to the west coast of Africa on September 22nd, and on September it became category 4 with rapid intensification to category 5. What made Lorenzo unique was its track (Figure 1), which shifted to the east and hit Azores on October 2nd with the strongest winds in 20 years. Later it propagated towards Ireland as an extra-tropical cyclone. Hurricane Lorenzo had the maximum 1-minute sustained winds of 72 m/s, lowest pressure of 925 hPa, and resulted in $USD 362 in damage and seven fatalities. It has been reported that waves reached 15 m offshore the islands and 53 people had to be relocated. The most severe conditions occurred in Flores Islands. The combination of severity with the unique characteristics of Lorenzo makes this event especially important to be assessed and discussed.

Previous studies describe the difficulty of simulating ocean waves under extreme wind conditions, including Campos et al. (2019b), Van Vledder and Akpinar (2015), Cavaleri (2009), Ponce de Leon and Guedes Soares (2008), Cavaleri et al. (2007), and Swail and Cox (2000). Rogers et al. (2012) found the three most important sources of errors in wave modeling: numerics and resolution, physics, and forcing. The strong sustained winds combined with unstable atmospheric boundary layer and rapid changes in intensity and directions compose the most difficult environmental conditions to predict. Specific extreme events were unique for being rare and anomalously intense, and deserved separate studies; e.g., Cardone et al. (1996), Ponce de León and Guedes Soares (2015), and Dutra et al. (2017). Therefore, since Hurricane Lorenzo has been the first hurricane to directly hit Portugal, there is an urgent request to assess the wave forecast and analyze how operational centers predicted the storm.

2 METHODS AND DATA DESCRIPTION

2.1 *Cyclone tracking and diagnostics*

The track of Hurricane Lorenzo is illustrated in Figure 1. A complete description of the event can be found at: https://www.nhc.noaa.gov/archive/2019/LORENZO.shtml? Due to its track hitting Azores,

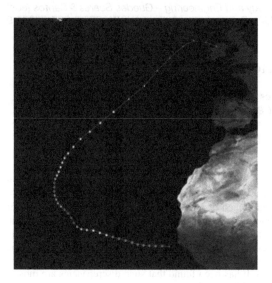

Figure 1. Track of Hurricane Lorenzo, generated at the coast of Africa with decay as an extratropical cyclone in Ireland.

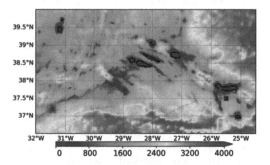

Figure 2. Wave measurements available during the passage of Hurricane Lorenzo through Azores (red markers). The red star represents the selected data, in Ponta Delgada, Sao Miguel, at 37.725°N/25.721°W moored at 90 m water depth.

the assessment is primarily based on wave measurements across the archipelago.

Figure 2 presents the stations with quality-controlled data for the duration of the hurricane, and consists of Datawell waverider buoys where bulk parameters are available. The parameters significant wave height (Hs) and peak wave period (Tp) measured near Ponta Delgada were selected for the assessments. The other two buoys further northwest were excluded because waves were attenuated by the islands, and would not be suitable for the evaluation of a global scale forecast.

The wave forecasts evaluated was provided by the National Centers for Environmental Prediction (NCEP/NOAA), the largest public available forecast product in the world, and consist of wave simulations from WAVEWATCH III version 6.07 (Tolman et al., 2019) with space resolution of 0.5°X0.5° for the global grid. There are four forecast cycles (FC) per day that produces forecasts of every hour from the initial time out to 120 hours, and then forecasts at 3-hour intervals out to 180 hours. Only the FC of 00Z has been selected for the assessment (with forecast range of 7.5 days for each cycle). The wave model is forced by 10-m winds from the Global Forecast System using its new implementation (GFS-FV3) since june-2019:
https://www.weather.gov/news/fv3

The assessment is based on four error metrics described by Mentaschi et al. (2013), where x is the wave forecast, y is the wave buoy data, and the overbar indicates the arithmetic mean. The correlation coefficient (CC) is also included (equation 4), where σ_x and σ_y are the standard deviations of the model and the observations respectively. Unlike the other metrics, CC values close to zero indicate poor results and the best models should be close to 1.

$$RMSE = \sqrt{\frac{1}{n}\sum_{i=1}^{n}(y_i - x_i)^2} \quad (1)$$

$$NBias = \frac{\sum_{i=1}^{n}(y_i - x_i)}{\sum_{i=1}^{n}x_i} \quad (2)$$

$$SI = \sqrt{\frac{\sum_{i=1}^{n}[(x_i - \bar{x}) - (y_i - \bar{y})]^2}{\sum_{i=1}^{n}y_i^2}} \quad (3)$$

$$CC = \frac{1}{n}\frac{\sum_{i=1}^{n}(x_i - \bar{x})(y_i - \bar{y})}{\sigma_x \sigma_y} \quad (4)$$

The error metrics above are applied to the time window of 36h during the passage of Lorenzo throughout the island. In addition, the difference in magnitude of the peak of the event is also computed ("PDiff", model minus observation) as well as the time lag ("Tlag") associated with the instant of peak (time difference between the time of peak of the forecast minus the peak of the observation), i.e., when Tlag is positive the forecast is delayed.

3 ASSESSMENT RESULTS

3.1 *In-situ analysis using buoy data*

The quality of NCEP wave forecast is analyzed as a function of the lead time, or forecast cycle prior to the event. The maximum Hs of Hurricane Lorenzo in Ponta Delgada occurred on October 2nd around 12Z. It is expected that the 00Z cycle of October 2nd produces a high-quality forecast, but as the cycle becomes more distant to the event, the chaotic behavior of the atmosphere deteriorates the predictability and increase the scatter errors. Therefore, the assessment compares the forecast cycles (FC) moving backwards in time but referring to the same day, when the maximum of Hs and Tp were recorded by the buoy.

Figure 3 presents the results, when the buoy recorded extreme waves up to 8 m of Hs on October - 2nd. The forecast cycle (FC) from September 26th, six days before to the event, predicted waves of 8.5 m with maximum at 09Z, i.e., the event was overestimated with earlier arrival compared to the observations. Nearly the same characteristic is obtained from the FC of September 27th. Moving to September 28th, four days prior to the maximum Hs in Azores, the forecast drastically changed, and the maximum was predicted to occur at 21Z. It is a significant modification on the prognostic for October 2nd, from the FC of September 27th compared to the 28th. Another rapid change is seen moving to the FC of September 29th, where the forecast becomes very accurate, with correct estimation of Hs and time of the peak.

On September 30th, two days before the measured peak of the storm in Azores, Figure 3 shows the forecast starts to underestimate the observations and the peak was delayed. In the next cycles the underestimation is amplified and Hs is reduced to 7 m on the forecast issued in the same day Lorenzo hit Azores. Therefore, the evolution of the forecast cycles moving forward in time and getting closer to extreme event in Ponta Delgada indicates a very dynamic behavior of the predictions, that changes especially in terms of the severity of the event and the peak time.

Table 1 summarizes the error metrics for the passage of the hurricane at Ponta Delgada. It is noticeable the degradation of the forecast at longer forecast ranges, especially beyond the fourth day – reflected especially on the RMSE, SI, and CC. Despite the limitations described above Table 1 shows the good predictability of Hurricane Lorenzo, with correlation coefficients above 0.9 within the four forecast days prior to the peak, and systematic errors up to 13% with absolute time lags of a few hours within the same

Table 1. Error metrics of Hurricane Lorenzo at Ponta Delgada, calculated for the period from October 2nd at 00Z to October 3rd at 12Z.

FC	RMSE (m)	Nbias (m)	SI	CC	PDiff (m)	Tlag (h)
Oct-02	0.47	0.05	0.08	0.98	-0.69	1.00
Oct-01	0.52	0.08	0.08	0.97	-0.26	1.00
Sep-30	0.56	0.09	0.07	0.98	-0.24	1.00
Sep-29	0.90	0.13	0.14	0.92	0.10	-1.00
Sep-28	1.59	0.22	0.25	0.82	1.38	4.00
Sep-27	2.12	0.16	0.41	0.52	1.12	-5.00
Sep-26	2.30	0.12	0.46	0.40	0.83	-7.00

interval. This level of accuracy allows analysts, forecasters, and decision makers to take correct measures to minimize risks and mitigate environmental threats.

The forecast analysis of the peak period (Tp) is shown in Figure 4. The same relation among FC is present in the evolution of Tp; however, they significantly differ from the observations. The maximum Tp, interestingly, happens on October 1st instead of 2nd, such as Hs. It indicates that the wave generation process and nonlinear interactions transferred energy towards the low frequency part of the spectrum (Tp around 20 seconds). The wave groups at lower frequencies and with larger lengths propagate faster than short-period waves and, in this case, faster than the cyclone propagation. Hence, the lowest frequencies travelled ahead of the atmospheric system and the main wave group with maximum energy and Hs.

From Figure 1, the wave forecast correctly captured the arrival of the low-frequency waves with Tp around 18 seconds, followed by the decay of Tp in the next days. However, it could not predict

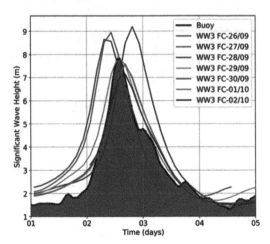

Figure 3. Assessment result of WW3/GFS NCEP forecast at Ponta Delgada as a function of forecast time, related to the forecast cycles (FC) prior to the event. The evolution of Hs is plotted.

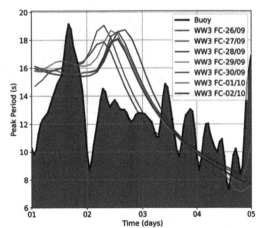

Figure 4. Assessment result of WW3/GFS NCEP forecast at Ponta Delgada as a function of forecast time, related to the forecast cycles (FC) prior to the event. The evolution of Tp is plotted.

accurately the instant of maximum Tp, suggesting possible misrepresentation of the wave spectra, especially at the lowest frequency ranges. Unfortunately, spectral information from the wave buoy is not available to investigate this issue.

3.2 Spatial distribution of forecasts

The previous assessments of Figure 3 and Figure 4 showed great changes in the time of the storm peak at Azores, with FC of September 26th and 27th indicating earlier arrival and the FC of the 28th significantly delayed. One could speculate the reasons for these differences, considering the dynamics of the atmospheric system and the wave propagation. Regarding the meteorological aspect (conjecture 1), the position of the cyclone directly determines the location of wave generation and thus the wave propagation and time for the wave group to arrive at the archipelago, which could explain such differences. On the other hand, regarding the wave aspect (conjecture 2), the misrepresentation of the wave spectra can lead to incorrect wave group propagation and consequent problems in the storm peak arrival. Since spectral data is not available, it is worth to look at the wind and wave fields in the North Atlantic Ocean, comparing the FC throughout the forecast ranges (Figure 5).

The most relevant FCs are presented in Figure 5, where it has been previously identified the largest modifications in consecutive cycles. The most important feature to be observed is the cyclone position, with location of the highest wind speeds, followed by the direct relation with Hs fields. Note that all maps are pointing to the metocean conditions on October 2nd at 12Z, the only difference is the FC from which such conditions were simulated.

Comparing the second and third columns of Figure 5, generated by the FC of September 28th and 29th when the largest modification of Tlag is verified, it is clear that the position of the hurricane is displaced. For the FC of September 28th the cyclone is further south, below 40°N, while for the FC of September 29th the cyclone is at 45°N. The wave fields directly follow the atmospheric evolution and indicated that the time discrepancies of the storm peak of Figure 3 come from the atmospheric forecast and the misrepresentation of the position of the storm (conjecture 1). Moreover, differences in the pronounced peak of the extreme event are also noticeable. The Hs field from the FC of September - 26th has a much smoother peak than the other FCs, where the maximum waves are more concentrated into a sharp peak at smaller area.

Such differences show the impact of each data assimilation cycle and model integration on the

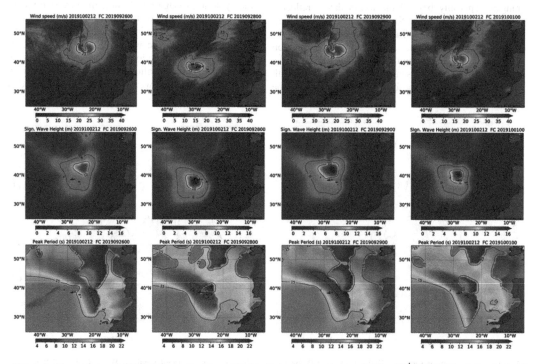

Figure 5. Comparison of different forecast cycles related to the same snapshot on October 2nd at 12Z. The left column if the FC of September 26th, six days before the peak of Lorenzo at Azores, and moving to the right columns it shows the FC of September 28th, 29th, and October 1st. The top line refers to wind speed, where the position of the Hurricane can be identified and directly associated with the generated wave field of Hs (middle line) and Tp (bottom line of plots).

forecast as it moves forward in time approaching the instant and occurrence of the storm at certain location. Interpreting different guesses and how it can change in time is part of the daily routine of forecasters worldwide and consist of a demanding task. The combination of Figure 3 to Figure 5 illustrates the amplitude of such discrepancies among the forecasts and how it improves with reduced lead times. Besides the predictability for Azores, this issue is a major subject for ship routing in the North Atlantic Ocean and nowadays, with the first hurricane to directly hit Portugal, the importance has increased.

4 CONCLUSIONS

The assessments of the NCEP wave forecast at Azores indicated reasonably good model performances since seven days prior to the event – where the extreme Hs was correctly predicted with only 0.5 m of error and seven hour of delay regarding the time of the peak of the storm in Ponta Delgada. The FCs are improved as the forecast range is reduced, as expected (Table 1), and the reasons for the changes in the prognostics of each FC have been investigated. The analysis of wind and wave fields (Figure 5) indicates that the variation on the time of the peak of the storm is associated with the cyclone position that shifts with different FC. Therefore, we conclude the structure of the hurricane and the wave modeling have been successfully represented, with the most critical forecast feature being the cyclone positioning.

Our results suggest that efforts on improving metocean forecasts, such as Ponce de León & Guedes Soares (2014) and Campos et al. (2019c), must address primarily the cyclone track evolution and position of the fetch throughout the forecast range – a great challenge that inevitably requires fully coupled atmospheric/ocean modeling with proper resolution and physics.

ACKNOWLEDGMENTS

This work was funded by the project "Extreme wind and wave modeling and statistics in the Atlantic Ocean" (EXWAV) financed by the Portuguese Foundation for Science and Technology (Fundação para a Ciência e Tecnologia-FCT) under contract PTDC/EAM-OCE/31325/2017 RD0504. The authors would like to acknowledge NCEP/NOAA for providing the forecasts. The authors are grateful to E.B. Azevedo and F. V. Reis for having made available the wave buoy data collected since 2005 by the project CLIMAAT (MAC/2.3/A3) and now obtained and processed under the framework of the ECOMARPORT project (MAC/1.1B/081). This work was performed within the scope of the Strategic Research Plan of the Centre for Marine Technology and Ocean Engineering (CENTEC), which is financed by the Portuguese Foundation for Science and Technology (Fundação para a Ciência e Tecnologia - FCT) under contract UIDB/UIDP/00134/2020.

REFERENCES

Bidlot, J.R., 2017. Twenty-one years of wave forecast verification. ECMWF Newsletter 150:31–36.

Bengtsson, L., Hodges, K. I., Esch, M., Keenlyside, N., Kornblueh, L., Luo, J.-J., and Yamagats, T., 2007. How may tropical cyclones change in a warmer climate? Tellus, V59A, 539–561.

Catto, J.L., Shaffrey, L.C., Hodges, K.I., 2011. Northern Hemisphere Extratropical Cyclones in a Warming Climate in the HiGEM High-Resolution Climate Model. Journal of Climate, 24, 5336–5352.

Campos, R.M., Alves, J.H.G.M., Penny, S.G., Krasnopolsky, V., 2019a. Global assessments of the NCEP ensemble forecast system using altimeter data. Ocean Dynamics, ISSN 1616-7341. https://doi.org/10.1007/s10236-019-01329-4.

Campos, R.M., Alves, J.H.G.M, Guedes Soares, C., Parente, C.E., Guimaraes, L.G., 2019b. Regional long-term extreme wave analysis using hindcast data from the South Atlantic. Ocean Engineering, 179, 202–212.

Campos, R.M., Krasnopolsky, V., Alves, J.H.G.M, Penny, S.G., 2019c. Nonlinear wave ensemble averaging in the Gulf of Mexico using neural networks. J Atmos Ocean Technol, 36, 113–127.

Cardone, V.J., Jensen, R.E., Resio, D.T., Swail, V.R., Cox, A.T., 1996. Evaluation of contemporary ocean wave models in rare events: the Halloween storm October and the storm of century of March 1993. J. Atmosph. Ocean Technol. 13, 198–230.

Cavaleri, L., 2009. Wave Modeling — Missing the Peaks. J. Phys. Oceanogr. 39, 2757–2778.

Cavaleri, L., Alves, J.H.G.M., Ardhuin, F., Babanin, A., Banner, M., Belibassakis, K., Benoit, M., Donelan, M., Groeneweg, J., Herbers, T.H.C., Hwang, P., Janssen, P.A.E.M., Janssen, T., Lavrenov, I.V., Magne, R., Monbaliu, J., Onorato, M., Polnikov, V., Resio, D., Rogers, W.E., Sheremet, A., McKee Smith, J., Tolman, H.L., Van Vledder, G., Wolf, J., Young, I., 2007. Prog. Oceanography 75, 603–674.

Dutra, L.M.M.D., Rocha, R.P., Lee, R.W., Peres, J.R.R., Camargo, R. 2017. Structure and evolution of subtropical cyclone Anita as evaluated by heat and vorticity budgets. Quarterly Journal of the Royal Meteorological Society, v. 1, p. 1–15.

Mentaschi L, Besio G, Cassola F, Mazzino, A., 2013. Problems in RMSE- based wave model validations. Ocean Model 72:53–58.

Ponce de Leon, S., Guedes Soares, C., 2008. Sensitivity of wave model predictions to wind fields in the Western Mediterranean sea. Coast. Eng. 55, 920–929.

Ponce de León, S., Guedes Soares, C., 2014. Extreme wave parameters under North Atlantic extratropical cyclones. Ocean Modelling 81, 78–88.

Ponce de León, S., Guedes Soares, C., 2015. Hindcast of the Hércules winter storm in the North Atlantic. Nat Hazards, 78:1883–1897.

Rogers, W.E., Dykes, J.D., Wang, D., Carroll, S.N., Watson, K., 2012. Validation test report for WAVEWATCH-III. NRL Memorandum Report 75 7320-12-9425.

Solomon, S., ed. Climate change 2007 - the physical science basis: Working group I contribution to the fourth assessment report of the IPCC. Vol. 4. Cambridge University Press.

Swail, V.R., Cox, A.T., 2000. On the use of NCEP-NCAR reanalysis surface marine wind fields for a long-term North Atlantic wave hindcast. J. Atmos. Oceanic Technol. 17, 532–545.

Tolman, H.L. & Development Group, 2019. User manual and system documentation of WAVEWATCH III version 6.07. NOAA/NWS/NCEP MMAB Tech. Note 333, 465 pp.

Van Vledder, G.Ph, Akpinar, A., 2015. Wave model predictions in the Black Sea: Sensitivity to wind fields. Appl. Ocean Res. 53, 161–178.

Distribution and characteristics of extreme waves generated by extratropical cyclones in the North Atlantic Ocean

C.B. Gramcianinov, R.M. Campos & C. Guedes Soares
Centre for Marine Technology and Ocean Engineering (CENTEC), Instituto Superior Técnico, Universidade de Lisboa, Lisbon, Portugal

R. de Camargo
Departamento de Ciências Atmosféricas, Instituto de Astronomia, Geofísica e Ciências Atmosféricas, Universidade de São Paulo, São Paulo, Brazil

ABSTRACT: Extreme waves at mid and high latitudes are closely associated with extratropical cyclones. The storm track position and intensity controls the wave climate across the oceans and they are crucial to ship routing and metocean design criteria. It is important to map the spatial distribution of cyclones associated with extreme waves, especially to define regions that present higher risks to shipping and offshore operations. This work aims to produce a climatology of extratropical cyclones, considering only the events associated with extremes waves in the North Atlantic. The season containing more extreme waves events associated with cyclones is the winter, also presenting the highest Hs values and largest extreme regions extension. The Northeastern of North Atlantic is the area with more occurrence of extreme wave events associated with cyclones. High cyclone intensification rate along the storm track allied to an increase of the fetch make the wave climate at this location dominated by cyclone-winds.

1 INTRODUCTION

The relevance of extratropical atmospheric activity for wind-wave generation is widely discussed in the literature (e.g. Young 1999, Bernardino et al. 2008, Hanafin et al. 2012, Bernardino & Guedes Soares 2016, Ponce de León & Guedes Soares 2014, 2016, Bell et al. 2017, Campos et al. 2018). Extratropical cyclones can be very effective to generate extreme events of winds and waves at mid and high latitudes all year long, even with distinct synoptic characteristics from season to season - in terms of wind magnitude, fetch area and system displacement. In general, the winter presents the most intense storms, due to enhanced temperature gradients and dynamic atmospheric instability mainly related to upper-level jet stream influences (Hoskin & Hodges 2002).

Usually, extreme wave climate studies are based in the climatological wind and wave fields (e.g. Young 1999, Takbash et al. 2019). This type of analysis excludes information regarding individual extreme event characteristics, such as persistence, important to shipping and offshore operations. The trajectory of the storms is an important aspect to be considered in extreme wave studies. Both position and intensity of the storm tracks are responsible to control the wave climate across the oceans, then being crucial for ship routing, storm avoidance and metocean design criteria (Vettor & Guedes Soares 2016a, b).

Objective methods for cyclone identification and tracking have been developed in past decades, mainly based on low-level vorticity or surface pressure criteria (e.g. Sinclair 1994; Murray & Simmonds 1991, Hodges 1994, 1995). Since then, a wide set of cyclone climatology has been developed, particularly to the North Atlantic basin (Hoskins & Hodges 2002, Pinto et al. 2005, Dacre & Grey 2009). The cyclone's climatologies have evolved in the past few years once storms characteristics can be added to each feature providing new insights of atmospheric patterns associated with a set of storms (e.g. Dacre & Grey 2009, Gramcianinov et al. 2019).

The basic product of a tracking method is the collection of all cyclone's trajectories within a region and a period. The spatial statistic distribution of this collection of trajectories can define the storm track position – the preferred location of extratropical cyclones propagation. The North Atlantic storm track extends northeastward across the basin, with maximum activity in January, during boreal winter (e.g. Sinclair 1997, Hoskins & Hodges 2002, Pinto et al. 2005, Wernli & Schwierz 2006).

Although the North Atlantic storm track has been deeply studied in the past years, an approach in extreme wave generation during cyclones is still missing. There is a need to separate those systems associated with persistent strong winds, from the weak and fast-moving cyclones that may not generate large waves and extreme events. Therefore, mapping those specific systems and knowing their spatial distribution and characteristics is very important, especially to improve the definition of regions with higher risks to offshore operations and navigation, which may also include the occurrence of abnormal waves, which may occur in those conditions (Guedes Soares et al. 2004; Slunyaev et al. 2005). In this sense, this work aims to contribute to establishing a new climatology of extratropical cyclones specifically related to wave extremes in the North Atlantic sector.

2 METHODS

2.1 Cyclone tracking and diagnostics

An automatic procedure is applied to the recent ERA5 reanalysis from the European Centre for Medium-Range Weather Forecast (ECMWF), a dataset with high temporal (1-hourly) and spatial resolution (0.125o in latitude and longitude).

Cyclones are identified in the newest major global reanalysis produced by the European Centre for Medium-Range Weather Forecast (ECMWF), the ERA5. This dataset provides hourly estimates of several atmospheric and oceanographic variables in a 30-km global grid. The description of ERA5 can be found in its documentation in the Copernicus Climate Change Service (2017), but the reanalysis is basically produced by an Atmospheric Global Circulation Model with a complex and robust assimilation system for several satellite products and observational data. The period considered in the present effort is a 5-year subset, from 2014 to 2018.

The TRACK program (Hodges 1994, 1995, 1999) is used to identify and track the cyclonic system within the North Atlantic region. Considering the amount of data produced by Global Circulation Models and Reanalysis, the automatic identification of atmospheric features is a powerful tool for objective analyses. Cyclonic features are identified using vorticity computed by u and v-components of the wind at 850 hPa. This field is computed in spherical coordinates to avoid projection distortion. The vorticity magnitude is directly proportional to the severity of the system, however, it is very noisy, particularly in a high-resolution grid. To cyclone identification, the vorticity field needs to be filtered to avoid small scale features (wavenumber > 42) and planetary waves (wavenumber < 5). The location of the cyclone center is made using the threshold of 1.0×10^{-5} s^{-1} and only systems with at least 24 h are used. Details about the TRACK algorithm and method can be found in Hoskins & Hodges (2002).

2.2 Extreme wave events selection

An extreme wave event can be defined by the significant wave height (Hs) field, considering a threshold that can be fixed (e.g. Bernardino et al. 2008) or computed statistically. For a spatial-temporal approach, it is simple to define a fixed threshold - here extreme wave is when Hs ≥ 5 m, following Bernardino et al. (2008). According to Young (1999), the maximum mean monthly value in North Atlantic is Hs = 5.2 m, in January.

Regions of extreme wave Hs are obtained and labeled through adjoined neighbor extreme points. The central latitude and longitude of each labeled region are computed using its center of mass, i.e. density of extreme points. Then, a search for a cyclone feature around the extreme is made to found the nearest cyclone. The distances between the extreme and cyclone centers are computed for each time frame in meters, considering the Earth curvature, to avoid projection distortion. One cyclone can be associated with more than one extreme region, but the opposite is not possible.

An example of cyclones and extreme wave selection method for one data frame is shown in Figure 1. If an extreme region has no cyclone within a 1500-km radius, it is considered being an extreme not generated by a local cyclonic feature, and it is excluded from the statistical analysis. The maximum distance of 1500-km was chosen to avoid the influence of another synoptic system winds, i.e. anticyclones, and is based in the size of a mid-latitude baroclinic wave (2000-3000 km).

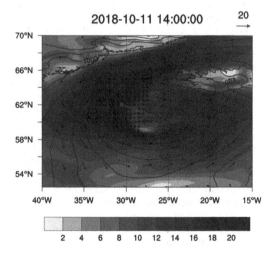

Figure 1. Example of the automatic scheme to identify and selection the extreme wave events associated with cyclones. The points with extreme wave values (Hs > 5m) are showed by the '+' signal. The center of mass of this continuous extreme region and the cyclone center are represented by the red and blue bullet, respectively. The distance computed between them is represented in the dashed line. The background field shows the 10-m wind velocity (magnitude and vectors; m s^{-1}) and sea level mean pressure (contoured every 4 hPa) on October 11th, 2018 at 14 UTC.

3 CYCLONES ASSOCIATED WITH EXTREME WAVE EVENTS

Table 1 shows the number of cyclones tracked in the North Atlantic domain and the number of the ones associated with extreme wave events. The winter leads, with the larger number of cyclones associated with extreme events, followed by autumn and spring. Winter is also the season that presents more cyclones associated with extreme wave events concerning its total, with just over half (51.7%). Autumn and spring present similar percentages of associated cyclones. Summer presents the larger difference in comparison to other seasons, with few cyclones associated with extreme events. It is important to note that the total number of cyclones passing through the domain does not change much with the season to justify the summer outlier value (standard deviation = 78.8).

The statistical characteristic of the extreme wave events associated with each cyclone is presented in Table 2. The most severe events occur in winter, considering all parameters displayed in Table 2. In this season it happens not only the most intense events regarding Hs but also the larger ones, considering the number of points affected per region. It is expected that the mean maximum Hs found here would be larger than the 5.2 m presented by Young (1999) once only extreme events above 5 m, are selected and also, the ones associated cyclone.

Table 1. Total number of cyclones passing though the North Atlantic domain, number of cyclones associated with extreme wave events and its percentage. The values were computed for each season and the entire analysis period (2014-2018).

Season	Total	Associated	%
Winter (DJF)	1372	709	51.7
Spring (MAM)	1371	457	33.3
Summer (JJA)	1211	96	7.9
Autumn (SON)	1362	503	36.9

Table 2. Maximum Hs (Hs_{max}), mean maximum Hs (mHs_{max}) and mean Hs (Hs_{mean}) of extreme events, in meters. Also, mean size of extreme region in grid points associated with one cyclone. These values were computed for each season, following the season definition presented in Table 1.

Season	Hs_{max}	mHs_{max}	Hs_{mean}	Size
Winter	20.347.15	5.72	731.4	1.4
Spring	14.026.70	5.62	408.1	1.3
Summer	11.446.17	5.48	92.7	1.1
Autumn	15.706.74	5.64	325.8	1.3

The spring and autumn present similar values, with the last one being slightly severe than the former. The summer shows the lowest values, as expected.

3.1 Extreme-wave cyclones

The spatial distribution of all cyclones tracks obtained for the period between 2014 and 2018 for the North Atlantic sector is presented in Figure 2, followed by the spatial distribution computed only using the trajectories of the cyclones associated with extreme wave events in Figure 3. Both Figures 2 and 3 present the track density separated by season. Note that the track density scale changes between Figures 2 and 3 due to the difference between the numbers of tracks used to compute the statistic in each case.

The North Atlantic cyclone track density per season (Figure 2) shows a northeast orientation across the basin, as described in previous studies (e.g. Hoskins & Hodges 2002, Dacre & Gray 2009). This configuration is directly related to the location of the branches of the jet stream, which oscillate typically between 35°N and 55°N along the year, reaching its northernmost position and lower intensity during the summer (Figure 2c). Two regions present high track density and their importance changes according to the season: the eastern North American coast and the Northeast portion of the basin, southward Greenland. During the winter and spring, the eastern coast of the USA leads, followed by the Northeast North Atlantic (NNA). In the autumn, the storm track strengthens northward, due to the jet stream variability, affecting the Canadian coast and reaching higher density in NNA (Figure 2d). The summer presents a dispersed storm track, mainly due to a weak and spread jet (Figure 2c). However, one can note that even with the northward position of the jet stream, the track density is not shifted as in autumn. Besides the spread upper-level jet, the southernmost latitude of the tracked area (35°N - 45°N), may present a signal of post-tropical depressions or subtropical cyclones. It is in the summer that most of the tropical-extratropical transition occurs, during the cyclone propagation along the eastern USA coast.

Interesting aspects emerge when only cyclones associated with the extreme wave events are taken into account (Figure 3). In the winter the storm track associated with the wave extreme events are similar to the main North Atlantic Storm track: the maximum along eastern USA coast and spreading toward the northeast.

The secondary storm track maximum in the NNA does not appear, indicating that a big part of the cyclones associated with extreme events in the basin comes though the eastern coast in this season. However the values along the entire winter storm track are high when compared to the other seasons, and even the western portion present large density values. The autumn and spring present a track density maximum northward, in central and northeastern

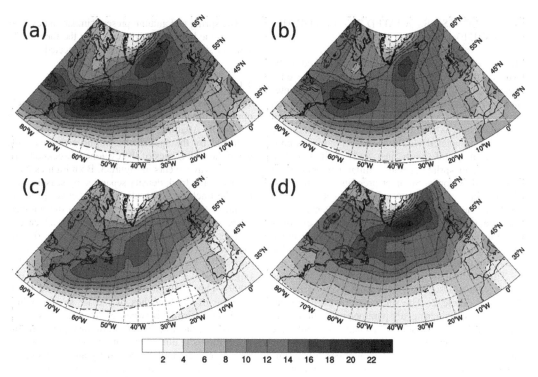

Figure 2. The cyclone track density for the (a) winter (DJF), (b) spring (MAM), (c) summer (JJA), and (d) autumn (SON). The densities are computed using all cyclones within North Atlantic domain in the period between 2014 and 2018. The density unit is cyclone per 10^6 km^2 per month.

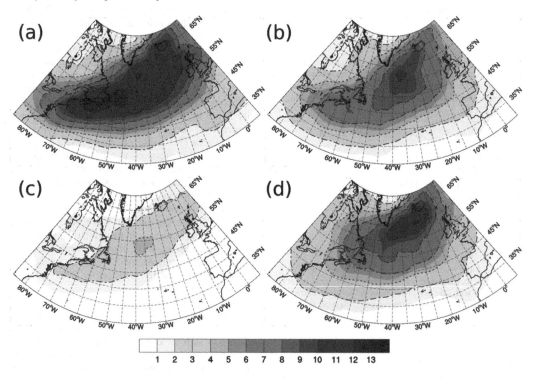

Figure 3. The track density computed only for the cyclones associated with extreme wave events for the (a) winter (DJF), (b) spring (MAM), (c) summer (JJA), and (d) autumn (SON). The densities are computed using all cyclones within North Atlantic domain in the period between 2014 and 2018. The density unit is cyclone per 10^6 km^2 per month.

portions of North Atlantic, which is expected for the autumn as seen in Figure 2d, but not for the spring. The spring track density for the associated cyclones indicates that the tracks at high latitudes (north of 45°N) present more influence to the extreme wave events within the domain. The summer presents the track maximum shifted to the center of the basin.

3.2 *The link between extreme wave events distribution and the storm track*

To support the discussion, Figure 4 presents the density of extreme wave events per area per month, in each season. In all seasons, the NNA presents a high density of events, in agreement with the extreme wave storm track presented in Figure 3. Despite that, it is interesting to see that the summer and spring present events more spread over the central part of the basin and along the USA east coast, in agreement with Figures 3b and 3c which shows a branch of the storm track at these locations. The density of events in the autumn correspond directly to the track density in Figure 3d, showing that cyclones passing through NNA plays an important role in the extreme wave events of this region.

One may note that, despite the high track density of associated cyclone in the USA eastern coast, winter extreme wave events are concentrated northward, and does not present a density core along North America coast, like summer or spring. Figure 5 shows the genesis density of cyclones associated with extreme wave events in the winter, which is similar to the genesis regions reported by Dacre & Grey (2009). The genesis density is computed considering only the first point of each track. All genesis regions within the domain are active to extreme wave cyclones: East Atlantic, Weast Atlantic, and Greenland (see Figure 2b, Dacre & Grey 2009). Cyclones generated at these distinct locations affect the North and Northeastern portion of the basin due to their track and to their intensification rate, which is maximum in the central North Atlantic for the East Atlantic cyclones. In fact, the regions where we find the highest density of extreme wave events are equivalent to the region of cyclones' maximum intensity found by Dacre and Grey (2009).

Young (1999), Young & Donelan (2018) and Talkbash et al. (2019) show the location of high density in Figure 4, as extreme Hs region. According to Young (1999), this sector of the North Atlantic presents the most extreme surface winds as well.

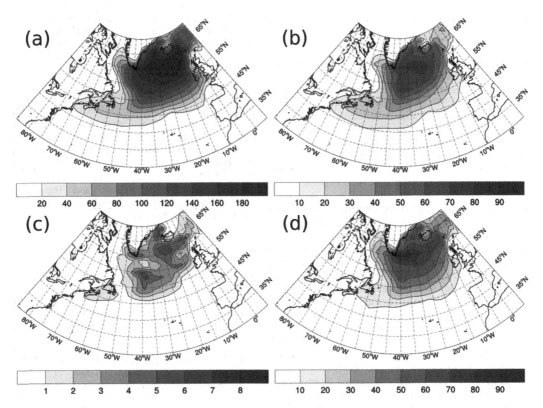

Figure 4. Extreme wave occurrence associated with cyclones in the (a) winter (DJF), (b) spring (MAM), (c) summer (JJA), and (d) autumn (SON). The occurrence is computed within a box of 2.5° × 2.5°, and the final unit is event per area per month, where the area is scaled to be 10^6 km^2.

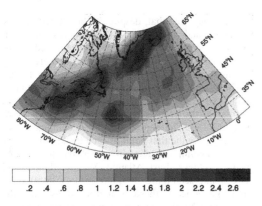

Figure 5. Genesis density computed only to the cyclones associated with extreme wave events in the winter (DJF). The density unit is cyclone per 10^6 km^2 per month.

These correspondences demonstrate de the important role of cyclones in the NNA, where the wind-sea waves dominate (Stopa et al. 2013). It is important to clarify that the method applied in this work, swell waves are not evaluated. However, the swell signal in the Hs may exist, particularly in the eastern North Atlantic (Young 1999).

4 CONCLUSIONS

This work produced a climatology of cyclones associated with extreme wave events (Hs > 5m) in the North Atlantic Ocean. The cyclones were identified and tracked using the TRACK program (Hodges 1994, 1995, 1999), with relative vorticity, while extreme wave events were selected using homogeneous areas with Hs > 5m. Once the extreme wave events were connected to the tracked cyclones spatial distribution maps of the events could be produced, resulting in a cyclone climatology that contains only cyclones that generated extreme local waves.

Winter leads the more severe season, as reported in the literature (e.g. Young 1999). It is the season with more cyclones associated with extreme wave events, and also the one which presents higher Hs values and extreme regions extension. Autumn and Spring are similar, but the former is slight severe. Summer remains as the weak season, supported by an also weak and spread storm track. The differences between the general storm track and the extreme cyclones track density reveals most of the extreme wave events in the basin are related to tracks that reach high latitudes (north of 45°N). The exception is the summer events that also are influenced by cyclones lower latitudes, which it is a signal of post-tropical cyclones and/or subtropical cyclone typical of this season. For this reason, the density of extreme wave events in the summer is more shifted southward in comparison with another season.

The Northeastern North Atlantic, near Greenland and Eastern Europe, is the area of major concern regarding the extreme wave events generated by cyclones in all seasons. The highest density of occurrence of extreme wave events associated with cyclones is in this location, similar to extreme wave climate compute by Talkbash et al. (2019) and Young (1999). This fact brings to evidence the importance of local cyclone-winds forcing in the wave climate of the region. First, there are the cyclones that develop in Greenland, and reaching their maximum intensification rates nearby (Dacre & Gray 2009). Secondly, there is the effect of the cyclones which originates in the East Atlantic and propagates towards Northeastern North Atlantic (e.g. Hanafin et al. 2012), with the possibility of fetch area increase allied to cyclonic winds intensification during the cyclone's lifecycle.

ACKNOWLEDGMENTS

This work is part of the project "Extreme wind and wave modeling and statistics in the Atlantic Ocean" (EXWAV) financed by the Portuguese Foundation for Science and Technology (Fundação para a Ciência e Tecnologia-FCT) under contract PTDC/EAM-OCE/31325/2017 RD0504, and by the São Paulo Research Foundation (Fundação de Amparo à Pesquisa do Estado de São Paulo - FAPESP) grant 2018/08057-5. The authors would like to acknowledge Kevin Hodges at the National Centre for Earth Observation, Dept. of Meteorology, University of Reading, Reading, UK, for the TRACK code. The ERA5 products were provided by the Copernicus Climate Change Service Information (2019). This work contributes to the Strategic Research Plan of the Centre for Marine Technology and Ocean Engineering (CENTEC), which is financed by the Portuguese Foundation for Science and Technology (Fundação para a Ciência e Tecnologia - FCT) under contract UIDB/UIDP/00134/2020.

REFERENCES

Bell, R.J., Gray, S.L. & Jones, O.P. 2017. North Atlantic storm driving of extreme wave heights in the North Sea. *J. Geophys. Res. Ocean* 122: 3253–3268.

Bernardino, M., Boukhanovsky, A. & Guedes Soares, C. 2008. Alternative Approaches to Storm Statistics in the Ocean. *Proceedings of the ASME 2008 27th International Conference on Offshore Mechanics and Arctic Engineering* ASME paper OMAE2008-58053.

Bernardino, M. & Guedes Soares, C. 2016. A climatological analysis of storms in the North Atlantic. In Guedes Soares, C. and Santos T.A., (eds.), *Maritime Technology and Engineering*, Taylor & Francis Group, London, UK. 1021–1026.

Campos, R.M., Alves, J.H.G.M., Guedes Soares, C., Guimaraes, L.G. & Parente, C.E. 2018. Extreme wind-wave modeling and analysis in the south Atlantic ocean. *Ocean Model*. 124: 75–93.

Copernicus Climate Change Service (C3S) 2017. ERA5: Fifth generation of ECMWF atmospheric reanalyses of the global climate. *Copernicus Climate Change Service Climate Data Store (CDS)*, July, 2019. https://cds.climate.copernicus.eu/cdsapp#!/home

Dacre, H.F. & Gray, S.L. 2009. The Spatial Distribution and Evolution Characteristics of North Atlantic Cyclones. *Mon. Wea. Rev.* 137: 99–115.

Gramcianinov, C.B., Hodges, K.I. & Camargo, R. 2019. The properties and genesis environments of South Atlantic cyclones. *Clim. Dyn.* 53: 4115–4140.

Guedes Soares, C.; Cherneva, Z., & Antao, E. 2004. Abnormal waves during Hurricane Camille. *Journal of Geophysical Research*. 109: C08008, doi:10.1029/2003JC002244.

Hanafin, J.A., Quilfen, Y., Ardhuin, F., Sienkiewicz, J., Queffeulou, P., Obrebski, M., Chapron, B., Reul, N., Collard, F., Corman, D., Azevedo, E.B. de, Vandemark, D. & Stutzmann, E. 2012: Phenomenal Sea States and Swell from a North Atlantic Storm in February 2011: A Comprehensive Analysis. *Bull. Amer. Meteor. Soc.*, **93**, 1825–1832.

Hodges, K.I. 1994. A general-method for tracking analysis and its application to meteorological data. *Mon Weather Rev* 122(11): 2573–2586.

Hodges, K.I. 1995. Feature Tracking on the Unit Sphere. Mon. *Weather Rev* 123: 3458–3465.

Hodges, K.I. 1999. Adaptative constraints for feature tracking. *Mon Weather Rev* 127: 1362–1373.

Hoskins, B.J. & Hodges, K.I. 2002. New Perspectives on the Northern Hemisphere Winter Storm Tracks. *J. Atmos. Sci.* 59: 1041–1061.

Hoskins, B.J. & Hodges, K.I. 2005. A New Perspective on Southern Hemisphere Storm Tracks. *J. Clim.* 18: 4108–4129.

Murray, R.J. & Simonds, I. 1991. A numerical scheme for tracking cyclone centres from digital data Part 1: development and operation of the scheme. *Aust Meteorol Mag* 39: 155–166.

Pinto, J. G., Spangehl, T., Ulbrich, U. & Speth, P. 2005. Sensitivities of a cyclone detection and tracking algorithm: Individual tracks and climatology. *Meteor. Z.* 14: 823–838.

Ponce de Leon, S. & Guedes Soares, C. 2014. Extreme wave parameters under North Atlantic extratropical cyclones. *Ocean Modelling*, 81:78–88.

Ponce de Leon, S. & Guedes Soares, C. 2015. Hindcast of Extreme Sea States in North Atlantic Extratropical Storms. *Ocean Dynamics*, 65:241–254.

Sinclair, M. R., 1994. An objective cyclone climatology for the Southern Hemisphere. *Mon. Wea. Rev.* 122 (10): 2239–2256.

Sinclair, M. R. 1997. Objective identification of cyclones and their circulation, intensity, and climatology. *Wea. Forecasting* 12: 595–612.

Slunyaev, A., Pelinovsky, E., & Guedes Soares, C. 2005. Modeling Freak Waves from the North Sea. *Applied Ocean Research*. 27(1):12–22.

Stopa, J.E., Cheung, K.F., Tolman, H.L. & Chawla, A. 2013. Patterns and cycles in the Climate Forecast System Reanalysis wind and wave data. *Ocean Model*.70: 207–220.

Takbash, A., Young, I.R. & Breivik, Ø. 2019. Global Wind Speed and Wave Height Extremes Derived from Long-Duration Satellite Records. *J. Climate* 32: 109–126.

Vettor, R. & Guedes Soares, C. 2016a. Development of a Ship Weather Routing System. *Ocean Engineering* 123: 1–14.

Vettor, R. & Guedes Soares, C. 2016b. Rough Weather Avoidance Effect on the Wave Climate Experienced by Oceangoing Vessels. *Applied Ocean Research* 59: 606–615.

Wernli, H. & Schwierz, C. 2006. Surface cyclones in the ERA-40 dataset (1958–2001). Part I: Novel identification method and global climatology. *J. Atmos. Sci.* 63: 2486–2507.

Young, I.R. 1999. Seasonal variability of the global ocean wind and wave climate. *Int. J. Climatol.* 19: 931–950.

Young, I.R. & Donelan, M.A. 2018. On the determination of global ocean wind and wave climate from satellite observations. *Remote Sens. Environ.* 215, 228–241.

Autonomous observing systems in fishing vessels

A.M.P. Piecho-Santos
IPMA-Portuguese Institute for the Ocean and Atmosphere, Lisbon, Portugal
CCMAR-Center of Marine Sciences of the University Algarve, Faro, Portugal

M.A. Hinostroza, T. Rosa & C. Guedes Soares
Centre for Marine Technology and Ocean Engineering (CENTEC), Instituto Superior Técnico, Universidade de Lisboa, Lisbon, Portugal

ABSTRACT: The ocean observing system will be totally autonomous and integrate several meteorological and oceanographic sensors to be installed onboard all types of fishing vessels. The system should allow high-resolution in situ monitoring and spatial coverage of the ocean and coastal areas. It is proposed that the system achieve a Technological Readiness Level of 7. The data acquired from this system will support the development of new products for more safe and efficient maritime operations, to support fishing activities and an integrated management of the marine ecosystems.

1 INTRODUCTION

1.1 *The project*

The project "OBSERVA.FISH- Autonomous Observing Systems in Fishing Vessels for the Support of Marine Ecosystem Management (PTDC/CTA-AMB /31141/2017)" is funded by the EU and FCT under the Portugal2020 Programme (Lisboa2020 and Algarve2020). The project started in September 1st, 2018 and will have a duration of 36 months (until August 31st, 2021). Its main objective is the development of a totally autonomous observing system (no human action), that could be installed onboard all types of fishing vessels (trawlers, purse-seiners, long-liners). Specific goals are: i) to develop more cost effective observing platforms with a large coverage and improved long-term capabilities; ii) to build consolidated data sets from all underway measurements that will be used to validate satellite-derived charts, and hydrodynamic and atmospheric models outputs; iii) to produce advisory products for the support of fishing operation and the management of marine ecosystems; iv) to support forecast and decision making regarding harmful algae blooms (support Bivalves Monitoring National Programme that covers the all coast) and v) to raise awareness among and knowledge transfer to the fishing industry for the acquisition and use of ocean observations and added value products. To attain these objectives the project will be divided in four tasks. Task 01 will include the discussion of the concept and design of the system that will lead to the creation of a Technical Report (Milestone M1) with the specifications of the system and recommend the best sensors to be acquired considering a cost-effective analysis. Based on these technical specifications the system will be built and a first prototype (M2) will be tested onboard IPMA's research vessels (Task 02), that will simulate the several types of fishing vessels. These field tests (Task 02) will produce information necessary for the improvement, adaptation and necessary changes to the system under Task 01 (M3-end-users suggestions report). After these interactions and the necessary changes the system will be delivered (M4) and installed in one of IPMA's research vessel for a continuous acquisition of data It is proposed that the system achieve a TRL 7 (Technological Readiness Level). A manual of installation and operation will be produced based on the experience of the field tests (M5). All the data acquired during the field tests and after the final installation will be analysed for validation (Task 03) using data collected at the same time by by top-of-the-range oceanographic equipments. All the data produced will be consolidated in a data set (M6) and processed jointly with other type of data (e.g., satellite-derived) to produce different advisory products (Task 03). At the end of the project a final report and a brochure (Task 04) will be produced summarizing the major outcomes of the project (M7).

1.2 *Background*

The oceans are vast and severely under-sampled, limiting their understanding and management. The high variability of the ocean processes and the need to assess marine environment state require a continuous monitoring at unprecedented resolution in time, space and quality. Operational oceanography routinely produces high quality observational and model data for fundamental studies and practical applications (McMeel et al. 2017). Ocean observations are expensive, e.g. the daily cost of a research vessel is between 10,000 € to more than 30,000 €.

The use of commercial voluntary Vessels of Opportunity (VOO) is one way to make longterm scientific measurements sustainable. The Global Ocean Surface Underway Data (GOSUD) programme of the Intergovernmental Oceanographic Commission (IOC) (http://www.gosud.org/) and the FerryBox initiative are two good examples of such use for data collection (Petersen et al. 2011).

Data from VOO are useful to establish the main routes of commercial shipping in N Atlantic, to estimate the climatic conditions along these routes and to determine the effect of bad weather avoidance (Vettor & Guedes Soares 2015, 2016, 2017). Fishing vessels are under-utilized as ocean observing platforms since ply coastal seas at all times of the year and in almost all weather conditions. To support the Mediterranean Forecasting System fishing vessels were equipped with a Fishery Observing System, an integrated device to collect data regarding catches, fishing operation position, depth and temperature during the hauls (Patti et al. 2016). In 2003, the RECOPESCA project put on fishing gears diverse sensors to measure fishing effort, temperature, salinity and turbidity (Martinelli et al. 2016). The equipment was self-powered and able to automatically send the data to a receiver onboard and after to land (Leblond et al. 2010). This approach makes available a great amount of daily data from a large area at low cost compared to usual scientific surveys and technological devices.

Off Portugal, the use of fishing VOO as observing platforms was first implemented under NATO SATOCEAN project (Laurs et al. 1989; Santos & Fiúza 1992; Santos et al. 2006). They used "bulk" thermometers and XBT probes to measure SST and obtain vertical profiles of temperature on board swordfish longline and sardine purse-seine fishing vessels. Despite the scientific success of these applications the need for human intervention was always a problem, preventing a true operational system. Later on, the European BASBLACK project, aimed to characterise the habitat of the deep-water species black scabbardfish (*Aphanopus carbo*) in the NE Atlantic by collecting environmental information (Temperature Depth Recorders) and record catches, on board a volunteer fishing vessel every month during 1 year (Santos et al. 1999), important to assess and manage the species. Methodologies to use fishing vessels as VOO were developed but again human intervention was needed.

Presently, fishing vessels activity is monitored for fisheries control by using vessel monitoring system (VMS) equipment, like the Portuguese MONICAP-Monitorização Contínua das Actividades de Pesca (Continous Fisheries Activity Monitoring) created in 1987 (the first to be implemented in Europe). VMS geo-referenced data includes information on vessel position, speed and heading over time. These data present a great potential for research and have been used over the past two decades to analyse fleet dynamics and estimate effective fishing effort. Coupling the georeferenced positions with landings or electronic fishing logbooks data, allows to follow the distribution patterns of targeted species and to estimate series of CPUE, a main indicator in fisheries management, often used as a proxy to resource abundance (e.g., Fonseca et al. 2008; Pilar-Fonseca et al. 2014a, b). However, vessel position is presently obtained every 2 hours which is not adequate for this kind of analysis. Within this project, spatial data of fishing activity will be obtained at a much higher resolution, allowing identifying the different operational phases within a fishing trip and increasing accuracy in effort estimation. The SADEP project, installed equipment to monitor wave conditions, the weight impact of fish onboard and the forces on the fishing gear to determine safety against capsizing. At the same time the system was estimating the wave field by measuring the motions of the vessel and analysing the signal in a similar way as from wave rider buoys. Pascoal et al. (2007, 2017) and Pascoal & Guedes Soares (2008, 2009) have been working on alternative parametric (PF) and non-parametric (NPF) formulations for wave spectra estimation in particular the final step of optimization computational bottleneck. They were the first to use genetic algorithms for global search in PF and the Kalman filter to estimate wave elevations in real time without requiring any cross spectral calculations (Hinostroza & Guedes Soares 2016a). Validations during sea operations were encouraging (Pascoal & Guedes Soares 2009; Hinostroza & Guedes Soares 2016b). These estimation procedure was incorporated in the onboard Decision Support Systems described in Rodrigues et al. (2012) for the safe operation of fishing vessels in waves (Perera et al. 2012) and for other types of vessels navigation under rough weather conditions, which continuously provide sea state data. Therefore, this type of system can be used in fishing vessels for continuous monitoring of the sea state conditions.

2 THE OBSERVING SYSTEM

2.1 General overview

The challenge is to develop a system that could be installed onboard fishing vessels engaged in different metiers (purse-seiners, longliners and trawlers) with no need of docking and of any human intervention during the operation (even no need to be turn on and off by the crew). The system will be composed by a set of sensors and equipment for collect meteorological and oceanographic information, monitoring ship motions, and eventually measures the loads in the crane of a fishing vessel. The sensors are the most adequate available in the market (e.g., wind, air

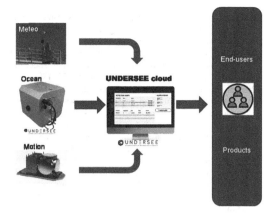

Figure 1. Data flow scheme.

Figure 2. The UNDERSEE_water device and UNDERSEE_cloud (from http://undersee.io/).

temperature, pressure, water temperature, salinity, sea state, pH, phytopigments, and turbidity) taking into account a cost effective analysis.

The observing system should integrate all the measurements with date, time and GPS position to produce single data points that could be send in near real-time or delay mode to a receiving centre on shore (Figure 1). Software will be developed, making possible the display of the data in a computer on board the fishing vessels. This software will have capabilities that allow real-time decision making related to navigation and fishing activities, although the present development only aims at the monitoring of meteorological and oceanographic data.

2.2 Meteorological unit

The Vantage Pro2™ (6152, 6153) Wireless Weather Stations will be used to collect meteorological information. This equipment includes two components: the Integrated Sensor Suite (ISS) which houses and manages the external sensor array, and the console which provides the user interface, data display, and calculations. The ISS and Vantage Pro2 console communicate via an FCC-certified, license-free, spread-spectrum frequency-hopping (FHSS) transmitter and receiver. User-selectable transmitter ID codes allow up to eight stations to coexist in the same geographic area. The frequency hopping spread spectrum technology provides greater communication strength over longer distances and areas of weaker reception. The Wireless Vantage Pro2 Plus weather station includes two additional sensors: the UV sensor and the solar radiation sensor. The console may be powered by batteries or by the included AC-power adapter. The wireless ISS is solar powered with a battery backup. Use WeatherLink® for Vantage Pro2 and Vantage Vue® to let your weather station interface with a computer, to log weather data, and to upload weather information to the internet.

2.3 Oceanographic unit

The UNDERSEE_water system from Matereospace Lda. (Portugal) will be used to measure continuously on the shipping routes the oceanographic parameters. UNDERSEE is a compact and easy to install in-situ water data acquisition system (UNDERSEE_water) and a user-friendly cloud platform (UNDERSEE_cloud) (Figure 2). UNDERSEE provide an end-to-end service with an integrated offering of hardware, software, installation, maintenance, customer support and automated decision-making tools. The service is composed by the following value layers and correspondent technologies: "Real-time water quality data (in-situ acquisition system)" and "Managing tools (Data Fusion & Web Services)".

2.4 Gyrocompass (IXSEA)

The manufacturer is IXSEA and the model is the Octans. It is both a fibre-optic survey-grade IMO-certified gyrocompass and a Motion Reference Unit for marine applications. It provides true-heading, roll, pitch, yaw, heave, surge, sway, rates of turn and accelerations (i.e. 6-DOF: 3 angular rates and 3 linear acceleration) even in highly volatile environments. The core of the sensor is a compact strapdown inertial measurement unit, which contains 3 accelerometers and 3 fibre optic gyroscopes, and a real-time computer.

3 CONCLUSIONS

This observation system should allow high-resolution in situ monitoring and spatial coverage of the ocean and coastal areas. The use of fishing voluntary Vessels of Opportunity (VOO) is one way to make long-term scientific measurements sustainable since fishing vessels ply coastal seas at all times of the year and in almost all weather conditions. Data from VOO are useful to establish the main routes of commercial shipping in N Atlantic, to estimate the climatic conditions along these routes and to determine the effect of bad weather avoidance.

The system has the potential of providing real-time data that can be assimilated in an existing regional area operational weather forecast system, which in addition to serving the general navigation can even be further developed to support the operation of fishing vessels and be associated to a weather routing system for saving fuel consumption.

Once the concept is proven, the future will be the collaboration with the fishing fleet for collecting data with large space coverage and high time resolution, difficult to obtain with other observing platforms. The data collected operationally will be validated and integrated into a wider observational programme that includes other in situ platforms, satellites and models. Their analyses will support the development of new products for more safe and efficient maritime operations, to support fishing activities, allowing master decisions on navigation and fishing operations. Furthermore, it will allow an integrated analysis of fishing success with marine environment and atmosphere to support fisheries and an integrated management of the marine ecosystems.

ACKNOWLEDGEMENTS

This study received Portuguese national funds from Foundation for Science and Technology (FCT) through projects OBSERVA.FISH (PTDC/CTA-AMB/31141/2017) and UID/Multi/04326/2019. OBSERVA.FISH is also supported by EU FEDER POR-Lisboa2020 e POR-Algarve2020 programmes.

REFERENCES

Fonseca, T., Campos, A., Afonso-Dias, M., Fonseca, P. & Pereira, J. 2008. Trawling for cephalopods off the Portuguese coast - fleet dynamics and landings composition. *Fisheries Research*, 92, 180–188.

Hinostroza, M. A. and Guedes Soares, C. 2016. Parametric estimation of the directional wave spectrum from ship motions. *International Journal of Maritime Engineering*. 158 (Part A2): pp. A121–A130

Hinostroza, M.A. & Guedes Soares, C. 2016b. Non-parametric estimation of directional wave spectra using two hyperparameters. *Maritime Technology and Engineering*, 3: 287–293.

Laurs, R.M., Fiúza, A.F.G. & Santos, A.M.P. 1989. *Plan for Satellite Remote Sensing Applications to Portuguese Fisheries*. Grupo de Oceanografia, Departamento de Física/Centro de Geofísica, Universidade de Lisboa, Relatório Técnico (1/89): 12 pp. [SATOCEAN Technical Report (1)].

Leblond, E., Lazure, P., Laurans, M., Rioual, C., Woerther, P., Quemener, L. & Berthou, P. 2010. The RECOPESCA project a new example of participative approach to collect fisheries and in situ environmental data. *Mercator Ocean Q. Newsl.*, 37: 40–48.

Martinelli, M., Guicciardi, S., Penna, P., Belardinelli, A., Croci, C., Domenichetti, F., Santojanni, A. & Sparnocchia, S. 2016. Evaluation of the oceanographic measurement accuracy of different commercial sensors to be used on fishing gears. *Ocean Engineering*, 111: 22–33.

McMeel, O., Pirlet, H. & Calewaert, J.-B. 2017. *Use and sharing of marine observations and data by industry. Good practice guide*. COLUMBUS project, 71 pp.

Pascoal, R. & Guedes Soares, C. 2008. Non-parametric wave spectral estimation using vessel motions. *Appl. Ocean Res.*, 30(1): 46–53.

Pascoal, R. & Guedes Soares, C. 2009. Kalman filtering of vessel motions for ocean wave directional spectrum estimation. *Ocean Engineering*, 36(6-7): 477–488.

Pascoal, R., Guedes Soares, C. & Sørensen, A.J. 2007. Ocean wave spectral estimation using vessel wave frequency motions. *J. Offshore Mech. Arct. Eng.*, 129 (2): 90–96.

Pascoal, R., Perera, L.P. & Guedes Soares, C. 2017. Estimation of directional sea spectra from ship motions in sea trials. *Ocean Engineering*, 132: 126–137.

Patti, B., Martinelli, M., Aronica, S., Belardinelli, A., Penna, P., Bonanno, A., Basilone, G., Fontana, I., Giacalone, G., Gabriele Gallì, N., Sorgente, R., Angileri, I.V.M., Croci, C., Domenichetti, F., Bonura, D., Santojanni, A., Sparnocchia, S., D'Adamo, R., Marini, M., Fiorentino, F. & Mazzola, S. 2016. The Fishery and Oceanography Observing System (FOOS): a tool for oceanography and fisheries science. *Journal of Operational Oceanography*, 9(S1): 99–118.

Perera, L.P., Rodrigues, J.M., Pascoal, R. & Guedes Soares, C. 2012. Development of an onboard decision support system for ship navigation under rough weather conditions. In: E. Rizzuto & C. Guedes Soares (eds.), *Sustainable Maritime Transportation and Exploitation of Sea Resources*: 837–844, Boca Raton: CRC Press/Balkema,Taylor & Francis Group.

Petersen, W., Schroeder, F. & Bockelmann, F.D. 2011. FerryBox-Application of continuous water quality observations along transects in the North Sea. *Ocean Dynamics*, 61(10): 1541–1554.

Pilar-Fonseca, T., Pereira, J., Campos, A., Moreno, A., Fonseca, P. & Afonso-Dias, M. 2014a. VMS-based fishing effort and population demographics for the European squid (Loligo vulgaris) off the Portuguese coast. *Hydrobiologia*, 725(1): 137–144.

Pilar-Fonseca, T., Campos, A., Pereira, J., Moreno, A., Lourenço, S. & Afonso-Dias, M. 2014b. Integration of fishery-dependent data sources in support of octopus spatial management. *Marine Policy*, 45: 69–75.

Rodrigues J.M., Perera, L.P. & Guedes Soares, C. 2012. Decision support system for the safe operation of fishing vessels in waves. In: C. Guedes Soares, Y. Garbatov, S. Sutulo & T.A. Santos (eds.), *Maritime Technology and Engineering*: 153–161, Boca Raton: CRC Press/Balkema,Taylor & Francis Group.

Santos, A.M.P. & Fiúza, A.F.G. 1992. Supporting the Portuguese Fisheries with Satellites. *ESA ISY-1* (ESA SP-341): 663–668.

Santos, A.M.P., Fiúza, A.F.G. & Laurs, R.M. 2006. Influence of SST on catches of swordfish and tuna in the Portuguese domestic longline fishery. *International Journal of Remote Sensing*, 27(15): 3131–3152.

Santos, A.M.P., Oliveira, L. & Aurélio, J. 1999. BASBLACK Project: an example of good collaboration between scientists and fishermen. *ICES CM 1999/Q:08*

Vettor, R. & Guedes Soares, C. 2015. Detection and analysis of the main routes of voluntary observing ships in the North Atlantic. *Journal of Navigation*, 68: 397–410.

Vettor, R. & Guedes Soares, C. 2016. Rough Weather Avoidance Effect on the Wave Climate Experienced by Ocean-going Vessels. *Applied Ocean Research*, 59:606–615.

Vettor, R. & Guedes Soares, C. 2017. Characterisation of the expected wave conditions in the main European coastal traffic routes. *Ocean Engineering*, 140: 244–257.

Modelling of the Surface Stokes drift in the Agulhas current system

S. Ponce de León & C. Guedes Soares
Centre for Marine Technology and Ocean Engineering (CENTEC), Instituto Superior Técnico, Universidade de Lisboa, Lisbon, Portugal

J.A. Johannessen
NERSC, Nansen Environmental and Remote Sensing Center, Bergen, Norway

ABSTRACT: The Stokes drift in the Agulhas current region is studied by performing high resolution spectral wave model simulations with ocean currents during a 3-month summer period of 2016. The current field comes from the European Space Agency project GLOBCURRENT. The validation of the numerical simulations is performed for the Significant Wave Height using satellite altimetry data from missions Saral-Altika, Jason-2 and Jason-3 showing a good correlation for the significant wave height (correlation coefficient ranging between 0.93-0.95). The summer mean Stokes drift in the Agulhas current region can reach magnitudes comparable to the local mean currents in the region. A direct correlation was found between the wind sea wave field and the Stokes drift patterns, especially in the southern limit of the domain that is affected by the strong circumpolar winds around Antartic and in the western African margin of Benguela. Currents increase the spatial variability of the Stokes drift field.

1 INTRODUCTION

The Agulhas Current system has been described as one of the strongest western boundary currents (up to 2 m/s) in the world's oceans (Johannessen et al., 2008). The Agulhas current is a relatively narrow current about 100 km wide that carries warm tropical and subtropical water southward. Having passed the Agulhas Bank, the Agulhas Current overshoots the African continent prograde into the South Atlantic Ocean where it experiences a strong change in direction (Bang 1970), retroflecting back into the South Indian Ocean (Lutjeharms & Ballegooyen 1988) as the Agulhas Return Current (Harris and Van Foreest 1978). There are several reasons why the Agulhas current deserves scientific studies. This particular current plays a key role in the inter-ocean exchange and in the global interchange of water masses (Lutjeharms 1981).

In addition, one of the global oceanic circulation processes that has received attention has been the concept of a global oceanic conveyor belt (Broecker 1991) in which the Agulhas Current plays a key role (Lutjeharms 2006). Besides, the Agulhas Current is important in the global ocean-atmosphere system because of its role in energy transport (de Vos et al., 2018). Besides, the Agulhas region is one of the places that show statistically substantial increase in mean Hs (Young & Ribal 2019). Satellite altimetry data and SAR allowed investigating different aspects, behavior and features of the Agulhas current (Lutjeharms 1981, Gründlingh 1994, Rouault et al., 2010, Johannessen et al., 2014).

The Stokes drift is nowadays estimated accurately directly from spectral wave models for realistic conditions (Webb & Fox-Kemper 2011, Tamura et al., 2012).

The present work analyzes the Stokes drift in the dynamic region of the strong Agulhas current system by performing a wave hindcast during the summer of 2016.

2 THE WAVE MODEL

2.1 *Set up*

The bathymetry grid data comes from the GEODAS NOAA's National Geophysical Data Centre (NGDC), with a resolution of 1 min of degree in latitude and longitude, which was linearly interpolated to the model grid. The WAM nested grid covers the Agulhas current system region from 50° S, 19° S up to 5° E, 45° E, at spatial resolution of 0.05°.

The configuration of the wave model estimates the wave spectrum for 36 directional bands measured clockwise with respect to true north, and 38 frequencies logarithmically spaced. The energy balance equation was integrated at 600 seconds.

The frequency range covers from 0.03 up to 1.0201 Hz.

A JONSWAP spectrum at every grid point is set as initial condition with the following parameters: Phillips' parameter 0.18; peak frequency 0.2 Hz; overshoot factor 3.0; left peak width 0.07; right peak width 0.09; wave direction 0°; fetch 30000 m.

The simulation covers a 3-month period from 01/01/2018 up to 30/03/2016. The wave hindcast was set to 1 hourly wind input and model output time steps. The wave model was forced by boundary conditions taken from the ERA5 model. In addition, the ERA-5 ECMWF reanalysis was chosen (Hersbach et al., 2019).

2.2 Validation

The verification of the hindcasts was done using satellite altimetry data from Jason2 and Jason3 the

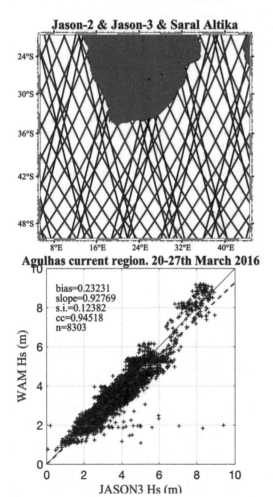

Figure 1. Orbits segments of Jason-2 (red), Jason-3 (blue) and Saral-Altika (black) (top panel). Scatter plots for the Hs after the collocation of WAM and JASON-3 (bottom).

Table 1. Statistics for the Hs for the periods from: 24-31 of January 2016 (Jason-2, Saral-Altika) and 20-27 of March 2016 (Jason-3) for the Agulhas Current system. S. I.-Scatter Index; CC-correlation coefficient, n-number of records. Bias, the best-fit scatter index and slopes between satellite altimeters observations and modelled Hs from WAM.

Parameter	Jason2	Jason3	Saral-Altika
Bias	0.342	0.232	0.360
Slope	0.887	0.927	0.881
S.I.	0.149	0.124	0.123
CC	0.924	0.950	0.932
n	8080	8303	7673

missions that coincided with the simulation period (Figure 1). The validation was performed for the significant wave height (Hs) using the collocation method of satellite altimetry data. The satellite observations were compared to model outputs by averaging the satellite measurements inside a grid cell, around the model output time, and comparing to the average of model output at the grid cell corners.

Table 1 shows some of the statistical parameters computed for each of the sensors and for two different periods (24-31 of January and 20-27 of March 2016). The validation was performed for the hindcasts performed for the wave-current case.

The bias was defined as the difference between the mean observation and the mean prediction. The scatter index (s.i.) was defined as the standard deviation of the predicted data with respect to the best fit line, divided by the mean observations.

The best correlation coefficient found corresponded to the collocated data of Jason-3 (0.95). In general, the best correlation in terms of lower scatter index (0.123), lower bias (0.23) and best slope (0.93) was obtained with Jason-3 as can be seen. It can be seen that both altimeters present some outliers (Figure 1). The worst correlation was obtained from Jason-2 with the higher scatter index and the lowest correlation coefficient. Outliers higher than 10 m were remove from the satellite altimetry data.

2.3 ESA GLOBCURRENT surface ocean current data

In the present study the geostrophic plus Ekman at 0 m was used. The fields were linearly interpolated to 1 hour from the 6-hourly GLOBCURRENT enhanced view of the ocean currents at the near surface product (Rio et al. (2014)) with a ¼° of resolution.

The GLOBCURRENT Ekman currents products are based on the Ekman model of Rio et al. (2014). The Ekman currents are provided at 15 m below the surface and at the surface (0 m), by estimating the

Ekman model parameters using the velocities derived from the trajectories of drifting buoys drogued at 15 m on the one hand and the velocities derived from the Argo float trajectories on the other (Rio et al., 2014).

To tune the Ekman model parameters, the drifting buoys data are filtered using an inertial-period-to-20-days band-pass filter, which corresponds to the frequencies of maximum coherency between the wind stress and the Ekman currents (Rio et al., 2014).

The Ekman model is then applied to the 3-hourly ECMWF wind stress fields (80 km of spatial resolution) to produce the GLOBCURRENT Ekman current products (Rio, 2015). This dataset contains global grids of 15 m depth Ekman velocities that have been resampled by linear interpolation on the GLOBCURRENT 0.1° resolution geographical grid.

3 RESULTS

3.1 Stokes drift

For wave motions that can be considered horizontally homogeneous and irrotational in the vertical plane, the expression of the Stokes drift can be written as:

$$US(z) = \mathbf{Us}.\exp(z/Ds) \quad (1)$$

where Us is the Stokes drift velocity at the surface (= $\sigma k\, a^2$), Ds is the Stokes depth scale (=1/2k), $\mathbf{k} = k(\cos\theta, \sin\theta)$ is the wave number vector, σ is angular frequency, k is wave number, θ is wave direction and a is wave amplitude.

Assuming that the wave field is homogeneous and stationary the Stokes drift for directional waves can be derived from Eq. (1) for the wave spectrum $F(\sigma, \theta)$ and for random directional waves as:

$$US(z) = 2/g \iint \sigma^3 F(\sigma, \theta)(\cos\theta, \sin\theta) d\sigma\, d\theta \quad (2)$$

where g is gravitational acceleration and $F(\sigma,\theta)d\sigma\, d\theta = 0.5\, a^2$

The exponential function in the integrand decays according to the wave number k, therefore the vertical profile of Stokes drift depends on the spectral shape.

3.2 Mean Stokes drift distribution

The map of mean austral summer Stokes drift (Figure 2, top -left panel) shows that the maximum values are located near the southern boundary, south of 48° S. There, the wave induced transport reaches

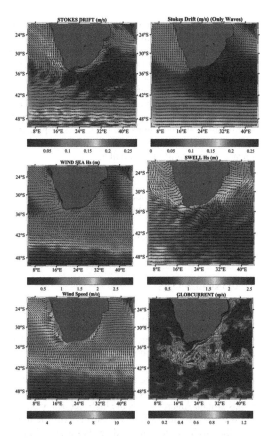

Figure 2. Three months mean distribution for Stokes drift considering currents (top-left); Stokes drift speed and direction without currents (top-right); wind sea Hs (middle-left); swell Hs (m) (middle right); ERA5 wind speed and direction (bottom-left); GLOBCURRENT current speed (bottom right); Averaging period: 01/01/2016-30/03/2016 from the WAM high spatial resolution grid (0.05°). The mean maps were obtained with a 6 hourly temporal resolution from 1 hourly simulations.

0.27 m/s, comparable to the mean current (Figure 2, bottom-right panel). Between 33° and 42° S the Stokes drift does not exceed 0.15 m/s, especially in the area east of the African continent's southern tip. This area of low Stokes drift coincides with region of the Agulhas Current Retroflection (Figure 2, bottom-right panel). In the Southwest African margin, Stokes drift values rise above 0.15 m/s, a value also attained in the coastal Agulhas current, that follows closely the coastline.

This distribution of the Stokes drift appears to be related to the wind field, through the wind sea. Indeed, comparing the maps of Stokes drift (Figure 2, top-left), wind sea (Figure 2, middle-left) and swell (Figure 2, middle-right) it can be seen that spatial correlation is stronger between the first two and weaker in the case of swell. This is higher frequency components of the wave spectrum have greater impact on the Stokes drift (Eq. 2), as was reported in Tamura et al (2012) for the Pacific Ocean. The wave model uses a wave-age based criterion to separate wind sea and swell (Komen et al., 1994).

There are also clear effects of the currents on the Stokes Drift distribution. To better appreciate these effects, we show also a map of Stokes drift from a simulation without currents (Figure 2, top right). Without currents the Stoke drift map is more uniform and its magnitude is smaller.

The effect of the currents is therefore to increase the spatial variability of the Stokes drift and also its magnitude. The magnitude change should be related to the frequency shift induced by the horizontal variations in the currents along the wave propagation direction, as this will change the value of the integral in Eq. (2).

4 CONCLUSIONS

The surface Stokes transport play an important role in upper-ocean dynamics through its contributions to the ocean's surface convergences and divergences. The summer mean Stokes drift in the Agulhas current region can reach values comparable to the mean currents in the region, especially in the southern limit of the domain that is affected by the strong circumpolar winds around Antarctic. It is the high frequency part of the wave spectra that affects the Stokes drift the most, i. e., the locally wind generated sea has a great impact in the Stokes drift. The Agulhas Current System causes a highly variable Stokes drift map with increased intensity due to the frequency shifting of the wave energy.

Results obtained in this work must be taken with caution since the present spatial resolution of GLOBCURRENT does not fully resolve the mesoscale vorticity and for this reason the simulation considering currents may likely underestimate the effects of currents on waves.

ACKNOWLEDGEMENTS

We are grateful for the opportunity to access and freely download the GLOBCURRENT data and information products. The development and validation of these products was funded by ESA under the DUE study contract number 4000109513/13/I-LG.

This work was performed within the scope of the Strategic Research Plan of the Centre for Marine Technology and Ocean Engineering (CENTEC), which is financed by the Portuguese Foundation for Science and Technology (Fundação para a Ciência e Tecnologia) under contract UIDB/UIDP/00134/2020.

REFERENCES

Bang, N.D. 1970. Dynamic interpretations of a detailed surface temperature chart of the Agulhas Current retroflexion and fragmentation area. South African Geographical Journal, 52(12): 67–76.

Broecker, W.S. 1991. The great ocean conveyor. Oceanography, 4(2): 79–89.

Harris, T.F.W. and D. van Foreest 1978. The Agulhas Current in March 1969. Deep-Sea Research, 25(6): 549–561.

de Vos, M., Backeberg, B., Counillon, F., 2018. Using an eddy-tracking algorithm to understand the impact of assimilating altimetry data on the eddy characteristics of the Agulhas system. Ocean Dynamics 68, 1071. http://dx.doi.org/10.1007/s10236-018-1174-4.

Gründlingh M.L., 1994. TOPEX/Poseidon observes wave enhancement in the Agulhas current. AVISO Altimeter Newsl. 3.

Hersbach H., Bell W., Berrisford P., Horányi A., Muñoz-Sabater J., Nicolas J., Radu R., Schepers D., Simmons A., Soci C., D. Dee, 2019. Global reanalysis: goodbye ERA-Interim, hello ERA5. Newsletter Feature Article #159, 17–24. Chapter Meteorology. http://dx.doi.org/10.21957/vf291hehd7.

Johannessen JA, Chapron B, Collard F, Kudryavtsev V, Mouche A, Akimov D, Dagestad KF., 2008, Direct ocean surface velocity measurements from space: improved quantitative interpretation of Envisat ASAR observations. Geophys Res Lett 35: L22608. doi: 10.1029/2008GL035709.

Johannessen, J. A., B. Chapron, F. Collard, B. Backeberg, 2014, Use of SAR data to monitor the Greater Agulhas Current, In Remote Sensing of the African Seas, edited by V. Barale and M. Gade, ISBN 978-94-017-8007-0, Springer.

Johannessen JA, B. Chapron, F. Collard, M.-H. Rio, J.-F. Piollé, L. Gaultier, G. Quartly, J. Shutler, R. Escola, R. P. Raj, C. Donlon, R. Danielson, A. Korosov, F. Nencioli, V. Kudryavtsev, M. Roca, J. Tournadre, G. Larnicol, G. Guitton, P. Miller, M. Warren and M. Hansen, 2016. Globcurrent: Multisensor synergy for surface current estimation. Journal ESA SP, Volume: SP-740. ISSN: 0379–6566. https://www.nersc.no/biblio/globcurrent-multisensor-synergy-surface-current-estimation.

Komen G.J., Cavaleri L., Donelan M. A., Hasselmann K, Hasselmann S, Janssen PAEM, 1994. Dynamics and Modelling of Ocean Waves. Cambridge University Press.

Lutjeharms, J.R.E. 1981. Features of the southern Agulhas Current circulation from satellite remote sensing. South African Journal of Science, 77(5): 231–236.

Lutjeharms, J.R.E., van Ballegooyen R.C., 1988. The retroflection of the Agulhas Current. Journal of Physical Oceanography, 18(11): 1570–1583.

Lutjeharms J.R.E. 2006. The Agulhas Current. ISBN-10 3-540-42392-3 Springer Berlin Heidelberg New York.

Rio, M.H., 2015. GLOBCURRENT Product Data Handbook: The Combined Geostrophy + Ekman Currents (ftp://ftp.ifremer.fr/ifremer/cersat/documentation/gridded/GLOBCURRENT/GLOBCURRENT_D-280_Product_Handbook_L4_combined_mhr.pdf).

Rio, M.-H., Mulet, S., Picot, N., 2014. Beyond GOCE for the ocean circulation estimate: synergetic use of altimetry, gravimetry, and in situ data provides new insight into geostrophic and Ekman currents. Geophys. Res. Lett. 41. http://dx.doi.org/10.1002/2014GL061773.

Rouault M.J., Mouche A., Collard F., Johannessen J.A., Chapron B., 2010. Mapping the Agulhas current from space: an assessment of ASAR surface current velocities. J Geophys Res 115:C10026. doi:10.1029/2009JC006050.

Tamura H., Miyazawa Y., Oey L-Y, 2012. The stokes drift and wave induced-mass flux in the North Pacific. JGR, VOL 117, C08021, doi:10.1029/2012JC008113.

Young I.R., Ribal A., 2019. Multiplatform evaluation of global trends in wind speed and wave height. Science 10.1126/science.aav9527.

Webb, A., and B. Fox-Kemper (2011), Wave spectral moments and Stokes drift estimation, Ocean Modell., 40, 273–288, doi:10.1016/j.ocemod. 2011.08.007.

Simulation of hurricane Lorenzo at the port of Madalena do Pico, Azores, by using the HIDRALERTA system

M.I. Santos
Gaspar Frutuoso Foundation, São Miguel, Azores, Portugal

L.V. Pinheiro, C.J.E.M. Fortes, M.T. Reis & V. Serrazina
National Laboratory for Civil Engineering, Lisbon, Portugal

E.B. Azevedo & F.V. Reis
IITAA – Universidade dos Açores, Terceira, Azores, Portugal

M. Salvador
Portos dos Açores SA, Terceira, Azores, Portugal

ABSTRACT: HIDRALERTA is a forecast, early warning and risk assessment system of port and coastal areas that uses measurements/estimates of sea-waves and water levels to evaluate overtopping/flooding. The calculation of the mean overtopping discharge over a maritime structure is performed through artificial neural network-based tools and/or empirical formulae. The system is composed of four modules developed in open source Web technology, mainly using the Python language, and is available online. This paper presents its application to reproduce the hurricane Lorenzo conditions and impacts at Madalena do Pico port, Azores, on October 2nd 2019. This hurricane was regarded as the strongest storm to hit Azores in 20 years. The system predicted the expected results for the hurricane wave characteristics, both offshore and at the port entrance. Other aspects of its validation still need to be improved with the collaboration of the local authorities and the use of historical data.

1 INTRODUCTION

The length of the Portuguese coast, the severity of the sea conditions and the importance of the coastal zone regarding socio-economic activities justify the relevance of studying wave-induced risks and, in particular, overtopping due to wave action. Indeed, emergency situations caused by adverse sea conditions are frequent and put in danger the safety of people and goods, with negative impacts for society, the economy and the environment, Figure 1.

Therefore, a methodology to assess the overtopping risk in port and coastal areas is essential for a proper planning and management of these areas. A detailed characterization of sea waves, water levels and currents is essential to improve risk assessment methodologies, increasing the reliability of the results, enabling the issue of warnings and supporting the preparation of mitigation plans.

In this context, the National Laboratory for Civil Engineering (LNEC), Portugal, has been developing the HIDRALERTA system (Poseiro, 2019), which is a set of integrated decision-support tools for port and coastal management, whose focus is to identify and prevent emergency situations and to enable the selection of measures by national authorities to avoid loss of lives and minimize damage. Moreover, the system may also act as a long-term management tool, since it can simulate the response to future scenarios related to climate change, such as the increase of the mean sea level and/or of the storm severity, which will increase coastal flooding probability and intensity.

In 2015, the first prototype of the HIDRALERTA system was implemented in the port of Praia da Vitória, in Terceira island, Azores, and it has been operating since then. Under the framework of the ECOMARPORT project (MAC/1.1b/081), other prototypes of the system have been under development and implemented at the ports of Madalena do Pico and S. Roque do Pico, both at the Pico island, Azores. Those prototypes assess, on a regular basis, the risk of wave overtopping and consequent flooding, and the risk to sea navigation (in particular as regards the safety of moored and maneuvered vessels), both risks triggered by wave conditions.

This paper presents the system application to reproduce the hurricane Lorenzo conditions and impacts at the port of Madalena do Pico, on October 2 2019. Methodologies and accomplishments of the HIDRALERTA project achieved so far are

DOI: 10.1201/9781003216599-89

Figure 1. Wave overtopping events at the Azores islands (Source: www.acorianooriental.pt, 2019).

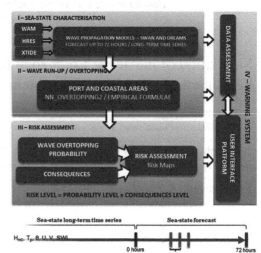

Figure 2. Schematic representation of the HIDRALERTA system.

herein described. Data from Graciosa buoy are used to validate one of the wave propagation models used in HIDRALERTA.

2 THE HIDRALERTA SYSTEM

The HIDRALERTA system (Poseiro *et al.*, 2013; Sabino *et al.*, 2018; Poseiro, 2019) is a wave overtopping/flooding forecast system with early warning and risk assessment capabilities. As a forecast and early warning tool, HIDRALERTA enables the identification, in advance, of the occurrence of emergency situations, prompting the responsible entities to adopt measures to avoid loss of lives and minimize damage. As a long-term planning tool, the system uses datasets of several years of sea-wave/water level characteristic (defined by the user, up to 40 years provided by ECMWF - European Centre for Medium-Range Weather Forecasts) and/or pre-defined scenarios, to evaluate wave overtopping and flooding risks of the protected areas, allowing the construction of risk maps based on the combined use of Geographic Information Systems (GIS) and the Analytic Hierarchy Process (AHP) (Poseiro, 2019).

The HIDRALERTA system was developed in a Python framework and it is accessible from a Web platform (www.aurora.lnec.pt). The development of the HIDRALERTA methodology used the basic conditions and requirements of the case study of Praia da Vitória. Nevertheless, the system was conceived with a generic architecture, which can be applied to other case studies.

The HIDRALERTA system encompasses four main modules (Figure 2), namely:

I. *Sea-state Characterization*, where the offshore wave conditions are propagated to inshore and inside ports using numerical models;
II. *Wave Run-up and Overtopping* determination, using Artificial Neural Network (ANN) tools or empirical formulae;
III. *Risk Assessment*, which defines a risk level for the predicted overtopping values;
IV. *Warning System*, which integrates all the information and disseminates warnings.

As a forecast and warning tool, the system uses modules I, II, and IV, as illustrated in this paper (section 3).

3 CASE STUDY – HURRICANE LORENZO AT MADALENA DO PICO PORT, AZORES

3.1 *Hurricane Lorenzo*

Hurricane Lorenzo was regarded as the strongest storm to hit the Azores islands in 20 years still as hurricane Category 2 to 1, breaking records as the most northeasterly Category 5 storm ever.

Lorenzo developed from a tropical wave that moved off the west coast of Africa on September 22, growing larger in size over the course of its development. The storm continued to intensify and reached its initial peak of intensity with maximum sustained winds of 230 km/h and a central pressure of 939 mbar early on September 27. Later on September 29, Lorenzo reached Category 5 strength, becoming the easternmost hurricane of such intensity recorded in the Atlantic basin, exceeding any of the 35 Category 5 hurricanes that have occurred in records since the 1920s. With a fastening northeastward track and expanding wind field, Lorenzo skirted the western

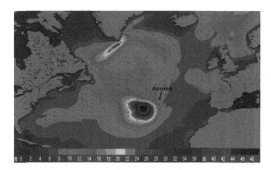

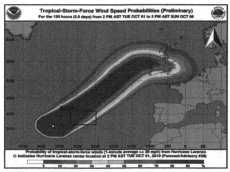

Figure 3. North Atlantic swell chart. on September 30 2019: hurricane Lorenzo located about 1600 km southwest of the Azores islands (Source: https://pt.magicseaweed.com, 2019).

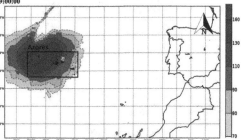

Azores on October 2, passing just west of Flores island between 4:00 and 4:30 am as a Category 2 to 1 hurricane, and brought high winds, pounding surf and storm surge to the islands, Figure 3. After hitting Azores, hurricane Lorenzo began its transition to an extratropical cyclone, racing towards Ireland and the United Kingdom.

Figure 4 shows the IPMA (Portuguese Institute for Sea and Atmosphere) report Nº9 with Lorenzo October 2 forecasts.

Wind gusts of 163 km/h were recorded at 8:25 am in Corvo island, while gusts at Faial and Flores islands reached 145 km/h at 5:00 am and 142 km/h at 4:00 am, respectively. Significant wave heights reached 15 m, coming mainly from the southwest, and were predicted to be between 9 m and 12 m in the central group of Azores. 171 incidents were reported, 66 in Faial, 23 in Flores, 28 in Pico, 8 in Graciosa, 20 in Terceira, 2 in São Miguel and 3 in Corvo, Figure 5. The reports mainly relate to road obstructions, housing damage, falling trees and flooding. 53 people were left homeless and had to be relocated. The most serious damage occurred in the western Azores, mainly at the port of Lajes das Flores, the only commercial port in Flores island, compromising energy, food, fuel and other essential supplies.

3.2 The Port of Madalena do Pico

The port of Madalena do Pico is located on the northwest coast of the Pico island and is protected by two breakwaters (Figure 6): the North and the West breakwaters.

The North breakwater represents the main port protection structure against sea waves, mainly from W-N. With a total length of approximately 530 m, only about 250 m correspond to the berthing quay, the so-called "Madalena Dock". At the breakwater root, the 3(V):4(H) armor is protected by two layers of 150 kN tetrapods, placed over a rock filter of 90-120 kN. Approximately 150 m after the breakwater bend, the weight of the tetrapod units increases to

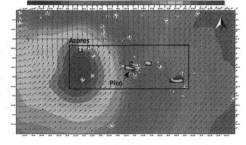

Figure 4. Forecast of hurricane Lorenzo, 2 October 2019 – Azores – Report Nº9 by IPMA.

240 kN, over a rock filter of 1-3 ton. At the breakwater head, the 1:2 armor is protected by 300 kN Antifer cubes. On the inner side, the 2:3 armor is protected by 5-8 ton rock units and a rock filter of 1-3 ton.

The West breakwater protects the port from the southwest wave conditions. It is a rubble mound breakwater with 300 kN Antifer cubes on a 2:3 slope, which ends on a 10-30 kN rock mattress located above the natural rocky bottom. Its deepest part is located at about -10.5 m (ZH). The breakwater crest is at +5.5 m (ZH), with ZH the chart datum.

According to local authorities, during Lorenzo hurricane, several overtopping events occurred, especially at the West and North breakwaters. Moreover, the wave conditions inside the port were significant, Figure 7.

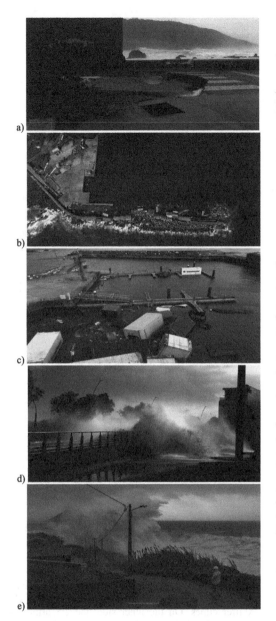

Figure 6. Pico Island, Madalena do Pico port.

Figure 5. Hurricane Lorenzo at a) Faial, b) and c) Flores, d) Pico and e) Terceira islands.

Figure 7. Lorenzo hurricane at Madalena do Pico port.

3.3 Application of HIDRALERTA

3.3.1 Module I – Wave characteristics

The system starts by requesting from the dada source (ECMWF - European Centre for Medium-Range Weather Forecasts) wave and wind fields from the WAM model (WAMDI Group, 1988) and pressure parameters from HRES (Persson, 2001). Data are supplied by ECMWF and the system downloads automatically sea-wave conditions every day. Then, it creates different charts for each instant to represent the offshore sea state (using *matplotlib* library from the *Python* programming language), firstly, for the North Atlantic and then to the Azores archipelago. Figure 8 illustrates the outputs charts produced by the system for 9 am of 2 October 2019, the most critical moment of the hurricane at Madalena do Pico.

Given the WAM model results, one selects the closest value to the Pico island that can represent the boundary conditions for sea-wave propagation models to be used afterwards. These values are transferred into a finer grid, one or several nested grids, firstly to the vicinity of the port of Madalena do Pico by using the spectral wave

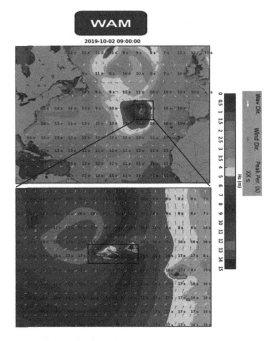

Figure 8. Example of outputs generated by the system for the WAM model for 2 October 2019, 9 am.

propagation model, SWAN (Booij et al., 1999) (Figure 9). The SWAN model is configured to use three nested grids with different resolutions. The coarse grid has a regular resolution of 1200 m and covers the central group of Azores. This grid is forced at the boundaries by the WAM wave condition and by the wind fields, both provided by the data source (ECMWF). The wind grid is composed by 29 (x-component) x 13 (y-component) points, with a mesh size of

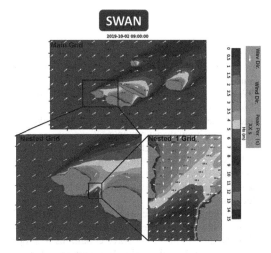

Figure 9. Outputs generated by the system for the SWAN model on 2 October 2019, 9 am, H_s and θ.

Figure 10. Location of the BOND5 buoy at coordinates 39° 05′ 24″ N and 27° 7′ 52″ W.

8720 m in x and 11097 m in y. The medium grid has a resolution of 600 m and is coupled to the coarse grid using the procedures described in the SWAN manual (The SWAN Team, 2018), where wave spectra from the coarse grid are employed as boundary conditions in the medium grid. Idem for the fine grid, which has a resolution of 100 m. The model includes physical processes as diffraction, friction, quadruplet and triad in all three grids.

In this paper, a comparison between the data measured by BOND5 buoy (CLIMAAT) (Azevedo et al., 2008), located at Graciosa (Figure 10), and the output from the WAM and the SWAN models is presented for the buoy location on 2 October 2019. Unfortunately, the closest buoy to the area, BOND4 (located at Faial), was not operational during that time.

Figure 11 presents the comparison of the wave parameters: BOND5 - significant wave height H_s, maximum wave period T_{max} and mean wave direction θ_m; and WAM and SWAN – spectral significant wave height H_{m0}, peak wave period T_p and mean wave direction θ_m for the buoy location.

On 2 October 2019, the buoy measurements ranged from approximately $1.5<H_s<3.5$ m, $10<T_p<21$ s and $150°<\theta_m<340°$. The peak of the storm occurred at approximately 9 am, with $H_s=3.5$ m, $T_p=21$ s and $\theta_m=340°$.

For all wave parameters, SWAN has a similar trend to that of BOND5 throughout the day, unlike what happens with WAM. The wave height is the only parameter clearly overestimated by the WAM model (by 4.5 m at 9 am). The SWAN model slightly overestimates the wave height (by 0.5 m at 9 am). The peak wave period is generally overestimated by WAM, although

819

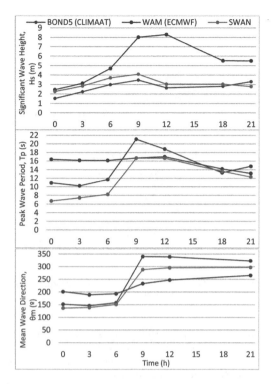

Figure 11. Comparison of H_s, T_p and θ_m from BOND5, WAM and SWAN for buoy location on 2 October 2019.

Table 2. Statistical analysis of the relation between measured T_{max} by BOND5 and predicted T_p by WAM and SWAN.

Peak wave period, T_p

	WAM (ECMWF)	SWAN
NRMSE	0.268	0.208
NBias	-0.089	0.189
r	0.211	0.928

Table 3. Statistical analysis of the relation between measured θ_m by BOND5 and predicted θ_m by WAM and SWAN.

Mean wave direction, θ_m

	WAM (ECMWF)	SWAN
NRMSE	0.247	0.116
NBIAS	0.101	0.104
r	0.894	0.996

there is underestimation between about 7 am and 5 pm (4 s at 9 am). Like BOND5 buoy, SWAN predicts a rotation of the mean wave direction from about 150° to 300° at 6 am (with θ_m=290° at 9 am), contrasting with the WAM model, which predicts mean directions between about 190° and 280° (with θ_m=230° at 9 am).

Table 1, 2 and 3, which present the statistical analysis of the correlation between measured and predicted wave parameters provided by the buoy and the numerical models, respectively, confirm the previous analysis. Various measures of statistical error have been used: Normalized Root Mean Square Error (NRMSE, Eq. 1), Normalized Simple Difference of the Error (NBIAS, Eq. 2) and Correlation Coefficient (r, Eq. 3).

Table 1. Statistical analysis of the relation between measured H_s by BOND5 and predicted H_{m0} by WAM and SWAN.

Significant wave height, H_{m0}

	WAM (ECMWF)	SWAN
NRMSE	1.131	0.205
NBias	-0.980	-0.146
r	0.705	0.762

$$NRMSE = \sqrt{\frac{1}{N}\sum_{n=1}^{N}\left(\frac{Buoy(n) - Num(n)}{Buoy(n)}\right)^2} \quad (1)$$

$$NBIAS = \sum_{n=1}^{N}\frac{Buoy(n) - Num(n)}{Buoy(n)} \quad (2)$$

$$r = \frac{\sum_{i=1}^{N}\left((Num(n) - \overline{Num}) - (Buoy(n) - \overline{Buoy})\right)}{\sqrt{\sum_{i=1}^{N}(Num(n) - \overline{Num})^2 \sum_{i=1}^{N}(Buoy(n) - \overline{Buoy})^2}} \quad (3)$$

where N is the number of buoy measurements used for comparison or the corresponding number of numerical model predictions (from WAM or SWAN), $Buoy(n)$ is the nth buoy measurement, $Num(n)$ is the nth model prediction, $\overline{Num}$ is the average of the numerical predictions and $\overline{Buoy}$ the avarage of the buoy measurements.

The results highlight the advantage of using SWAN for propagating the offshore wave climate to the buoy location, instead of adopting directly the wave characteristics provided by WAM for the same location.

The next step is the transference of the SWAN results into the Madalena do Pico port. DREAMS (Fortes, 2002) allows the wave conditions to propagate to both Madalena do Pico port entrance and inside the harbour. Figure 12 shows that the waves

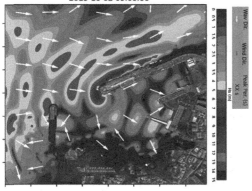

Figure 12. Madalena port. Outputs generated by the system for the DREAMS model on 2 October 2019, 9 am, H_s and θ.

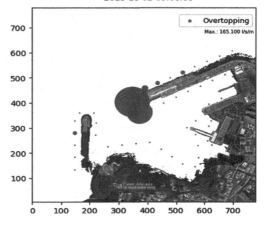

Figure 13. Overtopping output generated by the system on 2 October 2019, 9 am.

arrive at the port with a direction mainly from Northwest. The highest wave heights occurred in the North breakwater, beginning at the trunk and increasing towards the head (approximately 5 m<H_{mo}<9 m). At the West breakwater, the wave heights ranged between 4 m and 6 m, affecting both its trunk and head. The significant wave height in some areas inside the harbour was higher than 1.5 m, which prevents mooring operations. This is in agreement with *in situ* observations, Figure 7.

3.3.2 *Module II – Wave run-up and overtopping*
The estimates of overtopping are obtained by using the ANN tool NN_OVERTOPPING2 (Coeveld *et al.*, 2005). With the results of the DREAMS model at the toe of each structure of the port, and considering their main characteristics, it is possible to calculate mean overtopping discharges, q, at 50 cross-sections for the port of Madalena do Pico. From the overtopping predictions, an output chart is generated for each instant (Figure 13). To provide an idea of the overtopping intensity, red circles with different diameters are shown for the 50 cross-sections. The larger the circle, the highest the mean overtopping discharge. The chart also indicates the maximum mean overtopping discharge.

For the North breakwater, at 9 am, q increased towards the head, varying between 0.17 l/s/m and 165 l/s/m. For the West breakwater, the maximum predicted value of q, just before the breakwater head, was 1.9 l/s/m. Inside the port, no overtopping was predicted.

3.3.3 *Module IV – Warning system*
The maximum mean overtopping discharge predicted for the case study for each instant at each cross-section of the structures is compared with established pre-set thresholds of q. These thresholds have been defined in close collaboration with the local authorities of Madalena do Pico and are based on existing EurOtop (2007, 2018) recommendations on tolerable wave overtopping. Guidance on the pre-set thresholds and the warning levels may be found in Poseiro (2019).

Note that not all overtopping events are unacceptable. Some mean overtopping discharges may be tolerable and may not trigger any warning.

Figure 14 provides an example of the chart generated by the HIDRALERTA system for 9 am, with warning levels shown for each stretch of the structures.

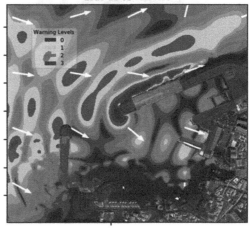

Figure 14. Warning output generated by the system on 2 October 2019, 9 am.

A red warning was issued only for the head of the North breakwater, whilst orange warnings were obtained for the trunk of both breakwaters. Note that these are only preliminary warnings, since module IV of the HIDRALERTA system is still being calibrated with past storms for Madalena do Pico.

The user interaction component is materialized in a Web application, in which the whole warning system is parameterized. The application is designed for use in traditional and mobile Web browsers, by adapting the information in accordance with the characteristics of the user's device.

The Web application (Figure 15) displays all the system forecasted data, which include the wave conditions from offshore to the foreshore, the wave overtopping discharges and the warning levels (including warning signals) obtained for each stretch of the structures.

Based on this information, a daily 72-hour forecast report is constructed (Figure 15) and it is sent by e-mail to institutions dealing with port/coastal management in Madalena do Pico, such as Portos dos Açores and the University of Azores. Data can be directly accessed at any time through the Web platform.

4 FINAL REMARKS

Currently, the HIDRALERTA system is in operation for the ports of Praia da Vitória, S. Roque do Pico and Madalena do Pico, with all the necessary elements to issue real-time warnings. However, to ensure the reliability of the system for the last two ports, there are still some aspects of its validation that need to be improved with the collaboration of the local authorities and the use of historical data, especially modules II and IV. Through reporting of dangerous situations by local authorities and residents, and their perception of existing risks, a better understanding of wave overtopping and flooding impacts in local communities may be achieved.

ACKNOWLEDGEMENTS

The works related with the participation of M.I. Santos, M. Salvador and E. B. de Azevedo on the simulation of the application of HIDRALERTA System to the Port of Madalena, have been done under the framework of the ECOMARPORT (MAC/1.1b/081), with the financial support of 85% by the EU (FEDER, MAC 2014-2020), and 15% from the Regional Government of the Azores. F. V. Reis is responsible for the wave data and wave database used by the system. The works of C.J.E.M. Fortes, M.T. Reis, L.V. Pinheiro and V. Serrazina have been developed under the framework of To-SEAlert, Ref. PTDC/EAM-OCE/31207/2017 and BSafe4Sea, Ref. PTDC/ECIEGC/31090/2017. The authors also acknowledge Portos dos Açores..

REFERENCES

Azevedo, E.B.; Mendes, P.; & Gonçalo, V. (2008). Projects CLIMAAT and CLIMARCOST climate and meteorology of the Atlantic archipelagos, maritime and coastal climate. *I Workshop Internacional sobre Clima e Recursos Naturais nos Países de Língua Portuguesa - WSCRA08*.

Booij, N.; Ris, R.C. & Holthuijsen, L.H. (1999). A third-generation wave model for coastal regions, Part I, Model description and validation. *J. Geographical Res.*, C4, 104, 7649–7666.

Coeveld, E.M.; Van Gent, M.R.A. & Pozueta, B. (2005). Neural Network: Manual NN_OVERTOPPING2. CLASH WP8 – Report BV.

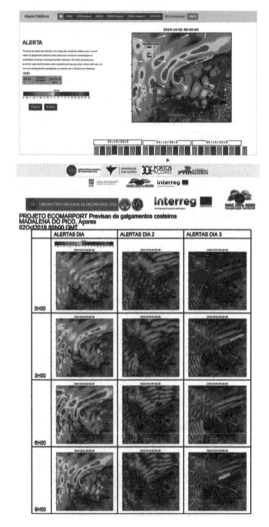

Figure 15. Examples of the HIDRALERTA platform. Daily forecast report.

EurOtop (2007). *Wave Overtopping of Sea Defences and Related Structures: Assessment Manual*. Pullen, T.; Allsop, N.W.H.; Bruce, T.; Kortenhaus, A.; Schuttrumpf, H. & Van der Meer, J.W.

EurOtop (2018). *Manual on Wave Overtopping of Sea Defences and Related Structures. An overtopping manual largely based on European research, but for worldwide application*. Van der Meer, J.W.; Allsop, N.W.H.; Bruce, T.; De Rouck, J.; Kortenhaus, A.; Pullen, T.; Schüttrumpf, H.; Troch, P. & Zanuttigh, B. www.overtopping-manual.com.

Fortes, C.J.E.M. (2002). *Transformações Não Lineares de Ondas em Zonas Portuárias. Análise pelo Método dos Elementos Finitos. PhD Thesis*, IST-UL.

Persson, A. (2001). *User Guide to ECMWF Forecast Products*. ECMWF.

Poseiro, P. (2019). *Forecast and Early Warning System for Wave Overtopping and Flooding in Coastal and Port Areas: Development of a Model and Risk Assessment*. PhD Thesis. IST-UL.

Poseiro, P.; Fortes, C.J.E.M.; Reis, M.T.; Santos, J.A.; Simões, A.; Rodrigues, C. & Azevedo, E. (2013). A methodology for overtopping risk assessment in port areas: Application to the port of Praia da Vitória (Azores, Portugal). *Proc. SCACR 2013*, 4–7 June, LNEC, Lisbon.

Sabino, A.; Poseiro, P.; Rodrigues, A.; Reis, M.T.; Fortes, C.J.E.M.; Reis, R. & Araújo, J. (2018). Coastal risk forecast system. *Journal of Geographical Syst.*, 20(2), 159–184. https://doi.org/10.1007/s10109-018-0266-5

The SWAN Team (2018). *SWAN User Manual. SWAN Cycle III version 41.20A*. Delft University of Technology, Environmental Fluid Mechanics Section, 133pp.

WAMDI Group (1988). The WAM Model - A third generation ocean wave prediction model. *Journal of Physical Oceanography*, 18, 1775–1810.

Author Index

Abad, R. 501
Abbasnia, A. 247
Abdelwahab, H.S. 341
Acanfora, M. 441
Altosole, M. 449, 463
Amoresano, A. 457
Anastas, G. 511
Andrés, M.A. 351
Araújo, G. 693
Araújo, J.P. 131
Arula, T. 721
Avalos, M. 403
Azevedo, E.B. 815

Bai, Y. 559
Balsamo, F. 449, 463
Bekker, A. 141, 255, 265
Belibassakis, K. 3, 519
Benvenuto, G. 463
Bernardino, M. 529
Bernardo, T.A. 685
Bettencourt, J.H. 785
Borges, H.M. 739
Bossau, J.C. 141, 255
Boukhanovsky, A.V. 767
Burloiu, M. 539

Callewaert, B. 247
Calvário, M. 597
Campora, U. 449, 463
Campos, A. 693, 713
Campos Filho, L.C.P. 63, 739
Campos, R.M. 791, 797
Carbajal, M.A.C. 159
Ch, P.K. 197
Chen, C. 11, 53, 91
Çiçek, D.D. 653
Chirosca, A.M. 75
Clarindo, G. 549
Coppola, T. 441
Costa, A.C. 151

Dai, H-N. 729
de Camargo, R. 797
de Figueiredo, N.M. 739
Diaz, H. 627
Díaz-Ruiz-Navamuel, E. 351
Ding, A. 361
Domínguez, J.M. 329
Duan, L. 169
Duarte, H.O. 159
d'Amore-Domenech, R. 501

Engelbrecht, M. 265
Esteve-Pérez, J. 19

Fang, Pan 559
Fasano, E. 441
Fellows, D.M. 747
Feng, Q.D. 275
Ferrari, V. 177
Ferreira, F.O. 421
Figari, M. 207
Flethes, B. 403
Fonseca, P. 693
Fortes, C.J.E.M. 341, 421, 511, 815

Gadelho, J.F.M. 81
Garbatov, Y. 705
Garcês, J.P. 699
Gaspar, J.F. 587, 597
Gasparotti, C. 75
Gil Rosa, J. 283
Gómez-Gesteira, M. 329
Gonçalves, M. 569, 791
González-Cao, J. 329
Gramcianinov, C.B. 797
Gu, X. 297
Guedes Soares, C. 81, 101, 119, 131, 151, 177, 187, 217, 227, 235, 247, 275, 283, 319, 329, 341, 371, 385, 395, 481, 491, 529, 549, 569, 577, 587, 597, 607, 617, 627, 639, 665, 673, 685, 705, 757, 775, 785, 791, 797, 805, 809
Guo, Y.C. 757
Gutiérrez-Romero, J.E. 19

Hallak, T.S. 577, 587, 597
Henriques, V. 693, 713
Hinostroza, M.A. 187, 227, 805
Hommik, K. 721
Hopman, H. 559
Huang, S. 91

Ibrahim, M.I. 403
Iodice, P. 457
Iseki, T. 169
Islam, H. 385, 395

Ji, C. 371
Jiang, X. 559
Jiao, J. 91
Johannessen, J.A. 809

Kaljuste, O. 721
Kalyuzhnaya, A.V. 767
Kamarlouei, M. 587, 597
Kan, J. 395
Karmakar, D. 577, 639
Katalinić, M. 37
Kishev, R. 747

Lameira, P.I.D. 63, 739
Lampreia, S. 475
Langella, G. 457
Legaz, M.J. 403
Leo, T.J. 501
Liang, M. 361
Liarokapis, D.E. 111, 415

Lin, Y. 297
Liu, J. 395
Liu, Z.C. 705
Lobo, V. 475
Luna-Abad, J.P. 19

Ma, N. 297
Maciel, G.F. 421
Magkouris, A. 519
Martelli, M. 207
Mattosinho, G.O. 421
Mauro, F. 27
Menon, A.K. 305
Michima, P.S.A. 159
Micoli, L. 441
Mikulić, A. 37
Mocerino, L. 449, 457
Mohapatra, S.C. 757
Mohseni, M. 101
Moraes, H.B. 63
Moreira, L. 131
Morgado, T. 475
Muiyser, J. 265
Murali, K. 607, 617

Nabergoj, R. 27
Navarro, E. 501
Neto, D. 699
Nikitin, N.O. 767
Nikolov, G. 747

Oğuz, E. 653
Ohsawa, T. 11
Oliveira, A.C.A. 159
Orihara, H. 429
Ortega-Piris, A. 351

Paramesh, S. 197
Parente, J. 693, 713
Parunov, J. 37
Peddamallu, P. 305
Pedišić Buča, M. 45

Pérez-Labajos, C.A. 351
Piaggio, B. 207
Picanço, H.P. 63
Piecho-Santos, A.M.P. 805
Pinheiro, L.V. 341, 511, 815
Pires da Silva, P. 217, 227
Polonskaia, I.S. 767
Polyzos, S. 111
Ponce de León, S. 809
Pousão-Ferreira, P. 699
Prosinečki, T. 45
Prpić-Oršić, J. 27, 53

Quaranta, F. 449, 457
Quental-Ferreira, H. 699
Querol, A. 403

Raed, K. 607, 617
Raid, T. 721
Rajendran, S. 197, 305
Ramos, S. 627
Reis, F.V. 815
Reis, M.T. 815
Rizzuto, E. 449
Rony, J.S. 639
Rosa, T. 805
Ruiz-Capel, S. 19
Rusu, E. 539
Rusu, L. 647

Saavedra, R.S. 739
Saks, L. 721
Salvador, M. 815
Santos, J.A. 341, 421, 511
Santos, M.I. 815
Sasa, K. 11, 53
Şentürk, A.E. 653
Sepp, E. 721
Serrazina, V. 815
Shukla, M.K. 729
Silva, D. 529, 627, 665

Silva, L.M.R. 775
Silva, L.Z.M. 319
Souza, P.A.P. 63
Sutulo, S. 177, 217, 227, 235, 247

Tadros, M. 481, 491
Takagishi, K. 429
Teixeira, A.P. 177
Terada, D. 11, 53
Theriaga, M. 699
Thiebaut, F. 597
Trachanas, G.P. 415
Tserpes, H. 111
Tzabiras, G.D. 111, 415

Uchiyama, R. 53
Uzunoglu, E. 673

Vairinhos, V. 475
van Zijl, C.M. 141
Ventura, M. 481, 491
Vettor, R. 319
Villalba-Herreros, A. 501
Viviani, M. 207

Wang, D. 297
Wang, Q. 729
Wang, Q. 729
Wang, S. 119, 275, 283, 329
Wang, X. 361, 395
Wen, L.J. 275
Wu, J.M. 275

Xiang, G. 119
Xu, H.T. 151
Xu, S. 361, 371

Yoshida, H. 429

Zamora-Parra, B. 19

Proceedings in marine technology and ocean engineering

1. Advances in Renewable Energies Offshore
   Edited by C. Guedes Soares
   ISBN: 978-1-138-58535-5 (Hbk + Multimedia)
   ISBN: 978-0-429-50532-4 (eBook)

2. Trends in the Analysis and Design of Marine Structures
   Edited by Josko Parunov & C. Guedes Soares
   ISBN: 978-0-367-27809-0 (Hbk + Multimedia)
   ISBN: 978-0-429-29887-5 (eBook)

3. Sustainable Development and Innovations in Marine Technologies, 2019
   Edited by P. Georgiev and C. Guedes Soares
   ISBN: 978-0-367-40951-7 (Hbk + Multimedia)
   ISBN: 978-0-367-81008-5 (eBook)

4. Developments in the Collision and Grounding of Ships and Offshore Structures, 2019
   Edited by C. Guedes Soares
   ISBN: 978-0-367-43313-0 (Hbk)
   ISBN: 978-1-003-00242-0 (eBook)

5. Developments in Renewable Energies Offshore, 2021
   Edited by C. Guedes Soares
   ISBN: 9780367681319 (Hbk)
   ISBN: 9781003134572 (eBook)

6. Developments in Maritime Technology and Engineering, 2021*
   Edited by C. Guedes Soares and T.A. Santos
   ISBN: 9780367773748 (Hbk)
   ISBN: 9781003171072 (eBook)

7. Developments in the Analysis and Design of Marine Structures, 2021
   Edited by J. Amdahl and C. Guedes Soares (Ed.).
   ISBN: 9781032136653 (Hbk)
   ISBN: 9781003230373 (eBook)

9780367773779